W9-CEP-072

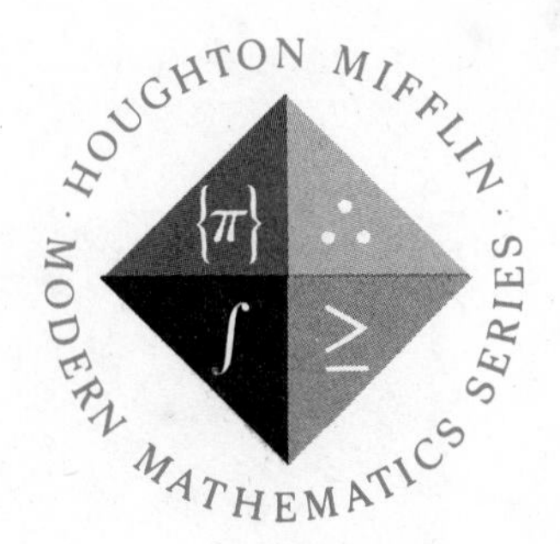

About the Cover

The design shown on the cover of this book was created by a special kind of photography. The artist-photographer calls the pictures "pendulum pictures." He used a pencil-type flashlight as his pendulum and suspended it by a string from the ceiling of a darkened room. Time exposures of the moving "pendulum" made with various color filters resulted in many beautiful patterns. The curves of these patterns are expressible in complicated mathematical equations such as this one,

$$F[(l^{-\frac{1}{2}} g^{\frac{1}{2}} \tau), (ml^{-\frac{2}{3}} g^{\frac{1}{2}} \mu^{-1}), \theta] = 0$$

Book Two
MODERN ALGEBRA AND TRIGONOMETRY

STRUCTURE AND METHOD

REVISED EDITION

Mary P. Dolciani

Simon L. Berman

William Wooton

Editorial Adviser

Albert E. Meder, Jr.

Houghton Mifflin Company • Boston
New York • Atlanta • Geneva, Illinois • Dallas • Palo Alto

ABOUT THE AUTHORS

Mary P. Dolciani, Professor and Chairman, Department of Mathematics, Hunter College of the City University of New York. Dr. Dolciani has been a member of the School Mathematics Study Group (SMSG) and a director and teacher in numerous National Science Foundation and New York State Education Department institutes for mathematics teachers.

Simon L. Berman, formerly Chairman, Department of Mathematics, Stuyvesant High School, New York. Mr. Berman has served on many mathematics curriculum committees, such as the Mathematics Syllabus Committee for New York State, and New York Regents Examination Committee.

William Wooton, Associate Professor of Mathematics, Los Angeles Pierce College. Mr. Wooton has been a teacher at the junior and senior high school levels. He has also been a member of the SMSG writing team and a team member of the National Council of Teachers of Mathematics summer writing projects.

EDITORIAL ADVISER

Albert E. Meder, Jr., Dean and Vice Provost and Professor of Mathematics, Emeritus, Rutgers University, The State University of New Jersey. Dr. Meder was Executive Director of the Commission on Mathematics of the College Entrance Examination Board, and has been an advisory member of SMSG.

STUDENT'S EDITION ISBN: 0-395-14256-3
STUDENT'S EDITION W/ODD ANSWERS ISBN: 0-395-14511-2
STUDENT'S EDITION W/ANSWERS ISBN: 0-395-14510-4
TEACHER'S EDITION ISBN: 0-395-14381-0

CONTENTS

ACKNOWLEDGMENTS

In writing *Modern Algebra and Trigonometry, Book Two*, the authors have had the advantage of comments and encouragement from many of their colleagues. They acknowledge with gratitude the assistance given by Mildred Blakeley, Somerville, Mass.; Hedwig Bergmann, Brookline High School, Brookline, Mass.; Minnie Belle Brewer, The Buckingham School, Cambridge, Mass.; Patricia S. Davidson, Arlington, Mass.; William C. Doyle, S. J., Rockhurst College, Kansas City, Missouri; Donald C. Duncan, Milton Academy, Milton, Mass.; Lawrence D. Hawkinson, George Washington High School, San Francisco; Professor M. Wiles Keller, Purdue University; George E. Kehoe, Bridgewater-Raynham High School, Bridgewater, Mass.; Carolyn Shine, Brookline High School, Brookline, Mass.; Gerhard Wichura, Wellesley High School, Wellesley, Mass.; and in particular by Julius Freilich, Brooklyn, N.Y.

The authors are grateful to Elsie Parker Johnson and Julius Freilich for the use of selected materials from *Algebra for Problem Solving, Book Two*, by Freilich, Berman, and Johnson, Copyright © 1957, 1953 by Houghton Mifflin Company.

Photograph Credits

COVER and Title Page photograph by Jack Sonatore, Design Photographers INTERNATIONAL, Inc.

PHOTOGRAPHS are by the courtesy of: NASA, p. xii; Columbia University Library, D. E. Smith Collection, p. 37; Itek Corporation, p. 38; General Dynamics Corporation, Convair Division, p. 68; E. Schaal, p. 76; ("Box 3" by John Healey), The Waddell Gallery, New York, p. 122; Science Service, p. 157; Geotronics, a Teledyne Company, p. 158; The Bettmann Archive, p. 197; Harold E. Edgerton, Edgerton, Germeshausen, and Grier, p. 208; Science Service, p. 249; Charles Pfizer and Company, Inc., p. 250; Brown Brothers, p. 297; Itek Corporation, p. 298; Sanders Associates Inc., p. 333; Polaroid Corporation, p. 338; Mount Wilson and Mount Palomar Observatories, p. 370; Fundamental Photographs, p. 420; Columbia University Library, D. E. Smith Collection, p. 461; Polaroid Corporation, p. 462; Baldwin Piano and Organ Company, p. 494; The Bettmann Archive, p. 523; William C. Coons, Lockheed Missiles and Space Company, p. 526; E. I. duPont de Nemours and Company, p. 549; The American Museum of Natural History, p. 550; Scripta Mathematica—Yeshiva University, p. 577; Harold E. Edgerton, p. 580.

CHAPTER 1

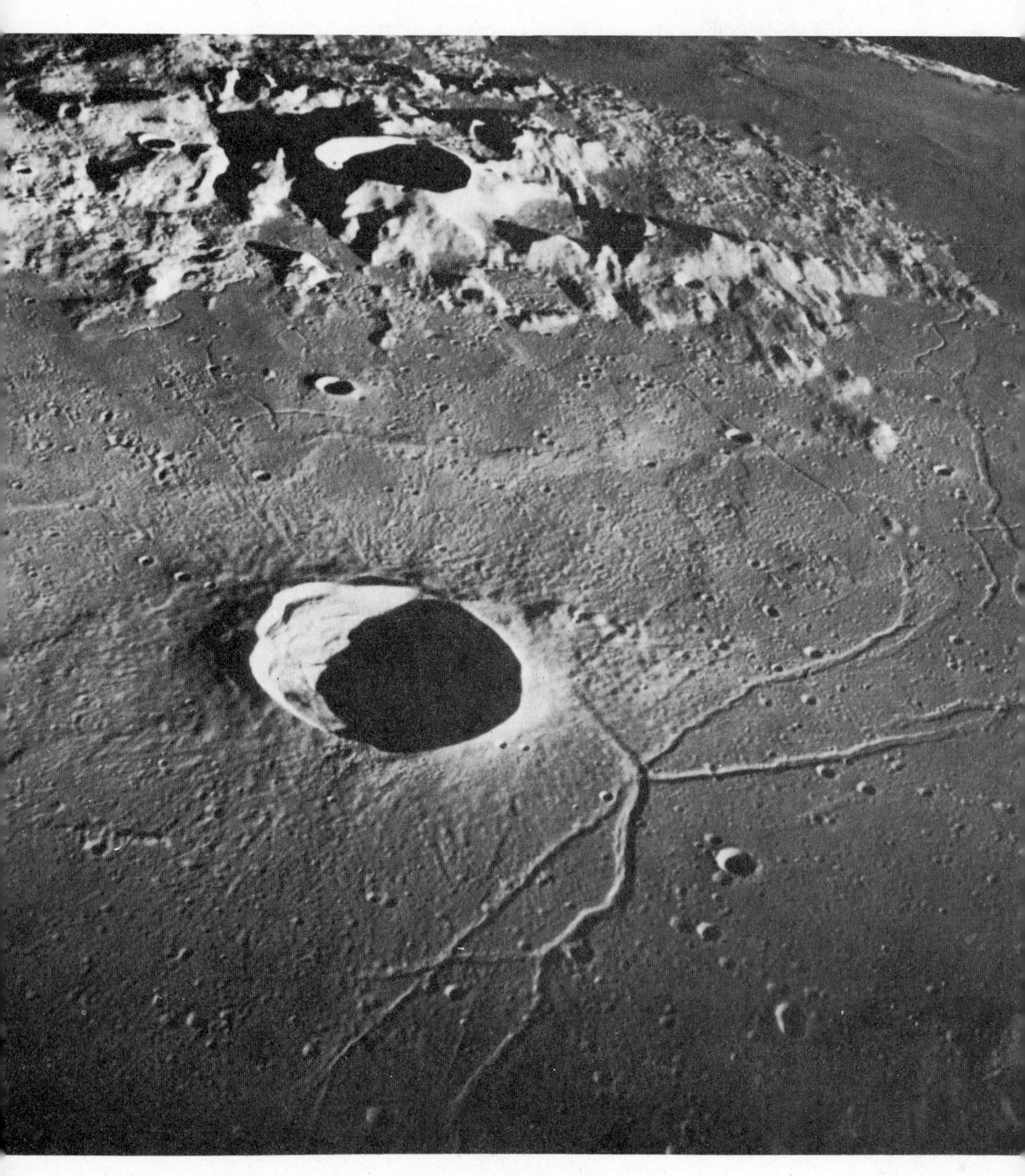

"That's one small step for a man, one giant leap for mankind."

Sets of Numbers; Axioms

Mathematics combines the old and the new. In this chapter you will study some things which your grandfather probably studied, but interwoven with them are other ideas which are so new that until recently they were studied only in graduate courses in the great universities. It is your privilege to learn now about sets and about the postulational basis of algebra.

SETS IN ALGEBRA

1–1 Sets and Their Relationships

What is the most fundamental concept in mathematics? You have met many mathematical ideas: number, addition, line, graph, and so on. All of these can be discussed in terms of the fundamental notions of *membership in a set* and of *equality*.

Many examples of sets are familiar to you: your algebra class, your favorite baseball team, the movies you have seen this year, all the whole numbers. The objects in a set are called **members** or **elements** of the set and are said to *belong to* or to be *contained in* the set. The symbol $\in$ is used to mean "is an element of," and $\notin$ to mean "is not an element of." Thus, if J is the set of whole numbers, $3 \in J$ and $\frac{1}{2} \notin J$.

To *specify* a set, you must identify its elements. Frequently you can specify a set by listing the names of its elements within braces, { }. For example, {0, 1, 2, 3}, read "the set, 0, 1, 2, 3," is a **roster** (list) of the set of numbers 0, 1, 2, 3; and {Gutenberg, Marconi} designates the set of the inventors of printing from movable type and of the wireless telegraph. The second example suggests another way of specifying a set: giving a rule or condition enabling you to decide whether or not an object belongs to the set. Thus, {the residents of New York City}, read "the set of the residents of New York City," specifies a set whose roster contains about eight million names.

Two sets are *equal* if and only if they have the same elements. Thus, {5, 3, 2} and {2, 5, 3} are equal, but {5, 3, 2} and {5, 3, 1} are not.

Although the sets {5, 3, 2} and {5, 1, 3} are not equal, there is an important relationship between them, illustrated by Figure 1–1. The elements of the two sets can be paired so that every member of each set has exactly one partner in the other set and no element in either set is without a partner. Such a pairing of the elements of two sets is called a **one-to-one correspondence.**

{5, 3, 2}
↕ ↕ ↕
{5, 1, 3}

· *Figure 1–1* ·

In counting the fingers of a hand (Figure 1–2), you establish a one-to-one correspondence between the set of fingers and {1, 2, 3, 4, 5}. If this process of counting all the elements comes to an end, the set is a **finite set.** In listing the members of the set of **natural numbers,** or **positive integers,** {1, 2, 3, 4, . . .}, the three dots after the 4 mean "and so on," indicating that the listing never comes to an end. When the process of counting the elements of a set continues without end, we call the set an **infinite set.** Other infinite sets of numbers are:

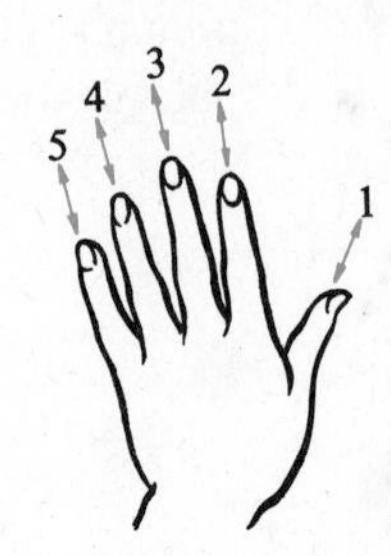

· *Figure 1–2* ·

{integers}	**{. . ., −3, −2, −1, 0, 1, 2, 3, . . .}**
{positive even integers}	**{2, 4, 6, 8, . . .}**
{negative odd integers}	**{−1, −3, −5, −7, . . .}**
{nonnegative integral multiples of 5}	**{0, 5, 10, 15, . . .}**

Do you see that every natural number belongs to the set of integers? Whenever each element of a set A is also an element of a set B, we say that A is a **subset** of B, written "$A \subset B$." Thus,

{natural numbers} ⊂ {integers} **and** **{women} ⊂ {human beings}.**

Diagrams such as the one shown may be used to illustrate a set and a subset.

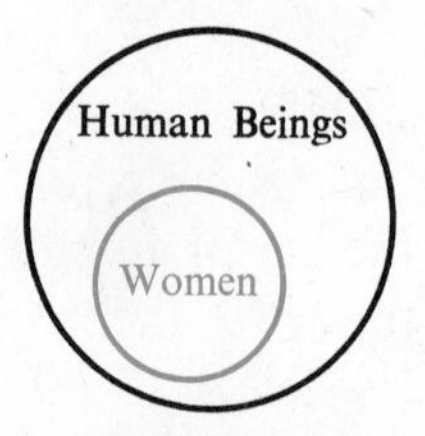

· *Figure 1–3* ·

Since every integer is a member of the set of integers, it is certainly true that the set of integers is a subset of itself. Indeed, the **improper subset** of each set is the set itself; every other subset is called a **proper subset** of the set.

Can you describe the set of natural numbers between $\frac{1}{4}$ and $\frac{1}{2}$? It has no members at all and is therefore called the **empty set** or **null set.**

The symbol ∅, written without braces, usually designates the empty set. By agreement there is only one empty or null set. Thus, the set of natural numbers between $\frac{1}{4}$ and $\frac{1}{2}$ and the set of square circles are the same set, namely, ∅. Furthermore, ∅ is accepted as a *proper* subset of every set except itself.

Set notation makes use of just a few of the many symbols of mathematics. Symbols used to designate numbers are called **numerals** or **numerical expressions.** The number three is represented by each of the numerical expressions, 3, III, $7 - 4$, $\sqrt{9}$, $\frac{8 + 7}{5}$. To indicate that two numerical expressions designate the same number, we use the symbol =, which stands for the word "equals," or for the words "is equal to." For example, $\sqrt{9} = 1 + 2$ and $7 - 4 = \text{III}$. Any statement of equality is called an **equation.** We use the symbol ≠, translated "is not equal to" or "does not equal," in an **inequality** such as $6 + 1 \neq \frac{18 + 1}{3}$, to show that two numerical expressions represent different numbers.

Oral Exercises

Specify each of the following sets by roster.

SAMPLE. {the letters in the word *missiles*}

What you say: {*m*, *i*, *s*, *l*, *e*}. Notice that each letter is listed only once.

1. {the vowels in the English alphabet}
2. {the letters in the word *philippic*}
3. {the days in a week}
4. {the first President of the U.S.A.}
5. {the positive integers less than 9}
6. {the negative integers greater than −5}
7. {the capital of Canada and that of the U.S.A.}
8. {the digits in this year's date}
9. {the even natural numbers less than 9}
10. {the integers whose squares equal 25}
11. {the countries bordering on Canada}
12. {the common fractions having numerator and denominator in {1, 2, 3}}

Tell whether or not each statement is true. Give a reason for each answer.

13. $10 \in \{9 + 2, 13 - 3, 7 \cdot 4\}$

14. $\frac{1}{4} \not\subset \{0.25, 0.5, 0.75\}$

15. $\{1, 9\} \subset \{\text{squares of integers}\}$

16. $\{\text{the even integers}\} \subset \{2, 4, 6\}$

17. $\emptyset = \{0\}$

18. $\{5 + 3, \frac{7}{7}, 1 + (-1)\} = \{1, 0, 8\}$

19. $\{3, 6\} \not\subset \{\text{multiples of } 3\}$

20. $87 \in \{8, 7, 6\}$

21. $\{0\} \in \{-7, 0, 7\}$

22. $7 \subset \{-7, 0, 7\}$

State which of the following sets are infinite and which are finite.

23. {residents of North America}

24. {grains of sand on the beaches of Cape Cod}

25. {triangles each with area 10 square inches}

26. {common fractions between 0 and 1}

27. {words in your dictionary}

28. {line segments 4 meters long}

In Column II find a set equal to each set in Column I.

Column I

29. $\{0, 1, 4, 9, 16, \ldots\}$

30. $\{0, 1\}$

31. {integral multiples of 4}

32. {the integer equal to its double}

33. $\{0, 2\}$

34. $\emptyset$

35. {the number whose sum with 5 is 5}

36. {negative integers between $-\frac{3}{2}$ and 4}

Column II

a. $\{-1\}$

b. {integers between $\frac{1}{2}$ and $\frac{3}{4}$}

c. {squares of the integers}

d. {nonnegative even integers less than 3}

e. {integers which equal their squares}

f. $\{\ldots, -12, -8, -4, 0, 4, 8, 12, \ldots\}$

g. $\{0\}$

Written Exercises

Copy each sentence, making it true by replacing each question mark with a numeral or with the sign = or ≠.

1. $4 + 9 = ? + 4$

2. $7 \times ? = 3 \times 7$

3. $? \times 14 = 5 - 5$

4. $6 + 6 \ ? \ 4 \times 3$

5. $? \div 2 = 1$

6. $8 + ? = 8$

7. $9 \times ? = 9$

8. $? \times 0 = 0$

9. $11 \times 2 \ ? \ 11 + 2$

10. $2 \times 2 \ ? \ 2 + 2$

11. $\dfrac{14 + ?}{2} = 10$

12. $\dfrac{18 + 3}{3} \ ? \ 6 + 3$

13. $\dfrac{6 \times 8}{2} \ ? \ 3 \times 4$

14. $3 \times 4 \times 5 = ? \times 60$

B

15. $\{4 + 2, 5 + 0\} \ ? \ \{4 + 1, 8 - 2\}$

16. $\{1, 3, 5\} \ ? \ \{\text{the odd integers}\}$

17. $\{6 \times 0\} \subset \{2, 4, ?\}$

18. $\{1 \times 7\} \subset \{?, 3, 5\}$

19. $\dfrac{6 \times ?}{3} \in \{6\}$

20. $\frac{1}{2} \times ? \notin \{\text{positive and negative numbers}\}$

Let $U = \{-7, 27, 14\}$. List all the subsets of U that:

21. Have exactly one element

22. Have exactly two elements

23. Have three elements

24. Have no elements

25. Have $\{-7, 7 + 7\}$ as a subset

26. Are subsets of {multiples of 7}

Determine whether there exists a one-to-one correspondence between the two sets specified in Exercises 27–34. Justify each answer.

27. $\{r, s, t, u\}$ and $\{4, 3, 9, 5\}$

28. {Tom, Dick, Harry} and {Sue, Mary}

29. {states of the United States} and {United States senators}

30. $\{1, 2, 3, 4\}$ and $\{6, 12, 18, 24\}$

31. {odd integers between 0 and 100} and {even integers between 1 and 10}

32. {even natural numbers less than 15} and {odd natural numbers less than 16}

C

33. {natural numbers} and {even natural numbers}

34. {natural numbers} and {integers}

35. Copy and complete the following table comparing the number of elements in a set U and the number of subsets of U.

U	Number of Elements of U	Number of Subsets of U
$\{r\}$	1	$2 = 2^1$
$\{r, s\}$	2	$4 = 2^2$
$\{r, s, t\}$	3	?
$\{r, s, t, u\}$	4	?

36. If U is a set with n elements, use the results of Exercise 35 to formulate a rule in terms of n for finding the number of subsets of U.

1–2 Sets and Variables

In discussing a set you often make statements about its members. For example, if M is the set of male college students, the sentence "He is a senior" is true for some members of M but false for others. Similarly, if $S = \{1, 2, 3, 4, 5, 6\}$, the sentence "x belongs to S, and $x + 2 = 6$" is true when x is replaced by 4 but false when the replacement is 3 or any other numeral that does not represent 4.

In the preceding sentences the pronoun *he* and the letter x play similar roles. Each is a symbol, called a **variable**; a variable may represent any element of a specified set. Thus, you may replace *he* by the name of any male college student and x by a numeral for any number in S. The set whose elements may serve as replacements for a variable is called the **domain**, or **replacement set**, or **universe**, of the variable. To indicate that the domain of x is S, you may write $x \in S$. The members of the domain are called the **values** of the variable. A variable with just one value is called a **constant**.

Sentences containing variables are called **open sentences**; for example, $x + 2 = 6$. An open sentence serves as a pattern for the various sentences, some true, some false, which you obtain by substituting in it numerals for the different values of the variable. The subset of the domain consisting of the elements of the domain for which the open sentence is true is called the **solution set** or **truth set** of the open sentence over that domain. Each element of the solution set is said to **satisfy** and to be a **root** or **solution** of the open sentence. Thus, if $x \in \{1, 2, 3, 4, 5, 6\}$, then $\{4\}$ is the solution set of $x + 2 = 6$. This may be written:

$$\{x\colon x \in S \text{ and } x + 2 = 6\} = \{4\}$$

read "the set of all elements x, such that x belongs to S and $x + 2 = 6$, is the set consisting of the number 4." In general, the statement $\{x\colon x + 2 = 6\} = \{4\}$ is true provided the domain of x contains the number 4.

The following statement may help you to fix the meaning of terms.

domain
replacement set
universe
set of values of the variable

If $S = \{1, 2, 3, 4, 5, 6\}$, *(variable)*
the sentence "x belongs to S, and $x + 2 = 6$" ← *open sentence*
is satisfied by the element 4 of S. **$\{4\}$** ← *solution set, truth set*

↑ *root, solution*

EXAMPLE. Specify by roster these subsets of the set of integers:

a. $K = \{x: 3 + x = 11\}$ **b.** $R = \{s: s + 2 = s + 3\}$

c. $Y = \{t: t + 3 + 2 = t + 4 + 1\}$

Solution: **a.** $K = \{8\}$. **b.** $R = \emptyset$.

c. $Y = \{\ldots, -3, -2, -1, 0, 1, 2, 3, \ldots\}$

Oral Exercises

Determine the solution set of the equation over the given set.

1. $x + 5 = 7$; $\{1, 2, 3, 4\}$
2. $y - 1 = 4$; $\{1, 3, 5, 7\}$
3. $v + v = 6$; $\{-1, 0, 1\}$
4. $7 + k = 7$; $\{-7, 0, 7\}$
5. $r + 5 = 0$; $\{-5, 0, 5\}$
6. $t \times 8 = 8$; $\{0, 1, 2\}$
7. $s - 3 = s$; {integers}
8. $r + 1 = r$; {integers}
9. $2 + h = 4$; {even integers}
10. $5 - n = 4$; {odd integers}

Tell which of the following statements are true.

11. Algebra $\in$ {m: m is a biological science}
12. You $\in$ {r: r is a human being}
13. A triangle $\notin$ {k: k is a plane quadrilateral}
14. An equilateral triangle $\notin$ {g: g is a regular polygon}
15. $\{5\} \subset$ {x: x is an integer and $5 + x = 0$}
16. $\{4\} \subset$ {y: y is an integer and $y \times 3 = 3 \times y$}

Written Exercises

List the members of the following sets.

A

1. {z: z was a United States President between 1941 and 1960}
2. {t: t is a New England state}
3. {y: y is a coauthor of this book}
4. {v: v is a planet in our solar system}
5. {k: k is a positive integer and k is even}
6. {a: a is a negative integer and a is odd}
7. {r: r is an integer and r is not 0}
8. {s: s is a positive integer and s is one more than an integral multiple of 3}

B

9. $\{R: R \text{ is a subset of } \{0, 1\}\}$

10. $\{S: S \text{ is a subset of } \{-1, 1\}\}$

11. $\{x: x \in \{5, 6\}\}$

12. $\{y: y = \emptyset\}$

13. $\{M: M \subset \{x: x \text{ is an integer and } x = x + 4\}\}$

14. $\{N: N \subset \{y: y \text{ is an integer and } y + 1 = 8\}\}$

AXIOMS FOR REAL NUMBERS

1–3 Order in the Set of Real Numbers

The set of all positive and negative numbers and zero is called the set of **real numbers**. Do you recall the picture of the real numbers as points on a line, Figure 1–4?

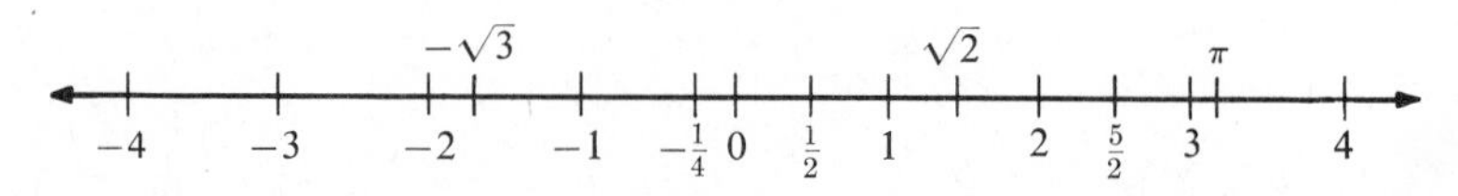

Figure 1–4

To construct such a *number line*, choose a starting point (**origin**) on a horizontal line; label it "0." At some convenient distance to the right of the origin select a second point; mark it "1." Then, using the distance between the points "0" and "1" as the unit distance on the line, you can associate each real number with that point whose distance from the origin is given by the number. The positive numbers are the partners of the points to the right of the origin and the negative numbers of points to the left of the origin. The point associated with a number is called the **graph** of the number, while the number paired with a point is the **coordinate** of the point.

The representation of real numbers as points on a line is based on several assumptions. In mathematics, assumptions are called **axioms** or **postulates**. One such axiom, known as the Axiom of Comparison, asserts that you can arrange the real numbers in a definite *order*. The inequality $4 > 1$ stands for "4 is greater than 1." Its interpretation on the number line is, "the graph of 4 is to the right of the graph of 1." The same information is conveyed by the inequality $1 < 4$, read, "1 is less than 4" and interpreted, "the graph of 1 is to the left of the graph of 4." Thus, a fundamental property of the set of real numbers is the existence of an *order relation*, denoted by the symbols $<$ or $>$ and satisfying the following axiom.

Axiom of Comparison. If a and b denote real numbers, then one and only one of the following statements is true: $a < b$, $a = b$, $a > b$.

To avoid confusing the *inequality symbols* $<$ and $>$, think of them as arrowheads always pointing to the numeral for the smaller number. A statement such as "$x < 2$ or $x = 2$" is usually written $x \leq 2$ and read, "x is less than or equal to 2." Similarly, $a \geq b$ stands for "a is greater than or equal to b."

On a number line you can picture any subset of the set of real numbers as a set of points, called the **graph of the subset**.

EXAMPLE. Graph the following subsets of the set of real numbers.

Solution:

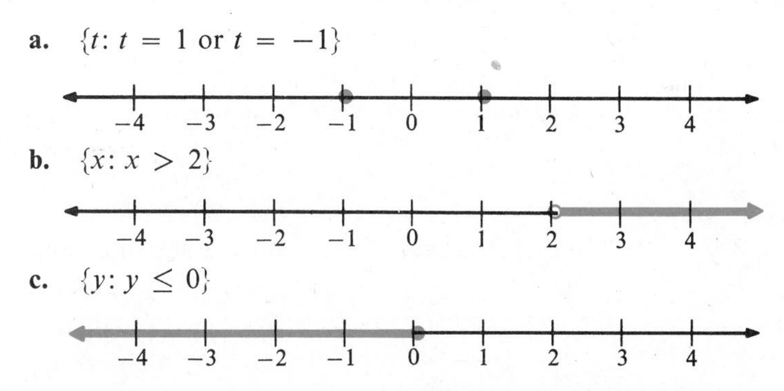

Note: A heavy dot • marks a point corresponding to a number in the set. A heavy portion of a line ▬ indicates that all points on it belong to the graph. Open dots ○ or thin portions of lines show points not belonging to the graph. A heavy arrowhead implies that the graph continues indefinitely in the indicated direction.

Another axiom, suggested by the number lines in Figure 1–5, is stated as follows:

Transitive Property of Order. Let a, b, and c denote real numbers.

1. If $a < b$ and $b < c$, then $a < c$.
2. If $a > b$ and $b > c$, then $a > c$.

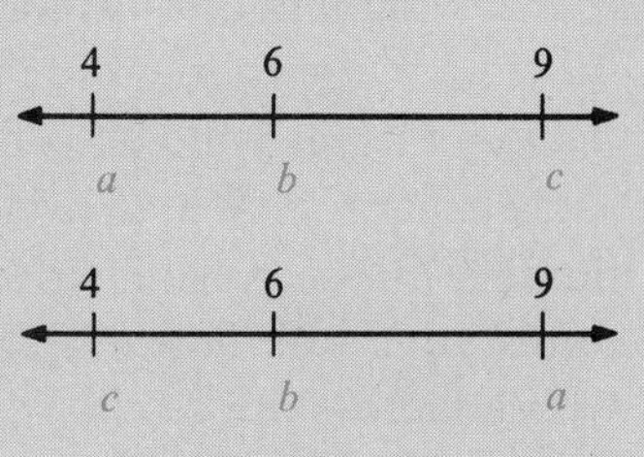

Figure 1–5

You usually write the pair of inequalities "$a < b$" and "$b < c$" in the combined form $a < b < c$, read "a is less than b, which is less than c," or "b is *between* a and c." Figure 1–6 shows the graphs of the solution sets of three such pairs over the set of real numbers.

$\{x: -2 < x < 3\}$ −3 −2 −1 0 1 2 3

$\{x: -2 < x \leq 3\}$ −3 −2 −1 0 1 2 3

$\{x: -2 \leq x \leq 3\}$ −3 −2 −1 0 1 2 3

· *Figure 1–6* ·

Written Exercises

Graph the following subsets of the set of real numbers.

A

1. $\{0, 1\}$
2. $\{-1, 0, 1\}$
3. $\{u: u \geq -1\}$
4. $\{y: y \leq 3\}$
5. $\{e: e = -2 \text{ or } e = 5\}$
6. $\{f: f = 0 \text{ or } f = 1\}$
7. $\{p: p \text{ is an integer and } p < 6\}$
8. $\{q: q \text{ is an integer and } q > -2\}$
9. $\{x: -2 \leq x < 4\}$
10. $\{y: -1 \leq y \leq 6\}$
11. $\{k: k \text{ is an integer and } -3 \leq k \leq 7\}$
12. $\{w: w \text{ is an integer and } 2 < w \leq 5\}$

1–4 Properties of Addition and Multiplication

The two basic operations on pairs of numbers are addition and multiplication. If a and b denote two numbers, then $a + b$, called the **sum** of a and b, represents the result of adding a and b; the **product**, denoted by $a \times b$, $a \cdot b$, $a(b)$, $(a)(b)$, or simply ab, is the result of multiplying a and b. In the sum $a + b$ the numbers a and b are called **terms**; in the product ab, they are called **factors**.

Do you recall the use of parentheses and other *symbols of inclusion*, such as brackets and a bar, to group symbols representing a single number? When you write $3 + (a + 2)$, you mean the sum whose terms are 3 and $(a + 2)$. Similarly, $3[a + 2]$ or $3\,\overline{a + 2}$ is a product whose factors are 3 and $[a + 2]$. Occasionally braces are used instead of parentheses.

Experience may suggest that when you add or multiply two real numbers, the result is always a real number. This is stated as an axiom:

Axiom of Closure for Addition and Multiplication. If a and b denote real numbers, then $a + b$ represents a unique (one and only one) real number, and ab represents a unique real number.

The term "closure" is used because any set of numbers is said to be *closed under an operation* performed on its elements if each result of the operation is a member of the set. Can you explain why the set $\{0, 1\}$ is closed under multiplication but not under addition?

The following axioms govern the use of the symbol $=$.

Axioms of Equality

Let a, b, c, and d denote real numbers.

1. **Reflexive:** $a = a$
2. **Symmetric:** If $a = b$, then $b = a$.
3. **Transitive:** If $a = b$ and $b = c$, then $a = c$.
4. **Substitution:** i. If $a = b$ and $a + c = d$, then $b + c = d$.
   ii. If $a = b$ and $ac = d$, then $bc = d$.

The substitution axiom guarantees that a sum or a product is not altered in meaning when equal numerals are used for a number. Thus, from $6 = 2 + 4$, and $6 + 5 = 11$ and $6 \cdot 5 = 30$, this axiom allows you to conclude that $(2 + 4) + 5 = 11$ and that $(2 + 4)5 = 30$.

Four other general principles are illustrated by the following particular statements:

$$4 + 6 = 6 + 4;\ 4 \cdot 6 = 6 \cdot 4;$$
$$(7 + 9) + 5 = 7 + (9 + 5);\ (7 \cdot 9)5 = 7(9 \cdot 5).$$

The first two illustrate the commutative axioms for addition and multiplication; the second two, the associative axioms.

Commutative Axioms: If a and b denote real numbers, then $a + b = b + a$ and $ab = ba$.

Associative Axioms: If a, b, and c denote real numbers, then $(a + b) + c = a + (b + c)$ and $(ab)c = a(bc)$.

Can you add *three* real numbers? If a, b, c denote real numbers, we *define* $a + b + c$ to be the sum $(a + b) + c$. Of course, because addition of real numbers is an *associative* and *commutative* operation, you may add the terms in a sum of two or more numbers in any *groups* of two and in any *order*.

$$14 + 101 + 33\tfrac{1}{2} + 46 + 99 + \tfrac{1}{2} = (101 + 99) + (14 + 46) + (33\tfrac{1}{2} + \tfrac{1}{2})$$

But $(101 + 99) + (14 + 46) + (33\tfrac{1}{2} + \tfrac{1}{2}) = 200 + (60 + 34)$

and $200 + (60 + 34) = 294$

Do you see why, besides the other axioms, you use the *transitive* property of equality twice to conclude from the preceding chain of equalities that $14 + 101 + 33\tfrac{1}{2} + 46 + 99 + \tfrac{1}{2} = 294$?

Similarly,

$$\tfrac{1}{2} \times 27 \times 8 \times \tfrac{5}{3} = (\tfrac{1}{2} \times 8)(27 \times \tfrac{5}{3})$$
$$= 4 \cdot 45 = 180$$

Oral Exercises

Name the property justifying each of the following sentences for any replacement of each variable by a real number.

SAMPLE. $5(7a) = (5 \cdot 7)a$

What you say: Associative Axiom for Multiplication

1. Given that $5 + 7 = 12$; therefore, $12 = 5 + 7$.
2. Given that $4 \cdot 2 = 8$ and $8 + 3 = 11$; therefore, $(4 \cdot 2) + 3 = 11$.
3. If $3 + 5 = 8$ and $8 + 1 = 9$, then $(3 + 5) + 1 = 9$.
4. $r + s = r + s$
5. $3 + \tfrac{1}{2}$ is a real number.
6. $10(-5)$ is a real number.
7. $(-9) + 0 = 0 + (-9)$
8. $\tfrac{3}{4} \times (5 + 8) = (5 + 8) \times \tfrac{3}{4}$
9. $5k + (3k + 4) = (5k + 3k) + 4$
10. $(b + c)a = a(b + c)$
11. $12 \cdot (8t) = (12 \cdot 8)t$
12. $7 + (19 + y) = (7 + 19) + y$
13. Given that $4(-2) + 3 = -8 + 3$ and $-8 + 3 = -5$; therefore, $4(-2) + 3 = -5$.
14. Given that $[(-3) + (-2)] + 5 = (-5) + 5$ and $(-5) + 5 = 0$; therefore, $[(-3) + (-2)] + 5 = 0$.
15. Given that $a = b$ and $c = b$; therefore, $a = c$. (Two properties)
16. Given $a = b$, $a = c$, $b = d$; therefore, $c = d$. (Three properties)

Name the axiom that justifies each step in each of the following chains of equalities. Assume that the domain of each variable is the set of real numbers, and that the number facts used are given. (*Note:* $\therefore$ means "therefore.")

SAMPLE. *Steps:*	*What you say:*
$6 + (v + 4) = 6 + (4 + v)$	Commutative property of addition.
$= [6 + 4] + v$	Associative property of addition.
$\therefore 6 + (v + 4) = [6 + 4] + v$	Transitive property of equality.
But $6 + 4 = 10$.	Given number fact.
$\therefore 6 + (v + 4) = 10 + v$.	Substitution axiom.

17.
$$\begin{aligned} (r + 4) + 5 &= r + (4 + 5) \\ \text{But } 4 + 5 &= 9. \\ \therefore (r + 4) + 5 &= r + 9 \\ &= 9 + r \\ \therefore (r + 4) + 5 &= 9 + r \end{aligned}$$

18.
$$\begin{aligned} 3(n \times 3) &= 3(3n) \\ &= (3 \cdot 3)n \\ \therefore 3(n \times 3) &= (3 \cdot 3)n \\ \text{But } 3 \cdot 3 &= 9. \\ \therefore 3(n \times 3) &= 9n \end{aligned}$$

19.
$$\begin{aligned} a(bc) &= (ab)c \\ &= (ba)c \\ &= b(ac) \\ &= b(ca) \\ \therefore a(bc) &= b(ca) \end{aligned}$$

20.
$$\begin{aligned} a + (b + c) &= (a + b) + c \\ &= (b + a) + c \\ &= b + (a + c) \\ \therefore a + (b + c) &= b + (a + c) \end{aligned}$$

21.
$$\begin{aligned} (a + 5) + (7 + b) &= [(a + 5) + 7] + b \\ &= [a + (5 + 7)] + b \\ \therefore (a + 5) + (7 + b) &= [a + (5 + 7)] + b \\ \text{But } 5 + 7 &= 12. \\ \therefore (a + 5) + (7 + b) &= (a + 12) + b \\ &= a + (12 + b) \\ &= a + (b + 12) \\ &= (a + b) + 12 \\ \therefore (a + 5) + (7 + b) &= (a + b) + 12 \end{aligned}$$

22.
$$\begin{aligned} (3c)(2d) &= [(3c)2]d \\ &= [(c \cdot 3)2]d \\ &= [c(3 \cdot 2)]d \\ \therefore (3c)(2d) &= [c(3 \cdot 2)]d \\ \text{But } 3 \cdot 2 &= 6. \\ \therefore (3c)(2d) &= (c \cdot 6)d \\ &= (6 \cdot c)d \\ &= 6(cd) \\ \therefore (3c)(2d) &= 6(cd) \end{aligned}$$

Written Exercises

Which of the following sets are closed under **(a)** addition and **(b)** multiplication? When a set is not closed, give an example which shows this.

SAMPLE. {positive odd integers} = {1, 3, 5, . . .}

Solution: **(a)** Not closed, as $1 + 3 = 4$ is not in the set. **(b)** Closed.

A

1. $\{0\}$
2. $\{1\}$
3. $\{0, 2\}$
4. $\{0, 1\}$
5. {natural numbers}
6. {integers}
7. {positive odd integers}
8. {positive even integers}
9. {squares of the integers}
10. $\{1, \frac{1}{3}, \frac{1}{9}, \frac{1}{27}, \ldots\}$

In each exercise an operation * is defined over the set of natural numbers. In each case (**a**) find $3 * 2$; (**b**) determine whether or not the set of natural numbers is closed under *; (**c**) state whether * is (1) commutative, (2) associative.

C

11. $r * s = r + (s + 1)$
12. $r * s = (r + s) + s$
13. $r * s = r + (r + s)$
14. $r * s = r - s$

1-5 Identity and Inverse Elements

Can you state a general principle illustrated by the statements: $0 + 4 = 4 + 0 = 4$, $0 + (-2) = (-2) + 0 = -2$? The number 0 plays a unique role in the set of real numbers: when 0 is added to any given number, the sum is *identical* with the given number. We call 0 the **identity element for addition** and state the following:

Axiom of Zero. The set of real numbers contains a unique element 0 having the property that if a denotes any real number, $0 + a = a$ and $a + 0 = a$.

Figure 1–7 illustrates a useful pairing of real numbers.

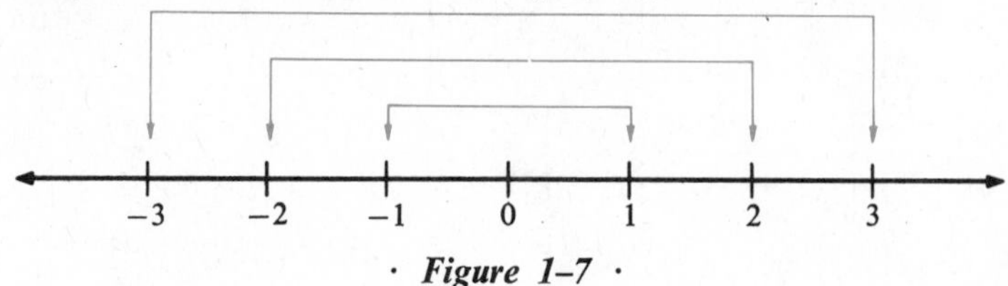

· *Figure 1–7* ·

Do you recall that the sum of the numbers in any of these pairs is 0? Thus, $-1 + 1 = 0$, $-2 + 2 = 0$, $3 + (-3) = 0$. Each number in a pair is called the *additive inverse*, *negative*, or *opposite* of the other number. The **additive inverse** of a real number a is the real number whose sum with a is 0, the additive identity element. It is denoted by $-a$. For example,

$-(2) = -2$, **read "the additive inverse of 2 is negative 2";**

$-(0) = 0$, **read "the additive inverse of 0 is 0";**

$-(-3) = 3$, **read "the additive inverse of negative 3 is 3."**

An important assumption about real numbers, illustrated on p. 14, is:

Axiom of Additive Inverses. If a denotes any real number, there is a unique real number denoted by $-a$, such that $a + (-a) = 0$ and $(-a) + a = 0$.

The symbol $-a$ should always be read "the additive inverse of a" or "the negative of a," because $-a$ may represent either a negative number, a positive number, or zero. Do you see that $-(-a) = a$?

For every nonzero real number a, we define its **absolute value**, denoted by $|a|$, to be the greater number of the pair a and $-a$. For example, $|3| = 3$, $|-2| = 2$, and $|-\frac{1}{4}| = \frac{1}{4}$. **The absolute value of 0 is 0.**

The role of 1 as the **identity element for multiplication** is illustrated by the statement $1 \cdot 4 = 4 \cdot 1 = 4$.

Axiom of One. The set of real numbers contains a unique element 1 having the property that if a denotes any real number, $1 \cdot a = a$ and $a \cdot 1 = a$.

Two numbers whose product is 1, the identity element for multiplication, are called **reciprocals** or **multiplicative inverses** of one another. For example, $\frac{1}{4}$ is the reciprocal of 4, and 4 is the reciprocal of $\frac{1}{4}$. Another pair of reciprocals is 5 and 0.2. Of course, 1 is its own reciprocal. The assumption that each number except zero has a reciprocal is stated as follows:

Axiom of Multiplicative Inverses. If a represents any nonzero real number, there is a unique real number denoted by $\frac{1}{a}$, such that $a \cdot \frac{1}{a} = 1$ and $\frac{1}{a} \cdot a = 1$.

Does 0 have a reciprocal? If it did, there would exist a real number satisfying the equation $0 \cdot x = 1$. But no such number exists, because the product of 0 and any real number is 0, a number different from 1. This familiar property is stated in the next axiom.

Multiplication Property of Zero. If a denotes any real number, then $0 \cdot a = 0$ and $a \cdot 0 = 0$.

Another axiom concerned with multiplication is the one below.

Property of the Reciprocal of a Product. If a and b denote nonzero real numbers, the reciprocal of their product is the product of their reciprocals: $\frac{1}{ab} = \frac{1}{a} \cdot \frac{1}{b}$.

To illustrate this result, you have: $\frac{1}{3 \cdot 7} = \frac{1}{3} \cdot \frac{1}{7}$ and $\frac{1}{\frac{5}{2} \cdot 4} = \frac{2}{5} \cdot \frac{1}{4}$.

A companion axiom is as follows:

Property of the Negative of a Sum. If a and b denote real numbers, the negative of their sum is the sum of their negatives: $-(a + b) = (-a) + (-b)$.

Using this axiom, you have: $-(2 + 3) = (-2) + (-3)$ and $-[(-4) + 7] = 4 + (-7)$.

Oral Exercises

Give the additive inverse and the absolute value of each number.

SAMPLE. -2 *What you say:* Additive inverse is 2; absolute value is 2.

1. 3	**4.** $\frac{1}{3}$	**7.** $-\frac{1}{5}$	**10.** 0
2. 7	**5.** -8	**8.** $-\frac{1}{9}$	**11.** $-(-2.5)$
3. $\frac{1}{4}$	**6.** -6	**9.** -1	**12.** $-(-.8)$

Give the reciprocal, if it exists, of each of the following numbers.

13. $\frac{5}{8}$	**15.** 0	**17.** 0.1	**19.** 1.1
14. $\frac{7}{4}$	**16.** 1	**18.** 0.01	**20.** 1.5

Give an expression for the additive inverse of each of the following.

SAMPLE. $2 + (-3)$ *What you say:* $-2 + 3$

21. $-1 + (-4)$

22. $-6 + 9$

23. $7 + 8$

24. $-4 + (-9)$

25. $10 + (-15) + (-3)$

26. $-2 + 7 + (-9)$

Tell which of these statements are true and which are false for all real values of any variables involved.

27. $|-3| = 3$

28. $|-5| \neq 5$

29. $-3 > |-10|$

30. $2 < |-4|$

31. $|7| + |-7| = 0$

32. $-|-6| = 6$

33. $\dfrac{1}{(-1)(2)} = \dfrac{1}{-1} \cdot \dfrac{1}{2}$

34. $\dfrac{1}{(3)(-5)} = \dfrac{1}{3} \cdot \dfrac{1}{-5}$

35. $-(-a) = a$

36. $-[-(-b)] = b$

37. $-(-a) = |a|$

38. $-(-a) = |-a|$

Justify each step in the following chains of equalities if *a*, *b*, and *c* denote real numbers.

39.
$$
\begin{aligned}
&(a + b) + [(-a) + (-b)] \\
&= (a + b) + [(-b) + (-a)] \\
&= [(a + b) + (-b)] + (-a) \\
&= [a + \overline{b + (-b)}] + (-a) \\
&= [a + 0] + (-a) \\
&= a + (-a) \\
&= 0
\end{aligned}
$$
$$\therefore (a + b) + [(-a) + (-b)] = 0$$

40.
$$
\begin{aligned}
&(ab) \cdot \left(\frac{1}{a} \cdot \frac{1}{b}\right) \\
&= (ab) \cdot \left(\frac{1}{b} \cdot \frac{1}{a}\right) \\
&= \left[(ab) \cdot \frac{1}{b}\right] \cdot \frac{1}{a} \\
&= \left[a\left(b \cdot \frac{1}{b}\right)\right] \cdot \frac{1}{a} \\
&= (a \cdot 1) \cdot \frac{1}{a} \\
&= a \cdot \frac{1}{a} \\
&= 1
\end{aligned}
$$
$$\therefore (ab)\left(\frac{1}{a} \cdot \frac{1}{b}\right) = 1$$

Written Exercises

Give the solution set of each of these equations over the set of real numbers.

A

1. $|p| = 6$
2. $|g| = 0$
3. $-x = 4$
4. $-y = -2$
5. $-z = 0$
6. $-(-t) = 1$
7. $-1 = |-u|$
8. $|-n| = 5$

9. $(-s) + 2 = 0$
10. $3 + (-k) = 0$
11. $|x| + 1 = 3$
12. $|v| + |-2| = 2$
13. $-[(-x) + (-2)] = 7$
14. $-[(-1) + (-y)] = 8$
15. $7|t| = |-7|$
16. $5|-y| = |5|$

Graph each nonempty solution set of the following open sentences over the set of real numbers.

B

17. $|y| < 0$
18. $|y| \leq 0$
19. $-r < 1$
20. $-p > 2$
21. $-v \leq -2$
22. $-c \leq -1$
23. $|p| \leq 2$
24. $|q| > 1$
25. $|x| < -x$
26. $|x| < x$
27. $|t| > 0$
28. $|t| \geq 0$
29. $y = |y|$
30. $|y| = -y$
31. $4 < |d| < 6$
32. $-1 < |f| \leq 1$
33. $-1 < -k < 2$
34. $2 \geq -h \geq -2$

USING AXIOMS

1–6 The Concept of Proof

The axioms, together with definitions which we make, describe *basic* properties of the system of real numbers. From these basic properties you can derive *other* properties of real numbers, such as the following:

Addition Property of Equality. If a, b, and c denote real numbers and if $a = b$, then $a + c = b + c$.

The reasoning from the *hypothesis* "a, b, and c denote real numbers and $a = b$" to the *conclusion* "$a + c = b + c$" is shown in the following sequence of statements, each justified by the indicated axiom or given fact.

1. a **and** c **are real numbers;** $a = b$.	**1. Given.**
2. $\therefore$ **there is a real number** d **such that** $a + c = d$.	**2. Axiom of closure.**
3. $b + c = d$	**3. Substitution axiom.**
4. $\therefore d = b + c$	**4. Symmetric property of equality.**
5. $\therefore a + c = b + c$	**5. Transitive property of equality.**

This form of logical reasoning from hypothesis to conclusion is called a **proof**. Assertions to be proved are called **theorems**. Can you prove the theorem stated below? (See Exercise 2, page 21.)

Multiplication Property of Equality. If a, b, and c denote real numbers, and if $a = b$, then $ac = bc$.

The next theorem states another useful fact about real numbers.

THEOREM. If b and c denote real numbers, then $(b + c) + (-c) = b$.

Proof

1. b and c denote real numbers.	**1.** Given.
2. $b + c$ is a real number.	**2.** Closure for addition.
3. $-c$ is a real number.	**3.** Axiom of additive inverses.
4. $(b + c) + (-c)$ is a real number.	**4.** Closure for addition.
5. $(b + c) + (-c) = b + [c + (-c)]$.	**5.** Associative axiom for addition.
6. $c + (-c) = 0$.	**6.** Axiom of additive inverses.
7. $(b + c) + (-c) = b + 0$.	**7.** Substitution axiom.
8. $b + 0 = b$.	**8.** Axiom of zero.
9. $(b + c) + (-c) = b$.	**9.** Transitive property of equality.

Frequently, to shorten the writing of a proof, some steps involving substitution and the transitive property of equality are not explicitly stated. For example, steps 5 through 9 in the preceding proof may be replaced by the following chain of equalities:

$(b + c) + (-c) = b + [c + (-c)]$	**Associative axiom for addition**
$= b + 0$	**Axiom of additive inverses**
$= b$	**Axiom of zero**
$\therefore (b + c) + (-c) = b$	**Transitive property of equality**

Assertions that have been proved may be used along with the axioms to derive other theorems. For example, you may use the theorem just proved to deduce the following.

THEOREM. If a, b, and c denote real numbers and if $a + c = b + c$, then $a = b$.

Proof

a, b, and c denote real numbers.	Given.
$a + c$ and $b + c$ are real numbers.	Closure for addition.
$-c$ is a real number.	Axiom of additive inverses.
$a + c = b + c$.	Given.
$(a + c) + (-c) = (b + c) + (-c)$.	Addition property of equality.
$(b + c) + (-c) = b$.	$(b + c) + (-c) = b$. (p. 19)
$(a + c) + (-c) = b$.	Transitive property of equality.
But $(a + c) + (-c) = a$.	$(b + c) + (-c) = b$. (p. 19)
$\therefore a = (a + c) + (-c)$.	Symmetric property of equality.
$\therefore a = b$.	Transitive property of equality.

Oral Exercises

Give the axiom, theorem, or definition justifying each step in the following proofs. Assume a, b, and c denote real numbers.

SAMPLE. Prove: $-(-b) = b$.

Steps	*What you say:*
b is a real number.	Given.
$-b$ is the additive inverse of b and $-(-b)$ is the additive inverse of $-b$.	Definition of the symbol for additive inverse.
$b + (-b) = 0$ and $-(-b) + (-b) = 0$.	Axiom of additive inverses.
$0 = b + (-b)$.	Symmetric property of equality.
$-(-b) + (-b) = b + (-b)$.	Transitive property of equality.
$\therefore -(-b) = b$.	If $a + c = b + c$, then $a = b$.

1. Prove: If $a = b$ and $c = b$, then $a = c$.

Proof

$a = b$ and $c = b$

$b = c$

$\therefore a = c$

2. Prove: If $a = b$, then $ac = bc$.

Proof

a, b, and c are real numbers. There is a real number d such that $ac = d$.

Since $a = b$, $bc = d$.

$d = bc$

$\therefore ac = bc$

3. Prove: If $a = b$, $a = c$, and $b = d$, then $c = d$.

Proof

$a = b$, $a = c$, and $b = d$

$b = a$

$\therefore b = c$

$c = b$

$\therefore c = d$

4. Prove: If $a = b$, then $c + a = c + b$.

Proof

a, b, and c are real numbers and $a = b$.

$a + c = b + c$

$a + c = c + a$ and

$b + c = c + b$

$\therefore c + a = c + b$

(See Exercise 3)

5. Prove: If $a = b$, then $-a = -b$.

Proof

a and b are real numbers. $-a$ and $-b$ are unique real numbers such that

$-b + b = 0$ and

$-a + a = 0$.

$a = b$

$\therefore -b + a = 0$

$-a + a = -b + a$

$\therefore -a = -b$

(See Exercise 1)

6. Prove: If $c \neq 0$, $(bc)\frac{1}{c} = b$.

Proof

b and c are real numbers and $c \neq 0$; bc is a real number.

$\frac{1}{c}$ is a real number

$(bc)\frac{1}{c}$ is a real number

$$(bc)\frac{1}{c} = b\left(c \cdot \frac{1}{c}\right)$$

$$= b \cdot 1$$

$$= b$$

$$\therefore (bc)\frac{1}{c} = b$$

Written Exercises

Prove each of the following theorems; a, b, c and d denote real numbers.

B

1. If $ac = bc$ and $c \neq 0$, then $a = b$.
2. If $ca = cb$ and $c \neq 0$, then $a = b$.
3. If $c + a = c + b$, then $a = b$.
4. If $a = b$ and neither a nor b is zero, $\frac{1}{a} = \frac{1}{b}$.
5. If $a + b = 0$, then $a = -b$ and $b = -a$.
6. If $ab = 1$ and neither a nor b is zero, then $a = \frac{1}{b}$ and $b = \frac{1}{a}$.
7. If $a = c$ and $a + b = c + d$, then $b = d$.
8. If $a = c$, $a \neq 0$, and $ab = cd$, then $b = d$.
9. If $a \neq 0$, $\frac{1}{\frac{1}{a}} = a$.
10. If $ab = b$, and $b \neq 0$, then $a = 1$.
11. If $b = d$ and $a - b = c - d$, then $a = c$.
12. If $a = bc$ and $b \neq 0$, then $c = a \cdot \frac{1}{b}$.

1–7 Adding and Subtracting Real Numbers

The axioms and the familiar addition facts for positive numbers enable you to find the sum of any two real numbers and to justify a general rule for finding sums.

EXAMPLE 1. Add: $-2 + (-3)$

Solution:

$-2 + (-3) = -(2 + 3)$ Property of the negative of a sum

$= -5$ Substitution

EXAMPLE 2. Add: $5 + (-3)$

Solution:

$$\begin{aligned} 5 + (-3) &= (2 + 3) + (-3) \\ &= 2 + [3 + (-3)] \\ &= 2 + 0 \\ &= 2 \end{aligned}$$

EXAMPLE 3. Add: $-5 + 3$

Solution:

$$\begin{aligned} -5 + 3 &= -(2 + 3) + 3 \\ &= [-2 + (-3)] + 3 \\ &= -2 + [-3 + 3] \\ &= -2 + 0 \\ &= -2 \end{aligned}$$

Can you supply the properties justifying the steps in Examples 2 and 3?

There is a useful interpretation of the addition of real numbers in terms of displacements (*changes of position*) on the number line. To add 3 to 2, start at 2 and move to the right a distance of 3 units. This displacement, shown by the red arrow in Figure 1–8, brings you to 5; thus, $2 + 3 = 5$.

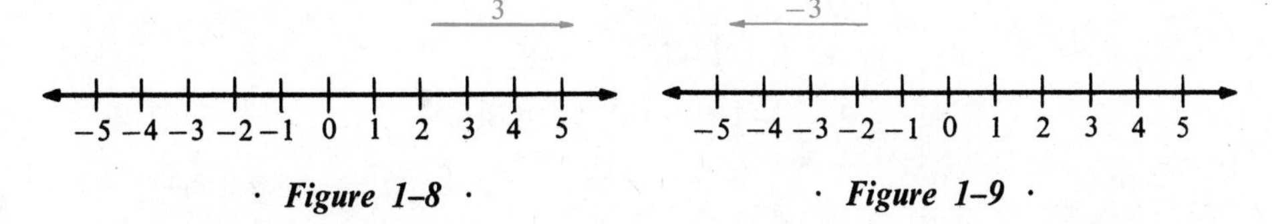

· *Figure 1–8* ·

· *Figure 1–9* ·

To add -3 to -2, start at -2, move 3 units to the left and arrive at -5 (Figure 1–9). You have $(-2) + (-3) = -5$. The sums $5 + (-3) = 2$ and $-5 + 3 = -2$ are pictured in Figures 1–10 and 1–11, respectively.

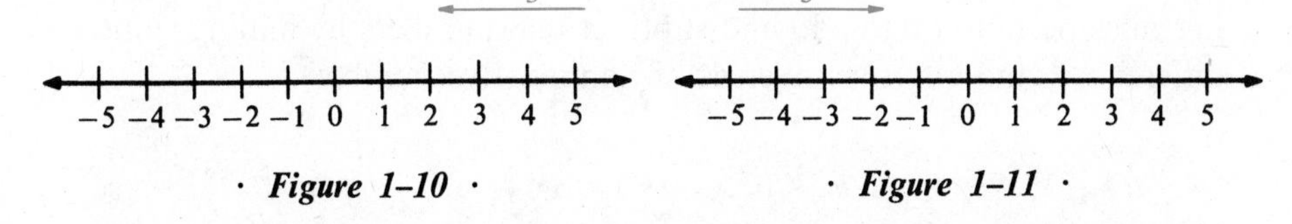

· *Figure 1–10* ·

· *Figure 1–11* ·

Subtraction in the set of real numbers is defined in terms of addition. Thus, $7 - 2 = 7 + (-2)$, $5 - (-3) = 5 + 3$, and $(-2) - (-1) = -2 + 1$. These examples illustrate the following definition:

If a and b denote real numbers, then $a - b = a + (-b)$.

To perform a subtraction, you replace the subtrahend by its negative, and add. Since every real number has a unique additive inverse, if you know b, then you know $-b$. Also, since $a + (-b)$ is a sum, it represents a real number. Hence, this definition implies that the set of real numbers is closed under subtraction.

Notice that $7 - 2 \neq 2 - 7$. Thus, subtraction of real numbers is *not* a commutative operation. Also, $(7 - 2) - 3 = 5 - 3 = 2$, whereas $7 - (2 - 3) = 7 - (-1) = 8$, so that subtraction of real numbers does *not* have the associative property. Consequently, to give a numerical expression like $7 - 2 - 3$ meaning, we agree on the following grouping: $7 - 2 - 3 = (7 - 2) - 3$. In general, we define:

$$a - b - c = (a - b) - c = a + (-b) + (-c).$$

In the absence of parentheses to indicate the order of operations in a sequence of additions and subtractions, you perform the operations as they occur in order from left to right.

EXAMPLE 4. Find: $4 - 12 + 7 - 2 - 9$

Solution: $4 - 12 = 4 + (-12) = -8, \quad -8 + 7 = -1,$

$-1 - 2 = -1 + (-2) = -3,$

$-3 - 9 = -3 + (-9) = -12,$ **Answer.**

or,

$(4 + 7) + [-12 + (-2) + (-9)] = 11 + (-23) = -12,$ **Answer.**

Since you can convert any subtraction into an addition, the following rules permit you to add and subtract real numbers by finding sums, differences, and additive inverses of nonnegative numbers:

1. **If $a \geq 0$ and $b \geq 0$, $a + b = |a| + |b|$.**

   EXAMPLE. $2 + 3 = 5$

2. **If $a \leq 0$ and $b \leq 0$, $a + b = -(|a| + |b|)$.**

   EXAMPLE. $-2 + (-3) = -(2 + 3) = -5$

3. **If $a > 0$ and $b < 0$ and $|a| \geq |b|$, $a + b = |a| - |b|$.**

   EXAMPLE. $5 + (-3) = 5 - 3 = 2$

4. **If $a \geq 0$ and $b < 0$ and $|a| < |b|$, $a + b = -(|b| - |a|)$.**

   EXAMPLE. $3 + (-5) = -(5 - 3) = -2$

Oral Exercises

a. Add the numbers. **b.** From the first number subtract the number listed below it.

1.	$\begin{array}{r}2\\3\end{array}$	**3.**	$\begin{array}{r}5\\-3\end{array}$	**5.**	$\begin{array}{r}-7\\4\end{array}$	**7.**	$\begin{array}{r}-8\\-9\end{array}$	**9.**	$\begin{array}{r}-6\\-4\end{array}$
2.	$\begin{array}{r}-5\\-5\end{array}$	**4.**	$\begin{array}{r}2\\-3\end{array}$	**6.**	$\begin{array}{r}4\\-1\end{array}$	**8.**	$\begin{array}{r}-4\\1\end{array}$	**10.**	$\begin{array}{r}-3\\-5\end{array}$

Find the following sums and differences.

11. $14 + (-7)$

12. $0 - (-6)$

13. $0 + (-9)$

14. $0 - 8$

15. $(-3) + (-4)$

16. $7 - (-2)$

17. $2 + (-9)$

18. $-4 - (-1)$

19. $100 - 100$

20. $2 + (-3)$

21. $-4 + -1$

22. $5 - (-5)$

Justify each step in the proofs of the following theorems, in each of which *a*, *b*, *c*, and *d* denote real numbers.

23. $a - (-b) = a + b$

Proof

a and b are real numbers.

$-b$ is a real number.

$a - (-b) = a + [-(-b)]$

$-(-b) = b$

$\therefore a - (-b) = a + b$

24. $-a + b = b - a$

Proof

a and b are real numbers.

$-a$ is a real number.

$-a + b = b + (-a)$

$b + (-a) = b - a$

$\therefore -a + b = b - a$

25. $-(a - b) = b - a$

Proof

a and b are real numbers.

$a - b = a + (-b)$

$-(a - b) = -[a + (-b)]$

$= (-a) + [-(-b)]$

$= -a + b$

$= b - a$

(See Exercise 24)

26. $a - (b - c) = (a - b) + c$

Proof

a, b, and c are real numbers.

$a - (b - c)$

$= a - (b + [-c])$

$= a + [-(b + [-c])]$

$= a + ([-b] + (-[-c]))$

$= a + ([-b] + c)$

$= (a + [-b]) + c$

$= (a - b) + c$

Written Exercises

Find the following sums and differences.

A

1. $47.5 + 50.5$
2. $-48 + (-36)$
3. $-71 - (-30)$
4. $-21 - (-29)$
5. $-19 + (-17)$
6. $12.9 + (-0)$
7. $(-0) + 61.2$
8. $-14 - (-81)$
9. $17.3 + (-17.3)$
10. $-46.5 - 50.5$
11. $-5.9 - (-6.2)$
12. $8.7 + (-9.3)$
13. $7 + (-8) + (-10) + 11$
14. $-13 + 6 + (-15) + (-6)$
15. $-21 - (-9) + (-0) + (-3)$
16. $-7 + 23 - 6 - (-10)$
17. $-13 + 15 - 18 + 2 - 7$
18. $8 - 11 - 3 - 14 + 9$
19. $19 + 3 - 8 - 10 - 4$
20. $23 - 7 - 6 - 10$

21.	22.	23.	24.
27	−38	58.3	−29.6
−9	−16	−17.2	38.5
−13	+47	−26.9	−12.1
−18	+7	−14.2	−59.7

25. Find the difference between a temperature of 8° and −2°.
26. Find the difference between a temperature of −10° and 2°.
27. Bill had a temperature of 103°F on Monday. Find the difference between this reading and the normal 98.6°F.
28. On Thursday Bill's temperature was 97.2°F. By how much did this differ from a normal temperature of 98.6°F.?

Show the computation of the following pairs of sums on a number line.

29. $-3 + (-7); -7 + (-3)$
30. $-8 + 4; 4 + (-8)$
31. $[-2 + (-1)] + 4; -2 + [-1 + 4]$
32. $[5 + (-3)] + (-2); 5 + [(-3) + (-2)]$

Determine which of the following subsets of the set of real numbers are closed under subtraction.

33. {natural numbers}
34. {integers}
35. {even integers}
36. {nonnegative even integers}

1–8 Multiplying and Dividing Real Numbers

Computations with numbers often involve both addition and multiplication. The *distributive axiom* serves as the link between these operations. The following examples employ the assumption that multiplication is *distributive* with respect to addition:

$$42(\tfrac{1}{3} + \tfrac{1}{7}) = (42 \cdot \tfrac{1}{3}) + (42 \cdot \tfrac{1}{7}) = 14 + 6 = 20$$

$$45 + 63 = (9 \cdot 5) + (9 \cdot 7) = 9(5 + 7) = 9(12) = 108$$

In general terms:

Distributive Axiom for Multiplication with Respect to Addition.

If a, b, and c denote any real numbers, then:

1. $a(b + c) = (ab) + (ac)$;
2. $(b + c)a = (ba) + (ca)$.

A very useful theorem that the distributive axiom enables you to prove is the **multiplication property of -1**, given below. This assertion means that multiplying a real number by -1 produces the additive inverse of the number. Thus, $4(-1) = -4$, $(-1)(-5) = 5$, and $(-1)(-1) = 1$.

THEOREM. If a denotes any real number, then $a(-1) = -a$ and $(-1)a = -a$.

Proof

a denotes a real number.	Given.
$a(-1)$ and $(-1)a$ denote real numbers.	Closure for multiplication.
$[a(-1)] + a$ is a real number.	Closure for addition.
$[a(-1)] + a = [a(-1)] + a$	Reflexive property of equality.
$= [a(-1)] + [a \cdot 1]$	Axiom of one.
$= a[(-1) + 1]$	Distributive axiom.
$= a \cdot 0$	Axiom of additive inverses.
$= 0$	Multiplication property of zero.
$\therefore [a(-1)] + a = 0$	Transitive property of equality.
$0 = (-a) + a$	Axiom of additive inverses.
$[a(-1)] + a = (-a) + a$	Transitive property of equality.
$\therefore a(-1) = -a$	If $a + c = b + c$, then $a = b$.
$(-1)a = a(-1)$	Commutative property of multiplication.
$\therefore (-1)a = -a$	Transitive property of equality.

The multiplication property of -1 together with the axioms and the multiplication facts for positive numbers enable you to multiply any two real numbers. For example,

$$
\begin{aligned}
4 \cdot 3 &= 12 \\
(-4) \cdot 3 &= (-1 \cdot 4)3 = -1(4 \cdot 3) = -1(12) = -12 \\
4(-3) &= 4[3(-1)] = (4 \cdot 3)(-1) = 12(-1) = -12 \\
(-4)(-3) &= (-1 \cdot 4)(-1 \cdot 3) = [-1(-1)](4 \cdot 3) = 1(12) = 12
\end{aligned}
$$

Similarly, for all real numbers a and b,

$$
\begin{aligned}
(-a)b &= (-1 \cdot a)b = -1(ab) = -ab \\
a(-b) &= a[b(-1)] = (ab)(-1) = -ab \\
(-a)(-b) &= (-1 \cdot a)(-1 \cdot b) = [-1(-1)](ab) = 1(ab) = ab
\end{aligned}
$$

Can you explain why the following statements are true?

1. The absolute value of the product of two or more real numbers is the product of the absolute values of the numbers.

2. A product of numbers of which an even number are negative is a positive number. A product of numbers of which an odd number are negative is a negative number.

We define the division of real numbers in terms of multiplication. For example,

$$14 \div 2 = 14 \cdot \frac{1}{2}, \qquad \frac{-28}{7} = -28 \cdot \frac{1}{7}, \qquad \frac{0}{3} = 0 \cdot \frac{1}{3}$$

In general:

If a and b denote any real numbers for which $b \neq 0$, then $\frac{a}{b} = a \cdot \frac{1}{b}$.

This definition means that to perform a division you replace the divisor by its reciprocal and multiply. Since every number except 0 has a unique reciprocal, and $b \neq 0$, $\frac{1}{b}$ represents a number. Since $a \cdot \frac{1}{b}$ is a product, it represents a number. Therefore, the definition implies that the real number system is closed under division, excluding division by 0.

Notice that in a fraction the bar acts as a symbol of inclusion, as well as a division sign. For example, $\frac{18 + 2}{3 + 2} = \frac{20}{5} = 4$; and,

$$\frac{a + b}{c} = \frac{1}{c}(a + b) = \frac{1}{c} \cdot a + \frac{1}{c} \cdot b = a \cdot \frac{1}{c} + b \cdot \frac{1}{c} = \frac{a}{c} + \frac{b}{c}.$$

Since $4 \div 2 \neq 2 \div 4$, division of real numbers is not a commutative operation. It is not an associative operation, either. For example, $(8 \div 4) \div 2 = 2 \div 2 = 1$, but $8 \div (4 \div 2) = 8 \div 2 = 4$.

For each a, b, and c, $b \neq 0$ and $c \neq 0$, we define:

$$a \div b \div c = (a \div b) \div c = \left(a \cdot \frac{1}{b}\right) \cdot \frac{1}{c}.$$

By agreement, the following steps give the order in which operations are to be performed.

Order of Operations

1. Simplify the expression within each symbol of inclusion, beginning with the innermost inclusion symbol.
2. Then, perform multiplications and divisions in order from left to right.
3. Then, perform additions and subtractions in order from left to right.

Note the following examples.

EXAMPLE 1. $5[3 + (7 \cdot 2)] = 5(3 + 14) = 5 \cdot 17 = 85$

EXAMPLE 2. Find $24 \div 6 \times (-3) \times 8 \div (-2)$

Solution: $24 \div 6 = 24 \cdot \frac{1}{6} = 4$, $4 \times (-3) = -12$, $-12 \times 8 = -96$

$-96 \div (-2) = -96 \cdot (-\frac{1}{2}) = 48$, **Answer.**

EXAMPLE 3. $3 \cdot a \div 3 + 2 - 7 \div b = \{[(3 \cdot a) \div 3] + 2\} - (7 \div b)$

Oral Exercises

Find the indicated products and quotients.

1. $(-2)(-7)$
2. $3(-4)$
3. $(-1)(-6)$
4. $0(-8)$
5. $(-\frac{1}{2})(-6)$
6. $(-3)(-8)$
7. $14 \div (-2)$
8. $-28 \div 4$
9. $0 \div 5$
10. $0 \div (-7)$
11. $(-32) \div (-16)$
12. $(-48) \div 6$

Without doing the computation tell whether each answer is a positive number, a negative number, or zero.

13. $(-3.5)(-.127)(-.49)$

14. $(-8)(2.3)(2.7)$

15. $\dfrac{(-8.1)(-7.3)(8.8)}{(2.1)(-3.7)}$

16. $\dfrac{(12.4)(-7.8)(6.5)}{(-3.2)(-1.4)(-1.7)}$

17. $\dfrac{(-2.9)(-3.7)(0)(-4.2)}{(-4)(-3.8)}$

18. $\dfrac{(-31.4)(-0)(7.2)}{(-1.1)(-8)}$

Written Exercises

Find the indicated products and quotients.

1. $-3 \cdot 0 \cdot -5 \cdot 8$
2. $-4 \cdot -2 \cdot -1 \cdot 6$
3. $(-14)(-12)(\frac{1}{7})$
4. $(-15)(\frac{1}{3})(-8)$
5. $29 \cdot 3 + 29 \cdot 7$
6. $31 \cdot 2 + 31 \cdot 8$
7. $10 - 5(17 + 3)$
8. $8 - 6 \cdot 12 - 8$
9. $-24 \div 4 \div (-3)$
10. $(-12)(-0)(-71)$
11. $0 \div 36 \div 6$
12. $64 \div (-16) \div (-2)$
13. $25(-3) \div (-5) \times 8 \div 3$
14. $12 \div (-\frac{1}{4}) \times (-15) \div (-9)$
15. $64 \div (-\frac{1}{8}) \times (-0) \times (-\frac{1}{4})$
16. $-100 \div (-\frac{1}{3}) \div (-5) \times (-2)$
17. $(-4)2 + 21 \div 3 + 4$
18. $15 - (4 + 8 \div 2) - 6$
19. $[36 - 4(3 + 1)] \div (4 - 6)$
20. $[64 - 5(1 + 4)] \div (-8 - 5)$

Prove each of the following theorems. *a*, *b*, and *c* denote real numbers.

B

21. $a(b - c) = ab - ac$

22. If $a \neq 0$, $\dfrac{1}{-a} = -\dfrac{1}{a}$

23. If $a \neq 0$, $\dfrac{a}{a} = 1$.

24. If $a \neq 0$, $\dfrac{-a}{a} = -1$.

25. If $a = b$ and $c \neq 0$, $\dfrac{a}{c} = \dfrac{b}{c}$.

26. $a \div 1 = a$

Chapter Summary

Inventory of Structure and Method

1. **Axioms** and **definitions** form the foundation of the set of real numbers. From these, you can derive **theorems** to build a logical structure on that

foundation. Every step in an exercise or in the proof of a theorem can be justified by an axiom, a definition, a given fact, or a theorem previously proved. On the next page are listed the axioms assumed in this chapter as part of the foundation of the set of real numbers.

2. From the axioms you can derive rules of operation such as the Multiplication Property of -1 (page 27).

3. To subtract a number, add its additive inverse: $a - b = a + (-b)$. To divide by a nonzero number, multiply by its multiplicative inverse: $\frac{a}{b} = a \cdot \frac{1}{b}$.
The Multiplication Property of Zero implies you may not divide by zero.

4. There is an agreement on the order in which operations are performed (page 29).

5. To solve an open sentence, determine which numbers of the domain of the variable(s) satisfy the sentence, that is, make it a true statement.

Vocabulary and Spelling

Review each term by reference to the page listed.

set (*p. 1*)
member (element) of a set (*p. 1*)
specifying a set (*p. 1*)
equal sets (*p. 2*)
one-to-one correspondence (*p. 2*)
finite set (*p. 2*)
infinite set (*p. 2*)
subset, proper and improper (*p. 2*)
empty, or null, set (∅) (*p. 2*)
numeral (*p. 3*)
numerical expression (*p. 3*)
equation (*p. 3*)
inequality (*p. 3*)
variable (*p. 6*)
domain (*p. 6*)
values of the variable (*p. 6*)
replacement set (universe) (*p. 6*)
constant (*p. 6*)
open sentence (*p. 6*)
solution (truth) set (*p. 6*)
root (solution) (*p. 6*)
real numbers (*p. 8*)
number line (*p. 8*)
origin (*p. 8*)
graph of a number (*p. 8*)
coordinate of a point (*p. 8*)
graph of a subset (*p. 9*)
term (*p. 10*)
factor (*p. 10*)
symbols of inclusion (*p. 10*)
unique (*p. 11*)
closed under an operation (*p. 11*)
additive inverse, or negative (*p. 14*)
absolute value (*p. 15*)
reciprocal (*p. 15*)
multiplicative inverse (*p. 15*)
hypothesis (*p. 18*)
conclusion (*p. 18*)
proof (*p. 19*)
theorem (*p. 19*)

PROPERTIES OF REAL NUMBERS

In the following list of properties of the set of positive and negative numbers and zero, a, b, c, and d denote any real numbers.

	FOR ADDITION	FOR MULTIPLICATION
CLOSURE AXIOMS	$a + b$ represents a unique real number.	ab represents a unique real number.
COMMUTATIVE AXIOMS	$a + b = b + a$	$ab = ba$
ASSOCIATIVE AXIOMS	$(a + b) + c = a + (b + c)$	$(ab)c = a(bc)$
IDENTITY ELEMENT	0 is the unique element such that $0 + a = a$ and $a + 0 = a$.	1 is the unique element such that $1 \cdot a = a$ and $a \cdot 1 = a$.
INVERSE ELEMENTS	There is a unique real number $-a$, the additive inverse of a, such that $a + (-a) = 0$ and $(-a) + a = 0$.	Provided a is not 0, there is a unique real number $\frac{1}{a}$, the multiplicative inverse of a, such that $a \cdot \frac{1}{a} = 1$ and $\frac{1}{a} \cdot a = 1$.
INVERSES OF SUMS AND PRODUCTS	$-(a + b) = (-a) + (-b)$	If neither a nor b is zero, $\frac{1}{ab} = \frac{1}{a} \cdot \frac{1}{b}$.
MULTIPLICATION PROPERTY OF ZERO		$a \cdot 0 = 0$ and $0 \cdot a = 0$

DISTRIBUTIVE AXIOM

$$a(b + c) = ab + ac$$
$$(b + c)a = ba + ca$$

PROPERTIES OF ORDER

AXIOM OF COMPARISON — One and only one of the following statements is true: $a < b$, $a = b$, $a > b$.

TRANSITIVE PROPERTY

1. If $a < b$ and $b < c$, then $a < c$.
2. If $a > b$ and $b > c$, then $a > c$.

PROPERTIES OF EQUALITY

REFLEXIVE $a = a$

SYMMETRIC If $a = b$, then $b = a$.

TRANSITIVE If $a = b$ and $b = c$, then $a = c$.

SUBSTITUTION

1. If $a = b$ and $a + c = d$, then $b + c = d$.
2. If $a = b$ and $ac = d$, then $bc = d$.

In Chapters 2 and 7, the remaining axioms characterizing the real number system will be added to the list.

Chapter Test

1–1 State whether the given sets are equal.

1. {letters in the word *honest*} ; {letters in the word *denotes*}

Identify the following set as being either finite or infinite.

2. {possible lengths of sides of triangles having perimeter 15 in.}

3. If $\{3 + 7, 8 - 1\} \subset \{1, 3, 7, *\}$, then $*$ must represent __?__.

1–2 Specify by roster.

4. $S = \{x\colon x - 3 \neq 2 \text{ and } x \in \{4, 5, 6, 7\}\}$

1–3 Show the graph of the following subsets of the set of real numbers.

5. $\{k\colon k \text{ is a negative integer and } -3 \leq k < -2\}$

6. $\{m\colon m > 3\}$

1–4 Is the given set closed under **(a)** addition and **(b)** multiplication, of two of its elements? If the set is not closed, give an example to show this.

7. {negative odd integers}

Give the property justifying each of the following. Consider the set of real numbers as the domain of each variable.

8. If $8 = x + 3$, then $x + 3 = 8$.

9. If $n = -3 + (-5)$, then n is a real number.

10. If $m = 6$, then $m + 2 = 6 + 2$.

1–5 Solve for the indicated variable over the set of real numbers. Graph any nonempty solution set.

11. $|t| + (-3) = 0$ **12.** $5 + |-s| = 0$

1–6 Justify each step in the proof below by a definition, an axiom, a given fact, or a proved theorem. Each variable represents a real number.

13. Prove: If $a = b$ and $c = d$, then $a + c = b + d$.

1. $a = b$
2. $a + c = b + c$
3. $c = d$
4. $b + c = b + d$
5. $\therefore a + c = b + d$

1–7 **14.** Find the sum: $-7.3 - (-3.7) + (-2.6)$

1–8 **15.** Find the product: $(-16) \div \frac{3}{4} \times (-8)$

16. If a, b, and d are real numbers, $d \neq 0$, and $\frac{a}{d} = \frac{b}{d}$, then $a = b$. Prove.

Chapter Review

1–1 Sets and Their Relationships *Pages 1–5*

1. *Specify by roster:* {living ex-Presidents of the U.S.A.}.

2. *Specify by rule:* {12, 15, 18}.

3. Two sets are __?__ if they contain the same elements.

4. When each member of each of two sets can be paired with exactly one member of the other set, the sets are in __?__ to __?__ correspondence.

In each case, is the statement true or is it false?

5. Every set has at least two subsets.

6. {trees in Yosemite National Park} is finite.

7. $\frac{9+3}{3} \neq \frac{12+4}{4}$

8. {multiples of 5} $\subset$ {even integers}

9. {letters in the word *sentences*} = {letters in the word *cents*}.

1–2 Sets and Variables *Pages 6–8*

10. The solution set of an open sentence must be a subset of the __?__ of the variable.

11. If $x \in \{0, 1, 3, 5\}$, the solution set of $x + 3 = 5$ is __?__.

12. If $r \in \{0, 1, 3, 5\}$, then 3 is a __?__ of the open sentence $7 - r = 4$, since 3 is a member of the __?__ of r and 3 __?__ the open sentence.

Specify each set.

13. $A = \{m\colon m + 3 + 5 = 9 - 1 \text{ and } m \in \{0, 12, 3\}\}$.

14. $B = \{n\colon n \in \{\text{subjects in your present program}\}\}$.

15. $C = \{r\colon \text{twice } r \text{ is a positive even number}\}$.

16. $D = \{s\colon 7 \times s = 7 \text{ or } s \in \{0, 1, 2\}\}$.

17. $M = \{t\colon t + 6 = 6 + t \text{ and } t \in \{\text{integers}\}\}$.

18. $N = \{z\colon z \times 3 = z \times 4 \text{ and } z \in \{4, 3, 2, 1, 0\}\}$.

19. $R = \{x\colon x + 5 = x + 3 \text{ and } x \in \{\text{integers}\}\}$.

1–3 Order in the Set of Real Numbers *Pages 8–10*

20. The positive and negative numbers and __?__ make up the set of __?__ numbers.

21. The graph of a __?__ is paired with the __?__ of a point on the number line.

22. If $a > b$ and $b > 5$, then a must be __?__ than __?__.

23. The inequalities $x > -3$ and $x < 2$ may be written in the form __?__ < __?__ < __?__.

24. An __?__ or a __?__ is an assumption.

Graph the following subsets of the set of real numbers.

25. $\{x: x \geq -1\}$

26. $\{n: -2 < n \leq 4\}$

27. $\{r: r \neq -1 \text{ and } r \neq 3\}$

28. $\{s: s = 0 \text{ or } s = 2\}$

1–4 Properties of Addition and Multiplication *Pages 10–14*

Which of the following sets are closed under **(a)** *addition and* **(b)** *multiplication? When a set is not closed, show an example.*

29. $\{0, 1\}$

30. $\{\frac{1}{2}, \frac{1}{3}, \frac{1}{4}, \ldots\}$

31. $\{-2, -1, 0, 1, 2\}$

32. $\{-1, -2, -3, \ldots\}$

Give the properties used in each case.

33. If $x = y + t$ and $y + t = n$, then $x = n$.

34. $r + 3 \cdot 2 = r + 2 \cdot 3$

35. If $y = 3$, then $y + x = 3 + x$.

36. roll + (hot dog + mustard) = (roll + hot dog) + mustard.

37. $4 \times (3 \times 2) = 12 \times 2$.

38. If $p = (-2)(6)$, then p is a real number.

39. If $n + a = 5$ and $a = 3$, then $n + 3 = 5$.

1–5 Identity and Inverse Elements *Pages 14–18*

40. If an operation on two numbers produces the __?__ element for that operation, then each number is the __?__ of the other for that operation.

41. The __?__ inverse of 1 is -1.

42. The absolute value of a real number may be __?__ or zero, but it cannot be __?__.

43. The negative of $3 + (-2)$ is __?__.

Solve over the set of real numbers. Graph each nonempty solution set.

44. $|-x| + (-2) = 0$

45. $\frac{1}{a} = -\left|-\frac{2}{5}\right|$

46. $|-s| + (-4) = s$

47. $|-t| = t$

48. $-|r| = |r|$

49. $3 + (-k) = 4$

50. $|n| > 2$

1–6 The Concept of Proof *Pages 18–22*

51. Each step in a proof must be justified by a given fact, an __?__, a definition, or a __?__ previously proved.

52. *Justify each step in the given proof.* (m, n, r, and s are real numbers.)

Prove: If $m = n$, $r = s$, $r \neq 0$, and $s \neq 0$, then $\frac{m}{r} = \frac{n}{s}$.

(a) m, n, r, and s are real numbers.

(b) $r \neq 0$, $s \neq 0$

(c) $\frac{m}{r}$, $\frac{n}{r}$, and $\frac{n}{s}$ are real numbers.

(d) $m = n$

(e) $\frac{m}{r} = \frac{n}{r}$

(f) $r = s$

(g) $\frac{n}{r} = \frac{n}{s}$

(h) $\therefore \frac{m}{r} = \frac{n}{s}$

53. *Prove:* If x, y, k, and t are real numbers, and $x = y$ and $k = t$, then $x + (-k) = y + (-t)$.

1–7 Adding and Subtracting Real Numbers *Pages 22–26*

54. Subtracting a real number is the same as __?__ its __?__.

55. If $a \neq b$, then $a - b \neq b - a$, since __?__ is not a __?__ operation.

State whether each set is closed under subtraction. If it is not, show by an example.

56. {negative integers}

57. {positive and negative numbers}

Add and then subtract in each of the following.

58.	**59.**	**60.**	**61.**	**62.**
-7	3	4	-1	-4
2	-5	-3	-6	-4

Compute.

63. $-2.8 + (-5.4) - (-6.3)$

64. $36 - [17 + (-3) - (-22)]$

1–8 Multiplying and Dividing Real Numbers *Pages 26–30*

Find each indicated product or quotient.

65. $21 \times (-14) \div (-7)$

66. $(-196) \div (-49) \div (-7)$

67. $(-183) \div (3 \times 30.5)$

68. $31.4 \div (-15.7) \times 0 \div 8.6$

69. *Prove:* For every real number a, b, c, with $c \neq 0$,

$$\frac{a - b}{c} = \frac{a}{c} - \frac{b}{c}.$$

70. *Simplify.* $118 \div [9(7 - 1) + 5]$

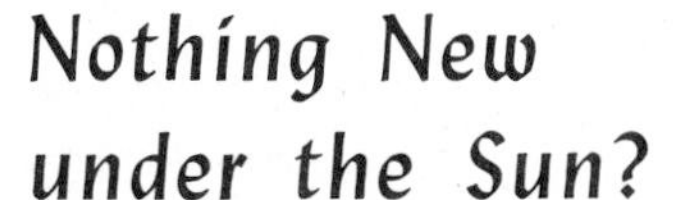

Nothing New under the Sun?

To be the creator, the inventor, of a new device such as television is quite wonderful. It is even more wonderful to create a new idea. Few mathematicians have originated as far-reaching an idea as did the German mathematician Georg Cantor, who lived from 1845 to 1918. It was when he was about thirty years old that Cantor announced a new theory of mathematics, the theory of sets. As is so often the case with new ideas and their creators, Cantor was derided by his colleagues, who found his concept revolutionary and unacceptable. The main criticism against his work arose because he was concerned with a mathematical approach toward the concept of the infinite.

Cantor was of a mild disposition, unable to hold his own in the bitter arguments. Opposition was so strong that he was denied an appointment at the University of Berlin. However, Cantor did live to see, though regrettably not until just before his death, the recognition of his work by mathematicians the world over.

The great strides in mathematics in this century rest upon foundations laid by this brilliant man. In this chapter you have become acquainted with some of the basic and simpler ideas of his theory. A complete study of the subject must wait until your college years, when you have become more mature mathematically. As you continue your study, you will come to appreciate the truth of Cantor's words:

The essence of mathematics lies in its freedom.

CHAPTER 2

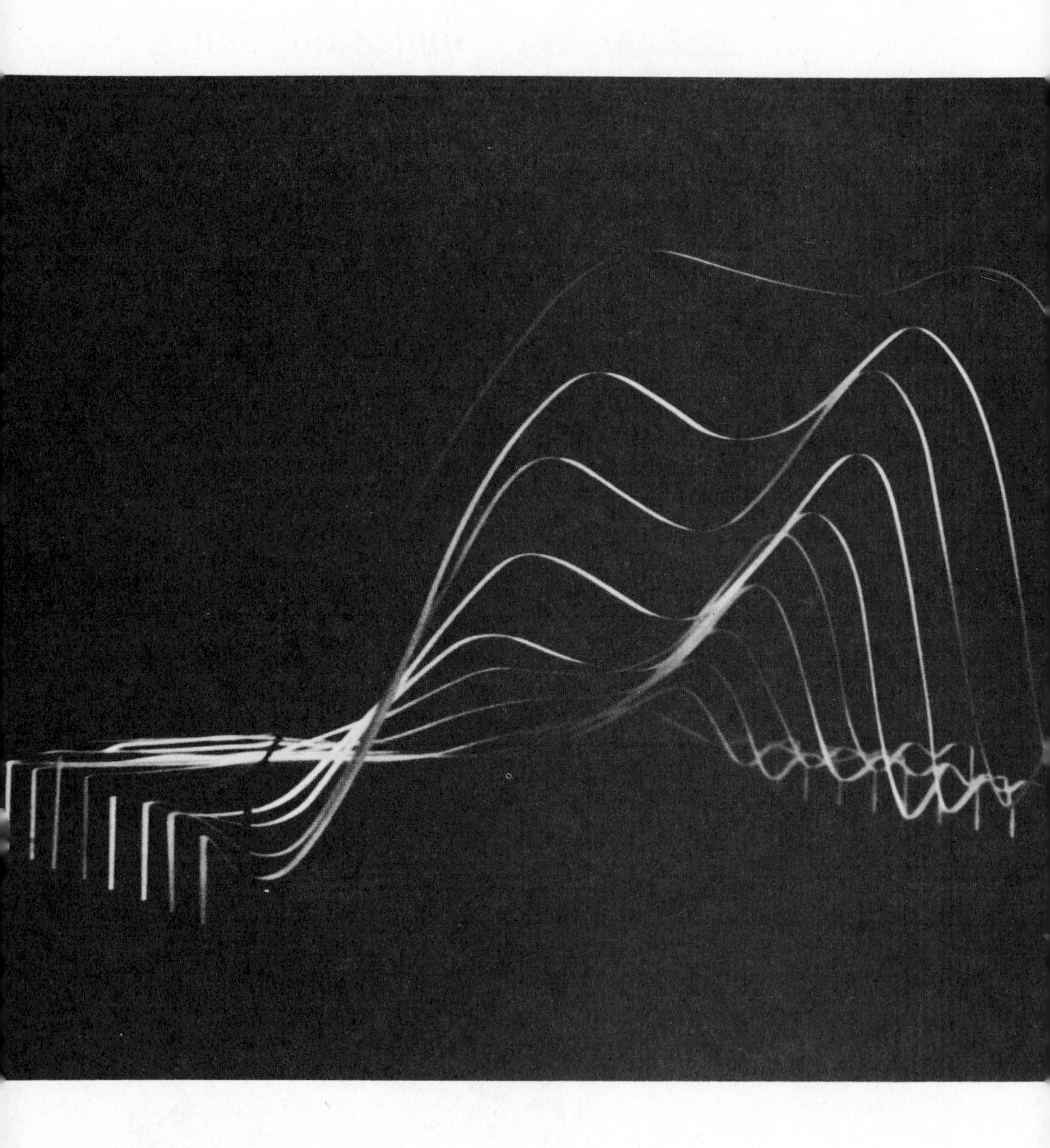

. . . a three-dimensional model of a computer-generated mathematical expression used to describe electronic performance

Open Sentences in One Variable

One of the principal skills to be acquired in the study of algebra is facility in solving open sentences. The main purpose of this chapter is to extend your understanding and knowledge so that you can deal easily with both equations and inequalities in one variable. A few new axioms will be added to those of Chapter 1 because they are needed in the work with inequalities.

EQUIVALENT EXPRESSIONS

2–1 Algebraic Expressions

Numerical expressions, variables, and indicated sums, products, differences, and quotients containing variables, such as 7, $2t$, $ab + ac$, $3y - 4$, and $\frac{x - 7}{y}$, are called **algebraic expressions**. Do you recall how exponents are used in such expressions? We call 5^4, "the fourth *power* of 5," and use it in place of $5 \cdot 5 \cdot 5 \cdot 5$. The *exponent* ^{4} shows that the *base* 5 is used as a *factor* 4 times. In general, if n denotes a positive integer and a, a real number, then the product of n factors each of which is a is called the **nth power** of a and is denoted by a^n. In the expression a^n, a is called the **base** and n is called the exponent of the base.

Here are some powers of a:

First power $a^1 = a$

Second power $a^2 = a \cdot a$ (also read, "a squared or a-square")

Third power $a^3 = a \cdot a \cdot a$ (also read, "a cubed or a-cube")

Fourth power $a^4 = a \cdot a \cdot a \cdot a$ (also read, "a fourth")

A term which is either a numeral (-3), a variable (x), or a product of a numeral and one or more variables $(5x, x^3, 3a^2b)$ is called a **monomial**. A term such as $\frac{1}{x}$, in which the variable appears in the denominator, is not a monomial. Monomials which are numerals, such as 2 and -3, or monomials which have the same variable factors, such as $9xy^3$ and $6xy^3$, are said to be **similar** or **like**. The **degree of a monomial** is the sum of the exponents of its variables. The degree of $9xy^3$ is 4, because $1 + 3 = 4$. A numeral other than 0 is a monomial of degree 0. The monomial 0 has no degree. The numerical factor of a monomial is called the **numerical coefficient** (or simply the **coefficient**) **of the monomial**. For example, the coefficient of $9xy^3$ is 9, and of $-z^4$ is -1.

A monomial or a sum of monomials is called a **polynomial**. The **degree of a polynomial** is the greatest of the degrees of its terms. The degrees of the terms of $4x^4 + 7x^2y^6 - 3$ are, in order, 4, 8, and 0. The degree of this polynomial is, therefore, 8.

To call attention to the particular variables in a polynomial, we speak of a *polynomial in one or more given variables*. For example, $2x^2 - x + 5$ is a polynomial in x, and $5ab + b^3$ is a polynomial in a and b.

A polynomial is in **simple form** in a given variable when no two of its terms are similar and when its terms appear in order of either decreasing or increasing degree in that variable. Thus, $4x^2 + 7$ is a polynomial of two terms, a **binomial**, which is in simple form. The **trinomial**, or polynomial of three terms, $32 + 6ab^2 + 7b^4$, is in simple form in the variable b.

Oral Exercises

Identify each of the following polynomials as a monomial, binomial, or trinomial and give the degree.

1. x

2. xyz

3. $y^2 - 2x^2y$

4. 0

5. $30 + 7x - y$

6. $11 \cdot 3$

7. $5x^4y^3 + x^3 - 3xy^2$

8. $y^4 - 10$

9. $3^2 - 1$

10. $9y^5 + 8x$

Express these polynomials in simple form in a.

11. $6a^2 + a^3 - 2ab$

12. $a^8b^8 + 15a^2b^3 + 6a^5$

13. $2 + a^3b^2 - 10ab^3$

14. $a^4b^7 + b$

15. $8b^2 + 7a^2b^6 - 3ab^3$

16. $b^3 + 3a^2b + 3ab^2 + a^3$

2–2 Simplifying Expressions

Because the variables in a polynomial represent real numbers, we can use the properties of real numbers to simplify the polynomial.

EXAMPLE 1. Simplify: $[6x^2 - 2x] + [4x + x^2]$

Solution:

$[6x^2 - 2x] + [4x + x^2]$	
$= [6x^2 + (-2x)] + [4x + x^2]$	Meaning of subtraction.
$= [6x^2 + (-2)x] + [4x + x^2]$	$-ab = (-a)b$.
$= 6x^2 + [(-2)x + (4x + x^2)]$	Associative axiom for addition.
$= 6x^2 + [\overline{(-2)x + 4x} + x^2]$	Associative axiom for addition.
$= 6x^2 + [(-2 + 4)x + x^2]$	Distributive axiom for multiplication with respect to addition.
$= 6x^2 + [2x + x^2]$	Substitution axiom.
$= 6x^2 + [x^2 + 2x]$	Commutative axiom for addition.
$= [6x^2 + x^2] + 2x$	Associative axiom for addition.
$= [6x^2 + 1 \cdot x^2] + 2x$	Axiom of 1.
$= [6 + 1]x^2 \quad + 2x$	Distributive axiom for multiplication.
$= 7x^2 + 2x$	Substitution Axiom.
$\therefore [6x^2 - 2x] + [4x + x^2]$ $= 7x^2 + 2x$	Transitive property of equality.

Because the axioms guarantee that the equation in the final step of this simplification is true for *every* numerical replacement of the variable, the expressions that form its *right member*, $7x^2 + 2x$, and its *left member*, $[6x^2 - 2x] + [4x + x^2]$, are called **equivalent expressions**, and the equation is called an **identity**.

Although in practice you do not write all the steps given in the preceding example, you should know how the simplification depends on the properties of real numbers and you should be able to give and justify all the steps. The next example shows a brief way of presenting a polynomial simplification.

EXAMPLE 2. Simplify: $(3y^2 + 5y^3 - 7y + 4) + (2 - y^2 + 7y)$.

Solution:

$$(3y^2 + 5y^3 - 7y + 4) + (2 - y^2 + 7y)$$
$$= 5y^3 + (3 - 1)y^2 + (-7 + 7)y + (4 + 2)$$
$$= 5y^3 + 2y^2 + 0y + 6$$
$$= 5y^3 + 2y^2 + 6$$

In subtracting polynomials, you use the property of the negative of a sum along with the other properties to simplify the difference.

EXAMPLE 3. Simplify: $(4b^2 + 3b - 2) - (7b^2 + 5b - 1)$.

Solution: $(4b^2 + 3b - 2) - (7b^2 + 5b - 1)$

$$= (4b^2 + 3b - 2) + [(-7)b^2 + (-5)b + 1]$$
$$= (4 - 7)b^2 + (3 - 5)b + (-2 + 1)$$
$$= -3b^2 - 2b - 1$$

To express a sum (or difference) of polynomials in equivalent simple form, you add (or subtract) the coefficients of similar terms.

The equation $W = I^2R$ is called a *formula.* It gives an expression for one variable, W, in terms of other variables, I and R. Given that $I = \frac{1}{2}$ and $R = 200$, you can find the corresponding value of W by **evaluating** as follows:

$$W = I^2R = (\tfrac{1}{2})^2(200) = \tfrac{1}{4} \cdot 200 \qquad \therefore W = 50$$

Oral Exercises

Read each polynomial in simple form and then give its degree.

SAMPLE. $4t + 2 + 8t - 5$

What you say: $12t - 3$; the degree is 1.

1. $7x + 3x$
2. $5z - 2z$
3. $9y + 2y + 3y$
4. $8n + 7n + 2n$
5. $2s^5 + 4 - 3s^5$
6. $9z^4 + 8 + 12z^4$
7. $3x^2 + x - 3x^2$
8. $4y^3 + y + 9y^3$
9. $2 + 2(b + 3)$
10. $3(4b + 5) + 1$
11. $5(2x^2 + 9) + 7x^2$
12. $2(k^4 + 3) + 10k^4$
13. $2y^2 + 8y^2 - 2y^2 + 7y^2$
14. $9t^3 - 3t^3 + 2t^3 - 5t^3$
15. $-7x + 2y + 2x + 9y$
16. $3t + 4v + 5t - 7v$

Written Exercises

Find an equivalent polynomial in simple form.

A

1. $50(\frac{1}{5} + \frac{1}{2})$
2. $(\frac{1}{3} + \frac{1}{7})42$
3. $10 + 14 \div (-2) + 3$
4. $(49 - 1) \div (7 + 1)$
5. $(49 - 1) \div (1 - 7)$
6. $3 \cdot 5 - (5 \cdot 3 + 4)$

7. $9x + (5x + 2) - (3x + 8)$
8. $2a - (7a + 3) + (5a + 6)$
9. $r + 7(r + s) - 8(r + s) + s$
10. $-2(t - v) - t + 3(t - v) + v$
11. $5 - 2(3r + 4) + r$
12. $7 - 3(2 - p) + 3p$
13. $30(x - y) - 8(x - y) + 10xy$
14. $8(a + b) - 6(a + b) + 2a^2b^2$

B

15. $(5x^3 + 7x^2 - 3x + 1) + (3x^3 + 5x - 18 + 4x^2)$
16. $(2a^4 + 3a^3 + 2 - 5a^2) + (3a^2 + 4a^3 - 8a^4 - 3)$
17. $(b^3 - 2b^2 + 3b + 4) - (b^2 - 4b^3 + 2b - 1)$
18. $(m^2 - 7m^3 - m - 3) - (10m^3 + m + 2 - m^2)$
19. $(2x^3 + 7x^2y^2 + 10xy^3) + (9x^2y^2 - 3x^3y)$
20. $(3c^2d + 2cd + 5d^3) + (9d^3 - 7c^2d - 2cd)$
21. $5t + 3s - 2(2t - 4s) + 3(5s + 8t)$
22. $8(7j + 4m) + 5(2m - 5j) - 6(m + j)$
23. $3[4a + 5(a + 2)] - 8$
24. $21 - 2[8k + 4(3k - 1)]$
25. $x(3x + 4) + 2(x^2 - 7x + 6) - 3x(1 - 5x)$
26. $4(5 - 2y - y^2) - y(y + 6) + 2y(7 - 8y)$

Evaluate the variable in the left member of each formula for the given values of the other variables.

27. $d = \frac{1}{2}at^2$; $a = 32$, $t = 3$ (freely falling body)
28. $k = \frac{1}{2}mv^2$; $m = 15$, $v = 2$ (kinetic energy)
29. $C = \frac{5}{9}(F - 32)$; $F = -4$ (Fahrenheit to centigrade)
30. $F = \frac{9}{5}C + 32$; $C = -20$ (centigrade to Fahrenheit)
31. $S = -\frac{1}{2}gt^2 + vt$; $g = 32$, $t = 2$, $v = 4$ (motion of a projectile)
32. $A = \pi(R^2 - r^2)$; $R = 9$, $r = 5$ (area of a ring). Use $\frac{22}{7}$ for π.
33. $R = \dfrac{kl}{d^2}$; $k = 9$, $l = 100$, $d = 5$ (resistance of a wire)
34. $L = g\left(\dfrac{t}{2\pi}\right)^2$; $g = 32$, $t = 0.3\pi$ (length of a pendulum)

Determine whether or not the number in red belongs to the solution set of the equation.

35. $x + 5 - \dfrac{x - 20}{x - 4} = 16$; 8
36. $s - 3 + \dfrac{5s - 5}{s - 2} = 10$; 7
37. $m(m + 3) = m^3 - 10$; -2
38. $(2 - k)(k + 1) = 2k - 5$; 3
39. $y^2 + 2y + 3 = 5y + 7$; -1
40. $5 - 3t + t^2 = 7 - 4t$; -2

EQUIVALENT OPEN SENTENCES

2-3 Equivalent Equations

Study the following two sequences of equations over the set of real numbers.

$x = 11$	Given.	$3x + 5 = 38$	
$3x = 3 \cdot 11$	Multiply by 3.	$3x + 5 - 5 = 38 - 5$	Add -5.
$3x = 33$		$3x = 33$	
$3x + 5 = 33 + 5$	Add 5.	$\frac{1}{3} \cdot 3x = \frac{1}{3} \cdot 33$	Multiply by $\frac{1}{3}$.
$\therefore 3x + 5 = 38$		$\therefore x = 11$	

Do you see that the properties of equality (Sec. 1–6) insure that if the first statement in either sequence is true for some real value of x, then the last statement in the sequence must also be true for that value of x? This means that $3x + 5 = 38$ and $x = 11$ must have exactly the same solution set, namely, $\{11\}$; that is, they are **equivalent**

The properties of equality guarantee that the following transformations of a given equation always produce an equivalent equation.

Transformations That Produce an Equivalent Equation

1. Adding to or subtracting from each member of the given equation the same polynomial in any variables appearing in the equation.
2. Multiplying or dividing each member by the same *nonzero* number.
3. Substituting for either member an expression equivalent to it.

You often use these transformations to convert an equation into an equivalent one whose solution set can be determined by inspection. The process of determining the solution set of an open sentence is called **solving the open sentence.**

Because errors may occur in transforming equations, you should check each apparent root by substituting it in the original equation.

Hereafter, you can assume, unless otherwise stated, that the domain of each variable is the set of real numbers.

EXAMPLE 1. Solve $2(3y + 5) - 12 = 3y - 8$.

Solution:

1. Copy the equation.	$\underbrace{2(3y + 5)} - 12 = 3y - 8$
2. Use the distributive axiom and simplify the left member.	$6y + 10 - 12 = 3y - 8$ $6y - 2 = 3y - 8$
3. Add 2 to each member and simplify each member.	$6y - 2 + 2 = 3y - 8 + 2$ $6y = 3y - 6$
4. Subtract $3y$ from each member in order that the variable will appear only in the left member.	$6y - 3y = 3y - 6 - 3y$ $3y = -6$
5. Divide each member by 3.	$\frac{3y}{3} = \frac{-6}{3}$ $y = -2$

Check:

$$2(3y + 5) - 12 \stackrel{?}{=} 3y - 8 \quad \leftarrow \text{original equation}$$
$$2[3(-2) + 5] - 12 \stackrel{?}{=} 3(-2) - 8$$
$$2(-6 + 5) - 12 \stackrel{?}{=} -6 - 8$$
$$2(-1) - 12 \stackrel{?}{=} -14$$
$$-2 - 12 \stackrel{?}{=} -14$$
$$-14 = -14 \checkmark$$

The question mark above the equal sign means, "Is this statement true?" The check (√) means "Yes, it is."

$\{-2\}$, **Answer.**

EXAMPLE 2. If b is a nonzero constant, solve for x: $xb = a$.

Solution:

$$xb = a$$
$$\frac{xb}{b} = \frac{a}{b}$$
$$x \cdot 1 = \frac{a}{b}; \qquad x = \frac{a}{b}. \qquad \left\{\frac{a}{b}\right\}, \text{ **Answer.**}$$

EXAMPLE 3. Solve for z: $z + b = a$.

Solution:

$$z + b = a$$
$$z + b - b = a - b$$
$$z + 0 = a - b$$
$$z = a - b \qquad \{a - b\}, \textbf{ Answer.}$$

In these examples the check is left to you.

The foregoing Examples suggest viewing division and subtraction as *inverse operations* to multiplication and addition:

$\frac{a}{b}$ is the number you multiply by b to obtain a; for example,

$$\tfrac{6}{2} = 3 \text{ because } 3 \cdot 2 = 6;$$

$a - b$ is the number you add to b to obtain a; for example,

$$7 - 2 = 5 \text{ because } 5 + 2 = 7.$$

This meaning of subtraction also suggests a number-line interpretation for $a - b$: the displacement from b to a.

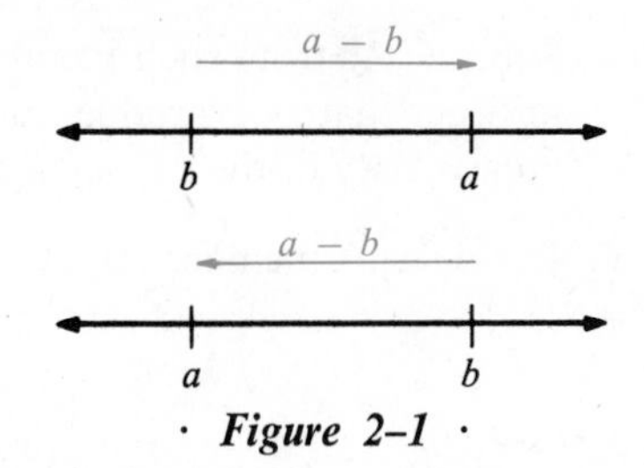

· *Figure 2–1* ·

Oral Exercises

Each of the following equations is the result of transforming $3ay = 27a$ into an equivalent equation. In each case give the transformations used. Assume that a is a nonzero constant.

1. $6ay = 54a$
2. $ay = 9a$
3. $3ay + 3a = 30a$
4. $3ay - 2a = 25a$
5. $2ay = a(27 - y)$
6. $6ay = 3a(9 + y)$
7. $3y = 27$
8. $\frac{y}{3} = 3$
9. $9a^2y = 81a^2$
10. $y = 9$
11. $3a(y - 9) = 0$
12. $3a(y + 9) = 54a$

Given $a + b = c$, $c = d + e$, tell which of the following statements are true for *all* real values of the variables. Assume $c \neq 0$.

13. $a = d + e + b$
14. $d = a - e + b$
15. $a + b = 2c - b - a$
16. $b + d = 2c + a - e$
17. $(a + b)^2 = c(d + e)$
18. $\frac{a + b}{d + e} = 1$
19. $\frac{a + b}{c} = \frac{c}{d + e}$
20. $\frac{a + b}{c} = \frac{c + d}{e}$

Written Exercises

Solve the following equations. Check your answers.

A

1. $2x + 3 = 9$
2. $4y - 1 = 31$
3. $5m + 4m + 72 = 0$
4. $-2n + 9n - 343 = 0$
5. $6x + 4 = 4x - 2$
6. $3y + 82 = 58 - y$
7. $3x + 16 = 5x + 8$
8. $7n - 6 = 9n - 114$
9. $\frac{3x}{7} = 21$
10. $\frac{5n}{3} = 60$
11. $2.6 = \frac{5r}{3}$
12. $3.5 = \frac{2x}{7}$
13. $\frac{x}{5} - \frac{3x}{5} = 1$
14. $\frac{2n}{3} - \frac{4n}{3} = 3$
15. $2(2x - 1) + 4 = 26$
16. $3(y + 4) + y = 20$
17. $\frac{7}{z} - 2 - \frac{1}{z} = 8$ (Hint: Replace $\frac{1}{z}$ by x.)
18. $\frac{8}{z} + 7 = \frac{5}{z} + 1$

In each of the following formulas substitute values for the variables as indicated, and then solve the resulting equation for the variable whose value is not given.

SAMPLE. $a = p(1 + rt)$ when $a = 2400, p = 1600, r = .05$

Solution:

$$a = p(1 + rt)$$
$$2400 = 1600(1 + .05t)$$
$$2400 = 1600 + 80t$$
$$800 = 80t$$
$$t = 10.$$ $\{10\}$, **Answer.**

19. $p = b + B + 2s$ when $p = 50, B = 11, s = 10$
20. $i = a - p$ when $i = 5.94, a = 154.44$
21. $p = 2(l + w)$ when $p = 723, l = 275$
22. $A = \frac{a + b}{2}$ when $A = 55, a = 72$
23. $L = 2\pi rh$ when $L = 12\pi, r = 1.5$
24. $T = 2\pi rh + 2\pi r^2$ when $T = 90\pi, r = 2$

Specify by roster the following subsets of the set of real numbers.

B

25. $\{z: 7z - (2 + z) = 2(3z - 1)\}$

26. $\{y: 8 - 4(10 - 3y) = 4y\}$

27. $\{x: 13x - 6(x + 3) = 10x - 3x\}$

28. $\{x: 9x + 17 = 1 - 3(8 - 3x)\}$

29. $\left\{n: \frac{5}{n} - 3 - \left(\frac{3}{n} - 1\right) = 7\right\}$

30. $\left\{n: 18 - 5\left(\frac{1}{n} + 2\right) = 2\right\}$

31. $\{x: 12x - (4x - 6) = 3x - (9x - 27)\}$

32. $\{z: 6z - (9 - 3z) = 6 - 3(z + 2)\}$

33. $\{s: s(s + 2) + 5 = 3 + s^2\}$

34. $\{y: 4 + y + y^2 = 7 - y(2 - y)\}$

35. $\{t: 2t(2 - t) = 1 + t(1 - 2t)\}$

36. $\{q: q(3q + 2) + 4 = 3(q^2 + q)\}$

37. $\{y: 9 - y(9 - y) = 3y(\frac{1}{3}y - 3)\}$

38. $\{k: \frac{1}{2}k(2k - 8) = -k(4 - k)\}$

Solve each of the following equations for the variable in red type. Use the resulting formula to find the value of that variable for the given values of the other variables.

C

39. $x(a - b) - x(a + b) + 4b^2 = 0; b = 3$

40. $r(m + n) - r(m - n) - n^2 = 0; n = 6$

41. $V = \frac{1}{3}\pi r^2 h; V = 48\pi, r = 3$

42. $V = \frac{1}{3}Bh; V = 450, B = 30$

43. $A = \frac{a + b + c}{3}; A = 81, a = 84, c = 78$

44. $T = mg - mf; T = 40, m = 10, g = 15$

45. $S = \frac{1}{2}n\,(a + l); S = 90, n = 15, l = 9$

46. $A = \frac{1}{2}h\,(b + c); A = 72, h = 9, b = 10$

2–4 Equivalent Inequalities

Look carefully at Figure 2–2. Do you see that adding the same number to each member of the inequality $-1 < 3$ does not change the **order**, or **sense**, of the inequality? This illustrates the property below Figure 2–2.

Given:	$-1 < 3$	**Given:**	$-1 < 3$
Add 2:	$-1 + 2 < 3 + 2$	Add -2:	$-1 + (-2) < 3 + (-2)$
	$1 < 5$		$-3 < 1$

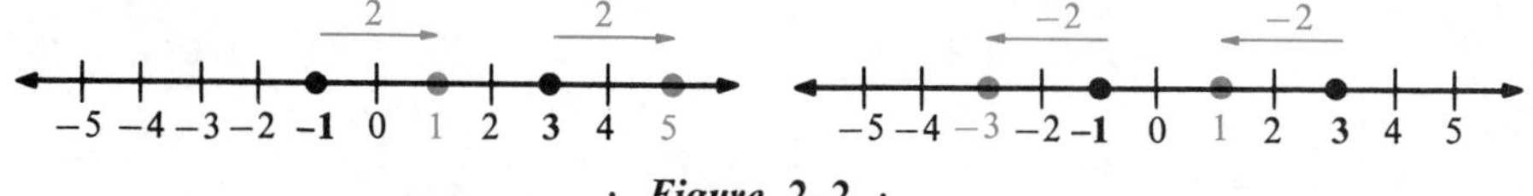

· *Figure 2–2* ·

Addition Property of Order. Let a, b, and c denote real numbers. If $a < b$, then $a + c < b + c$. If $a > b$, then $a + c > b + c$.

Note, in Figure 2–3, the results of multiplying each member of the inequality $-2 < 3$ by (**a**) 2, and (**b**) -2:

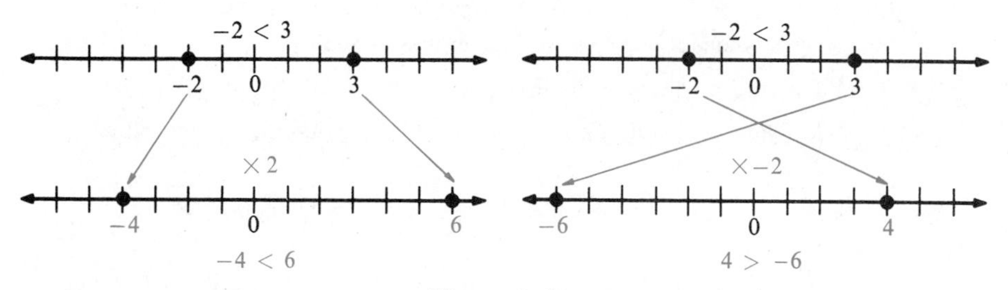

· *Figure 2–3* ·

These results illustrate the property given below.

Multiplication Property of Order. Let a, b, and c denote real numbers.

If $a < b$, then:	If $a > b$, then:
$ac < bc$, provided $c > 0$;	$ac > bc$, provided $c > 0$;
$ac > bc$, provided $c < 0$.	$ac < bc$, provided $c < 0$.

Notice that multiplying each member of an inequality by a positive number preserves the order of the inequality; but multiplication by a negative number reverses the order of the inequality. Multiplying an inequality such as $-2 < 3$ by 0 produces the equation $0 = 0$.

We will assume that substitution in an inequality is valid; that is: *If $a = b$, then $a < c$ implies $b < c$, and $d < a$ implies $d < b$.* Using this fact, it is possible to prove the following properties.

Subtraction and Division Properties of Order. Let a, b, and c denote real numbers.

If $a < b$, then:	If $a > b$, then:
$a - c < b - c$;	$a - c > b - c$;
$\frac{a}{c} < \frac{b}{c}$, provided $c > 0$;	$\frac{a}{c} > \frac{b}{c}$, provided $c > 0$;
$\frac{a}{c} > \frac{b}{c}$, provided $c < 0$.	$\frac{a}{c} < \frac{b}{c}$, provided $c < 0$.

The properties of order and equality insure that the following transformations of a given inequality always produce an **equivalent inequality**, that is, one with the same solution set.

Transformations That Produce an Equivalent Inequality

1. Adding to or subtracting from each member of the inequality the same polynomial in any variables in the inequality.
2. Multiplying or dividing each member by the same positive number.
3. Multiplying or dividing each member by the same negative number and reversing the order of the inequality.
4. Substituting for either member an expression equivalent to it.

EXAMPLES. Solve these inequalities and graph their solution sets:

1. $3v + 5 \geq v - 1$
2. $3(3 - k) - 10 > 2$

Solutions:

1.
$$3v + 5 \geq v - 1$$
$$3v + 5 - 5 \geq v - 1 - 5$$
$$3v \geq v - 6$$
$$3v - v \geq v - 6 - v$$
$$2v \geq -6$$
$$\frac{2v}{2} \geq \frac{-6}{2}$$
$$v \geq -3$$

$\{v\colon v \geq -3\}$, **Answer.**

2.
$$\underbrace{3(3 - k)} - 10 > 2$$
$$9 - 3k - 10 > 2$$
$$-3k - 1 > 2$$
$$-3k - 1 + 1 > 2 + 1$$
$$-3k > 3$$
$$\frac{-3k}{-3} < \frac{3}{-3}$$
$$k < -1$$

$\{k\colon k < -1\}$, **Answer.**

Oral Exercises

Each of the following inequalities is the result of transforming $12bx < -72b$ into an equivalent inequality. In each case give the transformations used. Assume $b > 0$.

1. $3bx < -18b$

2. $12bx + 5 < -72b + 5$

3. $24bx < -144b$

4. $3x < -18$

5. $-x > 6$

6. $x < -6$

7. $2bx < -b(72 + 10x)$

8. $6bx < -3b(2x + 24)$

9. $-6bx > 36b$

10. $12b(x + 6) < 0$

Justify the steps in the proofs of the following theorems. a, b, c denote real numbers.

11.

If $a < b$, then

$$a - c < b - c.$$

Proof

a, b, and c denote real numbers.

$-c$ is a real number.

$a + (-c) < b + (-c)$

$a + (-c) = a - c$ and

$b + (-c) = b - c$

$\therefore a - c < b - c$

12.

If $a < b$, then $-b < -a$.

Proof

a and b denote real numbers.

$-a$ and $-b$ are real numbers.

$(-a) + (-b)$ is a real number.

$$(-a) + (-b) = (-b) + (-a)$$

$$a < b$$

$a + [(-a) + (-b)] < b + [(-b) + (-a)]$

$[a + (-a)] + (-b) < [b + (-b)] + (-a)$

$$0 + (-b) < 0 + (-a)$$

$$\therefore -b < -a$$

Written Exercises

Solve each of the following inequalities and graph their solution sets.

1. $2x + 5 \leq 3$

2. $3y - 4 \geq 14$

3. $-5 - 4z > 35$

4. $7 - 5t < 32$

5. $2a + 8 \leq 3a - 4$

6. $7 + 5b \geq b - 1$

7. $m + 3 - 4m > 2m + 23$

8. $-14 + 2n < n + 7 - 5n$

9. $5(c + 3) + 4 < c - 1$

10. $6 + 3(d + 2) > d + 16$

11. $5(12 - 3t) > 15(t + 4)$

12. $-6(2 + s) < 2(3s - 6)$

13. $2 - (x + 3) < 4 - x$

14. $10 - y \geq 8 - (y - 2)$

B

15. $3[1 - (a - 2)] \leq 3 - 4(1 - a)$
16. $-5[2 - (1 + b)] \geq 25 + 7(2b - 3)$
17. $d(2 - d) - 8 < -(d^2 + d + 5)$
18. $k(1 - 2k) - 1 > 2[k(2 - k) - 1]$
19. $p(2p - 3) \geq p[2(p + 1) - 3]$
20. $-(3 - w + w^2) \leq 9 + w(5 - w)$
21. *Prove:* (a) If a and b are real numbers and $a < b$, then $a - b < 0$.
    (b) If a and b are real numbers and $a - b < 0$, then $a < b$.
22. *Prove:* (a) If a and b are real numbers and $a - b > 0$, then $a > b$.
    (b) If a and b are real numbers and $a > b$, then $a - b > 0$.
23. Show by an example that even though $a > b$ and $c > d$, it need not be true that $a - c > b - d$.
24. Show by an example that if $a > b$, it need not be true that $a^2 > b^2$.

C

25. Let a, b, c, and d denote real numbers. Prove that if $a > b$ and $c > d$, then $a + c > b + d$. (*Hint:* Show that $a + c > b + c$ and that $b + c > b + d$.)
26. Let a, b, c, and d denote real numbers. Prove that if $a > b > 0$ and $c > d > 0$, then $ac > bd$. (*Hint:* Show that $ac > bc$ and that $bc > bd$.)
27. Let a and b denote positive numbers. Prove that if $a < b$, then $a^2 < b^2$.
28. Let a and b denote negative numbers. Prove that if $a < b$, then $a^2 > b^2$.

2–5 Combining Open Sentences

To describe the graph of the solution set of $|x - 1| = 3$, note that $|x - 1|$ measures the distance between 1 and x on the number line. If that distance is 3, the point x must be located either 3 units to the left of 1 ($x - 1 = -3$) or 3 units to the right of 1 ($x - 1 = 3$); see Figure 2–4.

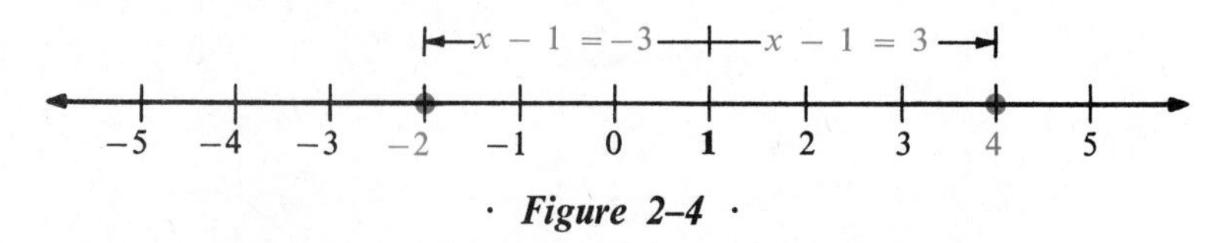

Figure 2–4

Thus, a value of x is a root of $|x - 1| = 3$, provided it belongs to the solution set of $x - 1 = -3$ or to the solution set of $x - 1 = 3$. Therefore, the sentence $|x - 1| = 3$ is equivalent to the following combination of open sentences:

either	$x - 1 = -3$	*or*	$x - 1 = 3$
	$x - 1 + 1 = -3 + 1$		$x - 1 + 1 = 3 + 1$
	$x = -2$		$x = 4$

$$\therefore \{x: |x - 1| = 3\} = \{-2, 4\}$$

Check: $|x - 1| = 3$

$|-2 - 1| \stackrel{?}{=} 3$	$|4 - 1| \stackrel{?}{=} 3$
$|-3| \stackrel{?}{=} 3$	$|3| \stackrel{?}{=} 3$
$3 = 3$ ✓	$3 = 3$ ✓

On the other hand, the roots of the inequality $|x - 1| \leq 3$ must correspond to all points at most 3 units from 1 on the number line (Figure 2–5).

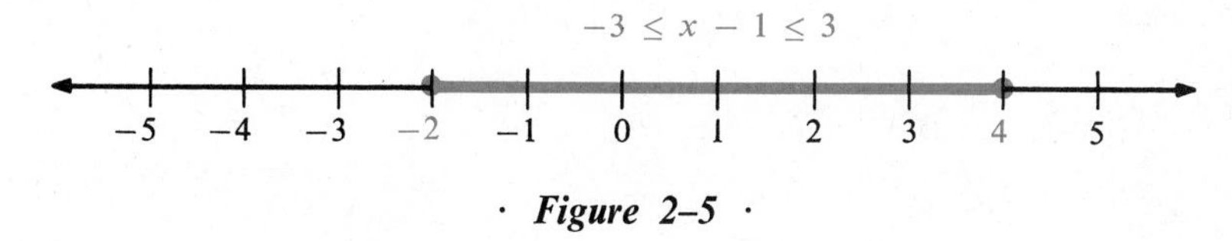

· *Figure 2–5* ·

Therefore, the sentence $|x - 1| \leq 3$ is equivalent to the sentence $-3 \leq x - 1 \leq 3$, that is, to the combination:

$-3 \leq x - 1$	*and*	$x - 1 \leq 3$
$-3 + 1 \leq x - 1 + 1$		$x - 1 + 1 \leq 3 + 1$
$-2 \leq x$		$x \leq 4$

$$\therefore \{x: |x - 1| \leq 3\} = \{x: -2 \leq x \leq 4\}$$

The graph of the solution set of $|x - 1| > 3$ consists of those points more than 3 units from 1 on the number line (Figure 2–6).

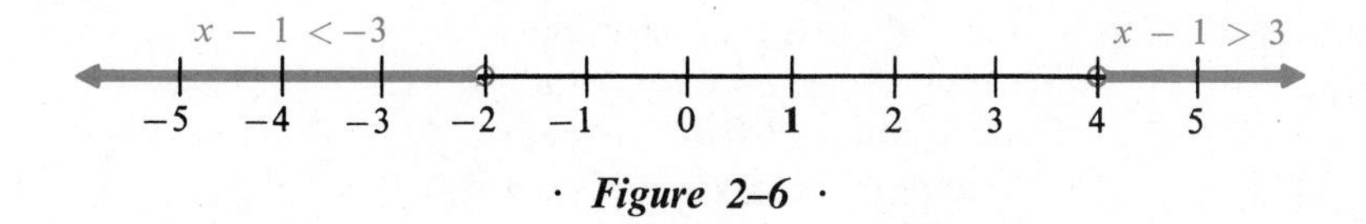

· *Figure 2–6* ·

Thus, $|x - 1| > 3$ is equivalent to the combination:

either	$x - 1 < -3$	*or*	$x - 1 > 3$
	$x < -2$		$x > 4$

In solving a combination of two open sentences (a *compound sentence*) it is essential to decide whether you want the numbers belonging to the solution set of *at least one* of the sentences or the numbers belonging to the solution sets of *both* of the sentences. You can use the language and symbolism of sets to describe these situations. The **union** of two sets A and B (in symbols, $A \cup B$) is the set consisting of the elements belonging to *at least one* of the given sets, while the **intersection** of A and B (in symbols, $A \cap B$) is the set made up of the elements belonging to *both* A and B. Thus:

$$\begin{aligned} \{x: |x-1| = 3\} &= \{x: x - 1 = -3\} \cup \{x: x - 1 = 3\} \\ &= \{-2\} \cup \{4\} \\ &= \{-2, 4\} \end{aligned}$$

$$\begin{aligned} \{x: |x-1| \le 3\} &= \{x: -3 \le x - 1\} \cap \{x: x - 1 \le 3\} \\ &= \{x: -2 \le x\} \cap \{x: x \le 4\} \\ &= \{x: -2 \le x \le 4\} \end{aligned}$$

EXAMPLE 1. Graph the set $\{k: |2k + 3| < 7\} \cap \{k: 1 - k \ge 0\}$.

Solution:

$$\begin{aligned} |2k+3| &< 7 \\ -7 < 2k + 3 &< 7 \\ -7 - 3 < 2k &< 7 - 3 \\ -10 < 2k &< 4 \\ -5 < k &< 2 \end{aligned}$$

and

$$\begin{aligned} 1 - k &\ge 0 \\ -k &\ge 0 - 1 \\ -k &\ge -1 \\ k &\le 1 \end{aligned}$$

-5 0 1 2 -5 0 1 2

The following number line shows the graph of the given set as the overlapping portion (the intersection) of the preceding graphs.

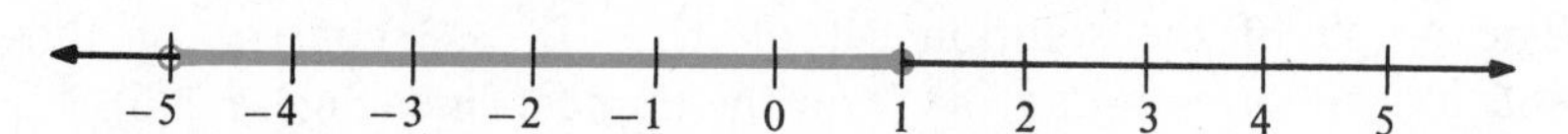

EXAMPLE 2. Let the regions within or on the indicated circles in the adjoining diagram represent the sets R, S, and T. Redraw the diagram and shade the region representing:

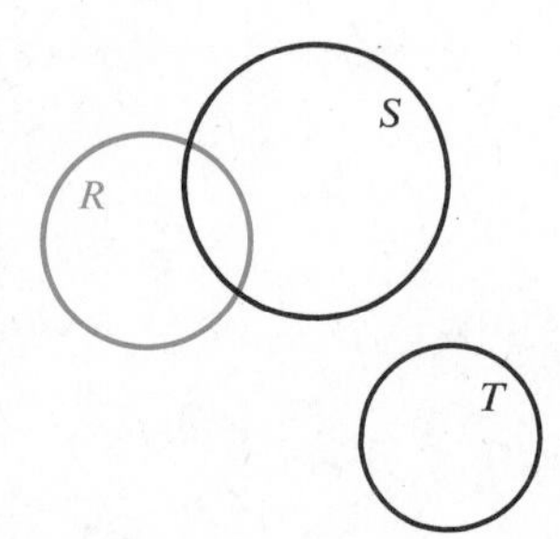

a. $R \cup S$ **c.** $R \cup T$

b. $R \cap S$ **d.** $R \cap T$

Solution:

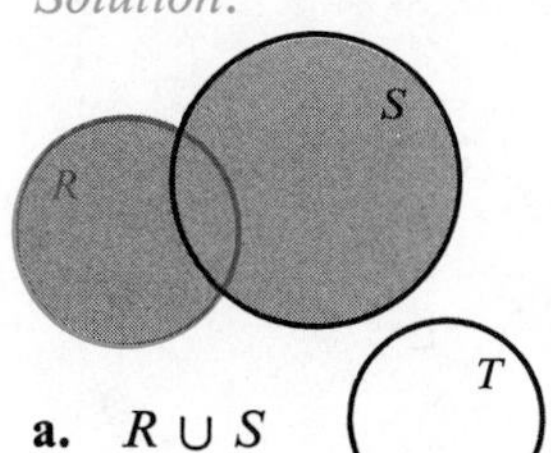

a. $R \cup S$

b. $R \cap S$

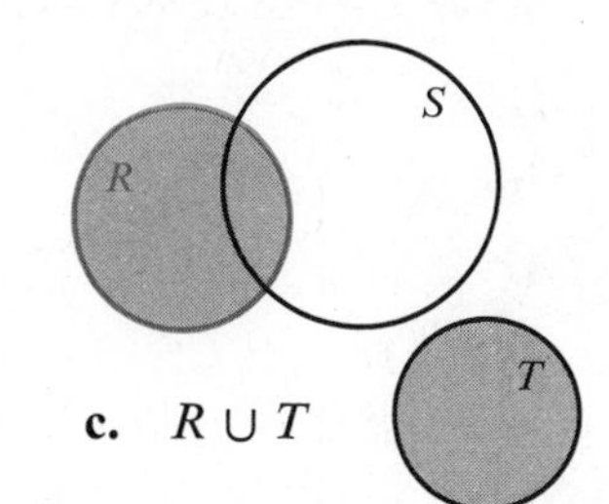

c. $R \cup T$

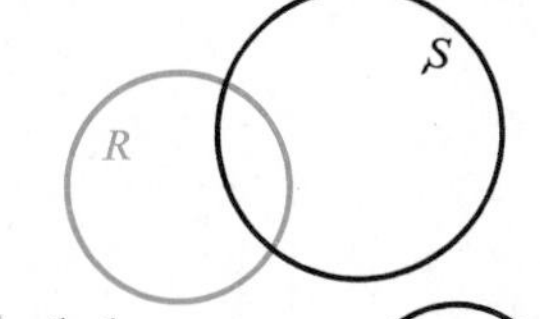

d. $R \cap T = \emptyset$

$\therefore$ no region is shaded

Oral Exercises

Specify by roster (a) the union, and (b) the intersection if not empty.

1. $\{3, 6, 9, 12\}$; $\{2, 4, 6, 8\}$
2. $\{3, 4, 2, 1\}$; $\{1, 2, -3, 0\}$
3. $\{2, 4, 8\}$; $\{4, 8, 2\}$
4. $\{5, 7\}$; $\{1, 2\}$
5. $\{a, b, c\}$; $\{e, g\}$
6. $\{r, t, s\}$; $\{s, r, t\}$
7. {even integers} ; {natural numbers}
8. {natural numbers} ; {nonnegative integers}
9. {nonpositive integers} ; {odd integers}
10. {natural numbers} ; {positive integers}

Written Exercises

Graph the solution set of each open sentence.

1. $|x| < 2$
2. $|y| > 1$
3. $|5 - y| = 7$
4. $|3 - z| = 4$
5. $|2x - 1| = 9$
6. $|3s - 4| = 22$
7. $|y - 4| > 3$
8. $|2 + x| < 1$
9. $|2y + 9| \leq 1$
10. $|3k - 7| \geq 2$
11. $|2 - 5h| \geq 3$
12. $|4 - 5k| \leq 9$

Specify by roster the following subsets of the set of integers.

B

13. $\{t: -8 \leq 2t + 5 \leq 11\}$

14. $\{s: 0 < 9 + 4s \leq 25\}$

15. $\{t: 7 \geq 2 - 5t > -13\}$

16. $\{f: 11 > 8 - 3f > -7\}$

17. $\{g: g - 2 \geq -2\} \cap \{g: 2g - 10 < 0\}$

18. $\{j: 2 + j \leq -1\} \cap \{j: -3 + j \geq -14\}$

19. $\{j: 2 + j < -1\} \cup \{j: -3 + j > -14\}$

20. $\{g: g - 2 > -2\} \cup \{g: 2g - 10 \leq 0\}$

Let the regions within or on the indicated rectangles in the adjoining diagram represent the subsets *R*, *S*, and *T* of a set *U*. In Exercises 21–30, redraw the diagram and shade the region representing the subset of *U* specified in each exercise.

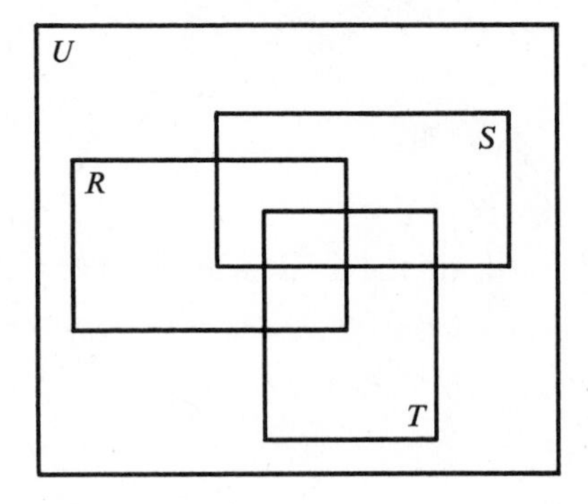

21. $R \cup S$

22. $S \cap T$

23. $\{y: y \in R \text{ or } y \notin S\}$

24. $\{t: t \in R, \text{ and } t \notin S\}$

25. $\{x: x \in R, x \in S, \text{ and } x \in T\}$

26. $\{m: m \in R, m \in S, \text{ or } m \in T\}$

C

27. $R \cup (S \cap T)$

28. $R \cap (S \cup T)$

29. $(R \cup S) \cap (R \cup T)$

30. $(R \cap S) \cup (R \cap T)$

In Exercises 31 and 32, let *A*, *B*, and *C* be subsets of $U = \{1, 2, 3, 4, 5, 6\}$. Specify the set *B* in each of the given situations.

31. $A = \{2, 4\}$, $B \cap C = \{2\}$, $B \cup C = \{1, 2, 3, 5, 6\}$, $A \cup C = \{1, 2, 4, 5\}$.

32. $B \cup C = U$, $B \cap C = \emptyset$, $C \cup A = \{1\}$, $A \cap A = \emptyset$.

2–6 Statements and Converses

Each of the statements, "If $x = 11$, then $3x + 5 = 38$," and "If $3x + 5 = 38$, then $x = 11$," is called the **converse** of the other, because the hypothesis of each statement is the conclusion of the other statement. Alternative ways of expressing a statement and its converse are shown in the following table.

STATEMENT	CONVERSE
If $x = 11$, then $3x + 5 = 38$.	**If $3x + 5 = 38$, then $x = 11$.**
Or: $3x + 5 = 38$, if $x = 11$.	**Or: $3x + 5 = 38$, only if $x = 11$.**

Thus, a sentence combining the indicated statement and its converse is:

$3x + 5 = 38$ if and only if $x = 11$.

You will see the words, "if and only if" in the statements of many theorems. One example is the following proposition.

THEOREM. Let a and b denote real numbers. Then, $ab = 0$ if and only if either $a = 0$ or $b = 0$.

Recall that "either $a = 0$ or $b = 0$" includes the possibility that both a and b equal 0. The use of the words "if and only if" makes the theorem a combination of two assertions.

I. If either $a = 0$ or $b = 0$, then $ab = 0$.

Proof: This follows directly from the multiplication property of zero.

II. If $ab = 0$, then either $a = 0$ or $b = 0$.

Proof: There are two cases to consider.

1. $a = 0$.
   In this case the conclusion is true. Therefore, assertion II holds.

2. $a \neq 0$.

$\therefore \frac{1}{a}$ is a real number.	Axiom of multiplicative inverses.
But $ab = 0$	Given.
$\therefore \frac{1}{a}(ab) = \frac{1}{a} \cdot 0$	Multiplication property of equality.
But $\frac{1}{a} \cdot 0 = 0$	Multiplication property of zero.
and $\frac{1}{a}(ab) = b$	Why?
$\therefore b = 0$	Repeated application of the transitive property of equality.

Therefore, given that $ab = 0$, it follows that either $a = 0$ or $b = 0$.

Another way to state this theorem is:

A product of real numbers is zero if and only if at least one of its factors is zero.

You can use this fact to solve an equation having one member 0, and the other member a product of linear binomials.

EXAMPLE. Solve $(x + 3)(x - 1) = 0$.

Solution: The theorem just proved implies that this equation is equivalent to the sentence

$$\text{either } x + 3 = 0 \quad \text{or} \quad x - 1 = 0$$
$$x = -3 \quad \Big| \quad x = 1$$

$\therefore$ the solution set of the given equation is $\{-3\} \cup \{1\} = \{-3, 1\}$, **Answer.**

To check the solution, you can substitute each apparent root in the original equation

$$(x + 3)(x - 1) = 0$$

$(-3 + 3)(-3 - 1) \stackrel{?}{=} 0$	$(1 + 3)(1 - 1) \stackrel{?}{=} 0$
$0(-4) \stackrel{?}{=} 0$	$4(0) \stackrel{?}{=} 0$
$0 = 0$ ✓	$0 = 0$ ✓

Oral Exercises

State a sentence equivalent to each of the following open sentences.

SAMPLE. $(2y - 6)(y + 5) = 0$. *What you say:* Either $2y - 6 = 0$ or $y + 5 = 0$.

1. $x(x + 3) = 0$
2. $(y - 11)(y + 4) = 0$
3. $(2t + 5)(t - 7) = 0$
4. $(v + 6)(3v - 1) = 0$
5. $t(t + 4)(t - 6) = 0$
6. $k(k - 7)(k - 8) = 0$

State the converse of each of the following propositions. State whether (a) the proposition, (b) its converse, is true for all real values of the variables. When both proposition and converse are true, restate them in combined form.

7. If $r = s$, then $r + t = s + t$.
8. If $r = s$, then $rt = st$.
9. If $r = s$ and $t = v$, then $r + t = s + v$.

10. If $r < s$, then $r - t < s - t$.
11. If $r > 0$ and $s > 0$, then $rs > 0$.
12. If $rs < 0$, then $r > 0$ and $s < 0$.
13. If $r > s$, then $rt > st$.
14. If $rs > 0$, then $r > 0$ and $s > 0$.
15. If two sides of a triangle have the same length, the angles opposite these sides have the same measure.
16. If a pair of opposite sides of a quadrilateral are parallel, then the quadrilateral is a parallelogram.
17. If two angles have equal measures, then each is a right angle.
18. If two squares have equal areas, then a side of one square has the same length as a side of the other.

Written Exercises

Determine the solution set of each of the following equations.

A

1. $(5t - 10)(4t + 24) = 0$
2. $(7n + 14)(6n - 18) = 0$
3. $0 = r(7r + 210)$
4. $0 = s(14s + 196)$
5. $t(2t + 1)(6t - 48) = 0$
6. $m(3m - 1)(12m + 96) = 0$
7. $(2p - 3)(p - 4)(12 - 4p) = 0$
8. $(5q + 4)(q + 7)(15 - 3q) = 0$

SAMPLE. $\left(\frac{1}{t} - 3\right)\left(\frac{1}{2t} + 4\right) = 0$

Solution: $\frac{1}{t} - 3 = 0$ *or* $\frac{1}{2t} + 4 = 0$

$\frac{1}{t} = 3, \quad t = \frac{1}{3}$ $\qquad \frac{1}{2t} = -4, \quad 2t = -\frac{1}{4}, \quad t = -\frac{1}{8}$

$\{\frac{1}{3}, -\frac{1}{8}\}$, **Answer.**

B

9. $\left(\frac{1}{x} - 2\right)\left(\frac{1}{x} + 3\right) = 0$
10. $\left(\frac{1}{y} + 4\right)\left(7 - \frac{1}{y}\right) = 0$
11. $0 = \frac{1}{x}(7x + 56)$
12. $0 = \frac{1}{k}(9k + 72)$
13. $0(12k - 11) = 0$
14. $0(5m + 4) = 0$

Prove the theorems stated in Exercises 15, 16. Assume b denotes a real number.

C

15. $b > 0$ if and only if $-b < 0$.
16. $-b > 0$ if and only if $b < 0$.

USING VARIABLES TO SOLVE PROBLEMS

2–7 Interpreting Algebraic Expressions and Sentences

An important application of algebra is the use of algebraic expressions and open sentences as **models**, or mathematical descriptions of practical situations. Thus, the expression $4p + 6$ can represent the perimeter of a rectangular field whose length is 3 feet more than its width (Figure 2–7). In this interpretation the domain of the variable p is the set of positive real numbers.

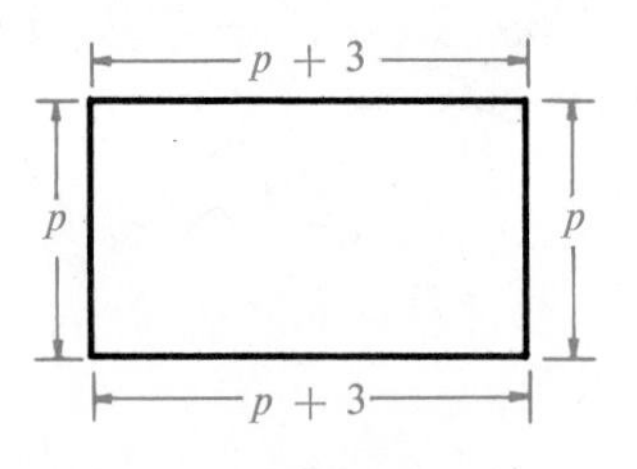

· *Figure 2–7* ·

The open sentence $4p + 6 = 3810$ describes mathematically the situation in which the perimeter of the given field is 3810 feet. When you find $\{951\}$ to be the solution set of the equation, you can determine that the dimensions of the field are 951 ft. $\times$ 954 ft.

Of course, $4p + 6 = 3810$ may also describe other situations. Consider the following problem.

During a test run, Machine A produced p cans; Machine B turned out twice as many ($2p$); Machine C produced 6 more cans than A, that is, $p + 6$. The total production during the run $[p + 2p + (p + 6)]$ was 3810 cans. How many cans did each machine produce?

To answer the question, you solve the equation

$$p + 2p + (p + 6) = 3810, \quad \text{or} \quad 4p + 6 = 3810.$$

Note that in this situation the replacement set of p is the set of non-negative integers, and the machines A, B, and C produce 951, 1902, and 957 cans respectively.

Another interpretation concerns consecutive integers. Recall that if p represents an integer, then $p + 1$, $p + 2$, and $p + 3$ represent in order the next three consecutive integers. Now consider the following problem.

The sum of four consecutive integers is 3810. Find the integers.

To solve the problem, you seek integers satisfying this sentence.

$$\mathbf{p + (p + 1) + (p + 2) + (p + 3) = 3810 \quad \text{or} \quad 4p + 6 = 3810.}$$

Now you can complete the problem.

Can you interpret the open sentence $4p + 6 = 3810$ to mean "6 more than 4 times a certain integral multiple of 5 equals 3810"? The replacement set is now $\{\ldots, -15, -10, -5, 0, 5, 10, 15, \ldots\}$ and this problem has no solution.

Written Exercises

Give two interpretations for each expression or sentence. In each case specify a suitable replacement set for the variable.

SAMPLE. $7 + \frac{1}{2}k = 21$

Solution: 1. Seven more than half a certain number is 21. $k \in \{\text{real numbers}\}$

2. Phil, who owns 21 model planes, has 7 more than half as many as Roger. $k \in \{\text{nonnegative integers}\}$

A

1. $4x$

2. $5y$

3. $x + 2$

4. $y - 1$

5. $3r - 4 = 19$

6. $2s + 3 = 21$

7. $g + 2(g + 3) = 12$

8. $(k + 1)^2 - k^2$

9. $\frac{x}{3} - 2 = 7$

10. $4 - \frac{t}{5} = 1$

11. $a + (a + 1) + 3a = 31$

12. $2x + 2(x + 5) = 60$

B

13. $q + (q + 2) + (q + 4) = -90$

14. $a + (a + 30) + (2a + 10) = 180$

15. $w(w + 3) \geq 154$

16. $\frac{1}{2}b(2b + 1) \geq 78$

17. $|x - 125| < 5$

18. $|y - 22| < 1\frac{1}{4}$

2–8 Solving Problems

The key to solving "word problems" is skill in translating English phrases and sentences about numbers and their relationships into algebraic expressions and open sentences. Study the following examples.

EXAMPLE 1. The sum of three consecutive even integers is 10 more than twice the smallest of the three integers. Find the largest of these integers.

Solution:

1. The first step in solving this problem is to choose a variable to use in representing the numbers described in the problem. Let x represent the smallest of the integers. The replacement set of x is the set of even integers, $\{\ldots, -4, -2, 0, 2, 4, \ldots\}$. Since consecutive even integers differ by 2, the next two integers described in the problem are represented by $x + 2$ and $x + 4$. Also, twice the smallest integer is $2x$, and 10 more than twice the smallest integer is $2x + 10$.

2. The second step is to write an open sentence based on relationships stated in the problem.

   The sum of the integers is 10 more than twice the smallest

   $$\underbrace{x + (x + 2) + (x + 4)}_{\text{The sum of the integers}} \underset{\text{is}}{=} \underbrace{2x + 10}_{\text{10 more than twice the smallest}}$$

3. The third step is to solve the open sentence.

   $$3x + 6 = 2x + 10$$
   $$3x = 2x + 4$$
   $$x = 4;\ x + 2 = 6;\ x + 4 = 8$$

   $\therefore$ The three even integers are 4, 6, and 8.

4. The fourth step is to check your results with the requirements stated in the problem. Are 4, 6, and 8 consecutive even integers? Yes ✓
   Is their sum 10 more than twice the least of them?

   $$4 + 6 + 8 \stackrel{?}{=} 2 \cdot 4 + 10$$
   $$18 \stackrel{?}{=} 8 + 10$$
   $$18 = 18 \qquad \text{Yes ✓}$$

   $\therefore$ The largest of the three integers is 8, **Answer.**

The four steps taken to solve the preceding problem are useful as a plan in solving any problem.

1. Choose a variable with an appropriate replacement set, and use the variable in representing each described number.
2. Form an open sentence using facts given in the problem.
3. Solve the open sentence.
4. Check your results with the requirements stated in the problem.

In solving problems about geometric figures, sketches drawn according to the facts of the problem may help you see relationships.

EXAMPLE 2. The base of a triangle has the same length as the side of a square. A second side of the triangle is 1 inch longer than the base, and the third side is 5 inches shorter than 3 times the base. If the perimeter of the triangle equals that of the square, find the length of the longest side of the triangle.

Note: In problem work the symbol = is used to mean "represent" or "represents."

Solution:

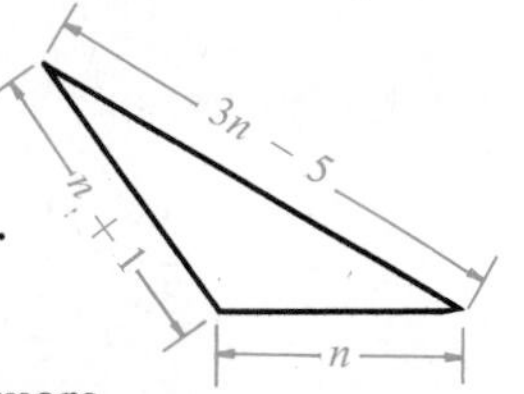

1. Let n = the number of inches in the length of the base of the triangle.
   Then $n + 1$ = length of second side, in inches.
   $3n - 5$ = length of third side, in inches.

2. Perimeter of triangle equals perimeter of square

$$\underbrace{n + n + 1 + (3n - 5)}_{\text{Perimeter of triangle}} \underset{\downarrow}{=} \underbrace{n + n + n + n}_{\text{perimeter of square}}$$

3.
$$\begin{aligned} 5n - 4 &= 4n \\ 5n - 4n &= 4 \\ n &= 4 \\ n + 1 &= 5 \\ 3n - 5 &= 7 \end{aligned}$$

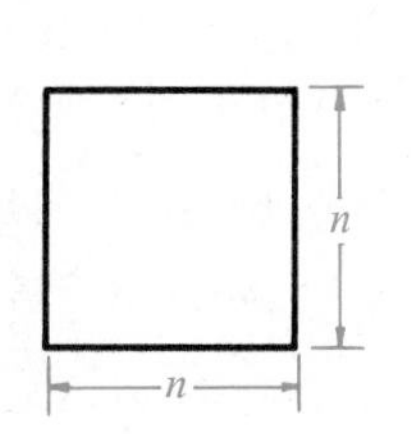

4. Is the second side 1 inch longer than the base? Yes, because $5 = 4 + 1$ ✓

   Is the third side 5 inches shorter than 3 times the base?
   Yes, because $7 = 3 \cdot 4 - 5$ ✓

   Does the triangle have the same perimeter as the square? Yes, because $4 + 5 + 7 = 4 \cdot 4$
   $16 = 16$ ✓

∴ Longest side, 7 inches, **Answer.**

Charts often help you to see relationships in a problem.

EXAMPLE 3. Mr. Kaye is 11 times as old as his daughter Lynn. Thirty-six years from now he will be at most twice as old as Lynn. At most, how old is Lynn?

Solution:

1. Let y = the number of years in Lynn's age now.

2. Arrange the facts of the problem in the adjoining chart.

	Lynn	**Mr. Kaye**
Age now	y	$11y$
Age 36 yr. hence	$y + 36$	$11y + 36$

3. Thirty-six years from now

Mr. Kaye's age in years will be at most twice Lynn's age

$$11y + 36 \leq 2(y + 36)$$
$$11y + 36 \leq 2y + 72$$
$$9y \leq 36$$
$$y \leq 4$$

4. If Lynn is 4 years old, Mr Kaye is 44 years old. Will he be at most twice as old as she 36 years from now?

Yes, because $44 + 36 = 80$ and $2(4 + 36) = 80$
so that $44 + 36 \leq 2(4 + 36)$. ✓

But, if Lynn were more than 4 years old, then $y > 4$ and $9y > 36$ Therefore, 36 years hence, Mr. Kaye's age $(11y + 36)$ would exceed twice Lynn's age $2(y + 36)$ because:

$$11y + 36 = (2y + 9y) + 36 = (2y + 36) + 9y$$

$(2y + 36) + 9y > (2y + 36) + 36$ and

$(2y + 36) + 36 = 2(y + 36)$

$\therefore 11y + 36 > 2(y + 36)$. ✓

Lynn is at most 4 years old, **Answer.**

Formulas from mathematics and science are often used in solving problems.

EXAMPLE 4. At noon two trains leave from towns 200 miles apart. One train averages 52 miles per hour, and the other, 48 miles per hour. When do they meet?

Solution: Use the formula, rate $\times$ time $=$ distance ($rt = d$). Let t $=$ number of hours until the trains meet.

Then $52t$ = mileage covered by the first train;

$48t$ = mileage covered by the other train.

|—— $52t$ ——+—— $48t$ ——|

|———— 200 mi ————|

Mileage (1st train) + mileage (2nd train) equals total distance

$$\mathbf{52t} \quad + \quad \mathbf{48t} \quad = \quad \mathbf{200}$$

Steps 3 and 4 are left to you.

Table 1 of the Appendix provides a list of several useful formulas from geometry. To solve problems concerned with angle measure, recall that two angles are **complementary angles** if the sum of their measures is 90° (the measure of a **right angle**), and they are **supplementary angles** if the sum is 180° (the measure of a **straight angle**). Also, the total number of degrees t in the measures of the interior angles of a polygon of n sides (or angles) is given by: $t = 180°(n - 2)$. In particular, the sum of the measures of the angles of a triangle is $180°(3 - 2) = 180°$.

Problems

1. The diameter of Uranus is ten times that of Mercury. If the sum of the diameters of these planets is 34,100 miles, find each diameter.

2. Find four consecutive even integers whose sum is 236.

3. One tree is 7 times as old as another. Five years from now it will be 4 times as old. Find the present ages of the trees.

4. Judy, who is 17 years old, has a grandmother aged 77 years. How many years ago was Judy's grandmother 6 times as old as Judy?

5. A newsboy notices that he has four times as many dimes as quarters. If his dimes and quarters total \$1.95, how many of each has he?

6. A dealer has gasoline worth 30 cents a gallon and some worth 35 cents a gallon. How many gallons of each kind must she take to produce 50 gallons worth 32 cents a gallon?

7. How many pounds of coffee worth \$.72 a pound should be mixed with 20 pounds worth \$.90 a pound to produce a mixture worth \$.78 a pound?

8. A glass packer is paid 8 cents for each article packed but is fined 25 cents for each one he breaks. His net earnings for a day where he successfully packed 10 more than thirty times as many articles as he broke were \$18. How many articles did he successfully pack that day?

9. The measures of the sides of a triangle are given by consecutive integers, each indicating a number of inches. If the perimeter is 6 feet, find the length of each side.

10. Each leg of an isosceles triangle exceeds twice the base by 5 inches. Find each side of the triangle if the perimeter is 5 feet.

11. If the perimeter of a square is 36 inches, find the area of the square.

12. If one side of a square is increased by 8 feet and an adjacent side decreased by 2 feet, a rectangle is formed whose perimeter is 40 feet. Find the length of a side of the square.

13. When a certain number is divided by 11, the quotient is 7 and the remainder is 5. Find the number.

14. When you divide a certain number by 13, the quotient is -8 and the remainder is 7. Find the number.

15. At 2:00 P.M. two cars start to meet each other from towns 240 miles apart. If the rate of one car is 10 miles per hour faster than the other, how fast does each car go if they meet at 5:00 P.M.?

16. At 10:00 A.M. two planes leave an airport. If the northbound plane flies at 280 miles per hour, and the southbound plane flies at 320 miles per hour, at what time will they be 1000 miles apart?

17. Emily leaves on a bicycle trip at the rate of 8 miles per hour. One hour later, her father, realizing that Emily forgot some camping gear, sets out by car. How fast must her father drive to overtake Emily in 15 minutes?

18. One of two supplementary angles is 3 degrees less than twice the other. Find the measures of the angles.

19. An angle is 5 times its complement. Find the measure of the angle and its complement.

20. Miss Avis made a certain trip in 3 hours, while the return trip took $3\frac{1}{2}$ hours. If her speed going was 5 miles per hour more than her speed returning, how many miles was the round trip?

21. If each of the base angles of an isosceles triangle is 5 less than twice the vertex angle, find the measure of each angle.

22. In a certain parallelogram, the obtuse angles are three times as large as the acute angles. Find the measure of each angle.

23. The length of a certain rectangle is twice its width. If the length is decreased by 3 centimeters, the area of the resulting rectangle is 12 square centimeters less than the area of the original rectangle. Find the original dimensions.

24. The area of a square is 18 square inches less than twice the area of a triangle. The base of the triangle is 3 inches longer and the altitude is the same length as the side of the square. Find the side of the square.

B

25. Said Bill to Mary: "I earn just $25.00 less than twice as much as you do each week." If this extravagant couple needed a joint weekly income of at least $170.00 to make ends meet, what was the least that each of them had to earn to avoid debt?

26. After washing a rectangular scarf whose length was 4 times its width, Mrs. Hill found it to be unchanged in width, but to be 2 inches shorter than it was before. If the scarf decreased at most 24 square inches in area, find the maximum values of its original dimensions.

27. A factory can produce 1 chair in 24 minutes and 1 table in 32 minutes. If it plans to turn out twice as many chairs as tables, what is the maximum number of complete units of each item it can produce in an eleven-hour workday?

28. If Bea were able to increase her cycling speed by 4 miles per hour, she would be able to cover in 2 hours a distance at least as great as that which now takes her 3 hours. What is the best speed she achieves at present?

29. Mr. Howard left an estate estimated at between $12,000 and $18,000. His widow is to receive one-third of the estate, and the remainder is to be divided equally among his four sons. What are the maximum and minimum expectations of the widow and each son?

30. A certain mathematics teacher learned that the range of normal weight for her height is 135 to 145 pounds. She figured that if she weighed 100 pounds less than twice her present weight, she would be in the normal range. In what range is her present weight?

Space Technology

In 1865 the French writer Jules Verne published the provocative science fiction novel *From the Earth to the Moon.* During the past decades, the spaceships of fiction have been replaced by the space crafts of modern science. Space technology has become one of the most challenging of today's professions.

The problems of space technology, however, are manifold. The lunar module which first touched down on the moon faced potential difficulties at all stages of operation. Although safety checks have been built into all systems on the manned flights, a minor problem with equipment or an error in calculation could reduce a scheduled moon landing to a routine orbiting of the earth. A major difficulty could send the craft hurtling into space.

The men who walk the moon have to be protected from its hostile environment. The first lunar astronauts were encased in over 180 pounds of equipment, which included oxygen packs and heating and ventilating systems. Due to the moon's weak gravity, however, the weight of the fully equipped astronauts averaged only 60 pounds.

The lunar flights continue to provide scientists with information from space long after the crafts complete their missions. Instruments left by the astronauts relay readings to the earth. A seismometer mounted on the moon's surface records even mild lunar quakes, and an array of reflectors serve as precise measuring instruments when laser beams are aimed at them from the earth.

Without an advanced mathematical science, Jules Verne's fable could never have been realized. With mathematics and modern technology, however, travel to the moon and beyond has become an accepted part of man's accomplishments.

A successful space flight depends on the smooth functioning of all systems in the craft. Here engineers double check an electrical circuit design for possible errors.

Extra for Experts

More about Proof

Can you prove that $1 > 0$? This familiar relationship is a by-product or **corollary** of the following theorem.

THEOREM. If a denotes a real number and $a \neq 0$, then $a^2 > 0$.

Proof

Since $a \neq 0$, the axiom of comparison (page 9) implies that there are two cases to consider:

Case 1: $a > 0$	*Case 2:* $a < 0$
Then, $a \cdot a > 0 \cdot a$	Then, $-a > 0$ (See Oral Exercise 12, page 51)
But $a \cdot a = a^2$	$(-a)(-a) > 0(-a)$
$0 \cdot a = 0$	But $(-a)(-a) = a \cdot a$ (see page 28)
$\therefore a^2 > 0$	$= a^2$
	$0(-a) = 0$
	$\therefore a^2 > 0$

Can you provide the reasons for the steps in the preceding arguments?

Now, if you apply the theorem just proved with 1 in place of a, you discover that $1^2 > 0$. But $1^2 = 1$; therefore, $1 > 0$. This proof and the others you have studied and constructed in this course have verified a theorem by means of logically justified assertions leading directly from the hypothesis of the theorem to its conclusion. Another method of proof, called the **indirect method**, begins by assuming that the conclusion of the theorem is false, even though the hypothesis is accepted as true. You then show that a sequence of logically correct steps leads to a contradictory statement. Because the assumption that the conclusion of the theorem is false leads to a contradiction, you know that the conclusion cannot be false, and thus that the theorem must be true.

As an example of this kind of reasoning, let us prove the following theorem.

THEOREM. 1. If c denotes a real number and $c > 0$, then $\frac{1}{c} > 0$.

2. If c denotes a real number and $c < 0$, then $\frac{1}{c} < 0$.

Proof of Part 1

To show that $\frac{1}{c} > 0$, we must show that assuming that $\frac{1}{c}$ is *not* greater than 0 leads to a contradiction. If $\frac{1}{c}$ is not greater than zero, then by the axiom of comparison there are two cases to consider:

Case 1: Assume that $\frac{1}{c} = 0$.

$$\frac{1}{c} \cdot c = 0 \cdot c$$

$$\frac{1}{c} \cdot c = 1$$

$$0 \cdot c = 0$$

$$\therefore 1 = 0$$

Case 2: Assume that $\frac{1}{c} < 0$.

$$c > 0$$

$$\frac{1}{c} \cdot c < 0 \cdot c$$

$$\frac{1}{c} \cdot c = 1$$

$$0 \cdot c = 0$$

$$\therefore 1 < 0$$

Be sure to give the reasons for each step.

In each case the final assertion contradicts the fact just proved: $1 > 0$. Therefore, the assumption that $\frac{1}{c}$ is not greater than zero must be false, and $\frac{1}{c} > 0$.

The proof of Part 2 is left as an exercise for you (Ex. 3 below).

Exercises

1. Given that $1 + 1 = 2$, prove that $2 > 1$.
2. Prove that $-1 < 0$. (*Hint:* Use Oral Exercise 12, page 51.)
3. Prove: If c denotes a real number and $c < 0$, then $\frac{1}{c} < 0$.
   (*Hint:* Assume (1) $\frac{1}{c} = 0$; (2) $\frac{1}{c} > 0$.)
4. Use the theorem on this page, and the meaning of division, to prove the division property of order (page 50).

Prove. In Exs. 9, 10, use the indirect method.

5. $\frac{a}{b} > 0$, if $a > 0$ and $b > 0$

6. $\frac{a}{b} < 0$, if $a < 0$ and $b > 0$

7. $\frac{a}{b} < 0$, if $a > 0$ and $b < 0$

8. $\frac{a}{b} > 0$, if $a < 0$ and $b < 0$

9. If $a \neq 0$, then $-a \neq 0$.

10. If $a \neq 0$, then $\frac{1}{a} \neq 0$.

Chapter Summary

Inventory of Structure and Method

1. You apply the **Distributive Axiom** in writing

$$8a^3b - 3a^3b = (8 - 3)a^3b = 5a^3b.$$

2. Transformations that produce an equivalent equation are:

1. Adding the same polynomial to each member of the given equation.
2. Multiplying or dividing each member by the same nonzero number.
3. Substituting for either member an expression equivalent to it.

To solve an open sentence, apply suitable transformations until you reach an equivalent sentence whose solution set is evident. Verify each solution by substituting it in the original sentence.

3. To solve an inequality use the following properties:

Addition Property of Order: Adding the same real number to each member of an inequality preserves the order (sense) of the inequality. **Multiplication Property of Order:** Multiplying each member of an inequality by a real number preserves the order of the inequality if the number is positive, but changes the order of the inequality if the number is negative.

4. The solution set of an inequality such as $|x - 1| > 2$ is the **union** of the two sets:

$\{x: x - 1 < -2\} \cup \{x: x - 1 > 2\}$, that is, $x < -1$ **or** $x > 3$.

The solution set of an inequality such as $|x - 1| < 2$ is the **intersection** of the two sets: $\{x: x - 1 > -2\} \cap \{x: x - 1 < 2\}$, that is, $x > -1$ **and** $x < 3$, written $-1 < x < 3$.

The theorem, $ab = 0$ if and only if $a = 0$ **or** $b = 0$ for real numbers a and b, allows you to find the solution set of a sentence such as $(x - r)(x - s) = 0$ as $\{x: x - r = 0\} \cup \{x: x - s = 0\}$, that is, $\{r, s\}$.

5. The steps in **solving problems algebraically are:**

1. Choose a variable with a suitable domain and use the variable in representing each described number.
2. Write an open sentence based on relationships and facts given in the problem.
3. Solve the open sentence.
4. Check your results with the requirements **stated in the problem.**

Vocabulary and Spelling

algebraic expression (*p. 39*)
power (*p. 39*)
exponent (*p. 39*)
base (*p. 39*)
factor (*p. 39*)
monomial (*p. 39*)
similar (like) terms (*p. 40*)
degree of a monomial (*p. 40*)
coefficient of a monomial (*p. 40*)
polynomial (*p. 40*)
degree of a polynomial (*p. 40*)
simple form (polynomial) (*p. 40*)
binomial (*p. 40*)
trinomial (*p. 40*)
right member (*p. 41*)
left member (*p. 41*)
equivalent expression (*p. 41*)
identity (*p. 41*)
formula (*p. 42*)
evaluating a formula (*p. 42*)
equivalent equation (*p. 44*)
solving an open sentence (*p. 44*)
order (sense) of an inequality (*p. 48*)
properties of order (*pp. 49 & 50*)
equivalent inequality (*p. 50*)
union of sets ($A \cup B$) (*p. 54*)
intersection of sets ($A \cap B$) (*p. 54*)
converse (*p. 56*)
complementary angles (*p. 65*)
right angle (*p. 65*)
supplementary angles (*p. 65*)
straight angle (*p. 65*)

Chapter Test

2–1 **1.** Write in simple form in m:
$3m^2r^3 - 2mr^4 + m^3r^2 - 3$, and state the degree of the polynomial.

2–2 **2.** Express as a polynomial in simple form:
$2a^2 - 3(ab + 2a - 3b) + 2a(5a - 4b) - (6a - 5b)$

2–3 **3.** Solve: $2 - 3(2x - 5) = 2x - 7$

4. If $A = \frac{h}{2}(a + b)$, find a when $A = 65$, $h = 5$, and $b = 10$.

2–4 **5.** Solve: $3 + 2(3n - 5) \geq 2n - 3(1 - 2n)$

2–5 **6.** Graph the solution set: $|3 - 2t| > 1$

7. Graph: $\{h: |4h - 2| < 10\} \cap \{h: 2 - 2h \leq 0\}$

2–6 **8.** Write the converse of: *If snow has fallen, then you can ski.*

9. Solve: $(3m + 1)(2m - 5) = 0$

2–7 **10.** Interpret the given sentence in two ways. Include a suitable domain for the variable. $\frac{1}{2}n + \frac{2}{3}(n + 1) = 24$

2–8 **11.** How many pounds of cashews at 89 cents a pound should be mixed with 18 pounds of peanuts at 39 cents a pound to make a blend worth 59 cents a pound?

12. A pilot is allowed between 4 hours 20 minutes and 4 hours 40 minutes to make a test run on a newly scheduled flight of 1820 miles. She finds that if she flies her new plane at 120 miles an hour less than twice the speed of her present plane, she will be able to keep within the time limits. Find the speed range of her present plane.

Chapter Review

2–1 Algebraic Expressions *Pages 39–40*

1. A monomial may not have a __?__ containing a variable.

2. The degree of the polynomial $3xy + x$ is __?__; the degree of $abc^3 - 3b^2c^2 + 2$ is __?__.

3. A polynomial is a __?__ or a sum of __?__.

2–2 Simplifying Expressions *Pages 40–43*

Express as a polynomial in simple form.

4. $(8r^3 - 3r + 7 - 5r^2) + 3(2r^2 - 3r^3 - 7r + 2)$

5. $(3s^2t - 4st^2 + 2st) - 2(2ts^2 - \frac{1}{2}ts + 5st^2)$

6. Find F when $m = 63$, $v = 45$, $r = 1.5$, and $F = \dfrac{mv^2}{r}$.

2–3 Equivalent Equations *Pages 44–48*

7. The equations $x + 2 = 5$ and $x - 1 = 2$ are __?__ since they have the same __?__ __?__.

8. You should __?__ each apparent root of an open sentence to determine whether it belongs to the __?__ __?__ of the open sentence and to the __?__ of the variable.

Solve and check.

9. $3y - 5(4y - 3) = 6(5 - 2y)$

10. $x + 2[3 - 5(1 - x)] = 3(x - 3) + 5$

11. $\{n: \frac{2n}{3} - 4(n + 2) - 22 = 0\}$

12. $3(a + \frac{1}{3}) - 2a(5a - 4) = 10(a - a^2) + a$

13. If $A = 2\pi r(h + r)$, find h when $A = 132$ and $r = 3$. Use $\pi = \frac{22}{7}$.

14. If $V = \frac{\pi D^2 H}{12}$, **(a)** solve for H, and **(b)** find H when $V = 157$ and $D = 10$. Use $\pi = 3.14$.

2–4 Equivalent Inequalities *Pages 48–52*

In Exercises 15–17, if the statement is true for all real numbers, answer True; otherwise, answer False.

15. If $a > b$, then $a < -b$.

16. If $a > b$, then $a + (-c) > b - (c)$.

17. If $a > b$, then $a(-c) < b(-c)$.

Solve, and graph each solution set.

18. $d(3 - d) + 2 \geq 2d - (d^2 + d)$

19. $3(4m - 5) \not< 1 - 4(6 - 4m)$

2–5 Combining Open Sentences *Pages 52–56*

20. $\{2, 4, 6\} \cup \{2, 3, 4\} =$ __?__

21. $\{2, 4, 6\} \cap \{2, 3, 4\} =$ __?__

22. The solution set of $|2x - 1| > 7$ is represented by the __?__ of two sets, but the solution set of $|2x - 1| < 7$ is represented by the __?__ of two sets.

23. $\{x: |2x - 1| < 7\} \cap \{x: |2x - 1| > 7\}$ is __?__.

Graph.

24. $|2r + 5| > 3$

25. $|4s - 3| \leq 9$

26. $\{m: 2m - 7 \geq 1\} \cap \{m: |m + 1| \leq 5\}$

27. $\{n: -3 < n + 1 < 1\} \cup \{n: -1 < 2n + 3 < 7\}$

Let the regions within or on the squares represent the sets as indicated in the diagram at the right. Redraw the diagram and shade the region representing

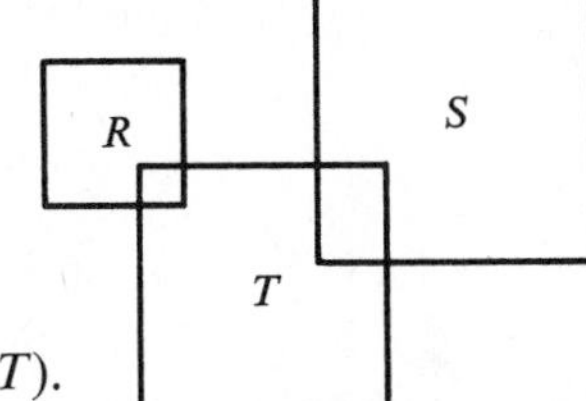

28. $R \cap T$.

29. $R \cap S$.

30. $R \cup S$.

31. $(R \cap T) \cup (S \cap T)$.

2-6 Statements and Converses *Pages 56–59*

32. The converse of the statement: *If blackberries are green, then they are red,* is __?__.

33. The converse of the statement: *If P moves from* -2 *to 3 along the number line, P moves a distance of five units,* is __?__.

34. The statement: $3x - 5 > 1$ *if and only if* $x > 2$, is equivalent to the statement: __?__ and its converse __?__.

Solve.

35. $p(p + 3) = 0$

36. $(5n - 3)(2n + 1) = 0$

2-7 Interpreting Algebraic Expressions and Sentences *Pages 60–61*

37. In interpreting an algebraic expression you should include the __?__ of the variable.

Give two interpretations of each sentence.

38. $a + (a + 15) + (a - 30) = 180$

39. $2r + 25 \geq 75$

2-8 Solving Problems *Pages 62–67*

40. Find four consecutive odd integers whose sum is 128.

41. A number is 5 more than 4 times another. The larger number decreased by $\frac{2}{3}$ the smaller gives 20 as a result. Find the larger.

42. An angle measures at least $\frac{2}{3}$ of its supplement and at most 5 times its complement. Find the possible measures of the angle.

43. When a rectangle is formed by doubling the length of a side of a square and decreasing the length of an adjacent side by 2 feet, the perimeter of the rectangle is 10 feet greater than that of the square. Find the dimensions of the rectangle.

44. A "Local" leaves a station and runs at an average rate of 35 miles an hour. An hour and a half later, an "Express" leaves the station and travels at an average rate of 56 miles an hour on a parallel track. How many hours after it starts will the Express overtake the Local?

CHAPTER 3

. . . the cantilevered roof of a sports stadium, hanging without visible support, but secured by a perfect balance of force

Systems of Linear Open Sentences

In advanced mathematics you need to know how to solve open sentences containing many variables. You take a step forward in this chapter as you become skillful in the handling of both equations and inequalities in two variables. Graphs form an interesting phase of the work.

LINEAR EQUATIONS AND THEIR GRAPHS

3–1 Open Sentences in Two Variables

The mathematical description of practical situations sometimes calls for the use of two or more variables. For example, a physicist may study the motion of a particle which starts at a point on a line and moves along the line for two seconds with a certain velocity, and then for three seconds with another velocity.

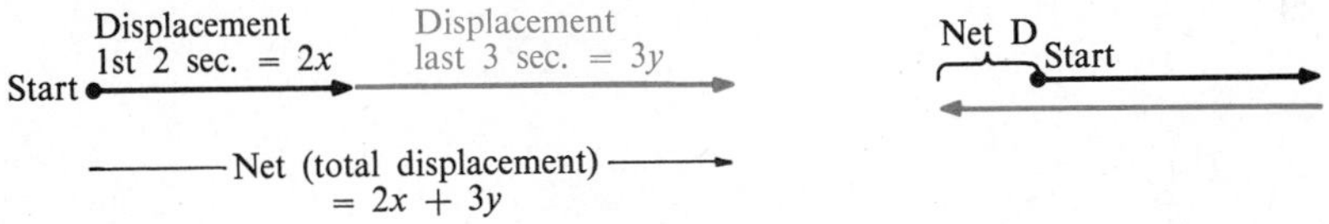

Displacement 1st 2 sec. $= 2x$

Displacement last 3 sec. $= 3y$

Start

Net (total displacement) $= 2x + 3y$

Net D

Start

· *Figure 3–1* ·

During each time interval the particle may travel in either direction along the line and at an average rate of any number of centimeters per second. Therefore, to write an expression for the *net displacement* of the particle, the physicist uses one variable, say x, to represent the average velocity during the first two seconds, and another variable, y, to denote the average velocity during the last three seconds. The replacement set of each variable is the set of real numbers, and an expression for net displacement is $2x + 3y$.

If the physicist told you that the net displacement was 27 centimeters, could you determine the average velocities? To solve an open sentence like $2x + 3y = 27$, you must determine each value of x and the corresponding value of y for which the equation is true. We write these corresponding values as ordered pairs (x, y); x is called the **first coordinate** and y the **second coordinate**. For example, the ordered pair $(9, 3)$ is a root of the sentence because $2 \cdot 9 + 3 \cdot 3 = 27$ is a true statement. Two ordered pairs are **equal** if and only if their first coordinates are equal and their second coordinates are equal. Thus, $(9, 3) = (3^2, \frac{6}{2})$, but $(9, 3) \neq (3, 9)$.

The **solution set of an open sentence in two variables** is the set of ordered pairs of numbers which belong to the replacement sets of the variables and for which the sentence is true. Each member of the solution set is said to be a **root** or **solution** of the open sentence and to **satisfy the sentence**. Do you see that the solution set of $2x + 3y = 27$ is an infinite set? To determine members of this set, transform the sentence into an equivalent one expressing y in terms of x. Then by assigning values to x you can use the equation $y = 9 - \frac{2}{3}x$ as a formula for finding the corresponding values of y, as shown in the adjoining table.

$$\begin{aligned} 2x + 3y &= 27 \\ 3y &= 27 - 2x \\ y &= 9 - \tfrac{2}{3}x \end{aligned}$$

x	$9 - \frac{2}{3}x$	y
0	$9 - \frac{2}{3} \cdot 0$	9
1	$9 - \frac{2}{3} \cdot 1$	$\frac{25}{3}$
3	$9 - \frac{2}{3} \cdot 3$	7
9	$9 - \frac{2}{3} \cdot 9$	3
-3	$9 - \frac{2}{3}(-3)$	11
-6	$9 - \frac{2}{3}(-6)$	13

Thus, a few of the members of $\{(x, y)\colon 2x + 3y = 27\}$ are $(0, 9)$, $(1, \frac{25}{3})$, $(3, 7)$, $(9, 3)$, $(-3, 11)$, $(-6, 13)$.

Written Exercises

The replacement set of each of the variables in the following open sentences is given. Giving coordinates in the order specified in red type, name three roots of each sentence.

A

1. $2x + y = 10$; {real numbers}. (x, y)
2. $3x - y = 4$; {real numbers}. (x, y)
3. $5x - 7y = 1$; {real numbers}. (x, y)
4. $3x + 2y = 4$; {real numbers}. (x, y)
5. $3r + 4s = -1$; {integers}. (r, s)
6. $2t + 5v = -3$; {integers}. (t, v)

7. $7 - (x - y) = 2x + 4$; {integers}. (x, y)
8. $5x - 8 = y - (-4 - x)$; {integers}. (x, y)
9. $a + 4b = 10 - a$; {nonnegative integers}. (a, b)
10. $3a - 1 = 6 - b$; {nonnegative integers}. (a, b)
11. $2(m + n) = 2n + 4$; {real numbers}. (m, n)
12. $15 - 3m = 3(n - m)$; {real numbers}. (m, n)

B

13. $2x - y \geq 4$; {real numbers}. (x, y)
14. $3x + y \geq 5$; {real numbers}. (x, y)
15. $2(k + t) - 3t < t - k$; {integers}. (k, t)
16. $2k - t > 5k - 3(k + t)$; {integers}. (k, t)
17. $|x| + |y| = 2$; {integers}. (x, y)
18. $|x| - |y| = 2$; {integers}. (x, y)
19. $|x| - y^2 = 4$; {negative integers}. (x, y)
20. $x^2 - |y| = 4$; {negative integers}. (x, y)

Find all real values of x and y for which these ordered pairs are equal.

21. $(x + 4, 2y - 3) = (2x + 7, 3y + 8)$
22. $(3x - 6, y - 8) = (15 - 4x, 5 - y)$
23. $(|x|, y) = (3 - |x|, -y)$
24. $(-x, |y|) = (x, 1 - y)$

Problems

Write an open sentence in two variables describing each situation. Then, as directed, find one or more roots of the sentence.

SAMPLE. A numeral is to have two digits such that the units digit is 5 less than twice the tens digit. Find all positive integers represented by such numerals.

Solution: Recall that every nonnegative integer can be expressed as a sum of different powers of 10 each multiplied by a number belonging to $\{0, 1, 2, 3, 4, 5, 6, 7, 8, 9\}$. For example, the integer $653 = 6 \cdot 10^2 + 5 \cdot 10 + 3$; in this example, 3 is the units digit, 5 is the tens digit, and 6 is the hundreds digit.

1. Since the integer described in the problem has two digits in its numeral, we choose two variables:

Let u = units digit
t = tens digit; $\therefore$ the integer $= 10t + u$

(*continued on next page*)

2. Units digit is twice tens digit less five.

$$\underset{u}{\downarrow} \quad \underset{=}{\downarrow} \quad \underbrace{\qquad}_{2t} \quad \underset{-}{\downarrow} \quad \underset{5}{\downarrow}$$

3. Since $t \in \{1, 2, 3, 4, 5, 6, 7, 8, 9\}$ and $u \in \{0, 1, 2, \ldots, 9\}$, you can show by substitution that $\{(t, u)\colon u = 2t - 5\} = \{(3, 1), (4, 3), (5, 5), (6, 7), (7, 9)\}$.

4. $\therefore$ the integers represented by $10t + u$ are 31, 43, 55, 67, or 79, **Answer.** The check is left to you.

A

1. The average of two integers is 76. Give **(a)** two such positive integers, and **(b)** two such integers, one positive and the other negative.
2. The sum of one integer and half another integer is 15. Find two such pairs of integers.
3. Jack is 8 years more than twice as old as Fran. Give two possibilities for their ages.
4. Fred is 5 years less than three times as old as May. Give two possibilities for their ages.
5. Together Jack and Jill carried at most 11 full pails of water. Find two possibilities for the number of full pails each carried.
6. After balancing income and outgo, Mrs. Kline has a net income of less than \$50.00. Give two pairs of corresponding values for income and outgo.
7. The sum of the digits of a positive integer whose decimal numeral has two places is 13. Find all possible integers meeting this description.
8. The units digit in a certain three-digit numeral is 5. If the sum of all three digits is 15, find all possible integers represented.

B

9. A rectangle has a perimeter of 30 inches. Give all integral possibilities for its length and width in inches.
10. An isosceles triangle has a perimeter of 14 feet. Give all integral choices for the lengths of its sides in feet.
11. On a certain day the price of a particular stock varied no more than one point from the opening price. Find two pairs of values for the opening and closing prices, one showing a price rise and the other a drop.
12. At the end of his army service, Peter's weight differed from his weight on induction by less than 5 pounds. Find two pairs of his possible weights, one showing a gain and the other a loss.

Describe a situation to fit each open sentence.

13. $2x - 3y = 10$
14. $xy = 15$
15. $2u + t = 18$
16. $10d + 25q \leq 500$

3–2 Graphs of Linear Equations in Two Variables

Do you recall how to graph the solution set of an equation in two variables such as $2x + 3y = 27$? In a plane choose two reference lines or **axes**, intersecting at right angles at a point O, the **origin**. Using convenient units of length, make each axis a number line whose zero point is O. You usually consider one axis horizontal (the x-axis) and the other vertical (the y-axis) with positive and negative numbers assigned to points on the axes as shown in Figure 3–2. The four regions, or **quadrants**, into which the plane is divided by the axes are also indicated in the figure.

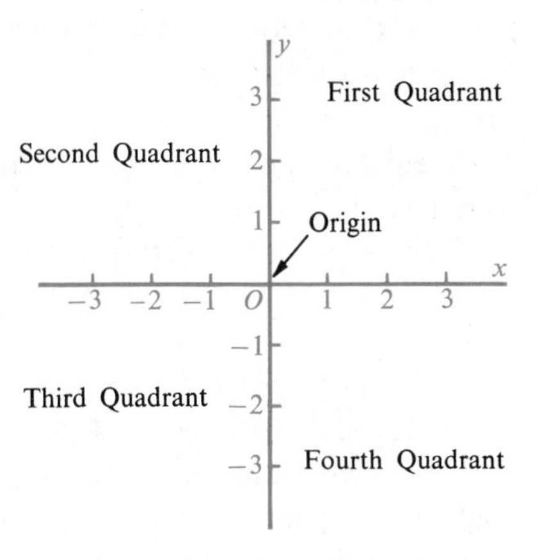

· *Figure 3–2* ·

To associate any ordered pair of numbers such as (9, 3) in the solution set of $2x + 3y = 27$ with a particular point in the plane, draw a vertical line through the graph of 9 on the x-axis and a horizontal line through the graph of 3 on the y-axis (Figure 3–3). P, the point of intersection of these lines, is the **graph** of (9, 3). You say that the coordinates of P are (9, 3), and you call 9, the first or *x-coordinate*, the **abscissa** of P, and 3, the second or *y-coordinate*, the **ordinate** of P. In Figure 3–3 check the **plotting**, or locating, of $Q\,(0, 9)$, $R\,(3, 7)$, and $S\,(-3, 11)$, other points in the solution set of $2x + 3y = 27$. If you could plot *all* the points associated with the ordered pairs in the solution set of this equation, you would obtain the straight line partially shown in Figure 3–4. You say that the line is the *graph of the equation* $2x + 3y = 27$, and that $2x + 3y = 27$ is an *equation of the line.*

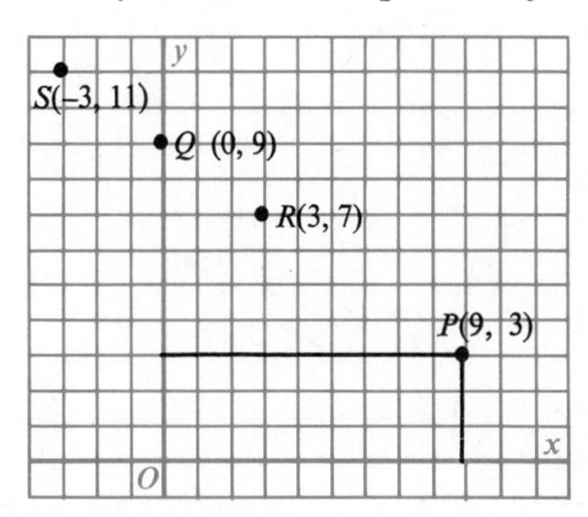

· *Figure 3–3* ·

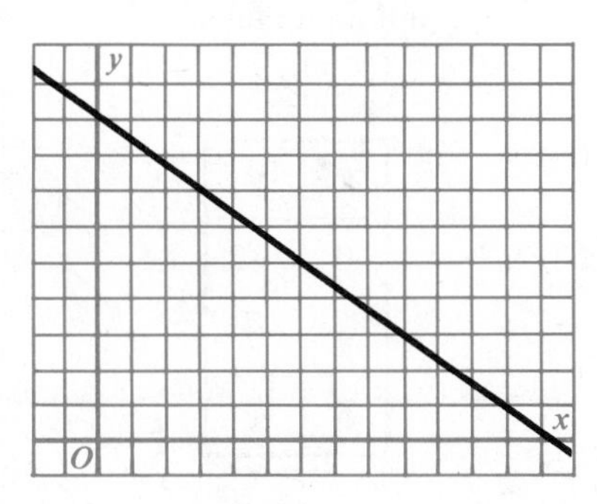

· *Figure 3–4* ·

The set of all points associated with ordered pairs of numbers in the solution set of an open sentence in two variables is called the **graph of the solution set**, or simply, the **graph of the open sentence**. The graph of every equation equivalent to one of the form $Ax + By = C$, where A, B, and C are constants such that not both A and B equal 0, is a straight line. Notice that in any **linear equation**, $Ax + By = C$, each term is either a constant or a monomial of degree 1. Hence, $2x + 3y = 27$ is a linear equation; but $y = x^2$ and $xy = 5$ are not, and their graphs are not straight lines.

The one-to-one correspondence established between the set of all points in a plane and the set of all ordered pairs of real numbers is called a **plane rectangular coordinate system**, or a **Cartesian coordinate system** (in honor of René Descartes, the French mathematician who introduced coordinates). Because of this correspondence you can think of an ordered pair of numbers as pictured by a point, and the solution set of an open sentence in two variables as the set of *all those points and only those points whose coordinates satisfy the sentence.*

Although you need plot only two points to determine the graph of a linear equation over the real numbers, it is good practice to plot a third point as a check. Points having at least one coordinate zero are convenient to plot, unless they are close to each other.

EXAMPLE 1.

Graph: $3x - 5y = 10$.

Solution: $3x - 5y = 10$

Let $x = 0$ and solve for y. Then, let $y = 0$, and $y = 1$, in succession. The table at the lower left may be formed.
$(0, -2)$, $(\frac{10}{3}, 0)$, and $(5, 1)$ determine the straight line in the adjoining figure.

x	y
0	-2
$\frac{10}{3}$	0
5	1

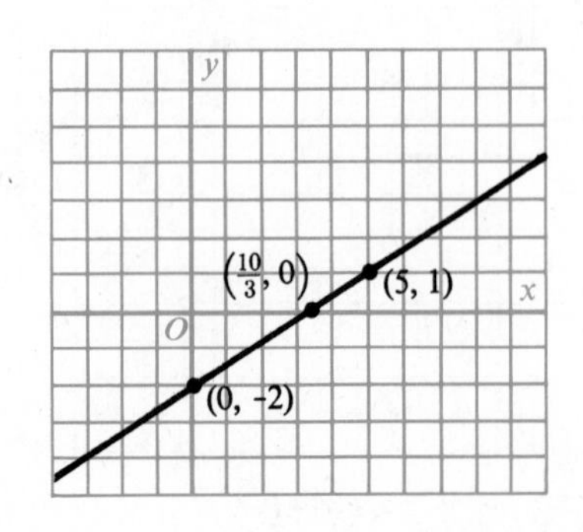

EXAMPLE 2. Graph: $\{(x, y): 3x + 2y = 0, x \geq 0, \text{ and } y > -6\}$.

Solution:

$$3x + 2y = 0$$
$$2y = -3x$$
$$y = -\tfrac{3}{2}x$$

x	$-\frac{3}{2}x$	y
0	$-\frac{3}{2} \cdot 0$	0
2	$-\frac{3}{2} \cdot 2$	-3
4	$-\frac{3}{2} \cdot 4$	-6

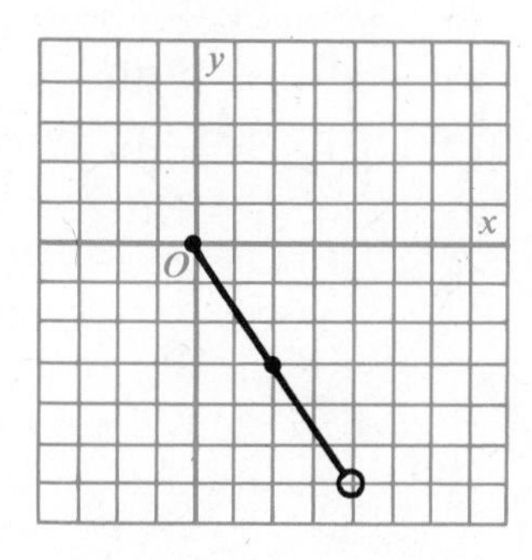

Note that the graph is a line segment including only one of its end points.

EXAMPLE 3. Graph: $\{(x, y): y = -1\}$.

Solution: The equation can be written $0 \cdot x + y = -1$. Its graph is the horizontal line shown.

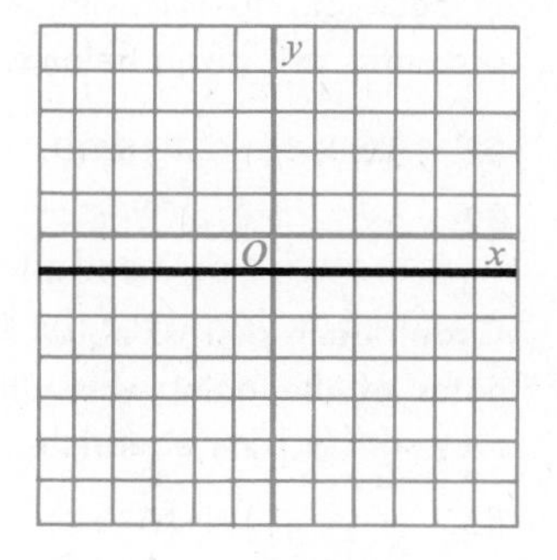

Oral Exercises

State the coordinates of the points in which the graph of each of the following equations intersects the axes.

SAMPLE. $5x - 2y = 10$ *What you say:* $(0, -5)$ and $(2, 0)$

1. $x + y = 5$
2. $x + y = -5$
3. $x - y - 5 = 0$
4. $x - y + 5 = 0$
5. $x - y = 0$
6. $x + y = 0$
7. $y - 8 = 0$
8. $y + 3 = 0$
9. $x + 1 = 0$
10. $x - 5 = 0$
11. $6x + y - 8 = 0$
12. $3x - y + 6 = 0$
13. $7x - y - 2 = 0$
14. $y - 2x = 5$
15. $y - 3x = 4$
16. $7x + y = 5$
17. $2x - 3y = 6$
18. $3x - 2y - 6 = 0$

19. $2x + 3y + 6 = 0$

20. $3x + 2y + 6 = 0$

21. $2x - 5y = 10$

22. $2y - 5x = 10$

23. $x - 5y = 10$

24. $3x + 2y = 0$

25. $0.1x + 0.2y = 0.3$

26. $0.2x - 0.1y = 0.3$

27. $\frac{1}{2}x + 3y = 5$

28. $3x - \frac{1}{4}y = 1$

29. $\frac{2}{3}x - \frac{1}{3}y = 1$

30. $\frac{1}{2}x - \frac{2}{3}y = 1$

Written Exercises

A **1–30.** Graph each of the equations listed in the Oral Exercises above.

In each of the following exercises determine k so that the point whose coordinates are given belongs to the graph of the equation.

B **31.** $3x + ky = 16; (2, -1)$

32. $5y = kx - 3; (-2, -1)$

33. $2ky + x - 3 = 0; (-5, 2)$

34. $(k - 3)x - ky = 2(k + 1); (2, -2)$

Graph each pair of equations in the same coordinate plane. Name the coordinates of the point where the graphs intersect, and show by substitution that they satisfy both equations.

35. $x - 4y = 10, x + y = 5$

36. $2x + y = 4, x - y = 5$

37. $3x = y - 9, 5x + 2y + 4 = 0$

38. $4y + 3x = 0, x = y$

Graph the following equations in the coordinate plane.

C **39.** $|y| = 3$ **40.** $|x| = 2$ **41.** $y = |x|$ **42.** $y = |x + 1|$

LINES AND THEIR EQUATIONS

3–3 The Slope of a Line

If a hill rises 15 feet for every 100 feet of horizontal distance, the steepness or *grade* of the hill is the ratio $\frac{15}{100}$, or 15% (Fig. 3–5). To describe the steepness or *slope* of a line, such as the graph of $2x - 3y = 12$ in Figure 3–6, choose two points on it, for example, $M(-3, -6)$ and $N(9, 2)$, and compute a similar quotient:

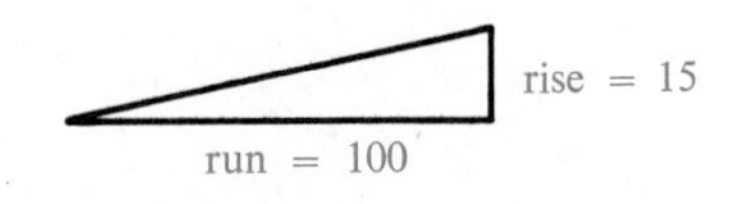

· *Figure 3–5* ·

$$\textbf{slope} = \frac{\textbf{rise}}{\textbf{run}} = \frac{\textbf{ordinate of } N - \textbf{ordinate of } M}{\textbf{abscissa of } N - \textbf{abscissa of } M}$$

$$= \frac{2 - (-6)}{9 - (-3)} = \frac{2 + 6}{9 + 3} = \frac{8}{12}$$

$$\therefore \textbf{slope} = \tfrac{2}{3}$$

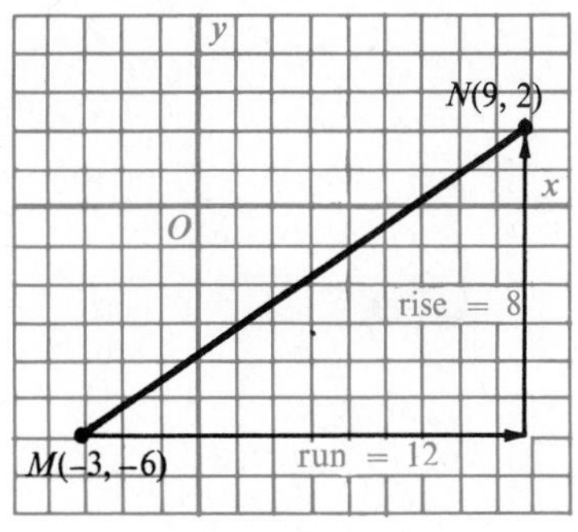

· *Figure 3–6* ·

To show that the slope of the line does not depend on the particular points selected, let $P(x_1, y_1)$ and $Q(x_2, y_2)$ be any two different points of the line. (*Note:* $P(x_1, y_1)$ is read "the point P, x sub one, y sub one.") Now use the fact that a point belongs to the graph of an equation if and only if its coordinates satisfy the equation:

Q is on the line; $\quad \therefore 2x_2 - 3y_2 = 12$

P is on the line; $\quad \therefore 2x_1 - 3y_1 = 12$

$$\therefore 2(x_2 - x_1) - 3(y_2 - y_1) = 12 - 12$$

$$-3(y_2 - y_1) = -2(x_2 - x_1)$$

$$\textbf{slope} = \frac{\textbf{ord. of } Q - \textbf{ord. of } P}{\textbf{abs. of } Q - \textbf{abs. of } P} = \frac{y_2 - y_1}{x_2 - x_1} = \frac{2}{3}$$

By transforming the equation $2x - 3y = 12$ into the equivalent equation $y = \frac{2}{3}x - 4$, you may see the relationship between the coefficients of the equation and the slope of the line: $y = \frac{2}{3}x - 4$.

This example suggests the following definition and theorem.

If $x_1 \neq x_2$, the slope m of the line joining the points whose coordinates are (x_1, y_1) and (x_2, y_2) is $m = \dfrac{y_2 - y_1}{x_2 - x_1}$.

THEOREM. If (x_1, y_1) and (x_2, y_2) belong to the solution set of

$$Ax + By = C \text{ and if } B \neq 0, \text{ then } \frac{y_2 - y_1}{x_2 - x_1} = -\frac{A}{B}.$$

The proof of the theorem employs the same reasoning as used above in the case of the equation $2x - 3y = 12$, and is left as Exercise 38, page 90.

A related theorem enabling you to draw a line when given its slope and one of its points is the following one, whose proof forms oral exercises 19–26 in the set on page 88.

THEOREM. If (x_1, y_1) belongs to the solution set of $Ax + By = C$, if $B \neq 0$, and if $\frac{y_2 - y_1}{x_2 - x_1} = -\frac{A}{B}$, then (x_2, y_2) also belongs to that solution set.

Both of these theorems are used in the following example.

EXAMPLE 1. **a.** Determine the slope m of the line whose equation is $5x + 4y = 20$.

b. Determine the coordinates of the point which the line has in common with the y-axis.

c. Use the results of **(a)** and **(b)** to draw the line.

Solution: **a.** The equation $5x + 4y = 20$ is of the form

$$Ax + By = C. \qquad \therefore m = -\frac{A}{B}, \text{ or } -\frac{5}{4}.$$

b. Substitute 0 for x and solve for y.
$5(0) + 4y = 20$; $y = 5$

$\therefore$ the point common to the y-axis and the line is (0, 5).

c. From (0, 5) measure 4 units to the right and then 5 units down to reach the point (4, 0). This point together with the point (0, 5) determine the line.

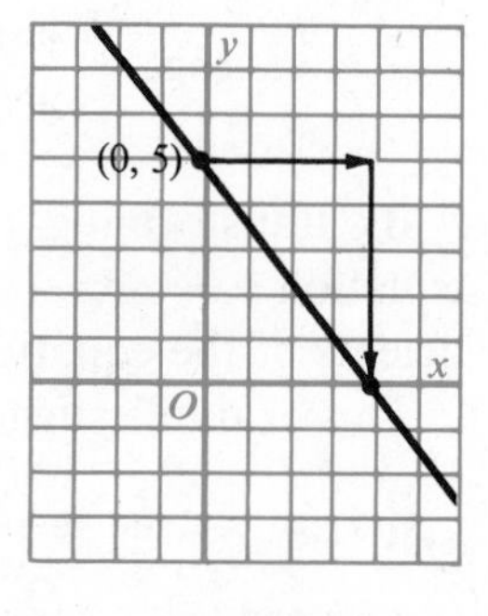

Notice that as a point moves from left to right along a line the slope gives the change in its ordinate (the vertical change) for each change of 1 unit in its abscissa (the horizontal change). Thus, if $(-5, 2)$ is a point on a line of slope 3, another point on the line is $(-5 + 1, 2 + 3)$ or $(-4, 5)$, Figure 3–7.

But, if $(-5, 2)$ is on a line of slope -3, another point of the line is $(-5 + 1, 2 + [-3])$, or $(-4, -1)$, Figure 3–8. Do you see that

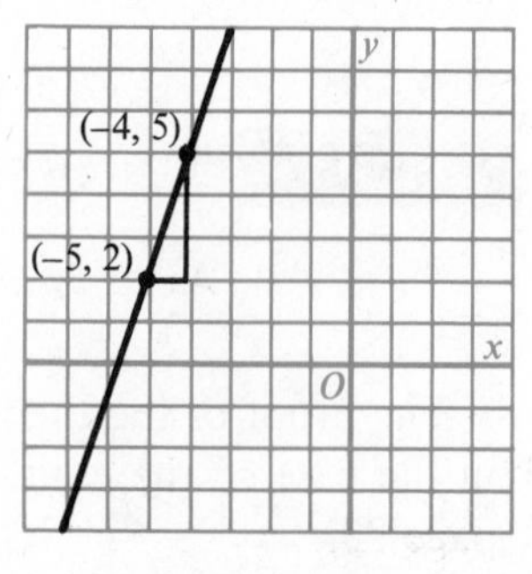

Figure 3–7

when a line rises from left to right, its slope is a positive number (Figure 3–7), but that when it falls from left to right its slope is negative (Figure 3–8)?

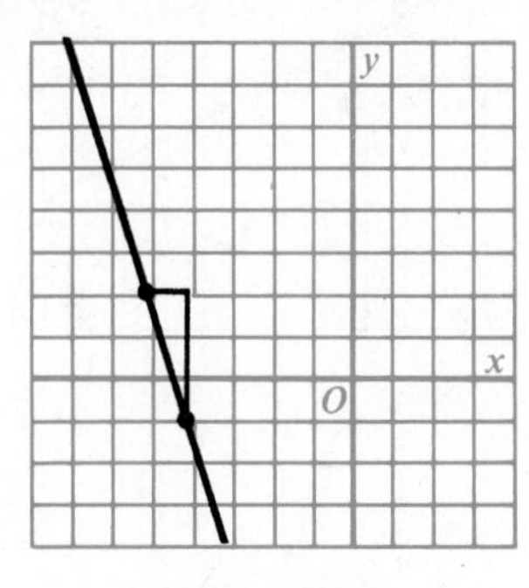

· *Figure 3–8* ·

$S(-7, 4)$ $R(3, 4)$

· *Figure 3–9* ·

Can the slope of a line be 0? The slope, m, of the line joining $R(3, 4)$ and $S(-7, 4)$ in Figure 3–9 is $m = \frac{4 - 4}{-7 - 3} = \frac{0}{-10} = 0$. As in this example, you can show that the slope of every horizontal line is 0.

The abscissas of any two points on a vertical line are equal, so that the slope computation for Figure 3–10 will give a fraction with denominator 0. Since you may not divide by 0, the line containing T and W, *like every vertical line*, has no slope.

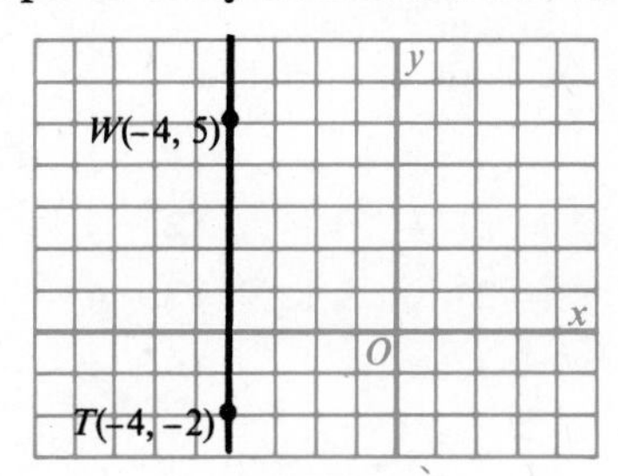

· *Figure 3–10* ·

Oral Exercises

Give the slope of each line in the accompanying diagrams.

1.

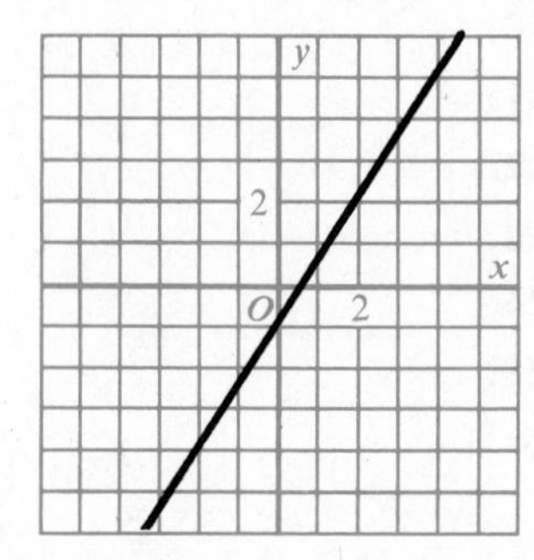

2.

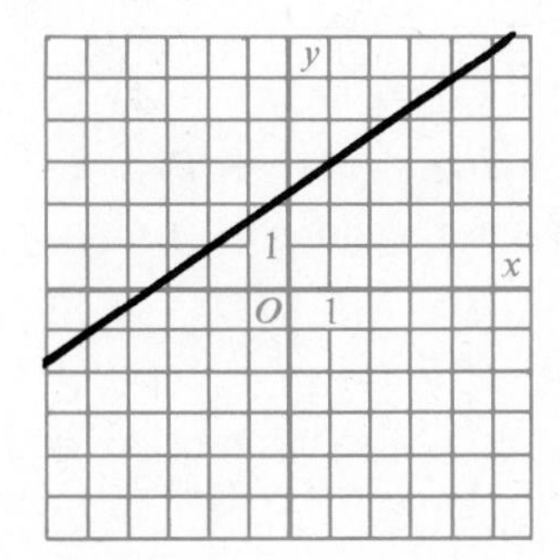

3.

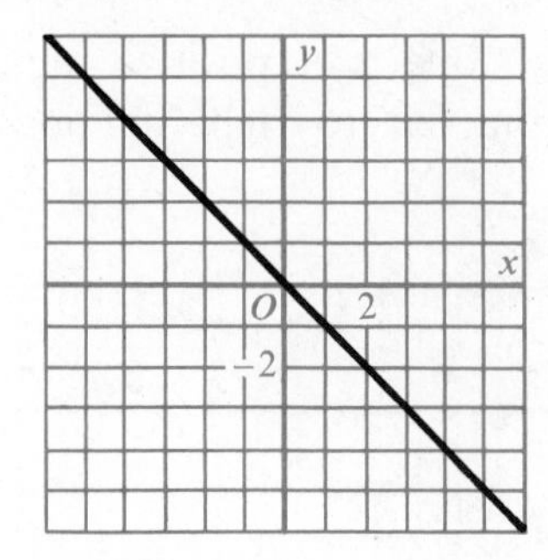

4.

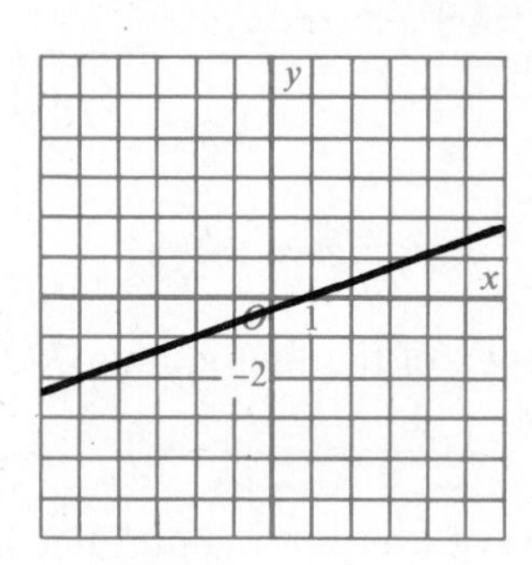

5.

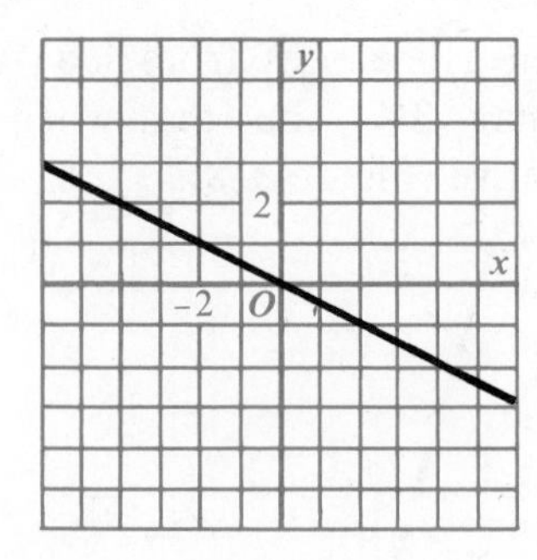

6.

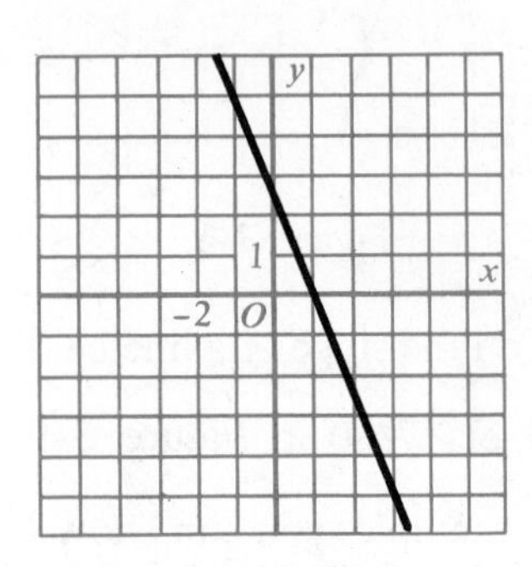

State the slope of each line.

7. $y = -3x + 2$	**11.** $2y = 4x - 12$	**15.** $4x - 6y = 0$
8. $y = 5x - 7$	**12.** $3y = 9x + 15$	**16.** $5x + 10y = 0$
9. $y = 2x$	**13.** $6 - x = y$	**17.** $x - 3 = 2$
10. $y = -6x$	**14.** $x - y = 1$	**18.** $x + 1 = 4$

In Exercises 19–26 give the reasons for the indicated steps in the proof of the theorem on page 86. Do not write in the book.

Proof

Step	*Reason*
$\dfrac{y_2 - y_1}{x_2 - x_1} = -\dfrac{A}{B}$	**19.**
$B(y_2 - y_1) = -A(x_2 - x_1)$	**20.**
$By_2 - By_1 = -Ax_2 + Ax_1$	**21.**
$Ax_2 + By_2 = Ax_1 + By_1$	**22.**
(x_1, y_1) is a solution of $Ax + By = C$	**23.**
$Ax_1 + By_1 = C$	**24.**
$\therefore Ax_2 + By_2 = C$	**25.**
$\therefore (x_2, y_2)$ is a solution of $Ax + By = C$	**26.**

Written Exercises

Plot each pair of points, draw a straight line through them, and determine the slope of the line from the graph. Check by using the slope formula.

1. $(2, 3); (4, 5)$
2. $(6, 1); (10, 3)$
3. $(1, -2); (4, 6)$
4. $(-2, 1); (2, -2)$
5. $(5, -1); (-5, -1)$
6. $(-2, 3); (-3, 3)$
7. $(2, 1); (-3, 0)$
8. $(-1, 3); (-2, 7)$
9. $(1, 2); (3, 6)$
10. $(5, -1); (0, 5)$
11. $(-1, 5); (-1, -5)$
12. $(2, -6); (2, 0)$

Through the given point, draw a line with the given slope, m.

13. $(-1, 2); m = 1$
14. $(-3, 0); m = -2$
15. $(2, 3); m = -\frac{1}{4}$
16. $(-1, 3); m = -\frac{3}{4}$
17. $(-2, 4); m = 0$
18. $(-4, 1)$; no slope

Do the points given in each table lie on a line? If so, give its slope.

SAMPLE.

	3	3	3	

x	0	3	6	9
y	1	3	5	7

	2	2	2	

Solution: As indicated in the table, each change of 3 in x is accompanied by a change of 2 in y. Hence the points are *collinear;* that is, they lie in a straight line having the slope $\frac{2}{3}$.

19.

x	0	1	2	3
y	5	7	9	11

20.

x	0	1	2	3
y	2	4	6	8

21.

x	-2	-1	0	1
y	1	2	1	0

22.

x	-3	-2	-1	0
y	-2	1	4	7

23.

x	2	4	6	8
y	-2	-5	-8	-11

24.

x	3	6	9	10
y	-1	1	3	5

25.

x	7	4	0	-5
y	0	6	14	24

26.

x	1	3	6	10
y	2	0	-3	-7

For each line with the indicated equation determine **(a)** the slope and **(b)** the point where the line intersects the *y*-axis. Use the results of **(a)** and **(b)** to draw the line.

B

27. $3x - 4y = 8$

28. $5x - 2y = 6$

29. $5x + 3y + 6 = 0$

30. $2x + 5y + 10 = 0$

Determine *a* so that the slope *m* of the line containing each pair of points has the given value. Check your solution by graphing the points you find.

31. $(0, 5a); (-4, 3a), m = \frac{1}{2}$

32. $(2, a); (5, -a), m = \frac{4}{3}$

33. $(4, 0); \left(5, \frac{1}{a}\right), m = -2$

34. $\left(2, \frac{1}{a}\right); (1, 0), m = -3$

C

35. $(1, |a|); (2, a), m = -1$

36. $(1, a); (2, |a|), m = 1$

37. Explain why the restriction $B \neq 0$ is made in the statement of the theorem on page 86.

38. Prove the theorem stated on page 85.

3–4 Determining an Equation of a Line

Given a linear equation, you know how to draw its graph. The theorems of the preceding section enable you to solve the converse problem: Given a line described by geometric conditions, find an equation of the line. For example, the line in Figure 3–11 has slope $\frac{3}{2}$ and passes through $(-1, -5)$. The theorems of the preceding section imply that a point (x, y), other than $(-1, -5)$ itself, lies on the line if and only if

$$\frac{y - (-5)}{x - (-1)} = \frac{3}{2}$$

$$\frac{y + 5}{x + 1} = \frac{3}{2}$$

$$y + 5 = \tfrac{3}{2}(x + 1)$$

$$\text{or} \quad 3x - 2y = 7$$

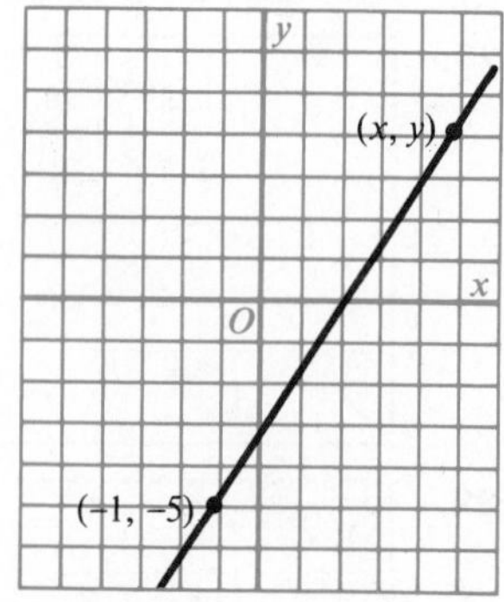

Figure 3–11

To verify that the graph of $3x - 2y = 7$ satisfies the prescribed conditions, we answer the following questions:

1. Does $(-1, -5)$ satisfy the equation?
   Yes, because $3(-1) - 2(-5) = -3 + 10 = 7$.
2. Is the slope of the graph $\frac{3}{2}$? Yes, because $3x - 2y = 7$ is equivalent to $-2y = -3x + 7$, or $y = \frac{3}{2}x - \frac{7}{2}$.

The preceding discussion illustrates the general method of finding an equation of a line having slope m and passing through a given point (x_1, y_1). Any other point (x, y) lies on this line if and only if

$$\frac{y - y_1}{x - x_1} = m.$$

Since $x \neq x_1$, the multiplication property of equality implies

$$y - y_1 = m(x - x_1).$$

Because the *derivation* of this equation applied only to points other than (x_1, y_1), we must verify by substitution that this pair will nonetheless satisfy the equation:

$$y_1 - y_1 \stackrel{?}{=} m(x_1 - x_1), \qquad 0 = 0 \checkmark$$

Thus, $y - y_1 = m(x - x_1)$, called the **point-slope form** of the equation of the line, is an algebraic statement of the geometric condition that the line must *contain the point* (x_1, y_1) and have *slope m*.

An especially simple case of the point-slope form results when the given point lies on the y-axis.

EXAMPLE 1. Write an equation of the line having slope 2 and containing $(0, -3)$.

Solution:

$$\begin{aligned} y - y_1 &= m(x - x_1) \\ &\downarrow \quad \downarrow \quad \downarrow \\ y - (-3) &= 2(x - 0) \\ y + 3 &= 2x \end{aligned}$$

$\therefore$ An equation of the line is $y = 2x - 3$, **Answer.**

In this equation the constant term, -3, is the y-coordinate of the point in which the line intersects the y-axis; it is called the **y-intercept** of the line.

Using the method in the solution of Example 1, you can show that the line having *slope m* and *y-intercept b* has an equation of the form

$$y = mx + b.$$

We call this open sentence the **slope-intercept form** of the equation of the line.

EXAMPLE 2. Find an equation of the line passing through the points whose coordinates are $(-1, 3)$ and $(2, -3)$.

Solution:

1. Slope $= \dfrac{-3 - 3}{2 - (-1)} = \dfrac{-6}{3} = -2.$

2. The slope-intercept form of the equation is

$$y = mx + b \text{ or } y = -2x + b.$$

Choose one point, say $(-1, 3)$. Since it lies on the line its coordinates must satisfy $y = -2x + b$.

$$3 = -2(-1) + b \text{ or } 3 = 2 + b$$
$$\therefore 1 = b$$

3. To check, show that the coordinates of the other point, $(2, -3)$, satisfy the equation:

$$y = -2x + 1$$
$$-3 \stackrel{?}{=} -2(2) + 1$$
$$-3 \stackrel{?}{=} -4 + 1$$
$$-3 = -3 \checkmark$$

$\therefore$ An equation of the line is: $y = -2x + 1$, **Answer.**

In a plane, different lines having the same slope, or having no slope, are called **parallel lines**.

Using the slope-intercept form, you can show why parallel lines have no point in common. For example, the graphs of $y = 3x - 2$ and $y = 3x + 4$, shown in Figure 3–12, cannot intersect because if $y = 3x - 2$ and $y = 3x + 4$ were both true statements for some ordered pair (x, y), then by substitution

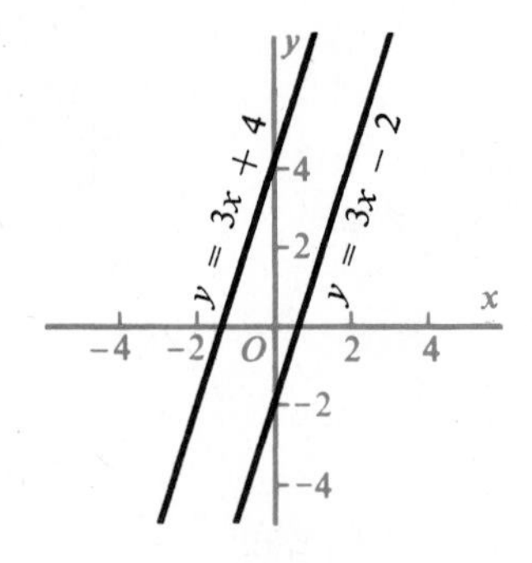

Figure 3–12

$$\mathbf{3x - 2 = 3x + 4, \text{ and}}$$
$$\mathbf{-2 = 4, \text{ a false statement.}}$$

It can be shown that, conversely, lines that lie in the same plane and do not intersect either have no slope (are vertical lines) or have the same slope.

EXAMPLE 3. Find an equation of a line parallel to $5x - 3y = 7$ and intersecting the x-axis at $(-6, 0)$.

Solution:

1. The slope of $5x - 3y = 7$ is $\frac{5}{3}$. Why?

   $\therefore$ The slope-intercept form of the described line is

$$y = \tfrac{5}{3}x + b$$

2. $(-6, 0)$ lies on the described line; therefore, replace x by -6, y by 0, and solve for b.

$$0 = \tfrac{5}{3}(-6) + b$$
$$0 = -10 + b$$
$$b = 10$$

$\therefore$ An equation of the line is $y = \frac{5}{3}x + 10$, or
$3y = 5x + 30$, **Answer.**

The x-coordinate of the point in which a line intersects the x-axis is called the **x-intercept** of the line. Thus, the line $3y = 5x + 30$ has an x-intercept equal to -6.

Oral Exercises

State the point-slope form of the equation of the line containing the given point and having the given slope.

1. $(1, 1)$; $m = 1$
2. $(2, 3)$; $m = 3$
3. $(1, -2)$; $m = -2$
4. $(3, -2)$; $m = -1$
5. $(1, 4)$; $m = -\frac{1}{2}$
6. $(3, 2)$; $m = -\frac{2}{3}$
7. $(2, -1)$; $m = 0$
8. $(-5, -7)$; $m = 0$
9. $(p, 2q)$; $m = r$
10. $(t, 2)$; $m = s$

State the slope and y-intercept of the graph of each equation.

11. $2x + y = 7$
12. $y - 5x = 4$
13. $2y - x = 12$
14. $x + 3y = 15$
15. $x - y + 10 = 0$
16. $0 = 5 - x - y$
17. $4x + 2y = 7$
18. $10x - 5y = 8$

State an equation of the line having the given slope and y-intercept.

19. $m = 1$; $b = 2$
20. $m = -2$; $b = 7$
21. $m = -5$; $b = -3$
22. $m = -\frac{1}{3}$; $b = 0$
23. $m = 0$; $b = -5$
24. $m = -\frac{1}{2}$; $b = 0$
25. $m = 4$; $b = -\frac{3}{4}$
26. $m = 5$; $b = -\frac{2}{5}$

Written Exercises

(a) Draw the line passing through the indicated point and having the given slope; **(b)** for each line determine an equation of the form $Ax + By = C$ where A, B, and C are integers.

A

1. $(2, 3); -1$
2. $(3, 4); -2$
3. $(-1, 2); 3$
4. $(-3, 1); 1$
5. $(2, -1); \frac{1}{2}$
6. $(3, 0); \frac{2}{3}$
7. $(0, 0); 1$
8. $(0, 0); -2$
9. $(-5, -2); 0$
10. $(-2, -5); 0$
11. $(10, 4)$; no slope
12. $(-7, 2)$; no slope

Find a linear equation whose graph contains the given points and which has the form $Ax + By = C$ where A, B, and C are integers.

13. $(3, 4); (6, 7)$
14. $(2, 5); (4, 7)$
15. $(-4, 3); (0, 2)$
16. $(0, -1); (4, 3)$
17. $(0, 0); (2, -1)$
18. $(5, 1); (0, 0)$
19. $(-3, -3); (-1, 2)$
20. $(0, -1); (-1, -1)$
21. $(2, 3); (3, 3)$
22. $(-3, 2); (2, 2)$
23. $(0, 0); (0, 1)$
24. $(2, 3); (2, 5)$

Determine an equation of the line satisfying the stated conditions.

B

25. With y-intercept 3 and parallel to the graph of $y = x$.
26. With y-intercept -4 and parallel to the graph of $x + y = 5$.
27. Through $(1, 3)$ and parallel to the graph of $2x + 3y = 4$.
28. Through $(1, -4)$ and parallel to the graph of $4x - 2y = 1$.
29. Through $(-5, 2)$ and parallel to the graph of $x = -2$.
30. Through $(0, 1)$ and parallel to the graph of $y = 5$.
31. With slope 3 and x-intercept 4.
32. With slope -4 and x-intercept -2.
33. Parallel to the y-axis and with x-intercept -5.
34. Parallel to the x-axis and with y-intercept -8.
35. Through $(-2, 1)$ and parallel to the line joining $(1, 4)$ and $(2, -3)$.
36. Through $(-3, 2)$ and parallel to the line joining $(2, 3)$ and $(1, -2)$.
37. With x-intercept 2 and y-intercept 3.
38. With x-intercept -5 and y-intercept 2.

C

39. Through $(a, 3a)$ with slope $\frac{1}{a}$.
40. Through $(b, -2b)$ with slope $\frac{2}{b}$.
41. Show that the figure whose vertices are $(2, 1)$, $(4, 2)$, $(5, 2)$, and $(7, 3)$ is a parallelogram.
42. Repeat Exercise 41 for vertices $(4, 5)$, $(3, 3)$, $(0, 6)$, and $(1, 8)$.

43. If a line has x-intercept a ($a \neq 0$) and y-intercept b ($b \neq 0$), show that an equation of the line (called the *intercept form* of the equation) is: $\frac{x}{a} + \frac{y}{b} = 1$.

44. If (x_1, y_1) and (x_2, y_2) are two points of a line and if $x_1 \neq x_2$, then an equation of the line (called the *two-point form* of the equation) is $y - y_1 = \frac{y_2 - y_1}{x_2 - x_1}(x - x_1)$.

45. Show that if the graphs of the linear equations $A_1x + B_1y = C_1$ and $A_2x + B_2y = C_2$ are parallel, then $A_1B_2 = A_2B_1$.

46. Show that if $A_1B_2 = A_2B_1$, then the graphs of the linear equations $A_1x + B_1y = C_1$ and $A_2x + B_2y = C_2$ are either the same line or are parallel lines.

3–5 Systems of Two Linear Equations in Two Variables

When you graph two linear equations over the real numbers on the same axes, the result is one of three types of graphs, as illustrated.

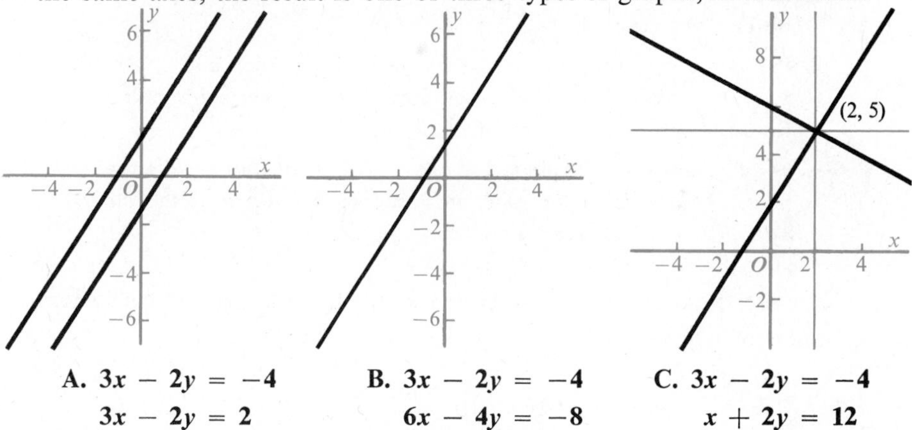

A. $\mathbf{3x - 2y = -4}$
$\mathbf{3x - 2y = 2}$

B. $\mathbf{3x - 2y = -4}$
$\mathbf{6x - 4y = -8}$

C. $\mathbf{3x - 2y = -4}$
$\mathbf{x + 2y = 12}$

· *Figure 3–13* ·

If S and T are the solution sets of two linear equations, the sets can have in common:

A. No point — the lines are parallel. $S \cap T = \emptyset$, and the equations are called inconsistent.

B. All their points — the lines coincide. $S \cap T = S = T$; the equations are equivalent and are called dependent.

C. Just one point — the lines intersect. $S \cap T$ contains a single ordered pair; the equations are called independent and consistent.

Because two such equations represent two conditions imposed at the same time on the same variables, we say that they form a system of **simultaneous equations**. Any ordered pair satisfying both equations is called a **solution**, or **root**, of the system.

If two systems of equations have the same solution set, the systems are said to be **equivalent**. Do you see that the system "$3x - 2y = -4$ and $x + 2y = 12$" is equivalent to the system "$x = 2$ and $y = 5$," whose graphs are the red lines in Figure 3–13C? Algebraic methods of solving a pair of linear equations in x and y aim to find such an equivalent system whose solution can be obtained by inspection.

The properties of equality (Sec. 1-6) insure that if you perform any *sequence* of the following transformations on a system of two equations in two variables, the resulting pair of equations is equivalent to the original system.

Transformations That Produce an Equivalent System of Linear Equations

1. Replace either equation by an equivalent equation in the same variables. (See page 44.)
2. Replace either equation by the sum of that equation and any real number multiple of the other equation. The replacement is called a **linear combination** of the given equations.
3. In either equation substitute for one variable (a) an equivalent expression in terms of the other variable as derived from the other equation or (b) its value if known.

You use these transformations to replace an equation of the system by one in which 0 is the coefficient of one of the variables.

EXAMPLE 1. Solve
$$x + 2y = 10$$
$$3x + 4y = 8$$

Solution 1: (*Linear Combination Method*)

1. To obtain equations having the same number as coefficient of x, multiply each member of the first equation, $x + 2y = 10$, by 3. (Transformation 1)

$$\begin{cases} 3x + 6y = 30 \\ 3x + 4y = 8 \end{cases}$$

2. In the new system keep the second equation but replace the first equation by the difference of the equations in Step 1. (Transformation 2)

$$\begin{cases} 2y = 22 \\ 3x + 4y = 8 \end{cases}$$

3. Solve $2y = 22$ for y. (Transformation 1) $\quad y = 11$

4. Substitute 11 for y in $3x + 4y = 8$. (Transformation 3) $\quad 3x + 4(11) = 8$

5. Solve for x. (Transformation 1)

$$3x + 44 = 8$$
$$3x = -36$$
$$x = -12$$

6. Verify that $(-12, 11)$ is a solution of *both* of the *original* equations.

$$-12 + 2(11) \stackrel{?}{=} 10$$
$$-12 + 22 \stackrel{?}{=} 10$$
$$10 = 10 \ \checkmark$$
$$3(-12) + 4(11) \stackrel{?}{=} 8$$
$$-36 + 44 \stackrel{?}{=} 8$$
$$8 = 8 \ \checkmark$$

$\{(-12, 11)\}$, **Answer**

Solution 2. (*Substitution Method*)

1. Transform the first equation to express x in terms of y. (Transformation 1)

$$x + 2y = 10$$
$$x = 10 - 2y$$

2. Substitute this expression for x in the other equation. (Transformation 3)

$$3x + 4y = 8$$
$$3(10 - 2y) + 4y = 8$$

3. Solve the result for y. (Transformation 1) $\quad 30 - 6y + 4y = 8; y = 11$

4. Substitute the value of y in the expression for x. (Transformation 3) $\quad x = 10 - 2(11)$

5. Solve for x. (Transformation 1) $\quad x = -12$

6. Check is the same as Step **6** in Solution 1. $\quad \{(-12, 11)\}$, **Answer**

EXAMPLE 2. Find $\{(x, y)\colon 4x - 2y = 3 \text{ and } -6x + 3y = 1\}$.

Solution:

1. To obtain equations having the coefficients of one variable (say y) equal in absolute value, multiply the first equation by 3, and the second by 2.

$$12x - 6y = 9$$
$$-12x + 6y = 2$$

2. Replace either equation (say the first) by the sum of the equations.

$$0 = 11$$
$$-12x + 6y = 2$$

Since the given system is equivalent to a system in which one equation has no solution ($0 = 11$ is a false statement), the given equations have no common solution and are inconsistent. Therefore,

$$\{(x, y)\colon 4x - 2y = 3 \text{ and } -6x + 3y = 1\} = \emptyset, \text{ **Answer.**}$$

EXAMPLE 3. Solve $2x + y = 1$ and $6x + 3y = 3$ simultaneously.

Solution: Three times the first equation is $6x + 3y = 3$, which is the second equation. Because the second equation is three times the first, the equations are dependent. Therefore the solution set of the system coincides with the infinite set of ordered pairs satisfying the first equation, $2x + y = 1$, **Answer.**

Another way to show that the equations are dependent is to (1) solve the first equation for y, and (2) substitute the result in the second equation:

(1) $\mathbf{2x + y = 1}$

$\mathbf{y = 1 - 2x}$

(2)

$$\begin{aligned} 6x + 3y &= 3 \\ 6x + 3(1 - 2x) &= 3 \\ 6x + 3 - 6x &= 3 \\ 3 &= 3 \end{aligned}$$

Since Steps 1 and 2 replace the second equation by the identity $3 = 3$, the solution set of the given system coincides with the solution set of the first equation, $2x + y = 1$.

Oral Exercises

Tell how to combine the two equations to obtain one with 0 as coefficient of the indicated variable, in red.

SAMPLE 1. $7x - 2y = 5$
$4x + 3y = 25$ $\quad y$

What you say: Multiply the first equation by 3, the second by 2, and add the resulting equations.

1. $3x - 2y = 7$
$5x + y = 3$ $\quad y$

2. $2x - 7y = 6$
$x + 3y = 2$ $\quad x$

3. $3a + 5b = 7$
$a - 2b = 4$ $\quad a$

4. $4u - 3v = 7$
$-2u + 7v = 6$ $\quad u$

5. $2p + 6q = 7$
$5p - 2q = 6$ $\quad q$

6. $20r - 2s = 5$
$4r + 7s = -2$ $\quad r$

7. $5x - 7y = 3$
$-3x + 6y = 4$ $\quad x$

8. $12x - 3y = 6$
$7x + 11y = 27$ $\quad y$

9. $6x - \frac{1}{2}y = 1$, $11x + y = 7$ $\quad y$

10. $\frac{1}{3}x + y = 7$, $x - 6y = 2$ $\quad x$

11. $4x - 7y = 24$, $6x + 11y = 12$ $\quad x$

12. $-6x - 3y = 5$, $9x + 22y = 35$ $\quad x$

Transform each equation into an equivalent one expressing the indicated variable in terms of the other variable.

SAMPLE 2. $2t + r = 4,\ r.$ *What you say:* $r = 4 - 2t.$

13. $2y = 4x - 6,\ y$

14. $x + y = 7,\ y$

15. $m - n = 0,\ m$

16. $5m - n = 7,\ n$

17. $2x = 4 - y,\ y$

18. $3y = 5 - x,\ x$

19. $3t + 2v = 6,\ v$

20. $2t - 3v = 12,\ t$

21. $0 = p + q + 3,\ p$

22. $0 = 2p - s + 7,\ s$

The systems in Exercises 23–28 are equivalent. State how to transform the first system into the second (in red).

23. $5x + y = 7$, $2x - y = 5$ $\qquad 5x + y = 7$, $7x = 12$

24. $3x - y = 4$, $-3x + 2y = 8$ $\qquad 3x - y = 4$, $y = 12$

25. $4c - d = 3$, $2c + 7d = 9$ $\qquad -15d = -15$, $2c + 7d = 9$

26. $5a + 6b = 9$, $2a + 3b = 1$ $\qquad a = 7$, $2a + 3b = 1$

27. $x = 2y + 4$, $x - 3y = 7$ $\qquad x = 2y + 4$, $2y + 4 - 3y = 7$

28. $y = 5 - x$, $2x + y = 8$ $\qquad y = 5 - x$, $2x + 5 - x = 8$

Written Exercises

Solve each system, and state whether the equations in the system are dependent, inconsistent, or independent. Illustrate Exercises 1–10 by graphs.

A

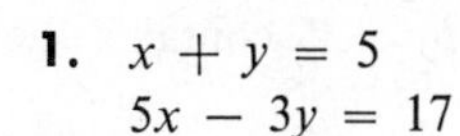

1. $x + y = 5$, $5x - 3y = 17$

2. $3x + y = 7$, $2x - 5y = -1$

3. $u = v$, $4u = 2v - 6$

4. $a = 3b$, $3b - 6 = 2a$

5. $x + y = 10$
$x - y = 8$

6. $8x - y = 29$
$2x + y = 11$

7. $r - 8s = 11$
$2r - 16s = 22$

8. $2p + q = 5$
$4p + 2q = 6$

9. $2a + b = -2$
$6a - 5b = 18$

10. $a - 9b = 2$
$3a - 3b = -10$

11. $x - y - 73 = 0$
$2x + 7y - 29 = 0$

12. $m - n - 52 = 0$
$3m - 8n - 6 = 0$

13. $2a + 5b - 18 = 0$
$3a + 4b - 7 = 0$

14. $2s - 3t - 1 = 0$
$3s - 4t - 7 = 0$

15. $9x - 8y = 1$
$6x + 12y = 5$

16. $4x - y - 10 = 0$
$3x + 5y = 19$

17. $10t + 15u = 3$
$6t + 9u = 4$

18. $2x - 3z = 5$
$4x - 6z = 10$

19. $3r - 4s = 15$
$8s - 6r + 30 = 0$

20. $8t = 7 - 2s$
$3s + 12t = 5$

Solve for x and y.

B

21. $x - y = 3a$
$x + y = 2a$

22. $x - y = -3a$
$2x + y = 6a$

23. $x + y = 2a$
$2x - 3y = 5b - a$

24. $2x - y = 3a$
$x - 2y = -2b$

25. $ax + by = c$
$bx + ay = d$

26. $cx - dy = 0$
$dx + cy - a = 0$

27. $rx + sy = t$
$2rx - sy = 2t$

28. $ux + vy = u^2$
$vx + uy = v^2$

C

29. $ax + by = a + b$
$abx + aby = a^2 + b^2$

30. $cx + dy = c$
$c^2x + d^2y = c^2$

31. Determine a and b so that the graph of $ax + by = 5$ contains the points $(2, -3)$ and $(1, 4)$.

32. Determine a and c so that the graph of $ax + 3y = c$ contains the origin and the point $(-6, -10)$.

Problems

Use two variables in solving each problem.

SAMPLE. A boat can travel 6 miles downstream in 40 minutes. The return trip requires an hour. Find the rate of the boat in still water and the rate of the current.

Solution: **1.** Let x = the rate of the boat (mi./hr.) in still water

y = the rate of the current (mi./hr.)

Then $x + y$ = the boat's rate downstream

$x - y$ = the boat's rate upstream

$\frac{2}{3}(x + y)$ = distance traveled downstream in 40 minutes ($\frac{2}{3}$ hr.)

$x - y$ = distance traveled upstream in 1 hour

2. Write two open sentences involving x and y.

$$\underbrace{\text{Downstream distance}} = 6 \text{ and } \underbrace{\text{upstream distance}} = 6$$

$$\frac{2}{3}(x + y) = 6 \text{ and } x - y = 6$$

3. Solve the system:

$$\begin{aligned} \tfrac{2}{3}(x + y) &= 6 \\ x - y &= 6 \end{aligned} \quad \text{or} \quad \begin{aligned} x + y &= 9 \\ x - y &= 6 \end{aligned}$$

Complete Step 3, and check your results in the words of the problem (Step 4).

A

1. Three times one number equals $\frac{1}{4}$ another number. If the sum of 4 times the first number and 12 equals three times the second number, what are the numbers?

2. Half the sum of two numbers is $-\frac{1}{2}$, while half their difference is $\frac{3}{2}$. Find the numbers.

3. The measure of one of two complementary angles is 2 degrees less than three times that of the other. How large are the angles?

4. The measure of one of two supplementary angles is 6 degrees less than twice that of the other. How large are the angles?

5. Tickets for a pre-Broadway showing of a play sold at \$4.00 for the main floor and \$2.75 for the balcony. If the receipts from the sale of 1600 tickets was \$5525, how many tickets were sold at each price?

6. Tickets to a class play were 25 cents and 50 cents. In all, 275 tickets were sold, and the total receipts were \$118.75. Find the number of tickets sold at each price.

7. A glass manufacturer makes two grades of glass which differ in silica content. If she has 1800 pounds of silica with which to make one batch of each type, and she uses 216 more pounds of silica for one type than for the other, how many pounds of silica were used for each type?

8. A collection of nickels and dimes has a total value of \$2.40 and contains 35 coins. How many of each kind of coin are there in the collection?

9. Flying with the wind, an airplane can travel 1080 miles in six hours, but flying against the wind it goes only $\frac{1}{3}$ the distance in half the time. Find the speed of the plane in still air and the wind speed.

10. Traveling downstream, a boat can go 12 miles in 2 hours. Going upstream, it makes only $\frac{2}{3}$ this distance in twice the time. What is the rate of the boat in still water, and what is the rate of the current?

11. There are 37 students in an algebra class. If there are 9 more boys than girls in the class, how many boys and how many girls are in the class?

12. An English class has 29 students enrolled. The number of girls in the class is one less than three times one half the number of boys. How many boys and how many girls are in the class?

13. Mary weighs three pounds more than Jane, and together they weigh 16 pounds less than the center on the football team who weighs 213 pounds. How much does each girl weigh?

14. The atomic number of antimony is one less than four times the atomic number of aluminum. If twice the atomic number of aluminum is added to that of antimony, the result is the atomic number of the element iridium, which is 77. What are the atomic numbers of antimony and aluminum?

B 15. Find values for A and B so that the set of ordered pairs

$$\{(x, y): Ax + By = 9\}$$

will contain (3, 2) and (9, −12).

16. Find values for a and b so that the set of ordered pairs

$$\{(x, y): y = ax^2 + b\}$$

will contain (2, 17) and (−1, 2).

17. If $\{(x, y): y = mx + b\}$ contains (1, 1) and (−2, −11), find m and b.

18. If $\{(x, y): y = mx + b\}$ contains (4, 7) and (−2, 4), find m and b.

19. Two temperature scales are established, one, the R scale where water under fixed conditions freezes at 15° and boils at 405°, and the other,

the S scale where water freezes at 5° and boils at 70°. If the R and S scales are linearly related, find an expression for any temperature R in terms of a temperature S.

20. The final velocity of a uniformly accelerated particle is linearly related to the elapsed time by the equation $v = v_0 + at$ where a and v_0 are constants. If $v = 20$ when $t = 5$, and $v = 35$ when $t = 10$, find values for v_0 and a.

In Problems 21–26 the original number is a positive integer whose numeral contains 2 places. Find this integer in each case.

21. The sum of the digits is 6. When the digits are interchanged, the new number represented is 3 times the tens digit of the original number.

22. The tens digit is twice the units digit. The sum of the original number and the number represented when the digits are interchanged is 66.

23. The tens digit is half the units digit. The sum of the original number and the number represented when the digits are interchanged is 99.

24. The sum of the digits is 10. The number is 1 less than twice the number represented when the order of the digits is reversed.

25. The units digit is 1 more than 3 times the tens digit. The number represented when the digits are interchanged is 8 times the sum of the digits.

26. The tens digit exceeds twice the units digit by 2. The number represented when the order of the digits is reversed is 5 more than 3 times the sum of the digits.

27. A river steamer travels 36 miles downstream in the same time that it travels 24 miles upstream. The steamer's engines drive in still water at a rate which is 12 miles an hour more than the rate of the current. Find the rate of the current.

28. Ava finds that in still water her outboard motor can drive her boat 4 times as fast as the rate of the current in Pony River. A 15-mile trip up the river and back requires 4 hours. Find the rate of the current.

C **29.** Two railroad workers are together in a 0.6-mile mountain tunnel. One walks east and the other west in order to be out of the tunnel before the Bad Creek Express comes through at 30 m.p.h. Each man reaches his respective end of the tunnel in 3 min. If the man walking east reaches the east entrance just before the train enters, and the train passes the other man 0.12 miles beyond the west end of the tunnel, at what rate did each man walk?

30. One mile upstream from her starting point, a rower passed a log floating with the current. After rowing upstream for one more hour, she rowed back and reached her starting point just as the log arrived. How fast was the current flowing?

3–6 Coordinates and Systems in Space

To select three coordinate axes in space, begin by choosing two lines intersecting at right angles, say a horizontal line to be called the y-axis and a vertical line, the z-axis. Their point of intersection is the **origin**, O. Then, as the third, or x-axis, choose the line passing through O at right angles to both the y- and the z-axes (Figure 3–14). Next, select a scale to make each axis a number line whose zero-point is the origin, and indicate the scale on the axes.

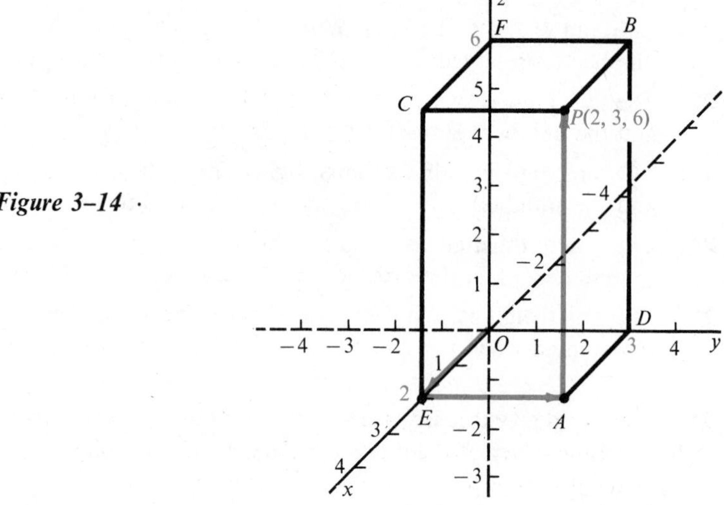

· *Figure 3–14* ·

Although you may label the axes and choose the positive directions on them as you wish, the choice shown in Figure 3–14 is a common one. Taken in pairs, the three coordinate axes determine three **coordinate planes**, called the xy-plane, the yz-plane, and the xz-plane.

To determine the coordinates of a point P, draw three planes through P, one perpendicular to the x-axis, another perpendicular to the y-axis, and the third perpendicular to the z-axis. The numbers paired with the points in which these planes intersect the respective axes are, in order, the **x-coordinate**, the **y-coordinate**, and the **z-coordinate** of P. For example, P in Figure 3–14 has coordinates $(2, 3, 6)$.

Notice that together with the coordinate planes, the three planes drawn through P form a *rectangular parallelepiped* (a box). Starting at the origin, you can arrive at P by moving along edges parallel to each axis in succession. One such path is shown in red in Figure 3–14: O to E, E to A, A to P. This suggests a procedure for locating a point whose coordinates are given. For example, Figure 3–15 shows the plotting of the point $T(4, -2, 5)$:

1. From the origin proceed 4 units along the x-axis.
2. Then move -2 units (2 units in the negative direction) parallel to the y-axis.
3. Then proceed 5 units parallel to the z-axis.

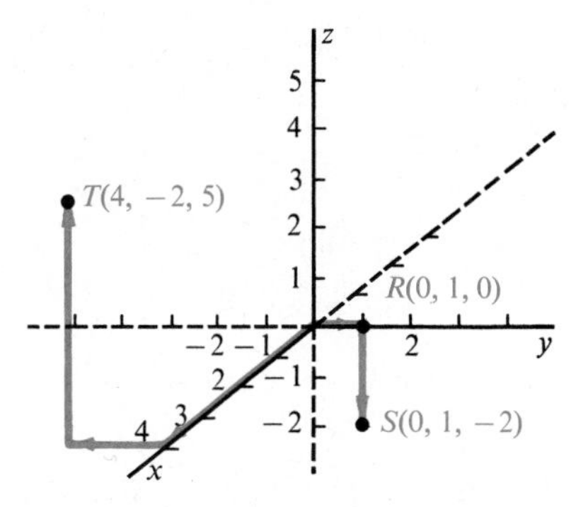

· *Figure 3–15* ·

The points $R(0, 1, 0)$ and $S(0, 1, -2)$ have also been plotted in Figure 3–15. Do you see that R and S belong to the yz-plane? Like every point of that plane, each has x-coordinate equal to 0. Indeed, the yz-plane is the set of points whose coordinates satisfy the linear equation $x + 0 \cdot y + 0 \cdot z = 0$, or simply $x = 0$. Similarly, the xy-plane is the solution set of the equation $z = 0$, while the xz-plane is the graph of $y = 0$.

It can be proved that if A, B, and C are constants, not all 0, then the graph of the linear equation in three variables $Ax + By + Cz = D$ is a plane, and conversely, every plane in space has an equation of this form.

To sketch a plane in a three-dimensional coordinate system, you use its lines of intersection **(traces)** with the coordinate planes. For example, to sketch the plane with equation $2x + y + z = 11$, you can first draw its xy-trace, that is, its line of intersection with the xy-plane. All points in this plane have coordinates $(x, y, 0)$, so that you want to sketch the graph of $2x + y + 0 = 11$, or, simply, $2x + y = 11$.

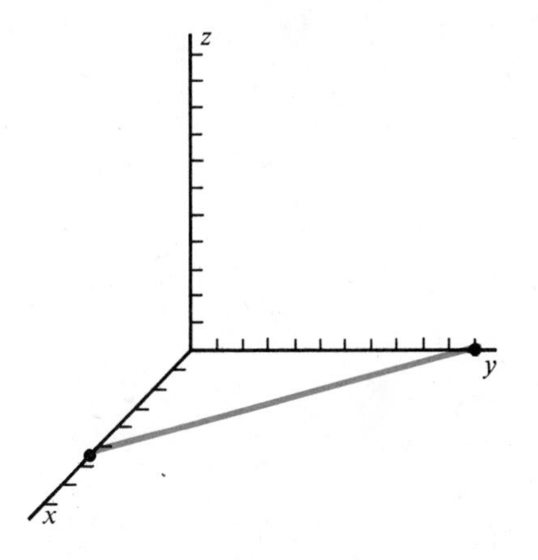

· *Figure 3–16* ·

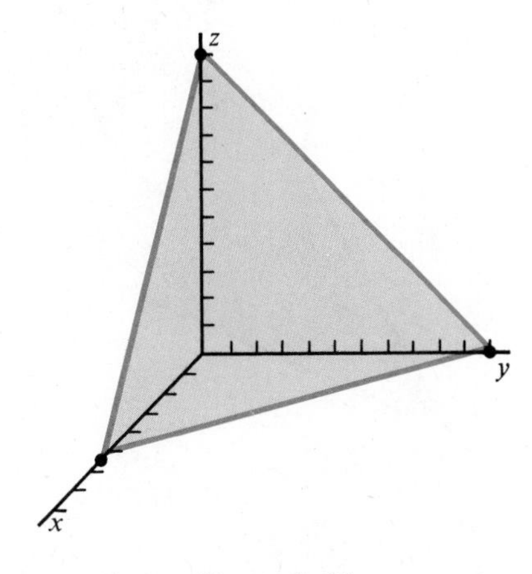

· *Figure 3–17* ·

Figure 3–16 shows this line. Next, you can sketch the xz- and yz-traces ($2x + z = 11$ and $y + z = 11$, respectively) to obtain the picture of the desired plane (Figure 3–17).

The equations in a system of three equations in three variables will have three planes as graphs. Three planes in space can intersect in a variety of ways, some of which involve a single point of intersection of the planes. The coordinate planes are three such planes — their only common point is the origin. The planes shown in Figure 3–18 are the graphs of $x + 2y = 8$, $2x + y + z = 11$, and $x + y + 2z = 13$. As the figure suggests, these planes also have exactly one point in common.

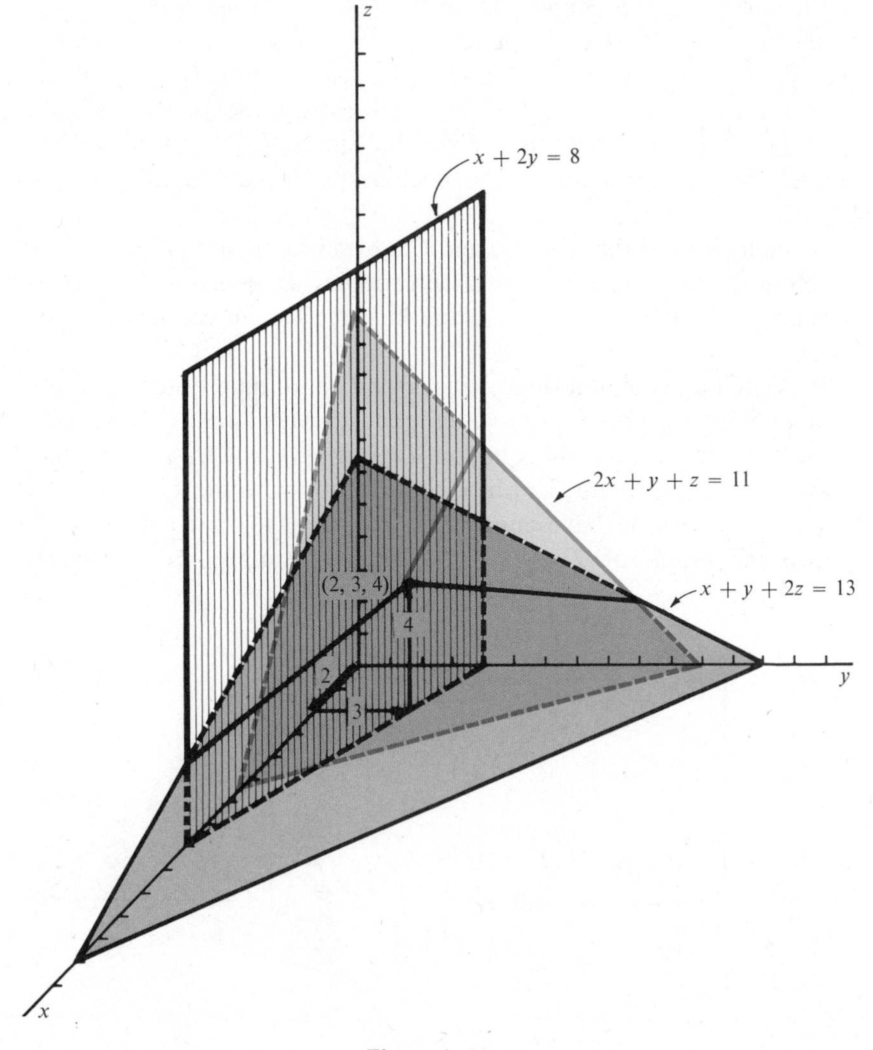

· *Figure 3–18* ·

This reflects the fact that this system of equations in three variables has one and only one solution. The equations in the system are said to be *consistent* and *independent.*

Of course, graphing planes is not a practical way to find the solution set of a system of equations in three variables. You can also solve this system by using substitution.

EXAMPLE 1. Determine the solution set of the system:

$$\begin{aligned} x + 2y &= 8 \\ 2x + y + z &= 11 \\ x + y + 2z &= 13 \end{aligned}$$

Solution:

1. Transform the first equation to express x in terms of y.

$$\begin{aligned} x + 2y &= 8 \\ x &= 8 - 2y \end{aligned}$$

2. Replace the second given equation by the one obtained from it by substituting $8 - 2y$ for x.

$$\begin{aligned} 2x + y + z &= 11 \\ 2(8 - 2y) + y + z &= 11 \\ -3y + z &= -5 \end{aligned}$$

3. Transform $-3y + z = -5$ to express z in terms of y.

$$z = 3y - 5$$

4. Replace the third given equation by the one obtained from it by substituting $8 - 2y$ for x and $3y - 5$ for z. Solve for y.

$$\begin{aligned} x + y + 2z &= 13 \\ (8 - 2y) + y + 2(3y - 5) &= 13 \\ 8 - 2y + y + 6y - 10 &= 13 \\ 5y &= 15 \\ y &= 3 \end{aligned}$$

5. Substitute 3 for y in the equations obtained in Steps 1 and 3 to find the values of x and z.

$$\begin{array}{l|l} x = 8 - 2y & z = 3y - 5 \\ x = 8 - 2(3) & z = 3(3) - 5 \\ x = 2 & z = 4 \end{array}$$

6. Check (2, 3, 4) in each of the given equations.

$$\begin{aligned} 2 + 2 \cdot 3 &\stackrel{?}{=} 8;\ 8 = 8 \\ 2 \cdot 2 + 3 + 4 &\stackrel{?}{=} 11;\ 11 = 11 \\ 2 + 3 + 2 \cdot 4 &\stackrel{?}{=} 13;\ 13 = 13 \end{aligned}$$

$\{(2, 3, 4)\}$, **Answer.**

When all three variables appear in each equation of a system, it is often convenient to replace two of the equations by linear combinations in which one of the variables does not appear.

EXAMPLE 2. Find the solution set of the system:

$$\begin{aligned} x + 2y + 2z &= 13 \\ 2x + y - z &= 3 \\ x - 4y + 3z &= 11 \end{aligned}$$

Solution:

1. To replace the second given equation by one not involving x, take these steps:
   (i) multiply the first equation by 2;
   (ii) from the result subtract the second equation.

$$\begin{aligned} 2(x + 2y + 2z) &= 2(13) \\ 2x + 4y + 4z &= 26 \\ 2x + y - z &= 3 \\ \hline 3y + 5z &= 23 \end{aligned}$$

2. To replace the third equation by one not involving x, subtract the first equation from it.

$$\begin{aligned} x - 4y + 3z &= 11 \\ x + 2y + 2z &= 13 \\ \hline -6y + z &= -2 \end{aligned}$$

3. The equations obtained in Steps 1 and 2 involve only y and z. You can use the methods for solving two equations in two variables to replace them by the equivalent pair $y = 1$ and $z = 4$.

4. Substitute 1 for y and 4 for z in the first of the given equations, and solve for x.

$$\begin{aligned} x + 2y + 2z &= 13 \\ x + 2(1) + 2(4) &= 13 \\ x &= 3 \end{aligned}$$

5. Checking (3, 1, 4) in each original equation is left to you.

$\{(3, 1, 4)\}$, **Answer.**

A system of three equations in three variables may have no solution, so that the equations are *inconsistent*. For example, the equations in the system $x = 0$, $y = 0$, and $x + 2y = 8$, whose graphs are the yz-plane, the xz-plane, and the plane indicated in Figure 3–19, evidently have no common solution because the graph of $x + 2y = 8$ is parallel to the line of intersection of the other planes (the z-axis). If you try to solve

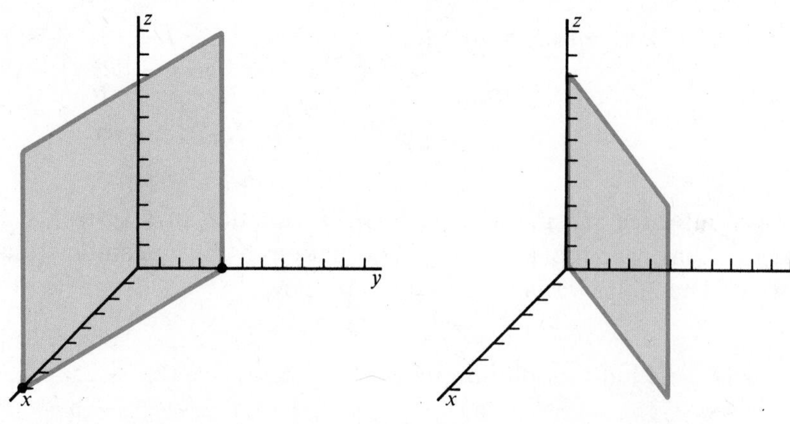

Figure 3–19 · *Figure 3–20*

this system by substituting 0 for x and for y in $x + 2y = 8$, the inconsistency shows up because you obtain the contradiction in $0 + 0 = 8$.

The system $x - y = 0$ (see Figure 3–20), $x = 0$, and $y = 0$ is satisfied by $(0, 0, 1)$, $(0, 0, 3)$, $(0, 0, -1)$, in fact by the coordinates of every point of the z-axis. The equations are *dependent*, and their graphs are planes containing the z-axis. When you substitute 0 for x and for y in $x - y = 0$, the fact that the equations are dependent shows up because you obtain the *identity* $0 - 0 = 0$.

Written Exercises

Plot the points with coordinates given below.

A

1. $(3, 4, 2)$
2. $(5, 0, 4)$
3. $(-1, 2, 5)$
4. $(3, -1, 7)$
5. $(-3, 0, 0)$
6. $(0, 3, 6)$

Find the equations of the traces of each plane whose equation is given below.

7. $x + 3y + 2z = 6$
8. $4x + y + 2z = 8$
9. $x + 5y = 10$
10. $y + 2z = 4$
11. $x + y = 0$
12. $x - z = 0$

Draw the graph of each equation.

13. $x + 3y + 2z = 6$
14. $4x + y + 2z = 8$
15. $x + 5y = 10$
16. $y + 2z = 4$

Find the solution set of each system.

17. $x + 2y + 3z = 0$
$x - 2z = 3$
$y + z = 1$

18. $x - y + z = 2$
$x + 2z = 7$
$y - z = 1$

19. $2x - y + z = 3$
$x + 2y - z = 3$
$3x - 4y + 2z = -1$

20. $3x + 2y - z = 4$
$2x - y + 3z = 5$
$x + 3y + 2z = -1$

21. $2l + m + 2n = 1$
$l + 2m - 3n = 4$
$3l - m + n = 0$

22. $p + q + 4r = 1$
$-2p - q + r = 2$
$3p - 2q + 3r = 5$

B

23. $2x + 3y + 3z = 8$
$3x + 2y - 2z = 14$
$4x + 5y + 3z = 38$

24. $2x + 5y - 2z = -6$
$7x + 2y - 5z = -4$
$-2x + 3y + 2z = -2$

25. $\frac{1}{x} + \frac{2}{y} - \frac{1}{z} = 3$
$\frac{3}{x} - \frac{4}{y} + \frac{2}{z} = -1$
$\frac{2}{x} + \frac{2}{y} - \frac{2}{z} = 5$

26. $\frac{3}{x} + \frac{1}{y} - \frac{4}{z} = 0$
$\frac{1}{x} + \frac{2}{y} - \frac{2}{z} = -1$
$\frac{4}{x} + \frac{4}{z} = 3$

In each of Exercises 27–34, if the given system has exactly one solution, find it; if the system has no solutions, state that fact; if the system has an infinite solution set, state that fact.

27. $x + y + 9z = 8$
$x + 3z - 1 = 0$
$y + 6z - 7 = 0$

28. $x + y + z = 1$
$-3x + 7y + 2z = 0$
$-2x + 8y + 3z = 4$

29. $4a - 4b - 3c = 2$
$4a + 3c - 3 = 0$
$4b + 6c - 3 = 0$

30. $2a + 3b = c - 2$
$a + 2b = 8 - 2c$
$5a + 9b = 22 - 5c$

31. $4x + 2y + 6z = 2$
$-7x + 3y - 3z = 2$
$3x + 5y + 9z = 4$

32. $3a - 2b + \frac{3}{c} = 6$
$a + b + \frac{1}{c} = 2$
$2a - b + \frac{1}{c} = 5$

33. $\frac{2}{r} + \frac{2}{s} - \frac{3}{t} = -1$
$\frac{1}{r} - \frac{2}{s} + 1 = 0$
$\frac{5}{r} - \frac{4}{s} - \frac{3}{t} = 5$

34. $\frac{1}{x} + \frac{2}{y} = 1$
$\frac{4}{y} - \frac{4}{z} = 3$
$\frac{3}{x} + \frac{10}{y} - \frac{4}{z} = 6$

Determine A, B, C so that the plane $Ax + By + Cz = 1$ contains the given points.

35. $(1, 0, 0)$; $(0, 2, 0)$; $(0, 0, 8)$

36. $(1, -1, 0)$; $(5, 0, 3)$; $(0, 4, 1)$

37. $(1, 0, 2)$; $(0, 2, 3)$; $(-1, 2, 0)$

38. $(3, 1, 0)$; $(2, 3, 1)$; $(-4, -1, 1)$

LINEAR INEQUALITIES

3–7 Linear Inequalities and Systems

Can you describe the relationship between the coordinates of points in the region above the graph of $y = x$ (Figure 3–21)? *On* the line the ordinate of each point equals the abscissa of the point. Therefore, *above* the line the ordinate of a point must exceed the abscissa. Thus, the coordinates of points above the line satisfy the inequality $y > x$. Similarly, the coordinates of points *below* the line form solutions of the inequality $y < x$.

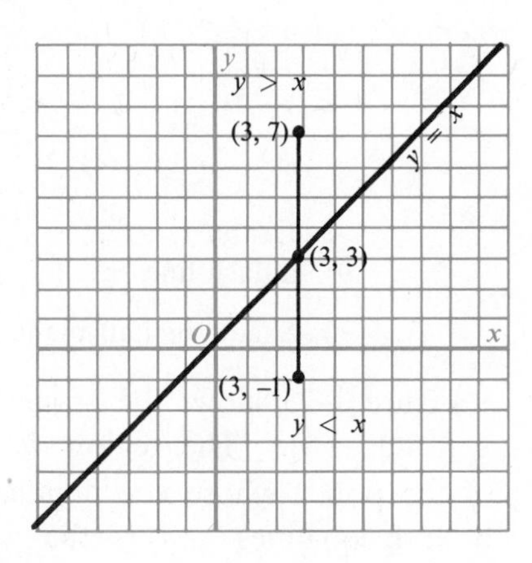

· *Figure 3–21* ·

Figure 3–22 shows partial graphs of four linear inequalities related to the equation $y = x$. Each graph, pictured as a shaded region, is a *half-plane* bounded by the graph of $y = x$. If the boundary is part of the region, the line is a solid line; if not, a dash line is used.

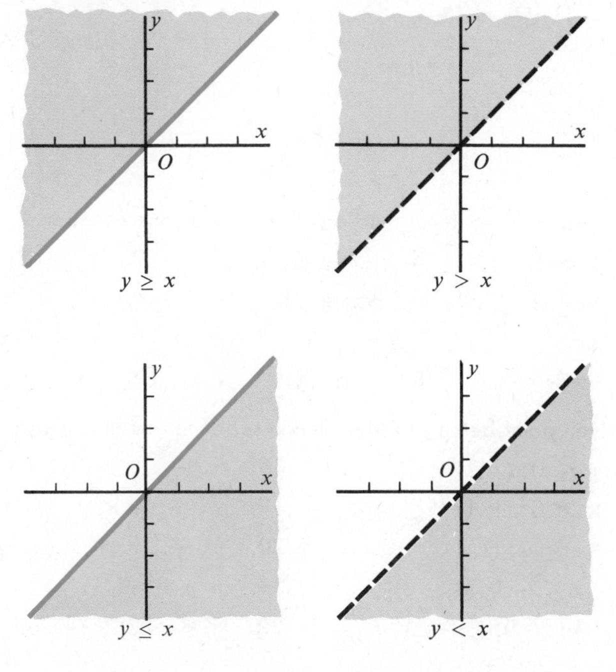

· *Figure 3–22* ·

EXAMPLE. Graph the inequality $2x - y < 3$.

Solution: **1.** Transform the inequality into an equivalent one having y as one member.

$$2x - y < 3$$
$$-y < 3 - 2x$$
$$y > 2x - 3$$

2. Graph $y = 2x - 3$, and show it as a dash line.

3. Shade the half-plane above the line.

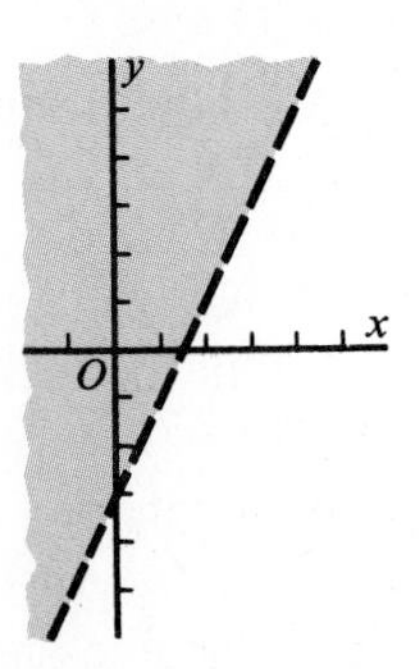

Figure 3–23 shows the graphs of the inequalities $2x - y < 3$ and $x \leq 3(1 - y)$. The region where the two colors overlap consists of the points whose coordinates satisfy both inequalities and is the graph of the solution set of the system of the two linear inequalities. You may specify this solution set as

$$\{(x, y): 2x - y < 3 \text{ and } x \leq 3(1 - y)\},$$

or $$\{(x, y): 2x - y < 3\} \cap \{(x, y): x \leq 3(1 - y)\}.$$

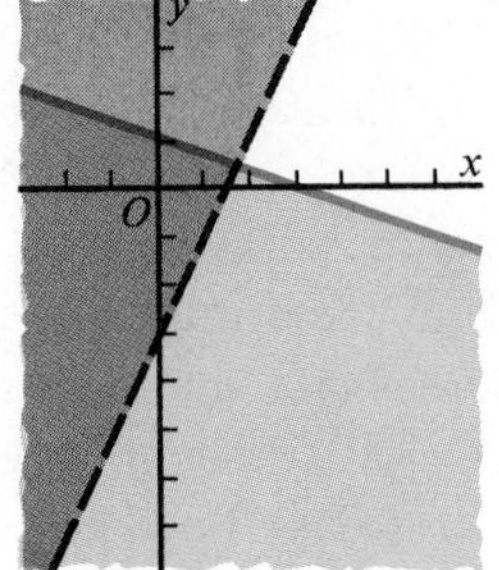

Figure 3–23

Oral Exercises

Transform each open sentence into one having y as one member.

1. $x + y > 6$
2. $y - x < 2$
3. $y - 3x \leq 4$
4. $5x + y \geq -1$
5. $2x + 6y < 0$
6. $9x + 3y \leq 0$
7. $x < 4y$
8. $x > 7y$
9. $8x - 2y \geq 0$
10. $10x - 5y < 0$
11. $x - y > -1$
12. $2x - y \geq 3$

Does the given point belong to the solution set of the open sentence?

13. $x - y \leq 0$; $(2, 2)$
14. $y - x \geq 0$; $(1, 1)$
15. $2y - x \geq 2$; $(1, 1)$
16. $2x + y \leq -1$; $(3, -3)$
17. $2x + 3y < 0$; $(3, -2)$
18. $3x - 2y > 0$; $(2, 3)$
19. $2x + 5y < -3$; $(-3, 0)$
20. $5x - 2y > 4$; $(2, 3)$
21. $y > 3$; $(2, 1)$
22. $x < -2$; $(-4, -2)$

Written Exercises

Graph the solution set of each open sentence or each system.

A

1. $y > x$

2. $y \geq 3x$

3. $y \leq 2x$

4. $y < -x$

5. $y > -2$

6. $x \geq 3$

7. $x \leq 0$

8. $y < 1$

9. $y + 5x > 0$

10. $x + y \geq 1$

11. $y - 4x \leq -2$

12. $y - 3x \leq 1$

13. $5y - 2x \geq 6$

14. $3x + 6y \leq 2$

15. $4y - 3x + 12 \geq 0$

16. $2x + 3y + 6 > 0$

17. $-y < 2x - 4$

18. $-2y > 3x - 3$

19. $-x < 0$

20. $-y \geq 0$

21. $y \leq x$
$y \geq -x$

22. $y \leq x$
$y \geq 0$

23. $y \geq x$
$x \leq 0$

24. $y \geq x$
$x \geq 0$

25. $y \geq x + 1$
$y \leq x + 2$

26. $y > 2x$
$y < 2x + 1$

27. $y \geq 2x - 3$
$y < 2 - x$

28. $y \leq 3x + 2$
$y \geq 2 - x$

29. $x + y \leq -6$
$y - 2x > 0$

30. $x + y \geq -6$
$y \leq -3$

31. $3x - 2y \leq 6$
$2x + 3y \geq 6$

32. $2x + 3y \leq 12$
$3x - 2y \leq 6$

SAMPLE. Graph: $x - 1 \leq y \leq x + 1$.

Solution: Graph $y \leq x + 1$ and $y \geq x - 1$. The region between and including the red lines contains the points whose coordinates satisfy both inequalities. It is, therefore, the graph of the given inequality.

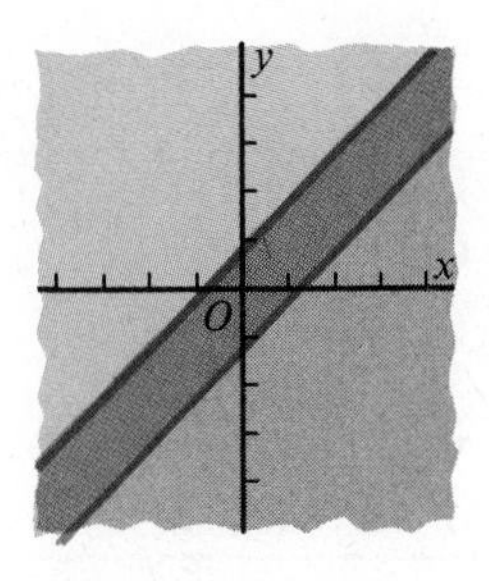

B

33. $0 \leq x \leq 2$

34. $2 \leq x \leq 3$

35. $x - 2 < -y < x$

36. $x < -y < x + 2$

37. $4 - x \leq y < 2 - x$

38. $-2x - 1 < y \leq -2x + 2$

39. $-5 < y - x \leq 5$

40. $-1 \leq x - y < 2$

C

41. $y = 3$ and $y < x$

42. $y = 0$ and $y \leq x + 1$

43. $x = 4$ and $x < -3 - y$

44. $x = 2$ and $x \leq 2 - y$

45. $y < x$
$0 \leq y \leq 1$

46. $y \leq x + 2$
$1 \leq x \leq 2$

47. $3 \leq x + y \leq 6$
$3 \leq x - y \leq 3$

48. $-6 \leq x + y \leq -3$
$3 \leq x - y \leq -3$

Extra for Experts

Linear Programming

Simultaneous linear inequalities appear in decision problems in applied mathematics. Consider the following situation:

To decide how much wheat and corn to produce on his acreage, a farmer analyzed the requirements for producing each grain. He found that the production of one hundred bushels of corn required 2.5 acres of land, $70 in capital, 2 hours of labor in August, and 2 hours of labor in September. To produce one hundred bushels of wheat, he needed 5 acres of land, $50 in capital, 4 hours of labor in August, and 10 hours of labor in September. Available to him were 100 acres of land, $2100 in capital, 200 hours of labor in August, and 160 hours of labor in September. If one hundred bushels of corn brought a return of $150 and 100 bushels of wheat $250, how should he have divided his production between corn and wheat to make the dollar return as large as possible? The data of the problem are arranged in the following chart.

	Input requirements per 100 bushels of		Available Material
	Corn	Wheat	
Land (acre)	2.5	5	100
Capital ($)	70	50	2100
Aug. labor (hr.)	2	4	200
Sept. labor (hr.)	2	10	160
Value of output of 100 bushels ($)	150	250	

Let x = the number of hundreds of bushels of corn produced;

y = the number of hundreds of bushels of wheat produced.

If R denotes the total return in dollars, then $R = 150x + 250y$.

The farmer had to *maximize* R (find its largest value) subject to these inequalities (*constraints*):

1. $2.5x + 5y \leq 100$
2. $70x + 50y \leq 2100$
3. $2x + 4y \leq 200$
4. $2x + 10y \leq 160$

The total amount of each input cannot exceed the material available.

$$\left.\begin{array}{ll} 5. & x \geq 0 \\ 6. & y \geq 0 \end{array}\right\}$$ The farmer cannot produce a negative number of bushels of either grain.

The graph of the intersection of the solution sets of these inequalities is shown as the shaded region in Figure 3–24 and is called the *feasible region*, because the coordinates of each of its points satisfy all the constraints. The boundary of the graph is called a *convex polygon*, and the intersection itself is called a *convex set*. Because the constraints, as well as R, are *linear* in x and y, this is called a *linear* programming problem.

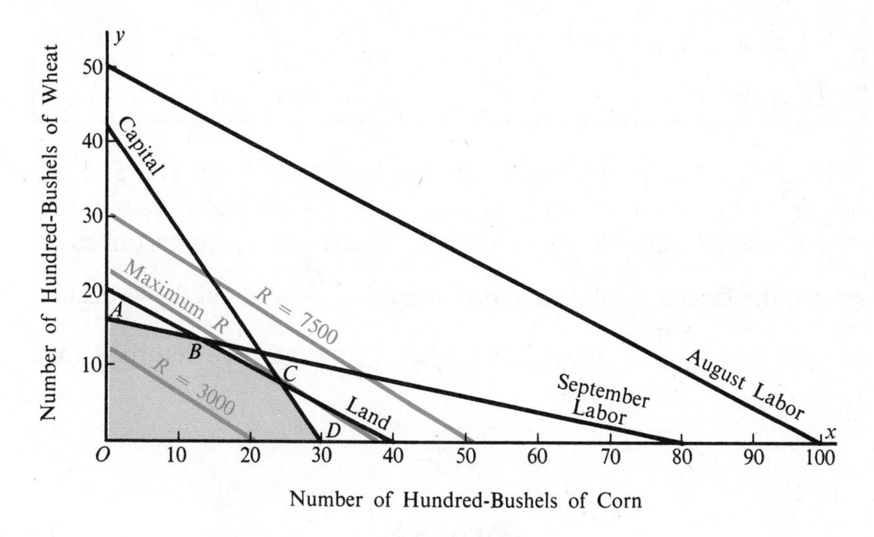

· *Figure 3–24* ·

For any value of R, such as $R = 3000$, the graph of the *return equation* $3000 = 150x + 250y$ is a straight line. For a greater value of R, say $R = 7500$, the graph of the return equation, is a line parallel to the graph of $R = 3000$, but with a larger y-intercept. Different values of R give a family of parallel lines each having y-intercept $\frac{R}{250}$. As the figure suggests, the line of the family having maximum y-intercept and, therefore, maximum R, and containing a point of the feasible region must intersect the region at a vertex. It can be shown in general that whenever a linear expression such as $150x + 250y$ is evaluated over a convex set, it must take on its maximum value at one of the vertices of the polygon bounding the set, and its minimum value at another vertex. By substitution you find that the expression for R takes on the following values at the vertices, whose coordinates are found by solving simultaneously the equations of adjacent sides of the polygon:

Vertex	$150x + 250y$	R
O (0, 0)	$150(0) + 250(0) = 0 + 0$	0
A(0, 16)	$150(0) + 250(16) = 0 + 4000$	4000
$B\left(\frac{40}{3}, \frac{40}{3}\right)$	$150\left(\frac{40}{3}\right) + 250\left(\frac{40}{3}\right) = 400\left(\frac{40}{3}\right)$	$5333\frac{1}{3}$
$C\left(\frac{220}{9}, \frac{70}{9}\right)$	$150\left(\frac{220}{9}\right) + 250\left(\frac{70}{9}\right) = \frac{50{,}500}{9}$	$5611\frac{1}{9}$
D(30, 0)	$150(30) + 250(0) = 4500 + 0$	4500

Thus, over the feasible region the maximum for R is $5611\frac{1}{9}$, and this occurs at the point C. The minimum for R is 0 and occurs at the origin; that is, when he plants nothing. Consequently, to maximize his return, the farmer should have produced $\frac{22{,}000}{9}$ or about 2,444 bushels of corn and $\frac{7000}{9}$ or about 778 bushels of wheat. His return is then about \$5,611.11.

Exercises

1. A convex polygon has vertices (1, 2), (3, 6), (4, 3), (4, 1), and (3, 0). What is the maximum and minimum value assumed by $3x - 4y$ over the set of ordered pairs represented by the polygon and its interior?
2. The vertices of a convex polygon are (4, 3), (4, 7), (5, 9), (7, 4), (6, 2), and (5, 2). What is the maximum and minimum value assumed by the expression $3y - 2x$ over the set of ordered pairs represented by the polygon and its interior?
3. Find the maximum and minimum values of the expression $3x - 2y$ over the intersection of the solution sets of $2 \leq x \leq 4$, $y \geq 1$, $y \leq -x + 7$.
4. Find the maximum and minimum values of the expression $\frac{1}{2}x - \frac{3}{2}y$ over the intersection of the solution sets of $x \leq 5$, $y \leq 6$, $y \leq x + 3$, $y \geq -x + 5$.

5. A manufacturer makes two kinds of television sets, a console and a portable. She has equipment to manufacture any number of console sets up to 400 per month or any number of portable sets up to 500 per month, but she can only manufacture 600 sets of both kinds per month in all. It takes 50 hours to manufacture either a console or a portable, and the manufacturer has available 30,000 work-hours per month.

a. If the manufacturer realizes a profit of $60.00 on each console set and $50.00 on each portable, find the number of each type of set she should manufacture to realize the greatest profit.

b. If the manufacturer realizes a profit of $70.00 on each console and $50.00 on each portable, find the number of each type she should manufacture to realize the maximum profit.

6. To fill his vitamin needs, a man is to buy 100 pills which must contain at least 750 units of B_1, 600 units of B_2, and 280 units of B_6. At 5 cents per pill, he can buy pill I, which contains 10 units of B_1, 5 of B_2, and 3 of B_6. At 6 cents per pill, he can buy pill II which has 12 units of B_1, 2 of B_2, and 11 of B_6. Also, pill III, which contains 6 units of B_1, 7 of B_2, and 2 of B_6, is available at 4 cents per pill. How many of each kind of pill should he use in order to fulfill his needs at lowest cost?

Chapter Summary

Inventory of Structure and Method

1. If an open sentence in two variables is a linear equation and the domain of each variable is the set of real numbers, its graph is a line; if a linear inequality, its graph is a half-plane.

2. If m is the **slope** of a line, $m = \dfrac{y_2 - y_1}{x_2 - x_1}$; that is, m is the change in ordinate per unit change in abscissa between any two points (x_1, y_1) and (x_2, y_2) on the line.

3. To find an equation of a specified line, use:

i. The **point-slope form** $y - y_1 = m(x - x_1)$ where point (x_1, y_1) is on the line.

ii. The **slope-intercept form** $y = mx + b$ where b is the y-intercept.

4. When the graphs of a pair of linear equations coincide, the solution set of the system consists of the coordinates of every point on the graph. When the graphs are parallel lines, the solution set is $\emptyset$. When the graphs intersect in just one point, the solution set of the system is the ordered pair associated with that point.

5. The following transformations convert a system of linear equations into an equivalent system.

   i. Replace either equation by an equivalent equation in the same variables.

   ii. Replace either equation by the sum of that equation and a real number multiple of the other equation.

   iii. In either equation, substitute for one variable an equivalent expression in terms of the other variable as derived from the other equation.

6. The graph of the solution set of a system of linear inequalities in two variables consists of the points common to the half-planes determined by the solution sets of the sentences.

Vocabulary and Spelling

first coordinate (*p. 78*)
second coordinate (*p. 78*)
equal ordered pairs (*p. 78*)
solution set of an open sentence (two variables) (*p. 78*)
axes (*p. 81*)
quadrants (*p. 81*)
x-coordinate (*p. 81*)
abscissa (*p. 81*)
y-coordinate (*p. 81*)
ordinate (*p. 81*)
plotting a point (*p. 81*)
equation of a line (*p. 81*)
graph of an open sentence (two variables) (*p. 82*)
linear equation (*p. 82*)
plane rectangular coordinate system (*p. 82*)
Cartesian coordinate system (*p. 82*)
slope (*p. 84*)
rise (*p. 85*)
run (*p. 85*)
point-slope form (*p. 91*)
y-intercept (*p. 91*)
slope-intercept form (*p. 91*)
parallel lines (*p. 92*)
x-intercept (*p. 93*)
inconsistent equations (*p. 95*)
dependent equations (*p. 95*)
independent equations (*p. 95*)
consistent equations (*p. 95*)
simultaneous equations (*p. 96*)
linear combination (*p. 96*)
coordinate plane (*p. 104*)
trace of a plane (*p. 105*)
half-plane (*p. 111*)

Chapter Test

3–1 **1.** The number of centimeters in the length of each side of a triangle is an integer and the length of one side is twice the length of another. If the perimeter is 17 centimeters, give two possibilities for the lengths of the sides.

3–2 **2.** If point $(0, -3)$ belongs to the graph of $3x - ky = 6$, find k.

3. Using the same coordinate axes, graph the given equations and give the coordinates of the point of intersection.

$$2x + y = 7 \qquad x - 2y = 6$$

3–3 **4.** Without graphing, find the slope of the line joining points $(3, -4)$ and $(-7, 1)$.

3–4 Find an equation of the line:

5. Having $m = \frac{1}{2}$ and passing through $(4, -1)$.

6. Having y-intercept -4 and passing through $(-3, -2)$.

3–5 Solve each system and state whether the equations are dependent, inconsistent, or independent.

7. $4x + y = 1$
$6x + 2y = 3$

8. $4x + 2y = -6$
$6x + 3y = -9$

3–6 **9.** Solve the system: $-x + y + 2z = 3$
$2x - y + z = 3$
$-4x + 2y + 3z = -1$

3–7 **10.** Graph the solution set of the system: $y \leq 2x - 3$
$x + 2y > 2$

Chapter Review

3–1 **Open Sentences in Two Variables** *Pages 77–80*

1. The solution set of an open sentence in two variables is a set of _?_ _?_ of _?_.

2. If the ordered pair $(a, -2)$ belongs to the solution set of $2x - 3y = 10$, then $a =$ _?_.

For the given replacement set, find three ordered pairs of numbers (x, y) satisfying the open sentence.

3. $3x + 4y = 5$; {integers} **4.** $3x - 2y = 1$; {positive integers}

5. The tens digit in a two-digit numeral is 1 more than twice the units digit. Find the positive integers represented.

3–2 Graphs of Linear Equations in Two Variables *Pages 81–84*

6. Point $(4, -3)$ lies in the __?__ quadrant.
7. If the ordinate of a point in the graph of $3x - 7y = -3$ is 6, the abscissa is __?__.
8. The graph of the equation $Ax + By = C$ intersects the y-axis in the point __?__, provided __?__ $\neq 0$.
9. If point $(-3, -4)$ belongs to the graph of $5kx + 2y = 7$, then $k \in \{$__?__$\}$.

Graph each pair of equations, using the same coordinate axes. Find the coordinates of the point of intersection.

10. $y = 1 - 2x;\ y = x + 7$ 11. $r + 2s = 6;\ r - s = 3$

3–3 The Slope of a Line *Pages 84–90*

12. A vertical line has __?__ slope; a horizontal line has __?__ slope.
13. The slope of a line through any two points is the change in __?__ per unit change in __?__ of the points.
14. Every portion of a specified line has the __?__ slope.

Find the slope of each line described.

15. Through points $(-8, 3)$ and $(6, -3)$.
16. Whose equation is $5y + 3 = 0$.
17. Whose equation is $3x - 5y = 6$.

Through the given point, draw a line whose slope is m.

18. $(4, -1);\ m = -2$ 19. $(-3, 0);\ m = \frac{2}{3}$

State whether the points represented in each table lie on a line.

20.

s	-3	-1	1	5
t	-4	-1	2	8

21.

x	0	-1	-2	-3
y	-1	0	3	8

22. Show that points $R(0, -3)$, $S(2, -2)$, and $T(8, 1)$ are collinear.

3–4 Determining an Equation of a Line *Pages 90–95*

23. If P is a point in a line, then the __?__ of P __?__ the equation of the line.
24. If you graph the lines whose equations are $2x - y = 1$ and $y = 2x$ in the same plane, the lines will be __?__ because they have the same __?__ but __?__ y-intercepts.

Find an equation of the line as specified.

25. $m = -1$; x-intercept, 3

26. x-intercept, $-\frac{1}{2}$; y-intercept, 2

27. Through $(-5, -1)$ and $(2, 6)$

28. Through $(2, -7)$ and parallel to the graph of $5x + 2y = 3$

29. y-intercept, -1; parallel to the graph of $4x - 6y = -1$

3–5 Systems of Two Linear Equations *Pages 95–103*

When the graphs of two linear equations in two variables:

30. Coincide, the equations are _?_ and their solution set is _?_ _?_ _?_ .

31. Are parallel, the equations are _?_ and their solution set is _?_.

32. Have unequal slopes, the lines _?_, the equations are _?_ and _?_, and the solution set contains _?_ ordered _?_.

Solve each system and state whether it is dependent, inconsistent, or independent.

33. $6x - 2y = 11$
$2x + y = 2$

34. $4r - 2s = 3$
$s = 2r - 1.5$

Use two variables to solve each problem.

35. A boat takes 2 hours to steam 20 miles up a river but only $1\frac{1}{3}$ hours for the return trip. Find the rate of the boat in still water and the rate of the current.

36. A collection of 28 coins consists of quarters and nickels and has a total value of $4. How many coins of each kind are there?

3–6 Coordinates and Systems in Space *Pages 104–110*

If the given system has exactly one solution, find it; if the system has no solutions, state that fact; if the system has an infinite solution set, state that fact.

37. $x + 3y + 2z = 5$
$-3x + 2y + z = -6$
$4x + 4y + 3z = 13$

38. $3x + 2y - z = 4$
$2x - 4y + z = -1$
$12x - 8y + z = 5$

3–7 Linear Inequalities and Systems *Pages 111–113*

39. The graph of a linear inequality in two variables consists of the points in a _?_.

40. The graph of the inequality $y > mx + b$ is the region _?_ the graph of _?_.

Graph the solution set of each system or sentence.

41. $3x - y \geq 1$

42. $x + 2y \geq 2$, $3x - 2y > -8$

CHAPTER 4

. . . an art form utilizing light projected through a series of lenses and color filters

Polynomials and Factoring

In this chapter you will concentrate your attention on operations with polynomials. Factoring will be applied to the solution of equations and inequalities. The chapter ends with an interesting and very useful theorem known as the Factor Theorem. Try to develop a high record of accuracy. This is necessary for success in the work with fractions in the next chapter.

PRODUCTS OF POLYNOMIALS

4–1 Positive Integral Exponents

Do you recall the laws of exponents illustrated in these examples?

1. $7^2 \cdot 7^3 = 7^{2+3} = 7^5$

2. $(2a)^4 = 2^4 \cdot a^4$

3. $(7^2)^3 = 7^{2 \cdot 3} = 7^6$

4. $\dfrac{5^7}{5^3} = 5^{7-3} = 5^4$

5. $\dfrac{5^3}{5^7} = \dfrac{1}{5^{7-3}} = \dfrac{1}{5^4}$

6. $\left(\dfrac{a}{2}\right)^4 = \dfrac{a^4}{2^4}$

We state the laws as follows:

Let a and b denote real numbers, and let m and n denote positive integers. In assertions 4–6, assume also that $b \neq 0$. Then:

1. $b^m \cdot b^n = b^{m+n}$

2. $(ab)^m = a^m b^m$

3. $(b^m)^n = b^{mn}$

4. $\dfrac{b^m}{b^n} = b^{m-n}$, if $m > n$

5. $\dfrac{b^m}{b^n} = \dfrac{1}{b^{n-m}}$, if $m < n$

6. $\left(\dfrac{a}{b}\right)^m = \dfrac{a^m}{b^m}$

The definition of a power, together with the properties of real numbers, makes it possible to prove any of these rules. Consider, for example, the proof of Law 1.

$b^m b^n = \underbrace{(b \cdot b \ldots b)}_{m\text{ factors}}\underbrace{(b \cdot b \ldots b)}_{n\text{ factors}}$	**Definition of a power.**
$= \underbrace{(b \cdot b \ldots\ldots\ldots\ldots b)}_{m+n\text{ factors}}$	**Associative axiom for multiplication.**
$= b^{m+n}$	**Definition of a power.**
$\therefore b^m b^n = b^{m+n}$	**Transitive property of equality.**

You can use Laws 1–3 together with the commutative and associative properties of multiplication to determine coefficients and the variable factors of monomial products such as the following.

EXAMPLES.
1. $(3tk^2)(-2t^3k^4) = (3)(-2)(t^1 \cdot t^3)(k^2 \cdot k^4) = -6t^4k^6$
2. $(-5x)^3 = (-5)^3x^3 = -125x^3$
3. $(-3p^2q^5)^4 = (-3)^4(p^2)^4(q^5)^4 = 81p^8q^{20}$

The proofs of Laws 4–6 depend on the *basic property of quotients* illustrated in this numerical example: $\frac{25 \cdot 6}{5 \cdot 3} = \frac{25}{5} \cdot \frac{6}{3} = 5 \cdot 2 = 10.$ Hence we can make the following general statement and give its proof.

THEOREM. If x, y, u, and v denote real numbers and if neither u nor v equals 0, then $\frac{xy}{uv} = \frac{x}{u} \cdot \frac{y}{v}$. **(Basic property of quotients)**

Proof

$\frac{xy}{uv} = xy \cdot \frac{1}{uv}$	Meaning of division.
$= xy\left(\frac{1}{u} \cdot \frac{1}{v}\right)$	Reciprocal of a product.
$= \left(x \cdot \frac{1}{u}\right)\left(y \cdot \frac{1}{v}\right)$	Commutative and associative axioms for multiplication.
$= \frac{x}{u} \cdot \frac{y}{v}$	Meaning of division.
$\therefore \frac{xy}{uv} = \frac{x}{u} \cdot \frac{y}{v}$	Transitive property of equality.

We need the following particular instances of the theorem.

$$\text{If } u = 1, \quad \frac{xy}{v} = x \cdot \frac{y}{v};$$

and

$$\text{if } x = 1, \quad \frac{y}{uv} = \frac{1}{u} \cdot \frac{y}{v}.$$

For example,

$$\frac{9 \cdot 12}{4} = 9 \cdot \frac{12}{4} = 9 \cdot 3 = 27;$$

$$\frac{16}{5 \cdot 4} = \frac{1}{5} \cdot \frac{16}{4} = \frac{1}{5} \cdot 4 = \frac{4}{5}.$$

Now we turn to the proof of Law 4.

To prove Law 4, notice that if $m > n$, $m - n > 0$; also, note that $(m - n) + n = m$. Hence, by Law 1, $b^m = b^{m-n} \cdot b^n$. Therefore,

$$\frac{b^m}{b^n} = \frac{b^{m-n} \cdot b^n}{b^n} = b^{m-n} \cdot \frac{b^n}{b^n} = b^{m-n} \cdot 1 = b^{m-n}.$$

The proofs of the other laws will be required in the exercises.

When simplifying quotients of monomials, you use Laws 4–6 along with the basic property of quotients.

EXAMPLES.

1. $\dfrac{24x^2y^5}{-6x^2y^3} = \dfrac{24}{-6} \cdot \dfrac{x^2}{x^2} \cdot \dfrac{y^5}{y^3} = -4 \cdot 1 \cdot y^{5-3} = -4y^2$, if $x \neq 0$ and $y \neq 0$.

2. $\dfrac{-5t^8k^4}{-25t^5k^6} = \dfrac{-5}{-25} \cdot \dfrac{t^8}{t^5} \cdot \dfrac{k^4}{k^6} = \dfrac{1}{5} \cdot t^3 \cdot \dfrac{1}{k^2} = \dfrac{t^3}{5k^2}$, if $t \neq 0$ and $k \neq 0$.

3. $\left(\dfrac{2z}{c^3}\right)^3 = \dfrac{(2z)^3}{(c^3)^3} = \dfrac{2^3z^3}{c^{3 \cdot 3}} = \dfrac{8z^3}{c^9}$, if $c \neq 0$.

Notice that Laws 1, 4, and 5 apply only when the bases of the powers are the *same*. You cannot use Law 5, for example, to simplify the quotient $\dfrac{z^3}{c^9}$ because the bases of the powers z^3 and c^9 are *different*.

Oral Exercises

Find the indicated products and quotients. Assume that variable expressions as exponents denote positive integers, and that variables in denominators do not equal 0.

1. $a^2 \cdot a^5$
2. $y^3 \cdot y^3$
3. $3^x \cdot 3^y$
4. $10^n \cdot 10$
5. $x^a \cdot x^b$
6. $b^4 \cdot b^x$
7. $t^{x-1} \cdot t^{x+1}$
8. $s^{1-x} \cdot s^{1+x}$
9. $y \cdot y^2 \cdot y^3$
10. $h^2 \cdot h^3 \cdot h^4$
11. $\frac{m^7}{m^3}$
12. $\frac{n}{n^4}$
13. $\frac{r^5}{r^5}$
14. $\frac{q^6}{q^4}$
15. $\frac{7^{2r}}{7^r}$
16. $\frac{4^s}{4^{3s}}$
17. $\frac{x^{2-a}}{x^a}$
18. $\frac{y^{5b}}{y^{7b}}$
19. $(2r)^3$
20. $(-3s)^5$
21. $\left(\frac{a}{3}\right)^2$
22. $\left(\frac{2}{b}\right)^4$
23. $(c^3)^3$
24. $(y^2)^5$
25. $\left(\frac{4}{z^2}\right)^3$
26. $\left(\frac{1}{r^2}\right)^4$
27. $(-5a^2)^2$
28. $(4b^3)^2$

Find the square of each of the following.

29. $2a^3$
30. $-3x^2$
31. $-5y^3$
32. $3xy^2$

Find the cube of each of the following.

33. $3r^2$
34. $2s^3$
35. $4xy$
36. $-2ab$

Written Exercises

Find the indicated products and quotients. Assume that variables in denominators do not equal 0.

A

1. $3x^3 \cdot 8x^3$
2. $4n^3 \cdot 5n$
3. $(-5a^2b)(-3ab^2)$
4. $(-9abc)(3a^2b^3c)$
5. $(12rst^2)(-3r^2s^2t)$
6. $(-2a)(-3a^2)(-4a^3)$
7. $(-3xy)(-4x)(5y^3)$
8. $(-2m^2)^3(3mx^2)^2$
9. $(-3s^3)^2(2sy)^4$
10. $(5ab)(-2a^2b)^3$
11. $(2rs^2t^3)^2(-3r^2s^3t)^3$
12. $(6a^2bc^2)^3(-2ab^3c^2)^2$

13. $\frac{64a^3b^2}{4ab^2}$

14. $\frac{-15r^4c^3}{5r^4c}$

15. $\frac{28mp^2}{-7m^3p}$

16. $\frac{5k^5v^4}{-45k^6v^8}$

17. $\frac{(-2x^2y)^3}{(6xy^2)^2}$

18. $\frac{(3ab^2)^4}{(-12a^2b)^2}$

19. $\left(\frac{12c^2b^3}{20c^4b^2}\right)^3$

20. $\left(\frac{18d^4h^5}{27d^3h^6}\right)^2$

Simplify each of the following expressions.

B **21.** $(-3b)^3(6b^2) - (2b^4)(5b)$

22. $(4c^3)(5c)^4 - (7c)^2(6c^5)$

23. $(2xy)^2 + (-2y)(4xy)(-3x)$

24. $(-3d^2)(-2c^2d) + (3d)(cd)(-5c)$

25. $(7x)(-3x) + (2x^2)^2 - (3x)(2x)^3 + \left(\frac{5x^4}{x^3}\right)^2$, if $x \neq 0$.

26. $(2x)^2(-3x) - \frac{9(x^3 + y^3)^2}{9(x^3 + y^3)} + y(-5y)^2$, if $x \neq -y$.

C **27.** Prove Law 5, page 123.

28. Prove Law 6, page 123.

29. Prove Law 2, page 123.

30. Prove Law 3, page 123.

4–2 Multiplying Polynomials

The distributive property, together with the laws of exponents and the other number properties, enables you to rewrite the product of a monomial and any polynomial. For example,

$$\begin{aligned} -5x^2(4x^2 + 2x - 3) &= (-5x^2)(4x^2) + (-5x^2)(2x) + (-5x^2)(-3) \\ &= -20x^4 - 10x^3 + 15x^2 \end{aligned}$$

In the following example, a binomial and a trinomial are multiplied.

$$\begin{aligned} &(3x + 2)(4x^2 + 2x - 3) \\ &= 3x(4x^2 + 2x - 3) + 2(4x^2 + 2x - 3) \\ &= 12x^3 + 6x^2 - 9x + 8x^2 + 4x - 6 \\ &= 12x^3 + 14x^2 - 5x - 6 \end{aligned}$$

Do you see that the product of two polynomials is the polynomial obtained by multiplying each term of one of the given polynomials by each term of the other, and then adding these monomial products?

Usually you can multiply *two binomials* at sight. The following example suggests the procedure for obtaining each term in the product.

$$(7y - 3)(2y + 5) = 14y^2 + 29y - 15$$

1. Multiply the first terms of the binomials.
2. Multiply the first term of each binomial by the second term of the other binomial; add the products.
3. Multiply the second terms of the binomials.

A special case of this procedure occurs when you square a binomial:

$$(a + b)^2 = a^2 + 2ab + b^2$$

1. Square the first term of the binomial.
2. Double the product of the two terms.
3. Square the second term of the binomial.

Similarly, $$(a - b)^2 = a^2 - 2ab + b^2$$

Thus, $(2m + 5)^2 = 4m^2 + 20m + 25$, $(7k - 4)^2 = 49k^2 - 56k + 16$, and $(-d + 3c^3)^2 = (3c^3 - d)^2 = 9c^6 - 6c^3d + d^2$

Another special case in the multiplication of two binomials arises when the first terms of the binomials are equal but the second terms are negatives of each other.

$$\begin{aligned}(a + b)(a - b) &= a^2 + (ab - ab) - b^2 \\ &= a^2 + 0 - b^2 \\ &= a^2 - b^2\end{aligned}$$

$$(a + b)(a - b) = a^2 - b^2$$

For example, $(6t^2 + 11)(6t^2 - 11) = 36t^4 - 121$.

Oral Exercises

Express the square of each of the following as a polynomial in simple form.

1. $2t$	**4.** $4z^2$	**7.** $2a - 1$	**10.** $y + 2$
2. $-3s$	**5.** $x + y$	**8.** $2a + 1$	**11.** $2a + 5$
3. $-3x^2$	**6.** $x - y$	**9.** $x - 2$	**12.** $5c - 2$

Express each product as a polynomial in simple form.

13. $(x + 1)(x + 3)$
14. $(n - 1)(n - 2)$
15. $(a + 4)(a - 1)$
16. $(t - 3)(t + 2)$
17. $(x + 5)(x - 5)$
18. $(2a + 1)(2a - 1)$
19. $(n - 7)(n + 7)$
20. $(x + 2y)(x + 3y)$
21. $(s - 3t)(s - 4t)$
22. $(a - 6b)(a + 2b)$
23. $(a + 6b)(a - 2c)$
24. $(4y + 3)(3y - x)$
25. $(3a - 7)(2a + 5)$
26. $(1 - 3y)(1 + 3y)$
27. $(1 + 4y)(1 - 4y)$
28. $(3 - 2n)(3 + 2n)$
29. $(3a - 2b)(3a + 2b)$
30. $(7ab + 1)(7ab - 1)$
31. $(3a - 2b)^2$
32. $(2a + 5)^2$

33. $4x^3(12x^5 - 3x^4 + 2x^2 - x + 9)$
34. $-3y(2 - 4y^2 + 5y^3 - 7y^6)$
35. $(-5a^2b)(21a^4b^2 - 6a^3b + 7ab^3 - b^4)$
36. $(7r^3s^2)(5rs^5 + 2r^2s^3 - 3rs^4 + s^6)$

Written Exercises

Write each of the following products as a polynomial in simple form. Assume that variables in exponents denote positive integers.

A

1. $(x^2 + 3)(x^2 + 1)$
2. $(a^2 - 2)(a^2 - 5)$
3. $(\frac{1}{2}n + 3)(n - 2)$
4. $(\frac{1}{2}c - 6)(\frac{1}{2}c + 2)$
5. $(0.3x + 1)(0.3x - 1)$
6. $(x^2 - 0.2)(x^2 + 0.2)$
7. $(z^3 - 3)^2$
8. $(x^3 + 2)^2$
9. $(2x^3 + 1)(x^3 - 5)$
10. $(a^n + bc)(a^n - bc)$
11. $(x^{2a} + 2)^2$
12. $(x^{3a} - 3)^2$
13. $(2a + 3b)^3$
14. $(5 - 2x)^3$
15. $(2y - 3)(4y^2 + 6y + 9)$
16. $(5t + 2)(25t^2 - 10t + 4)$
17. $(7z + 1)(49z^2 - 7z + 1)$
18. $(1 - 6d)(1 + 6d + 36d^2)$

B

19. $(a - 1)(a^2 - 2a - 1)$
20. $(2n - 3)(n^2 - 3n - 8)$
21. $(a - b)(a^2 + b^2 + 2ab)$
22. $(x + y)(x^2 + y^2 - xy)$
23. $(m + n)(m^2 - n^2)$
24. $(r^2 + s^2)(r - s)$
25. $x(x - 2)(x - 3)$
26. $y(y + 3)(y - 1)$
27. $-5x(x + 3y)^2$
28. $3a(a - 2b)^2$

29. $(x + 1)(x - 2)(x + 3)$

30. $(2n - 3)(n + 1)(3n - 2)$

31. $(2a + 1)(a - 2)^3$

32. $(m - n)^3(m + n)$

33. $3t^4\left(\frac{5}{t} + \frac{8}{t^2} - \frac{2}{t^3}\right)$

34. $-5a^3\left(\frac{6}{a} - \frac{3}{a^2} + \frac{4}{a^3}\right)$

35. $-6x^2\left(2x^2 - \frac{1}{2} + \frac{1}{6x} - \frac{1}{x^2}\right)$

36. $8y^2\left(3y^2 + \frac{1}{4} - \frac{1}{2y} + \frac{1}{y^2}\right)$

Find the value of k which makes each statement an identity.

C 37. $(2x - k)(x + k) = 2x^2 + 3x - k^2$

38. $(5x + k)(3x - k) = 15x^2 - 4x - k^2$

39. $(kn - 3)(kn + 1) = k^2n^2 - 4n - 3$

40. $(kn + 4)(kn - 2) = k^2n^2 + 6n - 8$

41. $(3r + k)(9r^2 + 21r + k^2) = 27r^3 + k^3$

42. $(5s - k)(25s^2 - 20s + k^2) = 125s^3 - k^3$

43. Solve: $(y + 1)^3 - (y - 2)^3 = 9(2 + y^2)$

44. Solve: $(t - 1)^3 = 9t(t - 4) + (t - 4)^3$

FACTORING

4–3 Factoring Monomials

When you write $72 = 8 \cdot 9$, you have *factored* 72 into a product of integers, and you call 8 and 9 *integral factors* of 72. In general, if a, b, and c denote integers such that $a = bc$, we say that b and c are **integral factors** of a. On the other hand, a is called an **integral multiple** of b and of c. Since $72 = 2^3 \cdot 3^2$, 2 and 3 are also integral factors of 72. Because any integer which is *greater than 1* and which has no positive integral factor other than itself and 1 is called a **prime** or a **prime number**, 2 and 3 are *prime factors* of 72.

When you factor a number, it is important to specify the set from which the factors may be selected, that is, the **factor set**. Thus, over the set of integers, 72 can be factored in many ways: $72 = 8 \cdot 9$, $72 = 4 \cdot 6 \cdot 3$, $72 = (-2)(-12)(3)$. But over the set of primes, $\{2, 3, 5, 7, 11, 13, 17, \ldots\}$, there is esssentially *one and only one* factorization of 72, namely, $2^3 \cdot 3^2$. Other prime factorizations merely vary the order in which the prime factors appear: $72 = 2 \cdot 3 \cdot 2 \cdot 3 \cdot 2$, $72 = 3 \cdot 2^3 \cdot 3$, etc.

A systematic way of finding the prime factors of a positive integer is shown in the adjoining example.

$$\begin{aligned} \mathbf{588} &= \mathbf{2 \cdot 294} \\ &= \mathbf{2 \cdot 2 \cdot 147} \\ &= \mathbf{2 \cdot 2 \cdot 3 \cdot 49} \\ &= \mathbf{2 \cdot 2 \cdot 3 \cdot 7 \cdot 7} \\ &= \mathbf{2^2 \cdot 3 \cdot 7^2} \end{aligned}$$

By factoring each of two integers, you can determine (1) their **greatest common factor** (G.C.F.), that is, the greatest integral factor of both of them; and (2) their **least common multiple** (L.C.M.), that is, the least positive integer having each as a factor. Suppose the integers are 72 and 588. Factoring,

$$\mathbf{72 = 2^3 \cdot 3^2} \quad \text{and} \quad \mathbf{588 = 2^2 \cdot 3 \cdot 7^2}$$

To find the G.C.F.

The greatest power of 2 common to 72 and 588 is 2^2, and the greatest common power of 3 is 3.

$$\text{G.C.F.} = 2^2 \cdot 3 = 12$$

No larger integer is a factor of both 72 and 588.

To find the L.C.M.

The least integer having both 72 and 588 as factors must have 2^3, 3^2, and 7^2 as factors. Hence,

$$\text{L.C.M.} = 2^3 \cdot 3^2 \cdot 7^2 = 3528$$

No smaller positive integer is divisible both by 72 and 588.

To **factor a monomial** with an integral coefficient, you seek other monomials whose coefficients are integers and whose product is the given monomial. Thus, one of the factors of $51x^2yz$ is $17x^2y$ because $51x^2yz = 17x^2y \cdot 3z$. Compare the degree of the factor $17x^2y$ with that of $51x^2yz$. (See page 40.)

To determine the G.C.F. of monomials, as for example $51x^2yz$ and $-9xy^3$, take these steps:

1. Find the **G.C.F.** of their numerical coefficients.

   $51 = 3 \cdot 17, \quad -9 = (-1)3^2 \qquad \therefore$ **G.C.F.** of coefficients is 3.

2. Compare the powers of each variable which is a factor of *both* monomials, and take the power in which the exponent is least.

   Compare x^2 and x; take x. Compare y and y^3; take y.

   $$\therefore \textbf{G.C.F.} = 3xy.$$

To find, for example, the L.C.M. of $51x^2yz$ and $-9xy^3$:

1. Find the **L.C.M.** of their numerical coefficients.

$$51 = 3 \cdot 17, \quad -9 = (-1)3^2$$

$$\therefore \textbf{L.C.M.} \text{ of coefficients is } 3^2 \cdot 17, \text{ or } 153.$$

2. Compare the power of each variable which is a factor of *at least one* of the monomials, and take the power in which the exponent is greatest.

   Compare x^2 and x; take x^2. Compare y and y^3; take y^3. Take z.

$$\therefore \textbf{L.C.M.} = 153x^2y^3z.$$

The monomial with the greatest constant coefficient and the greatest degree which is a factor of each of several monomials is called the **greatest common factor** (G.C.F.) of the monomials. The monomial with least positive constant coefficient and least degree which has each of several monomials as a factor is called the **least common multiple** (L.C.M.) of the monomials.

Written Exercises

Factor each integer over the set of primes.

A

1. 128	**3.** 630	**5.** 53	**7.** 5096
2. 343	**4.** 156	**6.** 2475	**8.** 67

Find **(a)** the G.C.F. and **(b)** the L.C.M. of the following monomials.

9. 125, 75	**13.** $2x^2y$, $10xy^3$	**17.** 1, $4x^2y$, z^2
10. 56, 49	**14.** $-3a^2b^3$, $12ab^4$	**18.** $3x$, $5y$, $4z$
11. -90, 225	**15.** $-4rs^2$, $-6r^3s$	**19.** $51xyz$, $-34x^2z^3$
12. 576, -336	**16.** $-15t^2v^3$, $-80t^3v^2$	**20.** $45a^2bc^3$, $90ab^3c$

B

21. List all the positive integral factors of 28, other than 28 itself, and show that the sum of the numbers in the list equals 28.

22. List all the positive integral factors of 496, other than 496 itself, and show that the sum of the numbers in the list equals 496.

23. Let p be an *odd prime* number. List the positive integral factors of $2p$, and show that their sum is $3(1 + p)$.

24. Let p be a *prime greater than* 3. List the positive integral factors of $3p$, and show that their sum is $4(1 + p)$.

25. The G.C.F. of two positive integers is 12. Their L.C.M. is 504. If one of the integers is 36, find the other integer.

26. The G.C.F. of two monomials is x^2y^3. Their L.C.M. is $15z(xy^2)^2$. If one of the monomials is $5x^2y^4$, find the other monomial.

4–4 Factoring Polynomials

The process of expressing a polynomial as a product of other polynomials belonging to a given set is called **polynomial factoring.** *Until otherwise stated, the factor set for a polynomial whose terms have integral coefficients will be the set of all polynomials whose terms have integral coefficients.*

To factor $20a + 24a^2$, you use the distributive property and write $20a + 24a^2 = 4a(5 + 6a)$. We call $4a$ the **greatest monomial factor** of the polynomial $20a + 24a^2$ because it is the greatest common factor of the terms of the polynomial. The first step in factoring a polynomial in simple form is to express it as a product of its greatest monomial factor and a polynomial whose greatest monomial factor is 1. Study the chart and notice how each polynomial is factored.

Given Polynomial	Factors		Factored Form
$2t^3 - 3t^2$	t^2	$2t - 3$	$t^2(2t - 3)$
$5x^4 - 320x^2$	$5x^2$	$x^2 - 64$	$5x^2(x^2 - 64)$
$9y^2 + 54y + 81$	9	$y^2 + 6y + 9$	$9(y^2 + 6y + 9)$
$50bz^3 - 80bz^2 + 32bz$	$2bz$	$25z^2 - 40z + 16$	$2bz(25z^2 - 40z + 16)$

Familiarity with the special product forms reviewed below will enable you to factor many binomials and trinomials whose greatest monomial factors are 1.

I. $\boldsymbol{a^2 - b^2 = (a + b)(a - b)}$

EXAMPLES. **1.** $x^2 - 64 = x^2 - 8^2 = (x + 8)(x - 8)$

2. $9a^2 - 144b^2 = 9(a^2 - 16b^2) = 9(a + 4b)(a - 4b)$

3. $m^4 - 1 = (m^2)^2 - 1 = (m^2 + 1)(m^2 - 1)$
$= (m^2 + 1)(m + 1)(m - 1)$

II. $\boldsymbol{a^2 + 2ab + b^2 = (a + b)^2}$
$\boldsymbol{a^2 - 2ab + b^2 = (a - b)^2}$

EXAMPLES. **1.** $y^2 + 6y + 9 = y^2 + 2 \cdot y \cdot 3 + 3^2 = (y + 3)^2$
2. $25z^2 - 40z + 16 = (5z)^2 - 2 \cdot 5z \cdot 4 + 4^2$
$= (5z - 4)^2$

III. $\boldsymbol{a^3 - b^3 = (a - b)(a^2 + ab + b^2)}$
$\boldsymbol{a^3 + b^3 = (a + b)(a^2 - ab + b^2)}$

EXAMPLES. **1.** $s^3 - 1 = s^3 - 1^3 = (s - 1)(s^2 + s + 1)$
2. $125v^3 + 8 = (5v)^3 + 2^3 = (5v + 2)(25v^2 - 10v + 4)$

By using the commutative and associative properties of addition to rearrange and group the terms of a polynomial, you can sometimes identify factors. In the following example the arrows indicate an appropriate grouping of the terms of the polynomial.

$$\begin{aligned} \boldsymbol{3ab - 20cd - 15ac + 4bd} &= \boldsymbol{(3ab - 15ac) + (4bd - 20cd)} \\ &= \boldsymbol{3a(b - 5c) + 4d(b - 5c)} \\ &= \boldsymbol{(3a + 4d)(b - 5c)} \end{aligned}$$

In the next example notice that the first three terms of the polynomial form the square of a binomial. When you group these terms, you see that the polynomial itself can be expressed as a difference of squares.

$$\begin{aligned} \boldsymbol{y^2 - 6y + 9 - z^2} &= \boldsymbol{(y^2 - 6y + 9) - z^2} \\ &= \boldsymbol{(y - 3)^2 - z^2} \\ &= \boldsymbol{[(y - 3) + z][(y - 3) - z]} \\ &= \boldsymbol{(y + z - 3)(y - z - 3)} \end{aligned}$$

Oral Exercises

State the factors of the following polynomials.

1. $2x - 2y$
2. $3a + 3b$
3. $m^2y + n^2y$
4. $ax + bx$
5. $ax^2 + 3ax^3$
6. $2my - 8m^2y$
7. $x^2 - 49$
8. $y^2 - 81$
9. $4a^2 - 1$
10. $9a^2 - 4$
11. $25 - b^2$
12. $1 - 16b^2$

13. $9a^2 - 100b^2$
14. $49c^2 - 36d^2$
15. $n^4 - 4x^2y^2$
16. $n^6 - 9x^2y^2$
17. $r^3 - 8$
18. $s^3 + 27$
19. $x^2 + 6x + 9$
20. $x^2 + 10x + 25$
21. $a^2 - 8a + 16$
22. $y^2 - 16y + 64$
23. $4a^2 + 4a + 1$
24. $9b^2 + 6b + 1$
25. $9x^2 + 30x + 25$
26. $9n^2 + 42n + 49$
27. $9a^2 - 12a + 4$
28. $4b^2 - 12b + 9$
29. $16x^2 - 24x + 9$
30. $25z^2 - 20z + 4$

Written Exercises

Factor the following polynomials.

A

1. $2x^2 - 18$
2. $3y^2 - 48$
3. $x^3 - 4x$
4. $9s^4 - 9s^2$
5. $a^4 - 16$
6. $a^4 - 625$
7. $5a^2 - 30a + 45$
8. $4a^2 + 16a + 16$
9. $-k^2 + 36k - 324$
10. $-x^2 + 50x - 625$
11. $ax - bx + ay - by$
12. $2ax + 3 + x + 6a$
13. $5b^2 + 70b + 245$
14. $6s^2 + 132s + 726$
15. $2x^2 - 64x + 512$
16. $3x^2 + 84x + 588$
17. $m^3 + n^3$
18. $r^3 - s^3$
19. $64x^3 - 1$
20. $8x^3 + 1$
21. $27y^3 - 1$
22. $125y^3 - 1$
23. $3a^2 - 2ax - 3a + 2x$
24. $a^2 + ab - 2a - 2b$
25. $125 - y^3$
26. $216 - z^3$
27. $729 - 8y^3$
28. $343 - 1000z^3$

B

29. $x^6 - 27$
30. $x^6 + 125$
31. $m^3n^6 + d^3$
32. $x^3 + y^3z^6$
33. $1 - 8n^6$
34. $1 + 125m^6$
35. $a^3 - a^2b - a + b$
36. $2x^3 - 3x^2 + 2x - 3$
37. $(x - 1)^2 - y^2$
38. $(x + 3)^2 - a^2$
39. $36 + 12(a + 5) + (a + 5)^2$
40. $49 - 14(2 - b) + (2 - b)^2$
41. $y^2 + 2y + 1 - 9t^2$
42. $4a^2 - 4ab - 36 + b^2$
43. $x^2 - y^2 + 4y - 4x$
44. $1 - n^2 - 2nx - x^2$

C

45. $x^{2a} - 1$
46. $1 - y^{2n}$
47. $t^{2p} - 2t^p + 1$
48. $r^{2k} + 6r^k + 9$
49. $(x - 2y)^3 - (x - 2y)^5$
50. $(a - b)^5 + 4(b - a)^3$
51. $(t - 1)^6 + (1 - t)^3$
52. $(s - 2)^2 - (s - 2)^5$

4–5 Factoring Quadratic Trinomials

A trinomial of the form $ax^2 + bx + c$ $(a \neq 0)$ is called a **quadratic trinomial** in x. In a polynomial in simple form a term of second degree such as ax^2 is called the **quadratic term** in x, a term of first degree such as bx is the **linear term**, and c is the **constant term**.

If the binomials $tx + r$ and $vx + s$ are the factors of $ax^2 + bx + c$, then the corresponding coefficients indicated in the following identity must be equal.

$$(tx + r)(vx + s) = tvx^2 + (ts + rv)x + rs = ax^2 + bx + c$$

EXAMPLE 1. Factor $x^2 - 7x + 10$.

Solution:

First clue: The product of the linear terms of the binomials must be x^2.

$\therefore$ The process of obtaining factors begins, $(x \quad)(x \quad)$.

Second clue: The product of the constant terms of the binomials must be 10, while their sum (which should equal the coefficient of the linear term of the trinomial) must be negative. $\therefore$ Both constant terms must be negative, and the only integral choices for them are -1 and -10 or -2 and -5. Thus, the possible factors are in this list:

Possible Factors	Corresponding Linear Term
$(x - 1)(x - 10)$	$-10x - x = -11x$
$(x - 2)(x - 5)$	$-5x - 2x = -7x$

Third clue: The linear term of the trinomial is $-7x$. Only the last possibility satisfies all three clues.

$\therefore x^2 - 7x + 10 = (x - 2)(x - 5)$.

Except for trivial changes in the factors such as writing them as $(2 - x)(5 - x)$ or interchanging them, as $(x - 5)(x - 2)$, this factoring of $x^2 - 7x + 10$ is unique, that is, the only factoring possible within the limitations of the factor set.

EXAMPLE 2. Factor $6y^2 - y - 2$.

Solution:

First clue: The product of the linear terms is $6y^2$.

$\therefore$ The factoring begins, $(y \quad)(6y \quad)$ or $(2y \quad)(3y \quad)$.

Second clue: The product of the constant terms is -2.

$\therefore$ One constant term must be positive and the other negative, and the only choices for them are -1 and 2, or -2 and 1. The list of possible factors is as follows.

Possible Factors	Corresponding Linear Term
$(y - 1)(6y + 2)$	$2y - 6y = -4y$
$(y - 2)(6y + 1)$	$y - 12y = -11y$
$(y + 2)(6y - 1)$	$-y + 12y = 11y$
$(y + 1)(6y - 2)$	$-2y + 6y = 4y$
$(2y - 1)(3y + 2)$	$4y - 3y = y$
$(2y + 2)(3y - 1)$	$-2y + 6y = 4y$
$(2y - 2)(3y + 1)$	$2y - 6y = -4y$
$(2y + 1)(3y - 2)$	$-4y + 3y = -y$

Third clue: The linear term of the trinomial is $-y$. Only the last possibility satisfies all three clues.

$\therefore 6y^2 - y - 2 = (2y + 1)(3y - 2)$.

EXAMPLE 3. Factor $z^2 + z + 4$.

Solution: The only possible factorings are $(z + 1)(z + 4)$ and $(z + 2)(z + 2)$. But, when you expand these products, you find that neither of the resulting trinomials has z as its linear term. Hence, $z^2 + z + 4$ cannot be factored over the set of polynomials with integral coefficients.

A polynomial which cannot be expressed as a product of polynomials of lower degree belonging to a given set is said to be **irreducible** over that set. An irreducible polynomial whose greatest monomial factor is 1 is called a **prime polynomial** over the set. Thus, $z^2 + z + 4$ is a prime polynomial over the set of polynomials with integral coefficients, while $2z^2 + 2z + 8 = 2(z^2 + z + 4)$ is irreducible, but not prime.

The factoring of a polynomial over a set is **complete** when each factor is either a constant, a prime polynomial, or a power of a prime polynomial. To factor $12x^6 - 192x^2$ completely over the set of polynomials with integral coefficients, you write

$$12x^6 - 192x^2 = 12x^2(x^4 - 16) = 12x^2(x^2 + 4)(x^2 - 4)$$
$$= 12x^2(x^2 + 4)(x + 2)(x - 2).$$

Written Exercises

Factor each of the following completely. Variables in exponents denote positive integers.

A

1. $x^2 + 6x + 5$
2. $x^2 - 4x + 3$
3. $n^2 + 5n + 6$
4. $n^2 - 11n + 24$
5. $m^2 + 3ms - 4s^2$
6. $m^2 - 5mx - 14x^2$
7. $y^2 + 4y - 12$
8. $y^2 - y - 30$
9. $t^2 + 2t - 80$
10. $t^2 - 14t - 72$
11. $6 - x - x^2$
12. $36 + 5x - x^2$
13. $36s^2 + 12s + 1$
14. $4 - 12s + 9s^2$
15. $2n^2 + n - 6$
16. $3n^2 - 10n - 8$
17. $n^2 - 20n - 3500$
18. $12x^2 - 8x - 15$
19. $12y^2 + 2y - 14$
20. $18y^2 - 21y - 9$
21. $m^2 - 35mn + 300n^2$
22. $m^2 + 2mn - 360n^2$
23. $n^2 - 9nr - 360r^2$
24. $n^2 + 23nr - 420r^2$
25. $6x^2 + 30x - 900$
26. $8x^2 - 24x - 1440$

B

27. $2a^4 + 10a^3 - 72a^2$
28. $x^4 - 3x^2 - 40$
29. $x^{2a} - 3x^a + 2$
30. $y^{2b} + 6y^b + 5$
31. $x^4 + x^3 + x^2$
32. $y^3 - y^4 + y^5$
33. $16x^3 - 2$
34. $3y - 81y^4$
35. $z^4 + 4z^2$
36. $z^6 - 64$

C

37. $3t^{4m} - 10t^{2m} + 3$
38. $y^{6n} - 5y^{3n} + 6$
39. $(3x - 1)^2 - 3(3x - 1) - 10$
40. $10(r + s)^2 + 11(r + s) + 3$
41. $(y^2 + y - 2)^2 - (y^2 - y - 6)^2$
42. $x^4 - (4x - 5)^2$

4-6 Greatest Common Factors and Least Common Multiples of Polynomials

A **common factor** of two or more polynomials is a polynomial which is a factor of each of them, while a **common multiple** of the polynomials is a polynomial having each of them as a factor. To find the greatest common factor and the least common multiple of $9x^3 - 9x^2 - 18x$ and $6x^5 - 24x^4 + 24x^3$, first express the polynomials in completely factored form and then take the steps indicated on the next page.

$9x^3 - 9x^2 - 18x$
$= 9x(x^2 - x - 2)$
$= 9x(x + 1)(x - 2)$

1. Find the G.C.F. of the constant factors.

   $9 = 3^2,\ 6 = 2 \cdot 3$

   $\therefore$ G.C.F. of the constants is 3.

2. Compare the powers of each prime polynomial which is a factor of *both* polynomials, and take the power in which the exponent is least. Compare x and x^3; take x. Compare $(x - 2)$ and $(x - 2)^2$; take $(x - 2)$.

   $\therefore$ G.C.F. $= 3x(x - 2)$.

$6x^5 - 24x^4 + 24x^3$
$= 6x^3(x^2 - 4x + 4)$
$= 6x^3(x - 2)^2$

1. Find the L.C.M. of the constant factors.

   $9 = 3^2,\ 6 = 2 \cdot 3$

   $\therefore$ L.C.M. of the constants is 18.

2. Compare the powers of each prime polynomial which is a factor of *at least one* of the polynomials and take the power in which the exponent is greatest. Compare x and x^3; take x^3. Compare $(x - 2)$ and $(x - 2)^2$; take $(x - 2)^2$. Take $(x + 1)$.

   $\therefore$ L.C.M. $= 18x^3(x - 2)^2(x + 1)$.

Do you see that the **greatest common factor** of two or more polynomials is the common factor which in completely factored form has the greatest degree and the greatest constant factor? The **least common multiple** of the polynomials is the common multiple which in completely factored form has the least degree and the least positive constant factor.

Written Exercises

Find **(a)** the G.C.F. and **(b)** the L.C.M. of the following polynomials.

A

1. $2t + 6;\ t + 3$
2. $2 - x;\ 2x - 4$
3. $s^2 - 25;\ 2s + 10$
4. $y^2 - 81;\ 2y + 18$
5. $x;\ x^2;\ -x^3$
6. $-r;\ r^4;\ r^2$
7. $48y^2(y + 2)(y - 3)^2;\ 32y^3(y - 3)$
8. $-35t^3;\ -25t(t - 1)(t + 5)$

B

9. $y;\ 3y^3;\ 6y - 6y^3$
10. $-21t^2;\ 14t^4;\ 2t - 2t^3$
11. $6x^2 - 6x;\ 4x^2 - 24x + 20$
12. $10v^2 + 30v;\ -5v^2 - 35v - 60$
13. $t^4 + t^3;\ t^7 - t^5$
14. $r^3 - 1;\ r - r^3$
15. $z^2 - 36;\ 6 + z;\ 6 - z$
16. $2 + 3k;\ 9k^2 - 4;\ 2 - 3k$
17. $a + 1;\ (a - 1)^2;\ a^2 - 1$
18. $2a + 6;\ 2a;\ 6$

C **19.** $16tv^2 - t^5v^2$; $vt^3 - 8v$

20. $x^2 - 3xy - 4y^2$; $4y^2 + 3xy - x^2$

21. $4a^3b - 20a^2b^2 + 24ab^3$; $2a^4 - 2a^3b - 12a^2b^2$

22. $18k^4 + 15k^3t - 12t^2k^2$; $54k^2 - 45kt + 9t^2$

FACTORING IN OPEN SENTENCES

4–7 Using Factoring to Solve Equations

You can use the theorem proved on page 57 to solve an equation having one member 0 and the other a polynomial you can factor.

EXAMPLE 1. Solve: $y^3 - 3y = y$.

Solution:

1. Transform to an equivalent equation with 0 as right member.
$$y^3 - 3y = y$$
$$y^3 - 4y = 0$$

2. Factor the left member completely.
$$y(y^2 - 4) = 0$$
$$y(y + 2)(y - 2) = 0$$

3. Solve the equivalent compound sentence.
$$y = 0 \text{ or } y + 2 = 0 \text{ or } y - 2 = 0$$
$$y = 0 \quad \Big| \quad y = -2 \quad \Big| \quad y = 2$$

4. Verify each value in the original equation.

$$y^3 - 3y = y$$

$0^3 - 3 \cdot 0 \stackrel{?}{=} 0$	$(-2)^3 - 3(-2) \stackrel{?}{=} -2$	$2^3 - 3(2) \stackrel{?}{=} 2$
$0 - 0 \stackrel{?}{=} 0$	$-8 + 6 \stackrel{?}{=} -2$	$8 - 6 \stackrel{?}{=} 2$
$0 = 0$ ✓	$-2 = -2$ ✓	$2 = 2$ ✓

$\{0, -2, 2\}$, **Answer.**

Sometimes the polynomial member of an equation has two or more identical factors. Such factors will yield a *double* or *multiple root*, which should be written only once in the roster of the solution set.

EXAMPLE 2. Solve: $5t^2 - 30t + 45 = 0$.

Solution:

1. Factor the left member completely.
$$5t^2 - 30t + 45 = 0$$
$$5(t^2 - 6t + 9) = 0$$
$$5(t - 3)(t - 3) = 0$$

2. Since $5 \neq 0$, the equivalent compound sentence has just two parts, which are identical.

$$t - 3 = 0 \text{ or } t - 3 = 0$$
$$t = 3 \quad \Big| \quad t = 3$$

3. Check in the original equation.

$$5t^2 - 30t + 45 = 0$$
$$5(3)^2 - 30(3) + 45 \stackrel{?}{=} 0$$
$$45 - 90 + 45 \stackrel{?}{=} 0$$
$$0 = 0 \checkmark$$

$\{3\}$, **Answer.**

EXAMPLE 3. The altitude h of an object t seconds after being thrown vertically upward with a starting speed of r feet per second from an altitude of k feet is given by the formula: $h = rt - 16t^2 + k$. Use this fact to determine when a ball tossed upward with a speed of 48 feet per second from a terrace 300 feet above the ground will be 236 feet above the ground.

Solution: **1.** Let t represent the number of seconds for the ball to reach an altitude of 236 feet.

$h = 236, r = 48, k = 300.$

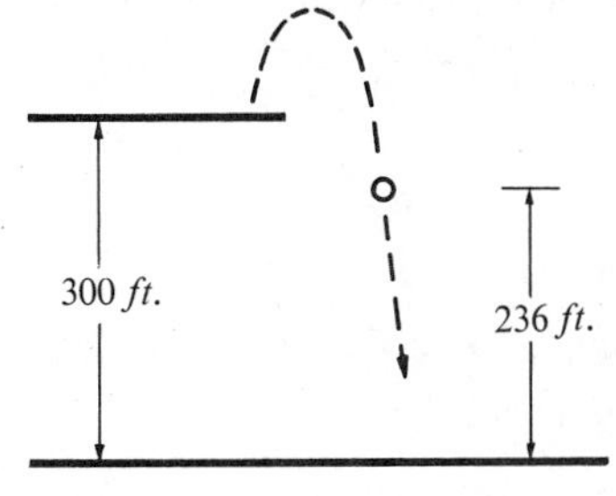

2. $h = rt - 16t^2 + k$

$236 = 48t - 16t^2 + 300$

3. $16t^2 - 48t - 64 = 0$

$16(t - 4)(t + 1) = 0$

$$t - 4 = 0 \quad \Big| \quad t + 1 = 0$$
$$t = 4 \quad \Big| \quad t = -1 \text{ rejected}$$

4. Will the ball take 4 seconds to reach an altitude of 236 feet if tossed upward with a rate of 48 feet per second from a height of 300 feet?

$$h = rt - 16t^2 + k$$
$$236 \stackrel{?}{=} 48(4) - 16(4)^2 + 300$$
$$236 = 236 \checkmark$$

The ball is 236 ft. above ground 4 sec. after being thrown, **Answer.**

The root -1 was rejected because it represents a time before the ball was thrown. Note that you solve the problem by reasoning that, to satisfy the conditions of the problem, t must satisfy the equation obtained in Step 2. However, just because a value of t satisfies the equation, you cannot conclude that it will also fulfill the conditions of the problem. The solution set of the equation gives the *possible solutions* of the problem. By checking these possibilities in the words of the problem, you find the *actual solutions* of the problem.

Oral Exercises

State a compound sentence equivalent to each of the following open sentences.

SAMPLE. $(x - 2)(x + 5) = 0$

What you say: Either $x - 2 = 0$ or $x + 5 = 0$.

1. $x(x + 3) = 0$
2. $(y - 11)(y + 4) = 0$
3. $(2t + 5)(t - 7) = 0$
4. $(v + 6)(3v - 1) = 0$
5. $t(t + 4)(t - 6) = 0$
6. $k(k - 7)(k - 8) = 0$
7. $x^2(2x + 1) = 0$
8. $y^2(5y - 2) = 0$
9. $a^2 = 2a$
10. $b^2 = -b$

Written Exercises

Determine the solution set of each of the following equations over the set of real numbers. Check your solution.

A

1. $x^2 - 4x + 3 = 0$
2. $x^2 - 9x + 8 = 0$
3. $r^2 - 4r - 32 = 0$
4. $r^2 + 3r - 54 = 0$
5. $x^2 - 9x = 0$
6. $x^2 + 4x = 0$
7. $n^2 - 6n + 9 = 0$
8. $n^2 + 8n + 16 = 0$
9. $x^2 - 9 = 0$
10. $2x^2 - 2 = 0$
11. $10y = 4y^2$
12. $4y = 6y^2$
13. $z^2 + 12 = 8z$
14. $15 - 2z = z^2$
15. $2a^2 - 5a + 2 = 0$
16. $3a^2 - 10a + 3 = 0$
17. $6r^2 + 7r = -2$
18. $20r^2 - 15 = 13r$
19. $(x - 2)(x + 2) = -3$
20. $(x + 2)(x - 2) = 3x$
21. $15t^2 + 5t - 10 = 0$
22. $15t^2 - 21t - 18 = 0$
23. $(5 - y)^2 + y^2 = 13$
24. $(5 - 2y)^2 + y^2 = 10$
25. $2n^2 - 18n = 720$
26. $5n^2 + 75n = 3500$

Solve each equation for x.

B

27. $x^2 - 6ax = 16a^2$
28. $x^2 + 3ax - 10a^2 = 0$
29. $n^2x^2 + 3nx = 40$
30. $a^2x^2 - 8ax = 20$
31. $x(x - 3)(x + 2) = 0$
32. $(x + 1)(x + 7)(2x - 1) = 0$
33. $x^3 - 7x^2 + 6x = 0$
34. $3x^3 + 18x^2 - 48x = 0$
35. $x^4 - 5x^2 + 4 = 0$
36. $x^4 - 25x^2 + 144 = 0$

C

37. $x^5 - 10x^3 + 9x = 0$

38. $625x - 50x^3 + x^5 = 0$

39. $a^2x + b = b^2x + a$

40. $6ax - 4x = 3a^2 - 5a + 2$

41. $2x^3 - 9x^2 = 2x - 9$

42. $4x - 4b + x^2b - x^3 = 0$

43. $ax - bx - a^2 + b^2 = 2a - 2b$

44. $nx - n + 3x - 3 = n^3 + 3n^2$

Problems

Solve and check each problem, omitting impossible solutions.

1. Find four consecutive integers such that the sum of the squares of the first and fourth is 45.

2. Find four consecutive integers such that 3 added to the sum of the squares of the first and second gives the square of the fourth.

3. If the length of one side of a square is increased by 1 inch and that of another side is diminished by 2 inches, a rectangle is formed whose area is 180 square inches. Find the length of a side of the square.

4. The width and height of a room with a square floor total 24 feet. If the floor and ceiling areas together equal the total area of the four walls, find the dimensions of the room.

5. A missile is fired from ground level with an upward velocity of 6400 feet per second. When will it return to the ground? (See Example 3.)

6. How much time will elapse before a missile fired with an upward velocity of 8000 feet per second from the edge of a cliff 1300 feet high again reaches an altitude of 1300 feet? (See Example 3.)

7. The base of a triangle is 2 feet greater in length than its altitude. If the area of the triangle is 40 square feet, find the lengths of the base and the altitude of the triangle.

8. The base of a triangle is 2 inches shorter than twice the altitude. If the area is 30 square inches, how long are the base and altitude?

9. The sum of two adjacent sides of a rectangle is 16. Its area is 48 square units. Find the dimensions.

10. A rectangular plot is so laid out that the length exceeds twice the width by 10 feet and the area is 4500 square feet. Find the dimensions.

11. Find three consecutive even integers such that the product of the first two increased by the product of the last two gives 200 as a result.

12. Find three consecutive odd integers such that the square of the sum of the first two exceeds the square of the third number by 15.

13. A rectangular lawn is 40 feet by 60 feet. The grass is cut in a uniform strip along the edges so that one third of the grass remains uncut. How wide is the strip?

14. A rectangular swimming pool whose length is twice its width is to be surrounded by a cement walk 4 feet wide. The total area of the pool and the walk is to be 2880 square feet. Find the dimensions of the pool.

B

15. In the circle at the left below, $CD = 14$, $AE = 3$, and $EB = 16$. Find CE and ED. $(AE \cdot EB = CE \cdot ED)$

16. In the figure at the right below, $AB = 8$, and AC exceeds AD by 12. Find AC. $(AC : AB = AB : AD)$

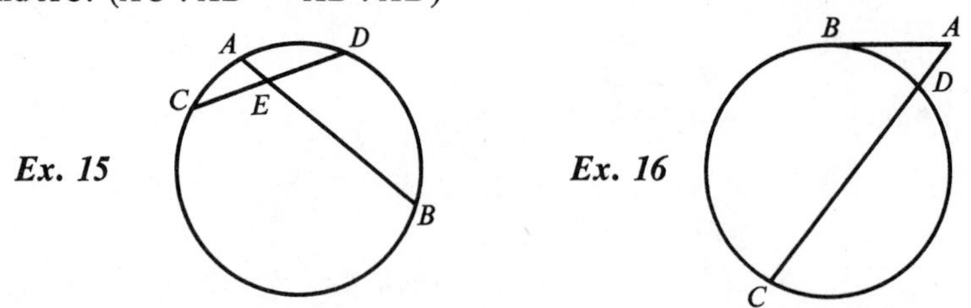

17. One leg of a right triangle is 5 inches longer than the other. If the hypotenuse is 25 inches long, find the lengths of the legs.

18. Mr. N and Mr. W start at the same time from a point and travel north and west respectively. Mr. W's rate is 4 miles an hour greater than twice that of Mr. N. After one hour, they are 26 miles apart. Find the rate of each.

19. From an airplane whose altitude is 2064 feet a bullet is fired with an upward muzzle velocity of 3200 feet per second. When will the bullet's altitude be 8400 feet? Explain the two solutions.

20. When will a ball thrown with a downward velocity of 64 feet per second from the roof of a building 720 feet high hit the ground? (Hint: $r = -64$)

21. What is the error in the following argument?

$$x^2 - 3x + 2 = 6$$
$$\therefore (x - 1)(x - 2) = 6 = 2 \cdot 3$$
$$\therefore \text{either } x - 1 = 2 \text{ or } x - 2 = 3$$
$$x = 3 \quad | \quad x = 5$$
$$\therefore \text{the solution set is } \{3, 5\}.$$

22. A box containing 180 cubic inches is constructed by cutting from each corner of a cardboard square a small square with side 5 inches, and then turning up the sides. Find the area of the original piece of cardboard.

4–8 Using Factoring to Solve Inequalities

Can you decide when the product of two or more nonzero real numbers is greater than zero?

> **A product of nonzero factors is positive, provided the number of negative factors is even. The product is negative when the number of negative factors is odd.**

These observations enable you to solve certain inequalities.

EXAMPLE 1. Graph the solution set of $x^2 + x > 6$ over the set of real numbers.

Solution:

$$x^2 + x > 6$$
$$x^2 + x - 6 > 0$$
$$(x + 3)(x - 2) > 0$$

The latter inequality will be satisfied if and only if the factors of the left member are either *both positive* or *both negative.*

Both Positive	or	Both Negative
$x + 3 > 0$ and $x - 2 > 0$		$x + 3 < 0$ and $x - 2 < 0$
$x > -3$ and $x > 2$		$x < -3$ and $x < 2$
The intersection of the solution sets of these inequalities is $\{x: x > 2\}$.		The intersection of the solution sets of these inequalities is $\{x: x < -3\}$.

$\therefore$ the solution set of the given inequality is $\{x: x < -3\} \cup \{x: x > 2\}$, whose graph is:

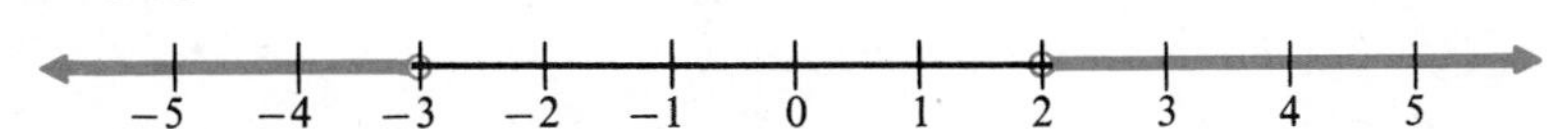

Written Exercises

Graph the solution set of each of the following inequalities over the set of real numbers.

1. $t^2 - 4t < 0$
2. $2n - n^2 < 0$
3. $(x - 1)(x + 7) > 0$
4. $(y + 2)(y - 3) \geq 0$
5. $t^2 + 3t - 18 \leq 0$
6. $s^2 + 7s + 10 < 0$
7. $v^2 - 25 \leq 0$
8. $36 - u^2 \geq 0$
9. $k^2 + 2k \geq 3$
10. $m^2 - m > 6$

B

11. $t^3 - 9t < 0$
12. $d^3 - 25d > 0$
13. $m^3 + 9m \geq 6m^2$
14. $10q^2 > 25q + q^3$
15. $x^2 + 1 < 0$
16. $x^2 + 1 > 0$
17. $16 \leq r^4$
18. $81 \geq s^4$

DIVISION OF POLYNOMIALS

4–9 Dividing Polynomials

You use the distributive property, $\frac{a+b}{c} = \frac{a}{c} + \frac{b}{c}$, to express the quotient of a polynomial and a monomial as a sum of fractions, as a polynomial, or as a sum of a polynomial and one or more fractions.

EXAMPLES.

1. $\frac{15t^3 + 24t^2 - 6t}{3t^4} = \frac{15t^3}{3t^4} + \frac{24t^2}{3t^4} - \frac{6t}{3t^4} = \frac{5}{t} + \frac{8}{t^2} - \frac{2}{t^3}$

2. $\frac{u - 2u^2 - u^5}{u} = \frac{u}{u} - \frac{2u^2}{u} - \frac{u^5}{u} = 1 - 2u - u^4$

3. $\frac{12x^4 - 3x^2 + x - 6}{6x^2} = \frac{12x^4}{6x^2} - \frac{3x^2}{6x^2} + \frac{x}{6x^2} - \frac{6}{6x^2} = 2x^2 - \frac{1}{2} + \frac{1}{6x} - \frac{1}{x^2}$

The familiar long division process of arithmetic leads you to write the quotient $\frac{313}{21}$ in the form $14\frac{19}{21}$:

$$\begin{array}{r} 14 \\ 21\overline{)313} \\ 210 \\ \hline 103 \\ 84 \\ \hline 19 \end{array}$$

210 ← subtract 10 × 21
84 ← subtract 4 × 21

$\therefore\ 313 - 10 \cdot 21 - 4 \cdot 21 = 19$ *or,*

$313 = 14 \cdot 21 + 19$ *or,*

$\frac{313}{21} = 14 + \frac{19}{21}$

Note that the process stops when the absolute value of the remainder is less than that of the divisor.

Analogously, the algebraic division process converts $\frac{z^2 - z + 5}{z + 1}$ into the equivalent expression $z - 2 + \frac{7}{z+1}$:

$$
\begin{array}{r l}
 & \boxed{z - 2} \leftarrow \text{quotient} \\
\text{divisor} \leftarrow \boxed{z + 1}\,\big) & \boxed{z^2 - z + 5} \leftarrow \text{dividend} \\
 & \left.\begin{array}{l} \underline{z^2 + z} \\ \quad -2z + 5 \end{array}\right\} \text{subtract } z(z + 1) \\
 & \left.\begin{array}{l} \quad \underline{-2z - 2} \\ \qquad\quad \boxed{7} \end{array}\right\} \text{subtract } -2(z + 1) \\
 & \qquad\quad \uparrow \text{remainder}
\end{array}
$$

Check: Dividend = Quotient × Divisor + Remainder

$$z^2 - z + 5 \stackrel{?}{=} (z - 2)(z + 1) + 7$$
$$z^2 - z + 5 \stackrel{?}{=} z^2 - z - 2 + 7$$
$$z^2 - z + 5 = z^2 - z + 5 \ \checkmark$$

Notice that in dividing one polynomial by another you arrange the terms of both dividend and divisor in order of decreasing degree in one variable. You end the division process *when the degree of the remainder in that variable is less than that of the divisor or when the remainder is 0.* The next example shows how to insert missing terms in a dividend by using 0 as a coefficient.

EXAMPLE 4. Divide $2a^3 - b^3 - ba^2$ by $2a^2 + ba + b^2$.

Solution:

$$
\begin{array}{r l}
 & \quad a - b \\
2a^2 + ba + b^2\,\big) & 2a^3 - ba^2 + 0 \cdot a - b^3 \\
 & \underline{2a^3 + ba^2 + b^2a} \\
 & \quad -2ba^2 - b^2a - b^3 \\
 & \quad \underline{-2ba^2 - b^2a - b^3} \\
 & \qquad\qquad\qquad 0
\end{array}
$$

$$\therefore \frac{2a^3 - b^3 - ba^2}{2a^2 + ba + b^2} = a - b, \textbf{ Answer.}$$

Check:

$$2a^3 - b^3 - ba^2 \stackrel{?}{=} (a - b)(2a^2 + ba + b^2)$$
$$2a^3 - b^3 - ba^2 \stackrel{?}{=} (2a^3 + ba^2 + b^2a) - (2ba^2 + b^2a + b^3)$$
$$2a^3 - b^3 - ba^2 = 2a^3 - ba^2 - b^3 \ \checkmark$$

Written Exercises

Perform the indicated divisions.

1. $\dfrac{25x^3 + 15x^2 - 30x}{5x}$ **2.** $\dfrac{21a^4 - 14a^3 + 7a^2}{7a}$

3. $\dfrac{16x^3y - 24x^2y^2 - 64xy^3}{-8xy}$

4. $\dfrac{36a^4 + 18a^3b - 24a^2b^2}{-6a^2}$

5. $\dfrac{3a^4 - 3a^3 + 3a^2}{-3a^2}$

6. $\dfrac{r^2s - r^2s^2 - 5rs^2}{-rs}$

7. $\dfrac{12a^3 - 9a^2 + 3a}{3a^2}$

8. $\dfrac{-15x^3 + 30x^2 + 5}{5x^3}$

9. $\dfrac{x^2 + 15x + 36}{x + 3}$

10. $\dfrac{y^2 + 17y + 52}{y + 4}$

11. $\dfrac{6n^2 + 11n - 35}{3n - 5}$

12. $\dfrac{12a^2 - 4ab - b^2}{2a - b}$

13. $\dfrac{15x^2 - x - 6}{5x + 3}$

14. $\dfrac{6x^2 + 2x - 28}{3x + 7}$

15. $\dfrac{6n^3 + 5n^2 + 9}{2n + 3}$

16. $\dfrac{8x^3 - 4x + 1}{2x - 1}$

17. $\dfrac{x^2 + 4x - 14}{x + 6}$

18. $\dfrac{x^2 + x - 8}{x - 3}$

19. $\dfrac{x^2 - 6}{x + 3}$

20. $\dfrac{x^2 - 4}{x - 1}$

21. $\dfrac{6a^3 + 11a^2 - 4a - 4}{3a - 2}$

22. $\dfrac{8a^3 - 22a^2 - 5a + 12}{4a + 3}$

B

23. $\dfrac{y^2 + a^2}{y + a}$

24. $\dfrac{z^2 - b}{z - b}$

25. $\dfrac{x^3 + a^3}{x + a}$

26. $\dfrac{x^3 - a^3}{x - a}$

27. $\dfrac{3 + 2t - 2t^3}{1 - t}$

28. $\dfrac{5 - s^2 + 7s}{1 + s}$

29. $\dfrac{4 - x^3 - 4x}{2 + x}$

30. $\dfrac{9 - v - v^3}{3 + v}$

31. $\dfrac{b^4 + 4b^3 + 10b^2 + 12b + 9}{b^2 + 2b + 3}$

32. $\dfrac{r^4 - 4r^3 + 2r^2 + 4r + 1}{r^2 - 2r - 1}$

33. $\dfrac{2x^4 - 9x^3 + 6x + 6 - 14x^2}{2 - 3x - x^2}$

34. $\dfrac{9 + 4y^2 - 12y - y^4}{3 - 2y - y^2}$

35. One factor of $a^4 + 4$ is $a^2 - 2a + 2$. Find the other factor.

36. One factor of $x^4 - 3x^2 + 1$ is $x^2 + x - 1$. Find the other factor.

37. Is $3x - 2$ a factor of $6x^3 - x^2 - 5x + 2$? Justify your answer.

38. Is $4y + 5$ a factor of $4y^3 + y^2 - 8y + 10$? Justify your answer.

C

39. Determine k so that $x - 4$ is a factor of $x^2 - 6x + k$.

40. Determine h so that $q + 3$ is a factor of $q^2 + hq + 12$.

41. If the quotient obtained in dividing $x^2 - 7x + b$ by $x + a$ is $x - 2$, and the remainder is 5, find the values of a and b.

42. If the quotient obtained in dividing $y^2 + ay + 6$ by $y + 3$ is $y - b$ and the remainder is 1, find the values of a and b.

4–10 The Factor Theorem (Optional)

Is $x - 2$ a factor of any polynomial (P) in the first column of the following chart?

P	Q	R	Is $x - 2$ a factor of P?	Is 2 a root of $P = 0$?
$x^2 - x - 6$	$x + 1$	-4	No	$2^2 - 2 - 6 = -4$, No
$x^2 - 5x + 6$	$x - 3$	0	Yes	$2^2 - 5 \cdot 2 + 6 = 0$, Yes
$x^3 - 4x^2 + 6x - 4$	$x^2 - 2x + 2$	0	Yes	$2^3 - 4 \cdot 2^2 + 6 \cdot 2 - 4 = 0$, Yes
$x^3 + 2x^2 - 7x + 4$	$x^2 + 4x + 1$	6	No	$2^3 + 2 \cdot 2^2 - 7 \cdot 2 + 4 = 6$, No

To answer the question, you can divide each polynomial in turn by $x - 2$, and determine the quotient (Q) and the remainder (R) as shown. By replacing x by 2 in each polynomial, you can also answer the question heading the last column in the chart. Do you see that $x - 2$ is a factor of one of the polynomials if and only if you obtain 0 as the value of the polynomial when you replace x by 2?

After studying the chart, you might guess that the following assertion, called the **Factor Theorem**, is true.

THEOREM. Let P denote a polynomial in x. Then, $x - a$ is a factor of P if and only if a is a root of the equation $P = 0$.

Although we will not discuss its proof until Chapter 14, you may use the Factor Theorem now to help determine factors of a polynomial. For example, if you want to factor $x^3 - 3x + 2$ over the set of polynomials with integral coefficients, the only linear factors to consider are of the form $x - a$, where a is an integral factor of the constant term, 2.

Can you explain why? This means $a \in \{-1, 1, -2, 2\}$. When you substitute 1 for x in the given polynomial, you find:

$$1^3 - 3(1) + 2 = 1 - 3 + 2 = 0.$$

Therefore, $x - 1$ is a factor of the polynomial. By division, you obtain:

$$x^3 - 3x + 2 = (x - 1)(x^2 + x - 2).$$

Using the Factor Theorem or the methods of Section 4–5, you can express the quadratic factor $x^2 + x - 2$ as $(x - 1)(x + 2)$. Thus:

$$x^3 - 3x + 2 = (x - 1)^2(x + 2).$$

Written Exercises

Use the Factor Theorem to determine whether the first polynomial in each pair is a factor of the second.

A

1. $x - 7$; $x^2 - 5x + 14$

2. $x - 5$; $x^2 - 2x + 15$

3. $x - 3$; $2x^3 - 11x^2 + 12x + 9$

4. $x - 2$; $x^3 + 2x^2 - 5x - 6$

5. $x + 3$; $x^4 - 3x^3 + 9x - 27$

6. $x + 1$; $2x^3 - 3x^2 - 2x + 6$

7. $y - 1$; $y^4 + 5y^3 - 13y^2 - 53y + 60$

8. $t + 5$; $t^4 + 16t^3 + 86t^2 + 176t + 105$

9. Show that $x + 2$ is a factor of $2x^3 - x^2 - 7x + 6$, and find the remaining linear factors of the polynomial.

10. Show that $x + 1$ is a factor of $2x^3 - x^2 - 5x - 2$, and find the remaining linear factors of the polynomial.

11. Show that $x - 1$ is a factor of $2x^3 + x^2 - 5x + 2$, and find the remaining linear factors of the polynomial.

12. Show that $x - 2$ is a factor of $2x^3 + x^2 - 7x - 6$, and find the remaining linear factors of the polynomial.

Factor each of the following polynomials completely.

13. $6x^3 - 7x^2 - 7x + 6$

14. $2x^3 + 7x^2 - 21x - 54$

15. $y^4 - 16y^3 + 86y^2 - 176y + 105$

16. $14t^3 - 23t^2 - 60t + 9$

17. $y^3 + 3y^2 - 9y + 5$

18. $z^3 - 3z^2 - 9z - 5$

19. $x^3 - 1$ by Factor Theorem

20. $x^3 + 1$ by Factor Theorem

21. $3t^2 - 4t + t^3 - 12$

22. $s^3 + 18 - 9s - 2s^2$

B **23.** Show that $x - a$ is a factor of $x^3 + (a + 1)x^2 + a^2 - 2a^2x - 2a^2$.

24. Show that $x - 2b$ is a factor of $x^3 + (4 - b)x^2 - 2(2b + b^2)x - 8b^2$.

25. Find m so that $z^3 - 2z^2 + 3z + m$ has $z - 3$ as a factor.

26. Find m so that $2v^4 - 3v^2 + 2v + m$ has $v + 1$ as a factor.

27. If the remainder in dividing $2t^3 + 3t^2 - kt + 10$ by $t - 2$ is 0, find k.

28. If the remainder in dividing $p^3 - 3p^2 + kp - 4$ by $p - 1$ is 0, find k.

C **29.** Use the Factor Theorem to prove that $x - a$ is a factor of $x^n - a^n$ where n is any positive integer.

30. Use the Factor Theorem to prove that $x + a$ is a factor of $x^n - a^n$ where n is any even positive integer.

31. Prove that $x + a$ is a factor of $x^n + a^n$ if n is any positive odd integer.

32. Observe that $x^{k+1} - a^{k+1}$ can be written $x^{k+1} - a^k x + a^k x - a^{k+1}$. Then show that if $x - a$ is a factor of $x^k - a^k$, it is also a factor of $x^{k+1} - a^{k+1}$, k a positive integer.

Chapter Summary

Inventory of Structure and Method

1. The **Laws of Exponents** apply to multiplication and division of powers of the same base:

For a and b real numbers, and m and n positive integers,

1. $b^m b^n = b^{m+n}$
2. $(ab)^m = a^m b^m$
3. $(b^m)^n = b^{mn}$
4. $\dfrac{b^m}{b^n} = b^{m-n}$, if $m > n$ and $b \neq 0$
5. $\dfrac{b^m}{b^n} = \dfrac{1}{b^{n-m}}$, if $m < n$ and $b \neq 0$
6. $\left(\dfrac{a}{b}\right)^m = \dfrac{a^m}{b^m}$, $b \neq 0$

To prove Laws 4–6, use the **Basic Property of Quotients:** $\dfrac{xy}{uv} = \dfrac{x}{u} \cdot \dfrac{y}{v}$, where u, v, x, and y denote real numbers with $u \neq 0$, $v \neq 0$.

2. The Distributive Axiom allows you to write a product of polynomials as a sum of monomials:

$$(a + b)(c + d) = a(c + d) + b(c + d) = ac + ad + bc + bd$$

You reverse this process when you **factor** a polynomial, that is, express it as a product of other polynomials. First, find all common monomial factors. Special polynomial forms, such as $(a + b)^2 = a^2 + 2ab + b^2$, $a^2 - b^2 = (a + b)(a - b)$, $a^3 - b^3 = (a - b)(a^2 + ab + b^2)$ and $a^3 + b^3 = (a + b)(a^2 - ab + b^2)$ provide factoring patterns. Finally, clues appearing in a quadratic trinomial help you to factor it.

3. Factoring may be used in solving equations and inequalities.
4. Algebraic division is analogous to arithmetic division. The division process terminates when the remainder is zero or when its degree is less than that of the divisor.
5. **Optional** — The **Factor Theorem** asserts that $x - a$ is a factor of P, a polynomial in x, if and only if a is a root of $P = 0$.

Vocabulary and Spelling

basic property of quotients (*p. 124*)
prime number (*p. 130*)
factor set (*p. 130*)
greatest common factor (G.C.F.)
  of monomial (*p. 132*)
  of polynomial (*p. 139*)
least common multiple (L.C.M.)
  of monomial (*p. 132*)
  of polynomial (*p. 139*)
quadratic trinomial (*p. 136*)
quadratic term (*p. 136*)
linear term (*p. 136*)
irreducible polynomial (*p. 137*)
prime polynomial (*p. 137*)
multiple root (*p. 140*)
Factor Theorem (*p. 149*)

Chapter Test

4–1 Find the indicated products, quotients, and powers. Assume that no denominator represents zero and that variables in exponents denote positive integers.

1. $(3ab^3)^4 \div 3(6a^2b^4c)^2$

2. $(3n^3 \cdot 10^{2n-1})^2 \times (-2n^2 \cdot 10^{1-n})^3$

4–2 Write as a polynomial in simple form.

3. $(3t^2 + 2)(9t^4 - 6t^2 + 4)$ **4.** $(x - 1)(2x - 3)(x + 2)$

4–3 Find **(a)** the G.C.F. and **(b)** the L.C.M.

5. $18rs^2t^3,\ 12rs^3t^5,\ -16s^4t^6$

4–4 Factor completely.

6. $3a^3y^4 - 27a^3y^2$

7. $81x^4 - 18x^2 + 1$

8. $24x^4 - 3x + 8x^3 - 1$

4–5 Factor completely.

9. $2n^2 - 34n - 168$ **10.** $12k^2 + k - 6$

4–6 Find **(a)** the G.C.F. and **(b)** the L.C.M.

11. $n^2 - 9n + 8,\ 4n^2 - 4,\ 2 - 2n$

4–7 Solve over the set of real numbers.

12. $4h^2 - h = 0$ **13.** $9n^2 + 3n = 42$

14. Mrs. Ott owns a square plot of land in the corner of a rectangular lot. The entire lot is 10 feet longer than Mrs. Ott's property and 24 feet wider than her plot. If the area of the entire lot is 4150 square feet more than the area of Mrs. Ott's property, find the length of her plot.

4–8 **15.** Solve the inequality and graph its solution set: $x^2 + 7x \geq 8$

4–9 **16.** Divide $8c^3 - 26c^2 - c$ by $2c - 5$.

4–10 **17.** Factor $d^3 - 7d - 6$ (Optional).

Chapter Review

4–1 **Positive Integral Exponents** *Pages 123–127*

1. The laws of exponents for multiplication and division apply only when the _?_ of the powers are the same.

2. When you multiply powers of a base, you _?_ exponents; when you divide powers of a base, you _?_ exponents.

Find the indicated products and quotients. Assume that variable expressions as exponents denote positive integers.

3. $(4c^2d^3)^3 \div 2(8ac^4d)^2$ **5.** $-2n^2 \div 6n^{6s}$

4. $8^{4n-1} \times 8^{3n+1} \times 8$ **6.** $(b^{2c+1})^3 \cdot (-b^{1-3c})^2$

4–2 **Multiplying Polynomials** *Pages 127–130*

7. The product of two binomials of the form $m + n$ and $m - n$ is the _?_ of two squares, namely _?_.

8. $(r + 1)^2 =$ _?_

Write as a polynomial in simple form.

9. $(x + 5)(x - 2)(x - 3)$ **10.** $(1 + 3t^2 + 9t^4)(1 - 3t^2)$

4–3 **Factoring Monomials** *Pages 130–133*

Find **(a)** *the G.C.F.* and **(b)** *the L.C.M.*

11. 186, 124 **12.** $8r^2v^3,\ -6v^2x^3,\ 12rv^5x^2$

4–4 Factoring Polynomials *Pages 133–135*

Factor.

13. $72s^2 + 24s + 2$

14. $9mn^2x^4 - mn^2y^2$

15. $1 + 16a^4b^4 - 8a^2b^2$

16. $2n^2 - c + cn - 2n$

17. $x - 5 + ax - 5a$

18. $y^3 + 125 + y^4 + 125y$

4–5 Factoring Quadratic Trinomials *Pages 136–138*

Factor.

19. $2m^2 + 30m + 108$

20. $c^2 - 24cd - 81d^2$

21. $8h^2 + 61h - 24$

22. $9n^2 + 113n - 420$

4–6 G.C.F. and L.C.M. of Polynomials *Pages 138–140*

Find **(a)** *the G.C.F. and* **(b)** *the L.C.M., in each case.*

23. $3n - 9, 3n, 3 - n$

24. $b^2 - 4, (b - 2)^2, b^2 - 2b$

4–7 Using Factoring to Solve Equations *Pages 140–144*

Solve for x in each case.

25. $x^2 = 9a^2x$

26. $9x^3 - 16x = 0$

27. $x^2 - 16 = 6x$

28. $6x^2 - 48x + 96 = 0$

29. $12x^2 + 11x - 36 = 0$

30. $mx + nx = 2m^2 - 2n^2 \ (m \neq -n)$

31. A rectangle is formed by increasing the length of a side of a square by 12 inches and decreasing an adjacent side by 2 inches in length. If the area of the rectangle is just double the area of the square, find the length of a side of the square.

4–8 Using Factoring to Solve Inequalities *Pages 145–146*

32. If a and b are real numbers and $ab < 0$, then either a __?__ 0 and b __?__ 0, or a __?__ 0 and b __?__ 0.

Solve and graph the solution set.

33. $6k - 3k^2 \leq 0$

34. $v^2 \geq 4(v + 3)$

4–9 Dividing Polynomials *Pages 146–149*

35. In the quotient $131 \div 15 = 8\frac{11}{15}$, the remainder is __?__.

36. When the remainder is 0, the __?__ is a __?__ of the dividend.

37. The process of dividing a polynomial by another is terminated when the __?__ of the remainder is __?__ than the __?__ of the divisor or when the remainder is __?__.

38. *Divide:* $\dfrac{6n^3 - 31n^2 + 34n + 10}{2n - 5}$

4–10 The Factor Theorem (Optional) *Pages 149–151*

39. If 3 is a root of $P = 0$, where P is a polynomial in x, then __?__ is a factor of P.

40. If $x + 5$ is a factor of $x^3 + ax^2 + bx + c$, where a, b, and c are integers, then __?__ must be an integral multiple of -5.

41. *Factor:* $2z^3 - 7z^2 - 28z - 12$

Extra for Experts

Euclid's Algorithm

What is the G.C.F. of 460 and 1449? You can find the required factor as follows.

1. Divide 1449 by 460.

$$\begin{array}{r} 3 \\ 460\overline{)1449} \\ 1380 \\ \hline 69 \end{array}$$

$\therefore\ 1449 = 3 \cdot 460 + 69$

2. Divide 460 by 69.

$$\begin{array}{r} 6 \\ 69\overline{)460} \\ 414 \\ \hline 46 \end{array}$$

$\therefore\ 460 = 6 \cdot 69 + 46$

3. Divide 69 by 46.

$$\begin{array}{r} 1 \\ 46\overline{)69} \\ 46 \\ \hline 23 \end{array}$$

$\therefore\ 69 = 1 \cdot 46 + 23$

4. Divide 46 by 23.

$$\begin{array}{r} 2 \\ 23\overline{)46} \\ 46 \\ \hline 0 \end{array}$$

$\therefore\ 46 = 2 \cdot 23 + 0$

Now, writing each of the four steps in the form

$$\text{dividend} = \text{quotient} \times \text{divisor} + \text{remainder},$$

1. $1449 = 3 \times 460 + 69$
2. $460 = 6 \times 69 + 46$
3. $69 = 1 \times 46 + 23$
4. $46 = 2 \times 23 + 0$,

you can see that 23 is a divisor of each divisor and also of each remainder. It must, therefore, be a divisor of each dividend, and the G.C.F. of 460 and 1449 is the same as that of 46 and 23, namely, 23.

In general, if a and b are positive integers, and $a > b$, then for some integer q_1 and some integer r_1, $0 \leq r_1 < b$,

$$\boldsymbol{a = q_1 b + r_1}.$$

Since $r_1 < b$, you can write

$$b = q_2 r_1 + r_2$$

where q_2 and r_2 are integers with $0 \leq r_2 < r_1$. Successive division produces the sequence of equalities

$$\begin{aligned} a &= bq_1 + r_1 & 0 &\leq r_1 < b \\ b &= r_1 q_2 + r_2 & 0 &\leq r_2 < r_1 \\ r_1 &= r_2 q_3 + r_3 & 0 &\leq r_3 < r_2 \\ &\vdots & &\vdots \end{aligned}$$

where $b > r_1 > r_2 > r_3 \ldots$. Since the successive remainders are decreasing nonnegative integers, you must ultimately arrive at a 0 remainder. The G.C.F. of a and b is the last positive remainder in this sequence.

The process of obtaining a G.C.F. in this way is attributed to Euclid, and is referred to as the Euclidean Algorithm.

Exercises

Find the G.C.F. for each pair of integers by means of the Euclidean Algorithm.

1. 28, 35

2. 34, 85

3. 126, 180

4. 328, 1804

5. 1360, 9639

6. 1976, 7429

7. Note that $a = q_1 b + r_1$ implies that $r_1 = a + (-q_1)b$. Similarly, in the sequence in the text, $b = q_2 r_1 + r_2$ implies that $r_2 = b + (-q_2)r_1$, and so on. Use these facts to show that if d is the G.C.F. of a and b, then, for some integers l and m, $d = la + mb$.

8. Find integers l and m so that the G.C.F. of 28 and 35 is expressed by $28l + 35m$.

9. Find integers l and m so that the G.C.F. of 126 and 180 is expressed by $126l + 180m$.

10. Use the results of Exercise 7 above to argue that if the G.F.C. of a and b in the equation $ax + by = c$ (a, b, and c integers) is a factor of c, then the equation has a solution in the integers, that is, a solution where x and y are integers. *Hint:* If d is the G.C.F. of a and b, then for some integers l and m, $al + bm = d$. Now use the fact that you are given that $c = kd$ for some integer k.

Oceanography

The unexplored "inner space" of the ocean world provides scientists with a frontier as challenging as that of outer space. Although the oceans cover nearly three quarters of the earth's surface, relatively little is known of them. Many questions, partly examined, have yet to be answered in detail.

What, for example, is the configuration of the ocean floor? What are the variations in temperature, density, and salinity from one part of the ocean to another? What is the circulation pattern of ocean currents? What is the distribution of marine organisms at various points in the ocean? To answer these questions, the oceanographer or his team must be geologist, chemist, physicist, and biologist all in one. Like all scientists, the oceanographer begins a research problem with a simple charting of data, but he ultimately seeks to understand the relationships between the phenomena which he observes.

Some oceanographers devote themselves to discovering the effect of oceanic conditions on the climate and weather of bordering land masses. Those who understand the circulation of ocean waters may then investigate such problems as means of disposal of radioactive waste. Other scientists examine samples of oceanic bottom deposits, in order to learn more about the earth's history. Special teams of oceanographers are attempting to drill a core through the miles of rock and sediment comprising the earth's crust. They believe that the information thus gained about the structure of the earth may settle the controversies over the origin of our planet.

But perhaps of most immediate importance is the work of those scientists who may help to solve some of the food problems of a rapidly expanding population. Most of the hungry nations of the world have access to the seas, and oceanographers hope to find ways for them to farm the waters as effectively as the land.

A scientist from the Woods Hole Oceanographic Institute, Massachusetts, supervises the collection of deepsea samples. The samplings later will be analyzed in the laboratory.

CHAPTER 5

Viewed aerially, the branching channels of a river delta look like a tree scorched by flames.

Rational Numbers and Expressions

Facility in operations with fractions is an essential skill in applying algebra in all the sciences and in many nonscientific occupations. Much of this chapter will review knowledge gained in your earlier mathematics. Then in the last two sections you will be acquiring skill in numerical calculations of the type needed in work in such sciences as chemistry, physics, and biology.

EXTENSION OF LAWS OF EXPONENTS

5–1 Zero and Negative Exponents

Can you assign a meaning to such expressions as 10^0, 10^{-3}, or, more generally, to b^{-n} where $n \in \{0, 1, 2, 3, \ldots\}$? Your guide in extending the meaning of a power to include *any integer* as an exponent is the requirement that operations with powers must continue to obey the laws already established for positive integral exponents (page 123).

You know that $\frac{10^3}{10^3} = 1$. However, if Law 4 (page 123) were to hold for this fraction, you would obtain: $\frac{10^3}{10^3} = 10^{3-3} = 10^0$. This suggests that it is appropriate to define 10^0 to be 1, and, in general, to make the following definition of $\boldsymbol{b}^0$ (read *b exponent 0*):

$$b^0 = 1 \text{ for every nonzero } b.$$

No meaning is assigned to the expression 0^0.

Now consider the fraction $\frac{10^4}{10^7} = \frac{1}{10^{7-4}} = \frac{1}{10^3}$. If you were to apply the first quotient law, you would obtain: $\frac{10^4}{10^7} = 10^{4-7} = 10^{-3}$. This suggests that you write $10^{-3} = \frac{1}{10^3}$ and that you make the general definition:

> **If n denotes any positive integer and $b \neq 0$, then $b^{-n} = \dfrac{1}{b^n}$; that is, b^{-n} is the reciprocal of b^n.**

Under these definitions, the laws of exponents that you have learned continue to apply. For example,

$$b^{-2} \cdot b^{-3} = b^{-2+(-3)} = b^{-5}.$$

To justify this statement, you may proceed this way:

$$b^{-2} \cdot b^{-3} = \frac{1}{b^2} \cdot \frac{1}{b^3} = \frac{1 \cdot 1}{b^2 \cdot b^3} = \frac{1}{b^{2+3}} = \frac{1}{b^5} = b^{-5}$$

You can also justify each of the following for every nonzero value of each variable:

$$\frac{b^{-4}}{b^{-6}} = b^{-4-(-6)} = b^2 \qquad \frac{10^{-2}}{7^{-3}} = \frac{7^3}{10^2} = \frac{343}{100} = 3.43$$

$$3a^4 \cdot 5a^{-3} = 15a^{4-3} = 15a \qquad \left(-\frac{1}{a^6}\right)^{-3} = (-a^{-6})^{-3} = -a^{18}$$

$$\frac{1}{b^{-4}} = b^4 \qquad \frac{(r^0s^{-2})^3}{2r^{-1}} = \frac{s^{-6}}{2r^{-1}} = \frac{r}{2s^6}$$

$$\left(\frac{1}{r}\right)^{-1} = r \qquad a^{-1} + b^{-1} = \frac{1}{a} + \frac{1}{b}$$

Oral Exercises

Express each of the following as a numeral or as a power of a variable (variable $\neq 0$).

1. $5^{-2} \cdot 5^3$
2. $7^{-4} \cdot 7^6$
3. $c^{-2} \cdot c^{-5}$
4. $x^2 \cdot x^{-1}$
5. $a^m \cdot a^{-7}$
6. $a^{-2} \cdot a^x$
7. $2^m \cdot 2^n$
8. $6^r \cdot 6^{-s}$
9. $y^{2m} \cdot y^m$
10. $v^m \cdot v^{-m}$
11. $b^n \cdot b^0$
12. $d^{-6} \cdot d^0$
13. $\dfrac{r^{-5}}{r^3}$
14. $\dfrac{s^8}{s^{-4}}$
15. $a^3 \div a^{-4}$
16. $n^{-2} \div n^{-6}$
17. $\dfrac{m^0}{m^k}$
18. $\dfrac{n^{x+2}}{n^0}$

19. $m^x \div m$

20. $n \div n^x$

21. $a^{6m} \div a^{2m}$

22. $c^{2k} \div c^{\quad k}$

23. $\dfrac{t^{3m+1}}{t^{-m+1}}$

24. $\dfrac{10^{2n+1}}{10^{n+1}}$

25. $(a^2)^{-3}$

26. $(b^{-2})^5$

27. $(c^{-3}b^{-1})^{-4}$

28. $(k^{-5}h^{-2})^3$

29. $(x^{-3})^0$

30. $(y^0)^{-2}$

31. $3a^0$

32. $(3a)^0$

33. $(a - b)^0$

34. $(3a + b)^0$

35. $\dfrac{1}{a^0 + 1}$

36. $\dfrac{1}{a^0 + b^0}$

37. $\left(\dfrac{1}{2^3}\right)^{-1}$

38. $\left(\dfrac{1}{3^2}\right)^{-1}$

39. $\left(\dfrac{1}{t^4}\right)^{-2}$

40. $\left(\dfrac{1}{s^5}\right)^{-3}$

41. $\left(\dfrac{1}{a^{-1}}\right)^{-1}$

42. $\left(\dfrac{1}{b^{-1}}\right)^{-1}$

Using only positive exponents, express each term.

SAMPLE. $\dfrac{2b^{-2}}{c^{-3}}$ *What you say:* $\dfrac{2b^{-2}}{c^{-3}} = \dfrac{2c^3}{b^2}$

43. $3z^{-2}$

44. $8y^{-3}$

45. r^2t^{-2}

46. $c^{-3}d^4$

47. $-5x^{-1}y^{-2}$

48. $-2w^{-3}v^{-1}$

49. $(r^{-1}s^2)^{-1}$

50. $(t^3z^{-1})^{-1}$

51. $\dfrac{3a^{-1}b^{-2}}{2^{-1}c^{-1}}$

52. $\dfrac{7r^{-2}t^{-4}}{3^{-1}s^{-1}}$

Written Exercises

Express each number in simplest form.

1. $(\frac{1}{2})^{-4}$

2. $(\frac{1}{3})^{-3}$

3. $(5 + 2)^{-2}$

4. $(5 - 2)^{-2}$

5. $(-3)^{-2}$

6. $(-3)^{-5}$

7. $(\frac{2}{3})^{-3}$

8. $(\frac{3}{2})^{-2}$

9. $(-3 \cdot 2)^{-3}$

10. $(-1 \cdot 5)^{-4}$

11. $(121^0 \cdot 5^{-2})^{-2}$

12. $(75^0 \cdot 3^{-3})^{-2}$

13. 2.45×10^{-1}

14. 3.45×10^{-2}

15. $\dfrac{1}{3^{-2}} + \dfrac{1}{2^{-2}}$

16. $\dfrac{1}{6^{-2}} - 1^{-4}$

Express each of the following in equivalent form without negative exponents.

17. $\dfrac{x^{-2}y^3}{x^3y^{-2}}$

18. $\dfrac{a^{-5}b^3}{ab^{-4}}$

19. $\dfrac{2^{-1}a^{-1}}{3a^2b^{-1}}$

20. $\dfrac{3^{-1}u^{-1}v^2}{2u^3v^{-4}}$

21. $\dfrac{p^{-4}q^5r^{-6}}{pq^{-2}r^3}$

22. $\dfrac{s^{-1}m^{-4}n}{s^{-2}mn^{-3}}$

23. $\dfrac{4a}{a^{-1}} + \dfrac{3}{a^{-2}}$

24. $\dfrac{3m}{n^{-1}} + \dfrac{2n}{m^{-1}}$

By assigning the indicated values to the variables, show that the following statements are *not true* for *all* real numbers.

25. $(x + y)^{-1} = x^{-1} + y^{-1};\ x = 1, y = 1$

26. $(x^{-1} + y^{-1})^{-1} = x + y;\ x = 1, y = 1$

27. $3a^{-4} = (3a)^{-4};\ a = 2$

28. $1 + a^{-1} = \dfrac{1}{1 + a};\ a = 1$

Express each of the following (Exercises 29–38) as the product of a power and a polynomial.

SAMPLE. $x^{-4} + 5x^{-2} - 12$

Solution: $x^{-4} + 5x^{-2} - 12 = x^{-4}(1 + 5x^2 - 12x^4)$, **Answer.**

B

29. $2x^{-3} - x^{-2} - 16x^{-1} + 4$

30. $5y^{-5} + y^{-2} + 7y^{-1} - 3$

31. $7z - z^{-1} + 2z^{-2} - z^{-4}$

32. $6u + 2u^{-1} - 3u^{-2} - u^{-3}$

33. $\dfrac{2}{t^3} - \dfrac{3}{t^2} + \dfrac{5}{t} + 4 + t$

34. $\dfrac{5}{s^4} + \dfrac{2}{s^2} - \dfrac{1}{s} + 3s$

C

35. $(x^2 - 1)^{-2} - 4x^2(x^2 - 1)^{-3}$

36. $(1 - y^2)^{-3} + 6y^2(1 - y^2)^{-4}$

37. $2(v - 1)(2v + 1)^{-1} - 2(v - 1)^2(2v + 1)^{-2}$

38. $4(2t + 1)(1 + 4t)^{-1} - 4(2t + 1)^2(1 + 4t)^{-2}$

39. Prove: If n is a positive integer, and b a nonzero real number, then

$$\frac{1}{b^{-n}} = b^n.$$

40. Prove: If n is a positive integer, and $ab \neq 0$, then $(ab)^{-n} = a^{-n}b^{-n}$.

OPERATIONS WITH FRACTIONS

5–2 Rational Algebraic Expressions

Because powers involving negative exponents can be expressed as fractions, operations with such powers depend on the properties of fractions. For example, the bases of these powers are restricted to nonzero numbers because a fraction has meaning if and only if its denominator is not 0. To see why a quotient like $\frac{a}{0}$ cannot be defined in the set of real numbers, recall that if $\frac{a}{0} = c$, then $a = 0 \cdot c$. But $0 \cdot c = 0$. Hence, if $a \neq 0$, *no value* of c can make the statement $a = 0 \cdot c$ true, while if $a = 0$, *every value* of c will make the statement true. Thus, $\frac{a}{0}$ either has *no value* or is *indefinite in value.* Consequently, a fraction $\frac{a}{b}$ or a power b^{-n} (n, a positive integer) is uniquely defined if and only if $b \neq 0$.

Can you explain why the domain of any variable in a fraction must exclude every real number for which the denominator equals 0? To find such excluded numbers, set the denominator equal to 0, and solve the resulting equation. The following chart shows several examples.

Fraction	$\frac{3}{x}$	$\frac{y^2 + 8y - 9}{y + 6}$	$\frac{2t + 7}{t^2 - 9}$	$\frac{z}{5}$
Equation	$x = 0$	$y + 6 = 0$	$t^2 - 9 = 0$, or $(t + 3)(t - 3) = 0$	$5 = 0$
Excluded numbers	0	-6	-3 and 3	No exclusions

A real number is called a **rational number** if and only if it can be represented by a fraction whose numerator is an integer and whose denominator is a nonzero integer. For example, because $5\frac{1}{2} = \frac{11}{2}$, $0.3 = \frac{3}{10}$, $-\frac{4}{5} = \frac{-4}{5}$, $7 = \frac{7}{1}$, and $0 = \frac{0}{1}$, the numbers $5\frac{1}{2}$, 0.3, $-\frac{4}{5}$, 7, and 0 are rational numbers. The fractions in the chart are called **rational algebraic expressions**, because their numerators and denominators are polynomials. For all real values of the variables for which the denominators $\neq 0$, rational algebraic expressions represent real numbers.

Written Exercises

Write each of the following as a rational algebraic expression. Determine all real values of the variables for which the expression is not defined.

A

1. $3 \div x$
2. $-8 \div t$
3. $0.7x$
4. $1.3y$
5. $(t - 2)t^{-1}$
6. $(r - 1)r^{-1}$
7. $r(r - 1)^{-1}$
8. $t(t - 2)^{-1}$
9. $5 \div (7k + 14)$
10. $8 \div (9m + 36)$
11. $x[x(x + 3)]^{-1}$
12. $y[y(y + 2)]^{-1}$

B

13. $\dfrac{5x + 15}{x^2 - 2x - 3}$
14. $\dfrac{6y - 18}{y^2 + 4y + 3}$
15. $(v - 4)(v^2 - 4)^{-1}$
16. $(l + 9)(9 - l^2)^{-1}$
17. $\dfrac{z - 1}{z^2 - 1}$
18. $\dfrac{w + 2}{4 - w^2}$
19. $5u(u^2 + 36)^{-1}$
20. $12t(t^2 + 1)^{-1}$
21. $(3 + k)[k(k - 1)(k + 3)]^{-1}$
22. $(m - 4)[m(m + 2)(m - 5)]^{-1}$
23. $\dfrac{c - 1}{3c^3 - 9c^2 - 30c}$
24. $\dfrac{b - 1}{20b - 6b^2 - 2b^3}$

C

25. $[5r(r + s)]^{-1}$
26. $[0.1k(k - 1)]^{-1}$
27. $\dfrac{ab}{a^2 - 2ab + b^2}$
28. $\dfrac{mn}{m^2 + 2mn + n^2}$
29. $\dfrac{t - p}{t^2 - p^2}$
30. $\dfrac{q + r}{q^2 - r^2}$

Determine the values of the variables for which each of the following represents a real number having a reciprocal.

31. $\dfrac{x - 3}{x^3 - 25x}$
32. $\dfrac{y + 7}{y^3 - 9y}$
33. $\dfrac{n}{n^3 + n}$
34. $\dfrac{s}{s^3 + 4s}$

5–3 Simplifying Rational Expressions

The property of quotients (page 124) enables you to replace one fraction by an equivalent one. For example,

$$\frac{24}{16} = \frac{3 \cdot 8}{2 \cdot 8} = \frac{3}{2} \cdot \frac{8}{8} = \frac{3}{2} \cdot 1 = \frac{3}{2}$$

In general, if neither b nor c equals 0,

$$\frac{ac}{bc} = \frac{a}{b} \cdot \frac{c}{c} = \frac{a}{b} \cdot 1 = \frac{a}{b}$$

Since this chain of equalities can be reversed, you can prove the following **Property of Fractions.**

THEOREM. Dividing or multiplying the numerator and denominator of a fraction by the same nonzero number produces a fraction equal to the given one.

$$\frac{ac}{bc} = \frac{a}{b} \text{ and } \frac{a}{b} = \frac{ac}{bc}, \text{ provided } b \neq 0 \text{ and } c \neq 0.$$

Thus,

$$-\frac{13}{52} = -\frac{1 \cdot 13}{4 \cdot 13} = -\frac{1}{4}$$

and

$$\frac{36(x+1)}{9(x+1)^3} = \frac{4 \cdot 9(x+1)}{(x+1)^2 \cdot 9(x+1)} = \frac{4}{(x+1)^2}, \text{ if } x \neq -1$$

A rational algebraic expression is said to be in **lowest terms** (or **simple form**) when the greatest common factor of its numerator and denominator is 1. **Reducing a rational algebraic expression to lowest terms** (or **simple form**) is the process of dividing the numerator and denominator by their greatest common factor.

EXAMPLE 1. Write $(y^3 - 25y)(2y^2 - 11y + 5)^{-1}$ as a rational algebraic expression in lowest terms.

Solution:

Rewrite as a fraction. → $(y^3 - 25y)(2y^2 - 11y + 5)^{-1} = \dfrac{y^3 - 25y}{2y^2 - 11y + 5}$

Factor the numerator and denominator. → $= \dfrac{y(y+5)(y-5)}{(2y-1)(y-5)}$

Divide numerator and denominator by their G.C.F. → $= \dfrac{y(y+5)}{2y-1}$, if $y \notin \{\frac{1}{2}, 5\}$

Sometimes factors of the numerator and denominator are negatives of one another, as in the next example.

EXAMPLE 2. Simplify: $\dfrac{6 - 6a}{5a^2 - 3a - 2}$.

Solution: $\dfrac{6 - 6a}{5a^2 - 3a - 2} = \dfrac{6(1 - a)}{(5a + 2)(a - 1)}$

Express the numerator as a product having -1 as a factor. → $= \dfrac{6(-1)(a - 1)}{(5a + 2)(a - 1)}$

$= \dfrac{-6}{5a + 2}$, if $a \notin \{1, -\frac{2}{5}\}$

The fraction $\dfrac{-6}{5a + 2}$ may also be written $-\dfrac{6}{5a + 2}$, because $\dfrac{-6}{5a + 2} = (-1) \cdot \dfrac{6}{5a + 2}$.

Do you see that in each example restrictions have been imposed on the variables? The restrictions are needed because in each case the original fraction and the fraction in lowest terms are equal only for those real values of the variables for which neither denominator is zero.

Hereafter, in this book it will be assumed that the replacement sets of the variables in a fraction include no value for which the denominator is zero.

Written Exercises

Express each of the following as a polynomial or rational algebraic expression in simple form.

A

1. $15(27)^{-2}$

2. $-18(12)^{-1}$

3. $\dfrac{-2ab^2}{6a^2b}$

4. $\dfrac{8a^6b^3}{-6a^2b^2}$

5. $2^{-1}(2x + 6)$

6. $3^{-1}(6x - 15)$

7. $4t(4t - 12)^{-1}$

8. $3s(6s - 9)^{-1}$

9. $\dfrac{t - 1}{1 - t}$

10. $\dfrac{y^2 - 4}{4 - y^2}$

11. $\dfrac{(n + 3)^3}{(n + 3)^5}$

12. $\dfrac{(1 - k)^4}{(k - 1)^7}$

13. $(18 - 12x)(9 - 6x)^{-1}$

14. $(2a^2b - 4ab^2)(a - 2b)^{-1}$

15. $\dfrac{a^3y - a^2y}{a^2y(a - 1)^2}$

16. $\dfrac{c^2 - c^3}{c^2 - 1}$

17. $-(x^2 - 9)^{-1}(6 - 2x)$

18. $(x^2 - 1)^{-1}(x^2 - 3x + 2)$

19. $\dfrac{1 - 4c + 4c^2}{4c^2 - 1}$

20. $\dfrac{9x^3 - x}{3x^2 + 8x - 3}$

21. $\dfrac{x^2 + 5x - 6}{(x - 1)(x + 6)^2}$

24. $-(b - a)(a^2 - 5ab + 4b^2)^{-1}$

22. $\dfrac{2m - 2n}{2n^2 - mn - m^2}$

25. $\dfrac{k^3 - 1}{2k^2 + 2k - 4}$

23. $(t^2 + t - 6)(t^2 + 2t - 3)^{-1}$

26. $\dfrac{a^3 + b^3}{a^2 - ab + b^2}$

B 27. $-\dfrac{(a - b)(b - c)(a - c)}{(b - a)(c - b)(c - a)}$

30. $\dfrac{a^2 + ab}{a(a + b) - 2(a + b)}$

28. $\dfrac{(x - y)^{-3}}{(y - x)^{-5}}$

31. $\dfrac{5v - 20v^3}{10v^4 + 5v^3 - 10v(1 + 2v)}$

29. $\dfrac{x^4 - y^4}{4x - 4y}$

32. $\dfrac{196c - 4c^3}{2c^3 - 6c + 14c^2 - 42}$

C 33. $\dfrac{(t^2 - 6)^3(t^2 + 3)(4t) - (t^2 + 3)^2(t^2 - 6)^2(6t)}{(t^2 - 6)^6}$

34. $\dfrac{(x^2 + 1)^2(3x - 1)^2(9x) - (3x - 1)^3(x^2 + 1)(4x)}{(x^2 + 1)^4}$

35. $\dfrac{(2y + 1)^4(y^3 + 4)(6y^2) - (y^3 + 4)^2(2y + 1)^3(8y)}{(2y + 1)^8}$

36. $\dfrac{(3k + 2)^5(5 - k^4)(-8k^3) - (5 - k^4)^2(3k + 2)^4(15k)}{(3k + 2)^{10}}$

5–4 Multiplication and Division

The property of quotients, $\dfrac{xy}{uv} = \dfrac{x}{u} \cdot \dfrac{y}{v}$, gives an expression for the product of fractions: $\dfrac{x}{u} \cdot \dfrac{y}{v} = \dfrac{xy}{uv}$.

A product of fractions equals the fraction whose numerator is the product of the numerators and whose denominator is the product of the denominators of the given fractions.

$\dfrac{3}{8} \cdot \dfrac{7}{5} = \dfrac{21}{40}$; $\quad 2k^2 \cdot \dfrac{3k}{m} = \dfrac{2k^2}{1} \cdot \dfrac{3k}{m} = \dfrac{6k^3}{m}$; $\quad \dfrac{c}{d} \cdot \dfrac{d}{c} = \dfrac{cd}{dc} = \dfrac{cd}{cd} = 1$;

$$\frac{6}{x + y} \cdot \frac{x(x + y)}{3} = \frac{6x(x + y)}{3(x + y)} = \frac{2x \cdot 3(x + y)}{3(x + y)} = 2x$$

You can often simplify products of rational algebraic expressions by factoring numerators and denominators.

$$\frac{5v+5}{v^3-8}\cdot\frac{v^2-4v+4}{v^2-1} = \frac{5(v+1)}{(v-2)(v^2+2v+4)}\cdot\frac{(v-2)^2}{(v+1)(v-1)}$$
$$= \frac{5(v-2)(v+1)(v-2)}{(v-1)(v^2+2v+4)(v+1)(v-2)}$$
$$= \frac{5(v-2)}{(v-1)(v^2+2v+4)}$$

Recall that a quotient equals the product of the dividend and the reciprocal of the divisor (page 28). This fact, together with the fact that the reciprocal of $\frac{c}{d}$ is $\frac{d}{c}$, if $c \neq 0$ and $d \neq 0$, means that $\frac{a}{b} \div \frac{c}{d} = \frac{a}{b}\cdot\frac{d}{c} = \frac{ad}{bc}$. Note the following.

$$-\frac{16}{9} \div \frac{22}{15} = -\frac{16}{9}\cdot\frac{15}{22} = -\left(\frac{2^4\cdot 3\cdot 5}{2\cdot 3^2\cdot 11}\right) = -\left(\frac{2^3\cdot 5}{3\cdot 11}\right) = -\frac{40}{33}$$

$$\frac{15+2k-k^2}{1+2k+k^2} \div \frac{2k^2-12k+10}{k^2-1}$$
$$= \frac{15+2k-k^2}{1+2k+k^2}\cdot\frac{k^2-1}{2k^2-12k+10}$$
$$= \frac{(3+k)(5-k)}{(1+k)^2}\cdot\frac{(k+1)(k-1)}{2(k-5)(k-1)}$$
$$= \frac{(3+k)(-1)(k-5)(k+1)(k-1)}{2(1+k)(k-5)(k+1)(k-1)}$$
$$= \frac{(-1)(3+k)}{2(1+k)} = -\frac{3+k}{2(1+k)}$$

Written Exercises

Express each product or quotient in lowest terms.

1. $\frac{15}{28}(-\frac{42}{45})(\frac{2}{3})^{-1}$

2. $(-\frac{55}{36})(-\frac{21}{44})(-\frac{35}{8})^{-1}$

3. $\frac{12x^3}{5}\cdot\frac{10}{x^3}$

4. $\frac{8x^2}{3}\cdot\frac{6}{x^2}$

5. $\frac{5a^3}{2} \div \frac{a^2}{3}$

6. $\frac{5m^2}{6} \div \frac{5m}{3}$

7. $\frac{x-1}{5} \div \frac{x-1}{10}$

8. $\frac{x+1}{6} \div \frac{x+1}{3}$

9. $(2a^2)(3b)^{-1}(15b^3)(2a)^{-2}$

10. $(9xy^3)(3ay)^{-1}(8a^4x)(2y)^{-2}$

11. $\frac{6abc^2}{15a^2} \cdot \left(\frac{2bc}{3a}\right)^{-1}$

12. $\frac{24m^6n}{18m^3} \cdot \left(\frac{9n^4}{2m}\right)^{-1}$

13. $\frac{-8x^2}{y^3} \cdot \frac{15y}{4x}$

14. $\frac{2rs}{3} \cdot \frac{-3}{4s}$

15. $\frac{x^2+3x}{x^2+2x-3} \cdot \frac{x+1}{x}$

16. $\frac{x^2-9}{4x+12} \cdot \frac{6}{x-3}$

17. $\frac{y^2+6y-16}{y^2-64} \cdot (y-2)^{-1}$

18. $\frac{2y^2-50}{2y-10} \cdot (4y-2) \cdot (6y+30)^{-1}$

19. $\frac{2z-8}{z^2-4} \div \frac{z-4}{z^2+6z+8}$

20. $\frac{2z-14}{z^2-2z-35} \div \frac{6z^3}{z^2-25}$

21. $\frac{a^2-4a}{a^2+2a}\left(\frac{a^2-9a+20}{a^2-3a-10}\right)^{-1}$

22. $\frac{1+3b-18b^2}{6b^2-17b-3}\left(\frac{3b-1}{b-3}\right)^{-1}$

B 23. $\frac{3a+6c}{9a} \cdot \frac{12ac}{a^2-4c^2} \div \frac{18a^3c^3}{2a-4c}$

24. $\frac{5c^2-5c}{4a^3} \cdot \frac{c^2-9c-10}{4c-40} \div \frac{2-2c^2}{a}$

25. $\frac{12a^2-3}{15} \cdot (2a+1)^{-1} \cdot \frac{5}{2a+1}$

26. $\frac{r^2-4s^2}{r+2s} \cdot (r+2s)^{-1} \cdot \frac{2s}{r-2s}$

27. $\frac{15-13x+2x^2}{4x^2-9} \cdot \frac{2x+1}{1-2x} \cdot \left(\frac{5-x}{2x-1}\right)^{-1}$

28. $\frac{30-11p+p^2}{9p-6p^2+p^3} \cdot \frac{p^2-3p}{25-p^2} \cdot \left(\frac{p^2-9}{p^2+2p-15}\right)^{-1}$

C 29. Explain why the set of rational numbers is closed under multiplication.

30. Explain why the set of rational numbers is closed under division, excluding division by 0.

31. Prove: If x_1 and x_2 denote positive numbers, $\frac{y_1}{x_1} > \frac{y_2}{x_2}$ if and only if $y_1x_2 > y_2x_1$.

32. Prove: If x_1 and x_2 denote positive numbers, $\frac{y_1}{x_1} < \frac{y_2}{x_2}$ if and only if $y_1x_2 < y_2x_1$.

5–5 Addition and Subtraction

The distributive property, together with the meaning of division, provides a means of writing the sum of fractions with equal denominators as a single fraction:

$$\frac{a}{c} + \frac{b}{c} = a \cdot \frac{1}{c} + b \cdot \frac{1}{c} = (a + b)\frac{1}{c} = \frac{a + b}{c}.$$

The sum of fractions with equal denominators equals the fraction whose numerator is the sum of the numerators and whose denominator is the common denominator of the given fractions.

EXAMPLES. $\frac{3}{10} + \frac{2}{10} - \frac{7}{10} = \frac{3 + 2 - 7}{10} = \frac{-2}{10} = -\frac{1}{5}$

$$\frac{3a}{2a + 2b} - \frac{1}{2a + 2b} - \frac{a - 7}{2a + 2b} = \frac{3a - 1 - (a - 7)}{2a + 2b} = \frac{3a - 1 - a + 7}{2a + 2b}$$

$$= \frac{2a + 6}{2a + 2b} = \frac{2(a + 3)}{2(a + b)} = \frac{a + 3}{a + b}$$

When the fractions have unequal denominators, replace each of the fractions by an equivalent one having its denominator equal to the lowest common denominator (L.C.D.) of the fractions. Of course, the L.C.D. of the fractions is the least common multiple of the denominators of the fractions (page 131).

EXAMPLE 1. Add: $\frac{7}{54} + \frac{11}{90} + 1$

Solution:

1. Find the L.C.D. $\rightarrow$ $54 = 2 \cdot 3^3$ and $90 = 2 \cdot 3^2 \cdot 5$

$\therefore$ L.C.D. $= 2 \cdot 3^3 \cdot 5 = 270$

2. Transform each fraction into an equivalent one with the L.C.D. as denominator. $\rightarrow$

$$\frac{7}{54} = \frac{7 \cdot 5}{54 \cdot 5} = \frac{35}{270}$$

$$\frac{11}{90} = \frac{11 \cdot 3}{90 \cdot 3} = \frac{33}{270}$$

$$1 = \frac{270}{270}$$

3. Add, as in the preceding examples, and simplify if possible.

$$\frac{7}{54} + \frac{11}{90} + 1 = \frac{35}{270} + \frac{33}{270} + \frac{270}{270}$$

$$= \frac{35 + 33 + 270}{270}$$

$$= \frac{338}{270} = \frac{169}{135}, \text{ or } 1\tfrac{34}{135}, \textbf{ Answer.}$$

EXAMPLE 2. Simplify: $\dfrac{x+4}{2x-4} - \dfrac{2x+5}{x^2-x-2} + \dfrac{3}{4}$

Solution:

1. $2x - 4 = 2(x - 2)$, $x^2 - x - 2 = (x + 1)(x - 2)$, $4 = 2^2$

$\therefore$ L.C.D. $= 2^2(x - 2)(x + 1)$

2. Write with factored denominators.

$$\frac{x+4}{2(x-2)} - \frac{2x+5}{(x+1)(x-2)} + \frac{3}{2^2}$$

3. Replace each fraction by an equivalent fraction.

$$\frac{(x+4)\cdot 2(x+1)}{2(x-2)\cdot 2(x+1)} - \frac{(2x+5)4}{(x+1)(x-2)4} + \frac{3(x+1)(x-2)}{4(x+1)(x-2)}$$

4. Combine the fractions and simplify.

$$\frac{2(x+1)(x+4) - 4(2x+5) + 3(x+1)(x-2)}{4(x-2)(x+1)}$$

$$= \frac{2(x^2+5x+4) - 4(2x+5) + 3(x^2-x-2)}{4(x-2)(x+1)}$$

$$= \frac{2x^2+10x+8-8x-20+3x^2-3x-6}{4(x-2)(x+1)}$$

$$= \frac{5x^2-x-18}{4(x-2)(x+1)}$$

$$= \frac{(5x+9)(x-2)}{4(x+1)(x-2)} = \frac{5x+9}{4(x+1)}, \textbf{ Answer.}$$

Written Exercises

Simplify.

A

1. $\frac{3}{5} - \frac{7}{5} + \frac{11}{5}$

2. $\frac{13}{20} + \frac{39}{20} - \frac{77}{20}$

3. $\frac{5}{4} - \frac{7}{6} + 4$

4. $-\frac{2}{5} + \frac{9}{10} - 3$

5. $\frac{x}{x-1} - \frac{1}{x-1}$

6. $\frac{5}{2a+6} + \frac{3}{2a+6}$

7. $\frac{2}{3a} + \frac{7}{12a}$

8. $\frac{4}{3x} + \frac{5}{6x}$

9. $\frac{7}{3x} - \frac{2}{2x^2}$

10. $\frac{3}{ab} - \frac{4}{b^2}$

11. $\frac{8m}{3n} - \frac{m}{2n} + \frac{1}{12}$

12. $\frac{a}{bc} - \frac{b}{ac} + \frac{c}{ab}$

13. $\frac{1}{2} + \frac{3}{4a^2} - \frac{1}{a}$

14. $\frac{3}{4} + \frac{x}{2} - \frac{5}{2x}$

15. $\frac{x-1}{2} + \frac{x-4}{3}$

16. $\frac{2y+3}{6} - \frac{y+3}{4}$

17. $\frac{2n+1}{3n} - \frac{2-3n}{4n} + \frac{1}{2n^2}$

18. $\frac{x-4}{6x} - \frac{3+5x}{5x} + \frac{1}{10x}$

19. $1 + x^{-1}$

20. $x + x^{-1}$

21. $1 + 3(x+2)^{-1}$

22. $5 - 4(y+1)^{-1}$

23. $\frac{3}{x+1} - \frac{2}{3x}$

24. $\frac{4}{2x-1} - \frac{3}{2x}$

25. $\frac{2}{x-1} + \frac{2}{x+1}$

26. $\frac{ab}{a^2-b^2} - \frac{a}{a-b}$

27. $\frac{r-s}{3r+6s} - \frac{r-2s}{4r+8s}$

28. $\frac{x}{6x-3y} - \frac{y}{12x-6y}$

29. $3t + 1 + \frac{2}{3t-1}$

30. $x + 1 - \frac{5}{1-x}$

Note. With practice you will acquire skill enabling you to shorten your work by combining steps in the simplification.

B

31. $\frac{t+4}{2t^2-2t} - \frac{5}{2t-2}$

32. $\frac{b}{a^2+ab} - \frac{2b}{a^2-b^2}$

33. $-\frac{2}{y} + \frac{4y}{y^2-1} - \frac{2}{y+1}$

34. $-\frac{x}{2} + \frac{x}{x-1} - \frac{x+1}{2x-2}$

35. $\frac{2x}{1-2x} + \frac{3x}{2x+1} - \frac{3}{4x^2-1}$

36. $\frac{x}{x-y} + \frac{x^2+y^2}{y^2-x^2} + \frac{y}{x+y}$

37. $\frac{m+5}{2m^2-2} + \frac{3}{1-m} + \frac{5}{2m+2}$

38. $\frac{x+6}{4-x^2} - \frac{x+3}{x+2} + \frac{x-3}{2-x}$

39. $x^2 - 3 + \frac{x-3}{x^2+3}$

40. $y^2 - 1 + \frac{2y+3}{y^2-1}$

41. $\frac{1}{r+s} + \frac{rs-2s^2}{r^3+s^3}$

42. $\frac{1}{h-2k} - \frac{6hk}{h^3-8k^3}$

C

43. $\frac{2rs+r^2}{2s^2-3rs+r^2} + \frac{r-s}{2s-r}$

44. $\frac{m+n}{m^2+4mn+4n^2} - \frac{m-n}{2n+m}$

45. $\left(\frac{9y}{y^2-9} + \frac{3}{3-y}\right) \cdot \frac{y^2-y-6}{2y+3}$

46. $\left(\frac{x}{4-x^2} - \frac{1}{x+2}\right) \cdot \frac{x^2+2x-8}{x+1}$

47. Explain why the set of rational numbers is closed under addition.

48. Explain why the set of rational numbers is closed under subtraction.

5–6 Complex Fractions

A **complex fraction** is a fraction whose numerator or denominator, or both, contains one or more fractions or powers involving negative exponents. There are two methods of simplifying complex fractions.

Method I. Multiply the numerator and denominator by the L.C.D. of all the fractions within them.

Method II. Express the fraction as a quotient, using the sign ÷.

EXAMPLE. Simplify: $\dfrac{x - 9x^{-1}}{1 + \dfrac{x}{3}}$.

Solution (Method I):

$$\frac{x - 9x^{-1}}{1 + \frac{x}{3}} = \frac{\left(x - \frac{9}{x}\right)3x}{\left(1 + \frac{x}{3}\right)3x}$$

$$= \frac{3x^2 - 27}{3x + x^2}$$

$$= \frac{3(x^2 - 9)}{x(x + 3)}$$

$$= \frac{3(x - 3)(x + 3)}{x(x + 3)}$$

$$= \frac{3(x - 3)}{x}, \textbf{ Answer.}$$

Solution (Method II):

$$\frac{x - \frac{9}{x}}{1 + \frac{x}{3}} = \left(x - \frac{9}{x}\right) \div \left(1 + \frac{x}{3}\right)$$

$$= \frac{x^2 - 9}{x} \div \frac{x + 3}{3}$$

$$= \frac{x^2 - 9}{x} \cdot \frac{3}{x + 3}$$

$$= \frac{3(x - 3)(x + 3)}{x(x + 3)}$$

$$= \frac{3(x - 3)}{x}, \textbf{ Answer.}$$

Written Exercises

Determine a polynomial or rational algebraic expression in simple form equivalent to each of the following.

A

1. $\dfrac{1 + \frac{9}{16}}{1 - \frac{3}{4}}$

2. $\dfrac{\frac{5}{27} - 5}{\frac{1}{3} + 1}$

3. $\dfrac{a - 2}{1 - \dfrac{4}{a^2}}$

4. $\dfrac{\dfrac{9}{a^2} - 1}{a - 3}$

5. $\dfrac{x + y^{-1}x}{1 + y^{-1}}$

6. $\dfrac{b - ac^{-1}}{ab^{-1} - c}$

7. $\dfrac{\dfrac{a}{b} - \dfrac{b}{c}}{\dfrac{b}{a} - \dfrac{c}{b}}$

8. $\dfrac{\dfrac{3}{s} + \dfrac{5}{t}}{\dfrac{s}{3} + \dfrac{t}{5}}$

9. $\dfrac{n + 1 - \dfrac{2}{n}}{n + 4 + \dfrac{4}{n}}$

10. $\dfrac{m - \dfrac{1}{m}}{1 + \dfrac{4}{m} - \dfrac{5}{m^2}}$

11. $\dfrac{y^{-1} + 1}{y - 1}$

12. $\dfrac{1 - x}{x^{-1} - 1}$

13. $\dfrac{t - \dfrac{t^2 - 1}{t}}{1 - \dfrac{t - 1}{t}}$

15. $\dfrac{2a - 8a^{-1}}{8a^{-2} + 2a^{-1} - 1}$

14. $\dfrac{x + y + \dfrac{x - 2y}{2}}{x + y - \dfrac{x + 3y}{3}}$

16. $\dfrac{1 + b - 2b^{-1}}{6b^{-2} + b^{-1} - 1}$

17. $\dfrac{1}{a^{-1} + b^{-1}}$

18. $\dfrac{2}{r^{-2} + s^{-2}}$

19. $\left(2 - \dfrac{2}{a}\right) \div \left(1 - \dfrac{1}{a^2}\right)$

20. $\left(\dfrac{1}{d^2 - 1} + 1\right) \div \left(\dfrac{1}{d - 1} + 1\right)$

21. $\left(1 + \dfrac{t}{t - 1}\right)\left(4 + \dfrac{3}{t^2 - 1}\right)^{-1}$

22. $\left(2 - \dfrac{7z + 2}{z^2 - 1}\right)\left(z - 3 - \dfrac{5}{z + 1}\right)^{-1}$

23. $\dfrac{1 + (t + 1)^{-1}}{1 + 3(t - 1)^{-1}}$

24. $\dfrac{1 + 3(r + 1)^{-1}}{1 + (r + 3)^{-1}}$

25. $\dfrac{m^{-1} + n^{-1}}{m^{-3} + n^{-3}}$

26. $\dfrac{a^{-2} - b^{-2}}{a^{-1}b^{-1}}$

27. $\dfrac{c^{-4} - d^{-4}}{c^{-2} + d^{-2}}$

28. $\dfrac{r^{-3} + s^{-3}}{r^{-9} - s^{-9}}$

29. $1 + (a + a^{-1})^{-1}$

30. $[x + (x + x^{-1})^{-1}]^{-1}$

31. $\left(\dfrac{r + s}{r - s} + \dfrac{r}{s}\right)\left(\dfrac{rs}{r^2 - s^2} + \dfrac{r}{r + s}\right)^{-1}$

32. $\left(\dfrac{x + y}{x} - \dfrac{2y}{x + y}\right)\left(\dfrac{x - y}{y} + \dfrac{2x}{x - y}\right)^{-1}$

33. $\dfrac{a^{-2} - 2a^{-1} + 1}{(1 + a^{-1})(1 - a^{-1})}$

34. $\dfrac{(x + y)(x^{-1} - y^{-1})}{(x - y)(x^{-1} + y^{-1})}$

USING FRACTIONS TO SOLVE PROBLEMS

5–7 Polynomials with Rational Coefficients

Skill in determining least common denominators is useful in factoring polynomials whose coefficients are rational numbers and in solving open sentences whose numerical coefficients are fractions.

EXAMPLE 1. Express $\frac{x^2}{2} - \frac{7}{4}x - 1$ as the product of a rational number and prime polynomials with integral coefficients.

Solution: $\frac{x^2}{2} - \frac{7}{4}x - 1 = \frac{1}{4}(2x^2 - 7x - 4)$

$= \frac{1}{4}(2x + 1)(x - 4)$, **Answer.**

EXAMPLE 2. Solve: $\frac{4m}{15} - \frac{2m - 1}{10} = \frac{1}{2}$

Solution: The L.C.D. of the terms is 30.

Method 1

$$\frac{4m}{15} - \frac{2m - 1}{10} = \frac{1}{2}$$

$$30\left(\frac{4m}{15} - \frac{2m - 1}{10}\right) = 30\left(\frac{1}{2}\right)$$

$$30\left(\frac{4m}{15}\right) - 30\left(\frac{2m - 1}{10}\right) = 30\left(\frac{1}{2}\right)$$

$$8m - 6m + 3 = 15$$

Method 2

$$\frac{4m}{15} - \frac{2m - 1}{10} = \frac{1}{2}$$

$$\frac{8m}{30} - \frac{3(2m - 1)}{30} = \frac{15}{30}$$

$$\frac{8m - 6m + 3}{30} = \frac{15}{30}$$

$$\frac{2m + 3}{30} = \frac{15}{30}$$

$$2m + 3 = 15$$

$$m = 6$$

The check is left to you. $\{6\}$ **Answer.**

Oral Exercises

State the L.C.D. of the terms of each open sentence; then read the sentence after multiplying the terms by the L.C.D.

SAMPLE. $\frac{7r}{24} + \frac{r}{9} \geq 1$

What you say: The L.C.D. is 72; $21r + 8r \geq 72$

1. $\frac{5k}{4} - \frac{k}{3} = 2$

2. $\frac{2d}{7} + \frac{3d}{5} = 1$

3. $\frac{x}{4} - x \leq \frac{1}{6}$

4. $t + \frac{2t}{21} > -\frac{1}{7}$

5. $6 - k = \frac{1}{2}k + \frac{1}{6}k$

6. $\frac{1}{9}d - \frac{5}{6}d = 2 + d$

7. $\frac{x}{4} + \frac{y}{14} = 1$

8. $\frac{5r}{6} + \frac{s}{15} = 1$

9. $k^2 - \frac{7k}{6} + \frac{1}{3} = 0$

10. $m^2 - \frac{1}{2} = \frac{m}{12}$

11. $\frac{3q^2}{2} - \frac{q}{8} + \frac{3}{4} > 0$

12. $\frac{v^2}{6} - \frac{5v}{12} - \frac{3}{2} \leq 0$

Written Exercises

Determine the solution set of each equation or system of equations over the set of real numbers.

A

1. $\frac{x}{3} + \frac{x}{4} = \frac{7}{2}$

2. $\frac{t}{4} + \frac{t}{5} = \frac{9}{2}$

3. $\frac{2}{3}c + 1 = \frac{1}{2}c$

4. $\frac{3}{7}r - 4 = \frac{1}{3}r$

5. $\frac{3n - 2}{6} - \frac{2n + 5}{4} = 1$

6. $\frac{2c - 15}{12} - \frac{3c + 2}{9} + \frac{6c + 53}{36} = 0$

7. $0.05x + 0.07(10{,}000 - x) = 550$

8. $0.045y + 0.03(500 - y) = 18$

9. $a^2 + \frac{5}{6}a = \frac{2}{3}$

10. $2 = \frac{3}{2}x^2 + \frac{26}{3}x$

11. $\frac{p}{2}\left(\frac{p}{3} - 1\right) - \frac{2}{3} = 0$

12. $\frac{u}{5}\left(\frac{4u}{7} - 1\right) = \frac{3}{14}$

13. $\frac{12}{5}x^3 = \frac{x}{3}\left(2 - \frac{9x}{5}\right)$

14. $\frac{1}{2}\left(\frac{n}{2}\right)^3 + 2\left(\frac{n}{2}\right)^2 + n = 0$

15. $\frac{k}{3} - \frac{3k - 5}{2} - 8 = 0$

16. $3 - \frac{3v}{2} - \frac{8 - 4v}{7} = 0$

17. $\frac{4s + 3}{6} - \frac{4s - 1}{9} = \frac{1}{2}$

18. $\frac{1}{4} - \frac{3m - 2}{8} = \frac{2m + 3}{6}$

B

19. $\frac{1}{2}x + \frac{1}{3}y = 2$
    $\frac{1}{3}x + \frac{1}{9}y = 1$

20. $\frac{1}{5}c + \frac{1}{2}d + 1 = 0$
    $\frac{1}{4}d - \frac{1}{3}c + \frac{1}{2} = 0$

21. $\frac{x}{4} - \frac{y}{6} = 0$

$\frac{3x}{8} + \frac{5y}{12} = -4$

22. $\frac{2m}{3} + 2n = 1$

$\frac{4m}{9} - \frac{n}{3} = \frac{1}{9}$

23. $\frac{9 - 5x}{2} = y + 1$

$x = \frac{y}{3} - 3$

24. $\frac{x}{3} - 2 = y - 2$

$\frac{x + 6}{3} + 3(y - 2) = 0$

25. $\frac{x + 2y}{3} - \frac{2x - y}{3} = -3$

$\frac{3x - 2y}{14} - \frac{3x + 2y}{4} = \frac{3}{4}$

26. $\frac{3x - 2y}{6} + \frac{9x + y}{2} = -\frac{5}{3}$

$\frac{2x + 3y}{2} - \frac{7x - 4y}{3} = \frac{4}{9}$

Graph the solution set of each of the following inequalities or systems over the set of real numbers.

27. $\frac{n - 2}{4} + \frac{n}{6} + 1 \geq 0$

28. $\frac{x - 1}{10} - \frac{x}{25} \leq 7$

29. $\frac{5 + k}{12} - \frac{3 + k}{8} < 1$

30. $\frac{2 + d}{6} - \frac{d - 3}{9} > -7$

31. $z^2 + \frac{3}{2}z > 1$

32. $p^2 - \frac{8}{3}p < 1$

33. $\frac{2}{5}x + \frac{1}{3}y \leq 1$

$x - \frac{2}{3}y \geq 2$

34. $\frac{x}{6} + \frac{y}{3} > -1$

$\frac{x}{2} - y < -3$

Express each of the following as the product of a rational number and one or more prime polynomials with integral coefficients.

35. $x^2 - \frac{1}{81}$

36. $\frac{1}{25} - y^2$

37. $0.008 - y^3$

38. $z^3 - 0.027$

39. $a^2 - \frac{4}{3}a + \frac{4}{9}$

40. $b^2 + \frac{5}{2}b + \frac{25}{4}$

41. $t^2 - \frac{t}{6} - \frac{1}{6}$

42. $\frac{y^2}{5} - \frac{4y}{15} - 1$

43. $x^3 - \frac{x^2}{12} - \frac{x}{2}$

44. $6x^3 + 9.9x^2 + 3x$

5–8 Problems Involving Fractions

The mathematical descriptions of problem situations often involve fractions.

EXAMPLE 1. One high-speed computer system can prepare the weekly payroll of a large concern in 12 hours. A faster system can do the job in 8 hours. If both systems were in operation, how rapidly could the payroll be processed?

Solution: To solve such "work" problems, make two assumptions:

a. If w denotes the amount of work done by an individual, r the rate of doing work, and t the time worked, then $w = rt$;

b. The total amount of work done by several individuals working together is the sum of the individual amounts.

1. Let x represent the number of hours for the systems to process the payroll together.

$\frac{1}{12}$ = rate of the first system (one-twelfth of the job in one hour).

$\frac{1}{8}$ = rate of the second system (one-eighth of the job in one hour).

1 = total work done together (one whole job).

2. Total work is **part** done by the first plus **part** done by the second:

$$1 = \frac{1}{12}x + \frac{1}{8}x$$

3. To simplify the equation, you can multiply each term by the least common denominator of the terms, $3 \cdot 4 \cdot 2 = 24$. Since the L.C.D. is a nonzero constant, the resulting equation is equivalent to the original one.

$$24 \cdot 1 = 24 \cdot \frac{1}{12}x + 24 \cdot \frac{1}{8}x$$
$$24 = 2x + 3x$$

Complete Step 3 to find that working together the systems would require $4\frac{4}{5}$ hours. Check as usual.

A **per cent** denotes a fraction whose denominator is 100. For example, $73\% = \frac{73}{100}$ or 0.73, and $125\% = \frac{125}{100}$ or 1.25. When you multiply a number called the **base** (b), by a per cent (r), the product is called the **percentage** (p). The formula $p = br$ is a basic tool in solving many problems in science and business.

EXAMPLE 2. A 15-ounce solution of alcohol in water is 75% alcohol. At most, how many ounces of a 67% solution can be added, if the final solution is to be at least 72% alcohol?

Solution:

1. Let y denote the number of ounces of the 67% solution to be added.

$$15 + y = \text{the number of ounces in the final solution.}$$
$$0.72(15 + y) = 72\% \text{ of the final solution.}$$
$$0.67y = \text{the amount of alcohol in the added solution.}$$
$$0.75(15) = \text{the amount of alcohol in the original solution.}$$

2. Alcohol in the final solution

Alcohol in original solution	plus	Alcohol in added solution	is at least	72% of the final solution
$0.75(15)$	$+$	$0.67y$	$\geq$	$0.72(15 + y)$

3. $\therefore \quad 75(15) + 67y \geq 72(15 + y)$

Show that *at most* 9 ounces of the 67% solution can be added.

EXAMPLE 3. A man has two investments, one paying a 6% dividend. The other is $680 more than half the first and pays a 5% dividend. If the total return is $102, find the investments.

Solution:

1. Let x represent the number of dollars invested at 6%, and y the number of dollars invested at 5%.

   Then $0.06x$ = the return on the first investment, and $0.05y$ = the return on the second investment.

2. The second investment is $680 more than half the first: $y = 680 + \frac{x}{2}$

   The total return is $102: $0.06x + 0.05y = 102$

3. Solve this system by the method of substitution or by linear combinations, and show that the investment at 6% is $800, while the one at 5% is $1,080.

Problems

Use either one or two variables to solve these problems.

A

1. In the Saturn series the length of the C–5 rocket is 175% that of the C–1. Together the lengths of these rockets total 550 feet. How long is each rocket?

2. In a certain city a sociologist finds the ratio of the number of residents 30 years of age or older to the number under 30 to be 3:2. She plans to interview a sample of 250 residents. How many persons of each age group must she select, if a sample is to have the same age distribution as the city's population?

3. A publishing company has two monthly magazines, "News Report," which sells for 35 cents, and "Fashion World," which sells for 50 cents. Last month the combined circulation of the two was 283,500 and the receipts were $104,550. How many copies of each were sold?

4. The air-mail rate for letters to Europe is 15 cents per half-ounce and to Africa is 25 cents per half-ounce. If Mrs. Reuter paid $6.65 to send 35 half-ounce letters abroad, how many did she send to Africa?

5. The average of two numbers is 15. Find the numbers if the smaller is two-thirds the larger.

6. Cara can pick enough apples to fill a barrel in half an hour. Jim takes 42 minutes to do it. In how many minutes can they pick a barrelful if they work together?

7. One card-sorter can process a deck of punched cards in 30 minutes, while another can sort the deck in 45 minutes. How long would it take the two sorters together to process the cards?

8. One water purification plant can process a day's water supply in 18 hours. Another plant can complete the treatment in 21 hours. If both plants are in operation, how long does it take to process the day's water supply?

9. Miss Hodge likes to take a leisurely walk at 3 miles per hour and return home over the same route by bus at 12 miles per hour. If she wants to spend just $2\frac{1}{2}$ hours for the entire trip, find the greatest distance she may walk.

10. A rocket averaged a vertical speed of 750 miles per hour during its ascent. At the peak of its flight path, it released a capsule which made a controlled descent with an average vertical speed of 400 miles per hour. If the capsule returned $57\frac{1}{2}$ minutes after the rocket was launched, find the height reached by the rocket.

11. A sensory nerve stimulated by a light source carries an impulse from the eye to the brain in 0.0015 seconds. The brain then relays the impulse along the motor nerve network to the fingers in 0.01 seconds. If the distance the impulse travels to the brain is 7 inches less than $\frac{1}{3}$ the distance from the brain to the fingers, what is the speed of the impulse?

12. A baseball player's batting average $= \dfrac{\text{number of hits}}{\text{number of times at bat}}$. The Rangers' team average of 0.263 is 0.004 greater than the average of the slugger and the pitcher. If the slugger's average is 0.192 greater than the pitcher's, find their averages.

13. An after-shave lotion contains 50% ethyl alcohol. How much water must be added to 6 fluid ounces of this lotion to reduce it to one which is 75% nonalcoholic?

14. How much water should be added to 20 ounces of a 15% solution of argyrol in water to reduce it to a solution that is 90% water?

15. A solution of silver nitrate in water is 12% silver nitrate. How many ounces of the compound must be added to 23 ounces of this solution to produce a 20% solution?

16. A nurse has 2 quarts of 3% boric acid. How much of a 10% solution of the acid must she add to have a 4% solution?

17. One alloy of copper is 20% pure copper while another is 12% pure copper. How much of each alloy must be melted together to produce 60 pounds of alloy containing 9 pounds of copper?

18. An automobile radiator contains 16 quarts of a 20% solution of antifreeze. How much of the original solution must be drawn off and replaced by pure antifreeze to make a 25% antifreeze?

19. If the basic structure of a rocket has mass s, if its payload has mass p, and its fuel has mass f, then the mass-ratio of the rocket is $\frac{s + p + f}{s + p}$.
How much fuel must be loaded in a rocket whose basic structure and payload each have a mass of 1 ton, if the mass ratio of the rocket is to be 4?

20. Determine the total mass of a two-stage rocket whose payload is the rocket described in Exercise 19 and whose mass ratio is 4, if the mass of the basic structure of this rocket equals that of its payload.

B **21.** A vat can be filled by the hot-water faucet in 8 minutes and by the cold-water faucet in 6 minutes. It can be emptied through the drain in 4 minutes. If the drain is accidentally left open while both faucets are turned on, how long does it take to fill the vat?

22. Two equal masses of different types of rocket fuel burn at different, but constant, rates. If the first mass of fuel is consumed in 5 minutes, and the second in 4 minutes, when will the second mass be half the first?

23. After deducting her commission of 5% of the sale price, an agent returned more than $2413 to the dealer. Find the least possible commission.

24. When an article costs $6, for at least what price should it be sold if the profit is to be at least 20% of the selling price?

25. A discount-store owner pays $15 for a transistor radio on which she wishes to make a 30% profit based on the selling price after she has allowed a discount of 10% to her customer. What should she set as the list price of the radio?

26. A dentifrice company testing the effectiveness of its new formula has 7,336 volunteers between the ages of 7 and 50 brush with its product. If there are 32% more volunteers under 25 than between 25 and 35, and 15% more volunteers in the 25–35 group than in the 35–50 group, how many volunteers are under 25?

27. A ski lift brings a skier to the summit in 15 minutes. In $4\frac{1}{4}$ hours an instructor makes 3 runs with her class, and 2 by herself at a faster speed. If alone she takes only one-fourth the time used in skiing down with the class, how long does it take her to ski down alone?

28. A total of $6000 is to be invested, part at $3\frac{1}{2}$% and part at 6%. If the total income must be at least $300 per year, at most how much can be invested at $3\frac{1}{2}$%?

29. At most how much water may be evaporated from 300 pounds of a 2% salt solution to get a solution that is at most 3% salt?

30. One vegetable oil contains 6% saturated fats and a second contains 26% saturated fats. In making a salad dressing how many ounces of the second may be added to 10 ounces of the first if the per cent of saturated fats is not to exceed 16%?

C **31.** A speeder going 75 miles per hour passes a state trooper parked by the side of the thruway. The trooper gives chase; within $1\frac{1}{2}$ minutes he has reached a speed of 90 mph and has gone 0.15 miles. If he continues at this speed, how long does it take him to overtake the speeder?

32. In a sports car race, a Panther starts the course at 9:00 A.M. and averages 75 miles per hour. A Mallotti starts 4 minutes later and averages 85 miles per hour. If a lap is 15 miles, on which lap will the Panther be overtaken?

33. A deep-sea diver ascends one-quarter the distance to the surface at $\frac{3}{4}$ the rate he ascends the second quarter. He then ascends the third quarter at a rate $1\frac{7}{9}$ that of the first quarter and $\frac{1}{2}$ that of the final quarter. After each of the first three stages he waits 10 minutes in order to avoid "the bends." If he reached the surface in 43 minutes 50 seconds and ascended the second quarter at $19\frac{1}{2}$ feet per minute, how deep had he dived?

34. A private art collector who buys a valuable canvas is later forced to sell it to an art gallery at a 10% loss during a financial depression. Some years later she rebuys it at auction and sells it to a museum for $37,000 more than the auction price. If the gallery made a 25% profit and the collector made a 39.5% net profit on her original investment, for what price did she originally buy the picture?

5–9 Fractional Equations

An equation such as $1 + \frac{12}{x^2 - 4} = \frac{3}{x - 2}$ in which a variable appears in the denominator of a fraction is called a **fractional equation.** Transforming a fractional equation by multiplying each of its members by the least common denominator of the terms may *not* produce an equivalent equation!

EXAMPLE 1. Solve $1 + \frac{12}{x^2 - 4} = \frac{3}{x - 2}$ over the set of real numbers.

Solution:

$$1 + \frac{12}{x^2 - 4} = \frac{3}{x - 2}$$

$$(x^2 - 4)\left(1 + \frac{12}{x^2 - 4}\right) = (x^2 - 4)\frac{3}{x - 2}$$

$$x^2 - 4 + 12 = 3(x + 2)$$

$$x^2 - 3x + 2 = 0$$

$$(x - 2)(x - 1) = 0$$

$$x = 2 \mid x = 1$$

When you test 2 and 1 in the original equation, notice what happens:

$$1 + \frac{12}{2^2 - 4} \stackrel{?}{=} \frac{3}{2 - 2}$$

$$1 + \frac{12}{0} \stackrel{?}{=} \frac{3}{0}$$

The fractions $\frac{12}{0}$ and $\frac{3}{0}$ are meaningless; therefore, 2 is not a root of the given equation.

$$1 + \frac{12}{1^2 - 4} \stackrel{?}{=} \frac{3}{1 - 2}$$

$$1 + \frac{12}{-3} \stackrel{?}{=} \frac{3}{-1}$$

$$1 - 4 \stackrel{?}{=} -3$$

$$-3 = -3 \checkmark$$

$\therefore$ The solution set is $\{1\}$.

The equation obtained by multiplying the given equation by $x^2 - 4$ has the extra root 2, a number for which the multiplier represents zero. Whenever you multiply an equation by a polynomial, the solution set of the resulting equation includes the roots of the original equation, but may also contain numbers for which the multiplier is zero. Therefore, be sure to observe the following precaution.

> When you transform an equation by multiplying by a polynomial, always test each root of the resulting equation in the original equation. Only those values producing true statements belong to the solution set of the original equation.

EXAMPLE 2. A city owns a tabulator that can process the data of its yearly census in 28 days. To speed up the processing, the city rents a faster device. When both machines are used, the tabulation is finished in 12 days. How long would the job have required if only the rented tabulator had been used?

Solution:

1. Let t represent the number of days needed by the rented tabulator; then

$\frac{1}{t}$ = the rate of the rented tabulator (the **part** of the job done per day).

28 = the number of days needed by the city's tabulator

$\frac{1}{28}$ = the rate of the city's tabulator (**part** done per day)

12 = the number of days both machines work to finish the job

$\frac{1}{12}$ = the rate of the machines working together (**part** done per day)

2. In any one day,

part done by rented machine	plus	part done by city's machine	=	part done by both machines working together
$\frac{1}{t}$	$+$	$\frac{1}{28}$	$=$	$\frac{1}{12}$

3. $84 + 3t = 7t$

Complete the solution and check that the rented device would need 21 days.

EXAMPLE 3. An airplane makes a 990-mile flight with a tail wind and returns, flying into the same wind. The total flying time is 3 hours 20 minutes, and the airplane's speed in still air is 600 miles per hour. What is the speed of the wind?

Solution:

1. Let w represent the speed of the wind;

then $600 + w$ = the airplane's speed when flying with the wind;

$600 - w$ = the airplane's speed when flying against the wind;

990 = the number of miles flown in each direction.

2.

Time flown with the wind	plus	time flown against the wind	=	total flying time
$\frac{990}{600 + w}$	$+$	$\frac{990}{600 - w}$	$=$	$\frac{10}{3}$

$$990 \cdot 3(600 - w) + 990 \cdot 3(600 + w) = 10(600 + w)(600 - w)$$

Steps 3 and 4 are left to you.

Written Exercises

Solve and check.

A

1. $\frac{1}{x} + \frac{1}{2x} = \frac{1}{6}$

2. $\frac{7}{3x} + \frac{3}{x} = 1$

3. $\frac{3m - 1}{5m - 4} = \frac{2}{3}$

4. $\frac{4m + 3}{3m + 11} = \frac{3}{4}$

5. $\frac{n - 5}{n - 4} = \frac{3n}{3n + 1}$

6. $\frac{2n - 1}{n - 1} = \frac{2n}{n + 1}$

7. $\frac{2}{y + 2} - \frac{y}{2 - y} = \frac{y^2 + 4}{y^2 - 4}$

8. $\frac{x}{x + 4} - \frac{4}{x - 4} = \frac{x^2 + 16}{x^2 - 16}$

9. $\frac{2}{s + 1} + \frac{1 - s}{s} = \frac{1}{s^2 + s}$

10. $\frac{3}{r} + \frac{6}{r - 1} = \frac{r + 13}{r^2 - r}$

11. $\frac{a + 2}{2a - 6} + \frac{3}{3 - a} = \frac{a}{2}$

12. $\frac{5}{2t + 6} - \frac{1 - 2t}{4t} = 2$

13. $\frac{x}{x - 1} + 3 = \frac{1}{x - 1} - 1$

14. $\frac{1}{1 - m} = 1 - \frac{m}{m - 1}$

15. $\frac{24}{10 + c} + \frac{24}{10 - c} = 5$

16. $\frac{8}{r + 2} + \frac{8}{r - 2} = 3$

B

17. $\frac{5}{t - 3} - \frac{30}{t^2 - 9} = 1$

18. $\frac{6}{x - 1} = \frac{12}{x^2 - 1} - 2$

19. $\frac{y + 3}{3 - y} + \frac{3y + 1}{y^2 - 9} = \frac{1 - 5y}{y + 3}$

20. $\frac{r}{r - 1} - \frac{2}{1 - r^2} = \frac{8}{r + 1}$

21. $2x - y = 5$
    $\frac{x + 4}{y + 9} = \frac{3}{4}$

22. $\frac{x + 4}{2} + \frac{y}{3} = 2$
    $\frac{x + 6}{2y - 1} = \frac{4}{5}$

23. $t + u = 6$
    $\frac{10t + u}{t + u} = \frac{5}{2}$

24. $\frac{t + u}{3} - \frac{t - u}{2} = 1$
    $\frac{10t + u}{10u + t} = \frac{7}{4}$

C

25. $\frac{2}{x} + \frac{1}{y} = 3$
    $\frac{3}{x} - \frac{2}{y} = 8$

26. $\frac{2}{3x} - \frac{2}{y} = -8$
    $\frac{9}{2x} - \frac{5}{y} = \frac{11}{2}$

(Hint: Let $\frac{1}{x} = a$ and $\frac{1}{y} = b$. Solve for a and b.)

27. $3(2m)^{-1} - 3(4n)^{-1} = 1$
$4(3m)^{-1} - 11(9n)^{-1} = 2$

28. $4x^{-1} + 3(2y)^{-1} = 0$
$2(3x)^{-1} + 13(4y)^{-1} = 0$

29. $\dfrac{4}{y+1} - \dfrac{y^2 - 2y + 2}{y^2 - 2y - 3} = \dfrac{y}{3 - y}$

30. $\dfrac{2y - 1}{y + 3} + \dfrac{1}{y^2 + y - 6} = \dfrac{y - 4}{2 - y}$

31. $3 - \dfrac{1}{3^{-1} + y^{-1}} = 3^{-1}$

32. $\dfrac{y+1}{y+3} - \dfrac{y+2}{y+4} = \dfrac{y+3}{y+5} - \dfrac{y+4}{y+6}$

Problems

A

1. A bus trip of 90 miles would have taken an hour less if the average speed had been increased by 3 miles per hour. Find the usual average speed of the bus.

2. One pipe can fill a tank in 3 hours. With a second pipe also in operation the tank can be filled in 2 hours. How long would it take the second pipe alone to fill the tank?

3. A Roman 40-oar galley rows 33 miles from Icaria to Samos with the wind in $1\frac{1}{2}$ hours. If the ship returns in $4\frac{1}{8}$ hours, what is the speed of the wind?

4. After making a trip of 126 miles, a man found that if he had increased his average speed by 8 miles per hour, he could have made the trip in 1 hour less time. Find his original rate.

5. To accommodate its members who were attending a convention, a society hired space in a hotel for \$360. When 6 members could not attend, however, each member had to be taxed \$2 more to provide the \$360. How many members attended?

6. The teacher and students of an American Government class are to share the \$540 expenses of a special bus trip to Washington, D.C. When 5 students were unable to go, the cost per person was \$1.50 greater. How many people made the trip?

7. Two numbers are in the ratio 6:11. If the first number is decreased by 4 and the second increased by 6, the resulting numbers are in the ratio 4:9. Find the original numbers.

8. If 2 is added to the numerator of a fraction, the value of the fraction becomes $\frac{1}{2}$. If 2 is subtracted from the numerator of the original fraction, the value of the fraction becomes $\frac{1}{6}$. Find the original fraction.

9. A fraction equals $\frac{8}{9}$. The numerator is 2 more than 6 times the quotient of the denominator and 7. Find the reciprocal of the original fraction.

10. If a number is increased by 4 times its reciprocal, the sum is $4\frac{1}{6}$. Find the number.

11. Working alone, a mechanic can do a job in 6 hours, but her helper needs 15 hours when he works alone. Together they do the job when the helper works twice as long as the mechanic. How long does each work when they do the job together?

12. A cafeteria strike was settled when busboys earning $72 per week were given a salary increase of 20 cents per hour. As a result, each busboy worked four hours fewer each week for the same salary. Before receiving his hourly increase, how many hours did each work a week?

13. A crew times itself on a three-mile course. The three miles upstream take 20 minutes, and the three miles downstream take 12 minutes. Find the rate of the crew in still water.

14. With the wind behind her, a skater crossed a frozen river 1 mile wide in 3 minutes. She skated straight into the wind on her return trip, which took 15 minutes. Find the speed of the wind.

15. Working alone, Chuck, Mary, and Steve can shovel the snow from Mr. Elder's driveway in 4, 3, and 6 hours respectively. How long will it take them when they work together?

16. A carpenter can build a shed in 6 hours, but his apprentice needs 16 hours to do the same job. When they work together to build the shed, the apprentice works 5 hours more than the carpenter. How long does each work?

B **17.** The distance between two towns consists of two stretches of road whose lengths are consecutive integers. A man drives on the shorter stretch at 60 miles per hour and on the rest at 46 miles per hour, so that his average rate for the whole trip is 52 miles per hour. Find the total distance.

18. A dealer bought a number of articles for $18.20. When improper handling ruined 3 of the articles, she sold the rest at a gain of 15 cents per article, thus making a total profit of $1.80. How many articles did she sell?

19. If the numerator of a fraction is multiplied by a number 2 greater than the denominator, the product of the resulting fraction and the reciprocal of the original fraction is $\frac{3}{2}$ the original numerator or $\frac{3}{7}$ less than $\frac{11}{7}$ times this numerator. Find the original fraction.

20. If a pyramid could be completed in 20 years by 100,000 slaves or by 75,000 paid workers, how long would it take a work force composed of 50,000 slaves and 18,750 paid workers to build the pyramid?

21. When a man is walking, his heart pumps blood at a rate 15 pints/minute greater than when he is sitting. When he is sitting, his blood makes $\frac{1}{4}$ as many complete circulations in 10 minutes as when walking. Assuming the man's body contains 10 pints of blood, find the rate his heart pumps when he is walking.

22. A crop-dusting plane must dust a rectangular field 0.5 miles wide and 0.6 miles long. The plane can dust a 44-foot strip at one time. The plane flies the length of the field with a 6 mph tailwind and back against the same headwind; the ratio of the time flying against the wind to the time with the wind is 9:8. What is the speed of the plane in still air?

23. A wholesale dealer figures that 20% of the receipts from her selling prices goes to overhead, 10% goes to commissions, and 10% to profit. What is her markup on an item costing her $90?

24. What should be the marked price for an article, if the dealer wants to give a 20% discount and still make a profit of 25% on the $12 cost?

25. Alma bought a number of horses for $900. After training them, she sold all but one to a dude ranch owner at a profit of $110 each, thereby realizing a profit of 100% on the whole transaction. How many horses did Alma buy?

26. The simple interest on a certain sum of money for one year is $12. If the rate were 1% higher, $200 less would have to be invested to earn the same annual interest. Find the rate of interest and the principal.

27. Mr. Russo takes 3 minutes less than Mr. Lloyd to pack a case when each works alone. One day, after Mr. Russo had spent 6 minutes in packing a case, the boss called him away, and Mr. Lloyd finished packing in 4 more minutes. How many minutes would it take Mr. Russo alone to pack a case?

C **28.** Flying east between 2 cities, a plane's speed is 380 miles per hour. On the return trip, it flies at 420 miles per hour. Find the average speed for the round trip.

29. In going between two floors a man takes the freight elevator up and the passenger elevator down. What is his average rate in feet per minute for the entire ride, if the freight elevator travels at the average rate of 3 seconds per foot, while the passenger elevator goes at 3 feet per second?

30. A metal foundry has some gun metal which is 15% tin, the rest being copper. Determine the range for the number of pounds of pure tin to mix with 600 pounds of the 15% gun metal to produce a grade of gun metal containing at least 20%, but no more than 25% tin.

31. What are the limits on the number of ounces of copper to mix with 110 ounces of pure silver to produce an alloy that is between 81% and 90% silver?

DECIMALS; SCIENTIFIC NOTATION

5–10 Decimals for Rational Numbers

To express a rational number by a decimal numeral, write the rational number as a quotient of integers and perform the indicated division.

$\frac{21}{16} = 21 \div 16$ $\qquad$ $\frac{3}{22} = 3 \div 22$

```
        1.3125              0.13636
    16)21.0000          22)3.00000
       16                  22
        50                  80
        48                  66
         20                 140
         16                 132
          40                  80
          32                  66
           80                 140
           80                 132
            0                   8
```

The symbol 1.3125, called a *terminating* or *finite* decimal, is a brief way of writing $1 + \frac{3}{10} + \frac{1}{10^2} + \frac{2}{10^3} + \frac{5}{10^4}$. By using the properties of fractions, you can check that the sum does equal $\frac{21}{16}$.

The conversion of $\frac{3}{22}$ to decimal form never terminates, however, because the recurring remainders 8 and 14 produce the *repeating block* of digits 36 in the quotient. You write

$$\tfrac{3}{22} = 0.1\ 36\ 36\ldots \quad \text{or} \quad \tfrac{3}{22} = 0.1\,\overline{36},$$

where the dots and the bar indicate that the block is to be repeated unendingly. Such decimals are called *repeating* or *periodic* decimals. Also, because they continue without end, they are said to be *non-terminating* or *infinite* decimals.

The conversion of $\frac{21}{16}$ and $\frac{3}{22}$ to decimals illustrates what happens whenever you express a rational number by a decimal. When you divide an integer r by a positive integer s, the remainder at each step belongs to $\{0, 1, 2, \ldots, s - 1\}$. Therefore, within $s - 1$ steps after only zeros are left in the dividend, either 0 occurs as a remainder and the division process stops, or a nonzero remainder recurs, and the process thereafter produces a repeating sequence of remainders with a repeating block of digits in the quotient.

The decimal for any rational number $\frac{r}{s}$ either terminates or eventually repeats in a block of fewer than s digits.

The converse of this statement is also true:

All terminating decimals and all repeating decimals represent rational numbers.

In converting a terminating decimal into a quotient of integers, you simply add fractions: $1.27 = 1 + \frac{2}{10} + \frac{7}{100} = \frac{127}{100}$. The following examples show how to convert a repeating decimal into a common fraction.

EXAMPLE 1. Write $0.5\overline{12}$ as a common fraction.

Solution:

$$\begin{aligned} \text{Let } N &= 0.5\overline{12} \\ 100N &= 51.2\overline{12} \\ N &= 0.5\overline{12} \\ \hline 99N &= 50.7 \end{aligned}$$

$$N = \frac{50.7}{99} = \frac{169}{330}$$

EXAMPLE 2. Write $0.\overline{234}$ as a common fraction.

Solution:

$$\begin{aligned} 1000N &= 234.\overline{234} \\ N &= 0.\overline{234} \\ \hline 999N &= 234 \end{aligned}$$

$$N = \frac{234}{999} = \frac{26}{111}$$

In general, if the number of digits in the repeating block of the decimal for a number N is p, multiply N by 10^p. The result, $10^p \cdot N$, has the same repeating block as N. Hence, the difference, $10^p \cdot N - N$, is a terminating decimal and thus a rational number. This means that the difference, and therefore $\frac{N(10^p - 1)}{10^p - 1} = N$, is a rational number.

Written Exercises

Write as terminating or repeating decimals.

1. $\frac{3}{25}$ **3.** $-\frac{7}{11}$ **5.** $\frac{81}{8}$ **7.** $\frac{-14}{15}$

2. $\frac{7}{50}$ **4.** $\frac{-8}{3}$ **6.** $\frac{15}{16}$ **8.** $\frac{-10}{21}$

Write as ratios of integers.

9. 2.7777	**12.** -0.00058	**15.** $0.\overline{56}$	**18.** $40.1\overline{03}$
10. 3.8888	**13.** $0.\overline{2}$	**16.** $0.\overline{74}$	**19.** $-0.003\overline{5}$
11. -0.0012	**14.** $0.\overline{3}$	**17.** $32.\overline{1306}$	**20.** $0.0004\overline{7}$

B

21. Show that the usual method of adding finite decimals applies the commutative, associative, and distributive properties of numbers to combine like powers of 10.

22. Show that the usual method of multiplying finite decimals applies the commutative, associative, and distributive properties of numbers to multiply powers of 10 and then to combine like powers of 10.

23. If the representation of x as a common fraction in lowest terms has denominator 11, and the decimal representation is $0.\overline{1r}$, find x.

24. If the representation of y as a common fraction in lowest terms has denominator 111, and the decimal representation is $0.\overline{03b}$, find y.

5-11 Approximations

It is often convenient to break off, or **round**, a lengthy or infinite decimal, leaving an approximation of the number represented. Using $\doteq$ to mean "equals approximately," you may write

$$\frac{3}{22} \doteq 0.1, \qquad \frac{3}{22} \doteq 0.14, \qquad \frac{3}{22} \doteq 0.136$$

as approximations of $\frac{3}{22}$ to *the nearest tenth, the nearest hundredth*, and *the nearest thousandth*, respectively. In rounding use this rule:

To round a decimal, add 1 to the last digit retained if the first digit dropped is 5 or more; otherwise, leave the retained digits unchanged.

Under this rule the difference between a number and its approximation (the **round-off error**) is *at most* half the unit of the last digit retained. For example, the statement $s \doteq 1.32$ is equivalent to

$$1.32 - 0.005 \le s < 1.32 + 0.005 \quad \text{or} \quad 1.315 \le s < 1.325$$

Measurements always produce approximations. The **precision** of a measurement is given by the unit used in making it. For example, a chemist reporting the weight of a sample of uranium to be 0.0304 grams *precise to the nearest ten-thousandth of a gram* means that the true weight w satisfies this inequality: $0.03035 \le w < 0.03045$. The unit (precision) of this measurement is one ten-thousandth of a gram and the *maximum possible error* is half that unit, or 0.00005 gram. On the other hand, a rancher may list the weight of a steer as 775 pounds, *to the nearest pound.* In this measurement the precision is to the nearest pound and the maximum possible error is half a pound.

Can you tell which of the two weights given in the preceding paragraph is the more *accurate* measurement? We define the **accuracy** of a measurement to be the *relative error*, that is, the ratio of the maximum possible error in the measurement to the measurement itself. Thus, the accuracy of the chemist's measurement is

$$\frac{0.00005}{0.0304} = \frac{5}{3040} \doteq 0.002, \quad \text{or} \quad 0.2\%$$

The relative error of the rancher's measurement, however, is

$$\frac{0.5}{775} = \frac{5}{7750} \doteq 0.0006, \quad \text{or} \quad 0.06\%$$

Thus, the rancher has made the more accurate measurement!

To indicate the accuracy of a measurement, we use the following *standard*, or *scientific, notation*. Express the measurement as a product, $a \times 10^n$, where the absolute value of a, a rational number in finite decimal form, is between 1 and 10, and n is an integer. Because the decimal for a contains as many digits as the accuracy of the measurement justifies, these are called *significant digits*. For example:

The chemist writes	*The rancher writes*
$a = 3.04$	$a = 7.75$
$0.03_\wedge04 = 3.04 \times 10^{-2}$ (in grams)	$7_\wedge75 = 7.75 \times 10^{2}$ (in pounds)
$n = -2$	$n = 2$

significant digits

three: 3, 0, 4	three: 7, 7, 5

maximum possible error

$0.005 \times 10^{-2} = 5 \times 10^{-5}$ (in grams)	$0.005 \times 10^{2} = 5 \times 10^{-1}$ (in pounds)

relative error

$$\frac{5 \times 10^{-5}}{3.04 \times 10^{-2}} = \frac{5}{3.04} \times 10^{-3} \doteq 0.2\% \qquad \frac{5 \times 10^{-1}}{7.75 \times 10^{2}} = \frac{5}{7.75} \times 10^{-3} \doteq 0.06\%$$

In each example notice the red caret placed after the first significant digit in the given number. By counting the number of places *from the caret to the decimal point*, you obtain n. Do you see that n is positive or negative according as you count to the right or to the left from the caret?

Can you express a measurement of 200 meters in standard notation? You would write 2×10^2, 2.0×10^2, or 2.00×10^2 according as the measurement is accurate to the nearest hundred meters, the nearest ten meters, or the nearest meter. Notice that to express in standard notation a number given in ordinary decimal form, you take all nonzero digits to be significant. Also, a zero between two nonzero digits is always significant, as in 0.0304. But the leading zero(s) preceding the first nonzero digit in a decimal fraction can never be significant, as in 0.0304. However, whenever a measurement is given by an integer whose decimal ends in zeros, such as 200, you cannot tell without additional information which, if any, of the final zeros are significant.

You can easily compare numbers in scientific notation.

EXAMPLE 1. Unequal values of n.

$9.2 \times 10^3 < 7.14 \times 10^4$ because $3 < 4$

EXAMPLE 2. Equal values of n.

$5.1 \times 10^{-2} > 2.89 \times 10^{-2}$ because $5.1 > 2.89$

Expressing numbers in scientific notation enables you to *estimate* products and quotients rapidly.

EXAMPLE 3. Find a one-significant figure estimate of A, if

$$A = \frac{7499 \times 49.34 \times 276}{614.7}.$$

Solution:

1. Round each number to one significant figure.

$$A = \frac{7499 \times 49.34 \times 276}{614.7}$$

$$\therefore A \doteq \frac{7000 \times 50 \times 300}{600}$$

2. Convert each approximation into scientific notation.

$$A \doteq \frac{7 \cdot 10^3 \times 5 \cdot 10 \times 3 \cdot 10^2}{6 \cdot 10^2}$$

3. Compute and round the result to one significant figure.

$$A \doteq \frac{7 \cdot 5 \cdot 3}{6} 10^{3+1+2-2}$$

$\therefore A \doteq 20 \cdot 10^4$, or $2 \cdot 10^5$, or 200,000, **Answer.**

Oral Exercises

Approximate each number to the nearest tenth.

1. 5.714 **2.** 3.638 **3.** -2.449 **4.** -1.349 **5.** $271.3\overline{6}$ **6.** 390.55 . . . **7.** $\frac{3}{4}$ **8.** $\frac{1}{4}$ **9.** 31.96 **10.** 0.98

Give a three-significant figure approximation of each number.

11. 12.358 **12.** 46.263 **13.** 0.0015048 **14.** 0.0020021 **15.** 399,507 **16.** 596,312 **17.** $0.1\overline{94}$ **18.** $0.1\overline{83}$ **19.** 207.63 **20.** 849.72

Give the number of significant digits in each numeral in standard notation.

21. 2.41×10^7 **22.** 3.12×10^5 **23.** 1.003×10^{-2} **24.** 2.007×10^{-5} **25.** 3.7×10^{10} **26.** 2.9×10^{12} **27.** 5.00×10^{-4} **28.** 6.00×10^{-3}

Written Exercises

Write each of the following numerals in standard form. In doubtful cases, assume zeros to be insignificant.

1. 73.5 **2.** 81.9 **3.** 6.54 **4.** 1.237 **5.** 0.0176 **6.** 0.0245 **7.** 0.00709 **8.** 0.00802 **9.** 123,700 **10.** 2,451,000 **11.** 0.0000120 **12.** 0.00000510 **13.** 380 **14.** 1760

Write each of the following numerals in decimal form.

15. 10^4 **16.** 10^6 **17.** 10^{-5} **18.** 10^{-3} **19.** 1.23×10^3 **20.** 4.56×10^5 **21.** 9.873×10^{-2} **22.** 1.32×10^{-7}

Use the laws of exponents to perform the indicated operations in each of the following. Express all answers in decimal form.

23. $\dfrac{(4 \times 10^8)(4 \times 10^{-3})}{8 \times 10^3}$

24. $\dfrac{(9 \times 10^{-4})(5 \times 10^4)}{1.5 \times 10^{-5}}$

25. $\dfrac{(5.6 \times 10^5)(12 \times 10^{-2})}{4.2 \times 10^7}$

26. $\dfrac{(4.8 \times 10^{-4})(6 \times 10^{-3})}{(3 \times 10^{-1})(2.4 \times 10^{-3})}$

Give a one-significant figure estimate of each of the following.

27. $\dfrac{343.7 \times 72.484}{(0.62)^2}$

28. $\dfrac{(-11011)(0.953)}{(1.72)(0.3418)}$

29. $\dfrac{(50.78)(0.07)(0.345)}{231}$

30. $\dfrac{(-767.5)(3.14)}{(0.079)^3}$

Each of the following represents in standard notation a measurement in meters. For each give (a) the precision; (b) the maximum possible error; (c) the relative error as a per cent.

31. 4×10^{-2}

32. 1.5×10^{0}

33. 2.5×10^{2}

34. 3.80×10^{2}

35. 4.0×10^{-4}

36. 8.0×10^{-5}

37. 1.25×10^{5}

38. 3.6625×10^{8}

Problems

Give each result to the same number of significant figures as in the least accurate item of data.

1. During a meteoric shower the earth's atmosphere collects as much as 20,000,000,000 pounds of interplanetary dust in a day. Write this figure in scientific notation and find the maximum possible error.

2. Using at most one molecule of each of the 22 known amino acids, 3.9×10^{26} different kinds of protein molecules can be formed. How many million different protein molecules can be formed?

3. The coefficient of linear expansion, that is, increase in unit length per Centigrade degree, of quartz is 5.0×10^{-7} and that of aluminum is 2.3×10^{-5}. Find the ratio of these coefficients.

4. The mass of a neutron is 1.675×10^{-24} grams and the mass of an electron is 9.107×10^{-28} grams. Compare their masses by ratio.

5. A steady current of 1 coulomb will deposit 3.294×10^{-4} grams of copper from a water solution of copper sulfate upon an object to be plated. How many grams will 850 coulombs deposit?

6. The mean distance of the planet Pluto from the sun is 3.67×10^{9} miles. If one light-year equals 5.88×10^{12} miles, how many light-years is Pluto from the sun?

7. If 6.35×10^{4} wave lengths of violet light equal 1 inch, what is the wave length of violet light in centimeters (1 in. $\doteq$ 2.54 cm.)?

8. In the Einstein equation $E = Mc^2$, E denotes energy in ergs; M, mass in grams; and c, the speed of light (3.000×10^{10} centimeters per second). When 4.520 grams of mass are converted to energy in an atomic reaction, find the energy released **(a)** in ergs, and **(b)** in foot-pounds. Use 1 ft.-lb. $\doteq 1.356 \times 10^{7}$ ergs.

9. To the nearest foot, the length of a certain square is 4 feet. What are the least and the greatest possible values of the area of the square?

10. To the nearest foot, the length of a rectangle is 4 ft. and its width is 3 ft. What are the least and the greatest possible values of the area?

Gentleman and Scholar

How often have you said, "Now why didn't I think of that?" This is what many admiring mathematicians must have thought when they heard of Descartes's new idea some three hundred years ago. *To represent a pair of numbers by a point in a plane*—what a brilliantly simple idea!

It was in 1596 that René Descartes was born, near Tours, France. Of noble birth, he followed his father's wishes and entered the army. It was an exciting era in which to be alive. Recall that these were the years of colonization in the New World. Did some of the new maps which Descartes must have seen suggest the method of graphing to him? At any rate, he was a young man still in his twenties when he first hit upon the notion of coordinates as the link between algebra and classical geometry.

As his interests became more and more those of a scholar, Descartes decided to leave the army. He went to Holland and there spent practically the rest of his life. His interests were wide; he was not only a mathematician but a scientist and philosopher. He is best known to the world of mathematics, however, as the creator of analytic (coordinate) geometry; for this contribution he is regarded as one of the greatest mathematicians of all time.

In Chapter Three you learned a little about coordinate geometry. By the use of coordinates it is possible to describe a set of points not only in two-dimensional space (the plane), but also in three, four, ..., n dimensions. You will often see the term "Cartesian coordinates"; the word "Cartesian," which comes from the Latin form of Descartes, will remind you of this man whose influence has reached down through the years to your own exciting century of discovery.

Extra for Experts

Congruences

If the difference of two integers a and b is divisible by m, then a and b are said to be **congruent modulo m**. The German mathematician Carl F. Gauss invented a notation to express this fact. He wrote

$$a \equiv b \pmod{m}.$$

Another way to say the same thing is to write

$$a - b = km \quad \text{or} \quad a = b + km$$

for some integer k. For example, $17 \equiv 7 \pmod{5}$ because $17 - 7$ is divisible by 5. Furthermore,

$$17 - 7 = k(5) \quad \text{or} \quad 17 = 7 + k(5)$$

for the integer $k = 2$. Also, $-9 \equiv 11 \pmod{2}$ can be written alternatively

$$-9 - 11 = k(2) \quad \text{or} \quad -9 = 11 + k(2)$$

for the integer $k = -10$.

The congruence relation $a \equiv b \pmod{m}$ can be shown to have the following properties:

1. $a \equiv a \pmod{m}$.

2. If $a \equiv b \pmod{m}$, then $b \equiv a \pmod{m}$.

3. If $a \equiv b \pmod{m}$, and $b \equiv c \pmod{m}$, then $a \equiv c \pmod{m}$.

4. If $a \equiv b \pmod{m}$, and $c \equiv d \pmod{m}$, then

$$a + c \equiv b + d \pmod{m},$$

$$a - c \equiv b - d \pmod{m},$$

and

$$ac \equiv bd \pmod{m}.$$

Do you see that these relationships are the same as some of the formal properties of equality? To prove Property 3, you can argue that since $a \equiv b \pmod{m}$ and $b \equiv c \pmod{m}$, then

$$a - b = k_1m \quad \text{and} \quad b - c = k_2m.$$

By the addition property of equality,

$$a - b + b - c = k_1m + k_2m$$

or

$$a - c = (k_1 + k_2)m = k_3m$$

and thus

$$a \equiv c \pmod{m}.$$

Exercises

Verify each of the following.

1. $27 \equiv 12 \pmod 5$
2. $37 \equiv 19 \pmod 6$
3. $5^3 \equiv 2^3 \pmod 3$
4. $8 \equiv 16 \pmod 4$
5. $-11 \equiv -18 \pmod 7$
6. $18 \equiv -2 \pmod 5$
7. Show that if $a \equiv b \pmod m$ is defined to mean $a = k_1m + r$ and $b = k_2m + r$ for some integers k_1 and k_2 and fixed integer r, $0 \leq r < m$, then $a \equiv b \pmod m$ implies that $a - b$ is divisible by m, and hence formulate an equivalent definition (are the steps in your argument reversible?) for congruence.
8. Use the fact that $a \equiv b \pmod m$ means that $a = b + km$ to prove that if $a \equiv b \pmod m$ and $c \equiv d \pmod m$, then $a + c \equiv b + d \pmod m$.
9. Prove that if $a \equiv b \pmod m$, then $ka \equiv kb \pmod m$ where k is any integer.
10. Observe that any of the operations of addition, subtraction, and multiplication when applied to congruent numbers will give congruent results. Show, therefore, that

$$3^3 - 4 \cdot 3^2 + 7 \cdot 3 + 1 \equiv (-1)^3 - 4 \cdot (-1)^2 + 7(-1) + 1 \pmod 2.$$

11. Use the results of Exercise 10 to help you make a conjecture about substituting a and b in any polynomial over the integers if $a \equiv b \pmod m$. Can you prove your conjecture?
12. Observe that the corresponding coefficients of the polynomials

$$2x^2 - 2x + 6 \quad \text{and} \quad 5x^2 + x - 3$$

are congruent modulo 3. Show that if $a \equiv b \pmod 3$, then

$$2a^2 - 2a + 6 \equiv 5b^2 + b - 3 \text{ mod } 3.$$

13. Show that if the sum of the digits in the decimal representation of an integer is divisible by 9, then the integer is divisible by 9.

Chapter Summary

Inventory of Structure and Method

1. The laws of exponents may be extended to **negative** integers and zero as **exponents**:

$$b^{-n} = \frac{1}{b^n} \text{ for } b \neq 0 \text{ and } n \text{ a nonzero integer, } b^0 = 1 \text{ for } b \neq 0.$$

2. A rational algebraic expression represents a real number for all real values of the variables for which the denominator is not zero.

3. The **Property of Fractions** asserts that dividing or multiplying the numerator and denominator of a fraction by the same nonzero number produces a fraction equal to the given one. Its proof depends on the Axiom of One, and the fact that $1 = \frac{c}{c}$, if $c \neq 0$.

   To simplify a **product** or a **quotient** of **fractions**, factor each numerator and denominator to determine common factors. Then use the **property of fractions.** To simplify a **sum** or a **difference** of **fractions**, multiply numerator and denominator of each fraction by the number which will produce the L.C.D. of the fractions as a denominator. Then apply the **Distributive Axiom.**

   You may simplify a **complex fraction** by multiplying numerator and denominator by the L.C.D. of all the fractions in it, or by expressing numerator and denominator as single fractions to be divided.

4. To solve an equation containing fractions, multiply each member by the L.C.D. In a **fractional equation**, such multiplication may introduce a value for which the multiplier is zero but which does not belong to the solution set of the original equation.

5. A number can be represented by a terminating or repeating decimal if and only if it is a rational number.

   To **round a decimal** to a given precision, add 1 to the last digit to be retained if the following digit is 5 or more; otherwise, leave the retained digits unchanged.

6. The **accuracy** of a measurement depends on the **relative error**: the maximum possible error divided by the measurement itself.

7. To compare numbers or to estimate products and quotients rapidly, express each number in **standard** or **scientific notation**: $a \times 10^n$ where $1 \leq |a| < 10$ and n is an integer.

Vocabulary and Spelling

rational number (*p. 163*)
rational algebraic expression (*p. 163*)
property of fractions (*p. 165*)
lowest terms (simple form) (*p. 165*)
complex fraction (*p. 173*)
per cent (%)(*p. 179*)
base (of a per cent) (*p. 179*)
percentage (*p. 179*)
fractional equation (*p. 184*)
terminating (finite) decimal (*p. 190*)
repeating block (*p. 190*)
repeating (periodic) decimal (*p. 190*)
nonterminating (infinite) decimal (*p. 190*)
rounding a decimal (*p. 192*)
round-off error (*p. 192*)
precision (of a measurement) (*p. 192*)
maximum possible error (*p. 193*)
accuracy (of a measurement) (*p. 193*)
relative error (*p. 193*)
standard (scientific) notation (*p. 193*)
significant digits (*p. 193*)

Chapter Test

5–1 Simplify. **1.** $\left(\frac{4}{3}\right)^{-1} \times 10^{-2}$ **2.** $4 \times 3^0 - 4 \times 5^0$

Write with positive exponents only. **3.** $-\dfrac{3a^{-2}b^{-3}c^6}{b^{-1}c^{-2}}$

5–2 Find all real values of the variable for which the fraction is not defined.

4. $\dfrac{x-3}{x^3-9x}$ **5.** $\dfrac{x+3}{x^2+9}$

5–3 **6.** Reduce to lowest terms: $\dfrac{2n-32n^3}{20n^3-3n^2-2n}$

5–4 **7.** Simplify: $\dfrac{8a^3}{2a^4-8a^2}\cdot\dfrac{3a^2-2a-16}{4a^3+24a^2}\div\dfrac{3a-8}{a^2+4a-12}$

5–5 Write as a single fraction.

8. $\dfrac{c+3}{c^2-4}+\dfrac{1}{4-c^2}$ **9.** $\dfrac{r+3}{3}-\dfrac{2r+3}{r+3}-\dfrac{r^2}{3r+9}$

5–6 **10.** Simplify: $\dfrac{t-\dfrac{4s^2}{9t}}{\dfrac{3t}{2}+s}$

5–7 **11.** Solve: $\frac{x - 2}{8} - \frac{2x + 1}{12} = \frac{1}{3}$

5–8 **12.** How many ounces of a 90% solution of alcohol should be added to 30 ounces of a 60% solution to form a resulting solution which contains 70% alcohol?

5–9 **13.** A jet plane makes a trip of 2700 miles with a tail wind and returns over the same route against the same wind. If the plane flies at 570 miles per hour with no wind, and the round trip flying time is $9\frac{1}{2}$ hours, find the speed of the wind.

5–10 **14.** Express $1.45\overline{45}$ as a ratio of integers.

5–11 **15.** Write in standard form: 43200

16. Write in decimal form: 3.6×10^{-3}

Chapter Review

5–1 Zero and Negative Exponents *Pages 159–162*

1. When a power consists of a __?__ base with exponent __?__, the value of the power is 1.

2. To transform a power having an exponent $-n$ to one having the exponent n, use the __?__ of the base as the new base.

3. $(\frac{2}{3})^{-2} = (?)^2 = ?$

4. $\frac{6m^0}{2} = ?$ provided $? \neq 0$.

5. $(\frac{1}{2}s^{-3}t^2)^{-3} = ?$ [s and $t \neq 0$]

6. $x^3 \div x^{-3} = ?$

7. Transform $\frac{h^{-2}m^{-1}t^{-6}}{3h^0k^2m^{-2}t^{-3}}$ into an expression with **(a)** denominator 1; **(b)** positive exponents only.

5–2 Rational Algebraic Expressions *Pages 163–164*

8. The diameter and the circumference of a circle cannot both have integral measures because π is not a(n) __?__ number.

Determine the values of the variables for which the fraction is not defined.

9. $\frac{3}{x^2 - 4x}$

10. $\frac{m + 3}{m^2 + 2m - 3}$

11. $\frac{w + 2}{w^2 + 4}$

5-3 Simplifying Rational Expressions *Pages 164–167*

12. A rational algebraic expression is in lowest terms when the numerator and denominator contain no _?_ _?_ other than 1.

Reduce to lowest terms.

13. $\dfrac{4r^3x - rx}{2rx - x}$ **14.** $\dfrac{d^2 - 2d + 1}{(d - 1)^2}$ **15.** $\dfrac{h^3 - 64}{h^2 - 16}$

5-4 Multiplication and Division *Pages 167–170*

Express each product or quotient in simplest form.

16. $\dfrac{18}{35} \div \dfrac{45}{56} \cdot \left(-\dfrac{75}{32}\right)$ **17.** $\dfrac{32c^8d^2}{20c^2} \cdot \left(\dfrac{4d^3}{c^4}\right)^{-1}$

18. $\dfrac{64 - x^2}{24 + 13x - 2x^2} \cdot \dfrac{2x^2 + x - 3}{3x^2 - 24x}$

19. $\dfrac{y^6 - 2y^5}{y^4 - 16} \div \dfrac{y^2 - y - 6}{3 - y}$

5-5 Addition and Subtraction *Pages 170–173*

20. To add or subtract fractions having unequal denominators, first transform each fraction into one whose denominator is the _?_ _?_ _?_ of all the fractions.

21. $\dfrac{3}{4a + 2} = \dfrac{?}{12a^2 - 3}$

Express as a single fraction in lowest terms.

22. $\dfrac{c}{3c - 9} + \dfrac{c - 2}{3 - c}$ **24.** $\dfrac{n + 1}{4n + 2} - \dfrac{n}{4n^2 - 1}$

23. $\dfrac{3m - 1}{6} - \dfrac{3m + 5}{15}$ **25.** $\dfrac{5}{4x - 1} + \dfrac{5}{4x}$

5-6 Complex Fractions *Pages 173–175*

Simplify:

26. $\dfrac{\dfrac{1}{a} - 2}{\dfrac{1}{2a} - 1}$ **27.** $\dfrac{3x - \dfrac{1}{3x}}{3 + \dfrac{7}{x} + \dfrac{2}{x^2}}$

5-7 Polynomials with Rational Coefficients *Pages 175–178*

Solve:

28. $\frac{2z+2}{3} - \frac{7z-1}{8} \geq 1$ **29.** $\frac{3n}{8} - \frac{9n-1}{12} + \frac{6n-1}{16} = 0$

5-8 Problems Involving Fractions *Pages 179–183*

30. If you can process n envelopes in 5 hours, then, in h hours $(0 \leq h \leq 5)$, you can process _?_ envelopes.

31. If it takes you 2 hours to do a certain job but the same job takes your friend 3 hours, then, working together, the part of the job you can both do in 1 hour is _?_

32. If n ounces of a 10% solution of argyrol are added to 20 ounces of a 30% solution, then _?_ will represent the number of ounces of argyrol in the resulting solution.

33. If d dollars are invested at 4% and twice that sum is invested at 5%, the total annual income is represented by _?_ dollars.

34. One machine can plow a field in 6 hours, but an older model takes twice as long to plow the field. How many hours will it take them if they work together?

35. Machine A can print a certain number of circulars in 8 hours. Machine B does the job in 12 hours. They both start the job together, but Machine A breaks down after a while, and it takes Machine B 7 more hours to complete the work. How long did Machine A work before it broke down?

36. Sixty ounces of a 15% solution of ammonium chloride are to be mixed with a 70% solution. How many ounces of the stronger solution should be used if the result is to contain 40% ammonium chloride?

37. The income from a 4% investment exceeds the income from a 6% investment by \$3. If the total sum invested is \$1200, find each investment.

38. An article costs a dealer \$80. Find the least marking price which will enable the dealer to give a 20% discount on the marked price and still make a 30% profit on the cost.

5-9 Fractional Equations *Pages 184–189*

39. The L.C.D. of the terms of a fractional equation is a _?_ expression.

40. Multiplying the members of a fractional equation by their L.C.D. may produce an equation having one or more roots _?_ satisfying the given equation.

Solve:

41. $\dfrac{n^2 + 1}{n - 1} + 1 + \dfrac{1 + 3n}{2 - 2n} = 0$

42. $\dfrac{x}{x + 3} + \dfrac{3}{x - 3} = \dfrac{x^2 + 9}{x^2 - 9}$

43. $\dfrac{110}{r} - \dfrac{110}{r + 1} = 1$

44. Together, two machines can process a package of cards in 12 minutes. If one machine takes 30 minutes to do the job alone, how long will it take the other machine to process the package of cards alone?

45. Together, two clerks can count a certain number of coins in $7\frac{1}{2}$ minutes. If one clerk, working alone, takes 8 minutes more than the other needs to do the same work alone, how long would each clerk need to count the coins alone?

5–10 Decimals for Rational Numbers *Pages 190–192*

46. A decimal that is either __?__ or __?__ represents a rational number.

47. Write as a terminating or repeating decimal: $\frac{11}{14}$

Write as a ratio of integers.

48. $0.72\overline{72}$ **49.** $-2.5666\ldots$ **50.** $0.\overline{132}$

5–11 Approximations *Pages 192–196*

51. The precision of 5.036 is to the nearest __?__.

52. The maximum possible error in the measurement 5.036 is __?__.

53. The relative error in 5.036 is about __?__%.

54. The relative error in 0.0062 is about __?__%.

55. When a numeral is written in standard notation ($a \times 10^n$), the n is always a(n) __?__, but the a is such that $? \leq |a| < ?$.

Approximate to three significant figures:

56. 5.0847 **57.** 92.954

Write in standard notation:

58. 4090000 **59.** 0.000018

Write in decimal form:

60. 3.72×10^{-3} **61.** 1.8×10^4

Cumulative Review: Chapters 1-5

In Exercises 1–4, tell whether the statement is true for all values, some values, or no values of the variables in the domain of real numbers.

1. $0(1 - 2m) = 1$

2. $(2 - r)^2 = (r - 2)^2$

3. $\dfrac{2s + 3t}{6} = s + t$

4. $(n - 2)(n + 3) = 2n$

5. $18 + 12 + 6 - 4 \cdot 2 = ?$

6. Divide $6k^3 - 5k^2 - 13k + 13$ by $2k + 3$.

7. Express $0.\overline{42}$ as a ratio of integers.

8. Write 0.000073 in standard notation.

9. A line contains points $(-2, 6)$, $(8, -9)$, and also a point whose abscissa is 4. Find the ordinate of that point.

10. Find an equation of the line parallel to the graph of $2x - 4y = 3$ and passing through point $(6, -2)$.

In Exercises 11–14, simplify the given expression.

11. $(4m^{-3}n)^{-2}(2m^{-2}n^{-1})^2$

12. $8^{2x-2} \div 8^{x-1}$

13. $(3u - v)^0\ [3u \neq v]$

14. $-3a[4b - 2(a - 7b)]$

In Exercises 15–17, write as a single fraction in simple form.

15. $\dfrac{2x^3 + 6x^2}{8x^3 + 27y^3} \div \dfrac{x^2 + 6x + 9}{4x^2 - 9y^2}$

16. $\dfrac{3}{3x + 1} + \dfrac{4}{1 - 9x^2} + \dfrac{2}{3x - 1}$

17. $\dfrac{\dfrac{6n - 1}{3} - \dfrac{5}{n}}{2 - \dfrac{9}{2n^2}}$

18. Write the converse of the statement: *If a cereal is made from wheat, it is good for you.*

In Exercises 19 and 20, *a*, *b*, and *c* represent any real numbers. Prove that

19. $-a(b - c) = -ab + ac$

20. $\dfrac{ab}{c} > 0$, if $ab < 0$ and $c < 0$

In Exercises 21–25, solve for *x*.

21. $|2x - 1| = 4x + 5$

22. $\dfrac{4x - 2}{3} - \dfrac{3x + 5}{4} = 1$

23. $\dfrac{ax}{3} + a^2 - \dfrac{x}{3} = a$

24. $\dfrac{35}{x} - \dfrac{35}{x + 2} = 2$

25. $\dfrac{x}{a - x} + \dfrac{x}{x + a} = \dfrac{a(x + 3)}{x^2 - a^2}$

In Exercises 26–28, find and graph the solution set of each sentence.

26. $5n - 2 < n + 6 < 3n + 8$

27. $(y - 2)(3y + 5) > (y - 3)(3y + 8)$

28. $x(x + 3) \leq 28$

In Exercises 29–31, solve graphically.

29. $2x + y = 5$
$x - 2y = 10$

30. $6x + 4y = 7$
$9x + 6y = 7$

31. $\{(x, y)\colon x + y \leq 5\} \cap \{(x, y)\colon 3x - y < 3\}$

32. The sum of the reciprocals of two consecutive even integers is $\frac{7}{24}$. Find the integers.

33. When a number, denoted by a two-digit numeral, is divided by the difference of the digits, the quotient is 15 and the remainder is 2. When the number with digits interchanged is divided by the sum of the digits, the quotient is 6 and the remainder is 8. Find the original number.

34. Mrs. Hansen adds enough water to 20 ounces of a 90% solution of acid to make the result a 60% acid solution. When she finds that she needs an 80% solution, she then adds enough acid to get the desired result. How much acid does she add?

35. A vat can be filled in 10 hours through one pipe, in 8 hours through another, and emptied in 6 hours through a third pipe. Should all three pipes be left open, how long would it take to fill an empty vat?

36. Mr. Keane invests $9000, part at 3% and the rest at 7%, so that the total income will just pay his taxes of $45 monthly. How much is invested at each rate?

37. Mr. Black had to drive 12 miles in the city before he could get on the thruway. Once on the thruway, he averaged 5 miles per hour less than three times his average city speed. If he drove 132 miles on the thruway and stopped for lunch after driving 3 hours in all, find his average thruway speed.

38. The perimeter of a rectangle measures 40 inches and its area contains 96 square inches. Find its dimensions.

39. Tom's outboard can drive his boat at 7 miles an hour in still water. It takes him 10 minutes more to reach his friend's camp 4 miles up Rill River than to return. Find the rate of the current.

40. Several friends wanted to hire a summer cabana for $320. When 2 more people joined the group, each person's share was reduced by $8. How many were in the original group?

41. Frank's boss gave him $5 with instructions to spend between $4 and $5 in buying twice as many 4-cent stamps as 10-cent stamps. Under these conditions, what limits are there on the number of 4-cent stamps he can buy?

CHAPTER 6

. . . a multiple-exposure photograph of a baton, depicting motion as a function of time

Relations and Functions

Mathematics has a vocabulary of its own, for example, *multiply, divide, theorem*. Sometimes, however, it borrows everyday words and gives them new meanings. Two such words are "relation" and "function." Maybe *relation* to you now suggests your Uncle Jim and *function* the formal party you attended last week. After you have studied this chapter you will realize why these words are important enough in mathematics to be used for the title of the chapter.

SPECIFYING RELATIONS AND FUNCTIONS

6–1 Relations

Consider the pairing of scores for the home baseball games played by South High. You can display this table as the roster of a set of *ordered pairs* of numbers. In each pair the first number is a Visitors' score and the second number the corresponding South High score.

Visitors	7	2	0	2	5
South High	3	4	0	0	3

$$S = \{(7, 3), (2, 4), (0, 0), (2, 0), (5, 3)\}$$

Any set of ordered pairs of numbers is called a **relation**. The set of all the first coordinates is the **domain** of the relation; the set of all the second coordinates is its **range**. Thus, the pairing of baseball scores above defines a relation, S, whose domain is $\{0, 2, 5, 7\}$ and whose range is $\{0, 3, 4\}$. Figure 6–1 shows the graph of S. Notice that the abscissa of any point of the graph is the first coordinate of the corresponding number pair, while the ordinate is the second coordinate.

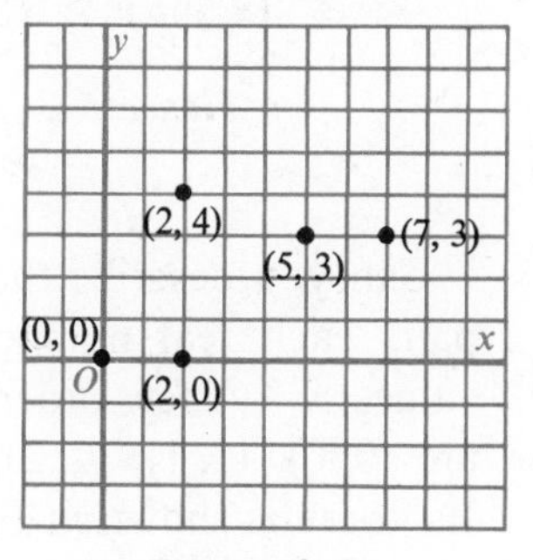

· *Figure 6–1* ·

Some relations can be specified by giving a rule enabling you to determine the member or members of the range paired with each element of the domain. For example, the solution set of an open sentence such as $x + 2y = 5$ is a relation R that you can specify as follows:

$$\mathbf{R = \{(x, y): x + 2y = 5, \text{ and } x \text{ and } y \text{ denote real numbers}\}.}$$

We say that the equation $x + 2y = 5$ *specifies the relation R over the set of real numbers*, and we show its graph in Figure 6–2.

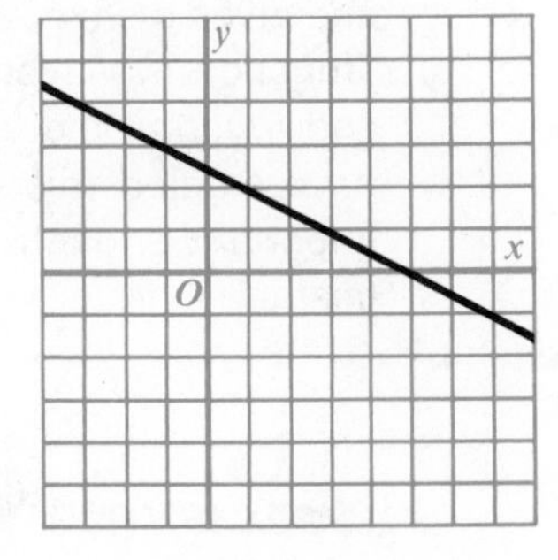

$\{(x, y): x + 2y = 5\}$

· *Figure 6–2* ·

For brevity, the words "and x and y denote real numbers" may be omitted from the rule specifying R. *Whenever an open sentence specifies a relation, and the domain and range are not mentioned, we agree to include in the domain and range those and only those real numbers for which the open sentence is true.* Thus, $\{(x, y): y \geq x\}$ is the relation whose graph is shown in Figure 6–3, while $\{(x, y): y \geq x$, and x and y are integers$\}$ is the *different* relation whose graph is shown in Figure 6–4.

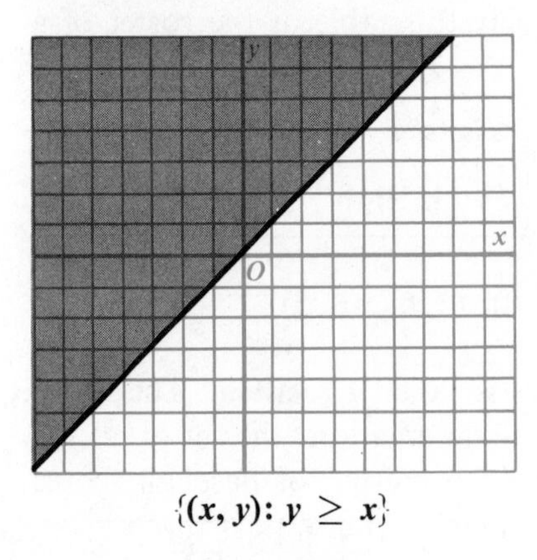

$\{(x, y): y \geq x\}$

· *Figure 6–3* ·

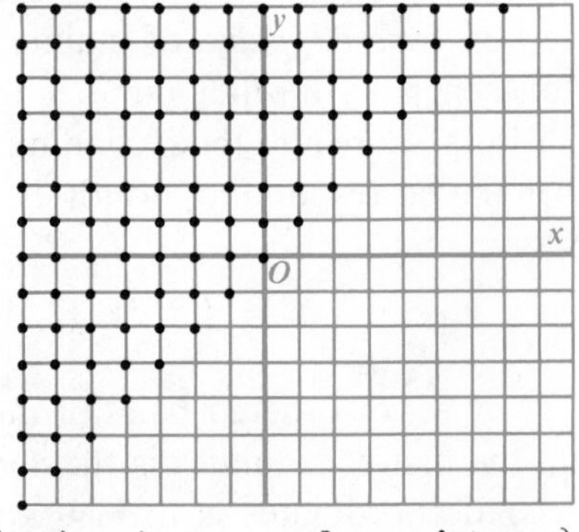

$\{(x, y): y \geq x,\ x \text{ and } y \text{ are integers}\}$

· *Figure 6–4* ·

Can you describe the relation $\{(x, |x|)\}$? It pairs each real number, x, with its absolute value, $|x|$. A few ordered pairs in this relation are $(0, 0)$, $(1, 1)$, $(2, 2)$, $(-1, 1)$, and $(-2, 2)$. Its graph is shown in Figure 6–5.

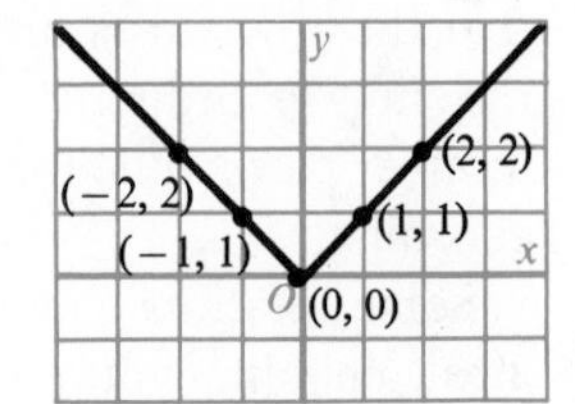

· *Figure 6–5* ·

Oral Exercises

State the domain and range of each of the following relations.

SAMPLE 1. $\{(-3, 2), (-2, 1), (4, 5)\}$

What you say: The domain is $\{-3, -2, 4\}$. The range is $\{1, 2, 5\}$.

1. $\{(1, 1), (2, 2), (3, 3)\}$
2. $\{(-2, 1), (-1, 2), (0, 3)\}$
3. $\{(3, -1), (2, -1), (1, -1)\}$
4. $\{(2, 1), (2, 2), (2, 3)\}$
5. $\{(3, 1), (3, 2), (2, 3)\}$
6. $\{(-1, 2), (-2, 2), (-3, 3)\}$
7. $\{(1, 0), (2, 0), (1, 1), (2, 1)\}$
8. $\{(3, 2), (4, -1), (3, -1), (3, 3)\}$

State the domain of each of the following relations over the set of real numbers.

SAMPLE 2. $\left\{(x, y): y = \frac{1}{1 - x^2}\right\}$

What you say: $\{x: 1 - x^2 \neq 0\}$; that is,
{all real numbers except 1 and -1}

9. $\left\{(x, y): y = \frac{1}{|x - 7|}\right\}$
10. $\left\{(x, y): y = \frac{1}{|x + 2|}\right\}$
11. $\left\{(u, v): v > \frac{1}{(u - 1)(u - 2)}\right\}$
12. $\left\{(k, r): r < \frac{1}{(k + 7)(k - 2)}\right\}$
13. $\left\{(a, b): b = \frac{a}{a^2 + 1}\right\}$
14. $\left\{(c, d): d = -\frac{c}{4 + c^2}\right\}$
15. $\{(x, y): |y| = x\}$
16. $\{(x, y): y^2 = x\}$
17. $\{(x, y): |x| + |y| = 1\}$
18. $\{(x, y): x^2 + y^2 = 1\}$

Written Exercises

Give the range and draw the graph of each of the following relations if $x \in \{-3, -2, -1, 0, 1, 2, 3\}$.

SAMPLE $\{(x, y): y = |x| - 1\}$

Solution: **1.** In the open sentence replace x in turn by each of its values, as shown in the table on the next page.

2. Determine *all* corresponding real values of y.

3. The pairs of corresponding values (x, y) comprise the relation whose range is the set of values of y. The range is $\{-1, 0, 1, 2\}$, **Answer.**

x	$\|x\| - 1$	$y = \|x\| - 1$
-3	$\|-3\| - 1$	2
-2	$\|-2\| - 1$	1
-1	$\|-1\| - 1$	0
0	$\|0\| - 1$	-1
1	$\|1\| - 1$	0
2	$\|2\| - 1$	1
3	$\|3\| - 1$	2

A

1. $\{(x, y): y = x - 1\}$
2. $\{(x, y): y = \frac{1}{2}x\}$
3. $\{(x, y): y \geq x - 2\}$
4. $\{(x, y): x \geq 2y - 3\}$
5. $\{(x, y): y = 2\}$
6. $\{(x, y): y = -1\}$
7. $\{(x, -|x|)\}$
8. $\{(x, 2|x|)\}$
9. $\{(x, y): x + 3y > 4\}$
10. $\{(x, y): 3x - 2y < 7\}$
11. $\{(x, y): y = 2|x + 1|\}$
12. $\{(x, y): y = |1 - x|\}$

B

13. $\{(x, y): y = x^2\}$
14. $\{(x, y): y = -x^2\}$
15. $\left\{(x, y): 0 \leq y \leq \dfrac{x^2}{2}\right\}$
16. $\{(x, y): x^2 - 4 \leq y < 10\}$

Draw the graph of each of the following relations over the set of real numbers.

17. $\{(a, b): 2a + 5b = -10\}$
18. $\{(c, d): 3c = 7d - 14\}$
19. $\left\{\left(x, \dfrac{1}{x}\right): x \neq 0\right\}$
20. $\left\{\left(x, -\dfrac{1}{x}\right): x \neq 0\right\}$
21. $\{(k, m): 5k \leq 10 + 2m\}$
22. $\{(p, t): 3t \geq 6 - p\}$

C

23. $\{(x, y): y < -|x|\}$
24. $\{(x, y): y \geq |x|\}$
25. $\{(d, v): v = 1 + \frac{1}{2}|d|\}$
26. $\{(n, s): s = 1 - 2|n|\}$

6–2 Functions

If you graph the relation $\{(-1, -1), (2, 0), (3, 1), (3, 3)\}$, you find that two points lie on the same vertical line (Figure 6–6). The element 3 in the domain appears in two ordered pairs, (3, 1) and (3, 3). This is not true of the relation $\{(-1, -1), (0, 2), (1, 3), (3, 3)\}$. No two points of its graph lie on the same vertical line (Figure 6–7). Such a relation is called a *function*.

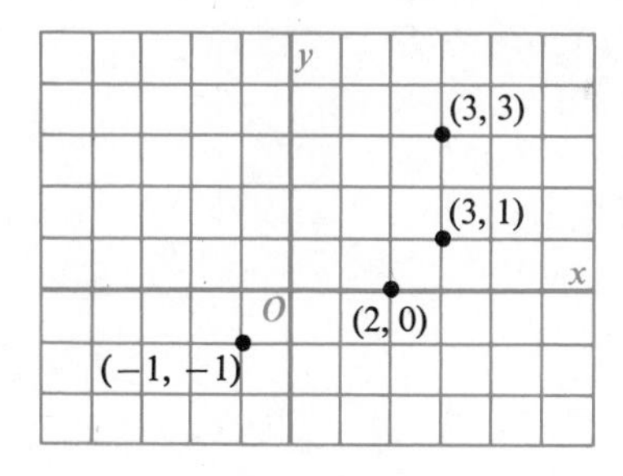

· *Figure 6–6* ·

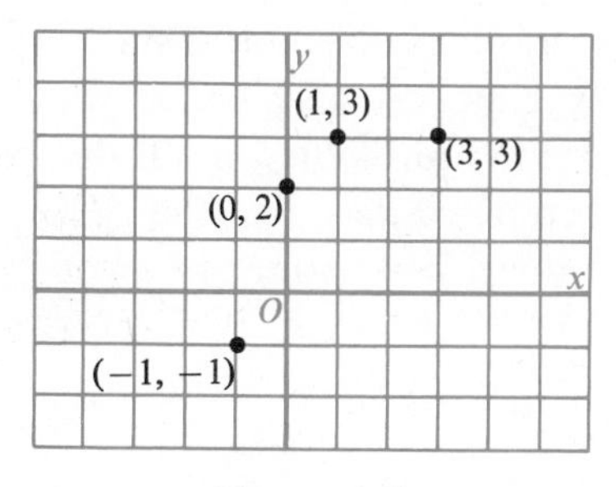

· *Figure 6–7* ·

A **function** is a relation which assigns to each element in the domain a *single* element in the range.

Like any other set, a function may be denoted by a letter such as f, g, H, or K. For example, you may write

$$f = \{(x, y): y = 2x + 1\}$$

to denote the function which pairs every real number with its double increased by 1. To designate the unique element in the range of f associated with the number 3 in the domain of f, we use the symbol

$f(3)$, read "f of 3" or "the *value* of f at 3."

Thus, $f(3) = 2 \cdot 3 + 1 = 7$. (Notice that $f(3)$ does *not* mean f multiplied by 3; it is a symbol for the number which the function f pairs with 3.) Similarly, $f(0) = 2 \cdot 0 + 1 = 1$, and $f(-1) = 2(-1) + 1 = -1$. In general, for any pair (x, y) in f, the second coordinate y is the **value of f at x**; therefore, another way to specify f is:

$$f = \{[x, f(x)]: f(x) = 2x + 1\}$$

When the values of a function f are indicated by a formula for $f(x)$ such as $f(x) = 2x + 1$, the domain unless otherwise specified consists of those real values of x for which the formula provides a unique real value for f; the range is the set of these values of f. Under this agreement, if $f(x) = 2x + 1$, the domain and range of f are each the set of real numbers. But, if $f(x) = \frac{1}{x^2}$, the domain is the set of all *nonzero* real numbers, and the range is the set of positive numbers.

Can you give the set notation for the function K if, for every real number, the value of K is 4? You can write $K = \{(x, y): y = 4\}$ or $\{[x, K(x)]: K(x) = 4\}$, or, simply, $K = \{(x, 4)\}$. Its graph is the horizontal line in Figure 6–8. Any function such as K which has the same second coordinate in all its ordered pairs is called a **constant function**. How many elements are there in the range of a constant function?

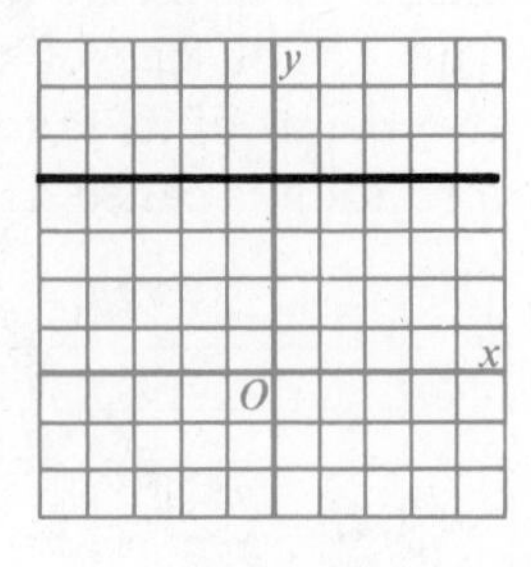

· *Figure 6–8* ·

Oral Exercises

State whether the relation indicated by graph, roster, or rule is a function. If it is not a function, explain why. If it is a function, give its domain and range.

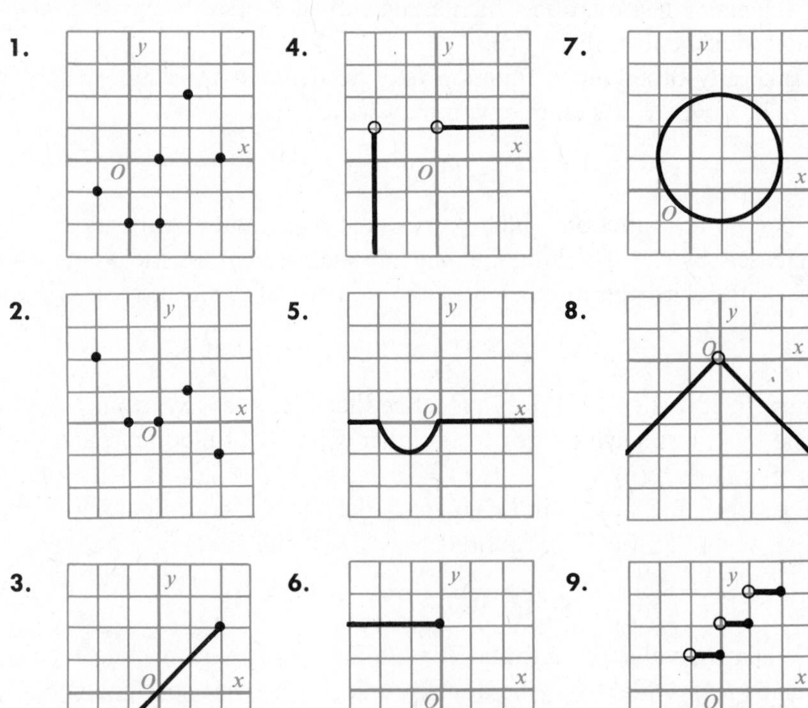

10.

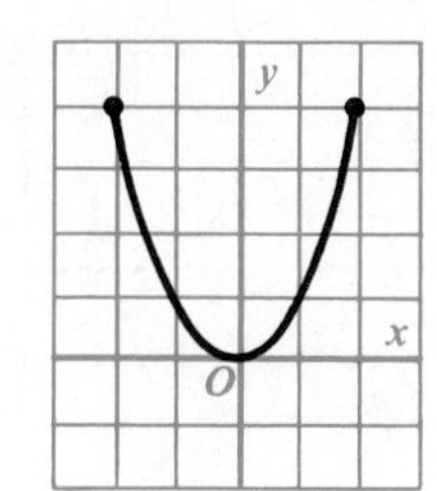

11.

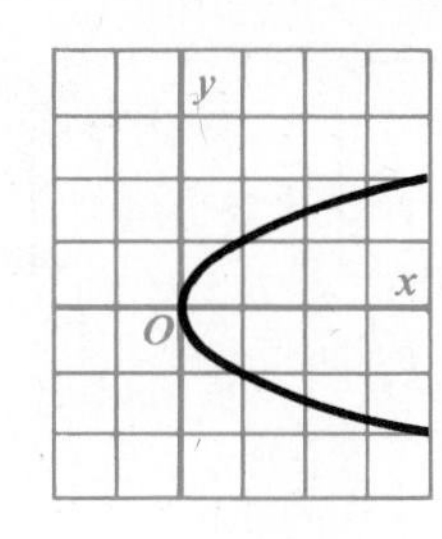

12.

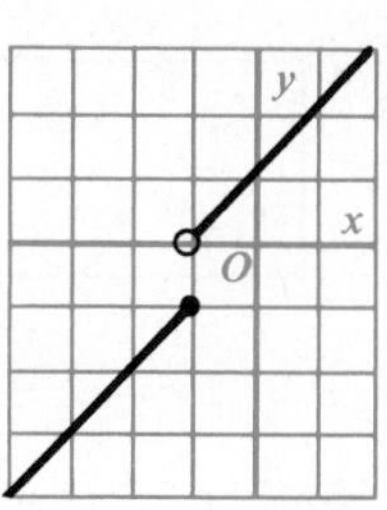

13. $\{(1, -2), (2, 3), (3, 4)\}$

14. $\{(3, 2), (2, -1), (3, 0)\}$

15. $\{(3, 2), (2, 2), (1, 2)\}$

16. $\{(2, 3), (2, 2), (2, 1)\}$

17. $\{(2, 1), (2, 2), (1, -3)\}$

18. $\{(2, -1), (2, 3), (1, 3)\}$

19. $\{(x, y): y = x\}$

20. $\{(x, y): x = y^2\}$

21. $\{(u, v): u \geq v\}$

22. $\{(t, p): t < p\}$

23. $\{(x, y): x = 3\}$

24. $\{(x, y): y = -1\}$

If $f(x) = 3x - 1$, give each of the following numbers.

25. $f(0)$ **27.** $f(-1)$ **29.** $f(\frac{1}{3})$ **31.** $f(-\frac{2}{3})$

26. $f(5)$ **28.** $f(-2)$ **30.** $f(-\frac{1}{3})$ **32.** $f(\frac{2}{3})$

Written Exercises

If $P(x) = x^2 - 2x + 1$, find each of the following.

A

1. $P(0)$ **3.** $P(2)$ **5.** $P(a)$ **7.** $P(a - 1)$

2. $P(-2)$ **4.** $P(3)$ **6.** $P(a^2)$ **8.** $P(a + 1)$

If $f(x) = x + 3$ and $g(x) = x - 3$, find the following.

9. $g(0)$ **11.** $3f(0)$ **13.** $f(1) - g(1)$ **15.** $f(3) \cdot g(3)$

10. $f(0)$ **12.** $4g(0)$ **14.** $f(2) + g(2)$ **16.** $\dfrac{f(4)}{g(4)}$

Graph the function F if its values are given by the indicated formula for $F(x)$ and if its domain is **(a)** {integers}, **(b)** {real numbers}.

17. $F(x) = 5$ **18.** $F(x) = -3$ **19.** $F(x) = 0$ **20.** $F(x) = \frac{1}{2}$

Each table specifies a function t. Give the domain of t and write a formula for $t(x)$.

21.

x	1	2	3	4
***t*(x)**	7	13	19	25

22.

x	1	2	3	4
***t*(x)**	5	8	11	14

23.

x	−1	0	1
$t(x)$	1	0	1

24.

x	−1	0	1
$t(x)$	−1	0	1

If $r(x) = 3x - 1$ and $t(x) = (x + 1)^2$, find the following.

SAMPLE. $t(r(2))$

Solution:

1. Find $r(2)$. $\quad r(x) = 3x - 1$
   $r(2) = 3 \cdot 2 - 1 = 5$

2. Then $t(r(2)) = t(5)$. $\quad t(x) = (x + 1)^2$
   Find $t(5)$. $\quad t(5) = (5 + 1)^2 = 36$

$\therefore\ t(r(2)) = 36$, **Answer.**

B

25. $t(r(0))$
26. $t(r(-1))$
27. $r(t(2))$
28. $r(t(0))$
29. $r(t(a))$
30. $t(r(a))$

If $P(x) = 2x + 6$ and $Q(x) = \frac{x}{2} - 3$, find **(a)** $P(Q(x))$ and **(b)** $Q(P(x))$, for each of the following values of x.

31. 5
32. -3
33. c
34. $-c$

35. Give an equation specifying the constant function whose graph passes through the point of intersection of the graphs of $\{(x, y): y = x - 5\}$ and $\{(x, y): y = 2x - 8\}$.

36. Give an equation specifying the constant function whose graph contains the point of intersection of the graphs of the equations $x - 2y = 3$ and $2x + y = 16$.

C

37. Let f be a function such that $f(x + 3) = f(x) + f(3)$ for every real number. Show that: **(a)** $f(0) = 0$; **(b)** $f(-3) = -f(3)$.

38. Let c be a function such that $c(x + \pi) = -c(x)$ for every real number x. Show that: **(a)** $c(0) = -c(\pi)$; **(b)** $c(-\pi) = c(\pi)$.

39. Suppose that for the function L, $L(mn) = L(m) + L(n)$ for all real numbers m and n. Show that $L(1) = 0$. (Hint: Let $m = n = 1$.)

40. Let E be a function for which $E(m + n) = E(m)E(n)$ for all real numbers m and n, and whose value is never 0.

    a. By setting $m = 0$, show that $E(0) = 1$.

    b. Then, show that $E(-n) = \dfrac{1}{E(n)}$.

LINEAR FUNCTIONS AND RELATIONS

6–3 Linear Functions and Direct Variation

A function such as

$$\{(x, y): y = -5x + 3\}$$

whose values are those of a polynomial of degree 1 is called a **polynomial function of degree 1**, or a **linear function**. As shown in Figure 6–9, the graph of the function

$$\{(x, y): y = -5x + 3\}$$

is a straight line with a slope -5 and y-intercept 3.

· *Figure 6–9* ·

In general, a function f is a **linear function**, provided there exist real numbers b and m, $m \neq 0$, such that for every x in the domain of f, $f(x) = mx + b$. Thus, if its domain is the set of real numbers, the graph of f is the straight line having slope m and intersecting the vertical axis in the point $(0, b)$. (See Section 3–4.) Do you see that for $m = 0$, f would be a constant function $[f(x) = b]$ instead of a linear one?

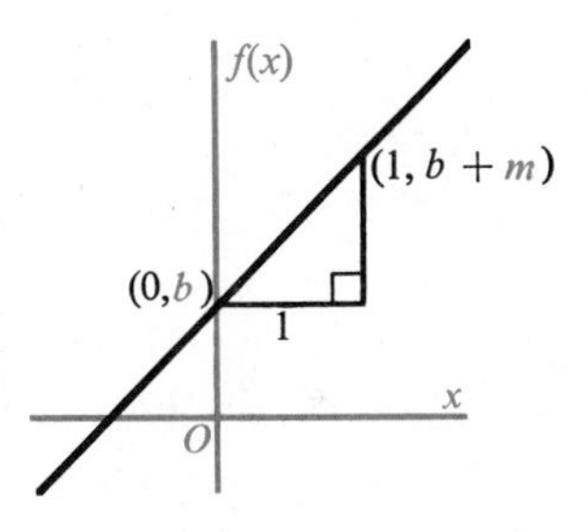

· *Figure 6–10* ·

The table shows the weight x in pounds of an object on earth and its estimated weight y on Mars. The ratio $\frac{y}{x}$ for every pair of numbers is the same; in fact, $\frac{y}{x} = 0.4$, or $y = 0.4x$. A linear function specified by an equation of the form $y = mx$, where m is a nonzero constant, is called a **direct variation**. We say that *y varies directly as x*, or *y is directly proportional to x*, or *y varies with x*; m is the **constant of proportionality** or **of variation**.

x	y	$\frac{y}{x}$
50	20	$\frac{20}{50} = 0.4$
100	40	$\frac{40}{100} = 0.4$
150	60	$\frac{60}{150} = 0.4$
200	80	$\frac{80}{200} = 0.4$

Do you see that the ordered pair (0, 0) belongs to every direct variation whose domain contains 0? Also, if (x_1, y_1) and (x_2, y_2) are two ordered pairs in a direct variation with $x_1 \neq 0$ and $x_2 \neq 0$ (Figure 6–11), you have

$$y_1 = mx_1 \text{ or } \frac{y_1}{x_1} = m;$$

and

$$y_2 = mx_2 \text{ or } \frac{y_2}{x_2} = m.$$

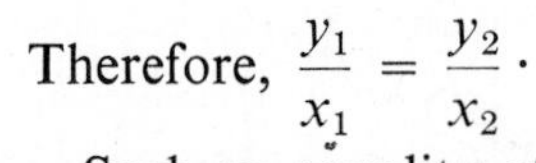

Therefore, $\dfrac{y_1}{x_1} = \dfrac{y_2}{x_2}$.

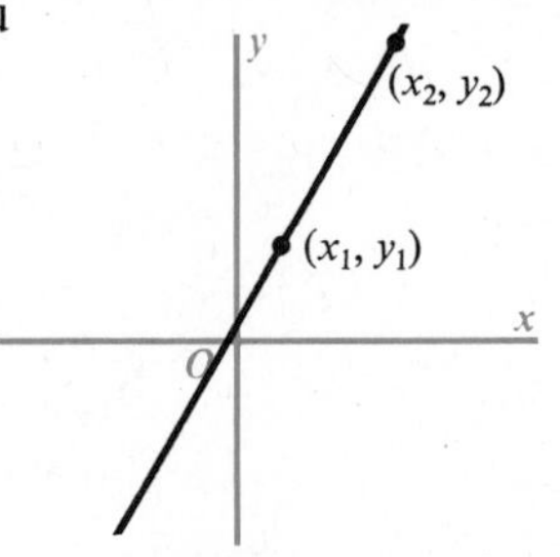

· *Figure 6–11* ·

Such an equality of ratios is called a **proportion**. It can be read "y_1 is to x_1 as y_2 is to x_2," and is sometimes written $y_1 : x_1 = y_2 : x_2$. In this proportion y_1 and x_2 are called the **extremes**, while x_1 and y_2 are called the **means**. Do you see that $x_1 y_2 = x_2 y_1$?

> In any proportion the product of the means equals the product of the extremes.

In solving problems about direct variation, you may use either the equation specifying the function or a proportion. In Example 1 the Solution uses one method and the Check employs the other.

EXAMPLE 1. If property tax varies directly as assessed valuation, determine the tax on a house assessed at \$14,000 in a community where a tax of \$382.50 is levied on property assessed at \$9,000.

Solution: Let T represent the tax in dollars and V the assessed valuation. Then $(9000, 382.50) \in \{(V, T): T = mV\}$.

To determine m:

$$T = mV$$
$$382.50 = m(9000)$$
$$\frac{382.50}{9000} = m$$
$$0.0425 = m$$

To determine T for $V = 14{,}000$:

$$T = 0.0425 \times V$$
$$T = 0.0425 \times 14{,}000$$
$$\therefore T = 595$$

Check:

$$T_1V_2 = T_2V_1$$
$$(382.50)(14{,}000) \stackrel{?}{=} (595)(9000)$$
$$5{,}355{,}000 = 5{,}355{,}000 \checkmark$$

$\therefore$ the property tax is \$595, **Answer.**

Note that 0.0425, the constant of variation, shows the tax rate.

EXAMPLE 2. The rate of consumption of the oxidizer used in a liquid-fuel rocket engine varies directly as the rate of consumption of fuel. If a rocket engine is consuming 2 lb. per second of aniline as fuel, and 5.6 lb. per second of red fuming nitric acid (RFNA) as oxidizer, what would be the rate of consumption of aniline when the rocket engine was consuming RFNA at the rate of 7 lb. per second?

Solution: Let x represent the rate of consumption of the fuel, and y the rate of consumption of the oxidizer.

Use: $x_2y_1 = x_1y_2$; $x_1 = 2$, $y_1 = 5.6$, $y_2 = 7$.

Then $x_2(5.6) = 2(7)$

$x_2 = 2.5$ 2.5 lb. per sec., **Answer.**

The check is left to you.

Oral Exercises

State a formula for the values of the following direct variations. Unless implied in the statement, the constant of proportionality m is given.

1. The circumference C of a circle varies directly as the length of its diameter d.
2. The perimeter P of a square varies directly as the length s of a side.
3. The distance d in meters that a moving object travels in 12 seconds is proportional to its average rate r in meters per second.
4. The distance d that an object travels at a uniform speed of 12 miles per hour is directly proportional to the number of hours t it travels.
5. If a record shop runs a 20% discount sale, the discount d varies directly as the list price l.
6. The annual income i on an investment at 6% varies directly as the number of dollars p invested.
7. The scaled distance s on a map is directly proportional to the actual distance a. ($m = 2 \times 10^{-4}$)

8. The heat H required to melt a quantity of lead varies with the mass M. $(m = 5.4)$

9. The volume V of a right circular cone having a base of fixed radius r varies directly as the length h of its altitude. $\left(m = \frac{\pi r^2}{3}\right)$

10. The volume V of a gas being kept at a constant pressure varies directly as the absolute temperature T. $(m = 3.66 \times 10^{-3})$

(a) Is there a linear function containing the ordered pairs (x, y) in each of the following tables? **(b)** If there is such a linear function, state the slope of its graph; and whether it is a direct variation.

SAMPLE.

1 2 4

x	1	2	4	8
y	1	3	7	15

2 4 8

What you say: **a.** The ordered pairs belong to a linear function because $\frac{y_2 - y_1}{x_2 - x_1} = 2$ for any two pairs (x_1, y_1) and (x_2, y_2).

b. The slope is 2. The function is not a direct variation because the ratio $\frac{y}{x}$ is not constant.

11.

x	3	4	5	6
y	−1	−2	−3	−4

12.

x	8	9	10	11
y	3	7	11	15

13.

x	2	3	4	5
y	4	6	8	10

14.

x	0	1	2	3
y	3	9	15	18

15.

x	4	6	8	10
y	1	2	3	4

16.

x	4	6	8	10
y	10	15	20	25

17.

x	−2	−1	0	1
y	4	−2	0	2

18.

x	3	0	3	9
y	−2	0	2	6

Written Exercises

A

1. If y varies directly as x and $y = 30$ when $x = 5$, find y when $x = 15$.
2. If y varies directly as x, and $y = 3$ when $x = 9$, find x when $y = 36$.
3. If C varies directly as D, and $C = 12\pi$ when $D = 12$, find C when $D = 3$.
4. If C and R are proportional, and $C = 6.28$ when $R = 1$, find R when $C = 18.84$.
5. If d varies directly as $|t|$, and two corresponding values of d and t are 60 and 2 respectively, find d when $t = -\frac{1}{2}$.
6. If C varies as $|n|$, $C_1 = 25$, and $n_1 = 10$, find C_2 if $n_2 = -4$.
7. If $y = k(x + 2)$ and $y = 35$ when $x = 5$, find the constant k.
8. If $y = k(x - 6)$ and $y = 45$ when $x = 15$, find the constant k.
9. If x varies directly as $2y - 1$, and $x = 9$ when $y = 2$, find y when $x = 15$.
10. If y is proportional to $3x + 5$, and $y = 14$ when $x = 3$, find x when $y = -7$.

If neither x_1, x_2, y_1, nor y_2 denotes zero, prove each of the following properties of the proportion $\frac{y_1}{x_1} = \frac{y_2}{x_2}$.

B

11. $x_1y_2 = x_2y_1$
12. $\frac{x_1}{y_1} = \frac{x_2}{y_2}$
13. $\frac{y_1}{y_2} = \frac{x_1}{x_2}$
14. $\frac{x_2}{x_1} = \frac{y_2}{y_1}$
15. $\frac{x_1 + x_2}{x_2} = \frac{y_1 + y_2}{y_2}$. (*Hint:* Add 1 to each member of $\frac{x_1}{x_2} = \frac{y_1}{y_2}$.)
16. $\frac{x_1 - x_2}{x_2} = \frac{y_1 - y_2}{y_2}$. (*Hint:* Add -1 to each member of $\frac{x_1}{x_2} = \frac{y_1}{y_2}$.)
17. If $y_1 \neq y_2$, $\frac{x_1 - x_2}{y_1 - y_2} = \frac{x_1}{y_1}$. (*Hint:* Use the results of Exercises 16 and 12.)
18. If $x_1 \neq x_2$ and $y_1 \neq y_2$, $\frac{x_1 + x_2}{x_1 - x_2} = \frac{y_1 + y_2}{y_1 - y_2}$. (*Hint:* Use the results of Exercises 15 and 16.)

C

19. If $f(x) = 3x + 2$, and a and c are distinct real numbers, find the value of $\frac{f(c) - f(a)}{c - a}$.

20. If $f(x) = mx + b$ $(m \neq 0)$, show that the graphs of $y = -f(x)$ and $y = f(-x)$ have the same slopes and hence are parallel lines.

21. Prove that if g is a direct variation over the set of real numbers, then for every pair of real numbers a and c, $g(a + c) = g(a) + g(c)$.

22. Prove that if g is a linear function other than a direct variation, then for every pair of real numbers a and c, $g(a + c) \neq g(a) + g(c)$.

Problems

A

1. For its propellant a rocket engine uses alcohol as fuel and liquid oxygen as oxidizer. The rate of consumption of alcohol varies directly with the rate of consumption of liquid oxygen. If the engine consumes 1.8 lb. per second of alcohol while consuming 6.3 lb. per second of liquid oxygen, what would be the rate of consumption of alcohol when liquid oxygen was being consumed at the rate of 7 lb. per second?

2. If the engine in Problem 1 consumes 2.4 lb. per sec. of alcohol while consuming 6 lb. per sec. of liquid oxygen, at what rate would it consume liquid oxygen when it was consuming 1.6 lb. per sec. of alcohol?

3. The amount of hydrogen produced when sodium is added to water varies directly as the amount of sodium added. If 138 grams of sodium produces 6 grams of hydrogen, how much sodium would be required to produce 7 grams of hydrogen?

4. If 2 grams of hydrogen unite with 16 grams of oxygen to form water, how many grams of hydrogen and how many grams of oxygen are required to produce 144 grams of water? (Assume that no loss takes place during the reaction.)

5. Mr. Carr owns 300 shares of stock in the Ace Company and receives $180 per year in dividends. How much does Mr. Adams receive for an annual dividend if he owns 450 shares in the same company?

6. The number of digits required to represent an integer in the binary system is roughly proportional to the number required in the decimal system. If 10 binary digits are needed to represent an integer whose decimal numeral contains 3 digits, about how many binary digits are needed to represent a number whose decimal numeral has 12 digits?

7. The speed of a body falling freely from rest is directly proportional to the length of time that it falls. If a body was falling at 144 ft. per second $4\frac{1}{2}$ seconds after beginning its fall, how fast was it falling $3\frac{3}{4}$ seconds later?

8. When water freezes, it expands 9% of its volume. How much water must freeze to form 545 cubic inches of ice?

9. The weight of an object on or beneath the surface of the earth varies directly as its distance from the center of the earth. The radius of the earth is approximately 4000 miles. If an object weighs 108 pounds on the surface of the earth, how far beneath the surface would the object have to be to weigh 81 pounds?

10. In Problem 9, if an object weighs 70 pounds when located 8 miles beneath the surface of the earth, how much does it weigh at the surface?

11. If 10 cc. of a normal specimen of human blood contains 1.2 grams of hemoglobin, how many grams of hemoglobin would 18 cc. of the same blood contain?

12. The average number of red cells in a cubic millimeter of blood is 5,000,000 for men and 4,500,000 for women. If a laboratory blood count procedure results in a dilution of 1 part of a man's blood to 199 parts of a saline solution, how many red cells should be contained in $\frac{1}{4000}$ cubic millimeter of the diluted solution?

13. Jack was standing on a direct line between Tom and the point on the surface of the earth where a bolt of lightning struck. If Tom heard the sound of the thunder associated with the lightning $5\frac{1}{2}$ seconds after it struck, how far was he standing from Jack if Jack was standing 4480 feet from the point where the bolt struck and heard the thunder $1\frac{1}{2}$ seconds before Tom?

14. At a rocket launching site a tracker located $1\frac{1}{2}$ miles from a rocket launch pad saw the first flame of the rocket on the pad $7\frac{1}{3}$ seconds before he heard the sound associated with the combustion. A tracker located at another site heard the sound $5\frac{1}{2}$ seconds after the flame began. How far was the second tracker from the launch pad?

15. In a circuit of 56 volts a voltmeter registers 77 on its scale 0–100. What is the maximum number of volts the meter can measure?

16. In a psychological test a man scored 115 on a scale of 0–160. Convert his score to a scale of 0–100.

B

17. Find a and b if $(1, 5)$ and $(3, 11)$ are members of the function $\{(x, y): y = 2ax + b\}$.

18. Find a and b so that $(1, 3)$ and $(-1, 7)$ are members of

$$\{(x, y): y = 3ax + b\}.$$

19. Find the slope of the graph of the linear function $\{(x, y): y = ax + 3b\}$ if $(1, 8)$ and $(-2, 2)$ belong to the function.

20. The linear function $\{(x, y): y = ax - 2b\}$ contains $(1, 1)$ and $(2, -2)$. What is the slope of the graph of the function?

6–4 Special Functions and Relations (Optional)

A function or relation may be specified by different rules over different subsets of its domain. For example, Figure 6–12 shows the graph of the function s, where

$$s(x) = \begin{cases} 1, \text{ if } x > 0; \\ 0, \text{ if } x = 0; \\ -1, \text{ if } x < 0. \end{cases}$$

· *Figure 6–12* ·

Can you suggest why s is called a *step-function*?

The step-function graphed in Figure 6–13 pairs the weight w in ounces of a letter with the postage p required to mail the letter by air. This function pairs each real number w between 0 and 8 with a multiple of 8 according to this rule: *air-mail postage is 8 cents for each ounce or fraction thereof up to 8 ounces.* Does 0 belong to the domain or range of this function? Does 6 belong to the domain?

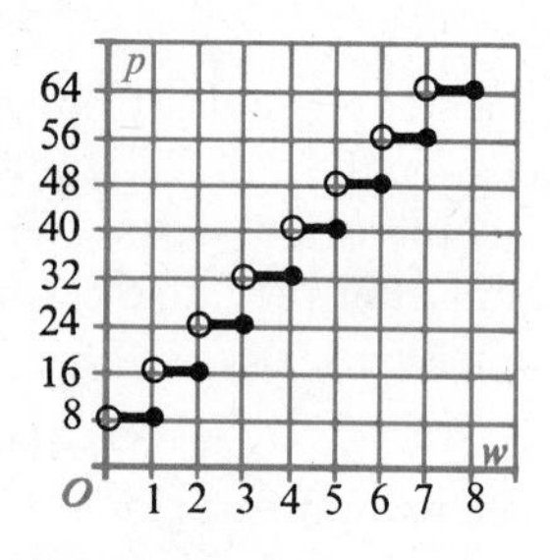

· *Figure 6–13* ·

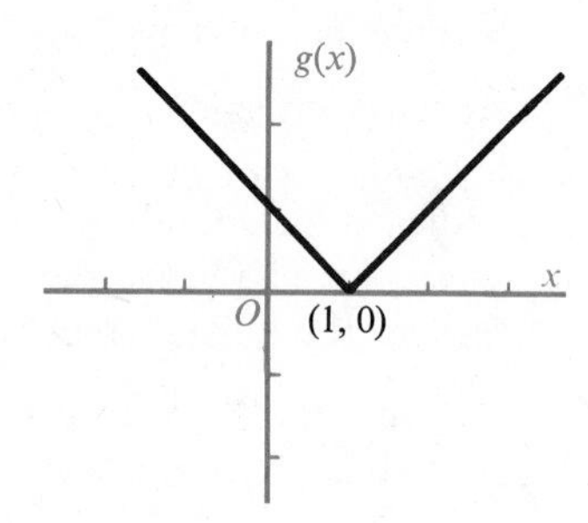

· *Figure 6–14* ·

Sometimes you can combine in a single open sentence the rules specifying a function or relation. Figure 6–14 shows the graph of the function g whose values are given by the rules:

$$g(x) = \begin{cases} x - 1, \text{ if } x \geq 1; \\ 1 - x, \text{ if } x < 1. \end{cases}$$

When you observe that $|x - 1| = x - 1$ if $x \geq 1$, but if $x < 1$, $|x - 1| = -(x - 1) = 1 - x$, you can indicate the values of g more compactly as follows: $g(x) = |x - 1|$.

Written Exercises

Graph the function F whose values are indicated.

B

1. $F(x) = \begin{cases} 1, \text{ if } x \geq 0; \\ 2, \text{ if } x < 0. \end{cases}$

2. $F(x) = \begin{cases} 3, \text{ if } x \leq 0; \\ -3, \text{ if } x > 0. \end{cases}$

3. $F(x) = \begin{cases} 3, \text{ if } x < 0; \\ 0, \text{ if } x = 0; \\ -1, \text{ if } x > 0. \end{cases}$

4. $F(x) = \begin{cases} 1, \text{ if } x > 0; \\ 0, \text{ if } x = 0; \\ -4, \text{ if } x < 0. \end{cases}$

5. $F(x) = \begin{cases} 0, \text{ if } x < -5; \\ 1, \text{ if } -5 \leq x \leq 0; \\ 2, \text{ if } x > 0. \end{cases}$

6. $F(x) = \begin{cases} -1, \text{ if } x < -3; \\ 0, \text{ if } -3 \leq x < 0; \\ 1, \text{ if } x \geq 0. \end{cases}$

7. $F(x) = \begin{cases} x, \text{ if } 0 \leq x < 3; \\ 5, \text{ if } x \geq 3. \end{cases}$

8. $F(x) = \begin{cases} \frac{1}{2}x, \text{ if } 0 \leq x < 4; \\ 2, \text{ if } x \geq 4. \end{cases}$

9. $F(x) = \begin{cases} 0, \text{ if } |x| \leq 1; \\ x - 1, \text{ if } |x| > 1. \end{cases}$

10. $F(x) = \begin{cases} 2 - x, \text{ if } |x| < 2; \\ 0, \text{ if } |x| \geq 2. \end{cases}$

11. $F(x) = \begin{cases} 2x, \text{ if } 2 \leq x < 3; \\ x + 2, \text{ if } 0 \leq x < 2; \\ 2, \text{ if } -3 \leq x < 0. \end{cases}$

12. $F(x) = \begin{cases} -1, \text{ if } x < -1; \\ -|x|, \text{ if } -1 \leq x \leq 1; \\ -1, \text{ if } x > 1. \end{cases}$

13. $F(x) = |2x - 1|$

14. $F(x) = -|3x + 1|$

15. $F(x) = 1 - |x + 2|$

16. $F(x) = |x - 2| - 1$

C

17. The rates charged by a hardware company for the rental of floor-sanding equipment for a maximum of seven days are as follows:

Rental Time	*Rental Fee*
One day or portion thereof	\$5.00
Over 1 day to 4 days	\$10.00
Over 4 days	\$15.00

Draw the graph of this rental-fee function.

18. First-class mail weighing 20 pounds or less is accepted for special delivery according to the following rate schedule:

Weight	*Special Delivery Fee*
2 pounds or less	30 cents
Over 2 pounds to 10 pounds	45 cents
Over 10 pounds	60 cents

Draw the graph of the special-delivery function.

Graph the relation $\{(x, y)\}$ specified by each set of rules.

19. $y = x$, if $0 < x \leq 3$
$y \leq 0$, if $x = 0$
$y = -x$, if $-3 \leq x < 0$

20. $y = 1 - |x|$, if $-1 \leq x \leq 1$
$y = \frac{1}{2}$, if $-\frac{1}{2} < x < \frac{1}{2}$

21. $|x| + |y| = 1$

22. $|x| + |y| \leq 2$

(Hint for Exercises 21 and 22: Draw the graph in one quadrant at a time.)

23. $|x| - 1 \leq y \leq -|x| + 1$

24. $|x + 1| \leq y \leq |x - 1|$

QUADRATIC FUNCTIONS AND RELATIONS

6–5 Quadratic Functions and Variation

A function whose values are given by a quadratic polynomial, $ax^2 + bx + c$, where a, b, and c are real numbers, $a \neq 0$, is called a **polynomial function of degree 2** or a **quadratic function**. To begin our study, we shall consider the simplest of quadratic functions, those specified by equations of the form $y = ax^2$.

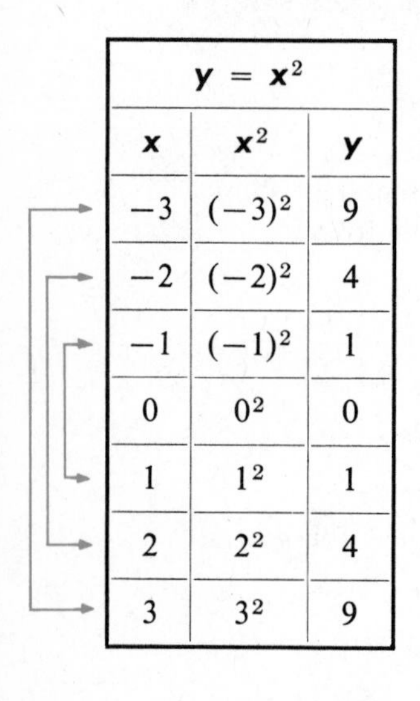

$y = x^2$		
x	x^2	y
-3	$(-3)^2$	9
-2	$(-2)^2$	4
-1	$(-1)^2$	1
0	0^2	0
1	1^2	1
2	2^2	4
3	3^2	9

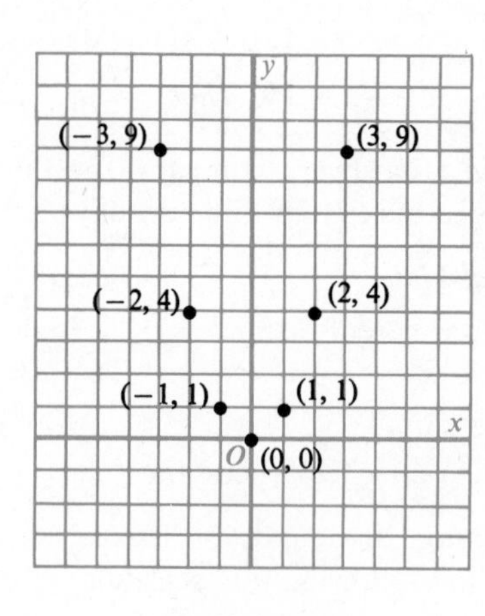

· *Figure 6–15* ·

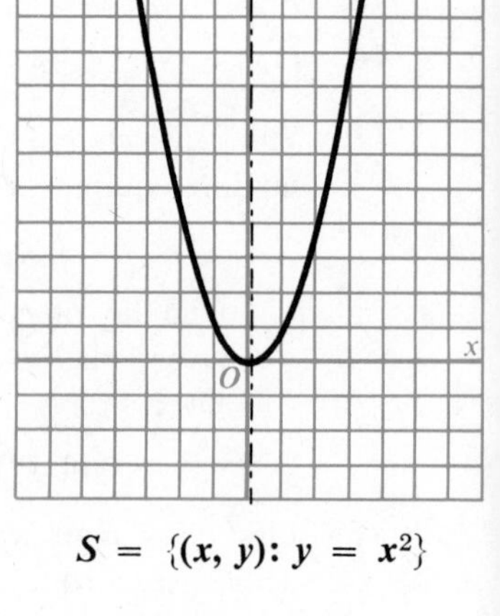

$S = \{(x, y): y = x^2\}$

· *Figure 6–16* ·

In Figure 6–15 several points of the graph of the quadratic function $S = \{(x, y): y = x^2\}$ have been plotted. As additional points are plotted, the pattern partially shown in Figure 6–16 emerges. It is a smooth curve connecting the points in order of increasing abscissa, and is the graph of the function S.

Do you see that the points of the graph can be paired so that the ordinates of the points in a pair are the same number, but the abscissas are negatives of each other: $(-1, 1)$ with $(1, 1)$; $(-2, 4)$ with $(2, 4)$; $(-3, 9)$ with $(3, 9)$; and so on? If a function f has the property that whenever the ordered pair (r, t) belongs to f, $(-r, t)$ also belongs to f, the graph of $y = f(x)$ is said to be **symmetric with respect to the y-axis.** If you were to imagine the coordinate plane folded along the y-axis, the part of the graph in the first quadrant would coincide with the part in the second quadrant. Since the graph of $S = \{(x, y): y = x^2\}$ is symmetric with respect to the y-axis, we call the y-axis the *axis of symmetry* of the curve and show it by alternate long and short dashes.

Another interesting fact about the function S is that it has a *least*, or *minimum, value*. For every nonzero value of x, $x^2 > 0$; therefore $S(x) > S(0)$ for $x \neq 0$. As a result, the point $(0, 0)$ lies below every other point on the graph of S and is called the *minimum point* of the curve.

By plotting enough points to enable you to draw a smooth curve, you will find that the graphs of $\{(x, y): y = 2x^2\}$, $\{(x, y): y = \frac{1}{2}x^2\}$, and $\{(x, y): y = -3x^2\}$ have the patterns indicated in Figure 6–17.

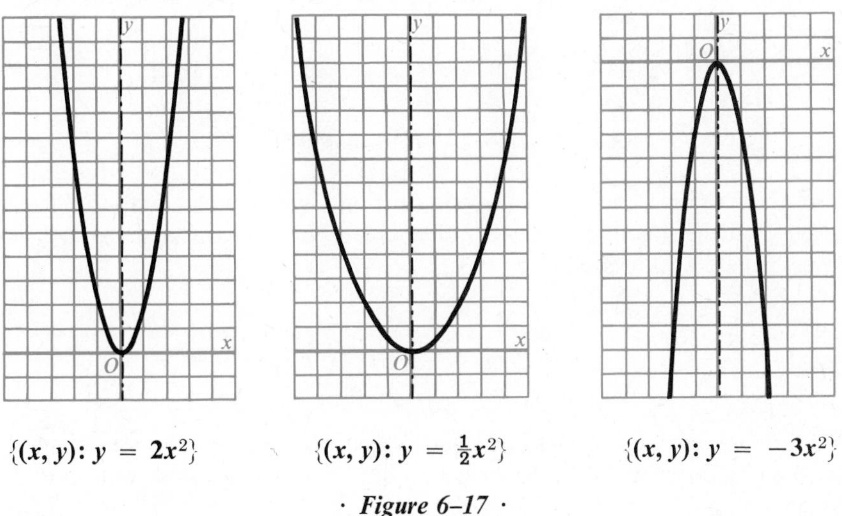

$\{(x, y): y = 2x^2\}$ $\{(x, y): y = \frac{1}{2}x^2\}$ $\{(x, y): y = -3x^2\}$

· *Figure 6–17* ·

All these curves are symmetric with respect to the y-axis; but, whereas the graphs of $y = 2x^2$ and $y = \frac{1}{2}x^2$ have minimum points at the origin, the graph of $y = -3x^2$ has its *maximum point* there. Can you explain why 0 is the greatest value of $\{(x, y): y = -3x^2\}$? The point in which the axis of symmetry intersects the graph of $\{(x, y): y = ax^2, a \neq 0\}$ is called the **vertex** of the graph. Do you see that the vertex is a minimum point if $a > 0$ and a maximum point if $a < 0$?

When a quadratic function is specified by an equation of the form $y = ax^2$, $a \neq 0$, we say that *y varies directly as x^2* or *y is directly proportional to the square of x.*

EXAMPLE. A stone dropped from the rim of a moon crater will fall 21.6 feet in 2 seconds. If the distance traveled in free fall from rest on the moon is directly proportional to the square of the time of fall, find how far the stone falls in 5 seconds.

Solution: Let d denote the distance, in feet, the stone falls in t seconds.

Method I

Use:
$$d = at^2$$
$$21.6 = a(2)^2$$
$$21.6 = 4a$$
$$5.4 = a$$
$$d = 5.4t^2$$
$$d = 5.4(5)^2$$
$$d = 135$$

Method II

Use:
$$\frac{d_1}{t_1^2} = \frac{d_2}{t_2^2}$$
$$\frac{21.6}{2^2} = \frac{d_2}{5^2}$$
$$\frac{21.6}{4} = \frac{d_2}{25}$$
$$135 = d_2$$

$\therefore$ 135 feet, **Answer.**

In this example, the constant of proportionality is the acceleration due to gravity on the moon: 5.4 ft./sec^2. The corresponding constant on Earth is approximately 32 ft./sec^2.

Oral Exercises

If F is a function whose values are given by the indicated formula, state whether **(a)** F is a quadratic function **(b)** the graph of $y = F(x)$ is symmetric with respect to the y-axis.

1. $F(x) = -5x^2$

2. $F(x) = \frac{1}{3}x^2$

3. $F(x) = \dfrac{5}{x^2}$

4. $F(x) = -\dfrac{1}{x^2}$

5. $F(x) = 2x^2 + \frac{1}{3}$

6. $F(x) = 3x^2 - \frac{1}{2}$

7. $F(x) = x^2 + \frac{1}{x}$

8. $F(x) = x^2 - \frac{1}{x}$

9. $F(x) = x(x + 3)$

10. $F(x) = (x - 1)^2$

11. $F(x) = 3(x + 7)^2$

12. $F(x) = (x + 1)(x - 10)$

13. $F(x) = 3x^2 - 9x + 4$

14. $F(x) = \frac{x^2}{4} + \frac{x}{2} - 1$

If $f(x) = 3x^2$, state the value of each of the following.

15. $f(3)$
16. $f(-1)$
17. $f(-3)$
18. $f(-2)$
19. $f(0)$
20. $f(2)$
21. $f(1)$
22. $f(\frac{2}{3})$

State whether the vertex of the graph of the given equation is a maximum or a minimum point of the curve.

23. $y = 3x^2$
24. $y = -\frac{1}{3}x^2$
25. $y = -\frac{1}{2}x^2$
26. $y = 10x^2$
27. $y = -4x^2$
28. $y = \frac{3}{5}x^2$

Written Exercises

Graph both functions in the same coordinate plane.

A

1. $\{(x, y): y = 3x^2\}$; $\{(x, y): y = \frac{1}{3}x^2\}$
2. $\{(x, y): y = 4x^2\}$; $\{(x, y): y = \frac{1}{4}x^2\}$
3. $\{(x, y): y = -5x^2\}$; $\{(x, y): y = -\frac{1}{5}x^2\}$
4. $\{(x, y): y = -2x^2\}$; $\{(x, y): y = -\frac{1}{2}x^2\}$
5. $\{(x, y): y = \frac{2}{3}x^2\}$; $\{(x, y): y = -\frac{2}{3}x^2\}$
6. $\{(x, y): y = \frac{3}{2}x^2\}$; $\{(x, y): y = -\frac{3}{2}x^2\}$

Determine which, if any, of the points with given coordinates belong to the graph of the function G, whose values are those of the indicated polynomial.

7. $G(x) = 5x^2$; $(2, 20)$; $(-2, -20)$
8. $G(x) = -2x^2$; $(-3, 18)$; $(3, -18)$
9. $G(x) = -4x^2$; $(-4, 1)$; $(-1, 4)$
10. $G(x) = \frac{1}{3}x^2$; $(-3, -3)$; $(-3, 3)$

Find the value of a if the function $\{(x, y): y = ax^2\}$ contains the given ordered pair of numbers.

11. $(3, 6)$
12. $(2, 16)$
13. $(3, -90)$
14. $(4, -\frac{16}{3})$
15. $(-\frac{1}{2}, -\frac{1}{8})$
16. $(-\frac{1}{5}, \frac{3}{25})$

17. If V varies directly as the square of s, and s is 4 when V is 48, find V when s is 6.

18. If v varies directly as t^2, and v is 45 when t is 3, find v when t is 5.

19. If S varies as r^2 and $S = \pi$ when $r = 0.5$, find r when $S = 36\pi$.

20. If h varies as v^2 and $h = \frac{1}{4}$ when $v = 4$, find v when $h = \frac{9}{16}$.

B

21. If y varies directly as x^4, and x is -2 when y is 6, find y when x is 4.

22. If h varies directly as the cube of d, and d is 3 when h is -3, find h when d is -6.

23. If s varies as the square of r, and r is proportional to t, what happens to the value of s when the value of t is doubled?

24. If A varies as the square of x, and x is proportional to y^2, what happens to the value of A when the value of y is doubled?

25. If k varies directly as the cube of t, determine how k changes when t is halved.

26. If R varies as the fourth power of S, determine how R changes when S is tripled.

C

27. If $\left(a, \frac{a}{4}\right) \in \{(x, y): y = ax^2\}$ and $a \neq 0$, determine all possible values of a.

28. If $\left(2a, \frac{a}{2}\right) \in \{(x, y): y = ax^2\}$ and $a \neq 0$, determine all possible values of a.

29. If $\left(k, \frac{k}{9}\right) \in f = \{(x, y): y = kx^2\}$, $k \neq 0$, replace the symbol ? by the term making the following statement true: $(2k, ?) \in f$.

30. If $\left(a, \frac{a}{2}\right) \in g = \{(x, y): y = ax^2\}$, $a \neq 0$, replace the symbol ? by the numeral making the following statement true: $(5, ?) \in g$.

Problems

A

1. A bomber-pilot coming out of a dive at a velocity of 600 feet per second experiences a centrifugal force of 1800 pounds. If centrifugal force is proportional to the square of velocity, find the force on this pilot flying the same path at 1000 feet per second.

2. The force exerted by the wind on a sail of fixed area varies directly as the square of the wind velocity. If the force exerted on a given sail is

180 pounds when the wind is blowing 15 miles per hour, what is the velocity of the wind when the force on the sail is 500 pounds?

3. The energy of a 2-pound satellite orbiting at 17,500 miles per hour is equivalent to 27,000 British thermal units of heat. If the amount of heat varies directly as the square of velocity, find the heat-equivalent of the energy of this satellite orbiting at 25,000 miles per hour.

4. The power expended by heat in an electric circuit of fixed resistance is directly proportional to the square of the current. If a circuit expends 180 watts when a current of 6 amperes is flowing, what is the heat expended when the current is 10 amperes?

5. The strength of a horizontal beam of rectangular cross section and fixed width and length varies as the square of the thickness. If a thickness of 6 inches is required to support a weight of 5400 pounds, how thick should a beam be to support a weight of 8000 pounds?

6. The rate of flow of water emerging from the end of a circular pipe under a fixed pressure is directly proportional to the square of the radius of the pipe. If a pipe of two-inch radius emits 864 cubic inches of water per second, at what rate will a pipe of $2\frac{1}{4}$-inch radius emit water under the same pressure?

7. The power required to drive a vessel varies as the cube of its speed. If 450 horsepower are needed to run the *Bombay Queen* at 6 knots, what horsepower is required to drive her at 8 knots?

8. The maximum deflection of a beam is directly proportional to the cube of its length. If a maximum deflection of 0.002 centimeters occurs in a beam 10 meters long, find the deflection in a 6-meter beam.

9. A square plate 3 inches wide has moment of inertia 6.75. What is the moment of inertia of a square plate 2 inches wide, if the moment of inertia varies as the fourth power of the width of the plate?

10. The crushing load of a circular pillar with a 10-inch diameter is 200 tons. Find the crushing load of a pillar of the same height and material but with a diameter of 14 inches, if the crushing load is directly proportional to the fourth power of the diameter.

B

11. The work done in stretching a spring is directly proportional to the square of the elongation. If 12 foot-pounds of work are done in stretching a spring 2 feet beyond its natural length of 10 feet, find the work done in stretching it to be a length of 13 feet.

12. The amount of silt carried by a stream is directly proportional to the sixth power of its velocity. A certain stream carries 150 tons of silt per day. Determine the amount of silt it would carry if its velocity were doubled.

13. The area bounded by the x- and y-axes and the graphs of the equations $y = 6x^2$ and $x = a$ is directly proportional to a^3. If the area is 16 when $a = 2$, find the area when $a = 5$.

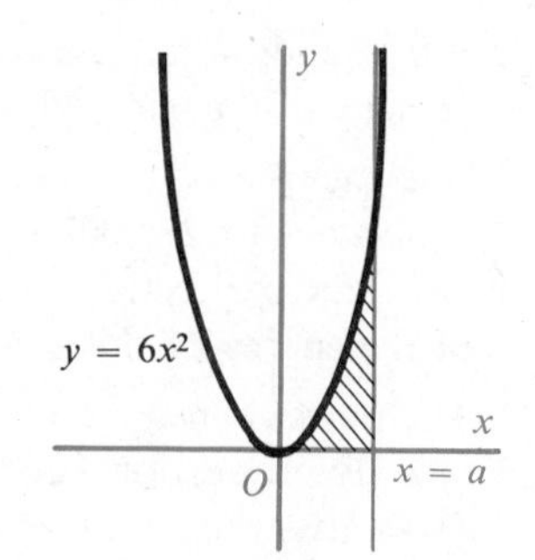

14. The slope of a line tangent to the curve whose equation is $y = x^3$ is directly proportional to the square of the abscissa at the point of tangency. If the line whose equation is $y = 12x - 16$ is tangent to the curve at (2, 8), find the equation of the line tangent at $(-1, -1)$.

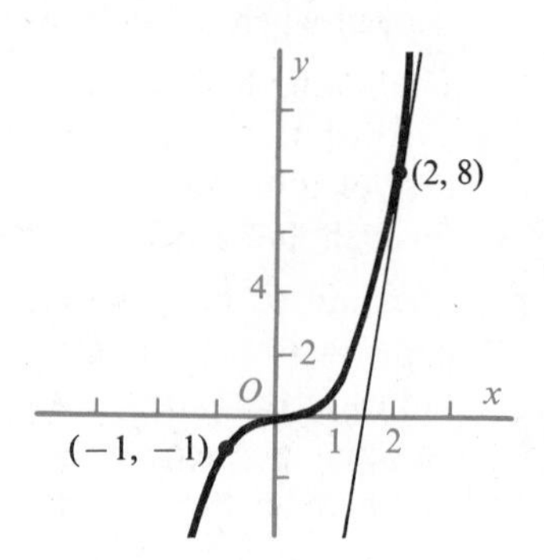

In Exercises 15–19 use these facts:

I. The areas of similar polygons and the surface areas of similar solids are proportional to the squares of corresponding linear dimensions.

II. The volumes of similar solids are porportional to the cubes of corresponding linear dimensions.

15. If one side of a parallelogram is $\frac{2}{3}$ as long as the corresponding side of a similar parallelogram, determine the ratio of the area of the first parallelogram to that of the second.

16. If the radius of one sphere is $\frac{4}{3}$ the radius of another, find the ratio of the volume of the smaller sphere to that of the larger.

17. A pyramid has a volume of 288 cubic meters and an edge of 6 meters. Find: **(a)** the volume of a similar pyramid whose corresponding edge is 15 meters long; **(b)** the ratio of the surface area of the first pyramid to that of the second.

18. The altitudes of two similar cylinders are 8 and 12 centimeters respectively. If the surface area of the smaller cylinder is 240 square centimeters, find **(a)** the surface area of the larger cylinder; **(b)** the ratio of their volumes.

19. If one side of a pentagon is 0.7 as long as the corresponding side of a similar pentagon, what is the ratio of their areas?

20. If canned tomatoes come in two sizes, with radius of one $\frac{2}{3}$ the radius of the other, find the ratio of the capacities of the two cans.

6–6 Quadratic Functions Specified by $y = a(x - h)^2 + k$

When you compare the values of the functions

$$S = \{(x, y): y = x^2\} \quad \text{and} \quad H = \{(x, y): y = x^2 + 5\}$$

for any real value of x, you can see that $H(x)$ is 5 more than $S(x)$.

x	S(x) = x²	H(x) = x² + 5
−3	9	9 + 5 = 14
−2	4	4 + 5 = 9
−1	1	1 + 5 = 6
0	0	0 + 5 = 5
1	1	1 + 5 = 6
2	4	4 + 5 = 9
3	9	9 + 5 = 14

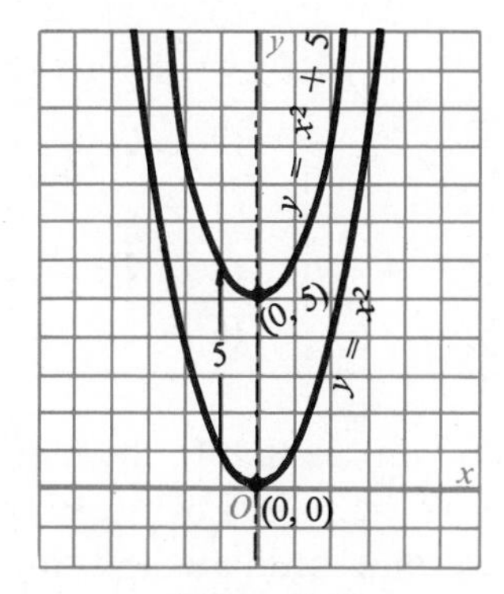

· *Figure 6–18* ·

Thus, the graph of H (Figure 6–18), like that of S, is symmetric with respect to the y-axis, but its vertex, the point (0, 5), is 5 units above the vertex (0, 0) of the graph of S.

Can you explain why every point on the graph of

$$L = \{(x, y): y = x^2 - 5\}$$

is 5 units *below* the corresponding point on the graph of S (Figure 6–19)?

Figure 6–20 shows the graphs of $\{(x, y): y = -\frac{1}{2}x^2\}$, $\{(x, y): y = -\frac{1}{2}x^2 + 3\}$, and $\{(x, y): y = -\frac{1}{2}x^2 - 3\}$.

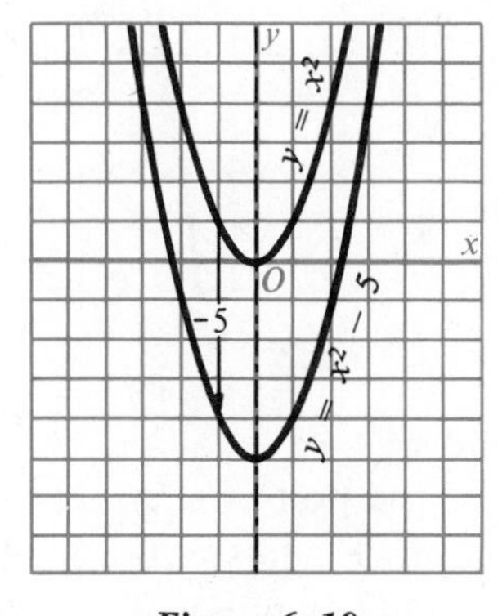

· *Figure 6–19* ·

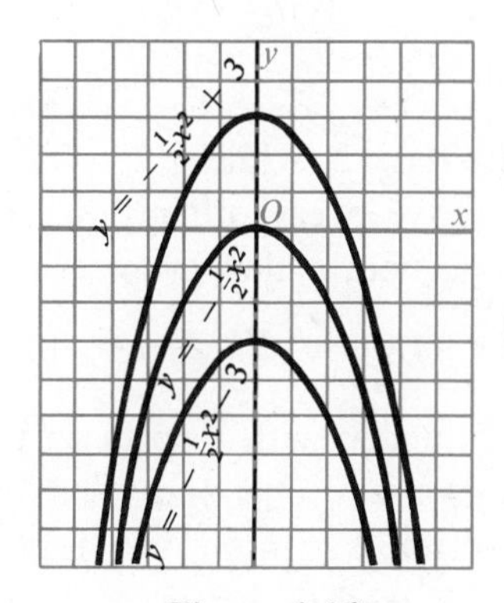

· *Figure 6–20* ·

Now study the following table of selected ordered pairs belonging to the function $f = \{(x, y): y = (x - 2)^2\}$, whose graph appears in Figure 6–21.

x	$f(x) = (x - 2)^2$
-1	$(-1 - 2)^2 = (-3)^2 = 9$
0	$(0 - 2)^2 = (-2)^2 = 4$
1	$(1 - 2)^2 = (-1)^2 = 1$
2	$(2 - 2)^2 = 0^2 = 0$
3	$(3 - 2)^2 = 1^2 = 1$
4	$(4 - 2)^2 = 2^2 = 4$
5	$(5 - 2)^2 = 3^2 = 9$

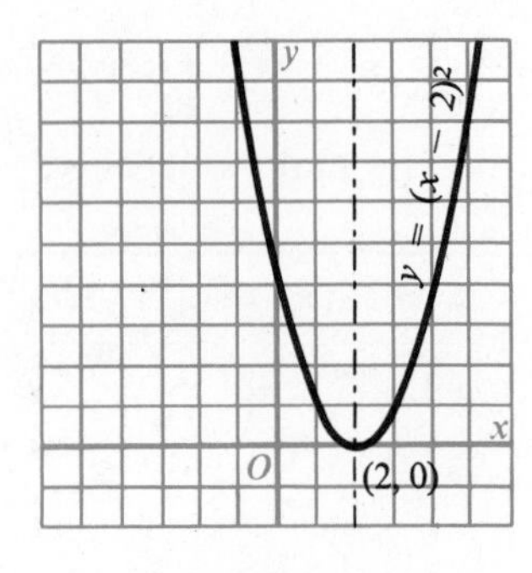

· *Figure 6–21* ·

Do you see that 0, the minimum value of the function, is $f(2)$? Moreover, the points of the graph can be paired so that paired points have the same ordinate and are equally distant from the line $x = 2$. For example,

$$(1, 1) \quad \text{and} \quad (3, 1) \qquad \text{or} \qquad (0, 4) \quad \text{and} \quad (4, 4)$$
$$|1 - 2| = 1 = |3 - 2| \qquad\qquad |0 - 2| = 2 = |4 - 2|$$

As a result, the graph of f has its vertex at $(2, 0)$ and is symmetric with respect to the line whose equation is $x = 2$.

The line $x = 2$ is also the axis of symmetry of the graph (Figure 6–22) of the function $g = \{(x, y): y = -(x - 2)^2 + 1\}$. To see why the point $(2, 1)$ is the vertex of the graph of g, notice that for $x \neq 2$, $(x - 2)^2 > 0$; therefore $-(x - 2)^2 < 0$ and $-(x - 2)^2 + 1 < 1$. Hence, $g(x) < 1$ unless x is 2, while $g(2) = 1$. Thus, $(2, 1)$ lies above every other point on the graph.

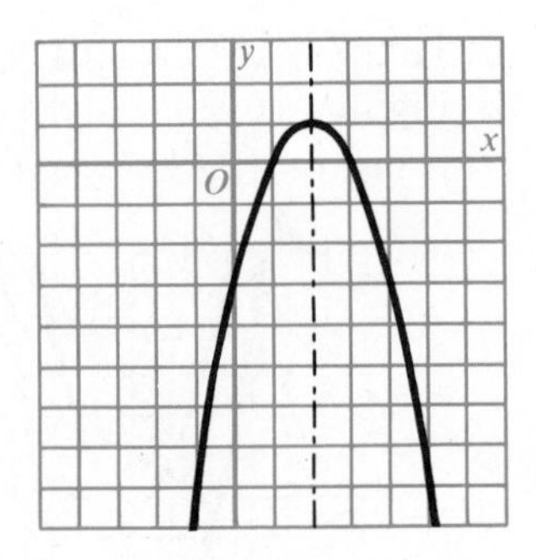

· *Figure 6–22* ·

In general, the graph of the function

$$\{(x, y): y = a(x - h)^2 + k\}, \quad a \neq 0,$$

is symmetric with respect to the line whose equation is $x = h$ and it has its vertex at the point (h, k). If $a > 0$, the vertex is a minimum point of the graph (Figures 6–18, 6–19, and 6–21); if $a < 0$, the vertex is a maximum point (Figures 6–20 and 6–22).

Oral Exercises

For the graph of each function state **(a)** the equation of the axis of symmetry; **(b)** the coordinates of the vertex; **(c)** whether the vertex is a maximum or whether it is a minimum point; **(d)** the corresponding maximum or minimum value of the function.

SAMPLE. $\{(x, y): y = -\frac{2}{3}(x + 1)^2 - 3\}$

What you say: **a.** $x = -1$ **c.** a maximum point
b. $(-1, -3)$ **d.** -3

1. $\{(x, y): y = 2(x - 1)^2 + 3\}$
2. $\{(x, y): y = 5(x - 7)^2 + 4\}$
3. $\{(x, y): y = -4(x - \frac{3}{2})^2 - 6\}$
4. $\{(x, y): y = -6(x - \frac{1}{3})^2 - 7\}$
5. $\{(x, y): y = 3(x + 3)^2 + 4\}$
6. $\{(x, y): y = 2(x + 3)^2 + 2\}$
7. $\{(x, y): y = -(x + 2)^2 - 1\}$
8. $\{(x, y): y = -(x + 5)^2 - 2\}$
9. $\{(x, y): y = -\frac{1}{2}(x + 9)^2 - \frac{1}{3}\}$
10. $\{(x, y): y = -\frac{3}{4}(x + 2)^2 - \frac{2}{5}\}$
11. $\{(x, y): y - 4 = (x + 1)^2\}$
12. $\{(x, y): y - 9 = (x + 4)^2\}$

The given ordered pair belongs to a quadratic function whose graph is symmetric with respect to the line whose equation is stated. Name a second ordered pair in the function.

13. $(5, 7);\ x = 9$
14. $(-3, 2);\ x = 4$
15. $(0, -4);\ x = -2$
16. $(0, 6);\ x = -3$
17. $(-3, 0);\ x + 1 = 0$
18. $(-7, 0);\ x + 2 = 0$
19. $(k + p, q);\ x = k$
20. $(p - k, q);\ x = -k$
21. Can the graph of a function be symmetric with respect to the x-axis? Justify your answer.
22. Can the graph of a function be symmetric with respect to any horizontal line? Justify your answer.

Written Exercises

Graph both functions in the same coordinate plane.

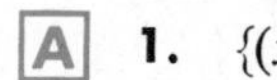

1. $\{(x, y): y = 2(x - 1)^2 + 4\};\ \{(x, y): y = 2(x - 1)^2 - 4\}$
2. $\{(x, y): y = -2(x + 1)^2 + 5\};\ \{(x, y): y = -\frac{1}{2}(x + 1)^2 + 5\}$
3. $\{(x, y): y = -(x + 1)^2\};\ \{(x, y): y = \frac{1}{3}(x + 1)^2\}$
4. $\{(x, y): y = -4(x - 3)^2\};\ \{(x, y): y = (x - 3)^2\}$

5. $\{(x, y): y = -3(x - \frac{1}{2})^2 + 2\}$; $\{(x, y): y = 3(x - \frac{1}{2})^2 - 2\}$
6. $\{(x, y): y = 5(x + \frac{2}{3})^2 - 1\}$; $\{(x, y): y = -5(x + \frac{2}{3})^2 + 1\}$
7. $\{(x, y): y = (2x - 1)^2 + \frac{3}{4}\}$; $\{(x, y): y = -(2x + 1)^2 + \frac{8}{5}\}$
8. $\{(x, y): y = (3x + 1)^2 - 2\}$; $\{(x, y): y = -(3x + 1)^2\}$

In each of the following determine all values of h or k so that the graph of the equation contains the indicated point.

9. $y = 2(x - 3)^2 + k$; $(6, 1)$
10. $y = -3(x + 4)^2 + k$; $(0, 9)$
11. $y = -\frac{1}{2}(x + 7)^2 + k$; $(0, 0)$
12. $y = \frac{4}{3}(x - 2)^2 + k$; $(-3, 8)$
13. $y = (x - h)^2 + 1$; $(0, 5)$
14. $y = (x - h)^2 + 5$; $(0, 14)$

B

15. $y = 2(x - h)^2 + 7$; $(3, 57)$
16. $y = -3(x - h)^2 + 6$; $(2, -42)$
17. $y = -\frac{1}{2}(x - h)^2 + 8$; $(-1, -10)$
18. $y = \frac{1}{3}(x - h)^2 - 4$; $(-2, 71)$

Determine all values of r so that $(r, 0)$ belongs to the given function.

19. $\{(x, y): y = \frac{1}{3}(x - 2)^2 - 3\}$
20. $\{(x, y): y = -7(x - 3)^2 + 7\}$
21. $\{(x, y): y = -\frac{1}{2}(x + 3)^2 + 2\}$
22. $\{(x, y): y = \frac{1}{2}(x + 4)^2 - 18\}$

Determine a and k so that both ordered pairs belong to the function.

23. $(0, 0)$; $(1, 12)$; $\{(x, y): y = a(x - 2)^2 + k\}$
24. $(5, 0)$; $(6, 20)$; $\{(x, y): y = a(x - 4)^2 + k\}$
25. $(-2, -1)$; $(3, 29)$; $\{(x, y): y = a(x + 1)^2 + k\}$
26. $(-2, 3)$; $(-1, 0)$; $\{(x, y): y = a(x + 3)^2 + k\}$

C

27. Show that the graph of $y = a(x - h)^2 + k$, $a \neq 0$, contains both of the points

$$\left(h + \frac{1}{2a}, k + \frac{1}{4a}\right) \quad \text{and} \quad \left(h - \frac{1}{2a}, k + \frac{1}{4a}\right).$$

28. Show that if $(r_1, 0)$ and $(r_2, 0)$, $r_1 \neq r_2$, belong to

$$\{(x, y): y = a(x - h)^2 + k, a \neq 0\}, \quad \text{then} \quad \frac{r_1 + r_2}{2} = h.$$

Draw the graph of the following functions.

29. $\{(x, y): y = |x^2 - 1|\}$
30. $\{(x, y): y = |9 - x^2|\}$

6–7 Quadratic Functions Specified by $y = ax^2 + bx + c$

Study the following procedure used to identify the axis of symmetry and the vertex of the graph of each of the following equations.

$y + 3 = x^2 - 2x + 1$	$y - 2 = 3x^2 + 30x + 75$
$y + 3 = (x - 1)^2$	$y - 2 = 3(x^2 + 10x + 25)$
$y = (x - 1)^2 - 3$	$y - 2 = 3(x + 5)^2$
	$y = 3(x + 5)^2 + 2$

$x - 1 = 0$, or $x = 1$ ← {equation of axis of symmetry} → $x + 5 = 0$, or $x = -5$

$(1, -3)$ ← {coordinates of vertex} → $(-5, 2)$

You can see that the identification depends on transforming the equation into an equivalent one of the form:

$$y = a(x - h)^2 + k$$

a constant (a); the square of a linear polynomial in which the coefficient of x is 1 ($(x - h)^2$); a constant (k)

EXAMPLE 1. Identify the axis of symmetry and the vertex of the graph of the function specified by the equation $y = 2x^2 - 12x + 7$. Draw the graph.

Solution:

1. Write an equivalent equation with only y and the constant term in the left member.

$$y = 2x^2 - 12x + 7$$
$$y - 7 = 2x^2 - 12x$$

2. Express the right member as the product of a constant and a binomial in which the coefficient of x^2 is 1.

$$y - 7 = 2(x^2 - 6x)$$

3. Add to both members the number making the expression within parentheses in the right member the square of a binomial.

add $18 = 2 \times 9$

$$y - 7 + 18 = 2(x^2 - 6x + 9)$$
$$y + 11 = 2(x - 3)^2$$

4. Write an equivalent equation with y as left member.

$$y = 2(x - 3)^2 - 11$$

∴ the equation of the axis of symmetry is $x - 3 = 0$, or $x = 3$; the vertex is the point $(3, -11)$. (The graph is on the next page.)

x	$y = 2x^2 - 12x + 7$
0	$2(0)^2 - 12(0) + 7 = 7$
1	$2(1)^2 - 12(1) + 7 = -3$
2	$2(2)^2 - 12(2) + 7 = -9$
3	$2(3)^2 - 12(3) + 7 = -11$
4	$2(4)^2 - 12(4) + 7 = -9$
5	$2(5)^2 - 12(5) + 7 = -3$
6	$2(6)^2 - 12(6) + 7 = 7$

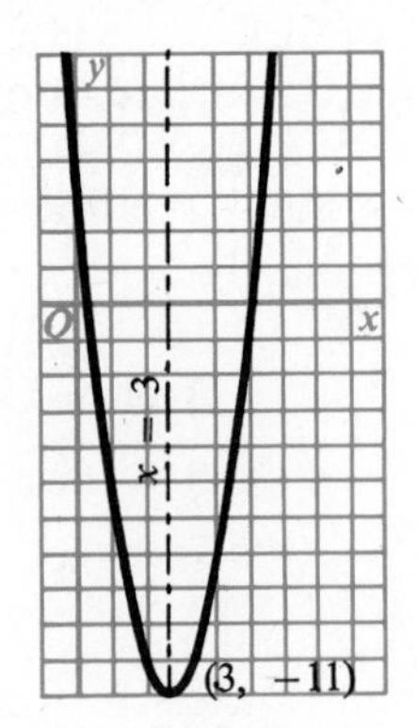

As a check on the work, notice that the table also shows the axis of symmetry to be the line whose equation is $x = 3$.

To apply the method of this example to any equation of the form

$$y = ax^2 + bx + c, a \neq 0,$$

or equivalently,

$$y - c = a\left(x^2 + \frac{b}{a}x\right),$$

you must be able to determine what to add to $x^2 + \frac{b}{a}x$ to produce the square of a binomial, a process called **completing the square.**

Analyze the following trinomials which are squares of binomials.

$$\mathbf{(x + 7)^2 = x^2 + 2 \cdot 7x + 7^2}$$

$$\mathbf{(x - 5)^2 = x^2 + 2(-5)x + (-5)^2}$$

$$\mathbf{(x - m)^2 = x^2 + 2(-m)x + (-m)^2}$$

$$\mathbf{\left(x + \frac{b}{2a}\right)^2 = x^2 + 2\left(\frac{b}{2a}\right)x + \left(\frac{b}{2a}\right)^2}$$

Do you see that in each case *the constant term is the square of half the coefficient of the linear term?* Thus, given $x^2 + \frac{b}{a}x$, you complete the square by adding $\left(\frac{1}{2} \cdot \frac{b}{a}\right)^2$, or $\frac{b^2}{4a^2}$.

Using this fact, you can derive the equation of the axis of symmetry of the graph of any quadratic function

$$\mathbf{f = \{(x, y): y = ax^2 + bx + c, a \neq 0\}.}$$

$$y = ax^2 + bx + c$$

$$y - c = a\left(x^2 + \frac{b}{a}x\right)$$

add $a \times \frac{b^2}{4a^2}$

$$y - c + \frac{b^2}{4a} = a\left(x^2 + \frac{b}{a}x + \frac{b^2}{4a^2}\right)$$

$$y - c + \frac{b^2}{4a} = a\left(x + \frac{b}{2a}\right)^2$$

$$y = a\left(x + \frac{b}{2a}\right)^2 + c - \frac{b^2}{4a}$$

$\therefore$ the equation of the axis of symmetry is $x + \frac{b}{2a} = 0$, or $x = -\frac{b}{2a}$;

and the coordinates of the vertex are $\left(-\frac{b}{2a}, c - \frac{b^2}{4a}\right)$.

Recall (page 228) that the vertex is the minimum or maximum point of the graph according as $a > 0$ or $a < 0$. Thus, $f\left(-\frac{b}{2a}\right)$ is the minimum or maximum value of f according as $a > 0$ or $a < 0$.

EXAMPLE 2. For the function $f = \{(x, y): y = 3x^2 - 4x + 2\}$ find:

a. the equation of the axis of symmetry of its graph;

b. its minimum or maximum value, if any.

Solution: **a.** $a = 3, b = -4;\ -\frac{b}{2a} = -\frac{-4}{2 \cdot 3} = \frac{2}{3}$

$x = \frac{2}{3}$, **Answer.**

b. $a > 0;\ \therefore f(\frac{2}{3})$ is the minimum value of f;

$$f(\tfrac{2}{3}) = 3(\tfrac{2}{3})^2 - 4(\tfrac{2}{3}) + 2$$
$$= \tfrac{4}{3} - \tfrac{8}{3} + 2$$
$$f(\tfrac{2}{3}) = \tfrac{2}{3}$$

$\therefore \frac{2}{3}$ is the minimum value, **Answer.**

Oral Exercises

State the value of n for which the trinomial is the square of a binomial.

1. $x^2 + 2x + n$

2. $x^2 - 6x + n$

3. $t^2 - 12t + n$

4. $k^2 + 20k + n$

5. $u^2 - u + n$

6. $u^2 + u + n$

7. $r^2 - 10r + n$

8. $b^2 + 16b + n$

9. $x^2 + 5x + n$

10. $x^2 + 7x + n$

11. $v^4 + \frac{v^2}{2} + n$

12. $w^4 - \frac{2w^2}{5} + n$

State the number to add to each member of the equation to make the expression in parentheses the square of a binomial.

SAMPLE. $y = 2(x^2 - 16x)$

What you say: Within the parentheses add $\left(\frac{-16}{2}\right)^2$ or 64;

$\therefore$ add $2 \cdot 64$, or 128, to each member.

13. $y = 3(x^2 + 8x)$

14. $y = 2(x^2 + 14x)$

15. $r = -2(t^2 + 6t)$

16. $q = -(s^2 - 4s)$

17. $v = -8(z^2 - z)$

18. $w = -16(p^2 + p)$

19. $y = 5(x^2 - \frac{4}{5}x)$

20. $y = 3(x^2 + \frac{4}{3}x)$

Written Exercises

Draw the graph of each of the following functions.

A

1. $\{(x, y): y = x^2 - 4x\}$

2. $\{(x, y): y = x^2 + 6x\}$

3. $\{[x, f(x)]: f(x) = 4x^2 - 8x\}$

4. $\{[(x, g(x)]: g(x) = 3x^2 + 9x\}$

5. $\{(x, y): y = x^2 - x - 6\}$

6. $\{(x, y): y = x^2 - 2x - 3\}$

7. $\{[x, r(x)]: r(x) = x^2 + 5x + 4\}$

8. $\{[x, t(x)]: t(x) = x^2 + 4x + 3\}$

9. G, if $G(x) = x^2 - 4x - 1$

10. H, if $H(x) = x^2 - 3x + 4$

11. F, if $F(x) = 2x^2 - 12x + 20$

12. m, if $m(x) = 3x^2 + 6x + 2$

13. $\{(x, y): y = 4x - x^2\}$

14. $\{(x, y): y = 3x - 2x^2\}$

15. $\{(x, y): y = x^2 + 6x + 9\}$

16. $\{(x, y): y = -4 + 4x - x^2\}$

17. $\{(x, y): y = x^2 - x + 3\}$

18. $\{(x, y): y = -4 - 3x - x^2\}$

Problems

B

1. If a stone is tossed upward with an initial velocity of 112 feet per second from a height of 700 feet above the surface of Mars, its height h above the surface t seconds later is given by $h = -5.6t^2 + 112t + 700$. Determine the maximum height reached by the stone.

2. If a stone is tossed upward with an initial velocity of 112 feet per second from a height of 700 feet above the surface of the earth, its height h above the ground t seconds later is given by $h = -16t^2 + 112t + 700$. What is the maximum height reached by the stone?

3. If $(8, 0) \in \{(x, y): y = bx + x^2\}$, what is the least value of this function in the interval $0 < x < 8$?

4. If $(-6, 0) \in \{(x, y): y = bx - x^2\}$, what is the greatest value of this function in the interval $-6 < x < 0$?

5. A missile fired from a launching pad followed a path whose equation is $y = x - 3.125 \times 10^{-6}x^2$. Determine

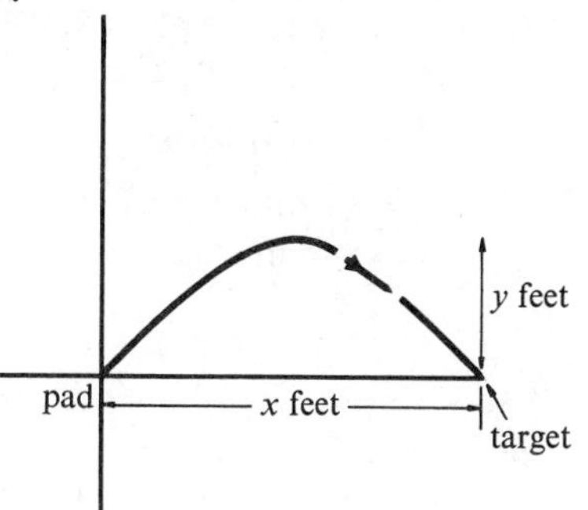

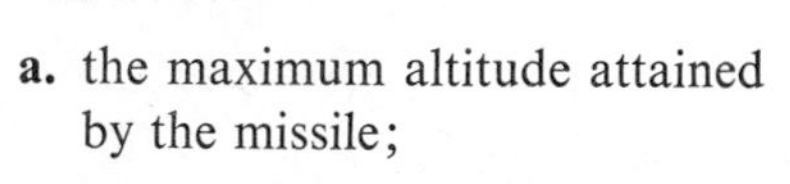

a. the maximum altitude attained by the missile;

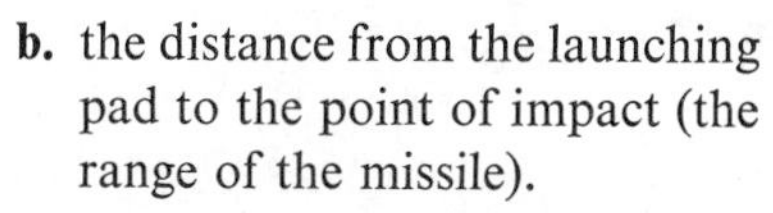

b. the distance from the launching pad to the point of impact (the range of the missile).

6. Each cable supporting the main span of the Golden Gate Bridge forms the graph of a quadratic function. If the supporting towers are 485 feet above the midpoint of the cable and are 4200 feet apart, determine an equation for the curve described by a supporting cable.

7. In a 110-volt circuit having a resistance of 11 ohms, the power W in watts when a current I is flowing is given by $W = 110I - 11I^2$. Determine the maximum power that can be delivered in this circuit.

8. A real-estate operator estimates that the monthly profit p in dollars from a building s stories high is given by $p = -2s^2 + 88s$. What height building would she consider most profitable?

C

9. Among all pairs of numbers whose difference is 64, determine the pair whose product is least.

10. Find the rectangle of maximum area that can be constructed with a perimeter of 44 inches.

11. A helicopter shuttle service operating between an airport and the center of a city charges a fare of \$10 and carries 300 persons per day. The manager estimates that she will lose 15 passengers for each increase of \$1 in the fare. Find the most profitable fare for her to charge.

12. The number n of units of a certain commodity sold at price p is given by $n = -0.2p + 50$. The revenue is the product of the selling price and the number of units sold. Find the maximum revenue for this commodity.

13. From a point P on a semicircle, a perpendicular PT is drawn to the diameter. If $RT = x$ and $RS = 6$,

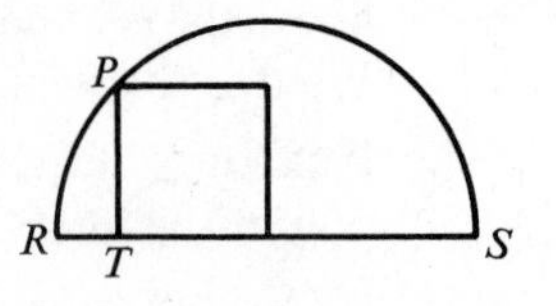

a. Express in terms of x the area of a square of side PT;

b. Find the maximum area for the square.

(*Hint.* $RT{:}PT = PT{:}TS$.)

14. From the rectangle $ABCD$, triangle RAS is cut. If $AB = 12$, $BC = 5$, and $DR = x = \frac{1}{2}SB$,

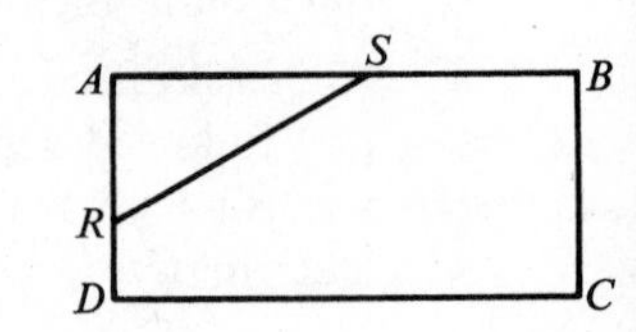

a. Express the area y of $RSBCD$ in terms of x;

b. Determine the length RA and AS so that y is maximum.

6–8 Using Graphs of Quadratic Functions

From the graph of the function, $\{(x, y): y = x^2 - 2x - 3\}$, you can determine or approximate the real roots of every equation of the form $x^2 - 2x - 3 = k$ where k denotes any real number. The roots of the equation are the x-coordinates of those points (if any) of the graph which have y-coordinates equal to k. For example, Figure 6–23 shows the solutions of $x^2 - 2x - 3 = 0$ to be -1 and 3, and those of $x^2 - 2x - 3 = 4$ to be approximately -1.8 and 3.8.

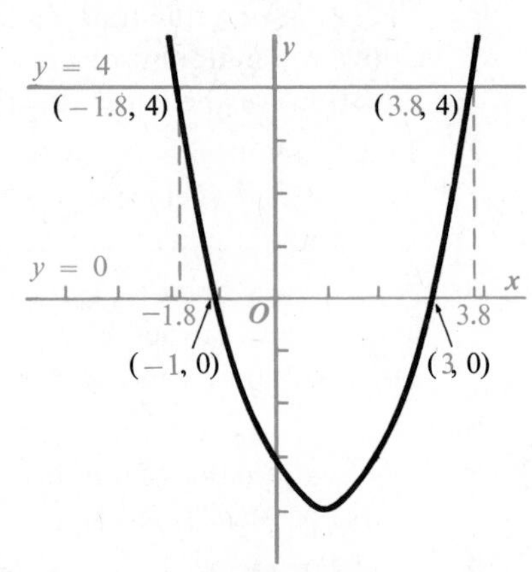

Figure 6–23

You also use the graph of a quadratic function in graphing quadratic inequalities like the one in the following example.

EXAMPLE. Graph the relation

$$\{(x, y): y < x^2 - 2x\}.$$

Solution: Show the graph of $y = x^2 - 2x$ as a dash curve, and shade the region below it.

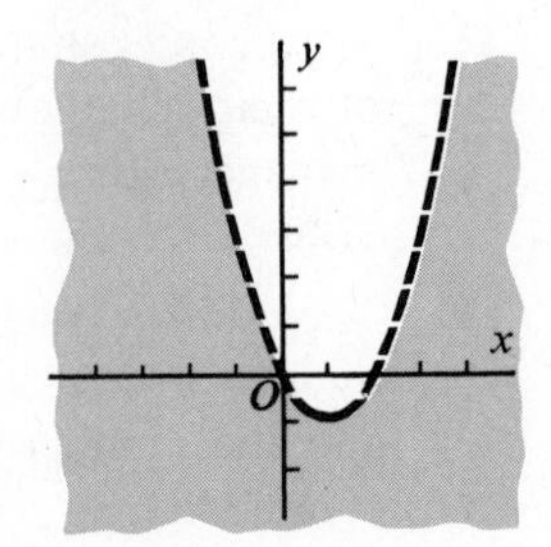

Written Exercises

Use a graph to approximate, correct to tenths, the real roots of each equation for the indicated values of k, in red.

A

1. $x^2 = k$; 3, 7
2. $x^2 - 5 = k$; 0, -3
3. $x^2 - 4x + 2 = k$; 0, 7
4. $x^2 + 2x - 4 = k$; 0, 1
5. $x^2 + 5x = k$; 0, -6
6. $x^2 - 3x + 1 = k$; 0, 2
7. $1 + 6x - 3x^2 = k$; 0, -2
8. $1 - 4x - 2x^2 = k$; 2, -3

Graph each open sentence.

9. $y \leq x^2$
10. $y \geq x^2$
11. $y > x^2 - 1$
12. $y < x^2 + 1$
13. $y < 2x - x^2$
14. $y \leq x - 2x^2$
15. $y \geq x^2 - 2x - 3$
16. $y > x^2 - 3x - 4$
17. $y \leq 2 - x - x^2$
18. $y \geq -4 + 5x - x^2$
19. $y \leq 2x^2 + x + 6$
20. $y < 2x^2 + 5x - 3$

B

21. $y \geq x^2$ and $y < 2$
22. $y \geq x^2 - 4$ and $y < 0$
23. $y \leq 4 - x^2$ and $y \geq -1$
24. $y > x^2 - 9$ and $y < -1$
25. $y \leq 4x - x^2$ and $y > x$
26. $y > x^2$ and $y + x < 3$

Graph each of the given relations.

C

27. $\{(x, y): y \leq |x^2 - 9|\}$
28. $\{(x, y): y \geq |4 - x^2|\}$
29. f, if $f(x) = \begin{cases} x^2, \text{ if } |x| \leq 1 \\ 1, \text{ if } |x| > 1 \end{cases}$
30. g, if $g(x) = \begin{cases} 0, \text{ if } |x| > 1 \\ 1 - x^2, \text{ if } |x| \leq 1 \end{cases}$

Chapter Summary

Inventory of Structure and Method

1. To specify a **relation**, you indicate by rule, roster, or graph the pairing of each element of one set (the domain) with one or more elements of another set (the range). For a relation to be a **function**, every element in its domain must be paired with one and only one element in its range.

2. If m is a nonzero constant, then the **linear function** $\{(x, y): y = mx\}$ is a **direct variation.** If (x_1, y_1) and (x_2, y_2) belong to a direct variation, then $y_1 : x_1 = y_2 : x_2$ provided $x_1 \neq 0$ and $x_2 \neq 0$.

3. The graph of the **quadratic function** $f = \{(x, y)\colon y = ax^2 + bx + c\}$, where $a \neq 0$, is **symmetric** with respect to a vertical line. When you transform $y = ax^2 + bx + c$ to the form $y = a(x - h)^2 + k$, $x = h$ is the equation of the **axis of symmetry** of the graph of f, and (h, k) are the coordinates of the vertex. The value of k is $f\left(-\frac{b}{2a}\right)$; it is a **maximum** value of the function when $a < 0$, and a **minimum** value when $a > 0$.
4. When $y = ax^2$, we say that y varies **directly as the square** of x.
5. The x-coordinates of the points having k as y-coordinate on the graph of $y = ax^2 + bx + c$ are the roots of the equation $ax^2 + bx + c = k$. You can graph a **quadratic inequality** in two variables by graphing the associated quadratic equation in two variables and shading the proper region.

Vocabulary and Spelling

relation (*p. 209*)
domain (*p. 209*)
range (*p. 209*)
function (*p. 213*)
$f(x)$ (*p. 213*)
constant function (*p. 214*)
polynomial function (*p. 217*)
linear function (*p. 217*)
direct variation (*p. 217*)
constant of proportionality (of variation) (*p. 217*)
proportion (*p. 218*)
extremes (*p. 218*)
means (*p. 218*)
quadratic function (*p. 226*)
symmetric (*p. 227*)
axis of symmetry (*p. 227*)
minimum point (*p. 227*)
maximum point (*p. 227*)
vertex (*p. 228*)
completing the square (*p. 238*)

Chapter Test

6–1 1. Give **(a)** the domain D, and **(b)** the range R of the relation

$$\left\{(x, y)\colon y = \frac{1}{2x - 1}\right\}.$$

2. If $x \in \{-5, -4, -3, -2, -1, 0, 1\}$, draw the graph of the relation $\{(x, y)\colon y = |2x + 4|\}$.

6–2 3. Is the set of ordered pairs (t, s) in the table a function? Justify your answer.

t	-2	-1	0	1	2
s	-4	0	-2	-4	0

4. If $f(n) = 2n^3 - 4n^2 + 1$, find $f(-2)$.

6–3 **5.** In the carbon dioxide-oxygen cycle, 44 grams of carbon dioxide produce 32 grams of oxygen. Assuming no loss in the process, state how many grams of carbon dioxide would produce 56 grams of oxygen.

6. If p varies as $2n + 1$, and $n = 4$ when $p = 6$, find n when $p = 18$.

6–4 **(Optional)**

7. Draw the graph of the function specified by

$$f(x) = \begin{bmatrix} x + 1 \text{ when } 0 \leq |x| < 4 \\ 4 \text{ when } 4 \leq |x| \leq 6 \end{bmatrix}.$$

6–5 **8.** State whether the graph of $f(x) = -8x^2$ has a maximum point or a minimum point and give its coordinates.

9. The areas of similar triangles vary directly as the squares of a pair of corresponding sides. If a pair of corresponding sides of two similar triangles are 6 in. and 8 in. long, and the combined area of the triangles is 250 sq. in., find each area.

6–6 **10.** For the function $\{(x, y): y = \frac{1}{2}(x + 4)^2 - 2\}$ find **(a)** the equation of the axis of symmetry, **(b)** whether the vertex is a maximum or a minimum point and give its coordinates, **(c)** the corresponding maximum or minimum value of the function.

6–7 **11.** If $y = -2(x^2 - 3x)$, find the number that must be added to each member to make the expression in parentheses the square of a binomial.

12. Draw the graph of $\{[x, f(x)]: f(x) = x^2 + 3x - 2\}$ for $-4 \leq x \leq 2$.

13. At a certain service station, an average of 4000 gallons of gasoline are sold daily at 35 cents per gallon. The owner estimates that he will sell 100 gallons less per day for every 1-cent increase in the price per gallon. Find the price which will give the owner maximum daily receipts.

6–8 **14.** Graph $\{(x, y): x^2 + 2x > 4 + y\}$.

Solve graphically.

15. $x^2 + 6x + 2 = k$, if **(a)** $k = 0$; **(b)** $k = -1$.

Chapter Review

6–1 **Relations** *Pages 209–212*

1. A relation is any ___?___ of ___?___ pairs.

2. A relation may be specified by a ___?___, a ___?___, or a ___?___.

3. When a relation is specified by a graph, the __?__ of the relation is the set of ordinates of the points on the graph.
4. The domain of the relation: $(1, -2), (0, -3), (-1, -2)$ is __?__; its range is __?__.
5. The domain of the relation: $\left\{(x, y)\colon y = -\dfrac{1 + |x|}{x^2}\right\}$ is __?__.
6. If $x \in \{-2, -1, 0, 1, 2, 3\}$, draw the graph of the relation: $\{(x, 1 - x^2)\}$.

6–2 Functions *Pages 213–216*

7. The relation: $\{(-2, 1), (-1, 2), (0, 1), (3, 0), (4, -1), (3, -3)\}$ is not a __?__ because it contains the ordered pairs __?__ and __?__.
8. No __?__ line may contain more than one point in the graph of a __?__.
9. If $f(t) = 1 + 2t - 3t^2 - t^3$, $f(-1) =$ __?__ and $f(2a) =$ __?__.

6–3 Linear Functions and Direct Variation *Pages 217–223*

10. The values of a __?__ function are those of a polynomial of degree 1.
11. A straight line whose slope is different from __?__ and whose y-intercept equals __?__ is the graph of a direct variation.

If (x_1, y_1) and (x_2, y_2) represent ordered pairs in a direct variation ($x_1 \neq 0$ and $x_2 \neq 0$), tell in each case whether the statement is true or false. (Assume k to be a nonzero constant.)

12. $x_1 = ky_1$
13. $x_1y_1 = x_2y_2$
14. $y^2 = kx^2$
15. $y = \dfrac{x}{k}$
16. If f is proportional to v, and $f = 15$ when $v = 3.9$, find v when $f = 6.5$.
17. If y varies directly as $5x - 3$ and $y = 18$ when $x = 3$, find y when $x = 5$.

6–4 Special Functions and Relations (Optional) *Pages 224–226*

18. The graph of the function specified by $y = |2x - 2|$ consists of the graphs of $y = 2x - 2$ when x __?__ and $y = 2 - 2x$ when $x <$ __?__.
19. Draw the graph of $y = |2x - 2|$.
20. Draw the graph of $\{(x, y)\colon 0 \leq y \leq 3 \text{ and } -1 \leq x \leq 4\}$.

6–5 Quadratic Functions and Variation *Pages 226–232*

21. If $(-3, 6)$ represents a point on the graph of $y = ax^2$, then (__?__, 6) represents another point on the graph.

22. The vertex of the graph of $y = 6x^2$ is the __?__ point of the graph.

23. The axis of symmetry of the graph of $y = ax^2$ always passes through the __?__ of the graph.

24. The graph of $y = ax^2$ has __?__ as its y-intercept and __?__ as its x-intercept, that is, the graph passes through the __?__.

25. Draw the graph of $y = -4x^2$ for $|x| \leq 3$. (Let each vertical division represent 4 units.)

26. The price of a diamond varies roughly as the square of its weight. If a diamond weighing 1.8 carats costs $1521, find the cost of a diamond of similar quality weighing 1.2 carats.

27. If $(2, -3)$ and $(k, -\frac{1}{3})$ are ordered pairs contained in $\{(x, y): y = ax^2\}$, find k.

6–6 Quadratic Functions: $y = a(x - h)^2 + k$ *Pages 233–236*

Exercises 28–31 refer to $g = \{(x, y): y = 1.5(x + 2)^2 - 4\}$.

28. Each point on its graph is __?__ units below the corresponding point of the graph of $y = 1.5(x + 2)^2$ for the same value of x.

29. The equation of the axis of symmetry of the graph is __?__.

30. If $x = n$ at the vertex of the graph, and $g(n + 2) = k$, then $g(n - 2) =$ __?__.

31. The vertex of the graph is the point __?__ which is the __?__ point on the curve.

6–7 Quadratic Functions: $y = ax^2 + bx + c$ *Pages 237–242*

32. Transform $y = 2x^2 - 6x$ into the form $y + m = p(x + s)^2$.

33. Without graphing, find the equation of the axis of symmetry of the graph of $y = 4x^2 + 2x + 1$.

34. If the equation of the axis of symmetry of the graph of $y = ax^2 + bx$ is $x = 3$ and the graph contains point $(-1, 5)$, find a and b.

35. Draw the graph of $\{(x, y): y = x^2 + 5x + 1\}$.

36. Draw the graph of $\{[x, f(x)]: f(x) = 4x - 2x^2\}$.

6–8 Using Graphs of Quadratic Functions *Pages 242–243*

37. Graph the relation defined by $y \geq 3x - x^2$.

38. The roots of $x^2 - 6x + 7 = 4$ are the x-coordinates of the points on the graph of $y = x^2 - 6x + 7$ for which the y-coordinate is __?__.

39. Graphically approximate to the nearest tenth the roots of $x^2 - 6x + 7 = 4$.

Extra for Experts

Denumerability

In counting the elements of a set, you establish a one-to-one correspondence between the members of the set and the members of a subset of the natural numbers. For example, the letters in "set" can be placed in one-to-one correspondence with the members of $\{1, 2, 3\}$, and hence you say that the word "set" has three letters. Any set whose elements can be counted is said to be **countable**, or **denumerable.**

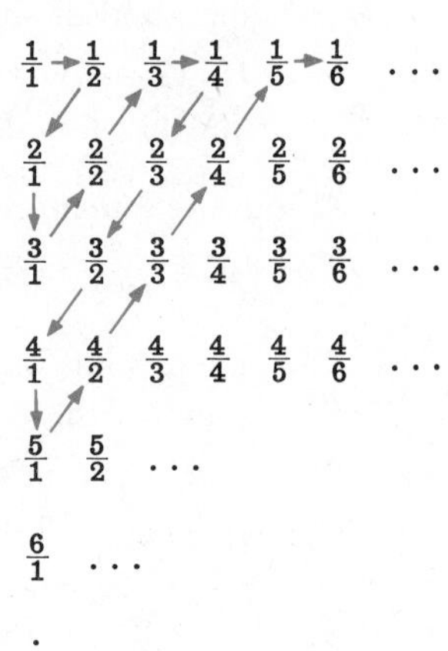

If a one-to-one correspondence can be established between the members of a given infinite set and {all natural numbers}, the given set is said to be **denumerably infinite**, and is assigned the symbol $\aleph_0$ (read "aleph null"). Notice that "$\aleph_0$" does not represent a natural number but is simply a symbol denoting a denumerable infinity of things.

The display at the right shows part of an array of all rational numbers. You can see that if you follow the red path through the array, you can assign a natural number to each rational number as you pass it. Hence, the rational numbers form a denumerably infinite set.

On the other hand, any "count" of the *real* numbers between 0 and 1, such as shown in the array at the right, will always omit at least one real number. To find $0.x_1x_2x_3\ldots$, the decimal for this omitted number, choose x_1 different from a_1 and 9, x_2 different from b_2 and 9, and so on. Since the number thus represented differs from every number in the array, the proposed counting has failed to include it. Because every such "count" fails similarly, the set of real numbers between 0 and 1 is *nondenumerable* and, therefore, so is the set of all real numbers.

$$\begin{array}{l}
1 \leftrightarrow 0.a_1a_2a_3a_4\ldots \\
2 \leftrightarrow 0.b_1b_2b_3b_4\ldots \\
3 \leftrightarrow 0.c_1c_2c_3c_4\ldots \\
4 \leftrightarrow 0.d_1d_2d_3d_4\ldots \\
\vdots \\
n \leftrightarrow 0.n_1n_2n_3n_4\ldots \\
\vdots
\end{array}$$

Exercises

1. Show that the set of all even natural numbers is denumerable.
2. Show that the set of all squares of integers is denumerable.
3. Show that the set of all integers is denumerable.
4. Addition of *natural numbers* arises when you count the members of the union of two sets having no common elements. How can you extend this notion of addition to include such sums as $\aleph_0 + 1$, $\aleph_0 + 2$, $1 + \aleph_0$, or $\aleph_0 + \aleph_0$? Can you explain why **(a)** $n + \aleph_0 = \aleph_0$ and $\aleph_0 + n = \aleph_0$ for every natural number n; **(b)** $\aleph_0 + \aleph_0 = \aleph_0$?

Medical Research

A century ago, most medical discoveries were made by practicing physicians, but today, medical science is so complex that a medical practitioner spends hours each week just in reading the professional journals to keep abreast of new findings, and the bulk of medical investigation must now be carried on by full-time scientists. Some of these workers have been educated as doctors; others, however, enter medical research from other fields of science.

Medicine is, in fact, heavily dependent on the "basic sciences." Pre-med students usually take a number of science courses, and the first-year medical school curriculum is largely devoted to such subjects as anatomy, physiology, biochemistry, and biomathematics.

Because it is concerned with a very broad area of learning, medical science is prone to increasing specialization. Thus, it is not surprising that medical research often enlists the aid of specialists from fields other than medicine. A neurology laboratory, for example, might employ an electrical engineer to design equipment for measuring the charge involved in nerve impulses. Or an orthopedics laboratory might employ a mineralogist to study the formation and atomic structure of human bone tissue. Many such specialists work in cooperation with medical personnel, each investigator attacking a small part of a complex problem. With an efficient pooling of resources, research teams of this sort can probably accomplish more in a few years than individuals working independently can hope to achieve in a lifetime.

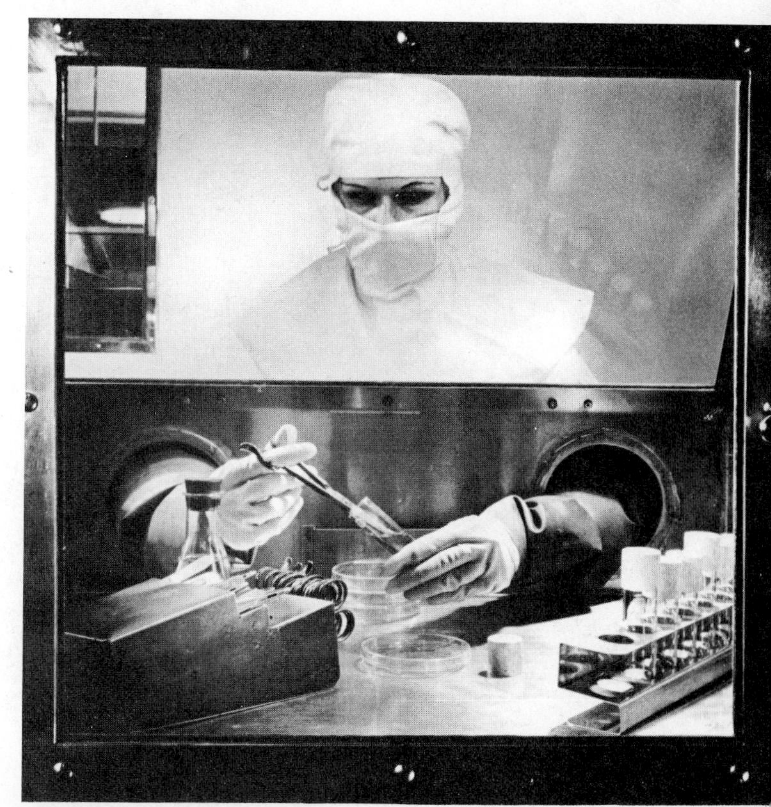

Scientist working under a protective hood prepares organic tissue that may be used in measles vaccine.

CHAPTER 7

. . . a photomicrograph of penicillin crystals

Irrational Numbers and Quadratic Equations

You have classified real numbers as positive, negative, or zero; and as integers or nonintegers. You have also identified certain real numbers as rational numbers. In this chapter you will continue this classification with a study of irrational numbers and their use in solving quadratic equations and inequalities.

REAL ROOTS OF REAL NUMBERS

7–1 Using Radicals to Express Roots

Does there exist one or more real roots of $x^2 = 9$? Is there a real number x such that $x^3 = 8$? Graphs offer a means of visualizing the answers to such questions. Plotting enough points to enable you to draw a smooth curve will suggest the patterns shown in Figures 7–1 and 7–2 as the graphs of the equations $y = x^2$, $y = x^4$, $y = x$, $y = x^3$.

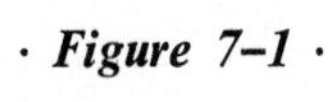
· *Figure 7–1* ·

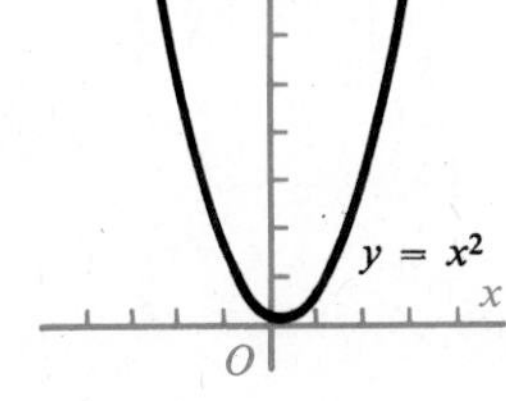

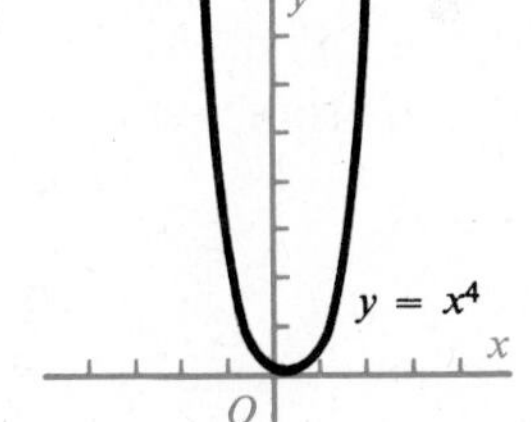

· *Figure 7–2* ·

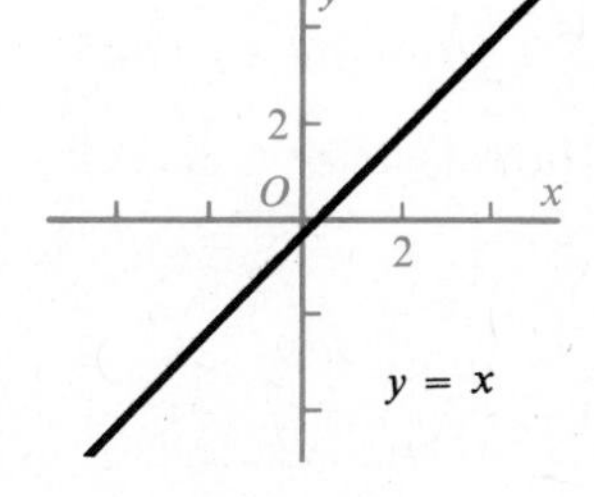

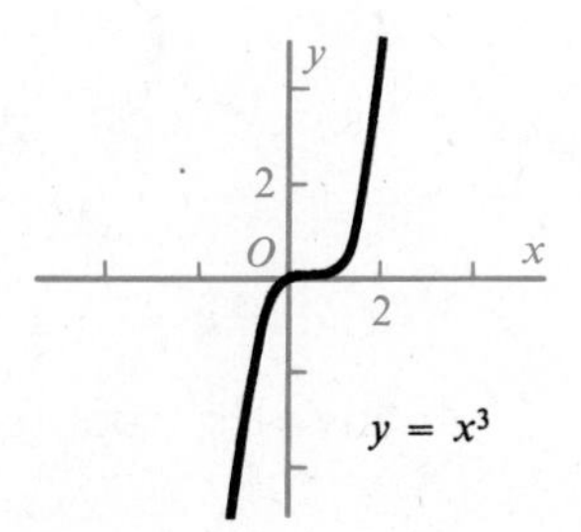

Notice that when n is an even positive integer (Figure 7–1), the graph of $y = x^n$ is symmetric with respect to the y-axis and has a minimum point at the origin. Thus, a horizontal line above the x-axis intersects the graph in two points whose abscissas are negatives of each other. For example, the graph of $y = 9$ intersects that of $y = x^2$ in the *two points* $(3, 9)$ and $(-3, 9)$, Figure 7–3. That is, for $y = 9$, the equation $y = x^2$ becomes $x^2 = 9$, which has two real roots, 3 and -3. On the other hand, the line whose equation is $y = -9$ has no point in common with the graph of $y = x^2$. Correspondingly, $x^2 = -9$ has *no real roots.*

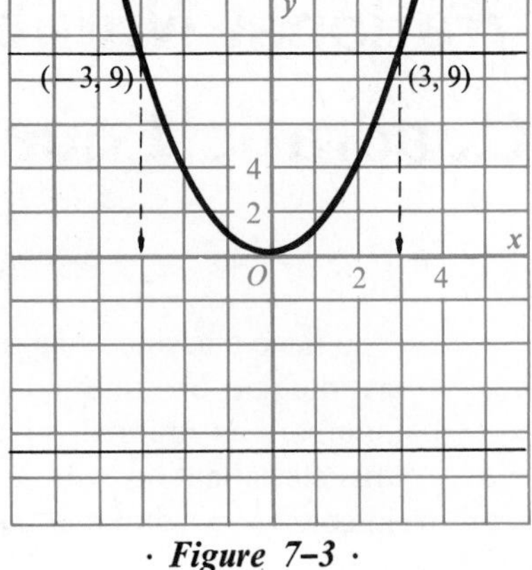

· *Figure 7–3* ·

If n is an odd positive integer (Figure 7–2), any horizontal line intersects the graph of $y = x^n$ in exactly one point. For example, Figure 7–4 shows that the graph of $y = 8$ intersects the graph of $y = x^3$ in the single point $(2, 8)$. Thus, $x^3 = 8$ has just one real root, namely, 2. Do you see that the line $y = -8$ cuts the curve only at $(-2, -8)$ and, therefore, that $x^3 = -8$ has the single real root -2?

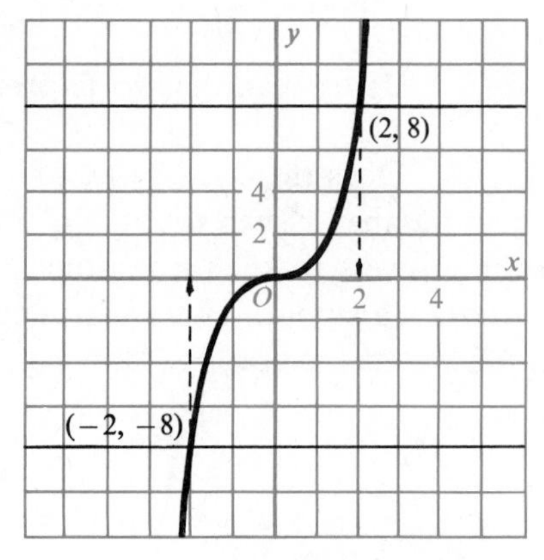

· *Figure 7–4* ·

For every positive integer n, any solution of $x^n = b$ is called an nth root of b.

Thus, for $n = 2$ and $b = 9$,

the solutions of $x^2 = 9$, namely, 3 and -3,

are 2nd roots (*square roots*) of 9.

And if $n = 3$ and $b = 8$, we have $x^3 = 8$;

2 is a 3rd root (*cube root*) of 8.

The following chart summarizes the facts about real nth roots of b suggested by considering the points common to the graphs of $y = b$ and $y = x^n$, as we did in Figures 7–3 and 7–4.

Number and Nature of Real *n*th Roots of *b*

For →	$b > 0$	$b < 0$	$b = 0$
when n is even	one positive root one negative root	no real roots	one real root, namely, 0
when n is odd	one positive root no negative root	one negative root no positive root	one real root, namely, 0

Special symbolism is used in indicating roots. The symbol $\sqrt[n]{b}$, called a **radical**, and read, "the principal nth root of b," or simply "the nth root of b," designates:

1. **The nonnegative *n*th root of *b* if *n* is even and $b \geq 0$. In this case $-\sqrt[n]{b}$ denotes the negative *n*th root of *b*, if $b \neq 0$.**

   For example, $\sqrt[2]{36} = 6$, $-\sqrt[4]{81} = -3$, $\sqrt[4]{0} = 0$.

2. **The single real *n*th root of *b* if *n* is odd.**

   For example, $\sqrt[3]{-125} = -5$, $\sqrt[5]{32} = 2$.

If n is even and $b < 0$, *no meaning is assigned* to the symbol $\sqrt[n]{b}$ in the system of real numbers. For example, $\sqrt[6]{-64}$ is not defined in the system of real numbers.

Notice that when $\sqrt[n]{b}$ is a real number, its definition implies $(\sqrt[n]{b})^n = b$. Can you simplify $\sqrt[n]{b^n}$? If n is an odd positive integer, $\sqrt[n]{b^n} = b$; for example, $\sqrt[3]{2^3} = 2$ and $\sqrt[3]{(-4)^3} = -4$. But, if n is an even positive integer, $\sqrt[n]{b^n} = |b|$, because radicals of even index designate nonnegative numbers; for example, $\sqrt[4]{2^4} = 2$ and $\sqrt[4]{(-2)^4} = |-2| = 2$.

Commonly, n, the **root index**, which signifies the root denoted, is omitted from square root radicals. In writing a radical, be sure the bar covers only the **radicand**, the expression whose root is denoted. Thus, $\sqrt{25 - 16} = \sqrt{9} = 3$, but $\sqrt{25} - 16 = 5 - 16 = -11$.

Oral Exercises

State the real roots of the equations.

SAMPLE 1. $3x^2 = 7$ *What you say:* $\sqrt{\frac{7}{3}}, -\sqrt{\frac{7}{3}}$.

1. $2x^2 = 5$
2. $8x^2 = 21$
3. $3x^3 = 1$
4. $5x^3 = -2$
5. $2x^4 - 1 = 0$
6. $3x^4 - 1 = 0$
7. $x^9 + 10 = 0$
8. $x^8 + 10 = 0$

State the restrictions, if any, on the real values of the variables for the given sentences to be true.

SAMPLE 2. $\sqrt{(x-2)^2} = x - 2$

What you say: $x - 2 \geq 0$; that is, $x \geq 2$.

9. $\sqrt{1+y} = 0$
10. $\sqrt{4-t} = 0$
11. $\sqrt[4]{(x+1)^4} = x + 1$
12. $\sqrt[4]{(y-2)^4} = |y-2|$
13. $\sqrt[3]{8x^9} = 2x^3$
14. $\sqrt[3]{-27y^{15}} = -3y^5$
15. $\sqrt{a^2+25} = a + 5$
16. $\sqrt[5]{b^5+32} = b + 2$
17. $\sqrt[6]{(r-1)^{12}} = (r-1)^2$
18. $\sqrt[8]{(p^2+1)^{24}} = (p^2+1)^3$
19. $\sqrt{r^2s^4t^2} = |r|s^2t$
20. $\sqrt[6]{a^6b^{18}c^{12}} = |a|b^3c^2$
21. $\sqrt[10]{w^3}$ denotes a real number.
22. $\sqrt[4]{16a^5}$ denotes a real number.
23. $\sqrt{4-y^2}$ denotes a real number.
24. $\sqrt{v^2-9}$ denotes a real number.

Written Exercises

Using large scales on the axes, carefully draw on separate sheets of paper graphs of $y = x^2$ and $y = x^3$ for $-2 \leq x \leq 2$. Refer to Tables 3 and 4, in the Appendix, for values of x^2 and x^3. Then, use the graphs to estimate to the nearest tenth of a unit each of the given numbers.

A

1. $\sqrt{3}$
2. $-\sqrt{3}$
3. $\sqrt{1.5}$
4. $\sqrt{0.5}$
5. $-\sqrt{\frac{7}{2}}$
6. $\sqrt{\frac{5}{2}}$
7. $-\sqrt{\frac{11}{5}}$
8. $-\sqrt{\frac{13}{5}}$
9. $\sqrt[3]{3}$
10. $\sqrt[3]{-5}$
11. $\sqrt[3]{-1.5}$
12. $\sqrt[3]{3.5}$
13. $\sqrt[3]{0.8}$
14. $\sqrt[3]{\frac{26}{5}}$
15. $\sqrt[3]{-\frac{11}{2}}$
16. $\sqrt[3]{-\frac{1}{2}}$

Solve. Use {rational numbers} as the replacement set of the variable.

SAMPLE. $25r^2 = 144$

Solution: $25r^2 = 144$

$r^2 = \frac{144}{25}$

$r^2 = (\frac{12}{5})^2$

or $r = \frac{12}{5}, -\frac{12}{5}$.

$\{-\frac{12}{5}, \frac{12}{5}\}$, **Answer.**

17. $36x^2 = 49$

18. $64y^2 = 121$

19. $64t^3 + 125 = 0$

20. $27t^3 - 343 = 0$

21. $625r^4 + 1 = 0$

22. $1 + 64s^6 = 0$

23. $1.21w^2 - 1 = 0$

24. $3.24k^2 - 1 = 0$

B **25.** Solve $\sqrt[4]{t^4} - t = 24$.

26. Solve $r - \sqrt[6]{r^6} + 16 = 0$.

27. If $a^2 + b^2 = 20$ and $ab = -2$, find the positive value of $a + b$.

28. If $k^2 + m^2 = 43$ and $km = -3$, find the negative value of $k - m$.

29. If $r^2 + s^2 = 13$ and $rs = 6$, find the negative value of $\frac{1}{r} + \frac{1}{s}$.

30. If $(t - v)^2 = 7$ and $tv = 14$, find the positive value of $\frac{1}{t} + \frac{1}{v}$.

C **31.** **a.** Prove: If $0 < x < 1$, then $0 < x^2 < x$ and $0 < x^3 < x$.

b. Use the results of **(a)** to explain why the graphs of $y = x^2$ and $y = x^3$ are below that of $y = x$ in the interval $0 < x < 1$.

32. **a.** Prove: If $x > 1$, then $x^2 > x$ and $x^3 > x$.

b. Use the result of **(a)** to explain why the graphs of $y = x^2$ and $y = x^3$ are above that of $y = x$, if $x > 1$.

33. Prove: If $a > b > 0$, then $\sqrt{a} > \sqrt{b}$.
Hint: $a - b = (\sqrt{a} + \sqrt{b})(\sqrt{a} - \sqrt{b})$.

34. Prove: If $\sqrt{a} > \sqrt{b}$, then $a > b$. (*Hint:* Show that $a > \sqrt{a}\sqrt{b}$ and $\sqrt{a}\sqrt{b} > b$.) Use this result to explain why a positive number cannot have more than one positive square root.

7–2 Rational and Irrational Roots

You recall that a rational number is a real number, such as $\frac{3}{4}$, $2\frac{1}{3}$, or -9, which can be expressed as a ratio of integers. Can you express numbers such as $\sqrt{2}$, $\sqrt[3]{5}$, and $-\sqrt[4]{3}$ as ratios of integers? Do you see that another way to state this question is to ask whether the equations $x^2 = 2$, $y^3 = 5$, and $z^4 = 3$ have rational roots?

To investigate the conditions a rational number must fulfill to be a root of a polynomial equation with integral coefficients, first consider the particular equation $21x^3 - 14x^2 + 30x - 20 = 0$, which has the root $\frac{2}{3}$, as shown by the substitution.

$$21x^3 - 14x^2 + 30x - 20 = 0$$
$$21(\tfrac{2}{3})^3 - 14(\tfrac{2}{3})^2 + 30(\tfrac{2}{3}) - 20 \stackrel{?}{=} 0$$
$$21 \cdot \tfrac{8}{27} - 14 \cdot \tfrac{4}{9} + 30 \cdot \tfrac{2}{3} - 20 \stackrel{?}{=} 0$$
$$\tfrac{56}{9} - \tfrac{56}{9} + 20 - 20 \stackrel{?}{=} 0$$
$$0 = 0 \checkmark$$

Do you see that 2, the numerator of the root $\frac{2}{3}$, is an integral factor of -20, the constant term of the equation? Notice also that 3, the denominator of $\frac{2}{3}$, is a factor of 21, the coefficient of the term of highest degree (called the **leading coefficient**).

What we have observed leads to the following theorem about rational roots of a **polynomial equation in simple form**; that is, an equation having 0 as one member and a polynomial in simple form as the other member.

THEOREM. If p and q denote integers ($q \neq 0$) such that $\frac{p}{q}$ is in lowest terms and represents a rational root of a polynomial equation in simple form with integral coefficients, then p must be an integral factor of the constant term and q an integral factor of the leading coefficient in the equation.

Before indicating the proof of this assertion, let us apply it.

EXAMPLE. Examine $x^2 = 2$ for rational roots.

Solution: In simple form the equation is $x^2 - 2 = 0$. The constant term is -2; the leading coefficient is 1. Therefore, if $\frac{p}{q}$, a fraction in lowest terms, denotes a root:

p is a factor of -2, that is, $p \in \{1, -1, 2, -2\}$	q is a factor of 1, that is, $q \in \{1, -1\}$

Thus, the only rational numbers to test as roots are the four *integers*, 1, -1, 2, -2. This is done by substituting 1, -1, 2, -2, in turn, in the equation $x^2 = 2$, as shown on the next page.

Test 1 and −1

$x^2 = 2$

$(1)^2 \stackrel{?}{=} 2 \qquad (-1)^2 \stackrel{?}{=} 2$

$1 = 2$ False

Test 2 and −2

$x^2 = 2$

$(2)^2 \stackrel{?}{=} 2 \qquad (-2)^2 \stackrel{?}{=} 2$

$4 = 2$ False

$\therefore x^2 = 2$ has no rational roots, **Answer.**

From this example it follows that $\sqrt{2}$ and $-\sqrt{2}$, the roots of $x^2 = 2$, are *not rational numbers.* Real numbers which are not rational are called **irrational numbers.** By considering the equation $x^n = b$, for any integer n exceeding 1 and any positive integer b, you can see that $\sqrt[n]{b}$ is an irrational number unless b is the nth power of an integer. Thus, $\sqrt[3]{5}$, $-\sqrt[4]{3}$, and $\sqrt[7]{64}$ are irrational numbers.

C

The proof of the theorem stated on page 256 is essentially the same for all positive integers n. Therefore, for simplicity take $n = 3$, and prove the theorem for the equation $ax^3 + bx^2 + cx + d = 0$, where a, b, c, and d denote integers, $a \neq 0$.

Proof

Let p and q be integers, $q \neq 0$, such that $\frac{p}{q}$ is in lowest terms.

1. Since $\frac{p}{q}$ is a root of the equation: $a\left(\frac{p}{q}\right)^3 + b\left(\frac{p}{q}\right)^2 + c\left(\frac{p}{q}\right) + d = 0$
2. Multiply each member by q^3: $ap^3 + bp^2q + cpq^2 + dq^3 = 0$
3. Add $-dq^3$ to each member: $ap^3 + bp^2q + cpq^2 = -dq^3$
4. Substitute $d(-q^3)$ for the right member: $ap^3 + bp^2q + cpq^2 = d(-q^3)$
5. Show p as a factor of the left member: $p(ap^2 + bpq + cq^2) = d(-q^3)$
6. Since q and $-q^3$ have the same *prime* factors (why?), and since p and q have 1 as their greatest common factor (why?), p and $-q^3$ have no integral factors in common but 1 and −1. Also, because sums and products of integers are integers, the left and right members of the equation in Step 5 denote integers. Since p is an integral factor of the left member, it is also a factor of the right member $d(-q^3)$, and, therefore, must be an integral factor of d. Hence, $p \in \{\text{integral factors of } d\}$.
7. To complete the proof, transform the equation in Step 2 to

$$q(bp^2 + cpq + dq^2) = a(-p^3).$$

Then reasoning as before, you can conclude $q \in \{\text{integral factors of } a\}$.

Oral Exercises

State a polynomial equation in simple form which has integral coefficients and the given number as a root.

SAMPLE 1. $\sqrt[3]{\frac{5}{2}}$ *What you say:* $x^3 = \frac{5}{2}$; $2x^3 - 5 = 0$

1. $\sqrt{3}$
2. $-\sqrt{11}$
3. $\sqrt[3]{9}$
4. $\sqrt[3]{-10}$
5. $\sqrt[5]{-3}$
6. $\sqrt[5]{10}$
7. $-\sqrt{\frac{1}{2}}$
8. $\sqrt{\frac{1}{7}}$
9. $\sqrt[4]{\frac{5}{3}}$
10. $\sqrt[4]{\frac{3}{11}}$
11. $-\sqrt[6]{\frac{13}{9}}$
12. $-\sqrt[6]{\frac{4}{17}}$

Name the rational numbers fulfilling the condition required of rational roots of the given equations.

SAMPLE 2. $3x^4 - 5x^2 - x - 7 = 0$

What you say: $1, -1, 7, -7, \frac{1}{3}, -\frac{1}{3}, \frac{7}{3}, -\frac{7}{3}$

13. $x^2 - 7 = 0$
14. $x^2 - 5 = 0$
15. $y^2 + 11 = 0$
16. $y^2 + 19 = 0$
17. $2m^3 - 3 = 0$
18. $3m^3 + 2 = 0$
19. $y^3 + y - 6 = 0$
20. $y^3 - y + 10 = 0$
21. $2t^4 - t^3 + 3t + 1 = 0$
22. $5t^3 - 2t^2 - 1 = 0$
23. $4z^2 + 2z + 2 = 0$
24. $9u^2 + u - 3 = 0$

Written Exercises

A

1–12. Use the method of the Example, page 256, to prove that each of the numbers listed in Oral Exercises 1–12 above is irrational. A proof for Sample 1 is given below.

SAMPLE. $\sqrt[3]{\frac{5}{2}}$

Proof: $\sqrt[3]{\frac{5}{2}}$ is a root of $2x^3 - 5 = 0$.

The only rational numbers to test as roots of this equation are denoted by $\frac{p}{q}$ where $p \in \{1, -1, 5, -5\}$ and $q \in \{1, -1, 2, -2\}$.

Therefore, $\frac{p}{q} \in \{1, -1, 5, -5, \frac{1}{2}, -\frac{1}{2}, \frac{5}{2}, -\frac{5}{2}\}$. Test each number by substitution, as follows:

$2(1)^3 - 5 = 0$ False $\quad 2(\frac{1}{2})^3 - 5 = 0$ False

$2(-1)^3 - 5 = 0$ False $\quad 2(-\frac{1}{2})^3 - 5 = 0$ False

$2(5)^3 - 5 = 0$ False $\quad 2(\frac{5}{2})^3 - 5 = 0$ False

$2(-5)^3 - 5 = 0$ False $\quad 2(-\frac{5}{2})^3 - 5 = 0$ False

$\therefore$ The equation has no rational roots, and so $\sqrt[3]{\frac{5}{2}}$ must be an irrational number.

The given number is a root of the equation. Use this fact to prove that the number is irrational.

13. $3 - \sqrt{7};\ x^2 - 6x + 2 = 0$

14. $-4 + \sqrt{17};\ y^2 + 8y - 1 = 0$

Find the rational roots of the given equations.

B

15. $y^3 - 2y^2 + 5y - 4 = 0$

16. $y^3 - 6y^2 + 11y - 6 = 0$

17. $z^3 - z^2 = 14z - 24$

18. $3z^2 + 10z = z^3 + 24$

19. $\frac{3}{2}t^3 - t^2 + t + \frac{1}{2} = 0$

20. $t^3 + t^2 - \frac{t}{4} - \frac{1}{4} = 0$

21. $2x^4 - 13x^3 - 13x^2 - 15x = 0$

22. $12x^4 - 20x^3 - x^2 + 6x = 0$

C

23. If b, c, and d are integers, explain why every rational root of the equation $x^3 + bx^2 + cx + d = 0$ must be an integer.

24. If b, c, and d are integers, explain why the only possible rational roots of $x^4 + bx^3 + cx^2 + dx + 1 = 0$ are 1 and -1.

25. Given that $\sqrt{2} + \sqrt{3}$ is a root of $x^4 - px^2 - qx + 1 = 0$, p and q being integers, show that $\sqrt{2} + \sqrt{3}$ is an irrational number.

26. Given that $\sqrt[3]{2} - \sqrt[3]{4}$ is a root of $x^3 + 6x + 2 = 0$, show that $\sqrt[3]{2} - \sqrt[3]{4}$ is an irrational number.

B 7-3 Rational Operations

The sum, product, difference, or quotient (divisor not zero) of two rational numbers is always a rational number. For this reason, addition, multiplication, subtraction, and division (except by 0) are called the **rational operations**

We now consider the nature of the result of combining a rational and an irrational number. The following example should be carefully studied.

EXAMPLE. Prove that $1 - \sqrt{2}$ is an irrational number.

Proof: (*Plan.* Show that the assumption *$1 - \sqrt{2}$ is a rational number* leads to a contradiction and so must be false.)
Suppose $1 - \sqrt{2}$ is a rational number, that is, there exist integers p and q ($q \neq 0$) such that

$$1 - \sqrt{2} = \frac{p}{q}$$

Then,
$$-\sqrt{2} = \frac{p}{q} - 1$$
$$\sqrt{2} = 1 - \frac{p}{q}$$
$$\therefore \sqrt{2} = \frac{q - p}{q}$$

But p, q, and therefore $q - p$, are integers and $q \neq 0$, so that $\frac{q-p}{q}$ denotes a rational number. But this contradicts the fact that $\sqrt{2}$ is irrational. Therefore, $1 - \sqrt{2}$ must be an irrational number.

The method employed in this example can be used to show that **any sum or difference of a rational and an irrational number is an irrational number.** Similar reasoning will prove that **the product or quotient of a nonzero rational and an irrational number will always be irrational.** Thus, from the fact that $\sqrt{2}$ is irrational, it follows that every number in this list is irrational:

$$1 + \sqrt{2}, \quad 2.5 + \sqrt{2}, \quad \sqrt{2} - 2, \quad 3\sqrt{2}, \quad \frac{1}{\sqrt{2}}, \quad -\tfrac{3}{2}\sqrt{2}, \quad 1 \div \frac{1}{\sqrt{2}}$$

The following illustrations show that the **rational operations performed with irrational numbers may result in either a rational or an irrational number.**

The result is rational	**The result is irrational**
$\sqrt{2} + (1 - \sqrt{2}) = 1$	$\sqrt[4]{5} + \sqrt[4]{5} = 2\sqrt[4]{5}$
$\sqrt{2} \times \sqrt{2} = 2$	$\sqrt{2}(1 - \sqrt{2}) = \sqrt{2} - 2$
$\sqrt[5]{6} - \sqrt[5]{6} = 0$	$2\sqrt[3]{11} - \sqrt[3]{11} = \sqrt[3]{11}$
$\frac{\sqrt[3]{7}}{\sqrt[3]{7}} = 1$	$\frac{\sqrt{2} - 1}{\sqrt{2}} = 1 - \frac{1}{\sqrt{2}}$

Written Exercises

Use the method of the example on page 260 to prove that each of the following numbers is irrational.

1. $\sqrt{15} - 1$
2. $2 + \sqrt{17}$
3. $2\sqrt[3]{9}$
4. $\frac{1}{2}\sqrt[5]{10}$
5. $-\frac{1}{\sqrt[3]{10}}$
6. $-\frac{4}{\sqrt[5]{3}}$
7. $\frac{1}{\sqrt{2}} + \frac{5}{2}$
8. $\frac{1}{\sqrt[3]{3}} - \frac{2}{3}$
9. Prove: If r is an irrational number, then $\sqrt{r}$ is also irrational.
10. Prove: If r is an irrational number, then $\sqrt[3]{r}$ is also irrational.

7–4 Decimals for Real Numbers

In Section 5–10 you studied the decimals of rational numbers. We now extend the discussion to include all real numbers.

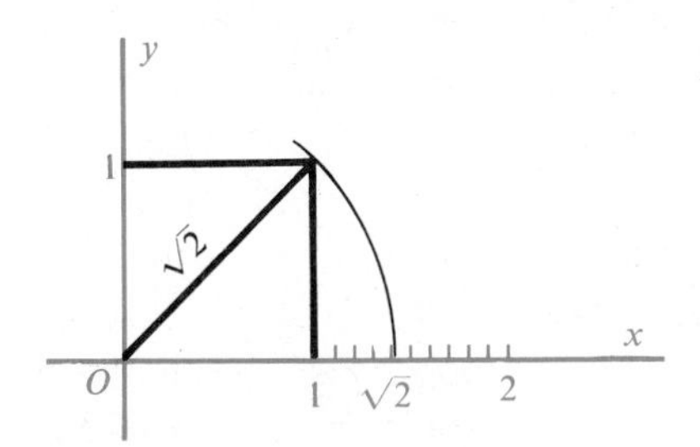

· *Figure 7–5* ·

One method of finding successive digits in the decimal for the irrational number $\sqrt{2}$ (the length of the diagonal of the unit square) is suggested in Figure 7–5. Since the point associated with $\sqrt{2}$ on the number line is between 1 and 2, you know that $1 < \sqrt{2} < 2$. By subdividing this unit interval into ten equal parts each of length 0.1, you can see that $1.4 < \sqrt{2} < 1.5$. To verify this fact, you may compute the successive squares: $(1.1)^2$, $(1.2)^2$, until you find that $(1.4)^2 = 1.96$ and $(1.5)^2 = 2.25$.

Next divide the interval from 1.4 to 1.5 into hundredths; computing squares, you discover $(1.41)^2 = 1.9881$ and $(1.42)^2 = 2.0164$. This means $1.41 < \sqrt{2} < 1.42$.

Dividing the interval from 1.41 to 1.42 into thousandths, you find that $1.414 < \sqrt{2} < 1.415$.

The chart summarizes the results (*p.* 261) and indicates that each time you repeat the procedure you obtain an additional digit in the decimal for $\sqrt{2}$. Will the process lead to a terminating or periodic decimal? The answer must be "No," because a terminating or periodic decimal represents a rational number, whereas $\sqrt{2}$ is irrational.

$1 < \sqrt{2} < 2$	$\sqrt{2} \doteq 1$
$1.4 < \sqrt{2} < 1.5$	$\sqrt{2} \doteq 1.4$
$1.41 < \sqrt{2} < 1.42$	$\sqrt{2} \doteq 1.41$
$1.414 < \sqrt{2} < 1.415$	$\sqrt{2} \doteq 1.414$
⋮	⋮

The procedure used to determine successive digits in the decimal for $\sqrt{2}$ is based on the following axiom of the set of real numbers:

Axiom of Completeness. Every decimal represents a real number, and every real number has a decimal representation.

Do you see that the set of rational numbers is not *complete* in the sense of this axiom? For example, if you write the decimal $5.050050005 \cdots$, which consists of a succession of 5's separated first by one 0, then two 0's, then three 0's, and so on, the decimal neither terminates nor repeats. Therefore, it cannot represent a rational number. However, because the set of *real* numbers is complete, this decimal does name a number, an *irrational* number.

In view of the axiom of completeness and the results of Section 5–10, you can classify real numbers according to the decimals representing them: *A rational number is a real number represented by a finite or periodic decimal; an irrational number is a real number represented by an infinite, nonperiodic decimal.*

Using decimal representations, you can illustrate the following property of the set of real numbers.

Property of density. Between any two real numbers, there is another real number.

EXAMPLE. Determine a rational number r and an irrational number s between $\frac{7}{5}$ and $\sqrt{2}$.

Solution: $\frac{7}{5} = 1.4$ and $1.41 < \sqrt{2}$.

Therefore, choose r and s so that $1.4 < r \leq 1.41$ and $1.4 < s < 1.41$. A few choices for r and s appear in the table. Can you describe the patterns in the decimals of the first two choices for s? The third choice is the number midway between $\frac{7}{5}$ and $\sqrt{2}$. Can you explain why this number is irrational?

r	s
1.401	1.4040040004 . . .
1.407	1.4071171117 . . .
1.4032	$\dfrac{\frac{7}{5} + \sqrt{2}}{2} = 0.7 + \frac{1}{2}\sqrt{2}$

Oral Exercises

Identify each of the following as a rational number or as an irrational one.

1. $0.12\overline{437}$
2. $\sqrt{2} + 0.\overline{3}$
3. $0.6 - \sqrt{3}$
4. $(0.\overline{2})(4.5)$
5. $0.8\overline{9} + 0.6\overline{25}$
6. $5 - 3.21\overline{43}$
7. $\sqrt[3]{2}\,(0.2\overline{71})$
8. $\dfrac{0.4\overline{1}}{\sqrt[5]{7}}$
9. 7.4343343334 . . .
10. 2.0101101110 . . .
11. The sum of the numbers in Exercises 9 and 10
12. The difference of the numbers in Exercises 9 and 10

Written Exercises

Use the method of this section to find the first three digits in the decimal for each of the following numbers.

A
1. $\sqrt{5}$
2. $-\sqrt{3}$
3. $-\sqrt[3]{2}$
4. $\sqrt[3]{7}$

Insert a rational and an irrational number between the given numbers.

5. $\frac{5}{8};\ \frac{3}{4}$
6. $\frac{2}{3};\ \frac{5}{6}$
7. $1\frac{2}{7};\ 1\frac{4}{9}$
8. $-2\frac{1}{3};\ -\frac{33}{10}$
9. $-\frac{4}{11};\ -0.367$
10. $0.464;\ \frac{5}{11}$

B
11. $\frac{63}{50}, \sqrt[3]{2}$
12. $\sqrt{2}, \sqrt{3}$
13. $\pi;\ \frac{22}{7}$
14. $-\pi;\ -\frac{157}{50}$. (Note: $\pi \doteq 3.14159$ and is irrational.)

C
15. Explain why the set of rational numbers has the property of density.
16. Explain why the set of integers does not have the property of density.

WORKING WITH RADICALS

7–5 Properties of Radicals

Can you see how the statements below imply useful properties of radicals? A comparison of results suggests the theorem which follows.

$$\sqrt[3]{27 \cdot 64} = \sqrt[3]{1728} = 12 \qquad \sqrt[3]{27} \cdot \sqrt[3]{64} = 3 \cdot 4 = 12$$
$$\therefore \sqrt[3]{27 \cdot 64} = \sqrt[3]{27} \cdot \sqrt[3]{64}$$

THEOREM. If n is a positive integer, and a, b, $\sqrt[n]{a}$ and $\sqrt[n]{b}$ denote real numbers, then $\sqrt[n]{ab} = \sqrt[n]{a}\sqrt[n]{b}$.

The proof of this **product property of radicals** involves two cases:

Case I. $a \geq 0$ and $b \geq 0$, with n a positive integer.

Case II. One or both of the numbers a and b negative, with n an odd positive integer.

Proof

Case I

Show that $\sqrt[n]{a}\sqrt[n]{b}$ is the nonnegative number whose *nth* power is ab.

1. Since $a \geq 0$ and $b \geq 0$, $\sqrt[n]{a} \geq 0$ and $\sqrt[n]{b} \geq 0$. (Why?)
   Therefore, $\sqrt[n]{a} \cdot \sqrt[n]{b} \geq 0$. (Why?)
2. Also, $(\sqrt[n]{a}\sqrt[n]{b})^n = (\sqrt[n]{a})^n(\sqrt[n]{b})^n$ (Why?)
   $= ab$ (Why?)

Steps 1 and 2 complete the proof of Case I. The proof of Case II is left as Exercises 57 and 58 on page 268.

When $a = b$ in the above theorem, you have $\sqrt[n]{b^2} = \sqrt[n]{b}\sqrt[n]{b} = (\sqrt[n]{b})^2$. This is a special case of the following theorem, to be proved as Exercise 61, page 268.

THEOREM. If m and n denote positive integers, and b and $\sqrt[n]{b}$ represent real numbers, then $\sqrt[n]{b^m} = (\sqrt[n]{b})^m$.

This theorem is especially useful in numerical work.

$$\sqrt[4]{16^3} = (\sqrt[4]{16})^3 = 2^3 = 8$$
$$\sqrt[3]{(-27)^2} = (\sqrt[3]{-27})^2 = (-3)^2 = 9$$

Check your understanding of the two theorems just given by expressing each of the following as a rational number or rational algebraic expression.

(1) $\sqrt[4]{8} \cdot \sqrt[4]{2}$	(4) $\sqrt[3]{9}\,\sqrt[3]{3}$	(7) $\sqrt{16^3}$	(10) $(2\sqrt{5})^2$
(2) $\sqrt[3]{2} \cdot \sqrt[3]{4}$	(5) $\sqrt{144w^4s^2}$	(8) $\sqrt{9^3}$	(11) $(\sqrt[4]{9})^2$
(3) $\sqrt[3]{5}\,\sqrt[3]{25}$	(6) $\sqrt{81a^8d^2}$	(9) $(3\sqrt{2})^2$	(12) $(\sqrt[3]{a})^6$

You can also obtain the following **quotient property of radicals:**

THEOREM. If n denotes a positive integer, and a, b, $\sqrt[n]{a}$, and $\sqrt[n]{b}$ represent real numbers ($b \neq 0$), then $\sqrt[n]{\dfrac{a}{b}} = \dfrac{\sqrt[n]{a}}{\sqrt[n]{b}}$.

$$\sqrt{\frac{y^8}{32{,}400}} = \sqrt{\frac{y^8}{4 \cdot 81 \cdot 100}} = \frac{\sqrt{y^8}}{\sqrt{4}\,\sqrt{81}\,\sqrt{100}} = \frac{y^4}{180}$$

$$\frac{\sqrt{98t^3}}{\sqrt{2t}} = \sqrt{\frac{98t^3}{2t}} = \sqrt{49t^2} = 7t, \text{ if } t > 0$$

The theorems of this section, together with the other number properties, enable us to simplify terms involving radicals of index n. Such terms are in *simple form* only when:

1. No integral radicand has as integral factor the nth power of any integer other than 1.
2. No polynomial radicand has as factor the nth power of any polynomial other than 1.
3. No fractions or powers involving negative exponents are under a radical sign.
4. No radical is in a denominator or appears with a negative exponent.

Study the following illustrations:

$$\sqrt[5]{32a^6} = \sqrt[5]{32a^5 \cdot a} = 2a\,\sqrt[5]{a}$$

$$\frac{6}{\sqrt{2}} = \frac{6 \cdot \sqrt{2}}{\sqrt{2} \cdot \sqrt{2}} = \frac{6\sqrt{2}}{2} = 3\sqrt{2}$$

$$\sqrt{\frac{7v^{-1}}{12}} = \sqrt{\frac{7}{12v}} = \frac{\sqrt{7}}{\sqrt{12v}} = \frac{\sqrt{7}}{\sqrt{4}\,\sqrt{3v}} = \frac{\sqrt{7} \cdot \sqrt{3v}}{2\sqrt{3v} \cdot \sqrt{3v}} = \frac{\sqrt{21v}}{6v}$$

$$\sqrt[3]{\frac{1}{200r^4}} = \frac{1}{\sqrt[3]{8r^3 \cdot 25r}} = \frac{1}{2r\sqrt[3]{25r}} = \frac{1 \cdot \sqrt[3]{5r^2}}{2r\sqrt[3]{25r} \cdot \sqrt[3]{5r^2}} = \frac{\sqrt[3]{5r^2}}{10r^2}$$

The last three examples illustrate the process, called **rationalizing the denominator**, of transforming a term involving radicals and fractions into an equivalent fraction with denominator free of radicals.

Oral Exercises

Express each of the following as a rational number, rational algebraic expression, or radical in simple form.

1. $\sqrt{12}$
2. $\sqrt{18}$
3. $\sqrt[3]{16}$
4. $\sqrt[3]{24}$
5. $\sqrt[3]{-125}$
6. $\sqrt[3]{-54}$
7. $-\sqrt{\dfrac{2a^2}{9}}$
8. $-\sqrt{\dfrac{3b^3}{4}}$
9. $\sqrt[3]{8^{-5}}$
10. $\sqrt[3]{64^{-2}}$

Identify each of the following as a rational or as an irrational number.

11. $\dfrac{\sqrt{8}}{\sqrt{2}}$
12. $\dfrac{\sqrt{10}}{\sqrt{2}}$
13. $\dfrac{\sqrt[4]{2}}{\sqrt[4]{16}}$
14. $\dfrac{\sqrt[3]{3}}{\sqrt[3]{81}}$
15. $\dfrac{-\sqrt{75}}{\sqrt{3}}$
16. $\dfrac{\sqrt{2}}{-\sqrt{72}}$

Written Exercises

Using Tables 3 and 4 in the Appendix give approximations correct to three significant figures of each of the following numbers.

SAMPLE 1. $\dfrac{1+\sqrt{3}}{\sqrt{2}}$

Solution:
$$\frac{1+\sqrt{3}}{\sqrt{2}} = \frac{1+\sqrt{3}}{\sqrt{2}} \cdot \frac{\sqrt{2}}{\sqrt{2}} = \frac{\sqrt{2}+\sqrt{6}}{2}$$
$$\doteq \frac{1.414 + 2.449}{2} \text{ (from Table 3)}$$
$$\doteq 1.93, \textbf{ Answer.}$$

SAMPLE 2. $\sqrt[3]{208}$

Solution: $\sqrt[3]{208} = \sqrt[3]{8}\sqrt[3]{26} = 2\sqrt[3]{26}$
$$\doteq 2(2.962) \text{ [Table 4] } \doteq 5.92, \textbf{ Answer.}$$

A

1. $3\sqrt{128}$
2. $\sqrt{1\frac{1}{8}}$
3. $\frac{2}{3}\sqrt{405}$
4. $\sqrt{1264}$
5. $\sqrt{.6}$
6. $\sqrt{.71}$
7. $\sqrt{35}\sqrt{\frac{3}{5}}$
8. $\sqrt{\frac{3}{4}}\sqrt{\frac{44}{3}}$
9. $(2\sqrt{60})(3\sqrt{30})$
10. $(\frac{1}{2}\sqrt{50})(\sqrt{10})$
11. $\dfrac{\sqrt[3]{-108}}{\sqrt[3]{2}}$
12. $\dfrac{\sqrt[3]{15}}{\sqrt[3]{-625}}$
13. $2\sqrt[3]{\frac{1}{9}}\sqrt[3]{1\frac{1}{8}}$
14. $\frac{1}{2}\sqrt[3]{\frac{5}{3}}\sqrt[3]{-4.8}$

Express each of the following in simple radical form. State restrictions, if any, on the values of the variables for the radicals to denote real numbers.

15. $\sqrt[4]{\frac{16}{27}}$
16. $\sqrt[4]{\frac{81}{8}}$
17. $4\sqrt[5]{-64}$
18. $20\sqrt[5]{-\frac{1}{625}}$
19. $\sqrt{32x^5}$
20. $\sqrt{242y^3}$
21. $\sqrt[3]{32x^3y}$
22. $\sqrt[3]{-54x^4y^4}$
23. $\sqrt[5]{a^6b^5}$
24. $\sqrt[5]{x^7y^{10}}$
25. $\sqrt[5]{\dfrac{1}{a^2}}$
26. $\sqrt[3]{\dfrac{1}{x^4}}$
27. $\sqrt[5]{k^{-6}}$
28. $\sqrt[5]{m^{-7}}$
29. $\sqrt[6]{128x^{-8}y^{12}}$
30. $\sqrt[6]{729t^{-9}v^{18}}$
31. $(5\sqrt[3]{-16ab^2})(3\sqrt[3]{-2a^2b})$
32. $(3\sqrt[3]{-12xy^2})(5\sqrt[3]{-3x^2y})$
33. $\sqrt[4]{9gh^4}\sqrt[4]{27gh}$
34. $\sqrt[4]{5c^4d^7}\sqrt[4]{125c^2d^3}$
35. $\dfrac{8\sqrt{54x^5}}{4\sqrt{3x}}$
36. $\dfrac{5\sqrt{250y}}{15\sqrt{5y^3}}$
37. $\dfrac{1}{\sqrt{3a^2+1}}$
38. $\dfrac{1}{\sqrt{5a^2+2}}$
39. $\sqrt[6]{4k^{14}} \div \sqrt[6]{32k^2}$
40. $\sqrt[7]{-a^3b^{15}} \div \sqrt[7]{a^{10}b}$
41. $\sqrt{a^2 - 4a + 4}$
42. $\sqrt{1 - 6n + 9n^2}$

43. $\sqrt[5]{\left(-\dfrac{r^{-10}}{243}\right)^{-4}}$
44. $\sqrt[3]{\left(-\dfrac{64t^{-3}}{v^{42}}\right)^{-5}}$
45. $\dfrac{\sqrt[4]{2a^{-1}}}{\sqrt[4]{128a^{-5}}}$
46. $\dfrac{\sqrt[4]{4b^{-6}}}{\sqrt[4]{1296b^{-2}}}$
47. $\sqrt{\dfrac{1}{x^5 - x^4}}$
48. $\sqrt{\dfrac{1}{y^4 + 2y^5}}$
49. $\sqrt{\dfrac{(x+3)^4}{x^3 - 14x^2 + 49x}}$
50. $\sqrt{\dfrac{(y-2)^8}{36y + 12y^2 + y^3}}$

Express each of the following as a fraction with numerator free of radicals.

51. $\sqrt{\dfrac{3a}{5}}$

52. $\sqrt{\dfrac{5c}{7}}$

53. $\sqrt[3]{\dfrac{6(x+1)^5}{3(x+1)}}$

54. $\sqrt[3]{\dfrac{4(y-1)^9}{12(y-1)^4}}$

55. $\sqrt[4]{7(t^2+3)}$

56. $\sqrt[6]{5(v^2+4)}$

Assuming that a and b denote real numbers and that n represents a positive integer, prove each of the following statements, subject to the indicated additional restrictions.

C

57. $\sqrt[n]{ab} = \sqrt[n]{a}\,\sqrt[n]{b}$; n odd, $a < 0$ and $b < 0$.
Hint: As Step 1, show that $\sqrt[n]{ab}$ and $\sqrt[n]{a}\,\sqrt[n]{b}$ both denote positive numbers.

58. $\sqrt[n]{ab} = \sqrt[n]{a}\,\sqrt[n]{b}$; n odd, and one of the numbers a, b negative.
Hint: As Step 1, show that $\sqrt[n]{ab}$ and $\sqrt[n]{a}\,\sqrt[n]{b}$ both denote nonpositive numbers.

59. $\sqrt[n]{\dfrac{a}{b}} = \dfrac{\sqrt[n]{a}}{\sqrt[n]{b}}$; $a \geq 0,\ b > 0$.

60. $\sqrt[n]{\dfrac{a}{b}} = \dfrac{\sqrt[n]{a}}{\sqrt[n]{b}}$; n odd; $\dfrac{a}{b} < 0$.

61. $\sqrt[n]{b^m} = (\sqrt[n]{b})^m$; $\sqrt[n]{b}$ denotes a real number, m a positive integer.

62. $\sqrt[n]{b^{-m}} = (\sqrt[n]{b})^{-m}$; $b \neq 0$; $\sqrt[n]{b}$ denotes a real number; m a positive integer.
Hint: Apply the quotient property of radicals to $\sqrt[n]{b^{-m}}$ or $\sqrt[n]{\dfrac{1}{b^m}}$, and use the result of Exercise 61.

Problems

Express each answer in simple radical form, and approximate it to the nearest integer. Where needed, use $\pi \doteq \frac{22}{7}$.

A

1. Find the time T in seconds for a complete swing of a pendulum whose length L is 12 feet. $\left(T = 2\pi\sqrt{\dfrac{L}{32}}\right)$

2. Determine in miles per second the escape velocity V at the surface of a planet whose radius R is 4000 miles and on which the acceleration due to gravity g is $\frac{1}{165}$ miles per sec^2. $(V = \sqrt{2gR})$

3. The altitude h of a cone with volume $201\frac{1}{7}$ cubic inches is 6 inches. Find the radius r. $(V = \frac{1}{3}\pi r^2 h)$
4. Find the length of the diameter d of a sphere whose volume is 539 cubic meters. $(V = \frac{1}{6}\pi d^3)$
5. The maximum height h in feet attained by an object fired with an initial vertical velocity of v feet per second is given by $h = \dfrac{v^2}{64}$ (neglecting air resistance). Find the velocity required to shoot a projectile to an altitude of 5000 feet.
6. A sky diver left her plane at 10,000 feet and fell freely to an altitude of 2000 feet, where she opened her parachute. Determine the time t in seconds that she fell before opening her chute, if the distance d in feet fallen in free flight is $d = 16t^2$.

B

7. Find the circumference of a circle whose area is 128 square centimeters.
8. A man derives a dollars from his business one year and b dollars the next. By varying the use of his resources, he can determine a and b according to the formula $b = 10000 - \dfrac{a^2}{4900}$. If he wants to take \$7500 next year, how much can he take this year?
9. A cube and a sphere have the same surface area, 60.0 square feet. What is the ratio of their volumes? (For a sphere of radius r, surface area S, and volume V, $S = 4\pi r^2$ and $V = \frac{4}{3}\pi r^3$.)
10. According to Kepler's third law of planetary motion, the cubes of the average distances of the planets from the sun are proportional to the squares of their times of one revolution around the sun. If Saturn is half as far from the sun as Uranus, find the ratio of their times of revolution.

7-6 Simplifying Sums of Radicals

The distributive property permits you to write as a single term sums of radicals with the same index and radicand.

$$2\sqrt[3]{x} - 5\sqrt[3]{x} = (2 - 5)\sqrt[3]{x} = -3\sqrt[3]{x}$$

On the other hand, sums of radicals with different indexes or radicands can only be indicated.

$$\sqrt[3]{5} + \sqrt[4]{5} + 7\sqrt[4]{5} = \sqrt[3]{5} + 8\sqrt[4]{5}$$

By expressing each radical in simple form, you can sometimes combine terms in a sum of radicals.

EXAMPLE. Simplify $a\sqrt{28a^2} - a^2\sqrt{56} + \sqrt{63a^4}$, if $a > 0$.

Solution:

$$\begin{aligned} a\sqrt{28a^2} - a^2\sqrt{56} + \sqrt{63a^4} &= a\sqrt{4a^2 \cdot 7} - a^2\sqrt{4 \cdot 14} + \sqrt{9a^4 \cdot 7} \\ &= a(2a\sqrt{7}) - a^2(2\sqrt{14}) + 3a^2\sqrt{7} \\ &= 2a^2\sqrt{7} - 2a^2\sqrt{14} + 3a^2\sqrt{7} \\ &= 5a^2\sqrt{7} - 2a^2\sqrt{14} \text{ or} \\ & a^2(5\sqrt{7} - 2\sqrt{14}), \textbf{ Answer.} \end{aligned}$$

To simplify sums involving radicals:

1. Express each radical in simple form.
2. Use the distributive property to combine radicals with the same index and radicand.

Written Exercises

a. State whether each of the following numbers is rational or whether it is irrational.

b. If it is an irrational number, use Table 3 or 4 to find an approximation correct to three significant figures.

1. $\sqrt{35} - 6\sqrt{5}$

2. $\frac{1}{3}\sqrt{27} - 2\sqrt{3}$

3. $\frac{1}{10}\sqrt{50} - \frac{1}{6}\sqrt{18}$

4. $\sqrt[3]{-16} + \frac{1}{3}\sqrt[3]{432}$

5. $\frac{1}{3}\sqrt[3]{135} - \sqrt[3]{-40}$

6. $-\sqrt{2\frac{2}{3}} + 2\sqrt{4\frac{1}{6}}$

7. $\frac{1}{3}\sqrt{54} - 3\sqrt{96} + 2\sqrt{24}$

8. $2\sqrt{27} - 3\sqrt{48} + \frac{1}{5}\sqrt{75}$

9. $\sqrt[3]{-6\frac{2}{3}} + 3\sqrt[3]{125} + 2\sqrt[3]{\frac{5}{6}}$

10. $\sqrt[3]{-0.008} + \sqrt[3]{37.5} - 5\sqrt[3]{\frac{3}{10}}$

11. $3\sqrt[3]{\frac{1}{19}} + 2\sqrt[3]{3.75}$

12. $\sqrt[3]{\frac{1}{200}} - 6\sqrt[3]{\frac{4}{2700}}$

Express each of the following in simple form.

13. $5\sqrt[4]{80} - 9\sqrt[4]{\frac{5}{16}}$

14. $\sqrt[5]{\frac{1}{8}} - \frac{1}{2}\sqrt[5]{972}$

15. $x\sqrt{4x} - 25\sqrt{25x^3} + \sqrt{81x^3}$, $x \geq 0$

16. $\sqrt{18a^4} - 3\sqrt{8a^4} + 2\sqrt{50a^4}$

17. $2\sqrt[4]{64y^8} - \sqrt[4]{4y^8} + \sqrt[4]{324}$

18. $x\sqrt[4]{16x} + 3\sqrt[4]{x^5} - x\sqrt[4]{2401}$, $x \geq 0$

19. $\sqrt[3]{625y^5} + y\sqrt[3]{5y^3} + \sqrt[3]{-40y^2}$

20. $\sqrt[5]{96z^{16}} + z^2\sqrt[5]{243z^6} - z\sqrt[5]{-9375z^{11}}$

21. $5\sqrt[3]{24y} - \frac{2y^2}{3}\sqrt[3]{\frac{81}{y^2}}, y \neq 0$

23. $\sqrt{\frac{n^2}{9} + \frac{n^2}{16}} + \frac{n}{5}, n < 0$

B

22. $z^3\sqrt[5]{\frac{10}{z^3}} - \frac{1}{2}\sqrt[5]{320z^{12}}, z \neq 0$

24. $2\sqrt[4]{5t^4 + \frac{t^4}{16}} + \sqrt[3]{t^3}, t < 0$

25. $\frac{1}{\sqrt{x^3}} - \frac{2}{x\sqrt{x}}, x > 0$

26. $\frac{1}{\sqrt[3]{(x-2)^2}} + \frac{1}{\sqrt[3]{(x+2)^2}}, x \notin \{2, -2\}$

Determine the real roots of each equation.

27. $x\sqrt{3} + \sqrt{6} = \sqrt{150} - x\sqrt{27}$

28. $\sqrt[3]{250} - t\sqrt[3]{32} = \sqrt[3]{4t^3} - \sqrt[3]{2}$

29. $\sqrt[3]{v} + 3\sqrt[3]{v} = 7 - \sqrt[3]{27v}$

30. $\sqrt[4]{y} + \sqrt[4]{625y} = 2(1 + \sqrt[4]{y})$

31. $(x - 1)^2 = 28$

32. $(x + 2)^2 = 45$

33. $121(t + 5)^2 = 2$

34. $49(3 - t)^2 = 7$

35. $x^4 - 11x^2 - 12 = 0$

36. $v^6 + 7v^3 - 8 = 0$

By assigning the given values to the variables, show that there are real numbers for which each statement is *false*.

37. $\sqrt{a + b} = \sqrt{a} + \sqrt{b}, a = 9, b = 16$

38. $\sqrt[3]{a} - \sqrt[3]{b} = \sqrt[3]{a - b}, a = 8, b = 1$

39. $\frac{\sqrt[3]{a + b}}{\sqrt[3]{a}} = 1 + \sqrt[3]{b}, a = 8, b = 19$

40. $\frac{1}{\sqrt{a}} + \frac{1}{\sqrt{b}} = \frac{1}{\sqrt{a + b}}, a = b = 1$

Products of Sums Containing Radicals

7–7 In working with products of sums whose terms involve radicals, you usually express results in simple form.

Simplify $(2 - \sqrt{3})(\sqrt{6} - \sqrt{2})$.

EXAMPLE 1.

Solution:

$$(2 - \sqrt{3})(\sqrt{6} - \sqrt{2}) = 2\sqrt{6} - 2\sqrt{2} - \sqrt{18} + \sqrt{6}$$
$$= 2\sqrt{6} - 2\sqrt{2} - 3\sqrt{2} + \sqrt{6}$$
$$= 3\sqrt{6} - 5\sqrt{2}, \textbf{ Answer.}$$

EXAMPLE 2. Rationalize the denominator of $\frac{3}{2\sqrt{7} - \sqrt{10}}$.

Solution: Use the fact that $(a + b)(a - b) = a^2 - b^2$; $(2\sqrt{7} - \sqrt{10})(2\sqrt{7} + \sqrt{10}) = (2\sqrt{7})^2 - (\sqrt{10})^2$.

$$\frac{3}{2\sqrt{7} - \sqrt{10}} \cdot \frac{2\sqrt{7} + \sqrt{10}}{2\sqrt{7} + \sqrt{10}} = \frac{3(2\sqrt{7} + \sqrt{10})}{28 - 10}$$

$$= \frac{3(2\sqrt{7} + \sqrt{10})}{18} = \frac{2\sqrt{7} + \sqrt{10}}{6}, \text{ **Answer.**}$$

Using radicals, you can factor certain quadratic polynomials which are irreducible over the set of polynomials with integral coefficients.

EXAMPLE 3. Factor $x^2 - 8$ completely over the set of polynomials with real coefficients.

Solution: $x^2 - 8 = x^2 - (\sqrt{8})^2 = (x + \sqrt{8})(x - \sqrt{8})$

$\therefore x^2 - 8 = (x + 2\sqrt{2})(x - 2\sqrt{2})$.

Written Exercises

Express in simple form.

A

1. $5\sqrt{10}(3\sqrt{2} - \sqrt{5})$

2. $-2\sqrt{21}(\sqrt{7} + 2\sqrt{3})$

3. $(\sqrt{6} - \sqrt{7})(\sqrt{6} + \sqrt{7})$

4. $(\sqrt{12} + \sqrt{20})(\sqrt{12} - \sqrt{20})$

5. $(\sqrt{3} + \sqrt{2})^2$

6. $(\sqrt{5} - \sqrt{7})^2$

7. $\left(\frac{1 + \sqrt{3}}{2}\right)^2$

8. $\left(\frac{4 - \sqrt{5}}{2}\right)^2$

9. $(5\sqrt{6} + 1)(2\sqrt{6} - 3)$

10. $(4\sqrt{11} - 3)(5\sqrt{11} - 2)$

11. $(\sqrt[4]{2} + 1)(\sqrt[4]{2} - 1)$

12. $(5\sqrt[3]{4} - 1)(5\sqrt[3]{4} + 1)$

13. $(\sqrt[3]{a^2} - 1)(\sqrt[3]{a} + a)$

14. $(\sqrt[4]{a^3} + a)(\sqrt[4]{a} - 1)$, $a \geq 0$

15. $\frac{3}{\sqrt{7} + 1}$

16. $\frac{3}{1 - \sqrt{3}}$

17. $-\frac{13}{\sqrt{3} + \sqrt{2}}$

18. $\dfrac{6}{\sqrt{5} - \sqrt{3}}$

19. $\dfrac{7}{2 + \sqrt{5}}$

20. $-\dfrac{9}{\sqrt{15} - 4}$

21. $\dfrac{13}{5\sqrt{3} - 7}$

22. $\dfrac{12}{4 + 3\sqrt{6}}$

B

23. $(\sqrt[3]{7} - \sqrt[3]{3})(\sqrt[3]{49} + \sqrt[3]{21} + \sqrt[3]{9})$

24. $(\sqrt[3]{5} + \sqrt[3]{2})(\sqrt[3]{25} - \sqrt[3]{10} + \sqrt[3]{4})$

25. $(\sqrt[3]{a} + \sqrt[3]{b})(\sqrt[3]{a^2} - \sqrt[3]{ab} + \sqrt[3]{b^2})$

26. $(\sqrt[3]{r} - \sqrt[3]{s})(\sqrt[3]{r^2} + \sqrt[3]{rs} + \sqrt[3]{s^2})$

27. $\dfrac{\sqrt{a} + \sqrt{b}}{\sqrt{a} - \sqrt{b}} + \dfrac{\sqrt{a} - \sqrt{b}}{\sqrt{a} + \sqrt{b}}, \ a > b > 0$

28. $\dfrac{\sqrt[3]{x}}{\sqrt[3]{x} - 1} + \dfrac{\sqrt[3]{x^2} - 1}{\sqrt[3]{x^2} + \sqrt[3]{x} + 1}$

29. $\dfrac{1}{3 + \sqrt{3}} + \dfrac{1}{\sqrt{3} - 3} + \dfrac{1}{\sqrt{3}}$

30. $\dfrac{\sqrt{x} - \dfrac{1}{\sqrt{x}}}{\dfrac{1 - \sqrt{x}}{\sqrt{x}}}$

31. $\dfrac{1}{\sqrt{x + 1} + 2}$

32. $\dfrac{5}{2 - \sqrt{1 - y}}$

33. $\dfrac{1}{\sqrt[3]{5} - 1}$

34. $\dfrac{1}{\sqrt[3]{7} + 1}$

35. $\dfrac{3\sqrt{2}}{2\sqrt{6} - \sqrt{3}}$

36. $\dfrac{2\sqrt{5}}{\sqrt{10} + 3\sqrt{2}}$

Express each of the following as a fraction with numerator free of radicals.

C

37. $\dfrac{z}{\sqrt{z - 1}} - \sqrt{z - 1}, \ z > 1$

38. $\dfrac{-2(a^2 - x^2)}{\sqrt{x^2 + a^2}} + \sqrt{x^2 + a^2}$

39. $\dfrac{x^2}{\sqrt[3]{(x^2 + 1)^2}} - \sqrt[3]{x^2 + 1}$

40. $\dfrac{2y^2 - a^2}{\sqrt[3]{y^2 - a^2}} - \sqrt[3]{(y^2 - a^2)^2}$

Factor each of the following completely over the set of polynomials with real coefficients.

41. $y^2 - 27$

42. $z^2 - 125$

43. $t^2 + 2\sqrt{6}\,t + 6$

44. $v^2 - 2\sqrt{10}\,v + 10$

45. $n^2 - 4\sqrt{3}\,n + 12$

46. $r^2 + 10\sqrt{2}\,r + 50$

47. $a^2 + 2ab + b^2 - 2$

48. $c^2 - 2cd + d^2 - 7$

RADICALS IN EQUATIONS

7–8 Using Radicals to Solve Quadratic Equations

The process of "completing the square" (page 238) can also be employed in solving quadratic equations. Study carefully the following parallel treatment.

$\mathbf{3x^2 + 10x + 2 = 0 \quad (3 \neq 0)}$	$\mathbf{ax^2 + bx + c = 0}$ **(assume** $\mathbf{a \neq 0}$**)**
$x^2 + \frac{10}{3}x + \frac{2}{3} = 0$	$x^2 + \frac{b}{a}x + \frac{c}{a} = 0$
$x^2 + \frac{10}{3}x = -\frac{2}{3}$	$x^2 + \frac{b}{a}x = -\frac{c}{a}$
$x^2 + \frac{10}{3}x + \left(\frac{5}{3}\right)^2 = \frac{-2}{3} + \left(\frac{5}{3}\right)^2$	$x^2 + \frac{b}{a}x + \left(\frac{b}{2a}\right)^2 = \frac{-c}{a} + \left(\frac{b}{2a}\right)^2$
$\left(x + \frac{5}{3}\right)^2 = \frac{-2}{3} + \frac{25}{9}$	$\left(x + \frac{b}{2a}\right)^2 = \frac{-c}{a} + \frac{b^2}{4a^2}$
$\left(x + \frac{5}{3}\right)^2 = \frac{19}{9}$	$\left(x + \frac{b}{2a}\right)^2 = \frac{b^2 - 4ac}{4a^2}$

For every real value of x, the left member of the last equation in each column denotes the square of a real number. Therefore, this equation is solvable in the set of real numbers if and only if its right member is greater than or equal to 0. Since 9 and $4a^2$ are the squares of nonnegative real numbers, they are positive. Hence we need consider the numerators only.

Since $\mathbf{19 \geq 0}$**:**	**Assume** $\mathbf{b^2 - 4ac \geq 0}$**:**
$x + \frac{5}{3} = \sqrt{\frac{19}{9}}$ or $-\sqrt{\frac{19}{9}}$	$x + \frac{b}{2a} = \sqrt{\frac{b^2 - 4ac}{4a^2}}$ or $-\sqrt{\frac{b^2 - 4ac}{4a^2}}$
$x + \frac{5}{3} = \frac{\sqrt{19}}{3}$ or $-\frac{\sqrt{19}}{3}$	$x + \frac{b}{2a} = \frac{\sqrt{b^2 - 4ac}}{2a}$ or $-\frac{\sqrt{b^2 - 4ac}}{2a}$
$x = -\frac{5}{3} \pm \frac{\sqrt{19}}{3}$	$x = \frac{-b}{2a} \pm \frac{\sqrt{b^2 - 4ac}}{2a}$
$x = \frac{-5 \pm \sqrt{19}}{3}$	$x = \frac{-b \pm \sqrt{b^2 - 4ac}}{2a}$ *
∴ the solution set is	∴ the solution set is
$\left\{\frac{-5 + \sqrt{19}}{3}, \frac{-5 - \sqrt{19}}{3}\right\}$	$\left\{\frac{-b + \sqrt{b^2 - 4ac}}{2a}, \frac{-b - \sqrt{b^2 - 4ac}}{2a}\right\}$

Do you see that $ax^2 + bx + c = 0$, $a \neq 0$, is equivalent to the compound open sentence:

$$\textbf{either} \quad x = \frac{-b + \sqrt{b^2 - 4ac}}{2a} \quad \textbf{or} \quad x = \frac{-b - \sqrt{b^2 - 4ac}}{2a}$$

which appears in combined form in the starred (*) step (page 274, bottom)? This combination of linear equations is called the **quadratic formula**. To solve any quadratic equation, you may substitute the values of a, b, and c in the quadratic formula, and find the root of each resulting linear equation.

EXAMPLE. Solve $3x^2 - 10x + 2 = 0$

Solution:

$$3x^2 - 10x + 2 = 0$$

$$x = \frac{-b \pm \sqrt{b^2 - 4ac}}{2a}; \ a = 3, \ b = -10, \ c = 2$$

$$x = \frac{-(-10) \pm \sqrt{(-10)^2 - 4(3)(2)}}{2(3)}$$

$$x = \frac{10 \pm \sqrt{100 - 24}}{6} = \frac{10 \pm \sqrt{76}}{6}$$

$$x = \frac{10 \pm 2\sqrt{19}}{6} = \frac{5 \pm \sqrt{19}}{3}$$

$\therefore$ the solution set is $\left\{\frac{5 + \sqrt{19}}{3}, \frac{5 - \sqrt{19}}{3}\right\}$, **Answer.**

To determine the *roots to the nearest tenth*, use Table 3, Appendix, to find $\sqrt{19}$ to *hundredths*, and substitute.

$$x \doteq \frac{5 - 4.35}{3}, \frac{5 + 4.35}{3}$$

$$x \doteq \frac{0.65}{3}, \quad \frac{9.35}{3}$$

$x \doteq 0.2, 3.1$, **Answer.**

Check:

$$3\left(\frac{5 + \sqrt{19}}{3}\right)^2 - 10\left(\frac{5 + \sqrt{19}}{3}\right) + 2 \stackrel{?}{=} 0$$

$$\frac{25 + 10\sqrt{19} + 19}{3} - \frac{50 + 10\sqrt{19}}{3} + 2 \stackrel{?}{=} 0$$

$$\frac{44 - 50 + 6}{3} \stackrel{?}{=} 0$$

Verifying the second root is left to you.

$$0 = 0 \checkmark$$

Oral Exercises

With the value of a positive, read each equation in the form $ax^2 + bx + c = 0$.

1. $7x^2 = 4x - 3$
2. $x^2 = 4 - x$
3. $4x = x^2$
4. $2x^2 = 9$
5. $5 = 4x - x^2$
6. $\frac{3}{2}x = 5x^2 + 8$
7. $-2x = 10 - 3x^2$
8. $2 - 5x - x^2 = 0$
9. $0 = 3 + \frac{7}{2}x - 2x^2$

Give the values of a, b, and c in each of the following equations.

10. $4x^2 - 3x - 7 = 0$
11. $2x^2 + 2x + 5 = 0$
12. $x^2 - 7 = 0$
13. $5x^2 - 9x = 0$
14. $x^2 + x + \sqrt{3} = 0$
15. $x^2 - \sqrt{2}x + 1 = 0$

Written Exercises

Use the indicated method to solve the following equations. Give irrational results in simple radical form and correct to tenths.

Solve by completing the square.

A

1. $t^2 - 6t - 7 = 0$
2. $y^2 - 4y - 21 = 0$
3. $v^2 - 8v - 1 = 0$
4. $k^2 - 10k + 1 = 0$
5. $3s^2 + 15s - 15 = 0$
6. $2d^2 - 6d - 54 = 0$
7. $6x^2 = 10 - 11x$
8. $11y = 10y^2 - 6$

Solve by using the quadratic formula.

9. $3r^2 + r = 1$
10. $5s^2 - s = 1$
11. $20 + 8y = 5y^2$
12. $2x + 7 = x^2$
13. $9n^2 + 24n + 16 = 0$
14. $4n^2 + 9 = 12n$
15. $3n^2 + 8n + 2 = 0$
16. $6n^2 + 10n + 3 = 0$
17. $\frac{y^2}{3} - \frac{y}{12} = \frac{1}{24}$
18. $\frac{t^2}{5} - \frac{t}{6} = \frac{1}{30}$
19. $2x(x - 2) = 3(4 - x)$
20. $5x(x + 2) = 4(3x + 1)$

Solve by any method.

B

21. $3.5y^2 - 0.1y - 0.6 = 0$
22. $0.03 = 0.17k - 0.2k^2$
23. $\frac{2}{a - 1} + \frac{1}{a + 1} = 3$
24. $\frac{3}{b - 2} - \frac{1}{b + 2} = 5$

25. $\dfrac{1}{m+3} - \dfrac{1}{3-m} = 2$

26. $\dfrac{1}{d+4} - \dfrac{1}{4-d} = 4$

27. $\dfrac{1}{t+3} + \dfrac{1}{t+1} = 1$

28. $\dfrac{1}{v+2} + \dfrac{1}{v+6} = 1$

29. $\dfrac{2r+10}{r+8} = \dfrac{r+5}{r+2} - \dfrac{9}{r^2+10r+16}$

30. $\dfrac{5p}{5p-2} = \dfrac{10p}{2-5p} + \dfrac{3}{25p^2-4}$

31. $5x^2 + x + 1 = 0$

32. $3u^2 + 2u + 4 = 0$

33. $k^2 - \sqrt{6}\,k + 1 = 0$

34. $t^2 + \sqrt{3}\,t - 2 = 0$

35. $d^2 + 2d = \sqrt{5}$

36. $m^2 - 3m = \sqrt{7}$

C

37. $\sqrt{2}\,x^2 - 2\sqrt{5}\,x = \sqrt{8}$

38. $\sqrt{27} - 2\sqrt{7}\,g = \sqrt{3}\,g^2$

39. $(1 - \sqrt{3})x^2 + (\sqrt{3} - 2)x + 1 = 0$

40. $(\sqrt{5} - 1)x^2 + (2 + \sqrt{5})x + 3 = 0$

41. $v^4 + 4v^2 - 1 = 0$

42. $1 - 6r^3 - r^6 = 0$

43. $(u^3 + 1)^2 - 2(u^3 + 1) - 2 = 0$

44. $(x^2 + x)^2 - 2(x^2 + x) + 3 = 0$

Factor each polynomial completely over the set of real numbers.

45. $x^2 - 2x - 1$

46. $x^2 + 2x - 2$

47. $y^3 + 6y^2 + 2y$

48. $y^3 - 8y^2 + 13y$

49. Show that if $c \neq 0$, an alternative form of the quadratic formula is

$$x = \frac{2c}{-b \pm \sqrt{b^2 - 4ac}}.$$

50. Prove that if each root of $ax^2 + bx + c = 0$, $a \neq 0$, is the reciprocal of the other, then $a = c$.

Problems

Unless otherwise directed, express irrational results in simple radical form.

1. One base of a trapezoid measures 5 cm. more than the other, while the altitude is $\frac{4}{5}$ as long as the longer base. Find the lengths of the bases if the area is 100 sq. cm.

2. The volume of a rectangular box 4 inches high is 136 cubic inches. If the perimeter of the base is 24 inches, find the dimensions of the box.

3. For the most pleasing effect, the ratio of the width of a rectangle to its length should equal the ratio of its length to the sum of its length and width. With this "Divine Proportion" in mind, design a rectangular picture frame having a perimeter of 50 inches. Give the dimensions to the nearest tenth of an inch.

4. The 86th floor observatory in the Empire State Building is 1050 feet above the street. The rate (in feet per minute) at which the elevator carries passengers to this level is 325 greater than 1000 times the time in minutes required for the trip. Find the rate of the elevator.

5. The volumes of two spheres differ by 336π cubic meters and the lengths of their radii differ by 6 meters. Find the length of the radius of the smaller sphere. ($V = \frac{4}{3}\pi r^3$)

6. The number of units of a certain commodity sold at price x is given by $90 - 0.1x$, while the total cost of producing and distributing these items is $0.1x^2 + 1.1x + 4$. If the profit on the sale is 865, find the number of units sold. (*Hint:* Profit = selling price − cost.)

B

7. From a rectangular sheet of metal 20 inches long and 12 inches wide an open rectangular box is made by cutting squares of equal area from the four corners and folding up the ends. If the area of the base of the box is 112 square inches, find the total area of the discarded squares.

8. As a result of tire trouble on the return leg of a 180-mile round trip that took 5 hours, Mr. Gorham's average speed coming home was 15 miles per hour less than his average speed going. If he had been able to maintain the same average speed coming home as going, what would his total driving time have been?

9. For any positive integer n, $n!$ is the product $1 \cdot 2 \cdot 3 \cdots n$. Determine the value for which $n! = 30(n-2)!$. (*Hint:* $n! = n(n-1) \cdot (n-2)!$ for $n \geq 3$.)

10. The sum of the squares of the first n consecutive integers, i.e., $1^2 + 2^2 + 3^2 + \cdots n^2$, is given by $\dfrac{n(n+1)(2n+1)}{6}$. The sum of the cubes of the first n integers is given by $\left[\dfrac{n(n+1)}{2}\right]^2$. Determine all values of n for which the sums of the first n squares and the first n cubes are equal.

11. An artist is to draw two rectangular diagrams of equal width. One is square. The height of the other is $\frac{1}{2}$ inch shorter than its width. If each dimension of each diagram is to be photo-reduced $\frac{1}{3}$ and the combined area of the two reduced diagrams is to be $7\frac{1}{3}$ square inches, what should be the dimensions of each diagram before reduction?

12. Mr. Friman is painting his rectangular kitchen, the length of which is 24.3 feet greater than its width. He does not paint the area occupied by the refrigerator, $2\frac{1}{2}' \times 2\frac{1}{2}'$; the sink, $2\frac{1}{2}' \times 2'$; the stove, $3.5' \times 1.75'$; and the built-in counter, $4' \times 1'$. If he paints an area of 752.125 square feet, what are the dimensions of the kitchen?

7–9 Relations between Roots and Coefficients of a Quadratic Equation

Do you recall (page 57) that the compound sentence "Either $x - 3 = 0$ or $x + 2 = 0$" is equivalent to the equation $(x - 3)(x + 2) = 0$? In general, if any real numbers r_1 and r_2 are the roots of a quadratic equation in x, then the quadratic equation must be equivalent to $(x - r_1)(x - r_2) = 0$ or

$$\boldsymbol{x^2 - (r_1 + r_2)x + r_1r_2 = 0}$$

By transforming the equation $ax^2 + bx + c = 0$, $a \neq 0$, to the equivalent form

$$\boldsymbol{x^2 + \frac{b}{a}x + \frac{c}{a} = 0,}$$

you can deduce the **property of the sum and product of the roots of a quadratic equation.**

THEOREM. The solution set of the equation $ax^2 + bx + c = 0$, $a \neq 0$, is $\{r_1, r_2\}$ if and only if $r_1 + r_2 = -\frac{b}{a}$ and $r_1r_2 = \frac{c}{a}$.

EXAMPLE 1. Is $\left\{\frac{1 + \sqrt{2}}{2}, \frac{1 - \sqrt{2}}{2}\right\}$ the solution set of $4x^2 - 4x - 1 = 0$?

Solution: $4x^2 - 4x - 1 = 0$; $a = 4$, $b = -4$, $c = -1$;

$$-\frac{b}{a} = 1, \quad \frac{c}{a} = -\frac{1}{4}.$$

$$r_1 + r_2 = \frac{1 + \sqrt{2}}{2} + \frac{1 - \sqrt{2}}{2} = 1 = -\frac{b}{a} \checkmark$$

$$r_1r_2 = \frac{1 + \sqrt{2}}{2} \times \frac{1 - \sqrt{2}}{2} = -\frac{1}{4} = \frac{c}{a} \checkmark$$

$\therefore \left\{\frac{1 + \sqrt{2}}{2}, \frac{1 - \sqrt{2}}{2}\right\}$ is the solution set of $4x^2 - 4x - 1 = 0$, **Answer.**

EXAMPLE 2. Find a quadratic equation whose roots are $1 + \sqrt{3}$ and $1 - \sqrt{3}$.

Solution:

$$(1 + \sqrt{3}) + (1 - \sqrt{3}) = 2 = -\frac{b}{a}$$

$$(1 + \sqrt{3})(1 - \sqrt{3}) = 1 - 3 = -2 = \frac{c}{a}$$

$\therefore x^2 - 2x - 2 = 0$, **Answer.**

Check: Show that the roots of $x^2 - 2x - 2 = 0$ are $1 \pm \sqrt{3}$ by using the quadratic formula. This check is left to you.

Oral Exercises

Give the sum and product of the roots of each equation.

1. $x^2 + 3x - 12 = 0$
2. $y^2 - 2y - 9 = 0$
3. $y^2 - 7y + 1 = 0$
4. $x^2 + 8x + 1 = 0$
5. $u^2 + 7u = 4$
6. $t^2 - 3t = 0$
7. $v^2 + dv + s = 0$
8. $w^2 - ew - f = 0$
9. $2p^2 + 3p = 0$
10. $3q^2 + 15q + 2 = 0$
11. $7x^2 - 14 = 0$
12. $6y^2 - 22 = 0$
13. $2x^2 + 8x - 1 = 0$
14. $4m^2 - m + 2 = 0$
15. $6n^2 - 3n = 4$

State a quadratic equation whose roots have the given sum and product.

16. $r_1 + r_2 = -8, r_1r_2 = 5$
17. $r_1 + r_2 = -7, r_1r_2 = 3$
18. $r_1 + r_2 = 6, r_1r_2 = -1$
19. $r_1 + r_2 = 9, r_1r_2 = -2$
20. $r_1 + r_2 = \sqrt{2}, r_1r_2 = 0$
21. $r_1 + r_2 = \sqrt{3}, r_1r_2 = 0$
22. $r_1 + r_2 = 0, r_1r_2 = 10$
23. $r_1 + r_2 = 0, r_1r_2 = -7$

Written Exercises

Write a quadratic equation in simple form having the given solution set.

A

1. $\{-3, -2\}$
2. $\{5, -7\}$
3. $\{-\frac{1}{2}, 2\}$
4. $\{-1, \frac{3}{4}\}$
5. $\{0, \frac{1}{3}\}$
6. $\{-\frac{1}{5}, 0\}$
7. $\{-\frac{1}{2}, -\frac{1}{3}\}$
8. $\{-\frac{1}{7}, -\frac{1}{9}\}$

9. $\{-2\}$
10. $\{-3\}$
11. $\{3 \pm \sqrt{2}\}$
12. $\{1 \pm \sqrt{5}\}$
13. $\left\{-\frac{1}{2} \pm \frac{\sqrt{3}}{4}\right\}$
14. $\left\{-\frac{1}{3} \pm \frac{\sqrt{7}}{2}\right\}$
15. $\{\sqrt{2} \pm \sqrt{3}\}$
16. $\{\sqrt{5} \pm \sqrt{7}\}$
17. $\{1 + \sqrt[3]{2}, 0\}$
18. $\{0, 1 - \sqrt[3]{4}\}$

B

19. If -5 is one root of $5x^2 + bx - 10 = 0$, find the other root and the value of b.
20. If 7 is one root of $14x^2 + bx + 7 = 0$, find the other root and write an equivalent equation with integral coefficients.
21. One root of $3x^2 - 12x + c = 0$ is $2 + \sqrt{3}$. Find the other root and the value of c.
22. One root of $2t^2 + 16t + c = 0$ is $-4 + \sqrt{7}$. Find the other root and the value of c.
23. If the equation $6x^2 + 18x + c = 0$ has equal roots, find the roots and the value of c.
24. One of the roots of $x^2 - mx - 25 = 0$ is the negative of the other. Find the roots and the value of m.

C

25. The linear term of a quadratic equation was incorrectly copied by a student who made no other mistake. She found the roots of her equation to be 6 and -2. Another student made an error only in copying the constant term and found -5 and -3 as the roots. What were the roots of the original equation?
26. Without solving the equation, find the sum of the reciprocals of the roots of $4x^2 + 6x - 15 = 0$.
27. Show that if $r_1 = \dfrac{-b + \sqrt{b^2 - 4ac}}{2a}$ and $r_2 = \dfrac{-b - \sqrt{b^2 - 4ac}}{2a}$, then $r_1 + r_2 = -\dfrac{b}{a}$ and $r_1 r_2 = \dfrac{c}{a}$.
28. Show that if r_1 and r_2 are the roots of $ax^2 + bx + c = 0$, then
$$r_1^2 + r_2^2 = \frac{b^2 - 2ac}{a^2}.$$

7–10 The Nature of the Roots of a Quadratic Equation

The graph of the function $f = \{(x, y): y = x^2 + 12x + 32\}$ appears as the curve farthest to the left in Figure 7–6 on the following page. Also in that figure are graphs of the functions $\{(x, y): y = -\frac{1}{2}x^2 + \sqrt{10}x - 5\}$ and $\{(x, y): y = x^2 - 14x + 53\}$.

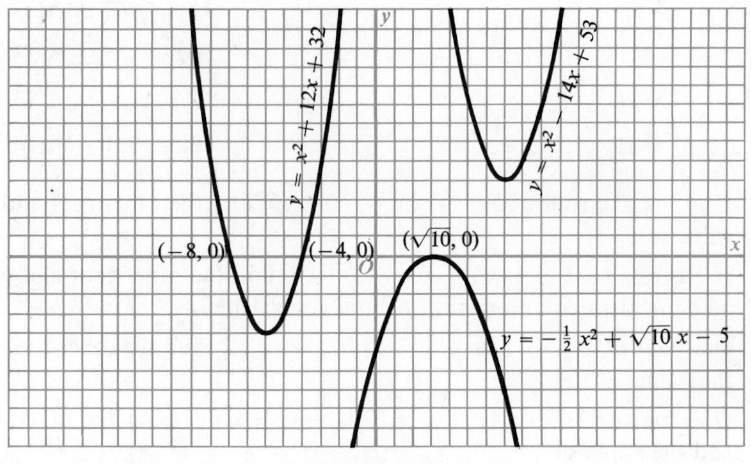

· *Figure 7–6* ·

Since the y-coordinate of every point on the x-axis is 0, you can determine the x-intercepts (if any) of each of these graphs by substituting 0 for y in the formula for the values of each function and solving the resulting quadratic equation in x.

Case 1

$$y = x^2 + 12x + 32$$
$$0 = x^2 + 12x + 32$$
$$x = \frac{-12 \pm \sqrt{144 - 128}}{2}$$
$$x = -6 \pm 2$$
$$x = -4 \text{ or } x = -8$$

Case 2

$$y = -\tfrac{1}{2}x^2 + \sqrt{10}\,x - 5$$
$$0 = -\tfrac{1}{2}x^2 + \sqrt{10}\,x - 5$$
$$x = \frac{-\sqrt{10} \pm \sqrt{10 - 10}}{-1}$$
$$x = \sqrt{10} - 0 \text{ or } \sqrt{10} + 0$$
$$x = \sqrt{10}$$

Case 3

$$y = x^2 - 14x + 53$$
$$0 = x^2 - 14x + 53$$
$$x = \frac{14 \pm \sqrt{196 - 212}}{2}$$
$$= \tfrac{1}{2}(14 \pm \sqrt{-16})$$

But $\sqrt{-16}$ does not exist in the set of real numbers.

The three cases are analyzed in the following chart.

	Number of points common to the x-axis and the graph of f	Number of different real roots of $f(x) = 0$	Value of $b^2 - 4ac$
Case 1	2	2	a positive number
Case 2	1	1, a double root	0
Case 3	0	0	a negative number

Do you see that the value of $b^2 - 4ac$ is the key to these cases? If $b^2 - 4ac > 0$, $\sqrt{b^2 - 4ac} > 0$. Thus, $ax^2 + bx + c = 0$ has two real unequal roots because

$$\frac{-b + \sqrt{b^2 - 4ac}}{2a} \neq \frac{-b - \sqrt{b^2 - 4ac}}{2a}.$$

But, if $b^2 - 4ac = 0$, then $\sqrt{b^2 - 4ac} = 0$; and hence the roots of $ax^2 + bx + c = 0$ are equal:

$$\frac{-b + 0}{2a} = \frac{-b - 0}{2a} = \frac{-b}{2a}.$$

But, for $b^2 - 4ac < 0$, no real root exists, since square roots of negative numbers do not exist in the real number system.

A quadratic equation with real coefficients can have

1. **Two different real roots,**
2. **a double real root, or**
3. **no real roots.**

Because the value of $b^2 - 4ac$ distinguishes the three cases, it is called the **discriminant** of the quadratic function; denote it by D.

The discriminant also enables you to tell whether the roots of a quadratic equation with *rational coefficients* are rational numbers. If a, b, and c are rational numbers, $a \neq 0$, $\frac{-b \pm \sqrt{b^2 - 4ac}}{2a}$ denotes a rational number if and only if $\sqrt{b^2 - 4ac}$ is rational (Section 7–3). But $\sqrt{b^2 - 4ac}$ is rational if and only if $b^2 - 4ac$ is the square of a rational number. Thus:

A quadratic equation with rational coefficients has rational roots if and only if its discriminant is the square of a rational number.

EXAMPLE 1. Determine the nature of the real roots of $2x^2 + 4x - 3 = 0$.

Solution: $2x^2 + 4x - 3 = 0;\ a = 2,\ b = 4,\ c = -3$

$$D = b^2 - 4ac = 4^2 - 4(2)(-3) = 40$$

Since $D > 0$, there are two unequal real roots.
Since D is not the square of a rational number, the roots are irrational numbers.

In the domain of a function f any value of x which satisfies the equation $f(x) = 0$ is said to be a **zero** of f. Notice that "zeros of the function f," "roots of the equation $f(x) = 0$," and "x-intercepts of the graph" are just different ways of referring to the same numbers.

EXAMPLE 2. What is the nature of the zeros of

$$\{(x, y): y = x^2 - 4\sqrt{3}\,x + 12\}?$$

Solution: $x^2 - 4\sqrt{3}\,x + 12 = 0;\ a = 1,\ b = -4\sqrt{3},\ c = 12,$

$$D = b^2 - 4ac = (-4\sqrt{3})^2 - 4 \cdot 1 \cdot 12 = 48 - 48 = 0$$

Since $D = 0$, there is one real zero.
Although D is the square of a rational number, $(0 = 0^2)$, the real zero is an irrational number because b is irrational.

Written Exercises

Without solving the equation, determine the nature of its roots.

A

1. $x^2 + 4x - 5 = 0$
2. $x^2 - 6x - 7 = 0$
3. $-3t^2 + 4t + 1 = 0$
4. $-5t^2 - t - 3 = 0$
5. $-7s^2 + 9s - 3 = 0$
6. $3s^2 - 4s + \frac{4}{3} = 0$
7. $\sqrt{5}\,z^2 = 6z - \sqrt{5}$
8. $x^2 + \frac{7}{4} = \sqrt{7}\,x$
9. $3x^2 + 7 = 0$
10. $\sqrt{2}\,v^2 - v = 0$

Without graphing the function, determine whether the graph has one, two, or no points in common with the x-axis. For each such point, state whether the coordinates are rational numbers.

11. $\{(x, y): y = -x^2 + 3x - 2\}$
12. $\{(x, y): y = x^2 + 8x + 16\}$
13. $\{(x, y): y = x^2 + 3x + 6\}$
14. $\{(x, y): y = 3x^2 - x - 1\}$

15. $\{(x, y): y = \frac{1}{2}x^2 + (1 - \sqrt{3})x - \sqrt{3}\}$
16. $\{(x, y): y = 2x^2 - 2\sqrt{2}\,x + 1\}$

Determine the values of k for which the graph of the function will have the indicated number of points in common with the x-axis.

17. $\{(x, y): y = x^2 + kx + 5\}; 1$
18. $\{(x, y): y = x^2 + kx + (k - 1)\}; 1$
19. $\{(x, y): y = x^2 + 4x - k\}; 0$
20. $\{(x, y): y = -x^2 + 8x - k\}; 2$

Let r denote a real constant. Show that over the set of real numbers $\emptyset$ is the solution set of each of the following equations in x.

C 21. $\dfrac{1}{x + r} = \dfrac{1}{x} + \dfrac{1}{r}$

22. $\dfrac{r}{x - r} = \dfrac{r}{x} - 1$

7–11 Solving Quadratic Inequalities

Figure 7–7 shows the graph of $\{(x, y): y = x^2 - 2x - 4\}$. Inspecting the graph, you see that $1 - \sqrt{5}$ and $1 + \sqrt{5}$, the roots of $x^2 - 2x - 4 = 0$, separate the other numbers of the x-axis into three sets:

$$R = \{x: x < 1 - \sqrt{5}\},$$
$$S = \{x: 1 - \sqrt{5} < x < 1 + \sqrt{5}\},$$
$$T = \{x: x > 1 + \sqrt{5}\}$$

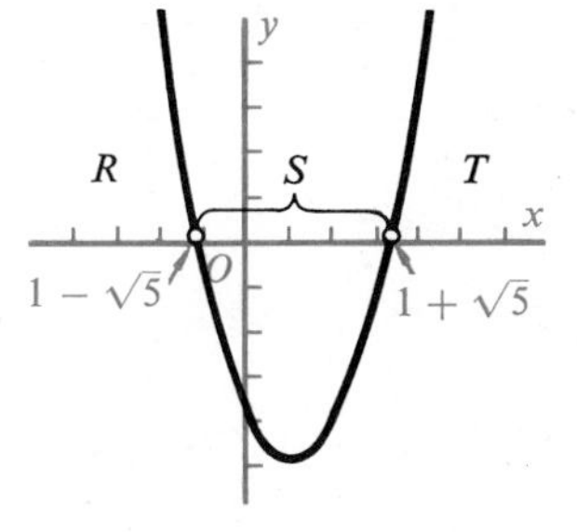

· *Figure 7–7* ·

Do you see that over any one of these subsets the value of $x^2 - 2x - 4$ (that is, the value of y) is *consistently positive* (graph is above the x-axis) or *consistently negative* (graph is below the x-axis)?

$x \in R$	$x \in S$	$x \in T$
$x^2 - 2x - 4 > 0$	$x^2 - 2x - 4 < 0$	$x^2 - 2x - 4 > 0$

Thus, to test whether $x^2 - 2x - 4$ denotes a positive number or whether it denotes a negative number for *every* value of x in one of these subsets, you need only determine the nature of $x^2 - 2x - 4$ for *any one* value of x in that subset.

EXAMPLE. Find the solution set of $3 - 4x - x^2 > 0$.

Solution:

1. Determine the roots of $3 - 4x - x^2 = 0$.

$$3 - 4x - x^2 = 0;\ a = -1,\ b = -4,\ c = 3$$

$$x = \frac{4 \pm \sqrt{(-4)^2 - 4(-1)(3)}}{2(-1)} = \frac{4 \pm \sqrt{28}}{-2}$$

$$x = -2 \pm \sqrt{7}$$

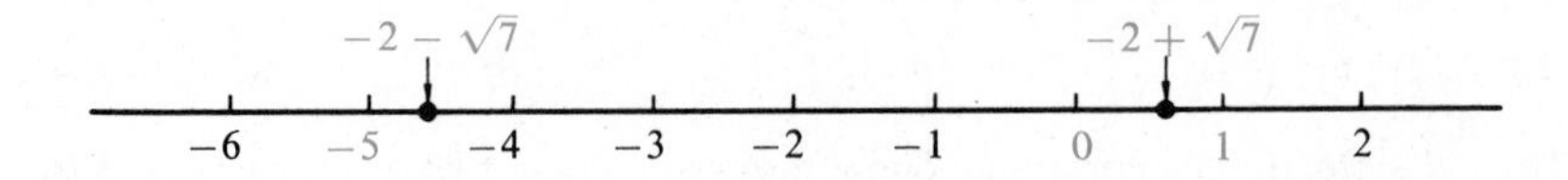

2. From each subset into which these numbers separate the set of real numbers, choose a number for which to evaluate $3 - 4x - x^2$.

Subset	Particular Number	$3 - 4x - x^2$
$x < -2 - \sqrt{7}$	-5	-2, negative
$-2 - \sqrt{7} < x < -2 + \sqrt{7}$	0	3, positive
$x > -2 + \sqrt{7}$	1	-2, negative

$\{x: 3 - 4x - x^2 > 0\} = \{x: -2 - \sqrt{7} < x < -2 + \sqrt{7}\}$, **Answer.**

Written Exercises

Determine the solution set of each inequality and show its graph on the number line.

A

1. $x^2 - 7 < 0$
2. $x^2 - 15 \geq 0$
3. $r^2 \geq \sqrt{3}\, r$
4. $p^2 < \sqrt{5}\, p$
5. $2t^2 + t \leq 6$
6. $2t^2 + 5t > 3$
7. $v^2 + 6v + 9 > 0$
8. $10s - s^2 - 25 < 0$
9. $x^2 + 10x \geq 11$
10. $x^2 - 8x \leq 6$
11. $d^2 + 3 \leq 2\sqrt{3}\, d$
12. $8 + w^2 \geq 4\sqrt{2}\, w$

B

13. $x^3 - 2x \geq 0$
14. $x^3 - 3x \leq 0$
15. $(x + 1)(x - 2)(x - 3) \leq 0$
16. $(x + 4)(x + 2)(x - 5) \geq 0$

Determine the values of k for which the equation will have the indicated number of different real roots.

C **17.** $z^2 + 2(k + 1)z + (2k + 3) = 0$; 2

18. $v^2 - (k - 1)v = 4\left(3 - \frac{k}{2}\right)$; 0

7–12 Irrational Equations

An equation having a variable in a radicand is called an **irrational** or a **radical equation**. A simple irrational equation is one like $\sqrt[3]{x - 1} = 2$, which you transform by cubing each member.

$$\sqrt[3]{x-1} = 2$$
$$(\sqrt[3]{x-1})^3 = 2^3$$
$$x - 1 = 8$$
$$x = 9$$

Check: $\sqrt[3]{9 - 1} \stackrel{?}{=} 2$

$\sqrt[3]{8} = 2$ ✓

$\therefore$ the solution set is $\{9\}$, **Answer.**

The first step in solving an equation having just one term with a variable in a radicand is to "isolate" that term in one member of the equation. Then raise each member to the integral power equal to the root index.

EXAMPLE 1. Solve $2 - y - 2\sqrt{y + 1} = 0$.

Solution:

1. Isolate the radical in one member of the equation.

$$2 - y - 2\sqrt{y+1} = 0$$
$$2 - y = 2\sqrt{y+1}$$

2. Square both members.

$$(2 - y)^2 = (2\sqrt{y+1})^2$$
$$4 - 4y + y^2 = 4y + 4$$

3. Solve the resulting equation.

$$y^2 - 8y = 0$$
$$y(y - 8) = 0$$
$$y = 0 \qquad y - 8 = 0$$
$$y = 8$$

4. Check.

Substitute and remember to take principal roots.

$2 - 0 - 2\sqrt{0+1} \stackrel{?}{=} 0$	$2 - 8 - 2\sqrt{8+1} \stackrel{?}{=} 0$
$2 - 2\sqrt{1} \stackrel{?}{=} 0$	$-6 - 2\sqrt{9} \stackrel{?}{=} 0$
$2 - 2 = 0$ ✓	$-6 - 6 \stackrel{?}{=} 0$, **No**

The solution set is $\{0\}$, **Answer.**

Can you explain why an "extraneous value" appeared, that is, why the "squared" equation in Step 2 is not equivalent to the given equation? Recall:

> If $a = b$, then $a^n = b^n$ for every positive integer n; but, *if n is an even integer* and $a^n = b^n$, *it need not be true that $a = b$.*

For example, $3^4 = (-3)^4$, but $3 \neq -3$.

To solve an equation having more than one term with a variable in a radicand, you may have to take the step of "raising to a power" more than once.

EXAMPLE 2. Solve $\sqrt{x} - 1 = \sqrt{2x + 1}$

Solution:

$$\begin{aligned} \sqrt{x} - 1 &= \sqrt{2x+1} \\ (\sqrt{x} - 1)^2 &= (\sqrt{2x+1})^2 \\ x - 2\sqrt{x} + 1 &= 2x + 1 \\ -2\sqrt{x} &= x \\ (-2\sqrt{x})^2 &= x^2 \\ 4x &= x^2 \\ x^2 - 4x &= 0 \\ x(x-4) &= 0 \end{aligned}$$

$$\begin{aligned} x &= 0 \\ \sqrt{0} - 1 &\stackrel{?}{=} \sqrt{2 \cdot 0 + 1} \\ -1 &\stackrel{?}{=} \sqrt{1} \\ -1 &\stackrel{?}{=} 1, \textbf{ No} \end{aligned}$$

$$\begin{aligned} x - 4 &= 0 \\ x &= 4 \\ \sqrt{4} - 1 &\stackrel{?}{=} \sqrt{2 \cdot 4 + 1} \\ 2 - 1 &\stackrel{?}{=} \sqrt{9} \\ 1 &\stackrel{?}{=} 3, \textbf{ No} \end{aligned}$$

The solution set is $\emptyset$, **Answer.**

Written Exercises

Find the solution set of each equation.

A

1. $\sqrt{m} - 8 = 0$
2. $\sqrt{t} - 4 = 0$
3. $\sqrt[3]{y + 2} = 4$
4. $\sqrt[3]{v + 1} = 3$
5. $\sqrt{5x + 1} + 6 = 10$
6. $\sqrt{1 + 2r} - 4 = -1$
7. $4 + \sqrt[4]{\frac{a}{2}} = 6$
8. $\sqrt[4]{\frac{b}{3}} - 2 = 1$
9. $\sqrt[3]{y^{-1}} = -2$
10. $\sqrt[3]{a^2} - 1 = 15$

11. $\sqrt{b^5} - 2 = 30$
12. $4\sqrt[3]{v^{-1}} + 12 = 0$
13. $\sqrt[4]{x^2 + x + 4} = 2$
14. $\sqrt[3]{s^2 + 2} - 3 = 0$
15. $\sqrt{y - 2} = 4 - y$
16. $\sqrt{x - 5} = x - 7$
17. $\sqrt{p^2 - 3} = p + 1$
18. $\sqrt{7 + a^2} = 1 - a$
19. $6 + 3\sqrt[3]{2n} = 0$
20. $6 + 2\sqrt{3n} = 0$
21. $2 + 5\sqrt{10n} = 0$
22. $2 - 3\sqrt[3]{2n + 1} = 0$
23. $\sqrt{3x^2 + 9x - 5} = 2x + 1$
24. $2\sqrt{x - 1} = x - 1$
25. $\sqrt{8m - 7} = m$
26. $\sqrt{19m - 12} = 2m$
27. $\sqrt{r^2 + 5} = r$
28. $\sqrt{4r^2 - 1} = 2r$

B

29. $\sqrt[3]{(5x + 7)^2} = 9$
30. $\sqrt{(3 + 3y)^3} = 27$
31. $\sqrt{x} + \sqrt{x - 3} = \dfrac{3}{\sqrt{x - 3}}$
32. $\sqrt{p + 6} - \dfrac{2}{\sqrt{p + 1}} = \sqrt{p + 1}$
33. $\sqrt{k - 5} = \sqrt{k} - 1$
34. $\sqrt{q + 12} + \sqrt{q} = 2$
35. $\sqrt{r + 5} + \sqrt{r} = 1$
36. $\sqrt{s - 8} + \sqrt{s} = 2$

Solve each of the following for the variable in red.

37. $r = \sqrt[3]{\dfrac{3w}{4\pi d}}$
38. $r = \sqrt[3]{\dfrac{2mM}{C}}$
39. $c = \sqrt{a^2 + b^2}$
40. $\sqrt{x + a} = \sqrt{x} + \sqrt{a},\ a > 0$
41. $v = \dfrac{1}{2}\sqrt{1 + \dfrac{T}{l}}$
42. $\dfrac{1}{d} = \sqrt{\dfrac{6F}{d} - 3}$

C

43. Determine a polynomial equation with integral coefficients and having $5 + 2\sqrt{7}$ as a root. Show that $5 - 2\sqrt{7}$ is also a root of the equation.
Hint: Start with $x = 5 + 2\sqrt{7}$.

44. Determine a polynomial equation with integral coefficients and having $\sqrt{2} + \sqrt{5}$ as a root. Using this equation, show that $\sqrt{2} + \sqrt{5}$ is an irrational number.
Hint: Start with $x = \sqrt{2} + \sqrt{5}$.

45. Prove: If r and s denote real numbers and $r^3 = s^3$, then

a. r and s are both zero, both positive, or both negative;

b. $r = s$.

Hint: Use the result of part **(a)** and $r^3 - s^3 = (r - s)(r^2 + rs + s^2)$.

46. Given that r and s are real numbers and $r^5 = s^5$, state all the conclusions you can draw about r and s. Prove your assertions.

Chapter Summary

Inventory of Structure and Method

1. For every positive integer n, any solution of $x^n = b$ is an ***n*th root** of b. The **radical** $\sqrt[n]{b}$ denotes the principal nth root of b. If n is odd, $\sqrt[n]{b^n} = b$; if n is even, $\sqrt[n]{b^n} = |b|$. For example, $\sqrt[5]{(-2)^5} = -2$, but $\sqrt[4]{(-2)^4} = 2$.

2. If a rational root of a polynomial equation in simple form with integral coefficients is expressed in lowest terms $\frac{p}{q}$, with $q \neq 0$, then p must be an integral factor of the constant term and q an integral factor of the leading coefficient. Any other real root of the equation is an **irrational number.**

3. **The Axiom of Completeness** guarantees that every decimal represents a real number and that every real number has a decimal representation. Decimals representing irrational numbers are neither repeating nor terminating. The **Property of Density** asserts that between any two real numbers, there is always another real number.

4. In simplifying radicals, you may use the **Product Property of Radicals,** $\sqrt[n]{ab} = \sqrt[n]{a} \cdot \sqrt[n]{b}$ (n, a positive integer, and $\sqrt[n]{a}$ and $\sqrt[n]{b}$, real numbers); the **Quotient Property of Radicals,** $\sqrt[n]{\frac{a}{b}} = \frac{\sqrt[n]{a}}{\sqrt[n]{b}}$ (with $b \neq 0$ an additional restriction); and the theorem: If m and n are positive integers and $\sqrt[n]{b}$ denotes a real number, then $\sqrt[n]{b^m} = (\sqrt[n]{b})^m$. A term containing a radical of index n is in simple form only when

   a. No integral factor (other than 1) of the radicand is an nth power.

   b. No polynomial factor (other than 1) of the radicand is an nth power.

   c. No fractions are in the radicand when expressed with positive exponents.

   d. No radical is in a denominator expressed with positive exponents.

5. You can write the **sum of radicals** having the same index and the same radicand as a single term by using the distributive property. You can

write the **product of radicals** having the same index as a single term by applying the product property of radicals.

6. The **Quadratic Formula,** $x = \frac{-b \pm \sqrt{b^2 - 4ac}}{2a}$ enables you to solve any quadratic equation of the form $ax^2 + bx + c = 0, a \neq 0$. The **sum of the roots** of such a quadratic equation is $-\frac{b}{a}$; the **product of the roots** is $\frac{c}{a}$; so that you may write $x^2 - (\text{sum of roots})x + (\text{product of roots}) = 0$ as an equivalent equation. From the value of the discriminant $b^2 - 4ac$ of a quadratic equation, you can tell whether its real roots are rational or irrational, and equal or unequal.
7. To solve an **irrational equation,** isolate the radical as one member and raise each member to the power corresponding to the root index.

Vocabulary and Spelling

nth root (of a number) (*p. 252*)
square root (of a number) (*p. 252*)
cube root (of a number) (*p. 252*)
principal root (of a number) (*p. 253*)
radical ($\sqrt[n]{b}$) (*p. 253*)
root index (*p. 253*)
radicand (*p. 253*)
polynomial equation in simple form (*p. 256*)
leading coefficient (*p. 256*)
irrational number (*p. 257*)
rational operation (*p. 259*)
property of density (*p. 262*)
product property of radicals (*p. 264*)
quotient property of radicals (*p. 265*)
rationalizing the denominator (*p. 266*)
quadratic formula (*p. 275*)
sum property of the roots (*p. 279*)
product property of the roots (*p. 279*)
discriminant (of a quadratic equation) (*p. 283*)
zero of a function (*p. 284*)
irrational (radical) equation (*p. 287*)

Chapter Test

7–1 **1.** Solve in {rational numbers}: $1 - 81n^4 = 0$

7–2 **2.** Given that $1 + \sqrt{2}$ is a root of $x^2 - 2x - 1 = 0$, prove that $1 + \sqrt{2}$ is an irrational number.

7–3 **3.** Use the method in Section 7–3 to show that $1 + \sqrt{3}$ is an irrational number.

7–4 **4.** Find **(a)** a rational number, and **(b)** an irrational number, between $\frac{4}{5}$ and $\frac{7}{8}$.

7–5 Express in simple radical form:

5. $3\sqrt{\frac{27}{8}}$ **6.** $\sqrt[3]{16x^3y^{-5}}$ $(y \neq 0)$

7–6 **7.** Express in simple form: $\frac{2}{3}\sqrt{108} - \frac{13}{2}\sqrt{128} + \sqrt{192}$

7–7 Express in simple form:

8. $\left(\frac{3 - 5\sqrt{3}}{3}\right)^2$ **9.** $\frac{2\sqrt{2}}{1 + 3\sqrt{5}}$

7–8 **10.** Express the roots of $4x^2 - 8x + 1 = 0$ **(a)** in simple radical form, **(b)** to the nearest tenth.

11. The length of a rectangle measures 4 cm. less than 4 times its width. If the area is 31.0 sq. cm., find the dimensions to the nearest tenth.

7–9 **12.** Write in simple form the quadratic equation in x whose roots are $\frac{5 \pm 3\sqrt{7}}{2}$.

7–10 **13.** Without solving the equation, determine the nature of the roots of $3x^2 - 6x + k = 0$ when k is **(a)** 1; **(b)** $1\frac{2}{3}$; **(c)** 3.

7–11 **14.** **(a)** Solve: $x^2 + 4x \geq 12$, and **(b)** graph the solution set on the number line.

7–12 **15.** Find the solution set: $2 - h = \sqrt{h + 10}$

Chapter Review

7–1 Using Radicals to Express Roots *Pages 251–255*

1. Because the graph of $y = k$, where $k > 0$, intersects the graph of $y = x^4$ in just __?__ point(s), the equation $x^4 = k$ has just __?__ real root(s).

2. When $n = -2$, $\sqrt{16n^2} =$ __?__; $\sqrt[3]{8n^3} =$ __?__.

3. Solve in {rational numbers}: $162 - 32y^4 = 0$

7–2 Rational and Irrational Roots *Pages 255–259*

4. For the equation $2x^3 - 5x + 6 = 0$ the only possible rational roots are __?__.

5. If $1 + \sqrt{5}$ is a root of the equation $x^3 - 8x = 8$, show that $1 + \sqrt{5}$ is irrational.

6. Find the rational roots of $x^3 - 7x + 6 = 0$.

7–3 Rational Operations *Pages 259–261*

7. An operation under which the set of rational numbers is closed is a(n) __?__ operation.
8. $a\sqrt{2}$ denotes an irrational number for every __?__ value of a.
9. Using the method of this section, show that $3 - \sqrt{7}$ is an irrational number.

7–4 Decimals for Real Numbers *Pages 261–263*

10. Because $(2.64)^2 = 6.9696$ and $(2.65)^2 = 7.0225$, you may write __?__ $< \sqrt{7} <$ __?__.
11. $\sqrt[3]{8}$ can be represented by a __?__ decimal, but the decimal for $\sqrt{8}$ is __?__ and __?__.
12. The set of real numbers between 1.1 and 1.2 is a(n) __?__ set.
13. Find **(a)** a rational number and **(b)** an irrational number, between $\sqrt{3}$ and $\frac{17}{10}$.

7–5 Properties of Radicals *Pages 264–269*

14. If $x\sqrt[3]{b} = b$, $x =$ __?__. $(b \neq 0)$

Simplify each of the following.

15. $-\frac{6}{5}\sqrt{\frac{25}{54}}$ 16. $\dfrac{2\sqrt{3}}{\sqrt{60}}$ 17. $\sqrt[3]{-8^2}$ 18. $\dfrac{6}{\sqrt[3]{2}}$

19. Rationalize the denominator and then use Table 3 to approximate $\dfrac{1 + \sqrt{7}}{\sqrt{28}}$ to three significant figures.
20. The lengths of the sides of three cubes are in the ratio 2:3:4 and the sum of their volumes is 7040 cubic inches. Find the length of a side of each cube to the nearest tenth of an inch.

7–6 Simplifying Sums of Radicals *Pages 269–271*

21. The sum of radicals can be expressed as a single radical only when the radicals have the __?__ __?__ and the __?__ __?__.
22. In a sum of radicals, first __?__ each radical, then __?__ terms, if possible.

Express each sum in simple form:

23. $\dfrac{18}{\sqrt{12}} + 10\sqrt{\frac{4}{5}} - 2\sqrt{180}$ 24. $\dfrac{4}{\sqrt[3]{32}} - 2\sqrt[3]{250} + 6\sqrt[3]{6.75}$

7–7 Products of Sums Containing Radicals *Pages 271–273*

Express in simple form:

25. $(3\sqrt{2} + 2\sqrt{3})(4\sqrt{6} - 3)$

26. $(2\sqrt[3]{3} + 5)(2\sqrt[3]{3} - 5)$

27. $\dfrac{6}{3 - \sqrt{7}}$

28. $\dfrac{n}{\sqrt{n + 1} + 1}$, $n \geq -1$

7–8 Using Radicals to Solve Quadratic Equations *Pages 274–279*

In Exercises 29–32, express the members of each solution set **(a)** *in simple radical form, and* **(b)** *to the nearest tenth.*

29. $x^2 - 2x = 10$

30. $3n^2 + 9n + 1 = 0$

31. $3r^2 + 2\sqrt{3}\,r = 2$

32. $\dfrac{1}{t - 2} - \dfrac{1}{t + 1} = 1$

33. A rectangular coal bin 5 feet high has a volume measuring 125 cubic feet. If the length of the base measures 2 feet less than three times the width, find, to the nearest tenth of a foot, the dimensions of the base.

7–9 Roots and Coefficients of a Quadratic Equation *Pages 279–281*

34. The sum of $\dfrac{-b + \sqrt{b^2 - 4ac}}{2a}$ and $\dfrac{-b - \sqrt{b^2 - 4ac}}{2a}$ is __?__; the product is __?__.

Give the sum and the product of the roots of each equation.

35. $6x^2 + 3x + 2 = 0$

36. $kx^2 - 2kx + k - 1 = 0$, $k \neq 0$

Write a quadratic equation in x having the given solution set.

37. $\{6, -\frac{2}{3}\}$

38. $\left\{\dfrac{3 \pm 2\sqrt{11}}{2}\right\}$

39. If one root of the equation $y^2 + 8y + k = 0$ is three times the other, find the value of k.

40. One root of the equation $x^2 + px + 11 = 0$ is $2\sqrt{3} - 1$. Find the value of p.

7–10 The Nature of the Roots of a Quadratic Equation *Pages 281–285*

41. The discriminant of $n^2 - 2\sqrt{10}\,n + 9 = 0$ is __?__.

Without solving, state whether the roots of the given equation are equal or unequal, and rational or irrational.

42. $3y^2 + 5y = 2$

43. $2s^2 + 5 = 2\sqrt{10}\,s$

44. $4x^2 + 20x + 25 = 0$

45. $x^2 + 4x = 4$

State the number of points that the graph of each equation will have in common with the x-axis.

46. $y = 7x^2 - 2\sqrt{14}\,x + 2$ **47.** $y = x^2 + 6x - 9$

7-11 Solving Quadratic Inequalities *Pages 285–287*

Determine the solution set and show its graph on the number line.

48. $x^2 + 2x < 15$ **49.** $4x - x^2 < 3$

7-12 Irrational Equations *Pages 287–290*

Find the solution set of each equation.

50. $\sqrt[3]{x^2 + x - 4} = 2$ **51.** $\sqrt{2r^2 - 5r + 7} = r + 1$

Extra for Experts

Continued Fractions

When you use the Euclidean Algorithm (pages 155–156) to show that the G.C.F. of 43 and 15 is 1, you obtain the following sequence of equations.

1. $43 = 2 \cdot 15 + 13,$ or $\frac{43}{15} = 2 + \frac{13}{15}$
2. $15 = 1 \cdot 13 + 2,$ or $\frac{15}{13} = 1 + \frac{2}{13}$
3. $13 = 2 \cdot 6 + 1,$ or $\frac{13}{2} = 6 + \frac{1}{2}$

The fractional forms of these equations (above right) exhibit an interesting pattern:

I. Each equation expresses the fraction in its left member as the sum of an *integral part* (the greatest integer not exceeding the fraction) and a *fractional part* (the difference between the fraction and its integral part).

II. The left member of each equation after the first is the reciprocal of the fractional part of the right member of the preceding equation.

The second property permits you to write:

$$\frac{43}{15} = 2 + \frac{1}{\frac{15}{13}} = 2 + \frac{1}{1 + \frac{1}{\frac{13}{2}}} = 2 + \frac{1}{1 + \frac{1}{6 + \frac{1}{2}}}$$

The final expression is called a *continued fraction* and is sometimes written in the more compact form: (2, 1, 6, 2).

As a check, we can simplify the fraction (page 173):

$$2 + \frac{1}{1 + \frac{1}{6 + \frac{1}{2}}} = 2 + \frac{1}{1 + \frac{2}{13}} = 2 + \frac{13}{15} = \frac{43}{15}$$

To find the continued fraction representing a positive irrational number such as $\sqrt{15}$, we set up a sequence of equations having properties I and II:

1. $\sqrt{15} = 3 + (\sqrt{15} - 3)$

2. $\dfrac{1}{\sqrt{15} - 3} = \dfrac{1}{\sqrt{15} - 3} \cdot \dfrac{\sqrt{15} + 3}{\sqrt{15} + 3} = \dfrac{\sqrt{15} + 3}{6} = 1 + \dfrac{\sqrt{15} - 3}{6}$

3. $\dfrac{6}{\sqrt{15} - 3} = \dfrac{6}{\sqrt{15} - 3} \cdot \dfrac{\sqrt{15} + 3}{\sqrt{15} + 3} = \sqrt{15} + 3 = 6 + (\sqrt{15} - 3)$

Because the fractional parts of the right members of the third and first equations are equal, the fourth equation will repeat the second, so that a recurring pattern of integral parts: 1, 6, 1, 6, . . . will continue without end. Thus, the *infinite, repeating* continued fraction $(3, \overline{1, 6})$ represents $\sqrt{15}$.

To check the work, let us determine the number x represented by the *purely* repeating fraction $(6, 1, \overline{6, 1})$. Since the value of this continued fraction is the same, whether we start with the first term or with the third, we have

$$x = 6 + \cfrac{1}{1 + \cfrac{1}{x}} = 6 + \frac{x}{x + 1} = \frac{7x + 6}{x + 1}$$

$\therefore\ x^2 - 6x - 6 = 0$, so that $x = 3 + \sqrt{15}$. Hence, $(6, 1, \overline{6, 1}) = 3 + \sqrt{15}$; thus, $(3, 1, 6, \overline{1, 6}) = 3 + \cfrac{1}{1 + \cfrac{1}{3 + \sqrt{15}}} = \sqrt{15}$.

As an exercise, you can verify that $\sqrt[3]{2} = (1, 3, 1, 5, 1, \ldots)$. This infinite continued fraction does *not* repeat because a number is represented by an infinite repeating continued fraction if and only if it is of the form $a + b\sqrt{c}$ where a, b, and c are rational, c not the square of a rational number.

Exercises

Find a continued fraction representing each number.

1. $\frac{47}{17}$ **2.** 3.14159 **3.** $\sqrt{6}$ **4.** $1 + \sqrt{2}$

Find the number represented by each continued fraction.

5. $(3, 1, 2, 4)$ **6.** $(7, 2, \overline{7, 2})$ **7.** $(1, \overline{1})$ **8.** $(3, \overline{3, 6})$

9. Prove that $(5, \overline{10}) = \sqrt{25 + 1}$ and, in general, that $(b, \overline{2b}) = \sqrt{b^2 + 1}$.

10. If $e = (2, 1, 2, 1, 1, 4, 1, 1, 6, 1, 1, 8, \ldots)$, determine rational approximations of e by dropping all but the first few terms.

A Modern Man of the Seventeenth Century

How much heat will be conducted by the heat shield of a space capsule upon its re-entry into the earth's atmosphere? The solution of this problem involves the use of partial differential equations, first developed in the vast work of the 17th century English scientist, Isaac Newton.

Newton is recognized as one of the most significant experimental and theoretical physicists of all time, ranking with Galileo and Kepler. His theory of universal gravitation is well known to any physics student, as are his basic laws of motion, which were presented in 1686 in his *Philosophiae Naturalis Principia Mathematica.* His principal work in mathematics was the development of the differential and integral calculus. Similar work with the calculus was being carried on independently during the same period by Leibniz in Germany. Since Newton did not publish his work until 20 years after he had first conceived of it, a controversy arose, goaded on by national pride and jealousies between the two countries, as to who was the discoverer of the calculus. Today both men are given credit.

Newton's extensive work in physics, mathematics, and celestial mechanics did not by any means occupy all his working hours. He was passionately interested in alchemy and theology and devoted time to devising logical justifications for portions of the Bible. His scientific discoveries had a profound effect on the philosophy of his time. From his law of gravitation emerged the concept of a clockwork universe governed by inalterable laws of nature, with the assumption that Man's position was to discover and accept these laws and to establish their proof by rational scientific reasoning.

CHAPTER 8

. . . a computer-generated elliptical pattern projected on a cathode ray tube

Quadratic Relations and Systems

The mathematical statement of problems in science and technology frequently involves nonlinear relations. In this chapter you will study quadratic relations which are simple, but fairly realistic, models of many physical situations.

COORDINATES AND DISTANCES IN A PLANE

8–1 Distance between Points

The assignment of coordinates to points enables you to translate into algebra the geometric concept of distance. For example, to find RS, the distance between the points R and S on a *number line* (Figure 8–1), you compute the absolute value of the difference between the coordinates of the points:

$$RS = |5 - 3| = 2$$

Similarly,

$$RT = |-1 - 3| = |-4| = 4$$

T R S
−3 −2 −1 0 1 2 3 4 5 6 7

· *Figure 8–1* ·

The formula for the distance between two points in a *coordinate plane* depends on the familiar theorem credited to Pythagoras.

THEOREM. In a right triangle the square of the length c of the hypotenuse equals the sum of the squares of the lengths a and b of the other two sides (the legs): $c^2 = a^2 + b^2$.

Recall that the **hypotenuse** is opposite the right angle and is the longest side of the triangle (Figure 8–2).

The converse of the Pythagorean theorem is also true:

If a, b, and c denote the lengths of the sides of a triangle, and if $c^2 = a^2 + b^2$, then the triangle is a right triangle.

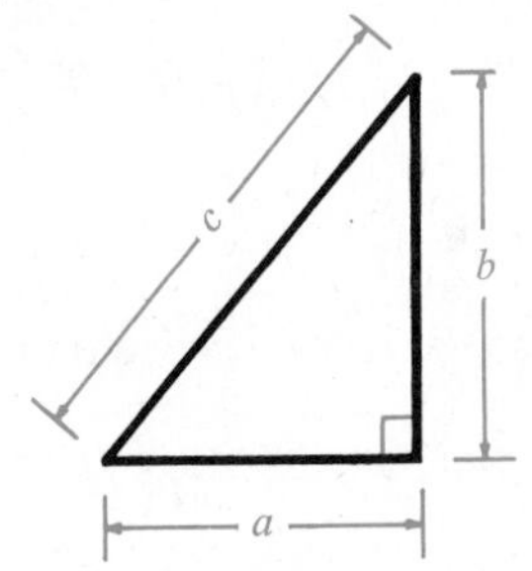

· *Figure 8–2* ·

To find the distance between any two points P_1 and P_2 in a coordinate plane (Figure 8–3), we construct a right triangle having the line segment P_1P_2 as hypotenuse. Let T be the point in which the horizontal line through P_1 intersects the vertical line through P_2. If (x_1, y_1) and (x_2, y_2) are the coordinates of P_1 and P_2 respectively, do you see that the coordinates of T are (x_2, y_1)? Therefore, P_1T, the distance between P_1 and T, is $|x_2 - x_1|$, and TP_2, the distance between T and P_2, is $|y_2 - y_1|$. Using the Pythagorean Theorem to find P_1P_2, the distance between P_1 and P_2, you have

$$\begin{aligned}(P_1P_2)^2 &= (P_1T)^2 + (TP_2)^2\\ &= |x_2 - x_1|^2 + |y_2 - y_1|^2.\end{aligned}$$

· *Figure 8–3* ·

Of course, $|x_2 - x_1|^2 = (x_2 - x_1)^2$ and $|y_2 - y_1|^2 = (y_2 - y_1)^2$. (Why?)

Thus,

$$P_1P_2 = \sqrt{(x_2 - x_1)^2 + (y_2 - y_1)^2} \quad \textit{[distance formula]}$$

EXAMPLE 1. Find the distance between $P_1(5, 4)$ and $P_2(8, -2)$.

Solution:

$$P_1P_2 = \sqrt{(8 - 5)^2 + (-2 - 4)^2}$$

$$P_1P_2 = \sqrt{45}. \qquad \therefore P_1P_2 = 3\sqrt{5}, \textbf{ Answer.}$$

EXAMPLE 2. Find a formula for the distance r between the origin and any point (a, b).

Solution:

$$r = \sqrt{(a - 0)^2 + (b - 0)^2}$$

$$\therefore r = \sqrt{a^2 + b^2}, \textbf{ Answer.}$$

EXAMPLE 3. Prove that

$$M\left(\frac{x_1 + x_2}{2}, \frac{y_1 + y_2}{2}\right)$$

is the midpoint of the line segment joining $P_1(x_1, y_1)$ and $P_2(x_2, y_2)$.

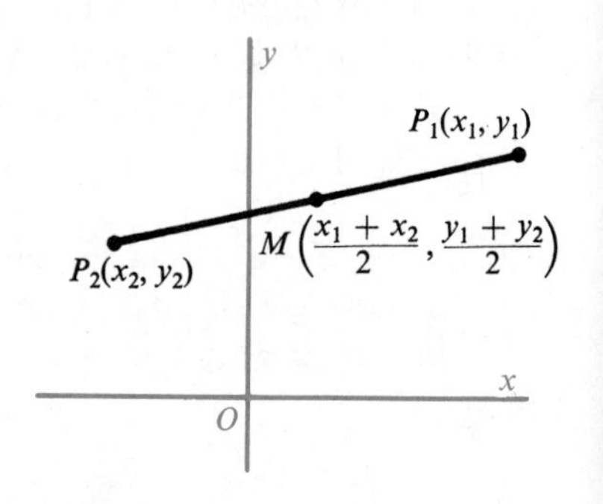

Proof: *Plan:* Show that $P_1M = \frac{1}{2}(P_1P_2)$ and $MP_2 = \frac{1}{2}(P_1P_2)$

$$P_1M = \sqrt{\left(\frac{x_1 + x_2}{2} - x_1\right)^2 + \left(\frac{y_1 + y_2}{2} - y_1\right)^2}$$

$$= \sqrt{\left(\frac{x_2 - x_1}{2}\right)^2 + \left(\frac{y_2 - y_1}{2}\right)^2}$$

$$\therefore P_1M = \tfrac{1}{2}\sqrt{(x_2 - x_1)^2 + (y_2 - y_1)^2}$$

$$\text{But } P_1P_2 = \sqrt{(x_2 - x_1)^2 + (y_2 - y_1)^2}$$

$$\therefore P_1M = \tfrac{1}{2}(P_1P_2);\ \text{similarly, } MP_2 = \tfrac{1}{2}(P_1P_2).$$

EXAMPLE 4. Given $P_1(5, 4)$ and $P_2(8, -2)$, the coordinates of M are

$$\left(\frac{5 + 8}{2}, \frac{4 + (-2)}{2}\right), \quad \text{or} \quad \left(\frac{13}{2}, 1\right).$$

Written Exercises

Find **(a)** the coordinates of the midpoint, and **(b)** the length of the line segment joining the points with given coordinates. Express all radicals in simple form.

A

1. $(-5, 3); (-5, -2)$
2. $(\frac{1}{2}, -1); (\frac{1}{2}, 4)$
3. $(3, \frac{2}{3}); (12, \frac{2}{3})$
4. $(5, 3); (-12, 3)$
5. $(3, -2); (4, -1)$
6. $(0, 1); (5, 13)$
7. $(\sqrt{2}, -1); (2\sqrt{2}, 3)$
8. $(2, \sqrt{2}); (6, -\sqrt{2})$
9. $(\sqrt{5}, 4\sqrt{7}); (3\sqrt{5}, 3\sqrt{7})$
10. $(2\sqrt{2}, \sqrt{3}); (\sqrt{2}, 2\sqrt{3})$
11. $(a, b); (3a, -b)$
12. $(-2r, 3s); (r, -3s)$

Find the coordinates of A if M is the midpoint of line segment AB.

B

13. $M(7, -3); B(5, 4)$
14. $M(-6, 2); B(-3, -1)$

The vertices of a triangle have the given coordinates. For the triangle, find **(a)** the perimeter; **(b)** whether it is isosceles; **(c)** whether it is a right triangle. If it is a right triangle, find its area.

15. $(1, 4); (5, 1); (5, 4)$
16. $(6, 4); (-2, 4); (2, 7)$
17. $(2, -1); (3, 4); (-7, 6)$
18. $(1, 0); (3, 4); (-7, 6)$
19. $(0, 0); (2, 2); (2, -2)$
20. $(2, 2\sqrt{3}); (0, 0); (3, -\sqrt{3})$

Show that the following points are collinear by using **(a)** the slope formula, and **(b)** the distance formula.

21. $R(7, -1); S(9, 4); T(13, 14)$
22. $R(-1, 6); S(2, 12); T(-4, 0)$

Problems

Sketch diagrams as necessary to help in solving these problems. Express irrational results in simple radical form and correct to tenths.

A

1. Find the length of the diagonal of a square whose area is 40 sq. in.
2. When a ladder 25 ft. long rests against the vertical wall of a building, its top is 17 ft. farther from the base of the building than is its foot. How high on the wall does the ladder reach?
3. Find the length of a wire from the top of a vertical pole 24 ft. tall to a point on the horizontal ground 7 ft. from the foot of the pole.
4. The ratio of the lengths of the legs of a right triangle is 3:4. If its area is 150 square centimeters, find the length of its hypotenuse.
5. How deep must the cut d be made to mill the square nut shown in the figure from a bar of four-inch round stock?

Ex. 5

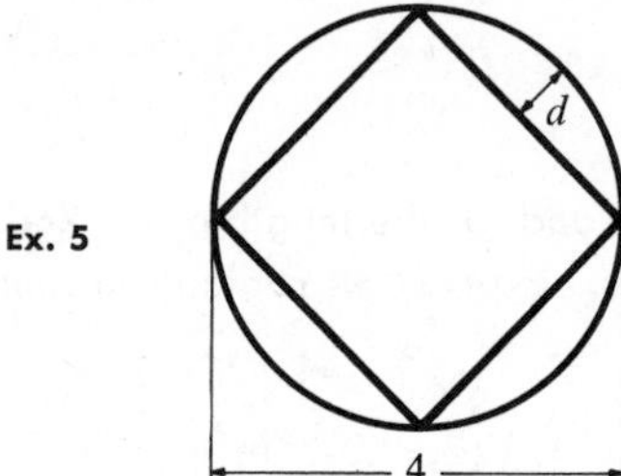

Ex. 6

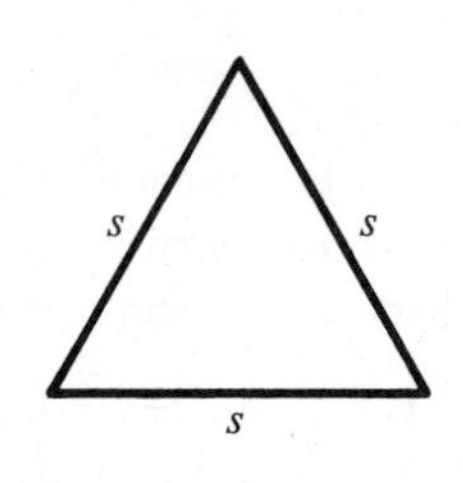

6. Prove that the area of an equilateral triangle of side s is $\frac{\sqrt{3}\, s^2}{4}$.

Determine the area of the shaded region in each figure if *AB* is 10 centimeters long.

7.

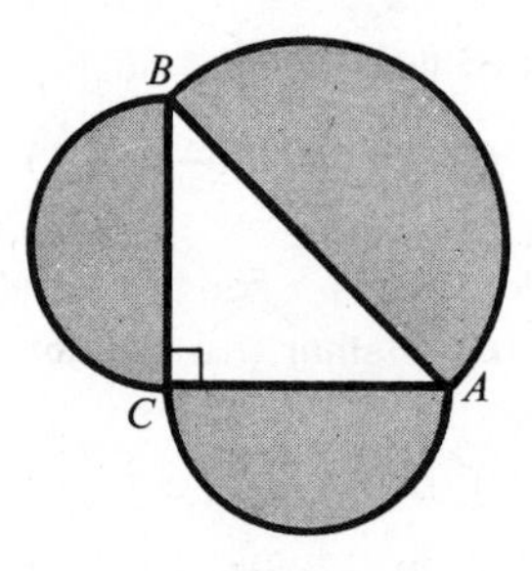

Semicircles

8.

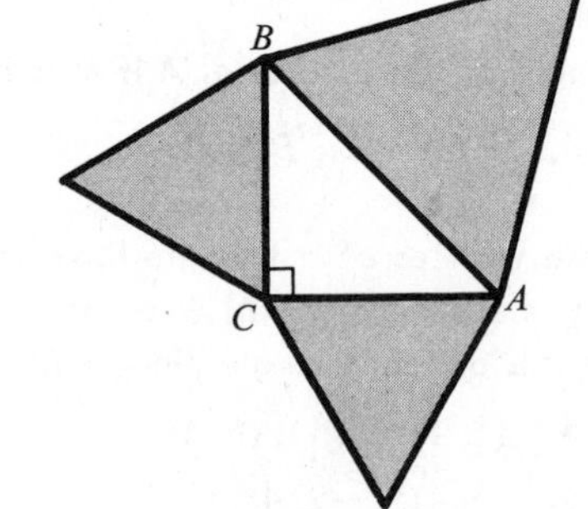

Equilateral Triangles

B

9. At noon a ship sailed due east from Key West. Two hours later another ship traveling 4 miles per hour faster sailed due south from that port. At 10 P.M. the same day (Key West time), the ships were 100 miles apart. What was the average speed of each?

10. Park City is 23 miles directly south of Adobe Flats. A train running due west at 40 miles per hour left Park City at the same time another train traveling due south at the same speed left Adobe Flats. How soon were the trains 17 miles apart?

11. Determine a linear equation expressing the condition that the point (x, y) be equidistant from the points $(0, 4)$ and $(6, 0)$.

12. Find every value of a for which the point $(a, 5)$ is 6 units from $(-2, 1)$.

13. Show that the sum of the squares of the four sides of the parallelogram with vertices $(0, 0)$, $(1, 1)$, $(2, 1)$, and $(1, 0)$ is equal to the sum of the squares of its diagonals. Is this true for every parallelogram?

14. Let $C(0, 0)$, $B(4, 0)$, and $A(0, 6)$ be the vertices of a right triangle. Show that the line joining C and the midpoint of side AB is half as long as that side.

C

15. Show that the length of the diagonal of a rectangular box a feet long, b feet wide, and c feet deep is $\sqrt{a^2 + b^2 + c^2}$ feet.

16. Let points $(0, 0)$, $(a, 0)$, and $(0, b)$ be three of the vertices of a rectangle. Find the fourth vertex and show that the diagonals of the rectangle bisect each other.

17. Let $O(0, 0)$, $A(a, 0)$, and $B(0, b)$ be the vertices of a right triangle. Show that the midpoint of side AB is equidistant from the three vertices.

18. Let $R(-a, 0)$, $S(a, 0)$, and $T(0, b)$ be vertices of an isosceles triangle. Prove that the medians bisecting sides RT and ST are equal in length.

8–2 Perpendicular Lines (Optional)

Two lines intersecting at right angles are called **perpendicular lines.** For example, every horizontal line in a plane, such as the graph of $y = 3$ in Figure 8–4, is perpendicular to each vertical line, as, for example, the graph of $x = -2$. In Figure 8–5 the graphs of the lines

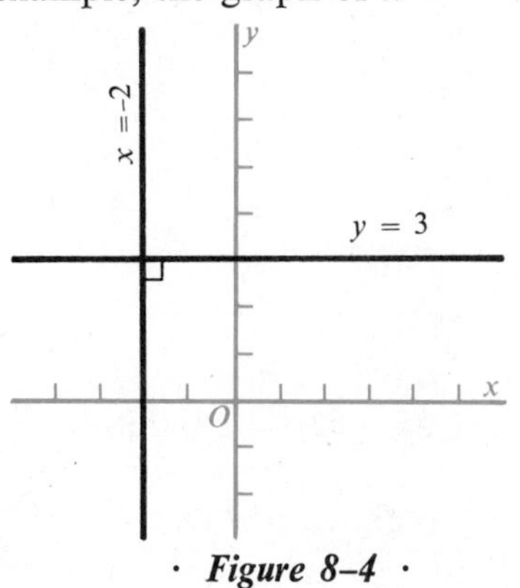

· *Figure 8–4* ·

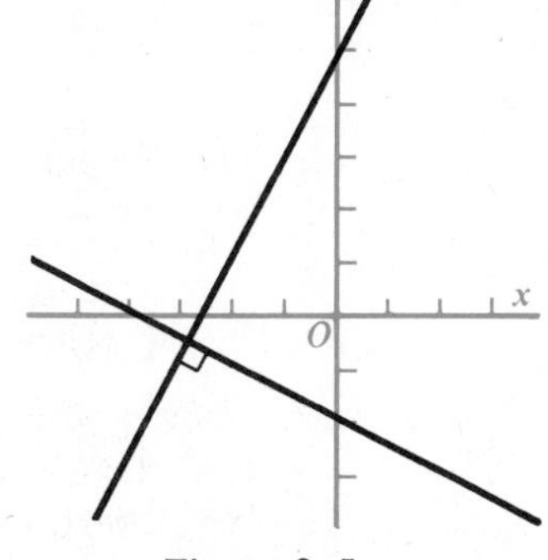

· *Figure 8–5* ·

whose equations are $y = 2x + 5$ and $y = -\frac{1}{2}x - 2$ are also perpendicular. Do you see that the product of the slopes of these lines is -1? $(2 \times (-\frac{1}{2}) = -1)$. This relationship is typical of every pair of perpendicular lines that are not parallel to either axis.

THEOREM. In a coordinate system, two lines, neither of which is parallel to a coordinate axis, are perpendicular if and only if the product of their slopes is -1.

Call the lines l_1 and l_2. Since neither line is vertical, each has a slope, say m_1 for l_1 and m_2 for l_2. There are two assertions to prove:

I. If l_1 and l_2 are perpendicular, then $m_1m_2 = -1$.

II. If $m_1m_2 = -1$, then l_1 and l_2 are perpendicular.

Before proving I and II, notice that $m_1m_2 = -1$ means $m_1 = -\dfrac{1}{m_2}$ and $m_2 = -\dfrac{1}{m_1}$. Thus, lines not parallel to either axis are perpendicular to each other if and only if their slopes are negative reciprocals of each other.

EXAMPLE. Determine an equation of the line through $(3, -1)$ perpendicular to the graph of $2x + 3y = 6$.

Solution: **1.** $2x + 3y = 6$

$$y = -\tfrac{2}{3}x + 2$$

$\therefore$ the slope of the graph of $2x + 3y = 6$ is $-\frac{2}{3}$. Any line perpendicular to it has slope

$$-\frac{1}{-\frac{2}{3}} = \frac{3}{2}.$$

2. Use the point-slope form:

$$\begin{aligned} y - y_1 &= m(x - x_1) \\ &\downarrow \quad \downarrow \quad\quad \downarrow \\ y - (-1) &= \tfrac{3}{2}(x - 3) \\ 2y + 2 &= 3(x - 3), \quad \text{or} \quad 3x - 2y = 11, \textbf{ Answer.} \end{aligned}$$

Now let us prove Assertions I and II of the above theorem.

C

Proof of I

Suppose l_1 and l_2 intersect at right angles in a point $P(r, s)$, as in Figure 8–6. Since P lies on l_1, a line with slope m_1, the point $T_1(r + 1, s + m_1)$ must also lie on l_1. Similarly, $T_2(r + 1, s + m_2)$ lies on l_2. Thus, the points T_1, P, and T_2 determine a triangle with right angle at P. Therefore, the Pythagorean theorem and the distance formula imply:

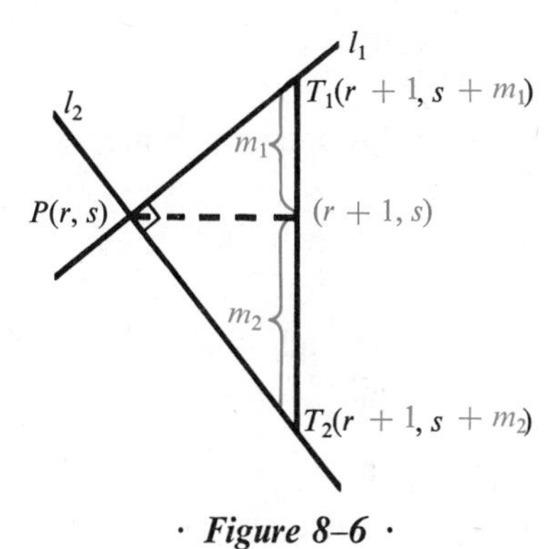

· *Figure 8–6* ·

$$
\begin{aligned}
(T_1T_2)^2 &= (PT_1)^2 + (PT_2)^2 \\
(m_1 - m_2)^2 &= (1 + m_1^2) + (1 + m_2^2) \\
m_1^2 - 2m_1m_2 + m_2^2 &= 2 + m_1^2 + m_2^2 \\
-2m_1m_2 &= 2 \\
\therefore\ m_1m_2 &= -1
\end{aligned}
$$

C

Proof of II

Since $m_1m_2 = -1$, l_1 and l_2 cannot be parallel lines. For $m_1 = m_2$ would mean $m_1^2 = -1$, a statement false for every real number m_1. Therefore, l_1 and l_2 must intersect in a point $P(r, s)$. Determine T_1 and T_2 as in part I. To prove l_1 perpendicular to l_2, we must show that $m_1m_2 = -1$ implies that triangle T_1PT_2 has a right angle at P, that is, that the statement $(T_1T_2)^2 = (PT_1)^2 + (PT_2)^2$ is true. This equality holds because:

$$
\begin{aligned}
(T_1T_2)^2 = (m_1 - m_2)^2 &= m_1^2 - 2m_1m_2 + m_2^2 \\
&= m_1^2 - 2(-1) + m_2^2 = m_1^2 + 2 + m_2^2 \\
\therefore\ (T_1T_2)^2 &= (1 + m_1^2) + (1 + m_2^2) = (PT_1)^2 + (PT_2)^2.
\end{aligned}
$$

Written Exercises

What is the slope of any line perpendicular to the line through the given points?

A

1. (2, 1); (−3, 2)

2. (1, 2); (3, 6)

3. (−2, 3); (−3, 3)

4. (−1, 3); (−2, 7)

5. (5, −1); (7, 5)

6. (2, −5); (2, 0)

Find an equation of the line satisfying the given conditions.

7. Passing through the point $(-3, 4)$ and perpendicular to the graph of $2x + 4y = 9$.

8. Passing through the point $(5, -7)$ and perpendicular to the graph of $3x - 9y = 4$.

9. Passing through the origin and perpendicular to the line joining points $(7, 6)$ and $(2, -1)$.

10. Passing through the origin and perpendicular to the line joining $(-5, 9)$ and $(2, 0)$.

B **11.** The perpendicular bisector of the line joining $A(7, -4)$ and $B(-5, -9)$.

12. The perpendicular bisector of the line joining $A(-8, -4)$ and $B(5, 2)$.

In Exercises 13 and 14, use (a) the slope relationship, and (b) the converse of the Pythagorean theorem, to prove that the line segments joining the points with the given coordinates are the vertices of a right triangle.

13. $(0, 8); (6, 2); (-4, 4)$ **14.** $(3, 4); (0, 6); (-4, 0)$

In Exercises 15 and 16, show that *ABCD* is a rectangle.

15. $A(-2, 2); B(1, 3); C(2, 0); D(-1, -1)$

16. $A(-2, 1); B(2, 5); C(8, -1); D(4, -5)$

C **17.** Prove that if $c \neq 0$, then (a, b), $(a + c, b)$, $(a + c, b + c)$, and $(a, b + c)$ are the coordinates of the vertices of a square. Also prove that the diagonals of the square are perpendicular to each other.

18. Prove that if the coordinates of the vertices of a triangle are (a, b), $(a + c, b)$, and $(a + c, b + c)$, the triangle is a right triangle.

GRAPHING QUADRATIC RELATIONS

8–3 Circles

Using the distance formula, you can express algebraically many geometrical relationships. For example, you know that a **circle** is the set of points equidistant from a given point, called the **center**. The **radius** of the circle is the distance between each of its points and the center. Thus, if the center is $C(-5, 3)$ and the radius is 4 (Figure 8–7), then a point P with coordinates (x, y) belongs to the circle, if and only if $PC = 4$.

$$\therefore \sqrt{[x - (-5)]^2 + (y - 3)^2} = 4, \text{ or } (x + 5)^2 + (y - 3)^2 = 16$$

Because the circle contains all those points and only those points whose coordinates satisfy $(x + 5)^2 + (y - 3)^2 = 16$, we call this open sentence an **equation of the circle**. In general, any open sentence which can be written in the form $(x - h)^2 + (y - k)^2 = r^2$ is an equation of a circle with radius r and center (h, k). (See Exercise 10, page 308.)

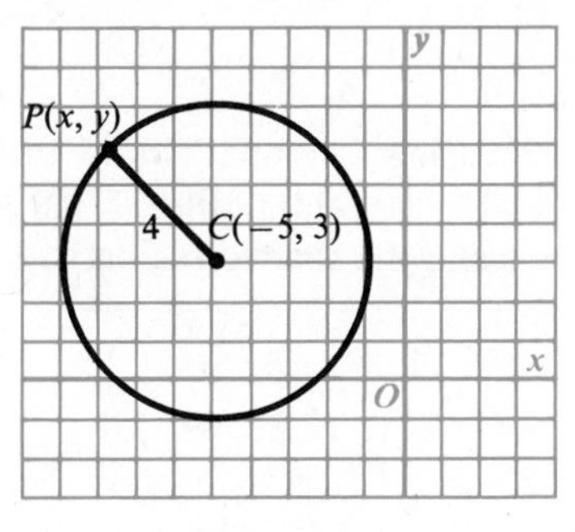

· *Figure 8–7* ·

EXAMPLE 1. Find an equation of the circle having center at the origin and radius 2.

Solution:

$$\sqrt{(x - 0)^2 + (y - 0)^2} = 2$$

$$x^2 + y^2 = 4, \textbf{ Answer.}$$

Do you see that $(x + 5)^2 + (y - 3)^2 = 16$ is equivalent to $x^2 + 10x + y^2 - 6y + 18 = 0$?

To transform $x^2 + 10x + y^2 - 6y + 18 = 0$ into the original form which tells directly the center and radius of the circle, you use the process of "completing the square" twice (see page 238).

1. Subtract 18 from each member. $\qquad x^2 + 10x + y^2 - 6y = -18$

2. Add to each member $\left(\frac{10}{2}\right)^2$, or 25, to complete the square in x, and $\left(-\frac{6}{2}\right)^2$, or 9, to complete the square in y. Simplify.

$$\underbrace{x^2 + 10x + 25}_{(x+5)^2} + \underbrace{y^2 - 6y + 9}_{(y-3)^2} = \underbrace{-18 + 25 + 9}_{16}$$

EXAMPLE 2. Draw the graph of the relation

$$\{(x, y): x^2 - 2x + y^2 + 4y \le 4\}$$

Solution:

1. Transform the inequality to the form $(x - h)^2 + (y - k)^2 \le r^2$.

$$x^2 - 2x + y^2 + 4y \le 4$$

$$x^2 - 2x + (-1)^2 + y^2 + 4y + 2^2 \le 4 + (-1)^2 + 2^2$$

$$(x - 1)^2 + (y + 2)^2 \le 9$$

$$(x - 1)^2 + [y - (-2)]^2 \le 3^2$$

(*continued on p.* 308)

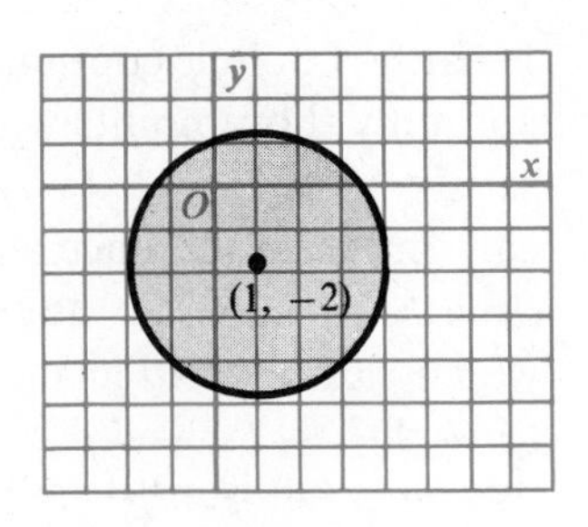

2. Using a compass, draw the circle with center (1, −2) and radius 3. The graph is the circle and the shaded region within it.

Written Exercises

Write an equation of the circle with the given center and radius.

A

1. $(0, 4); 3$
2. $(-2, 0); 1$
3. $(2, -2); \frac{7}{2}$
4. $(-9, -3); \frac{1}{2}$
5. $(-20, 30); \sqrt{5}$
6. $(7, -1); \sqrt{3}$
7. $(\frac{9}{4}, \frac{2}{5}); 1.5$
8. $(0.2, 0.25); \frac{1}{4}$
9. $(0, 0); r$
10. $(h, k); r$

Draw the graph of each relation that does not equal $\emptyset$.

11. $\{(x, y): x^2 + y^2 - 36 = 0\}$
12. $\{(x, y): x^2 + y^2 = 16\}$
13. $\{(x, y): -\frac{1}{2}x^2 - \frac{1}{2}y^2 + 50 = 0\}$
14. $\{(x, y): 3x^2 + 3y^2 - 108 = 0\}$
15. $\{(x, y): x^2 + y^2 - 2y = 8\}$
16. $\{(x, y): x^2 - 6x + y^2 - 16 = 0\}$

B

17. $\{(x, y): y^2 - 10x + x^2 + 6y + 18 \leq 0\}$
18. $\{(x, y): 4x^2 + 4y^2 + 4x + 1 < 4y\}$
19. $\{(x, y): 36x^2 + 36y^2 - 12y - 48x = -17\}$
20. $\{(x, y): x^2 + 16x - 6y + y^2 \leq -73\}$
21. $\{(x, y): x^2 + y^2 - 2x - 14y + 41 > 0\}$
22. $\{(x, y): x^2 + y^2 + 4y + 12 = 0\}$

Find the radius and an equation of the circle having C as center and containing the point P.

23. $C(0, 0); P(1, -3)$
24. $C(0, 0); P(-10, -10)$
25. $C(-1, 1); P(4, -3)$
26. $C(-7, -5); P(1, 2)$

Draw the graph of each relation.

C

27. $\{(x, y): y = \sqrt{9 - (x + 1)^2}\}$
28. $\{(x, y): 4 \leq x^2 + y^2 \leq 9\}$

8–4 Parabolas

In a plane, the set of points equidistant from a given point is a circle. Many other figures are defined as sets of points satisfying geometric conditions. For example, consider the set consisting of every point P whose distance from the point $F(3, 4)$ equals its perpendicular distance from the line l having equation $y = -2$. (See Figure 8–8.) Then:

$$PF = PD$$

$$\sqrt{(x-3)^2 + (y-4)^2} = \sqrt{(x-x)^2 + [y-(-2)]^2}$$

$$(x-3)^2 + (y-4)^2 = (y+2)^2$$

$$(x-3)^2 + y^2 - 8y + 16 = y^2 + 4y + 4$$

$$(x-3)^2 + 12 = 12y$$

$$y = \tfrac{1}{12}(x-3)^2 + 1$$

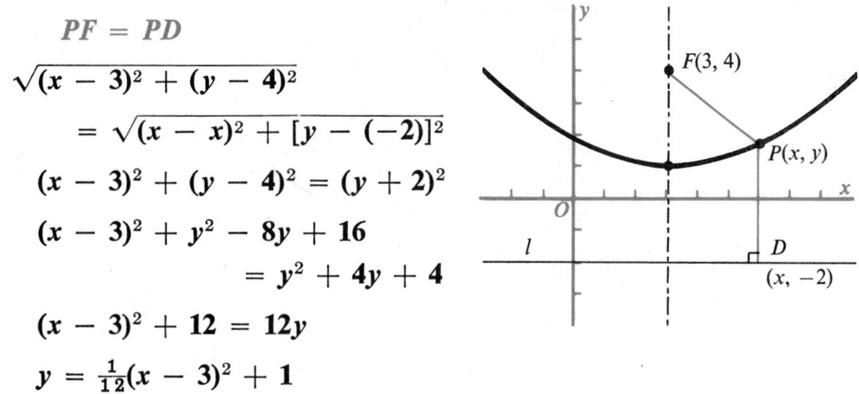

· *Figure 8–8* ·

Because the steps in the preceding sequence of equations can be reversed, a point in the plane belongs to the set *if and only if* its coordinates satisfy the equation $y = \frac{1}{12}(x-3)^2 + 1$. Thus, the set of points P is the graph of the quadratic function $\{(x, y): y = \frac{1}{12}(x-3)^2 + 1\}$. Using the methods of Chapter 6 to sketch the curve, you obtain the graph shown in Figure 8–9.

x	y
−3	4
−1	$\frac{7}{3}$
1	$\frac{4}{3}$
3	1
5	$\frac{4}{3}$
7	$\frac{7}{3}$
9	4

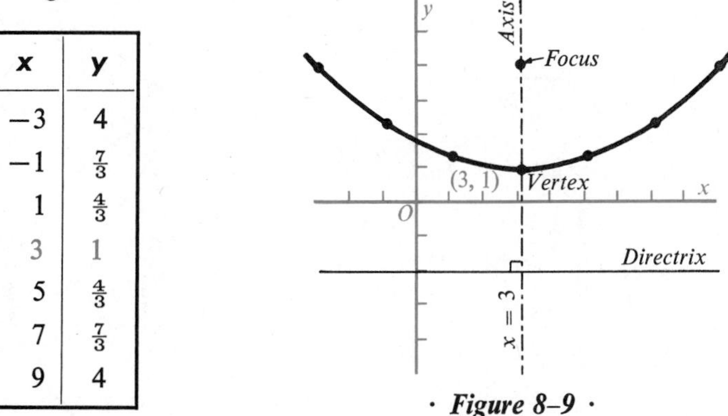

· *Figure 8–9* ·

In a plane, any curve consisting of the set of points equidistant from a line and a point not on the line is a **parabola**. The line is called the

directrix and the point, the **focus**. Figure 8–9 identifies two other features of a parabola:

axis of symmetry (or simply, **axis**), the line through the focus perpendicular to the directrix;

vertex, the point in which the parabola intersects its axis.

Do you see that the vertex is the midpoint of the segment of the axis between the focus and the directrix?

The example below involves a parabola whose directrix is parallel to the y-axis.

EXAMPLE. Find an equation of the parabola whose focus is the point $(-2, 0)$, and whose directrix is the line $x = 2$. Draw the parabola and label its focus, vertex, directrix, and axis.

Solution:

$$\begin{aligned} PF &= PD \\ \sqrt{[x - (-2)]^2 + (y - 0)^2} &= \sqrt{(x - 2)^2 + (y - y)^2} \\ (x + 2)^2 + y^2 &= (x - 2)^2 \\ x^2 + 4x + 4 + y^2 &= x^2 - 4x + 4 \\ y^2 &= -8x \\ x &= -\tfrac{1}{8}y^2 \end{aligned}$$

The table used to draw the parabola was obtained by assigning to y the values listed and then computing the corresponding values of x. Can you explain why the relation $\{(x, y): x = -\frac{1}{8}y^2\}$ is not a function?

$x = -\frac{1}{8}y^2$		
x	$-\frac{1}{8}y^2$	y
$-4\frac{1}{2}$	$-\frac{1}{8}(-6)^2$	-6
-2	$-\frac{1}{8}(-4)^2$	-4
$-\frac{1}{2}$	$-\frac{1}{8}(-2)^2$	-2
0	$-\frac{1}{8}\cdot 0^2$	0
$-\frac{1}{2}$	$-\frac{1}{8}\cdot 2^2$	2
-2	$-\frac{1}{8}\cdot 4^2$	4
$-4\frac{1}{2}$	$-\frac{1}{8}\cdot 6^2$	6

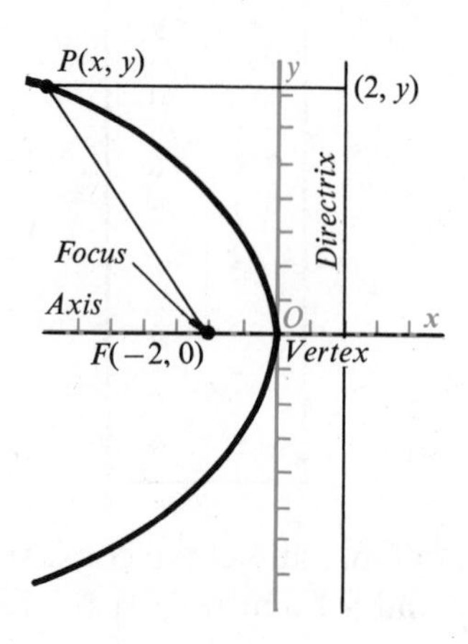

Notice that the points of the graph in the preceding example can be paired so that the x-coordinates of the points in a pair are the same but the y-coordinates are negatives of each other: $(-\frac{1}{2}, -2)$ with $(-\frac{1}{2}, 2)$; $(-2, 4)$ with $(-2, -4)$; and so on. If a curve has the property that whenever the point (r, t) belongs to it, the point $(r, -t)$ also belongs to it, then the curve is said to be **symmetric with respect to the x-axis**. Compare this definition with that of *symmetry with respect to the y-axis*, page 227.

Written Exercises

Draw the graph of each relation.

SAMPLE. $\{(x, y)\colon x = y^2 - 6y + 7\}$.

Solution:

$$x = y^2 - 6y + 7$$

1. To determine the vertex, complete the square in y.

$$x - 7 = y^2 - 6y$$
$$x - 7 + 9 = y^2 - 6y + 9$$

2. In plotting points, use the fact that the line $y = 3$ is the axis of symmetry and the point $(-2, 3)$ is the vertex.

$$x + 2 = (y - 3)^2$$
$$x = (y - 3)^2 - 2$$

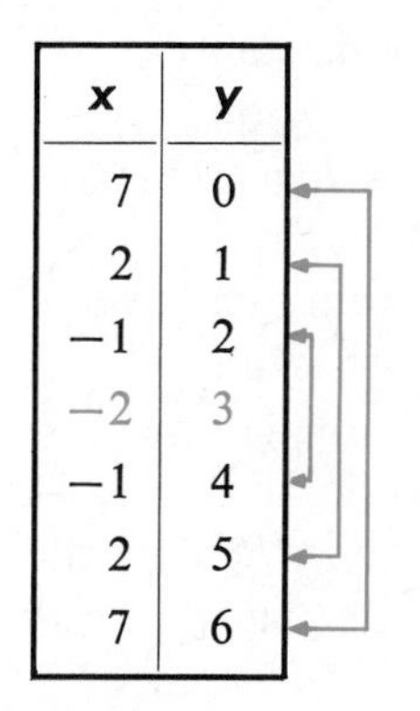

x	y
7	0
2	1
−1	2
−2	3
−1	4
2	5
7	6

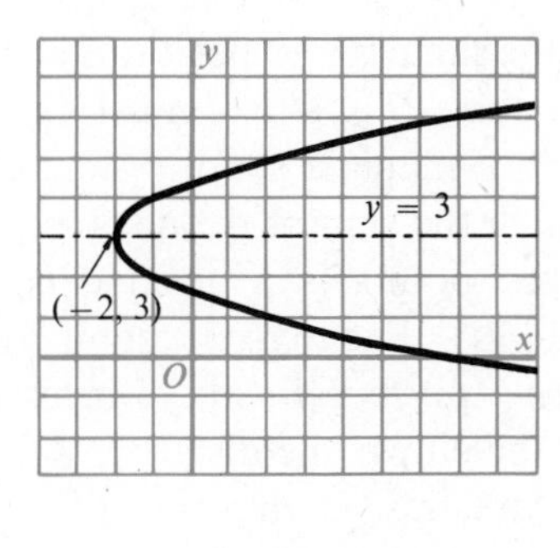

A

1. $\{(x, y)\colon y = 7 + 4x - x^2\}$
2. $\{(x, y)\colon y = 5 - 2x - x^2\}$
3. $\{(x, y)\colon x = 3y^2\}$
4. $\{(x, y)\colon x = -2y^2\}$
5. $\{(x, y)\colon x = -(y + 1)^2\}$
6. $\{(x, y)\colon x = \frac{1}{2}(y + 4)^2\}$
7. $\{(x, y)\colon x = y^2 - 4y + 1\}$
8. $\{(x, y)\colon x = y^2 + 8y + 6\}$
9. $\{(x, y)\colon x = 5 - 4y - 2y^2\}$
10. $\{(x, y)\colon 4x + y^2 = 8y + 16\}$

B

11. $\{(x, y): x = 3 + \sqrt{y - 7}\}$

12. $\{(x, y): y = 5 - \sqrt{x - 1}\}$

13. $\{(x, y): x \geq (y + 2)^2 + 3\}$

14. $\{(x, y): x \leq 5 - (y - 1)^2\}$

Determine the equation of the parabola with the given focus and directrix.

15. focus: $(4, 0)$; directrix: $x = -4$

16. focus: $(0, 5)$; directrix: $y = -5$

17. focus: $(-3, 4)$; directrix: $y = 6$

18. focus: $(2, -1)$; directrix: $x = 8$

Each statement describes a set of points $\{P(x, y)\}$. Find an equation satisfied by the coordinates of all points of the set, and graph the equation.

C

19. The slope of the line joining P and the point $(5, -1)$ is 4.

20. The perpendicular distance between P and the line $y = 3$ is 2.

21. The sum of the squares of the distances of P from the points $(-7, 0)$ and $(7, 0)$ is 20.

22. P is twice as far from the point $(3, 0)$ as from the point $(-3, 0)$.

8–5 Ellipses

Imagine a piece of string with ends fastened at two points F_1 and F_2 in a plane (Figure 8–10). The point P of a moving pencil which holds the string taut in the plane will describe the curve shown in the figure. Because the sum of the distances PF_1 and PF_2 equals the length of the string, this sum is the same for all positions of P. Do you see that $PF_1 + PF_2$ must exceed F_1F_2?

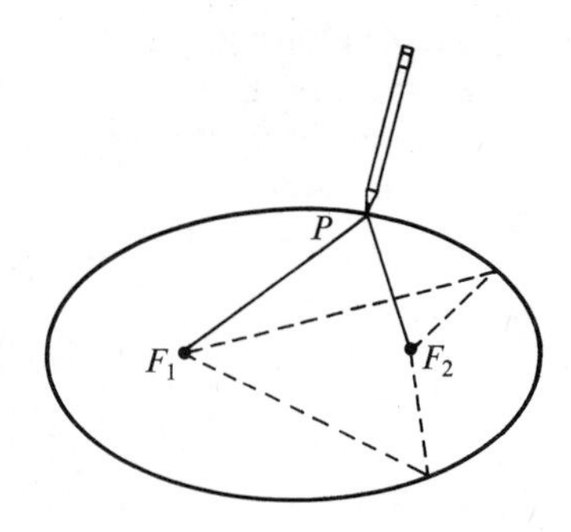

· *Figure 8–10* ·

In a plane, a set of points for each of which the sum of the distances from two given points is a given constant is an **ellipse**. Each given point is called a **focus** (pl. *foci* [**fo**-si]). For each point P of the ellipse the distances PF_1 and PF_2 are called the **focal radii** of P.

An ellipse having $(-c, 0)$ and $(c, 0)$ as the coordinates of its foci, and $2a$ as the sum of the focal radii for each of its points, has a simple equation, $\frac{x^2}{a^2} + \frac{y^2}{b^2} = 1$, where $b^2 = a^2 - c^2$. To verify this in the special case with $c = 3$ and $a = 5$, you can proceed as follows.

$$PF_1 + PF_2 = 10$$

$$\therefore \sqrt{(x+3)^2 + (y-0)^2} + \sqrt{(x-3)^2 + (y-0)^2} = 10, \quad \text{or}$$

$$\sqrt{(x+3)^2 + y^2} = 10 - \sqrt{(x-3)^2 + y^2}$$

Square each member and rearrange terms to obtain:

$$(x + 3)^2 + y^2 = 100 - 20\sqrt{(x - 3)^2 + y^2} + (x - 3)^2 + y^2, \quad \text{or}$$
$$3x - 25 = -5\sqrt{(x - 3)^2 + y^2}$$

Squaring again and simplifying, you have:

$$16x^2 + 25y^2 = 400, \quad \text{or} \quad \frac{x^2}{25} + \frac{y^2}{16} = 1, \quad \text{or} \quad \frac{x^2}{5^2} + \frac{y^2}{5^2 - 3^2} = 1,$$

an equation which must be satisfied by each point of the ellipse. On the other hand, it can be shown that any number pair satisfying this equation consists of the coordinates of a point P for which $PF_1 + PF_2 = 10$. The equation reveals why this ellipse has the shape suggested by Figure 8–10.

1. Whenever (r, t) satisfies $\frac{x^2}{25} + \frac{y^2}{16} = 1$, so also do $(r, -t)$ and $(-r, t)$.

$\therefore$ *the curve is symmetric with respect to both coordinate axes.*

2. Replacing y by 0, you obtain $\frac{x^2}{25} + \frac{0}{16} = 1$; $x^2 = 25$; $x = 5$ or $x = -5$.

$\therefore$ *the x-intercepts of the ellipse are* 5 *and* -5.

3. Replacing x by 0, you find $\frac{0}{25} + \frac{y^2}{16} = 1$; $y^2 = 16$; $y = 4$ or $y = -4$.

$\therefore$ *the y-intercepts are* 4 *and* -4.

4. Transforming the equation to express one variable in terms of the other, you find:

$\frac{x^2}{25} = 1 - \frac{y^2}{16}$	$\frac{y^2}{16} = 1 - \frac{x^2}{25}$
$x = \frac{5}{4}\sqrt{16 - y^2}$, or	$y = \frac{4}{5}\sqrt{25 - x^2}$, or
$x = -\frac{5}{4}\sqrt{16 - y^2}$	$y = -\frac{4}{5}\sqrt{25 - x^2}$
$\sqrt{16 - y^2}$ denotes a real number if and only if $\lvert y \rvert \le 4$	$\sqrt{25 - x^2}$ denotes a real number if and only if $\lvert x \rvert \le 5$

$\therefore$ *The ellipse is bounded by the rectangle formed by the lines* $y = 4$, $y = -4$, $x = 5$, $x = -5$.

With this information regarding symmetry, intercepts, and extent, and the table of coordinates of *first quadrant* points, you plot the ellipse shown in Figure 8–11 on the next page.

x	$\frac{4}{5}\sqrt{25 - x^2}$	[Q.I]	y
0	$\frac{4}{5}\sqrt{25 - 0}$	$= \frac{4}{5}\sqrt{25}$	4
2	$\frac{4}{5}\sqrt{25 - 4}$	$= \frac{4}{5}\sqrt{21}$	3.7
3	$\frac{4}{5}\sqrt{25 - 9}$	$= \frac{4}{5}\sqrt{16}$	3.2
4	$\frac{4}{5}\sqrt{25 - 16}$	$= \frac{4}{5}\sqrt{9}$	2.4
5	$\frac{4}{5}\sqrt{25 - 25}$	$= \frac{4}{5}\sqrt{0}$	0

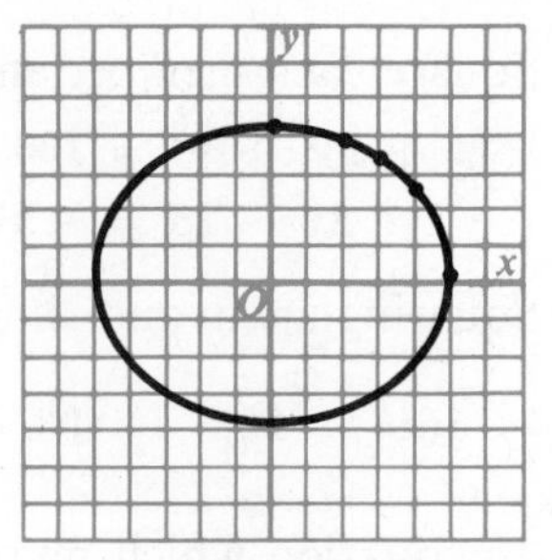

· *Figure 8–11* ·

When the foci of an ellipse are on the y-axis at $(0, c)$ and $(0, -c)$, and the sum of the focal radii is $2a$, you can show that the ellipse has an equation of the form $\frac{x^2}{b^2} + \frac{y^2}{a^2} = 1$, where $b^2 = a^2 - c^2$. The following example involves an ellipse of this kind.

EXAMPLE. Sketch the graph of the relation $\{(x, y)\colon 4x^2 + y^2 = 100\}$.

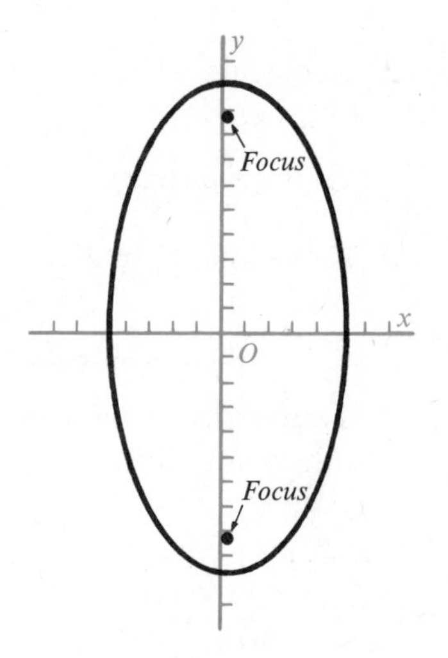

Solution: $4x^2 + y^2 = 100;\ \frac{x^2}{25} + \frac{y^2}{100} = 1$

1. Symmetric with respect to both axes
2. x-intercepts: 5 and -5
3. y-intercepts: 10 and -10
4. Extent: $-5 \le x \le 5;\ -10 \le y \le 10$
5. Table of *first-quadrant* points: $y = 2\sqrt{25 - x^2}$

x	0	3	4	5
y	10	8	6	0

Written Exercises

Graph each of the following relations.

1. $\left\{(x, y)\colon \frac{x^2}{9} + \frac{y^2}{4} = 1\right\}$
2. $\left\{(x, y)\colon \frac{x^2}{25} + \frac{y^2}{9} = 1\right\}$
3. $\left\{(x, y)\colon \frac{x^2}{36} + \frac{y^2}{49} = 1\right\}$
4. $\left\{(x, y)\colon \frac{x^2}{64} + \frac{y^2}{100} = 1\right\}$
5. $\{(x, y)\colon 4x^2 + y^2 = 100\}$
6. $\{(x, y)\colon x^2 + 4y^2 = 100\}$
7. $\{(x, y)\colon 49x^2 + 100y^2 = 4900\}$

8. $\{(x, y): 100y^2 + 49x^2 = 4900\}$

9. $\{(x, y): 4x^2 + 25y^2 < 100\}$

10. $\{(x, y): 25y^2 + 4x^2 \leq 100\}$

11. $\{(x, y): 4x^2 + y^2 \geq 16\}$

12. $\{(x, y): x^2 + 36y^2 > 144\}$

B **13.** $\{(x, y): 36 \leq 9x^2 + 4y^2 < 144\}$

14. $\{(x, y): 49 \leq x^2 + 49y^2 \leq 196\}$

From the definition determine an equation of the ellipse whose foci have the given coordinates if the sum of the focal radii for each of its points is the given number. Sketch the ellipses in Exercises 15–18.

15. $(3, 0); (-3, 0); 10$

16. $(0, 4); (0, -4); 12$

17. $(0, -5); (0, 5); 14$

18. $(-1, 0); (1, 0); 4$

C **19.** $(0, c); (0, -c); 2a$

20. $(c, 0); (-c, 0); 2a$

Graph.

21. $\{(x, y): y \geq 3\sqrt{4 - x^2}\}$

22. $\{(x, y): x \leq -2\sqrt{2 - y^2}\}$

23. $\left\{(x, y): \frac{(x-1)^2}{4} + \frac{(y+2)^2}{9} = 1\right\}$

24. $\left\{(x, y): \frac{(x+1)^2}{16} + \frac{(y-4)^2}{4} = 1\right\}$

8–6 Hyperbolas

Using a system of navigation called *Loran*, a pilot guides his aircraft by maintaining a *constant difference* between his distances from two fixed points, representing radio sending stations. The curve along which the pilot flies is called a *branch* of a *hyperbola*. (See Figure 8–12.)

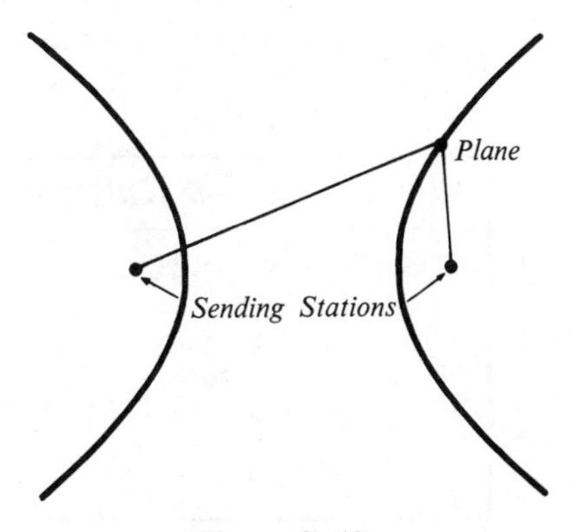

· *Figure 8–12* ·

A **hyperbola** is a set of points in a plane such that for each point of the set the *absolute value* of the difference of its distances from two given points, called **foci**, is a given constant.

If $P(x, y)$ is any point of a hyperbola whose foci are $F_1(-5, 0)$ and $F_2(5, 0)$, and if PF_1 and PF_2, the *focal radii*, differ by 6, then *either* $PF_1 - PF_2 = 6$ *or* $PF_1 - PF_2 = -6$. Thus, P belongs to the hyperbola if and only if its coordinates satisfy the compound open sentence:

$$\sqrt{(x+5)^2+y^2} - \sqrt{(x-5)^2+y^2} = 6$$

or

$$\sqrt{(x+5)^2+y^2} - \sqrt{(x-5)^2+y^2} = -6$$

Using the squaring process to obtain an equation free of radicals, you can show that this compound sentence is equivalent to $\frac{x^2}{9} - \frac{y^2}{16} = 1$. The equation reveals at once several properties of this hyperbola.

Property	Reason
1. It is symmetric with respect to both coordinate axes.	**1.** Whenever (r, t) satisfies $\frac{x^2}{9} - \frac{y^2}{16} = 1$, so also do $(r, -t)$ and $(-r, t)$.
2. Its x-intercepts are 3 and -3.	**2.** Replace y by 0: $\frac{x^2}{9} - \frac{0^2}{16} = 1$ $\therefore x = 3$, or $x = -3$
3. It has no y-intercept; in fact, it contains no point for which $\lvert x \rvert < 3$.	**3.** Solve for y: $\frac{y^2}{16} = \frac{x^2}{9} - 1$ $\therefore y = \frac{4}{3}\sqrt{x^2-9}$ or $y = -\frac{4}{3}\sqrt{x^2-9}$ $\therefore y$ denotes a real number if and only if $x^2 - 9 \geq 0$; that is, $x^2 \geq 9$ or $\lvert x \rvert \geq 3$.

With these facts and the following table of *first quadrant* points, you obtain the graph in Figure 8–13.

x	$y = \frac{4}{3}\sqrt{x^2-9}$ [Q.I]	y
3	$\frac{4}{3}\sqrt{9-9} = \frac{4}{3}\sqrt{0}$	0
4	$\frac{4}{3}\sqrt{16-9} = \frac{4}{3}\sqrt{7}$	3.5
5	$\frac{4}{3}\sqrt{25-9} = \frac{4}{3}\sqrt{16}$	5.3
6	$\frac{4}{3}\sqrt{36-9} = \frac{4}{3}\sqrt{27}$	6.9

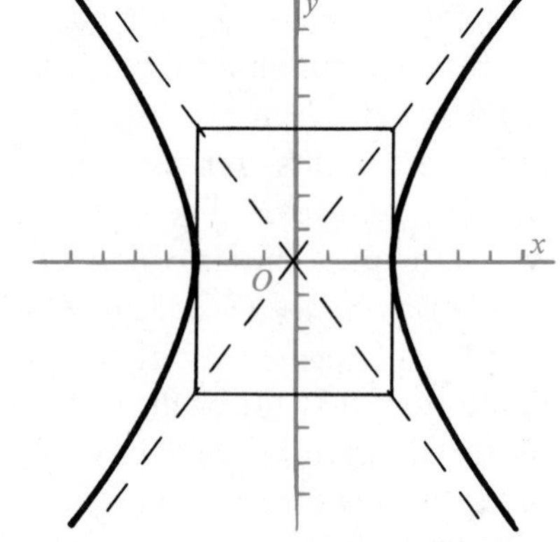

· *Figure 8–13* ·

Notice that the graph lies entirely within two of the sectors marked out by the diagonals of the rectangle formed by the lines $x = 3$, $x = -3$, $y = 4$, $y = -4$. The equations of these diagonals, called the *asymptotes* of the hyperbola, are $y = \frac{4}{3}x$ and $y = -\frac{4}{3}x$ It can be shown (Exercise 20, page 318) that, measured on the vertical line $x = r$, the distance between a branch of the hyperbola and the corresponding asymptote grows smaller as $|r|$ grows larger. This means that the hyperbola gets closer and closer to the diagonals, so that you can use these lines as guides in sketching the curve.

The preceding discussion suggests that a hyperbola with foci on the x-axis at $(c, 0)$ and $(-c, 0)$, and $2a$ as the difference of the focal radii, has an equation of the form $\frac{x^2}{a^2} - \frac{y^2}{b^2} = 1$ where $b^2 = c^2 - a^2$. On the other hand, with foci at $(0, c)$ and $(0, -c)$ on the y-axis, the hyperbola has the equation: $\frac{y^2}{a^2} - \frac{x^2}{b^2} = 1$.

EXAMPLE. Draw the graph of the relation $\{(x, y)\colon 16x^2 - 9y^2 = -144\}$.

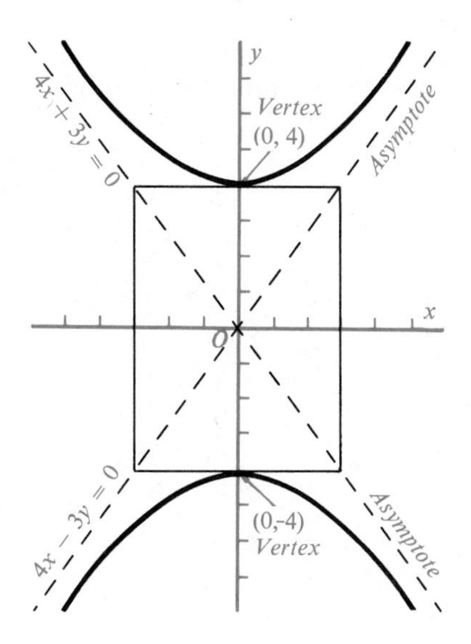

Solution:

$$16x^2 - 9y^2 = -144;\ \frac{y^2}{16} - \frac{x^2}{9} = 1$$

1. Symmetric with respect to both axes.
2. No x-intercept.
3. y-intercepts: 4 and -4
4. Asymptotes: $\frac{y}{4} - \frac{x}{3} = 0$ and $\frac{y}{4} + \frac{x}{3} = 0$.
5. Selected first quadrant points: $y = \frac{4}{3}\sqrt{9 + x^2}$

x	0	2	3	4
y	4	4.8	5.6	6.7

Written Exercises

Graph each relation.

A

1. $\left\{(x, y)\colon \frac{x^2}{9} - \frac{y^2}{25} = 1\right\}$

2. $\left\{(x, y)\colon \frac{x^2}{25} - \frac{y^2}{9} = 1\right\}$

3. $\left\{(x, y): \frac{y^2}{36} - \frac{x^2}{64} = 1\right\}$

4. $\left\{(x, y): \frac{y^2}{81} - \frac{x^2}{16} = 1\right\}$

5. $\{(x, y): x^2 - y^2 = 1\}$

6. $\{(x, y): y^2 - x^2 = 1\}$

7. $\{(x, y): 4x^2 - y^2 = 16\}$

8. $\{(x, y): x^2 - 9y^2 = 9\}$

9. $\{(x, y): 2x^2 - 2y^2 + 8 = 0\}$

10. $\{(x, y): 12x^2 - 3y^2 + 48 = 0\}$

If $R = \{(x, y): y = 2\sqrt{x^2 - 1}\}$, $S = \{(x, y): y = -2\sqrt{x^2 - 1}\}$

$T = \left\{(x, y): y = 2x\sqrt{1 - \frac{1}{x^2}}\right\}$, and $V = \left\{(x, y): y = -2x\sqrt{1 - \frac{1}{x^2}}\right\}$,

graph each of the following sets.

B

11. R
12. S
13. V
14. T
15. $R \cup V$
16. $S \cup T$
17. $R \cup T$
18. $S \cup V$

C

19. a. Show that for any constant k the hyperbolas having equations of the form $x^2 - y^2 = k$ have the same lines as asymptotes.

    b. Show that the asymptotes are perpendicular to each other. (*Optional*)

    c. In the same coordinate system draw the graphs if k is replaced by $9, -9, \frac{1}{9}, -\frac{1}{9}$, and 0.

20. In the figure, $T_1(r, t_1)$, a point in the first quadrant, belongs to $\left\{(x, y): \frac{x^2}{a^2} - \frac{y^2}{b^2} = 1\right\}$. $T_2(r, t_2)$ belongs to the asymptote $\left\{(x, y: \frac{x}{a} - \frac{y}{b} = 0\right\}$.

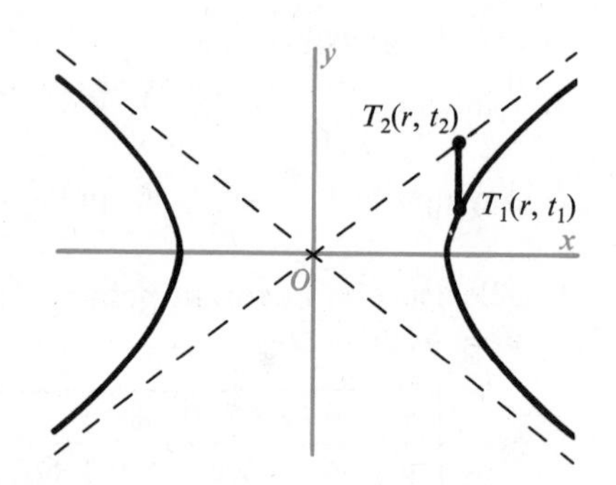

a. Prove that $T_1T_2 = \dfrac{ab}{r + \sqrt{r^2 - a^2}}$ and use this result to explain why T_1T_2 grows closer to 0 as r increases.

Hint: $T_1T_2 = t_2 - t_1 = \frac{b}{a}(r - \sqrt{r^2 - a^2})$.

b. Explain why symmetry implies corresponding results in the other quadrants.

Using the definition, determine an equation of the hyperbola whose foci have the given coordinates, if the absolute value of the difference between the focal radii for each of its points is the given number.

21. $(0, -5); (0, 5); 6$

22. $(-3, 0); (3, 0); 3\sqrt{2}$

23. $(-c, 0); (c, 0); 2a$

24. $(0, -c); (0, c); 2a$

8–7 Inverse Variation

When two pulleys are connected (Figure 8–14), the one with the smaller diameter revolves with the greater speed. In fact, if d_1 is the diameter of one pulley and n_1 the number of revolutions it makes per minute (rpm), while d_2 and n_2 are the corresponding numbers for the other pulley, then $n_1d_1 = n_2d_2$ or $\frac{n_1}{n_2} = \frac{d_2}{d_1}$. If you know $d_1 = 6$ inches, $n_1 = 150$ rpm, and $d_2 = 10$ inches, then you can determine n_2:

$$\frac{150}{n_2} = \frac{10}{6}$$

$$90 = n_2$$

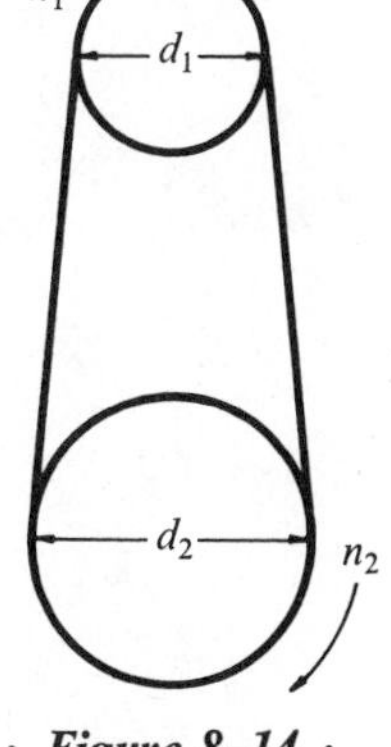

· *Figure 8–14* ·

In this system the product nd is constant: $nd = 900$. Because this equation is equivalent to $n = \frac{900}{d}$ or $d = \frac{900}{n}$, we say n and d *vary inversely as each other* or are *inversely proportional to each other.*

Any function $\{(x, y): xy = k\}$ where k is a nonzero constant is called an *inverse variation*, with k as **constant of proportionality** or

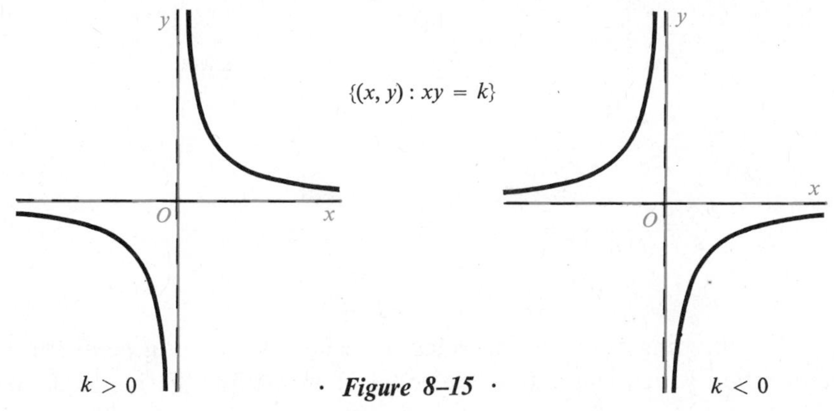

· *Figure 8–15* ·

variation. The graph of an inverse variation can be shown to be a hyperbola having foci equally distant from the origin on the line $y = x$ or on the line $y = -x$. As shown in Figure 8–15, the hyperbola has the coordinate axes as asymptotes. The curve is in the first and third quadrants if k is positive, but in the second and fourth if k is negative. Of course, in practical situations the domain of an inverse variation may be restricted to positive numbers, thus limiting the graph to one branch of the hyperbola.

Inverse variation involving a power appears in the following example.

EXAMPLE. The force of attraction between two particles, each with a mass of 1 gram, varies inversely as the square of the distance between their centers.

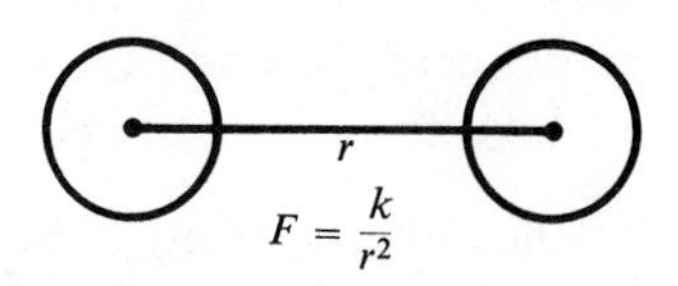

When the centers are 1 centimeter apart, the force of attraction is 6.67×10^{-8} dynes. What is the force of attraction when they are 1 *meter* apart?

Solution: Let F represent the force of attraction in dynes and r the distance in centimeters between the centers.

$$(1,\ 6.67 \times 10^{-8}) \in \left\{(r, F):\ F = \frac{k}{r^2}\right\}. \quad \text{Therefore:}$$

1. $F = \dfrac{k}{r^2}$

$$6.67 \times 10^{-8} = \frac{k}{1^2}$$

$$6.67 \times 10^{-8} = k$$

2. $F = \dfrac{6.67 \times 10^{-8}}{r^2}$

$$1 \text{ meter} = 100 \text{ or } 10^2 \text{ centimeters}$$

$$\therefore\ F = \frac{6.67 \times 10^{-8}}{(10^2)^2}$$

$$F = 6.67 \times 10^{-12}$$

6.67×10^{-12} dynes, **Answer.**

Check: $\dfrac{F_1}{F_2} \stackrel{?}{=} \dfrac{r_2^{\,2}}{r_1^{\,2}}$

$$\frac{6.67 \times 10^{-8}}{6.67 \times 10^{-12}} \stackrel{?}{=} \frac{(10^2)^2}{1^2}$$

$$10^4 = 10^4 \ \checkmark$$

The preceding example illustrates a special case of the general *law of gravitation* which states that the force of attraction (F) between two particles *varies jointly* as their masses (m and n) and *inversely* as the square of the distance r between their centers; in symbols:

$$F = \frac{kmn}{r^2}.$$

We call the variation of F with respect to m and n a **joint variation** because F varies directly as their product. We call the variation of F with respect to m, n, and r^2 a **combined variation** because it involves both direct and inverse variation.

Written Exercises

Graph each function.

A

1. $\{(x, y)\colon xy = 8\}$
2. $\{(x, y)\colon xy = 1\}$
3. $\{(x, y)\colon xy = -6\}$
4. $\{(x, y)\colon xy = -12\}$
5. $\{(x, y)\colon xy + 10 = 0\}$
6. $\{(x, y)\colon xy - 36 = 0\}$

Determine each value of c for which both ordered pairs belong to the same inverse variation.

7. $(10, 25); (2, c)$
8. $(9, 28); (c, 42)$
9. $(-60, -15); (-c, -c)$
10. $(5, 20), (c, c)$
11. $(\frac{4}{5}, \frac{2}{3}); (c, 6)$
12. $(0.28, 0.32); (8, c)$

Determine c so that each statement is true.

B

13. $\{(4, 3), (-2, c)\} \subset \{(x, y)\colon y \text{ varies inversely as } x^2\}$
14. $\{(2, 6), (8, c)\} \subset \{(x, y)\colon y \text{ varies inversely as } x^2\}$
15. $\{(\frac{3}{4}, 6), (4, c)\} \subset \{(x, y)\colon y \text{ varies inversely as } x^2\}$
16. $\{0.25, 0.48), (c, 3)\} \subset \{(x, y)\colon y \text{ varies inversely as } x^2\}$
17. $\{(16, -3), (c, -4)\} \subset \{(x, y)\colon y \text{ varies inversely as } \sqrt{x}\}$
18. $\{(-8, 5), (c, 125)\} \subset \{(x, y)\colon y \text{ varies inversely as } \sqrt[3]{x}\}$
19. If x varies jointly as y and z^2, and x is 48 when y is 8 and z is 3, what is the value of x when y is 12 and z is 2?
20. If y varies jointly as r, s, and t, and y is 30 when r is 3, s is 4, and t is 5, what is r when y is 40, s is 5, and t is 8?
21. If y varies directly as x and inversely as z^2, what is the resulting change in y when x and z are both doubled in value?
22. If y varies directly as x^2 and inversely as z, what is the resulting change in y when x and z are both halved in value?

Graph each relation.

C

23. $\{(x, y): xy < 100\}$
24. $\{(x, y): xy \leq 4\}$
25. $\{(x, y): xy \geq 6\}$
26. $\{(x, y): xy > 24\}$
27. $\{(x, y): |x|y = 4\}$
28. $\{(x, y): x|y| = 4\}$

Using the definition (page 315), find an equation of the hyperbola having the given points as foci and the given number as numerical difference of the focal radii.

29. $(1, 1); (-1, -1); 2$
30. $(-2, 2); (2, -2); 4$

Problems

A

1. The frequency of a radio wave is inversely proportional to the wave length. If a wave 250 meters long has a frequency of 1200 kilocycles per second, find the length of a wave with a frequency of 800 kilocycles per second.
2. A pulley with diameter 8 inches is running at 1452 revolutions per minute while belted to a 12-inch pulley. Find the speed of the larger pulley if the speeds of the pulleys are in inverse proportion to their diameters.
3. Two meshed gears have 35 and 56 teeth respectively. If the speeds are inversely proportional to the numbers of teeth, at what speed should the second gear be driven so that the first gear will run at 1450 revolutions per minute?
4. A certain project can be completed by 28 men in 90 days. In order to get a bonus, the contractor hires extra men so that the job can be done in 84 days. How many extra men does he hire?
5. The load that a wooden beam of given length can support varies jointly as its width and the square of its depth. If a beam whose width is 4 inches and whose depth is 2 inches can support a load of 880 pounds, find the load the beam can support when turned on its side, that is, with a width of 2 inches and a depth of 4 inches.
6. The heat developed in a wire carrying a current for a specified time varies jointly as the resistance and the square of the current. If a current of 8 amperes produces 153.6 calories in a wire whose resistance is 10 ohms, how many calories are produced by a current of 6 amperes in a wire whose resistance is 15 ohms?
7. A surface is now 10 feet from a source of light. How far from the source would the surface have to be in order to receive twice as much

illumination, if the intensity of illumination varies inversely as the square of its distance from the source of light?

8. When an object moves in a circular path, the centripetal force (F) varies directly as the square of the velocity (v) and inversely as the radius (r) of the circle. If $F = 64$ when $v = 2$ and $r = 5$, find F when $v = 3$ and $r = 4$.

B

9. If a satellite completes a circular orbit in 90 minutes flying 500 miles above the earth at 18,000 miles per hour, how long would it take a space capsule flying 300 miles above the earth at 18,950 miles per hour to complete one orbit? Consider 4000 miles as the radius of the earth, and use the fact that the period in hours for a satellite to complete a circular orbit varies directly as the radius of orbit and inversely as the orbital velocity.

10. A gas whose volume is 500 cubic centimeters is under a pressure of 30 inches of mercury at an absolute temperature of 300°. What pressure would be exerted by the gas if the volume rose to 570 cubic centimeters and its absolute temperature dropped to 285°? The pressure on any gas varies directly as its absolute temperature and inversely as its volume.

11. The weight of a body is inversely proportional to the square of its distance from the center of the earth. If a man weighs 147 pounds on the earth's surface, what will he weigh 200 miles above the earth? Assume the radius of the earth to be 4000 miles.

12. The amount of bending of a beam supported at each end and centrally loaded varies jointly as the load (pounds) and the cube of the length (feet) and inversely as the cube of its depth (inches). A beam 12 feet long, 6 inches thick, carrying a load of 2000 pounds, bends $\frac{1}{4}$ inch downward. What is the maximum load a 16-foot beam, of the same width and material, whose depth is 4 inches can carry at the center so as to bend not more than $1\frac{1}{8}$ inches at the center?

In Exercises 13 and 14, use the fact that a lever with arms of length d_1 and d_2, supporting weights w_1 and w_2, is in balance (neglecting its own weight) if and only if $w_1d_1 = w_2d_2$.

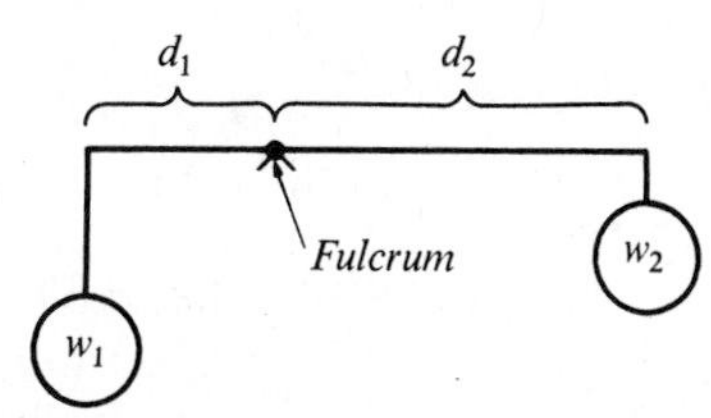

13. The arms of a lever are 8 feet and 12 feet respectively. What weights differing by 10 pounds will balance the lever?

14. To lift a 250-pound boulder an 11-foot crowbar was placed over a stone acting as a fulcrum. How far from the boulder must the stone be placed so that an 80-pound weight on the end of the crowbar will just raise the boulder?

SOLVING QUADRATIC SYSTEMS

8–8 Graphic Solutions

You can use graphs to determine or to estimate solutions of equations in two variables in which one or both of the equations are quadratic.

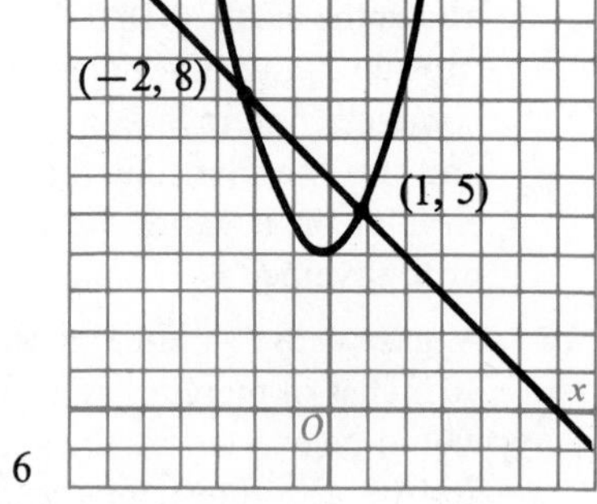

EXAMPLE. Find the solution set of the system

$$y = x^2 + 4$$
$$x + y = 6$$

Solution: Graph both equations on the same axes, and determine the coordinates of any points of intersection.

Check: $8 \stackrel{?}{=} (-2)^2 + 4$ $\quad (-2) + 8 \stackrel{?}{=} 6$

$8 = 8$ ✓ $\quad 6 = 6$ ✓

$5 \stackrel{?}{=} (1)^2 + 4$ $\quad 1 + 5 \stackrel{?}{=} 6$

$5 = 5$ ✓ $\quad 6 = 6$ ✓

$\{(-2, 8), (1, 5)\}$, **Answer**

In the Exercises that follow, you will discover that a system consisting of (1) a linear and a quadratic equation may have 2, 1, or 0 real solutions, and (2) two quadratic equations may have 4, 3, 2, 1, or 0 real solutions.

Oral Exercises

Identify the graph of each equation and state whether the graph is symmetric with respect to one, both, or neither of the coordinate axes.

SAMPLE. $x + y = 4$
$x^2 + y^2 + 2y = 3$

What you say: The graph of $x + y = 4$ is a straight line, symmetric with respect to neither axis.
The graph of $x^2 + y^2 + 2y = 3$ is a circle. It is symmetric with respect to the y-axis because, if (r, t) satisfies the equation, so does $(-r, t)$.

1. $y = x$
$x^2 + y^2 = 1$

2. $y = 2$
$x^2 + y^2 = 4$

3. $x^2 + y^2 = 9$
$x^2 + y^2 = 16$

4. $x^2 + 4y^2 = 16$
$x^2 + y^2 = 16$

5. $y = -3x$
$xy = -6$

6. $y = -5x + 1$
$xy = 6$

7. $x = y^2 - 4$
$x^2 - y^2 = 9$

8. $y = x^2 - 4$
$x^2 + y^2 = 16$

9. $y = x^2 - 2$
$y = 2 - x^2$

10. $x = y^2 + 1$
$x^2 + y^2 - 4y = 5$

Written Exercises

A

1–10. By making a rough sketch of each graph, find the *number* of real solutions of each system in Oral Exercises 1–10 above.

By drawing the graph of each equation, find the solution set of the system.

11. $y = 2x - 6$
$2y = x^2 - 4x$

12. $y = x + 1$
$y = x^2 - 4x - 2$

13. $2x - y = 1$
$4x^2 + y^2 = 36$

14. $x - y = 1$
$x^2 + 9y^2 = 25$

15. $2x = y + 6$
$x^2 = 36 - y^2$

16. $x = y + 1$
$x^2 + y^2 = 25$

17. $xy = 4$
$x^2 + y^2 = 16$

18. $xy = -4$
$x^2 + y^2 = 4$

19. $y = 2x$
$x^2 - y^2 = 4$

20. $x^2 + 4y^2 = 100$
$x^2 - 2y = 0$

B

21. $x^2 - y^2 = 9$
$x^2 + 9y^2 = 169$

22. $x^2 - 3y^2 = 9$
$4x^2 + y^2 = 9$

23. $3x^2 - y^2 = 9$
$y = x^2 + 5x - 5$

24. $x^2 - y^2 = 9$
$y = x^2 - 5x - 5$

25. $4x^2 + y^2 = 144$
$x^2 + y^2 = 16$

26. $x^2 + 4y^2 = 100$
$4x^2 + y^2 = 16$

27. $y = x^2 - 2x - 4$
$xy = 16$

28. $y = x^2 + 4x + 2$
$xy = -16$

Graph the solution set of each of the given systems.

29. $y \leq 2 - x^2$
$y \geq 1$

30. $y \leq 1 - x^2$
$y \geq -4$

31. $x^2 + y^2 \geq 4$
$x^2 + 3y^2 \leq 9$

32. $x^2 + y^2 \geq 4$
$x^2 + y^2 \leq 9$

33. $y \geq 1 - x^2$
$y \geq x^2 - 1$

34. $x^2 + y^2 \leq 4$
$y \geq x^2$

35. $y \geq x^2$
$y \leq 2x - x^2$

36. $xy \leq 4$
$y \leq 4x - x^2$

37. $xy \geq 4$
$x^2 + y^2 \leq 4$

38. $x^2 + y^2 \geq 4$
$y \geq |x|$

8–9 Linear-Quadratic Systems: Substitution

To solve a system involving a linear and a quadratic equation in two variables, you may use substitution (Section 3–5) to replace the quadratic equation by one in which one of the variables does not explicitly appear.

EXAMPLE. Find the solution set of the system

$$x - y + 1 = 0$$
$$x^2 + y^2 = 13$$

Solution:

Step	Work
1. Transform the linear equation to express one variable, say y, in terms of x.	$x - y + 1 = 0$ $y = x + 1$
2. Replace the given quadratic equation by the one obtained from it by substituting $x + 1$ for y. Solve the resulting equation in x.	$x^2 + y^2 = 13$ $x^2 + (x + 1)^2 = 13$ $x^2 + x^2 + 2x + 1 = 13$ $2x^2 + 2x - 12 = 0$ $x^2 + x - 6 = 0$ $(x + 3)(x - 2) = 0$ $x = -3 \quad x = 2$
3. Substitute -3 and 2 in turn for x in the linear equation. Write the corresponding ordered pairs.	$x - y + 1 = 0$ $-3 - y + 1 = 0$ | $2 - y + 1 = 0$ $-2 - y = 0$ | $3 - y = 0$ $y = -2$ | $y = 3$ $(-3, -2)$ | $(2, 3)$
4. Check each ordered pair in *both* equations.	$-3 - (-2) + 1 \stackrel{?}{=} 0$ | $2 - 3 + 1 \stackrel{?}{=} 0$ $0 = 0$ ✓ | $0 = 0$ ✓ $(-3)^2 + (-2)^2 \stackrel{?}{=} 13$ | $2^2 + 3^2 \stackrel{?}{=} 13$ $13 = 13$ ✓ | $13 = 13$ ✓ $\{(-3, -2), (2, 3)\}$, **Answer.**

Notice that the effect of the substitution performed in Step 2 above has been to *replace the circle* in Figure 8-16 by the *pair of red vertical lines*. Thus, the problem reduces to finding the points in which the given line $x - y + 1 = 0$ intersects each red vertical line (Step 3).

Could you have substituted for x instead of y in the equation of the circle (Step 2)?

Yes, because the effect would have been to replace the circle by the pair of horizontal lines shown by red dashes in the figure and you would have obtained the same points.

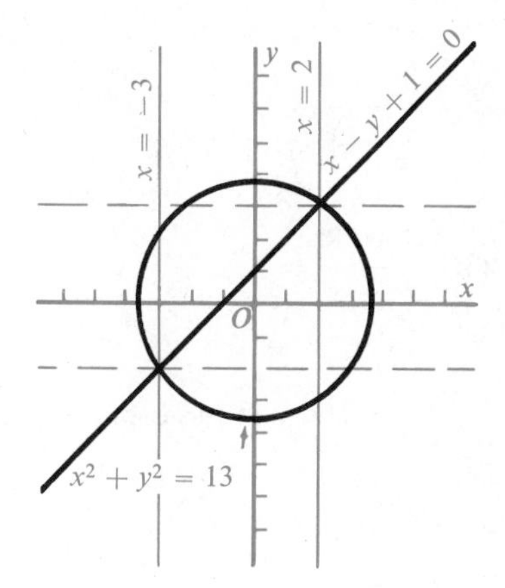

· *Figure 8–16* ·

Written Exercises

Find the solution set for each of the following systems.

1. $y = x^2 - 4$
$y = x - 5$

2. $y = x^2 + 3$
$y = 3x + 1$

3. $rs = 12$
$2r - s = 2$

4. $uv = 24$
$u - 3v = 6$

5. $x^2 + y^2 = 25$
$2x - 3y = -1$

6. $x^2 + y^2 = 100$
$2x - y = 8$

7. $a^2 + 4b^2 = 36$
$a - 2b = 6$

8. $4p^2 + q^2 = 17$
$2p - q = 3$

9. $x^2 - y^2 = 5$
$2x - y = 4$

10. $x^2 - y^2 = 8$
$y = x - 2$

11. $m^2 - n^2 = 15$
$2m - n = -2$

12. $a^2 - b^2 = 21$
$2a - b = -1$

13. $4x^2 + 4y^2 = 1$
$x + y = 1$

14. $y = 4x^2 + 1$
$4x - 3y = -4$

15. $16v^2 + 9w^2 = 13$
$8v - 3w = 4$

16. $6r^2 - 2t^2 = 37$
$r - 3t = 1$

17. $2m^2 - 3mt = 8$
$2m + t = 4$

18. $2a^2 - 2ab + b^2 = 10$
$2a - b + 2 = 0$

19. $2m^2 - mt = 30$
$m - 2t = -11$

20. $x^2 - 2xy + 2y^2 = 18$
$x - 2y = 6$

B

21. $\dfrac{2}{x} + \dfrac{2}{y} = 1$
$y = 2x$

22. $\dfrac{2}{x} - \dfrac{4}{y} = 2$
$y = -2x$

23. $\dfrac{3}{x} + \dfrac{8}{y} = 3$
$2x - y = 2$

24. $\dfrac{1}{x} - \dfrac{4}{y} = 3$
$y = x + 3$

25. $(c - 1)(n + 5) = 75$
$cn = 60$

26. $(c + 2)(n - 10) = 150$
$cn = 120$

Express x and y in terms of the variables in red.

C

27. $x^2 + cxy = c^2 + d^2$
$cx - d^2y = 0$

28. $m^2x^2 + y^2 = b^2$
$y = mx + b$

Problems

Use two variables to solve each problem.

1. Find the dimensions of a rectangle whose area is 35 square inches and whose length is 2 inches greater than its width.

2. Find the dimensions of a rectangle whose area is 15 square inches and whose perimeter is 16 inches.

3. A piece of wire 120 inches long is bent to form a right triangle having a hypotenuse of 51 inches. Find the length of each leg of the triangle.

4. Two men part and walk at right angles. One man walks 1 mile per hour faster than the other. At the end of one hour, the men are 5 miles apart. Find the rate at which each man walks.

5. The sum of two numbers is -2, their product is 1. Find the numbers.

6. Find two numbers whose difference is 2 and whose product is 2.

7. Find two numbers whose sum is 10 and the sum of whose reciprocals is $\frac{5}{12}$.

8. Find two numbers whose sum is 8 and the difference of whose reciprocals is $\frac{1}{3}$.

9. Find the value of k for which the graph of $y = 2x + k$ touches but does not cross (is tangent to) the graph of the parabola $y = x^2 + 1$. *Hint:* There will be one and only one point of intersection.

10. Find the value or values of k for which the graph of $y = 2x + k$ is tangent to the circle whose equation is $x^2 + y^2 = 25$.

8–10 Quadratic-Quadratic Systems

Substitution is often an easy method of solving systems of two quadratic equations in two variables.

EXAMPLE 1. Find the solution set of the system $x^2 - y^2 = 3$, $xy = 2$.

Solution:

1. Transform the second equation to express y in terms of x.	$y = \frac{2}{x}$
2. Substitute $\frac{2}{x}$ for y in the first equation.	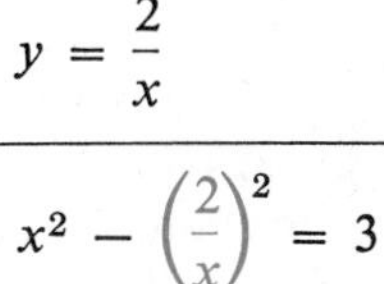 $x^2 - \left(\frac{2}{x}\right)^2 = 3$ $x^2 - \frac{4}{x^2} = 3$
3. Since 0 is not a root of the last equation in Step 2, you may multiply each of its members by x^2; then transform the result to simple form.	$x^4 - 4 = 3x^2$ $x^4 - 3x^2 - 4 = 0$ $(x^2)^2 - 3(x^2) - 4 = 0$
4. Solve the resulting quadratic equation in x^2. Since $x^2 + 1 = 0$ has no real roots, you need consider only the equation $x^2 - 4 = 0$.	$(x^2 - 4)(x^2 + 1) = 0$ $x^2 - 4 = 0, \quad x^2 + 1 = 0$ $(x - 2)(x + 2) = 0$ $x = 2 \quad \vert \quad x = -2$
5. Substitute 2 and -2 in turn for x in $y = \frac{2}{x}$ to obtain values for y. Checking the resulting ordered pairs of numbers in both equations is left to you.	$y = \frac{2}{2} \quad \vert \quad y = \frac{2}{-2}$ $y = 1 \quad \vert \quad y = -1$ $(2, 1) \quad \vert \quad (-2, -1)$ $\{(2, 1), (-2, -1)\}$, **Answer.**

Do you see that substitution in Step 2 replaced the hyperbola whose equation is $x^2 - y^2 = 3$ by the red vertical lines in Figure 8–17?

In addition to the substitution method, the method of linear combinations (Section 3–5) can be used in solving many systems of quadratic equations.

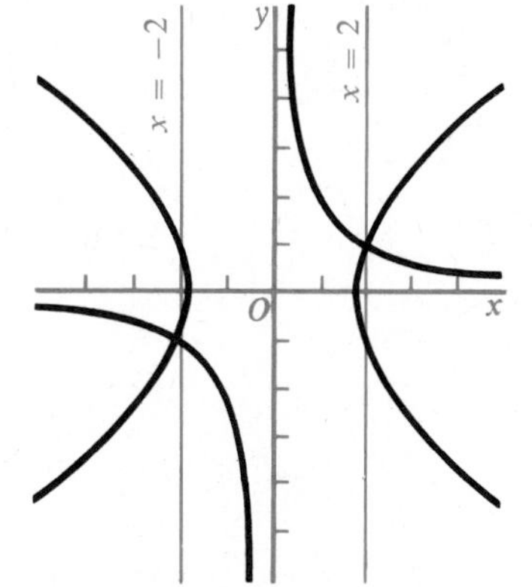

· *Figure 8–17* ·

EXAMPLE 2. Find the solution set of the system: $5x^2 - y^2 = 3$
$x^2 + 2y^2 = 5$

Solution:

1. To obtain equations having the coefficients of y^2 equal in absolute value, multiply the first equation by 2.

$$10x^2 - 2y^2 = 6$$
$$x^2 + 2y^2 = 5$$

2. Replace either equation in Step 1 (say the first) by the sum of the equations. Use this replacement to determine values of x.

$$11x^2 = 11$$
$$\therefore x^2 = 1$$
$$x = 1 \quad | \quad x = -1$$

3. Substitute 1 and -1 in turn for x in $x^2 + 2y^2 = 5$. Write the resulting ordered pairs of numbers.

$$1^2 + 2y^2 = 5 \quad | \quad (-1)^2 + 2y^2 = 5$$
$$2y^2 = 4$$
$$y^2 = 2$$
$$y = \sqrt{2}, \quad | \quad y = -\sqrt{2}$$
$$(1, \sqrt{2}), (1, -\sqrt{2}) \quad | \quad (-1, \sqrt{2}), (-1, -\sqrt{2})$$

4. The check is left to you. $\{(1, \sqrt{2}), (1, -\sqrt{2}), (-1, \sqrt{2}), (-1, -\sqrt{2})\}$, **Answer.**

As suggested in Figure 8–18, Step 2 replaces the given hyperbola by the red vertical lines.

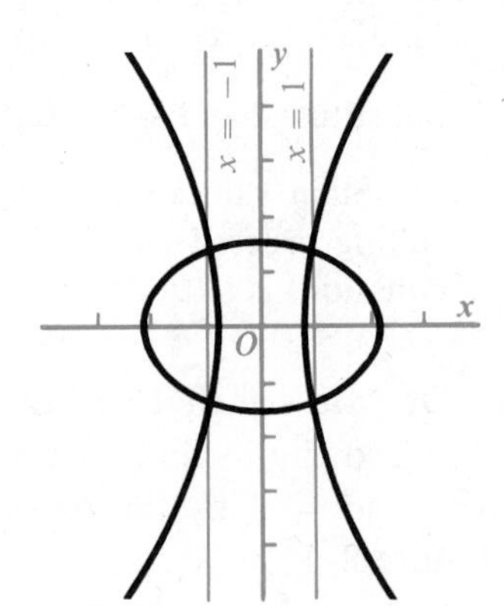

· *Figure 8–18* ·

Written Exercises

In the set of real numbers find the solution set of each system.

A

1. $x^2 + y^2 = 13$
   $y = x^2 - 7$

2. $x^2 + y^2 = 5$
   $y = x^2 - 5$

3. $2a^2 + b^2 = 33$
   $b^2 - a = 23$

4. $c^2 + 3d^2 = 7$
$d^2 = c - 1$

5. $x^2 + y^2 = 25$
$xy = 12$

6. $x^2 - 4y^2 = 5$
$xy = 3$

7. $u^2 + v^2 = 5$
$uv = 2$

8. $p^2 + q^2 = 12$
$pq = 4$

9. $4y = x^2$
$y = x^2 - 3$

10. $y = x^2 - 2x - 4$
$y = x^2 + 4x + 2$

11. $x^2 + y^2 = 25$
$x^2 - y^2 = 7$

12. $x^2 + y^2 = 4$
$x^2 - 2y^2 = 1$

13. $3x^2 - 2y^2 = 9$
$x^2 - y^2 = -1$

14. $4x^2 + 9y^2 = 36$
$x^2 + y^2 = 4$

15. $4x^2 + 9y^2 = 36$
$x^2 - y^2 = 36$

16. $2x^2 + 3y^2 = 23$
$3x^2 - y^2 = 7$

17. $4x^2 - y^2 = 7$
$2x^2 + 5y^2 = 9$

18. $5x^2 - y^2 = 3$
$x^2 + 2y^2 = 5$

B

19. $xy = 6$
$\frac{1}{x} + \frac{1}{y} = \frac{5}{6}$

20. $xy = 8$
$\frac{1}{x} + \frac{1}{y} = \frac{1}{4}$

21. $xy = 12$
$(x - 1)(y + 1) = 12$

22. $xy = 100$
$(x - 5)(y + 1) = 100$

23. $y = -\frac{1}{2}x^2 + 2x + 2$
$xy = 8$

24. $xy = 12$
$3y = 2x^2 + 4x - 18$

Problems

Solve each problem, using two variables.

A

1. Find two numbers such that the sum of their squares is 170 and the difference of their squares is 72.

2. Find two numbers such that the sum of their reciprocals is 4, and 4 times the product of their reciprocals is 15.

3. Find two numbers such that the square of their sum is 20 more than the square of their difference, and the difference of their squares is 24.

4. Find a fraction such that the difference of the squares of the denominator and numerator is 189, and the square of the numerator is 6 more than twice the denominator.

5. A corner lot is in the form of a right triangle whose hypotenuse measures 17 meters and whose area contains 60 square meters. Find the legs of the triangle.

6. An art dealer bought some paintings for $360. When a storm ruined 2 of them, he sold the rest for $380, thus making a profit of $8 on the original cost of each picture. How many pictures did he buy?

7. A group of people decided to buy a motor launch at the sale price of $792, each contributing equally. When 3 more joined in the project, the share of each participant was reduced by $27. How many were in the original group?

8. When a favorable wind caused an increase of 20 miles per hour over the usual speed of the plane, the pilot made the 980-mile trip between two cities in 7 minutes less time. Find the usual speed of the plane.

9. Mia wants to make a window box from a rectangular sheet of galvanized metal whose area contains 680 square inches. She cuts 6-inch squares from each corner and folds the sides to make a box whose base area measures 176 square inches. Find the dimensions of the original metal sheet.

10. The legs of a right triangle are represented by a and $a + b$, respectively, and the hypotenuse measures 15 feet. If the smaller leg is increased by 7 feet and the other leg remains unchanged, the hypotenuse is increased by 5 feet. Find the length of each leg.

B

11. A circle whose center is on the x-axis passes through points (3, 5) and (6, 4). Write an equation of the circle.

12. A hyperbola whose equation is of the form $\frac{x^2}{a^2} - \frac{y^2}{b^2} = 1$ contains points $(-8, \sqrt{3})$ and $(12, -2\sqrt{2})$. Find a^2 and b^2.

13. An ellipse whose equation is of the form $\frac{x^2}{a^2} + \frac{y^2}{b^2} = 1$ contains points $(6, \sqrt{7})$ and $(-4, -2\sqrt{3})$. Find a^2 and b^2.

14. An ellipse whose equation is of the form $\frac{x^2}{4a^2} + \frac{y^2}{b^2} = 1$ and a hyperbola whose equation is of the form $\frac{x^2}{a^2} - \frac{y^2}{b^2} = 1$ are drawn on the same axes. If one of the points of intersection is $(\frac{6}{5}\sqrt{10}, \frac{3}{5}\sqrt{15})$, write each equation.

Lasers

In today's world of modern technology, scientists are making rapid advancements in the use of highly amplified light waves in the field of communications. While light travels at the same high speed as radio waves, light has a much shorter wavelength than other kinds of electromagnetic waves, enabling it to carry enormous amounts of information. Laser beams, or rays of highly controlled light no bigger than pencil leads, are so powerful they may someday replace whole systems of communications now in use.

The potential of laser beams is not restricted to the transmission of information alone. Light which is generated by the laser is also a powerful transmitter of energy. Ordinary light radiates out in all directions from the source. Coherent light waves, which are the basis of the laser beam, travel parallel to each other in a single direction, and all the energy of the laser can therefore be focused onto a very small area. Laser beams which are formed by passing light through a ruby crystal generate more heat than the surface of the sun.

Because of this tremendous energy, lasers have been used to bore holes through materials once considered impenetrable. The beams can be focused on areas as small as one ten-thousandth of an inch in diameter, making them invaluable in the process of welding microscopic electronic equipment. Lasers have also been used in medicine to remove tumors, or to cut away tissue in painless surgery.

Much research must go into the development of more sophisticated laser beams. The devices which exist today are limited in the range of wavelengths which they can achieve, and the beams must be made more flexible before use in guidance and tracking systems becomes widespread. But the potential of harnessed light, as exhibited by the laser beam, is limitless.

Chapter Summary

Inventory of Structure and Method

1. The formula for the **distance between points** $P_1(x_1, y_1)$ and $P_2(x_2, y_2)$ is $d = \sqrt{(x_2 - x_1)^2 + (y_2 - y_1)^2}$. The **midpoint** of segment P_1P_2 is $M\left(\frac{x_1 + x_2}{2}, \frac{y_1 + y_2}{2}\right)$.

2. By applying the distance formula, you can derive the equation of a **circle** with center (h, k) and radius r; namely, $(x - h)^2 + (y - k)^2 = r^2$.

3. An equation of a **parabola** can be derived if you know its **focus** and its **directrix.**

4. When an equation of an **ellipse** is of the form $\frac{x^2}{a^2} + \frac{y^2}{b^2} = 1$ $(a \neq 0, b \neq 0)$, the ellipse intersects the coordinate axes in the points $(a, 0)$, $(-a, 0)$, $(0, b)$, $(0, -b)$ and is symmetric with respect to both coordinate axes.

5. When an equation of a **hyperbola** is of the form $\frac{x^2}{a^2} - \frac{y^2}{b^2} = 1$ or $\frac{y^2}{b^2} - \frac{x^2}{a^2} = 1$ $(a \neq 0, b \neq 0)$, the hyperbola is symmetric with respect to both coordinate axes. The **asymptotes,** $y = \frac{b}{a}x$ and $y = -\frac{b}{a}x$, may be used as guides in drawing the hyperbola.

6. In the function $\{(x, y): xy = k\}$, $k \neq 0$, the corresponding values of x and y **vary inversely**. The graph of an inverse variation is a hyperbola having the coordinate axes as asymptotes. **Joint variation** and **combined variation** are other types of relations.

7. The points of intersection of the graphs of the equations of a system represent the real solutions of the system. Linear-quadratic and quadratic-quadratic systems may be solved algebraically by substitution or by linear combination.

Vocabulary and Spelling

hypotenuse (*p. 299*)
Pythagorean Theorem (*p. 299*)
perpendicular (*p. 303*)
parabola (*p. 309*)
  focus (*p. 310*)
  directrix (*p. 310*)
ellipse (*p. 312*)
  foci (*p. 312*)
  focal radius (*p. 312*)
hyperbola (*p. 315*)
  foci (*p. 315*)
  asymptote (*p. 317*)
inverse variation (*p. 319*)

joint variation (*p. 321*)
combined variation (*p. 321*)
linear-quadratic system (*p. 326*)
quadratic-quadratic system (*p. 329*)

Chapter Test

8–1 **1.** **a.** Express, in simple form, the distance between $A(-2, 7)$ and $B(-8, 3)$. **b.** Find the midpoint of line segment AB.

8–2 **2.** (*Optional*) Write an equation of the line perpendicular to the line $x - 2y = 6$ at the point $(2, -2)$.

8–3 **3.** Without graphing, find the center and the radius of the circle whose equation is $x^2 + y^2 + 6x - 8y - 11 = 0$.

8–4 **4.** Draw the graph of the relation $\{(x, y): x = y^2 + 4y + 1$ and $-5 \leq y \leq 1\}$.

8–5 **5.** Find the points in which the ellipse $4x^2 + 25y^2 = 100$ intersects the coordinate axes.

8–6 **6.** Find the equations of the asymptotes of the hyperbola $x^2 - 16y^2 = 16$.

8–7 **7.** The total heat (H) on a given surface varies inversely as the square of its distance (d) from the source of heat. If a surface 30 inches from a heater gets 200 heat units, how far from the heater must the surface be in order to receive 450 heat units?

8–8 **Solve graphically, estimating solutions to the nearest tenth.**

8. $4x^2 + 25y^2 = 100$
$x^2 - 16y^2 = 16$

Find the solution set of the system:

8–9 **9.** $4x^2 - 2xy + y^2 = 13$
$2x - y = 4$

8–10 **10.** $2a^2 + b^2 = 11$
$ab = -3$

Chapter Review

8–1 **Distance between Points** *Pages 299–303*

1. The distance between points $(3, 9)$ and $(10, -15)$ is __?__.

2. For $P(-7, -3)$ and $Q(-2, -3)$, the midpoint of PQ is __?__.

8–2 **Perpendicular Lines (*Optional*)** *Pages 303–306*

3. If the slope of line l is 0.5, the slope of a line perpendicular to l is __?__.

8–3 Circles *Pages 306–308*

4. An equation of the circle whose center is the origin and whose radius is $2\sqrt{3}$ is ___?___.

8–4 Parabolas *Pages 309–312*

5. Graph the relation $\{(x, y): x \leq 4 + 2y - y^2\}$.

8–5 Ellipses *Pages 312–315*

6. Graph the relation $\{(x, y): y = -2\sqrt{4 - x^2}\}$.

8–6 Hyperbolas *Pages 315–319*

7. Draw the graph of $x^2 - 4y^2 = 4$.

8–7 Inverse Variation *Pages 319–323*

8. The graphs of $y = kx$ and $xy = k$ $(k \neq 0)$ will **(a)** always, **(b)** sometimes, or **(c)** never, intersect. State which.

8–8 Graphic Solutions *Pages 324–325*

Solve graphically, estimating solutions to the nearest tenth.

9. $x^2 + y^2 = 10$
$x + 2y = 4$

10. $x^2 + 9y^2 = 36$
$y = x^2 - 2x - 3$

11. $x^2 - 4y^2 = 9$
$xy = -4$

12. $xy = 8$
$x = y^2 - 2$

8–9 Linear-Quadratic Systems: Substitution *Pages 326–328*

Solve: **13.** $9x^2 - y^2 = 21$
$3x + y = 3$

14. $x + 2y = 3$
$x - xy = 6$

8–10 Quadratic-Quadratic Systems *Pages 329–332*

Solve: **15.** $2x^2 - y^2 = 6$
$5x^2 - 3y^2 = 6$

16. $r^2 + 2rs - 2s^2 = -3$
$rs = -10$

Extra for Experts

The Conic Sections

The diagrams show that the shape of the curve in which a plane intersects a cone whose base is circular and whose axis is perpendicular to the base depends on the angle between the plane and the axis of the cone and on whether the plane contains the vertex of the cone. But in every case the intersection is a figure you have studied: a circle, an ellipse, a parabola, a hyperbola, a point, a line, or a pair of intersecting lines. As a result, these sets of points are called **conic sections**.

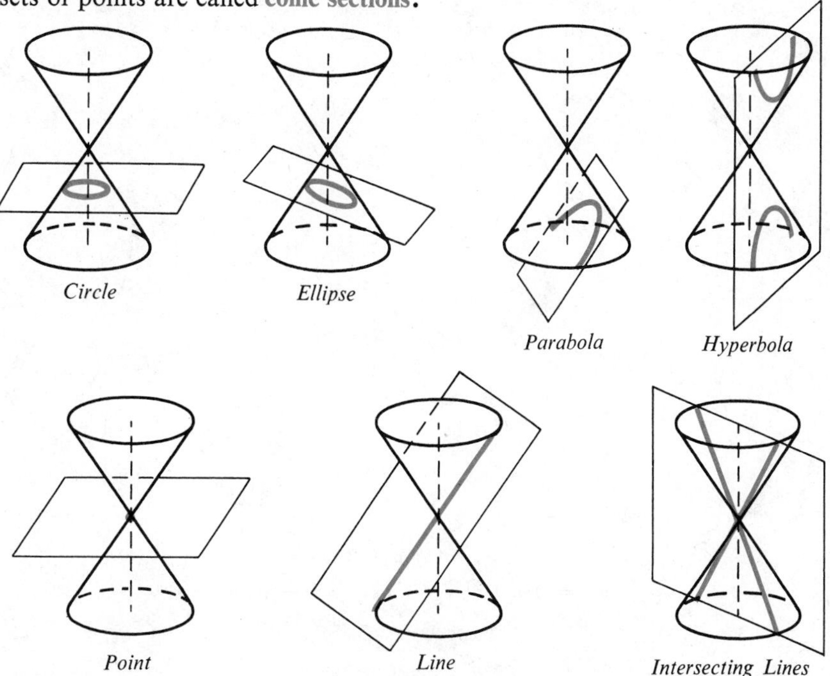

Conic sections also share a common definition as sets of points in a plane. A set of points each of whose distances from a given point F (the **focus**) is a constant e times its distance from a given line d (the **directrix**) is a conic section. Do you see that the parabola satisfies this definition with $e = 1$? The diagram below illustrates the effect of e, called the **eccentricity**, and suggests a means of classifying conics:

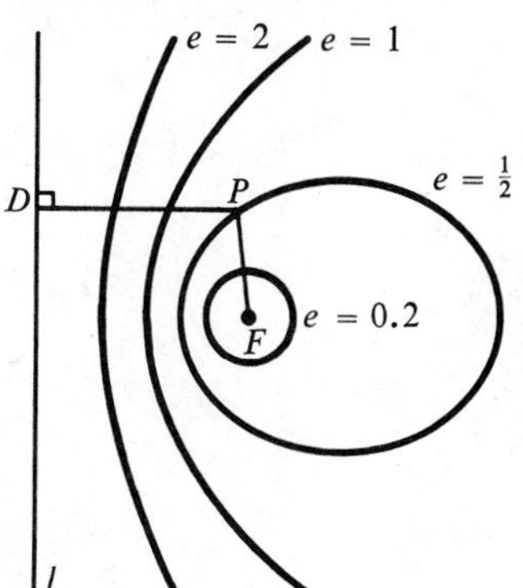

e	Conic
$0 < e < 1$	ellipse
$e = 1$	parabola
$e > 1$	hyperbola

Exercises

Find its equation and sketch the conic with given focus, directrix, and eccentricity.

1. $F(0, 1); y = -3, e = 1$
2. $F(3, 0); x = 12; e = \frac{1}{2}$
3. $F(4, 0); x = 1; e = 2$
4. $F(-\sqrt{2}, 0); x = -\frac{\sqrt{2}}{2}; e = \sqrt{2}$

CHAPTER 9

. . . varying frequencies of a laser beam recorded as concentric circles of light

Exponential Functions and Logarithms

The invention of useful symbolism has often stimulated the development of mathematics. The introduction of positional notation, for example, began a new era in arithmetic and number theory. In this chapter you will see how the extension of the use of exponents and the invention of logarithms contributed not only to efficient numerical calculation but also to the understanding of such concepts as function and inverse.

FROM EXPONENTS TO LOGARITHMS

9–1 Rational Numbers as Exponents

You know that any integer can be used as an exponent of any base b, $b \neq 0$. For example, $3^1 = 3$, $(-2)^4 = 16$, $4^0 = 1$, $5^{-2} = \frac{1}{25}$. Can we extend the meaning of exponents so that every member of the set of rational numbers may qualify as an exponent?

Look first at a special case, say $3^{\frac{1}{2}}$. For $3^{\frac{1}{2}}$ to have a meaning consistent with the familiar laws of exponents (pages 123, 159, 160), it should be true that $(3^{\frac{1}{2}})^2 = 3^{(\frac{1}{2}\cdot 2)} = 3^1 = 3$. Since $3^{\frac{1}{2}}$ is to denote a number whose square is 3, we will define it to be $\sqrt{3}$. (We choose $\sqrt{3}$ rather than $-\sqrt{3}$ so that the inequality $3^0 < 3^{\frac{1}{2}} < 3^1$ is true.) Similar reasoning requires that $3^{\frac{5}{2}} = (3^{\frac{1}{2}})^5 = (\sqrt{3})^5$, and $3^{-\frac{5}{2}} = (3^{\frac{1}{2}})^{-5}$ or $(\sqrt{3})^{-5}$. These observations suggest the following definition:

If p denotes an integer, r a positive integer, and b a positive real number, then

$$b^{\frac{p}{r}} = (\sqrt[r]{b})^p.$$

Using powers with rational exponents, you can write radical expressions in **exponential form**, that is, as powers or products of powers. Then, *because the laws of exponents apply to these powers* (Exercises 42, 43, 44, page 341), you can use the laws to simplify the exponential expressions.

EXAMPLE 1. $2\sqrt{9a^5bc^{-6}} = 2(9)^{\frac{1}{2}}(a^5)^{\frac{1}{2}}(b)^{\frac{1}{2}}(c^{-6})^{\frac{1}{2}} = 6a^{\frac{5}{2}}b^{\frac{1}{2}}c^{-3}$

EXAMPLE 2. $\sqrt{a^{-1}} \cdot \sqrt[3]{a^2} = a^{-\frac{1}{2}}(a^2)^{\frac{1}{3}} = a^{-\frac{1}{2}+\frac{2}{3}} = a^{\frac{1}{6}}$, or $\sqrt[6]{a}$

EXAMPLE 3. $(\frac{1}{16})^{-\frac{3}{4}} = 16^{\frac{3}{4}} = (16^{\frac{1}{4}})^3 = (\sqrt[4]{16})^3 = 8$

The second theorem on page 264 provides another expression for $b^{\frac{p}{r}}$, namely, $\sqrt[r]{b^p}$. This means that

$$(b^{\frac{p}{r}})^r = b^p.$$

Notice also that the laws of *integral* exponents permit you to write for any integer s

$$\begin{aligned}(b^{\frac{p}{r}})^{rs} &= [(b^{\frac{p}{r}})^r]^s \\ &= [b^p]^s \\ &= b^{ps}\end{aligned}$$

Because $b^{ps} = (b^{\frac{p}{r}})^{rs}$ and $b > 0$, you can assert $b^{\frac{ps}{rs}} = b^{\frac{p}{r}}$, or

$$\sqrt[rs]{b^{ps}} = \sqrt[r]{b^p}$$

if $s > 0$. For example, $49^{\frac{2}{4}} = 49^{\frac{1}{2}} = 7$, and $\sqrt[12]{25} = \sqrt[12]{5^2} = \sqrt[6]{5}$.

Note that in extending powers to include all rational exponents, we have restricted the base b to be a positive real number. Without that restriction, some of the familiar laws of exponents do not hold. (See Exercise 41, page 341.)

Oral Exercises

1. If $f(x) = 2^x$, find **(a)** $f(3)$; **(b)** $f(0)$; **(c)** $f(-2)$; **(d)** $f(-1)$.
2. If $f(x) = 4^x$, find **(a)** $f(2)$; **(b)** $f(\frac{1}{2})$; **(c)** $f(-\frac{1}{2})$; **(d)** $f(-\frac{3}{2})$.

Give the value of each symbol.

3. $4^{\frac{3}{2}}$ **5.** $27^{-\frac{1}{3}}$ **7.** $(\frac{4}{9})^{-\frac{1}{2}}$ **9.** $(64)^{\frac{2}{3}}$

4. $8^{\frac{5}{3}}$ **6.** $9^{-\frac{1}{2}}$ **8.** $(\frac{1}{32})^{-\frac{4}{5}}$ **10.** $-8^{\frac{4}{3}}$

State the value of b.

11. $b^{\frac{1}{3}} = 5$ **12.** $b^{\frac{1}{4}} = 2$ **13.** $b^{\frac{3}{2}} = 8$ **14.** $b^{\frac{2}{3}} = 4$

Written Exercises

Write in exponential form.

A

1. $\sqrt[4]{xy^5}$

2. $\sqrt[3]{m^2n^3}$

3. $\sqrt{9a^{-1}b^8}$

4. $\sqrt[4]{81a^{-6}b^3}$

5. $3\sqrt[3]{8x^{-9}z^{-5}}$

6. $2\sqrt{36b^{-9}c^{-8}}$

Simplify and express the answer in simple radical form.

7. $\sqrt[3]{2^5} \cdot \sqrt[4]{2}$

8. $\sqrt[3]{2^2} \cdot \sqrt[6]{2^7}$

9. $\sqrt[3]{4} \cdot \sqrt[4]{2}$

10. $\sqrt{8} \cdot \sqrt[4]{32}$

11. $\sqrt[6]{32} \div \sqrt[3]{2}$

12. $\sqrt[10]{18} \div \sqrt[5]{2}$

13. $\sqrt[8]{64} \div \sqrt[4]{4}$

14. $\sqrt[3]{81} \div \sqrt[6]{9}$

Evaluate.

15. $125^{-\frac{4}{3}}$

16. $64^{-\frac{5}{6}}$

17. $5 \div 4^{-\frac{3}{2}}$

18. $\frac{3}{4} \div (\frac{1}{8})^{-\frac{2}{3}}$

19. $0.027^{\frac{2}{3}}$

20. $0.16^{\frac{3}{2}}$

21. $32^{-\frac{6}{5}}$

22. $-64^{\frac{5}{6}}$

Simplify.

B

23. $10^{1.7} \times 10^{6.1} \div 10^{1.5}$

24. $10^{2.3} \times 10^{-0.8} \div 10^{-0.45}$

25. $\sqrt[3]{2^{3.1} \div 2^{0.4}}$

26. $\sqrt[4]{2^{1.6} \div 2^{-3.8}}$

27. $\sqrt[3]{\sqrt{27}}$

28. $\sqrt{\sqrt[3]{36}}$

29. $\left(\sqrt{\sqrt{\sqrt{a^{12}}}}\right)\left(\sqrt[3]{\sqrt[3]{\sqrt[3]{a^{12}}}}\right)$

30. $\left(\sqrt[5]{\sqrt[5]{b^{20}}}\right)\left(\sqrt{\sqrt{\sqrt{b^{30}}}}\right)$

31. $(a + 2\sqrt{ab} + b)^{\frac{1}{2}}$

32. $(r - 2\sqrt{rs} + s)^{\frac{1}{2}}$

33. $(t^{\frac{1}{2}} + t^{\frac{5}{2}})(t^{\frac{1}{2}} - t^{\frac{5}{2}})$

34. $(s^{\frac{7}{2}} - s^{\frac{1}{2}})(s^{\frac{7}{2}} + s^{\frac{1}{2}})$

Solve over the set of real numbers.

35. $t^{-\frac{3}{4}} = \frac{1}{8}$

36. $b^{-\frac{2}{3}} = 9$

37. $(x - 1)^{\frac{2}{3}} = 25$

38. $(y + 1)^{\frac{3}{2}} = 64$

39. $y = 6 - y^{\frac{1}{2}}$

40. $y = 10 + 3y^{\frac{1}{2}}$

(*Hint for Exs. 39, 40:* Let $x = y^{\frac{1}{2}}$, and solve for x.)

41. If $(-8)^{\frac{1}{3}} = \sqrt[3]{-8}$, show that $(-8)^{\frac{1}{3}} \neq (-8)^{\frac{2}{6}}$, even though $\frac{1}{3} = \frac{2}{6}$.

Let a and b denote positive real numbers, r and s positive integers, and p and q integers. Prove each of the following statements:

42. $b^{\frac{p}{r}} \cdot b^{\frac{q}{s}} = b^{\frac{ps + rq}{rs}}$

43. $(b^{\frac{p}{r}})^{\frac{q}{s}} = b^{\frac{pq}{rs}}$

(*Hint:* Raise each member of the equation to the rsth power.)

44. $(ab)^{\frac{p}{r}} = a^{\frac{p}{r}}b^{\frac{p}{r}}$

9-2 Real Numbers as Exponents

We have assigned a meaning to the symbol 2^x for every rational value of x. For example, $2^{-3} = \frac{1}{2^3} = \frac{1}{8}$, $2^0 = 1$, $2^{\frac{3}{2}} = \sqrt{2^3}$, and $2^{1.7} = 2^{\frac{17}{10}} = \sqrt[10]{2^{17}}$. Can we extend the meaning to include expressions such as $2^{\sqrt{3}}$, in which the exponent is an irrational number?

You can construct a table of coordinates of points of the graph of $\{(x, y)\colon y = 2^x\}$ for selected rational values of x:

x	-3	-2	-1	0	$\frac{1}{2}$	1	$\frac{3}{2}$	2
$y = 2^x$	$\frac{1}{8}$	$\frac{1}{4}$	$\frac{1}{2}$	1	1.4	2	2.8	4

For the graph to be represented by the smooth unbroken curve shown joining these points in Figure 9–1, it must be true that you can approximate a power such as $2^{\sqrt{3}}$, in which the exponent is irrational, as follows: Evaluate the successive powers

$$2^1, \quad 2^{1.7}, \quad 2^{1.73}, \quad 2^{1.732}, \ldots$$

in which the exponents are rational numbers obtained by taking more and more places in the decimal representing $\sqrt{3}$. Since these powers steadily increase but remain less than 2^2, it can be proved by advanced mathematical techniques that they get closer and closer to a certain positive real number which we call $2^{\sqrt{3}}$. As a matter of fact, to five significant figures $2^{\sqrt{3}} \doteq 3.3220$.

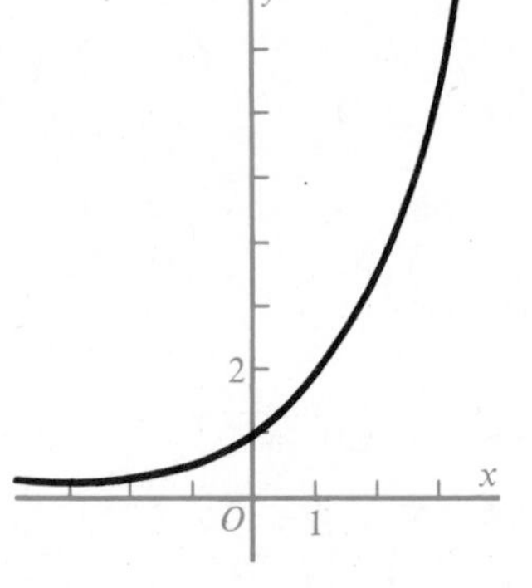

· *Figure 9–1* ·

Similar reasoning leads to the definition of b^x where b is any *positive* real number and x any irrational number. Furthermore, it can be proved that the laws of exponents continue to hold for these powers.

$$(3^{\sqrt{2}})^{\sqrt{2}} = 3^{\sqrt{2}\cdot\sqrt{2}} = 3^2 = 9; \qquad 2^{1-\pi} \cdot 2^{\pi} = 2^{(1-\pi)+\pi} = 2^1 = 2$$

The curve shown in Figure 9–1 continuously rises with increasing abscissa and is typical of the graph of every function of the form $\{(x, y)\colon y = b^x\}$ where b is a constant greater than 1. If $0 < b < 1$, the graph falls with increasing abscissa (Figure 9–2). In each case, however, any vertical line and any horizontal line above the x-axis intersects the graph in just one point. This means that $b^{x_1} = b^{x_2}$ *if and only if* $x_1 = x_2$.

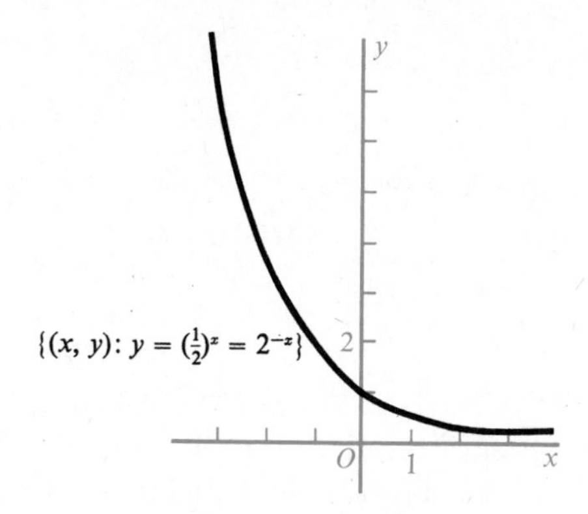

· *Figure 9–2* ·

EXAMPLE. Solve for n: $4^{n-1} = (\frac{1}{2})^{4n-1}$.

Solution:

1. Express each member of the equation as a power of the same base, 2. $\quad 4^{n-1} = (\frac{1}{2})^{4n-1}$; $\quad (2^2)^{n-1} = (2^{-1})^{4n-1}$
2. Simplify each member. $\quad 2^{2n-2} = 2^{1-4n}$
3. Equate exponents and solve for n. $\quad 2n - 2 = 1 - 4n$; $\quad 6n = 3$
4. The check is left to you. $\quad n = \frac{1}{2}$; $\{\frac{1}{2}\}$, **Answer.**

Written Exercises

Simplify.

A

1. $2(5^{\sqrt{3}})(5^{-\sqrt{3}})$
2. $(2^{\sqrt[3]{6}})^{\sqrt[3]{\frac{6}{3}}}$
3. $(5^{-\sqrt{2}})^{\sqrt{4}}$
4. $(\sqrt{2}^{-\pi})^{2/\pi}$
5. $10^{\sqrt{3}+1} \cdot 100^{-\sqrt{\frac{3}{2}}}$
6. $10^{3-2\sqrt[3]{2}} \cdot 100^{\sqrt[3]{2}}$
7. $36^{\sqrt{5}} \div 6^{\sqrt{40}}$
8. $2^{\sqrt{27}} \div 8^{\sqrt{3}}$

Solve.

9. $3^4 = 3^{2x+1}$
10. $10^{x+1} = 10^{3x+4}$
11. $7^m = 7^{2m^2-1}$
12. $4^{3n^2} = 4^{5n+2}$
13. $4^{3t} = 8^{t-2}$
14. $8^{k-1} = 16^{3k}$
15. $9^{c-1} = 27^c$
16. $125^{2v-1} = 625^v$

Using convenient scales on the axes, graph each function.

17. $\{(x, y): y = 3^x\}$
18. $\{(x, y): y = 4^x\}$
19. $\{(x, y): y = (\frac{1}{4})^x\}$
20. $\{(x, y): y = (\frac{1}{3})^x\}$

B

21. $\{(x, y): y = 2^x + 1\}$

22. $\{(x, y): y = 3^x - 2\}$

23. $\{(x, y): y = 3 \cdot 2^{x+1}\}$

24. $\{(x, y): y = 5 \cdot 2^{1-x}\}$

Graphically solve each system, estimating roots to the nearest half unit.

C

25. $y = 2^x, y = x + 1$

26. $y = 3^x, 3x - y = 0$

9-3 Relations and Their Inverses

You can think of a function whose domain is the set D and whose range is the set R as a mapping from D to R. Figure 9-3 pictures the function $\{(x_1, y_1), (x_2, y_1), (x_3, y_3)\}$ as a mapping under which two elements, x_1 and x_2, of D are mapped onto the same element, y_1, of R, while x_3 is mapped onto another element, y_3, of R. The function shown in Figure 9-4 is called a **one-to-one function** or **mapping**, because distinct elements of D are mapped onto distinct elements of R.

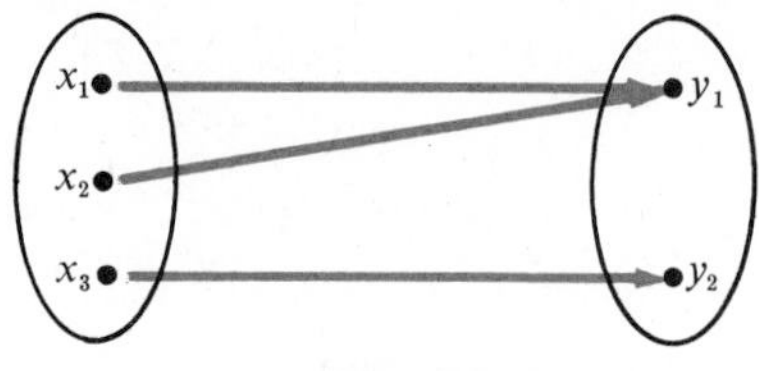

· *Figure 9-3* ·

· *Figure 9-4* ·

Now suppose that f is the one-to-one function which maps each real number onto its double increased by 1; that is, $f = \{(x, y): y = 2x + 1\}$. Also, let g be the function mapping each real number onto one-half the difference between the real number and 1; that is, $g = \{(x, y): y = \frac{1}{2}(x - 1)\}$. Then $f(3) = 2 \cdot 3 + 1 = 7$ and $g(7) = \frac{1}{2}(7 - 1) = 3$. Thus, if you apply the mapping f to the number 3, and then apply g to the result, 7, you come back to 3. This means that $g[f(3)] = g(7) = 3$. Similarly, $g[f(5)] = g(11) = 5$; and, in general, $g[f(x)] = g(2x + 1) = \frac{1}{2}[(2x + 1) - 1] = x$. You can also show that $f[g(x)] = x$. The functions f and g are called **inverse functions**, and we write $f = g^{-1}$ and $g = f^{-1}$, read "f is the inverse of g, and g is the inverse of f."

Figures 9-5 and 9-6 picture the relationship between f and f^{-1}. You obtain f^{-1} by interchanging the domain and range of f and reversing its mapping. In general, the **inverse of a relation** is the relation obtained by interchanging the coordinates in each ordered pair in the given relation.

Because it is customary to orient the graph of a relation so that numbers in the domain are paired with points of the horixontal axis and numbers in the range with points of the vertical axis, Figure 9-6 should be viewed from the other side of this sheet turned 90° clockwise. It would then appear as Figure 9-7.

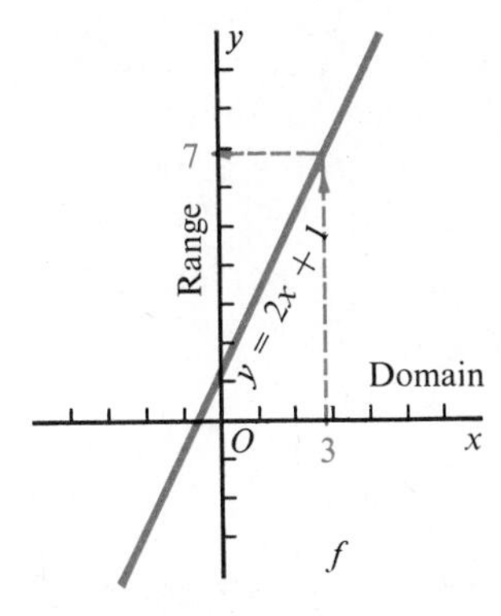

· *Figure 9–5* ·

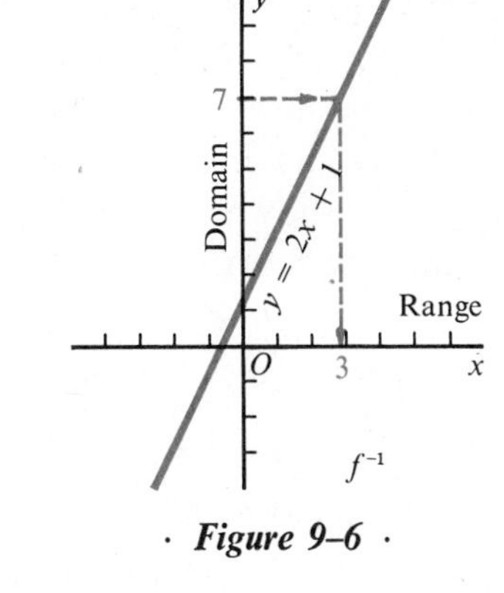

· *Figure 9–6* ·

Notice that the axes have been relabeled in Figure 9–7 to conform with the custom of representing elements of the domain by the variable x and elements of the range by the variable y. This means that you obtain the equation relating numbers in the domain and range of f^{-1} by interchanging x and y in the equation for f. Since $f = \{(x, y)\colon y = 2x + 1\}$, you have

$$f^{-1} = \{(x, y)\colon x = 2y + 1\},$$

$$\text{or } f^{-1} = \{(x, y)\colon y = \tfrac{1}{2}(x - 1)\}.$$

· *Figure 9–7* ·

The fact that you can obtain the ordered pairs in the inverse of a function by interchanging the coordinates in each of the ordered pairs of the function suggests a way of constructing the graph of f^{-1}. Since $(3, 7) \in f$, you know that $(7, 3) \in f^{-1}$. As indicated in Figure 9–8, the points $A(3, 7)$ and $B(7, 3)$ are symmetric with respect to the line $y = x$. This means that the line $y = x$ is the perpendicular bisector of line segment AB. Do you see that all the points of the graphs of f and f^{-1} can be paired in this way? If you were to fold the coordinate plane along the line $y = x$, the graphs of f and f^{-1} would coincide.

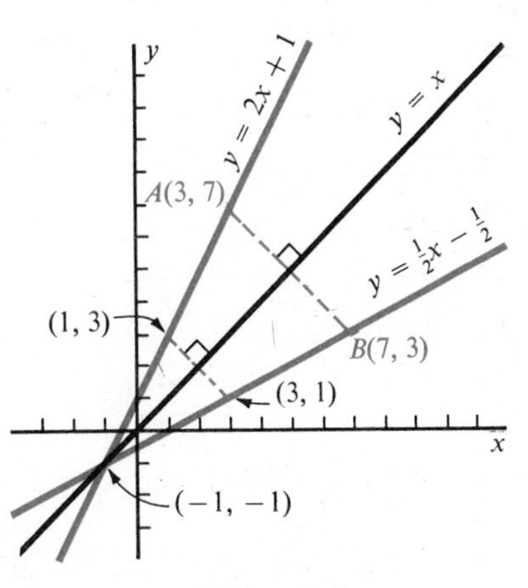

· *Figure 9–8* ·

Whenever a function is one-to-one, its inverse is also a function. The function $\{(x, y)\colon y = x^2\}$, whose graph appears in Figure 9–9, is not one-to-one, because it maps both 2 and -2 onto the same number, 4. Consequently, its inverse $\{(x, y)\colon x = y^2\}$, or $\{(x, y)\colon y = \sqrt{x}$ or $y = -\sqrt{x}\}$, shown in Figure 9–10 is a relation, but not a function. Notice that the inverse maps 4 onto both 2 and -2.

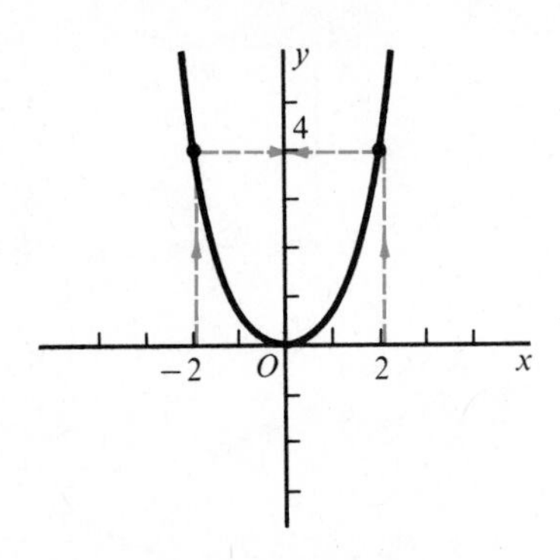

· *Figure 9–9* ·

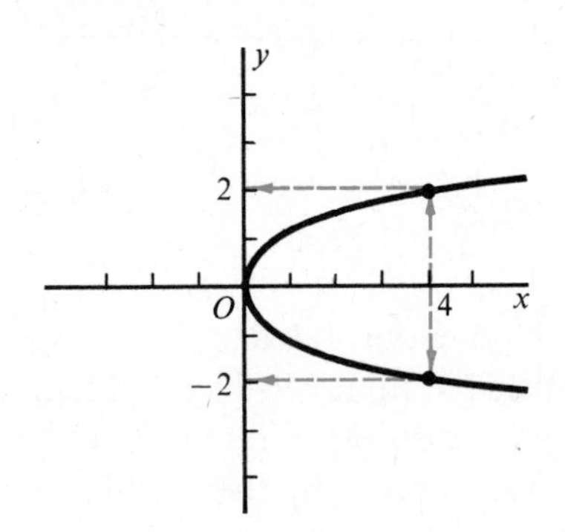

· *Figure 9–10* ·

Written Exercises

State the inverse of each of the following functions over the real numbers and tell whether the inverse is a function. Draw graphs of the function and its inverse.

A

1. $\{(x, y)\colon y = \frac{1}{3}x + 2\}$

2. $\{(x, y)\colon y = x^3\}$

3. $\{(x, y)\colon y = x^2 - 1\}$

4. $\{(x, y)\colon y = 2 - x^2\}$

5. $\{(x, y)\colon y = 2\}$

6. $\{(x, y)\colon y = -1\}$

7. $\{(x, y)\colon y = x\}$

8. $\left\{(x, y)\colon y = \dfrac{1}{x}\right\}$

9. $\{(x, y)\colon y = \sqrt{25 - x^2}\}$

10. $\{(x, y)\colon y = \sqrt{36 + x^2}\}$

11. $\{(x, y)\colon y = |x|\}$

12. $\{(x, y)\colon y = x^{\frac{1}{2}}\}$

13. Find a function which is its own inverse and which has the set of all real numbers as domain.

9–4 Exponential and Logarithmic Functions

The function of the form $\{(x, y)\colon y = b^x,\ b > 0,\ b \neq 1\}$ is called the **exponential function with base *b*.** Given the graph of an exponential function, you can use it to find an approximation of any power of the base. For example, in Figure 9–11 you find $10^{0.5} \doteq 3$ by drawing first the vertical line and then the horizontal line indicated in red. On the other hand, by reversing the construction (Figure 9–12),

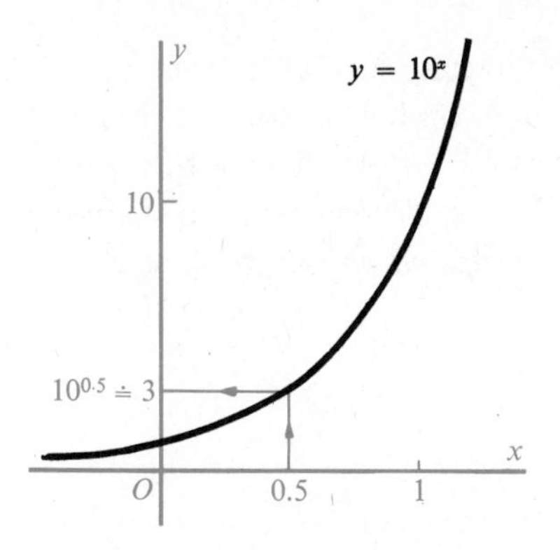

· *Figure 9–11* ·

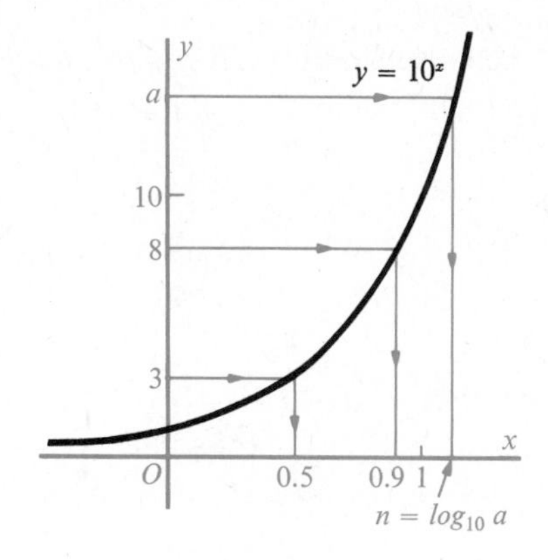

· *Figure 9–12*

you find that to express 3 as a power of 10 you use an exponent approximately equal to 0.5; that is, $3 \doteq 10^{0.5}$. This figure also shows $8 \doteq 10^{0.9}$.

The exponential function is a one-to-one function. As Figure 9–12 indicates, given any positive number a, there is a unique real number n such that $\boldsymbol{a = 10^n}$. We call n "the **logarithm** of a to the base 10" and write $\boldsymbol{\log_{10} a = n}$. For example:

$\log_{10} 100 = 2$ because $100 = 10^2$ | $\log_{10} 0.001 = -3$ because $0.001 = 10^{-3}$

In general, if a denotes any *positive* real number and b any positive real number except 1, there is a unique real number, called the **logarithm of a to the base b,** ($\log_b a$) which is the exponent in the power of b that equals a; that is, $\boldsymbol{\log_b a = n}$ if and only if $\boldsymbol{a = b^n}$. For example, $\log_{\frac{1}{2}} 4 = -2$ because $4 = (\frac{1}{2})^{-2}$.

We call $\{(x, y)\colon y = \log_b x,\ b > 0,\ b \neq 1,\ x > 0\}$ the **logarithmic function with base b.** Since you obtain this function by interchanging the coordinates in the ordered pairs of $\{(x, y)\colon y = b^x\}$, the exponential function with base b and the logarithmic function with base b are inverses of each other. As you saw in Section 9–3, Figure 9–13 demonstrates that the graphs of $y = b^x$ and $y = \log_b x$ are reflections of each other in the graph of $y = x$.

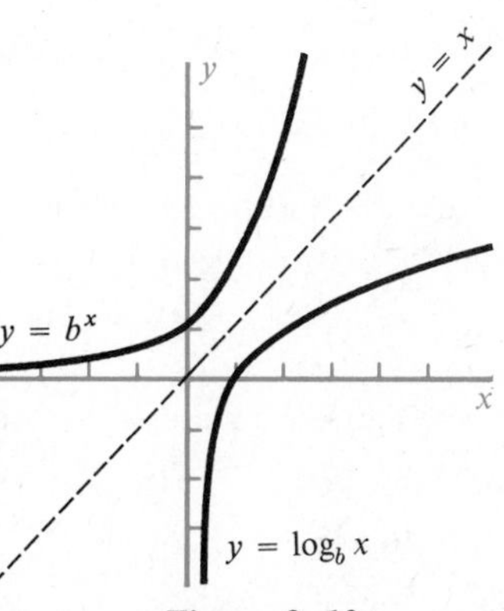

· *Figure 9–13* ·

Because the domain of the logarithmic function is the range of the exponential function, the logarithmic function has as domain the set of *positive real numbers.* Its range, the set of all *real numbers*, is the domain of the exponential function. Also, because $b^{y_1} = b^{y_2}$ if and only if $y_1 = y_2$, it follows that *$\log_b x_1 = \log_b x_2$ if and only if $x_1 = x_2$.*

EXAMPLE. Determine x if $\log_2(x^2 - 1) = \log_2 8$.

Solution:

$$\log_2(x^2 - 1) = \log_2 8$$
$$x^2 - 1 = 8$$
$$x^2 = 9$$
$$x = 3,\ x = -3.\quad \{3, -3\},\ \textbf{Answer.}$$

Written Exercises

Find each logarithm.

A

1. $\log_{10} 0.1$
2. $\log_{10} 0.01$
3. $\log_{27} 3$
4. $\log_{27} 9$
5. $\log_8 16$
6. $\log_4 \frac{1}{2}$
7. $\log_{\frac{1}{2}} \frac{1}{4}$
8. $\log_{\frac{1}{4}} \frac{1}{2}$
9. $\log_{\frac{1}{3}} 9$
10. $\log_{\frac{1}{5}} 25$
11. $\log_{\frac{1}{2}} 1$
12. $\log_{\frac{3}{4}} 1$

Find the value of x in each case.

SAMPLE. $\log_x 216 = 3$

Solution: $\log_x 216 = 3;\ \therefore x^3 = 216;\ x = \sqrt[3]{216} = 6$, **Answer.**

13. $\log_x 81 = 4$
14. $\log_x 10 = 1$
15. $\log_x 16 = 2$
16. $\log_x 125 = 3$
17. $\log_4 x = -4$
18. $\log_6 x = -2$
19. $\log_3 x = 0$
20. $\log_8 x = \frac{2}{3}$
21. $\log_{10} 100 = x$
22. $\log_9 27 = x$
23. $\log_{16} 8 = x$
24. $\log_2 0.5 = x$

B

25. $\log_{\sqrt{2}} x = 4$
26. $\log_{\sqrt{3}} x = 6$
27. $\log_x \sqrt{3} = \frac{1}{2}$
28. $\log_x \sqrt{2} = \frac{1}{6}$
29. $\log_{\sqrt{2}} 8 = x$
30. $\log_{\sqrt{5}} 25 = x$
31. $\log_{10}(x^2 + 36) = 2$
32. $\log_{10}(x - 1)^2 = -2$

Graph the functions in the same coordinate systems.

33. $\{(x, y): y = 3^x\}; \{(x, y): y = \log_3 x\}$
34. $\{(x, y): y = (\frac{1}{2})^x\}; \{(x, y): y = \log_{\frac{1}{2}} x\}$

Show that each statement is true.

35. $\log_2 64 = 3 \log_8 64$.
36. $\log_3 81 = \frac{4}{3} \log_2 8$.
37. $\log_2 8 \cdot \log_8 2 = 1$.
38. $\log_3 27 \cdot \log_{27} 3 = 1$.
39. For $a > 0$, $\log_a a^a = a$.
40. For $a > 0$, $\log_a a^2 = 2$.

USING LOGARITHMS

9–5 Common Logarithms

Originally invented to aid astronomers in their calculations, logarithms may be used to simplify computation. Because our numerals are based on 10, logarithms to the base 10, called **common logarithms**, are often used. Since it is customary to omit writing the base 10, we will agree that $\log x = \log_{10} x$.

You obtain common logarithms of integral powers of 10 by writing the power in exponential form and noting the exponent.

Exponential Form	*Logarithmic Form*
$0.01 = 10^{-2}$	$\log 0.01 = -2$
$0.1 = 10^{-1}$	$\log 0.1 = -1$
$1 = 10^{0}$	$\log 1 = 0$
$10 = 10^{1}$	$\log 10 = 1$
$100 = 10^{2}$	$\log 100 = 2$

To find the common logarithms of numbers that are not integral powers of 10, use a table which gives the first four decimal places in the logarithms of numbers between 1 and 10. The table on this page is an excerpt from Table 5 of the Appendix. To find an approximation for $\log x$ when $1 \leq x < 10$, find the first two digits of x in the column headed x and find the third digit in the row to the right of x.

x	0	1	2	3	4	5	6	7	8	9
11	0414	0453	0492	0531	0569	0607	0645	0682	0719	0755
12	0792	0828	0864	0899	0934	0969	1004	1038	1072	1106
13	1139	1173	1206	1239	1271	1303	1335	1367	1399	1430
14	1461	1492	1523	1553	1584	1614	1644	1673	1703	1732

To find log 1.24, look for 12 under x and move along row 12 to the column headed 4, where you find 0934. Since $\log x$ is between 0 and 1 when x is between 1 and 10, each entry in the table is understood to be preceded by a decimal point. Therefore, $\log 1.24 \doteq 0.0934$. In working with logarithms, it is customary to use the symbol $=$, rather than $\doteq$, although with only one exception (which one?), the logarithms in Table 5 are approximations. But if you write $\log 1.24 = 0.0934$, remember that the *equality holds only for four decimal places.*

The use of standard notation (page 193) enables you to find the logarithm of a positive number outside the interval from 1 to 10. For example,

$$12.4 = 1.24 \times 10^1$$

But

$$\log 1.24 = 0.0934, \text{ or } 1.24 = 10^{0.0934}$$

Therefore,

$$12.4 = 10^{0.0934} \times 10^1 = 10^{1.0934} \text{ or } \log 12.4 = 1.0934$$

Here are four more examples:

$$1_{\wedge}24 = 1.24 \times 10^2; \quad \therefore \log 124 = 2.0934$$

$$1_{\wedge}2400 = 1.24 \times 10^4; \quad \therefore \log 12400 = 4.0934$$

$$0.01_{\wedge}24 = 1.24 \times 10^{-2}; \quad \therefore \log 0.0124 = -2 + 0.0934$$

$$0.0001_{\wedge}24 = 1.24 \times 10^{-4}; \quad \therefore \log 0.000124 = -4 + 0.0934$$

Notice that the logarithm of a number has two parts: a decimal or fractional part called the **mantissa**, which is a *positive number* found in Table 5, and an integral or whole number part called the **characteristic**, which is the exponent of 10 in the standard notation for the number. To maintain this pattern, we usually do not simplify the sum $-2 + 0.0934$ by combining terms in a single negative number to obtain $\log 0.0124 = -1.9066$. Instead we will write $-2 = 8.0000 - 10$, giving us $\log 0.0124 = 8.0934 - 10$.

In using logarithms, you have to find the logarithm of a given number and also the number having a given logarithm. In either case, use Table 5.

EXAMPLE 1. Find log 8350.

Solution: In standard form $8350 = 8.35 \times 10^3$, so the characteristic is 3. Now look for line 83, column 5 in the table and find the mantissa 9217. $\therefore \log 8350 = 3.9217$, **Answer.**

EXAMPLE 2. The logarithm of a number is 2.8370. Find the number. This may be stated: $\log x = 2.8370$; find x.

Solution: Reverse the order of the steps in Example 1. The mantissa is .8370, so look for 8370 *among the mantissas* in the table. Notice that the entries increase in each line as you go to the right, and continue to increase in the next line. You locate 8370 in line 68, column 7, so the digits in x are 687. If the characteristic were 0, x would equal 6.87. Since the characteristic is 2, $x = 6.87 \times 10^2 = 687$, **Answer.**

If $\log x = a$, then x is called the antilogarithm of a.

EXAMPLE 3. Find antilog $9.8370 - 10$.

Solution: This means $\log x = 9.8370 - 10$; find x.
From Example 2, $\log 6.87 = 0.8370$, but here the characteristic is $9 - 10 = -1$.

$\therefore x = 6.87 \times 10^{-1} = 0.687$, **Answer.**

Written Exercises

Find each logarithm. Use Table 5.

A

1. log 92.5	**5.** log 3760	**9.** log 0.62	**13.** log 5.1
2. log 0.783	**6.** log 1.04	**10.** log 800	**14.** log 0.597
3. log 7	**7.** log 0.0209	**11.** log 62.4	**15.** log 60000
4. log 0.0693	**8.** log 8730	**12.** log 0.00058	**16.** log 0.00125

Find the antilogarithm in each case.

17. antilog 1.4362
18. antilog 0.8401
19. antilog 2.5403
20. antilog 9.0253 − 10
21. antilog 3.4200
22. antilog 8.6010 − 10
23. antilog 1.9750
24. antilog 2.1931
25. antilog 4.5911
26. antilog 9.6031 − 10
27. antilog 8.8603 − 10
28. antilog 6.9782 − 10
29. antilog 0.7388
30. antilog 3.3054
31. antilog 8.7709 − 10
32. antilog 7.0043 − 10

Solve each inequality.

C

33. $\dfrac{(x - 2)\log x}{x^2} > 0$

34. $\dfrac{\log(x - 1)}{x + 3} \leq 0$

9–6 Interpolation

Can you find log 1.374? Because Table 5 gives direct readings for the logarithms of numbers known to *at most three* significant figures, you can find entries for log 1.370 and log 1.380 but not for log 1.374.

To see how to compute log 1.374, look at Figure 9–14, which is a schematic diagram comparing the graph of $\{(x, y): y = \log x\}$ from point P to point Q with the straight line joining P and Q.

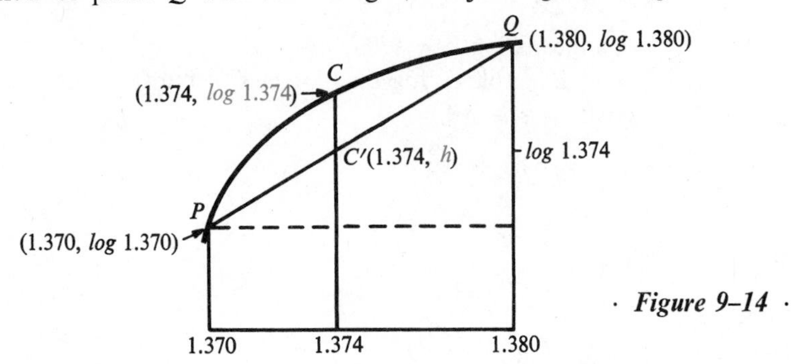

· *Figure 9–14* ·

The diagram suggests the assumption that we make: the ordinate h of point C' on the line is an acceptable approximation of log 1.374, the ordinate of C on the curve. This means we assume that because 1.374 is $\frac{4}{10}$ of the way from 1.370 to 1.380, log 1.374 is $\frac{4}{10}$ of the way from log 1.370 to log 1.380. Then, because P, C', and Q are collinear,

$$\underbrace{\textbf{the slope of segment } PC'}_{} = \underbrace{\textbf{the slope of segment } PQ}_{}$$

$$\frac{\log 1.374 - \log 1.370}{1.374 - 1.370} = \frac{\log 1.380 - \log 1.370}{1.380 - 1.370}$$

$$\frac{\log 1.374 - \log 1.370}{0.004} = \frac{\log 1.380 - \log 1.370}{0.010}$$

$$\therefore \log 1.374 - \log 1.370 = \tfrac{4}{10}[0.1399 - 0.1367] \quad \text{(Table 5)}$$

$$\log 1.374 - \log 1.370 = \tfrac{4}{10}(0.0032) = 0.00128$$

$$\log 1.374 = 0.1367 + 0.0013$$

$$\therefore \log 1.374 = 0.1380$$

Denoting log 1.374 − log 1.370 by d, you can arrange the work as follows:

		x	$\log x$		
0.010		1.380	0.1399		0.0032
	0.004	1.374	log 1.374	d	
		1.370	0.1367		

$d = \frac{4}{10} \times 0.0032 \doteq 0.0013$ (rounded to four places because mantissas in Table 5 are reliable only to four places)

$\therefore \log 1.374 = 0.1367 + 0.0013 = 0.1380$

This process, called **linear interpolation,** enables you to use a four-place table of logarithms to find the logarithm of a number known to four significant figures, with the result usually correct to four decimal places. To find the logarithm of a number known to more than four digits, first round the given number to four digits (page 192), then find the logarithm of the resulting number.

You can also interpolate in reverse to find x if $\log x$ is known and its mantissa is not an entry in the table.

EXAMPLE. Find antilog 1.0875.

Solution: In Table 5, find the consecutive entries 0864 and 0899 between which the mantissa 0875 lies, and note the corresponding four-digit sequences, 1220 and 1230. Then, make the following chart with 12.20 and 12.30 in the x-column because the characteristic 1 tells you that each antilog is between 10 and 100.

	x	$\log x$	
0.10	12.30	1.0899	0.0035
c	antilog 1.0875	1.0875	0.0011
	12.20	1.0864	

$$\frac{c}{0.10} = \frac{0.0011}{0.0035}; \quad c = \frac{1}{10} \cdot \frac{11}{35} \doteq 0.03$$

$$\therefore \text{antilog } 1.0875 = 12.20 + 0.03 = 12.23, \textbf{ Answer.}$$

Note that the value of c was rounded to one significant figure because reverse interpolation in a four-place table yields at most four significant digits for the number whose logarithm is given. With practice, much of the interpolation can be performed mentally.

Written Exercises

Find $\log x$.

A

1. $x = 32.45$
2. $x = 98.86$
3. $x = 0.5338$
4. $x = 38.55$
5. $x = 0.007524$
6. $x = 702.3$
7. $x = 3.142$
8. $x = 0.01257$
9. $x = 0.8676$
10. $x = 63394$
11. $x = 0.01541$
12. $x = 27,186$

Find antilog y.

13. $y = 2.8811$
14. $y = 1.2912$
15. $y = 8.2210 - 10$
16. $y = 9.8706 - 10$
17. $y = 0.9915$
18. $y = 3.7929$

19. $y = 4.6238$ **21.** $y = 8.5410 - 10$ **23.** $y = 1.8257$

20. $y = 2.9431$ **22.** $y = 7.6660 - 10$ **24.** $y = 1.5555$

9–7 Products and Quotients

Because logarithms are exponents, you can multiply and divide positive numbers by adding or subtracting their logarithms. To see how this is accomplished, consider the product ab, where a and b denote positive numbers. By definition,

$$10^{\log a} = a,\ 10^{\log b} = b, \text{ and } 10^{\log ab} = ab.$$

$$\therefore\ 10^{\log ab} = ab = (10^{\log a})(10^{\log b}) = 10^{\log a + \log b}.$$

Because equal powers of the same positive base (other than 1) have equal exponents,

$$\log ab = \log a + \log b.$$

Thus, *to find the logarithm of a product of numbers, you add the logarithms of the numbers.* Similarly, you can show that for positive numbers a and b,

$$\log \frac{a}{b} = \log a - \log b,$$

which says that *the logarithm of a quotient is equal to the logarithm of the dividend minus the logarithm of the divisor.*

As you study the three Examples which follow, use pencil and paper, and refer to the Tables as required. Notice also the following instructions.

In computing with four-place logarithms, results can be given to at most four significant figures. If, moreover, the numbers involved in the computation are approximations, the accuracy of the result may be further restricted. We use the following working rules to decide how to round the answer.

1. Give products, quotients, and powers to the same number of *significant figures,* as appear in the *least accurate* approximation involved.
2. Give sums and differences to the same number of decimal places, as appear in the approximation with the *least number* of decimal places.

A computation is worthless if it is not correct. To guard against error, you should adopt two practices as a matter of routine.

First, make an estimate of the result. This guards against such gross errors as misplacing a decimal point.

Second, plan and arrange your work systematically and neatly. This makes it easier to check for errors. A good rule to follow is always to write numbers that must be added or subtracted in vertical columns, aligning equality signs vertically and keeping decimal points directly under one another. You can indicate the operations (+), (−), or (×) and put in the characteristics in advance. Also label the steps of your computation, so that if you have to check back, you know what you are checking.

EXAMPLE 1. Compute 758×0.416 if each factor is a three-significant figure approximation.

Solution: Let $N = 758 \times 0.416$.

1. Make an estimate of N (see page 194).

$$758 \doteq 8 \times 10^2;\ 0.416 \doteq 4 \times 10^{-1}$$
$$\therefore N \doteq (8 \times 10^2)(4 \times 10^{-1}) \doteq 320$$

2. Write equations showing the plan of work and find $\log N$.

$$\begin{aligned} N &= 758 \times 0.416 \\ \therefore \log N &= \log 758 + \log 0.416 \\ \log 758 &= 2.8797 \\ \log 0.416 &= \underline{9.6191 - 10} \quad (+) \\ \log N &= 12.4988 - 10 = 2.4988 \end{aligned}$$

3. Since you can find N to at most three digits, you need not interpolate; simply determine the number whose logarithm is closest to $\log N$ in the table.

$$N = 315$$

4. As a partial check, note that when rounded to one significant digit, the result 315 and the estimate 320 agree.

To the nearest unit, N is 315, **Answer.**

Recall that $\log x$ is not defined for $x \leq 0$. Therefore, if negative numbers are involved in a calculation, first determine by inspection whether the result is a positive or a negative number. Then perform the computation using absolute values.

EXAMPLE 2. Compute $\dfrac{-6.770}{25.40}$.

Solution: 1. Let $N = \dfrac{-6.770}{25.40}$; by inspection, note that N is negative.

(*continued on p.* 356)

$$|N| = \frac{6.770}{25.40};\ |N| \doteq \frac{7}{3 \times 10} \doteq 0.2 \text{ (estimate)}$$

2. $\log |N| = \log 6.770 - \log 25.40$

$\log 6.770 = 0.8306$

$\log 25.40 = \underline{1.4048}\ (-)$

$?$

To obtain a difference in which the mantissa is positive, change the form of log 6.770 to 10.8306 − 10.

$$\begin{aligned} \log 6.770 &= 10.8306 - 10 \\ \log 25.40 &= \underline{\ \ 1.4048 \qquad\quad} \quad (-) \\ \log |N| &= 9.4258 - 10 \\ |N| &= 0.2666, \text{ by interpolation.} \end{aligned}$$

3. The result checks with the estimate 0.2. N is -0.2666, **Answer.**

The product and quotient properties stated for logarithms to the base 10 are also true for any other base. You can use this fact to solve certain equations involving logarithms.

EXAMPLE 3. Solve: $\log_4(x + 3) + \log_4(x - 3) = 2$.

Solution:

1. Use the product property to express the left member as the logarithm of a product. $\quad \underbrace{\log_4(x + 3) + \log_4(x - 3)} = 2$; $\quad \log_4(x + 3)(x - 3) = 2$
2. Transform the equation obtained in Step 1 to exponential form. $\quad \therefore\ (x + 3)(x - 3) = 4^2$; $\quad x^2 - 9 = 16$
3. Solve for x. $\quad x^2 = 25$
4. Verify results in the given equation. $\quad x = 5 \text{ or } -5$

$x = 5$	$x = -5$
$\log_4(5 + 3) + \log_4(5 - 3) \stackrel{?}{=} 2$	$\log_4(-5 + 3) + \log_4(-5 - 3) \stackrel{?}{=} 2$
$\log_4 8 + \log_4 2 \stackrel{?}{=} 2$	No, because logarithms of negative numbers have not been defined.
$\frac{3}{2} + \frac{1}{2} \stackrel{?}{=} 2$	
$2 = 2$ ✓	

$\{5\}$, **Answer.**

Oral Exercises

Without referring to tables, state the value of n.

1. $\log 2 + \log 3 = \log n$
2. $\log_3 5 + \log_3 6 = \log_3 n$
3. $\log_7 15 - \log_7 3 = \log_7 n$
4. $\log n = \log 4 - \log 20$
5. $\log_{\frac{1}{2}} n = \log_{\frac{1}{2}} 2 + \log_{\frac{1}{2}} 3 + \log_{\frac{1}{2}} 1$
6. $\log_{\sqrt{2}} n = \log_{\sqrt{2}} 3 + \log_{\sqrt{2}} 6 - \log_{\sqrt{2}} 2$

State the logarithmic equation you would use to compute each of the following.

SAMPLE. $(32.1)(2.14)$

What you say: $\log N = \log 32.1 + \log 2.14$

7. $(4.76)(86.1)$
8. $(5.88)(6.54)$
9. $(892)(0.271)$
10. $(0.0791)(8.17)$
11. $(211.4)(0.613)$
12. $(82.34)(25.5)$
13. $(813)(0.2141)$
14. $(238)(0.6162)$
15. $(-0.08125)(0.2317)$
16. $(-0.02176)(-0.9144)$
17. $\dfrac{80.7}{41.6}$
18. $\dfrac{7.02}{5.57}$
19. $\dfrac{329.0}{83.10}$
20. $\dfrac{0.4340}{0.1720}$
21. $\dfrac{2370}{8947}$
22. $\dfrac{70.52}{571.0}$
23. $\dfrac{0.40771}{0.30496}$
24. $\dfrac{0.31298}{0.7132}$
25. $\dfrac{-767.5}{-424.5}$
26. $\dfrac{8.312}{-23.11}$

Written Exercises

A

1–20. Use logarithms to perform the calculations indicated in Oral Exercises 7–26 above. Assume each number involved is an approximation.

Determine the solution set of each equation.

21. $\log n + \log 5 = 1$
22. $\log_3 n - \log_3 4 = 2$
23. $\log_5 x^3 - \log_5 x = 2$
24. $\log 9x + \log x = 4$
25. $\log_6 n - \log_6(n - 1) = \log_6 3$
26. $\log_8(m + 1) - \log_8 m = \log_8 4$

B

27. $\log_7(x + 1) + \log_7(x - 5) = 1$
28. $\log_6(y - 3) + \log_6(y + 2) = 1$
29. $\log_2(9t + 5) - \log_2(t^2 - 1) = 2$
30. $\log_3(2v - 5) - \log_3(v^2 + 4v + 4) = -2$

9–8 Powers and Roots

Logarithms provide a good means of evaluating expressions such as $\sqrt[7]{253}$ and $(0.12)^{27}$. But to perform these computations, you need an additional law of logarithms.

If a denotes any positive number, you know:

$$a = 10^{\log a}$$

$$\therefore\ a^n = (10^{\log a})^n = 10^{n \log a},$$

or

$$\mathbf{\log a^n = n \log a}$$

This means that *to find the logarithm of a power, you multiply the logarithm of the base by the exponent indicating the power.* For example:

$$\log 2^5 = 5 \log 2 = 5(0.3010) = 1.5050$$

$$\log \sqrt[3]{6.3^2} = \log 6.3^{\frac{2}{3}} = \tfrac{2}{3} \log 6.3 = \tfrac{2}{3}(0.7993) = 0.5329$$

$$\log \sqrt[6]{0.0719} = \tfrac{1}{6} \log (0.0719) = \frac{8.8567 - 10}{6}$$

To obtain an integral characteristic in the last example, replace 8.8567 − 10 by 58.8567 − 60. Then,

$$\log \sqrt[6]{0.0719} = \frac{58.8567 - 60}{6} = 9.8095 - 10$$

Do you see that if you wished to find $\frac{1}{3}$ of a logarithm such as 9.0820 − 10 you could change it to 29.0820 − 30?

EXAMPLE 1. Find $(0.814)^5$.

Solution: Let $N = (0.814)^5$.

To find an estimate, round *up* some factors and round *down* the rest.	$\log N = 5 \log 0.814$
$N \doteq (8 \times 10^{-1})^4(9 \cdot 10^{-1})$	$\log 0.814 = 9.9106 - 10$
$\doteq (64)^2 \cdot 9 \cdot 10^{-5}$	$5\ (\times)$
$\doteq (6 \cdot 10)^2 \cdot 9 \cdot 10^{-5}$	$\log N = 49.5530 - 50$
$\doteq 36 \cdot 9 \cdot 10^{-3}$	$\log N = 9.5530 - 10$
$\doteq (4 \cdot 10) 9 \cdot 10^{-3}$	$\therefore\ N = 0.357$
$\doteq 36 \cdot 10^{-2}$ or 0.36	0.357, **Answer.**

EXAMPLE 2. Find $\sqrt[4]{39.60}$.

Solution: Let $M = \sqrt[4]{39.60} = (39.60)^{\frac{1}{4}}$.

Estimate	*Computation*
$M \doteq 36^{\frac{1}{4}} = (36^{\frac{1}{2}})^{\frac{1}{2}}$	$\log M = \frac{1}{4} \log 39.60$
$\therefore M \doteq 6^{\frac{1}{2}} \doteq (6.25)^{\frac{1}{2}}$	$\log 39.60 = 1.5977$
$\therefore M \doteq 2.5$	$\frac{1}{4}\ (\times)$
	$\log M = 0.3994$
	$M = 2.508$

2.508, **Answer.**

Oral Exercises

State the value of n.

1. $\log n = 2 \log 5$
2. $\log_5 n = 3 \log_5 2$
3. $\log_7 n = \frac{1}{2} \log_7 36$
4. $\log n = \frac{1}{3} \log 8$
5. $3 \log n = \log 125$
6. $2 \log_8 n = \log_8 49$

State the logarithmic equation which you would use to compute each of the following.

SAMPLE. $(30.71)^5$ *What you say:* $\log N = 5 \log 30.71$

7. $(4.09)^3$
8. $(1.35)^{12}$
9. $(56.4)^{\frac{1}{3}}$
10. $(18.3)^{\frac{1}{2}}$
11. $\sqrt{731}$
12. $\sqrt[5]{79600}$
13. $\sqrt[4]{0.307}$
14. $\sqrt[3]{0.214}$
15. $(307.4)^6$
16. $(1.029)^{10}$
17. $(85.76)^{\frac{1}{10}}$
18. $(0.04881)^{\frac{1}{6}}$
19. $(637700)^3$
20. $(-0.009043)^7$
21. $\sqrt{63.776}$
22. $\sqrt[3]{-3.8972}$
23. $(0.5379)^{\frac{1}{3}}$
24. $(0.03285)^{\frac{1}{5}}$
25. $(872)^{\frac{3}{4}}$
26. $-(0.0065)^{\frac{2}{5}}$

Written Exercises

A **1–20.** Perform the operations indicated in Oral Exercises 7–26 above. Assume each number other than an exponent is an approximation.

B **21.** Determine the solution set of $\log x^2 = (\log x)^2$.

22. If $\pi = 3.14159\ldots$ and $e = 2.71828\ldots$, determine which number is the greater: π^e or e^π.

9–9 Combined Operations

You can apply the laws of logarithms to several operations at once. For example, to compute

$$N = \frac{\sqrt{3.612}\,(2.147)^2}{4\sqrt[3]{1318}}$$

you would use the logarithmic equation

$$\log N = [\tfrac{1}{2}\log 3.612 + 2\log 2.147] - [\log 4 + \tfrac{1}{3}\log 1318],$$

and to compute

$$N = \frac{[(2.314)^{\frac{1}{2}}(3.157)^{\frac{1}{3}}]^{\frac{1}{5}}}{(3.189)^6}$$

you would use

$$\log N = \tfrac{1}{5}[\tfrac{1}{2}\log 2.314 + \tfrac{1}{3}\log 3.157] - 6\log 3.189.$$

EXAMPLE 1. Compute: $\dfrac{(25.01)(0.9736)}{(63.18)(3.172)}$

Solution: 1. *Estimate:*

The numerator is approximately $25 \times 1 = 25$

The denominator is approximately $60 \times 3 = 180$

The fraction is then roughly $\frac{25}{200}$, so the answer will be about $\frac{1}{8}$ or 0.125.

2. *Plan of computation:*

log 25.01	=	1.	
log 0.9736	=	9. −10	(+)
log num.	=		┐
log 63.18	=	1.	│
log 3.172	=	0.	(+) │
log denom.	=		(−) ←
log fraction	=		
fraction	=		

[log fraction = log numerator − log denominator
= (log 25.01 + log 0.9736) − (log 63.18 + log 3.172)]

Completion of this Example is left to you. The answer is 0.1215.

EXAMPLE 2. Compute $3.28\sqrt[3]{\dfrac{690}{0.417 \times 1.84}}$.

Solution: Let $N = 3.28\sqrt[3]{\dfrac{690}{0.417 \times 1.84}}$.

1. $N \doteq 3\sqrt[3]{\dfrac{7 \cdot 10^2}{4 \cdot 10^{-1} \cdot 2}} \doteq 3\sqrt[3]{\frac{7}{8} \cdot 10^3} \doteq 3 \cdot 10$, or 30.

2. $\log N = \frac{1}{3}[(\log 690 - \log 0.417) - \log 1.84] + \log 3.28$

$$\begin{array}{rcll}
\log 690 & = & 12.8388 - 10 & \\
\log 0.417 & = & \underline{9.6201 - 10} & (-) \\
 & & 3.2187 & \\
\log 1.84 & = & \underline{0.2648} & (-) \\
 & & 2.9539 & \\
 & & \underline{\tfrac{1}{3}} & (\times) \\
\tfrac{1}{3}[\log 690 - \log 0.417 - \log 1.84] & = & 0.9846 & \\
\log 3.28 & = & \underline{0.5159} & (+) \\
\log N & = & 1.5005 & \\
N & = & 31.7, & \textbf{Answer.}
\end{array}$$

Many formulas can be evaluated by means of logarithms. Among these is the compound-interest formula. If P represents the principal invested at r per cent annual interest, and n represents the number of times the interest is compounded during a year, then the amount A accumulated after t years is given by

$$\boldsymbol{A = P\left(1 + \frac{r}{n}\right)^{nt}}$$

EXAMPLE 3. A bond paying 3% compounded semiannually is bought for $2000. To the nearest dollar, how much will it be worth when it matures 20 years from now?

Solution:

$$A = P\left(1 + \frac{r}{n}\right)^{nt}$$

$P = 2000$, $r = .03$, $n = 2$, and $t = 20$.

$$A = 2000\left(1 + \frac{.03}{2}\right)^{(2)(20)}$$

$$A = 2000(1.015)^{40}$$

$$\begin{array}{rcll}
\log A & = & 40 \log 1.015 + \log 2000 & \\
\log 1.015 & = & 0.0065 & \\
40 \log 1.015 & = & 0.2600 & \\
\log 2000 & = & \underline{3.3010} & (+) \\
\log A & = & 3.5610 & \\
A & = & \$3639, & \textbf{Answer.}
\end{array}$$

Oral Exercises

State the logarithmic equation you would use to compute each of the following.

SAMPLE. $s = \frac{1}{2}gt^2$

What you say: $\log s = \log g + 2\log t - \log 2$

1. $c = \pi r^2$
2. $A = \frac{1}{2}bh$
3. $G = \sqrt{AH}$
4. $F = \dfrac{mv^2}{r}$
5. $V = \frac{1}{12}\pi d^2 h$
6. $t = 2\pi\sqrt{\dfrac{l}{g}}$
7. $R = r\sqrt[3]{\dfrac{V}{v}}$
8. $r = \sqrt{\dfrac{V}{\pi h}}$
9. $H = \dfrac{\pi dfs}{33{,}000}$
10. $V = \frac{4}{3}\pi r^3$
11. $F = \dfrac{km_1m_2}{d^2}$
12. $A = \dfrac{s^2\sqrt{3}}{4}$

Written Exercises

Write the logarithmic equation you would use to compute each of the following.

A

1. $\dfrac{(86)(0.45)}{57.4}$
2. $\dfrac{(0.04)(256)}{72.6}$
3. $\dfrac{48.7}{(83.8)(3.14)}$
4. $\dfrac{0.87}{(28.9)(0.785)}$
5. $\dfrac{\sqrt[4]{34.7}}{2.981}$
6. $\dfrac{57.26}{\sqrt[3]{0.382}}$
7. $\dfrac{(0.961)(87.5)^2}{4850}$
8. $\sqrt[3]{\dfrac{9310}{(1.08)(62.4)^3}}$
9. $\dfrac{0.003634}{(47.00)(0.0980)^3}$
10. $\dfrac{(3072)\sqrt[3]{0.8400}}{(2.634)^2}$
11. $\pi\sqrt{\dfrac{42.68}{9801}}$
12. $\sqrt[3]{\dfrac{(3)(782.6)}{4\pi}}$
13. $-\dfrac{17}{7.1}\sqrt{\dfrac{(28.8)^3}{5390 \times 951}}$
14. $\dfrac{(86.2)^2(-37.3)}{(-591)\sqrt[3]{60}}$
15. $\dfrac{(780.6)^2\sqrt{3.000}}{4.000}$
16. $\dfrac{(0.9200)^5(7032)(1.367)}{317.0\sqrt{0.0684}}$

17–32. Perform the computations indicated in Exercises 1–16 by means of logarithms.

Without using a table of logarithms, find N.

33. $\log(N + 5)^2 - \log(N + 5) = \log 2$

34. $\log N + 2 \log N = \log 8$

35. $\log_5 \sqrt[3]{N} + \frac{2}{3} \log_5 N = 3$

36. $4 \log \sqrt[3]{N} + \log \sqrt[3]{N^2} = \log \frac{1}{8}$

B

37. $\log N = \frac{1}{3}[\log 3 - \log 5] + \frac{2}{3} \log 4 + \log 11$

38. $\log N = \frac{1}{5}[\log 7 + \frac{1}{2} \log 3] - [\log 5 + \frac{1}{3} \log 8]$

39. $\log N = \frac{1}{2}[\log(x^4 - 1) - \log(x^2 + 1)] + \log x$

40. $8 \log N = \log x^{\frac{3}{2}} + \log 2 - \frac{1}{2} \log x + \log x^3 - \log \dfrac{2}{x^4}$

C

41. Show that $\log \dfrac{x + \sqrt{x^2 - 1}}{x - \sqrt{x^2 - 1}} = 2 \log(x + \sqrt{x^2 - 1})$.

42. Show that $\dfrac{\log(x + h) - \log x}{h} = \log \left(1 + \dfrac{h}{x}\right)^{\frac{1}{h}}$.

43. Show that $\log \dfrac{y}{a + \sqrt{a^2 + y^2}} = \log \dfrac{\sqrt{a^2 + y^2} - a}{y}$.

44. Solve for x: $\log_4 |2x + 2| - \log_4 |3x + 1| = \frac{1}{2}$.

Problems

A

1. A certain savings bank pays 3% interest compounded semiannually. How much will \$2500 amount to if left on deposit for 20 years?

2. Find the amount in a savings and loan account if the company pays 4% compounded quarterly and \$1200 was deposited 5 years ago.

3. If \$2000 is invested at 3% interest compounded every four months, what will be the amount in the investment after 10 years?

4. If \$5000 is invested at 4% compounded quarterly, what will be the amount of the investment after 12 years?

5. How much should be invested now at 5% compounded semiannually to amount to \$915 in 14 years?

6. When David started school at six years of age, his father invested enough money at 4% compounded annually so that David received \$2500 when he finished medical school at the age of 26. How much was invested?

7. The formula $t = \pi\sqrt{\frac{l}{g}}$ relates to the motion of a pendulum. Find t to the nearest hundredth when $l = 46.5$ and $g = 32.2$.

8. In Exercise 7, find t if $l = 27.9$ when $g = 16.3$.

9. If energy and mass are related by the equation $E = mc^2$, where c is the velocity of light (approximately 3.00×10^{10} centimeters per second), find the energy available in a mass of 3 grams. *Note:* The energy resulting is expressed in ergs.

10. If 1 kilowatt-hour is equivalent to 3.60×10^6 joules, and 1 joule is equivalent to 1×10^7 ergs, find the energy in a mass of 3 grams (see Exercise 9) in terms of kilowatt hours.

B

11. A certain radioactive material decays at a rate given by $Q = Q_0 \cdot 10^{-kt}$ where Q is in grams and t is in years. If $Q_0 = 500$ grams, find k if $Q = 450$ grams when $t = 1000$ years.

12. Using the results of Exercise 11, find Q when $t = 2000$ years.

13. A certain culture of bacteria (provided it has sufficient nourishment) grows at the rate of $N = 1000(10)^{\frac{t}{48}}$ where N is the number of bacteria, and t is the elapsed time in hours. How many bacteria will be present after the elapse of 3 hours?

14. Using the relationship stated in Exercise 13, find how many bacteria were present at the end of one day.

15. A radioactive substance decays according to the equation $Q = Q_0(10)^{-0.024t}$ where t is in hours; find the half-life of the substance. That is, find t when $Q = \frac{1}{2}Q_0$.

16. If the half-life of a substance that decays according to the equation $Q = Q_0(10)^{-kt}$ is 2 hours, find a value for k.

17. If x is the thickness of an absorber, k is an absorption coefficient, and I the intensity of a beam of gamma radiation, the intensity of the beam after passing through a thickness x of absorber is given by $I = I_0(10)^{-kx}$. Find the absorption coefficient k of a material for which 9.4 centimeters thickness reduces a beam of 1 million electron volts to 100,000 electron volts intensity.

18. Find the "half-value thickness" of the material in Exercise 17. That is, find the thickness that will reduce I to $\frac{1}{2}I_0$.

19. How long will it take \$1000 invested at 4% compounded quarterly to double itself?

20. How long will it take \$1000 invested at 3% compounded semiannually to double itself?

9-10 Using Logarithms to Solve Equations

You can use logarithms in solving certain equations.

EXAMPLE 1. Determine x to three significant digits if $x^{\frac{2}{5}} = 3.91$.

Solution:

1. Equate the common logarithms of the members.

$$x^{\frac{2}{5}} = 3.91$$
$$\log x^{\frac{2}{5}} = \log 3.91$$

2. Use the laws of logarithms to simplify the left member; solve for $\log x$.

$$\tfrac{2}{5} \log x = \log 3.91$$
$$\log x = \tfrac{5}{2} \log 3.91$$
$$\log x = \tfrac{5}{2}(0.5922)$$
$$\log x = 1.4805$$

3. Find antilog 1.4805.

$$x = 30.2, \textbf{ Answer.}$$

EXAMPLE 2. Find the solution set: $5^x = 40$.

Solution:

$$5^x = 40$$
$$\log 5^x = \log 40$$
$$x \log 5 = \log 40$$
$$x = \frac{\log 40}{\log 5} \doteq \frac{1.6021}{0.6990}$$

To determine x:

$$\log x = \log \frac{1.602}{0.6990}$$
$$\log x = \log 1.602 - \log 0.6990$$
$$\log 1.602 = 10.2046 - 10$$
$$\log 0.6990 = 9.8445 - 10 \quad (-)$$
$$\log x = 0.3601$$
$$x = 2.292. \quad \{2.292\}, \textbf{ Answer.}$$

EXAMPLE 3. Express $\log_7 8$ in terms of common logarithms.

Solution: Let $x = \log_7 8$.

1. Write the equation in exponential form.

$$7^x = 8$$

2. Equate the common logarithms of the members of the equation obtained in Step 1, and solve for x.

$$\log 7^x = \log 8$$
$$x \log 7 = \log 8$$
$$x = \frac{\log 8}{\log 7}$$
$$\therefore \log_7 8 = \frac{\log_{10} 8}{\log_{10} 7}, \textbf{ Answer.}$$

The result of Example 3 suggests the relationship that holds, in general, between the logarithms of a number n to two different bases a and b:

$$\log_b n = \frac{\log_a n}{\log_a b}.$$

Can you justify the steps in the following proof of this relationship?

$$\text{Let } x = \log_b n$$
$$b^x = n$$
$$\log_a b^x = \log_a n$$
$$x \log_a b = \log_a n$$
$$\therefore x = \frac{\log_a n}{\log_a b}, \text{ or } \log_b n = \frac{\log_a n}{\log_a b}.$$

In particular, if $n = a$, you obtain $\log_b a = \dfrac{\log_a a}{\log_a b}$, or, since $\log_a a = 1$,

$$\log_b a = \frac{1}{\log_a b}.$$

Written Exercises

Solve each equation, using logarithm tables where necessary.

A

1. $4^n = 60$
2. $3^x = 2$
3. $11^x = 4.75$
4. $17^n = 71.5$
5. $x^{\frac{1}{4}} = 7.06$
6. $2s^{\frac{3}{4}} = 882$
7. $3y^{\frac{2}{5}} = 17.28$
8. $(\frac{1}{4})^{x-1} = 8^{2x-1}$
9. $27^{4-x} = (\frac{1}{9})^{x-1}$
10. $x = \log_5 7$
11. $x = \log_9 4$
12. $x = \log_{\frac{1}{2}} 9$
13. $x = \log_{\sqrt{2}} 1.3$
14. $\log_{2.718} 2 = k$
15. $\log_{2.718} 5 = k$

B

16. $3^{x+1} = 9.82$
17. $5^{x-3} = 27.1$
18. $7^{2x-3} = 31.7$
19. $3^{2s-1} = 64$
20. $10^{2t-2} = 143.7$
21. $10^{t+2} = 241.3$

Chapter Summary

Inventory of Structure and Method

1. A radical may be written in **exponential form**: $(\sqrt[r]{b})^p = b^{\frac{p}{r}}$, if $\sqrt[r]{b}$ and p are real numbers. The laws of exponents apply also to exponents that are real numbers.

2. By interchanging the coordinates in each of the ordered pairs belonging to the **exponential function** $\{(x, y): y = b^x, b > 0, b \neq 1\}$, you obtain the **logarithmic function** $\{(x, y): y = \log_b x\}$. If $a = b^n$, then $\log_b a = n$ or $a = b^{\log_b a}$ where a is any positive real number.
3. The **characteristic** of the common logarithm of a number is found by inspection of the number in standard form; the **mantissa** is determined from the table. In using **linear interpolation**, you assume that small portions of the graph of $y = \log x$ are straight lines. If $a < b < c$, then $\log a < \log b < \log c$, and we assume $\dfrac{\log b - \log a}{b - a} = \dfrac{\log c - \log a}{c - a}$.
4. The laws of exponents are the basis for the laws of logarithms: $\log ab = \log a + \log b$; $\log \dfrac{a}{b} = \log a - \log b$; $\log a^n = n \log a$.

   To find the logarithm of a number to another base, use the relationship: $\log_b n = \dfrac{\log_a n}{\log_a b}$.
5. Logarithms are used also in solving certain equations.

Vocabulary and Spelling

one-to-one function (*p. 344*)
inverse relation (*p. 344*)
exponential function (*p. 346*)
logarithm ($\log_b a$) (*p. 347*)
logarithmic function (*p. 347*)
common logarithm (*p. 349*)
mantissa (*p. 350*)
characteristic (*p. 350*)
antilogarithm (antilog x) (*p. 351*)
interpolation (linear) (*p. 353*)

Chapter Test and Review

9–1 **1.** Evaluate $(\frac{9}{25})^{-\frac{3}{2}}$.

9–2 **2.** Solve for t: $8^{t+2} = 16^{2t-1}$.

9–3 **3.** State the inverse of $\{(x, y): y = 3x + 6\}$.

9–4 **4.** Find x if **(a)** $\log_x \frac{2}{3} = -1$, **(b)** $\log_{10}(x^2 + 1) = 1$.

9–5 **5.** Find **(a)** log 0.724, **(b)** antilog 0.5740.

9–6 **6.** Find **(a)** log 3697, **(b)** antilog 8.7940 − 10.

9–7 **7.** Divide 46.9 by 63.3, using logarithms.

9–8 **8.** Find $(0.806)^{\frac{2}{5}}$ to the nearest thousandth.

9–9 **9.** Find $4.3\sqrt{\dfrac{277}{0.785}}$ to the nearest tenth.

9–10 **10.** Find $\log_{2.72} 3$ to the nearest hundredth.

Cumulative Review: Chapters 1-9

1. If k is a real number, does $\sqrt{k^2}$ always equal $\sqrt[5]{k^5}$? Justify your answer.

2. If s varies directly as t and inversely as the square of r, and $s = 108$ when $t = 3$ and $r = \frac{1}{3}$, find r when $t = \frac{1}{2}$ and $s = 64$.

3. Evaluate $2x^0 - 4x^{-\frac{2}{3}} + 1^x$ when $x = 64$.

4. Factor **(a)** $x^{6n} + 8$; **(b)** $2sx + 4tx - 6t - 3s$.

5. If the equations $3x - 4y = 6$ and $6x + by = c$ are dependent, then $b =$ __?__ and $c =$ __?__.

6. Write an equation of the line passing through $(-6, 2)$ and parallel to the graph of $3x + 6y = 2$.

7. Show that points $(8, -1)$, $(4, 1)$, and $(-2, 4)$ are collinear by using **(a)** the slope formula; **(b)** the distance formula.

8. Simplify **(a)** $\dfrac{s^2 - 5}{s^2 - 25} + \dfrac{s - 3}{5 - s}$; **(b)** $\dfrac{1 - \dfrac{11}{3r} - \dfrac{4}{3r^2}}{\dfrac{3r}{2} - \dfrac{1}{6r}}$

In Exercises 9–11, solve for x.

9. $\dfrac{2a}{3} - \dfrac{b}{x} = \dfrac{ab}{3x} - 2$

10. $\sqrt{2x^2 + 2n^2 - r^2} = x + n$ $(n \geq r \geq 0)$

11. $\left\{x: \dfrac{x - 5}{4} - \dfrac{x - 1}{2} < 0\right\} \cap \{x: 3x - 5 \leq 1\}$

12. **a.** Graph the function $\{(x, y): y = x^2 - 6x + 2\}$.
b. Give the equation of the axis of symmetry.
c. For which values of k will the roots of $x^2 - 6x + 2 = k$ be real?
d. Find x to the nearest tenth for $x^2 + 2 > 6x$.

13. Solve to the nearest tenth: $3x^2 + 8x + 2 = 0$.

In Exercises 14–19, give nonintegral values to the nearest tenth. Use the graphic method in Exercises 14, 17.

14. $2x + 2y = 3$
$4x - y = -19$

15. $3a + b + 2c = 5$
$2a - 3b + 4c = -1$
$5a + 2b - 6c = -14$

16. $5x^2 - 4y^2 = 40$
$2x^2 + 3y^2 = 246$

17. $x^2 + y^2 = 10$
$4x^2 - y^2 = 4$

18. $3x^2 - xy - 2y^2 = 25$
$xy = -6$

19. $2u - v = 4$
$v^2 + 2vu + 4u^2 = 7$

20. Without finding the roots of $3x^2 - 7x + 2 = 0$, give **(a)** their nature, **(b)** their sum, and **(c)** their product.

In Exercises 21–26, **(a)** describe the graph; **(b)** state whether it is symmetric to the *x*-axis, *y*-axis, both, or neither; **(c)** give the asymptotes, if a hyperbola.

21. $4x - \frac{y}{9} = 16$

22. $3x^2 + 6y^2 = 9$

23. $xy = -1$

24. $x^2 - 8y^2 = 10$

25. $x - \frac{y^2}{3} = 1 + y$

26. $4x^2 - 12x + 4y^2 = 39$

27. Express in simple form: **(a)** $3\sqrt[3]{108} - 6\sqrt[3]{\frac{1}{2}}$, **(b)** $\frac{6}{4 + 3\sqrt{2}}$

28. The sides of two cubes are in the ratio 5:3. If the sum of the volumes is 760 c.c., find the volume of the smaller cube and find its side correct to tenths.

29. If $\log m = 1.7123$ and $\log k = 9.4750 - 10$, find **(a)** $\log 10\sqrt[3]{k}$, **(b)** $\log \frac{m}{k^2}$, **(c)** $\log (km)^4$.

30. Evaluate to four significant figures: $\frac{\sqrt[6]{8300}}{(37.93)(1.070)^3}$.

31. Evaluate: $\log 15 + \log 6 - 2 \log 3$.

32. If $f(x) = a^x$ and $f(y) = a^y$, $a > 0$, show that $f(x) \cdot f(y) = f(x + y)$.

33. Mrs. Clay wishes to have $2500 available for a trip to Hawaii 5 years from now. If the bank gives 4% interest compounded quarterly, how much should Mrs. Clay deposit now for that purpose? Answer to the nearest dollar.

34. How many ounces of a 45% solution of acid should be added to 15 ounces of an 80% solution so that the result will contain 60% acid?

35. The base of a triangle measures 16 feet, and the lengths of the legs are in the ratio 3:4. If the perimeter is at most 80 feet, find the possible integral lengths of the legs.

36. By traveling an average of 5 miles per hour more than usual, Mr. Calhoun saved half an hour on a 275-mile trip. Find his usual speed.

37. Twice the tens digit of a 2-digit numeral decreased by the units digit equals 2. The number with digits interchanged exceeds 6 times the sum of the digits by 4. **(a)** Find the original numeral. **(b)** If the digits are proportional to the digits of another 2-digit numeral in that order, state the possibilities for the other numeral.

CHAPTER 10

. . . the Horsehead Nebula, a mass of tiny solid particles, appearing as a dark shadow against the brighter background of sky

Trigonometric Functions and Complex Numbers

Trigonometry is an ancient science with ultra-modern applications. Conceived in antiquity for the purpose of measuring angles and distances in surveying and astronomy, trigonometry today plays a major role in atomic research, electrical theory, thermodynamics, the study of mechanical vibrations, indeed in every area where phenomena have repetitive (periodic) characteristics. In this chapter and the next you will study trigonometry based on angles. In Chapter 12 we will discuss the concept of trigonometry without using angles.

COORDINATES AND TRIGONOMETRY

10–1 Rays, Angles, and Points

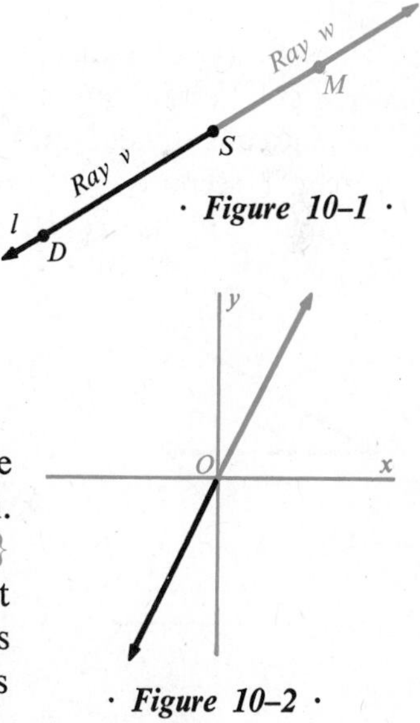

· *Figure 10–1* ·

· *Figure 10–2* ·

Any point of a line, such as point S on line l, in Figure 10–1, separates the line into two **opposite rays**, such as v and w, each having the point as **vertex**. You can specify a ray by indicating first its vertex and then another of its points. For example, in Figure 10–1, w is ray SM, and v is ray SD.

In a coordinate system a ray can also be specified as the graph of a linear relation. For example, $\{(x, y): y = 2x \text{ and } x \geq 0\}$ has as its graph the ray in the first quadrant with slope 2 and the origin as vertex (Figure 10–2). The opposite ray is the graph of $\{(x, y): y = 2x \text{ and } x \leq 0\}$.

The set of points composing two rays with a common vertex, together with a *rotation* that sends one ray into the other, is called a **directed angle**, or simply an **angle**. Counterclockwise rotation yields a **positive angle**; clockwise rotation yields a **negative angle**.

In Figure 10–3 ray p is the *initial side* (*ray*) and ray q is the *terminal side* (*ray*). The point O is the *vertex* of the angle.

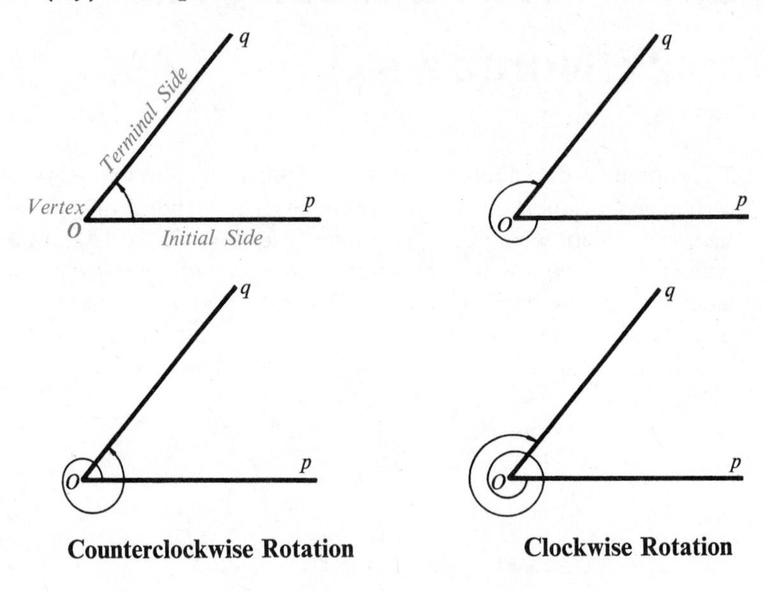

· *Figure 10–3* ·

A common unit of angle measure is a *degree*, written as 1°. **One degree** is $\frac{1}{360}$ of a complete counterclockwise rotation about a point. The degree is divided into minutes and seconds: 1 minute $= 1' = \frac{1}{60}$ degree; 1 second $= 1'' = \frac{1}{60}$ minute. Angles whose measures are 30° (read "30 degrees"), 90°, 180°, −180°, −405°, and −360° are shown:

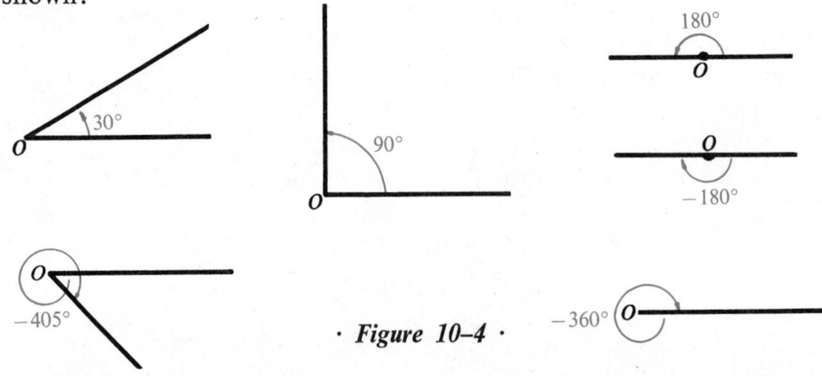

· *Figure 10–4* ·

Angles having the same initial and terminal sides are called **coterminal angles.** In a coordinate plane every point P other than the origin determines an infinite set of coterminal angles, each having the origin as vertex, the positive half of the x-axis as initial side, and ray OP

as terminal side. Each of these angles is said to be in **standard position** and to be a **position angle** of P. Notice that the measures of coterminal angles in standard position differ by integral multiples of 360°.

Knowing both the measure of a position angle of P and the distance OP between P and the origin, you can locate P in the plane.

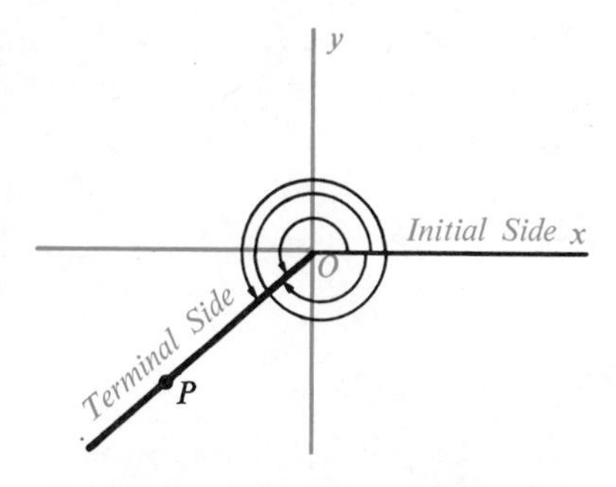

· *Figure 10–5* · **Coterminal Angles in Standard Position**

EXAMPLE. Locate point P, if $OP = 3$ and the measure of one of its position angles is $-40°$. Indicate and give the measure of a positive position angle of P.

Solution:

1. Draw ray q forming with the positive half of the x-axis an angle whose measure is $-40°$.
2. On q measure 3 units from O. The point reached is P.
3. A positive position angle of P has measure $(-40 + 360)°$, or 320°.

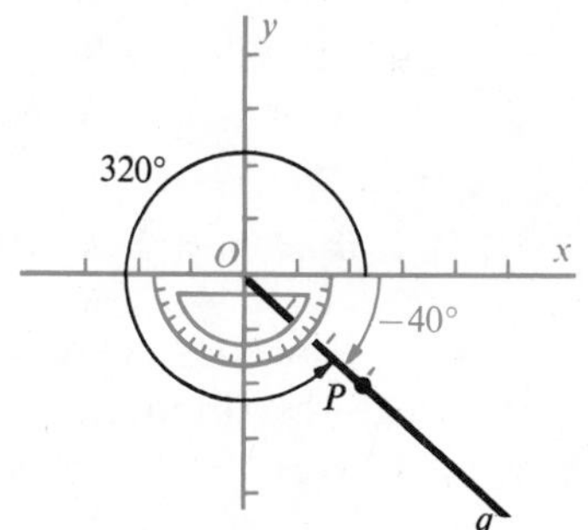

Written Exercises

At the given distance from the origin locate the point having a position angle with the stated measure. Indicate and give the measures of two other angles, one positive and one negative, that are also position angles of the point.

1. 2 (distance from origin); 180° (angle measure)

2. 3; 210°
3. 4; 60°
4. 1; −30°
5. 5; −45°
6. 7; 240°
7. $\frac{3}{2}$; −360°
8. $\frac{5}{2}$; −225°
9. $3\frac{1}{2}$; 720°
10. $\frac{1}{4}$; −540°
11. 0; 150°
12. 0; 330°

Draw the ray which is the graph of each relation, and indicate a positive and a negative angle in standard position having it as terminal side.

13. $\{(x, y)\colon y = \frac{1}{2}x \text{ and } x \geq 0\}$
14. $\{(x, y)\colon y = \frac{1}{3}x \text{ and } x \leq 0\}$
15. $\{(x, y)\colon y = -4x \text{ and } x \leq 0\}$
16. $\{(x, y)\colon y = -5x \text{ and } x \geq 0\}$
17. $\{(x, y)\colon x = 0 \text{ and } y \leq 0\}$
18. $\{(x, y)\colon y = 0 \text{ and } x \leq 0\}$

If point P has the given coordinates, draw ray OP, specify a relation having it as graph, and show a positive angle in standard position having it as terminal side.

SAMPLE. $P(-3, 4)$

Solution:

Slope of $OP = -\frac{4}{3}$.

$\therefore$ Ray OP is the graph of

$\{(x, y): y = -\frac{4}{3}x \text{ and } x \leq 0\}$, **Answer.**

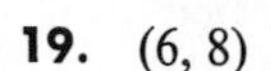

19. $(6, 8)$ **21.** $(-2, -1)$ **23.** $(-5, 10)$ **25.** $(4, 0)$

20. $(12, 5)$ **22.** $(3, -6)$ **24.** $(-9, 3)$ **26.** $(0, -2)$

27. Explain why the measures of coterminal angles in standard position differ by an integral multiple of 360°.

28. Explain why angles in standard position whose measures differ by an integral multiple of 360° are coterminal.

10–2 Sine and Cosine Functions

Consider a point P moving on the circle with radius 1 and center at the origin (the *unit circle*). As P moves counterclockwise from the point $(1, 0)$, the measure of its position angle runs through the set of values from 0° to 360° (Figure 10–6). By allowing P to repeat its counterclockwise motion on the unit circle, and also to travel in a clockwise direction, you can obtain in standard position an angle whose measure in degrees is any prescribed real number.

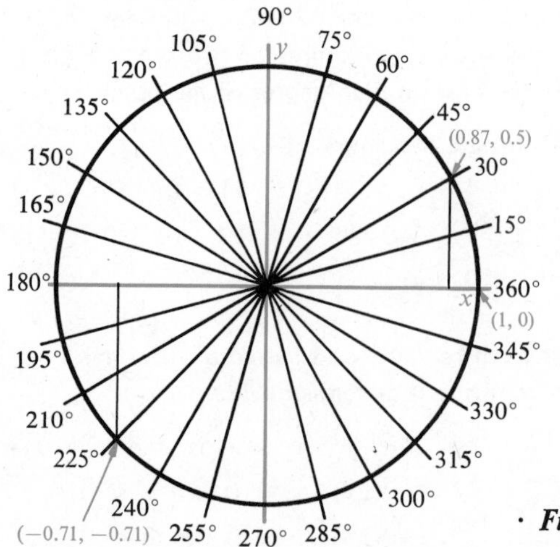

Measure of θ	a	b
0°	1	0
15°	0.97	0.26
30°	0.87	0.50
45°	0.71	0.71
90°	0	1
180°	−1	0
225°	−0.71	−0.71
270°	0	−1
360°	1	0

· *Figure 10-6* ·

Let the Greek letter θ (theta) be a variable whose domain is the set of all angles in standard position in the plane. As P moves on the circle, not only does its position angle θ change, but its coordinates (a, b) also change subject to the condition that the distance between P and the origin is 1; that is, $\sqrt{a^2 + b^2} = 1$. Indeed, for each angle θ there is a unique corresponding pair (a, b) whose coordinates can be estimated as shown for the angles of 30° and 225° in Figure 10–6. Use the figure to check the entries for the other angles given in the table.

The set of all ordered pairs (θ, a) determined by this procedure is called the **cosine function**; the set of all pairs (θ, b) is called the **sine function**. Do you see that the domain of each of these functions is the set of *angles in standard position*, and that the range is the set of *real numbers* between -1 and 1 inclusive? For any particular angle θ we call the values of these functions "the cosine of angle θ" and "the sine of angle θ" according to the following definition.

Let θ denote any angle in standard position. If (a, b) denote the coordinates of the point one unit from the origin on the terminal side of θ, then:

cosine of angle $\theta = a$ and sine of angle $\theta = b$.

We usually write **cos θ** as an abbreviation for "cosine of angle θ" and **sin θ** for "sine of angle θ." *Notice that $(\cos \theta, \sin \theta)$ are the coordinates of the point of intersection of the unit circle and the terminal side of θ.*

Given *any* point T, other than the origin, on the terminal ray of an angle θ in standard position, you can determine the coordinates of the point P in which the ray OT intersects the unit circle, $x^2 + y^2 = 1$. This means that you can find $\cos \theta$ and $\sin \theta$.

EXAMPLE 1. $T(-4, 3)$ is a point with position angle θ. Find $\cos \theta$ and $\sin \theta$.

Solution: Let P be the point of intersection of ray OT and the circle $x^2 + y^2 = 1$.

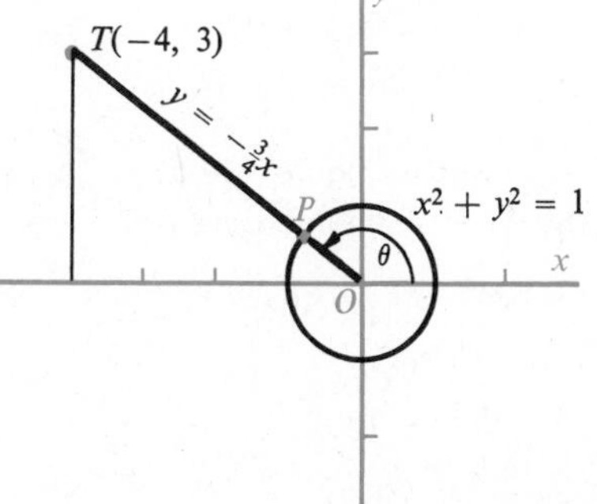

1. Ray OT is the graph of $\{(x, y)\colon y = -\frac{3}{4}x \text{ and } x \leq 0\}$.

2. The coordinates of P must satisfy the three open sentences:

$$x^2 + y^2 = 1$$
$$y = -\tfrac{3}{4}x$$
$$x \leq 0$$

(*continued on page* 376)

3. Solving $x^2 + y^2 = 1$ and $y = -\frac{3}{4}x$ simultaneously, you obtain two ordered pairs: $(-\frac{4}{5}, \frac{3}{5})$ and $(\frac{4}{5}, -\frac{3}{5})$. Only the first pair satisfies the condition $x \leq 0$.

$\therefore$ The coordinates of P are $(-\frac{4}{5}, \frac{3}{5})$, so that $\cos\theta = -\frac{4}{5}$, $\sin\theta = \frac{3}{5}$, **Answer.**

If you notice that 5, the denominator of each of the fractions $-\frac{4}{5}$ and $\frac{3}{5}$, measures r, *the distance from the origin to T*, ($5 = \sqrt{(-4)^2 + 3^2}$ where $r = \sqrt{a^2 + b^2}$), you can write the results of the preceding example as follows:

$$\cos\theta = \frac{\textbf{abscissa of } T}{r} \textbf{ and } \sin\theta = \frac{\textbf{ordinate of } T}{r}.$$

This suggests the following theorem:

THEOREM. If (a, b) are the coordinates of any point other than the origin on the terminal side of θ, an angle in standard position, then

$$\cos\theta = \frac{a}{r} \text{ and } \sin\theta = \frac{b}{r} \text{ where } r = \sqrt{a^2 + b^2}.$$

The proof of the theorem consists in carrying through the steps of the solution of Example 1 with (a, b) in place of $(-4, 3)$. Using the theorem, you can find the sine and cosine of an angle in standard position if you know the coordinates of any point other than the origin on its terminal side.

EXAMPLE 2. Determine $\cos\theta$ and $\sin\theta$ for the angle shown.

Solution: $a = -2$, $b = -1$; $r = \sqrt{(-2)^2 + (-1)^2} = \sqrt{5}$

$$\therefore \cos\theta = -\frac{2}{\sqrt{5}} = -\tfrac{2}{5}\sqrt{5};$$

$$\sin\theta = -\frac{1}{\sqrt{5}} = -\tfrac{1}{5}\sqrt{5}$$

Oral Exercises

Referring to Figure 10–6, page 374, describe the variation of **(a)** $\cos\theta$, and **(b)** $\sin\theta$, as the measure of θ increases from the first to the second value.

SAMPLE. 0° to 90° *Solution:* **(a)** $\cos\theta$ decreases from 1 to 0; **(b)** $\sin\theta$ increases from 0 to 1.

1. 90° to 180°
2. 180° to 270°
3. 270° to 360°
4. −90° to 0°
5. −180° to −90°
6. 360° to 450°

For what measures of θ between 0° and 360° are the given statements true?

7. $\sin\theta = 1$
8. $\cos\theta = 0$
9. $\cos\theta = -1$
10. $\sin\theta = 0$
11. $\sin\theta > 1$
12. $-1 \le \cos\theta \le 1$

Written Exercises

Using a large scale on the coordinate axes, copy Figure 10–6, page 374, and use it to find approximations to the nearest tenth of $\cos\theta$ and $\sin\theta$ for θ with the given measure.

1. 105°
2. 120°
3. 210°
4. 255°
5. 315°
6. 330°
7. 300°
8. −385°
9. −60°
10. −150°
11. −225°
12. −135°
13. 1080°
14. −810°
15. −80°
16. 140°

Determine $\cos\theta$ and $\sin\theta$ for any position angle θ of the point with given coordinates. Express radicals in simple form.

17. $(-8, -15)$
18. $(30, 16)$
19. $(-3, 0)$
20. $(0, -4)$
21. $(-2, 2)$
22. $(5, -5)$
23. $(4, 2)$
24. $(-6, -3)$

Determine $\cos\theta$ and $\sin\theta$ if θ is an angle in standard position whose terminal side is the graph of the given relation.

25. $\{(x, y)\colon 2x + 5y = 0, x \ge 0\}$
26. $\{(x, y)\colon 3x - 4y = 0, x \le 0\}$
27. $\{(x, y)\colon x + y = 0, y \ge 0\}$
28. $\{(x, y)\colon x - y = 0, y \le 0\}$
29. $\{(x, y)\colon y = 0, x \le 0\}$
30. $\{(x, y)\colon x = 0, y \ge 0\}$

θ is an angle in standard position with measure between 0° and 360°. Draw θ and determine all numerical replacements of the question mark for which the given statement is true.

31. $\sin\theta = \frac{1}{5}$ and $\cos\theta = \underline{\ ?\ }$
32. $\sin\theta = -\frac{2}{7}$ and $\cos\theta = \underline{\ ?\ }$
33. $\cos\theta = -\dfrac{\sqrt{2}}{2}$ and $\sin\theta = \underline{\ ?\ }$
34. $\cos\theta = \dfrac{\sqrt{3}}{2}$ and $\sin\theta = \underline{\ ?\ }$

10–3 The Trigonometric Functions

Certain combinations of sine and cosine values occur so often that we give them special names, as indicated on the next page.

Given the angle θ shown in Figure 10–7, $\cos\theta = \frac{8}{17}$ and $\sin\theta = -\frac{15}{17}$.

The quotient $\dfrac{\sin\theta}{\cos\theta} = \dfrac{-\frac{15}{17}}{\frac{8}{17}} = -\dfrac{15}{8}$ is the *tangent of angle* θ ($\tan\theta$),

$\dfrac{\cos\theta}{\sin\theta} = \dfrac{\frac{8}{17}}{-\frac{15}{17}} = -\dfrac{8}{15}$ is the *cotangent of angle* θ ($\cot\theta$),

$\dfrac{1}{\cos\theta} = \dfrac{1}{\frac{8}{17}} = \dfrac{17}{8}$ is the *secant of angle* θ ($\sec\theta$),

and $\dfrac{1}{\sin\theta} = \dfrac{1}{-\frac{15}{17}} = -\dfrac{17}{15}$ is the *cosecant of angle* θ ($\csc\theta$).

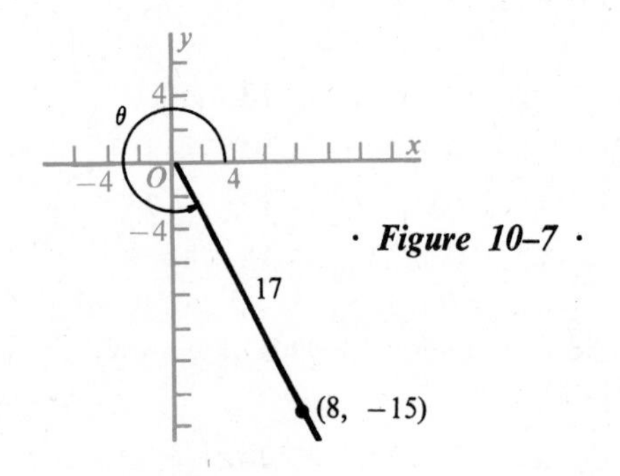

· *Figure 10–7* ·

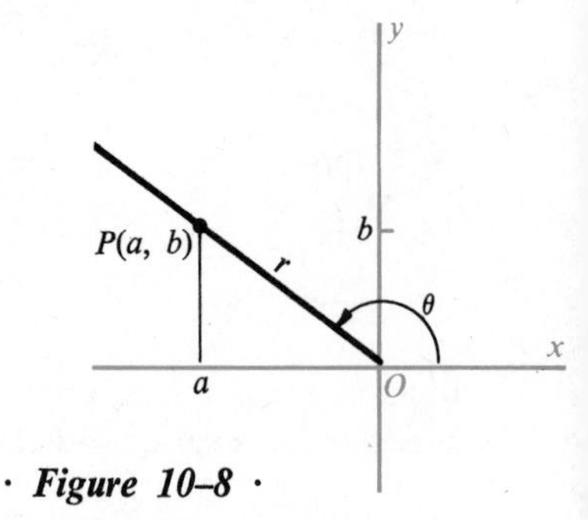

· *Figure 10–8* ·

We can now state the following definitions of four functions whose domains are subsets of the set of angles θ in standard position:

the tangent function $= \left\{(\theta, \tan\theta):\ \tan\theta = \dfrac{\sin\theta}{\cos\theta},\ \text{provided } \cos\theta \neq 0\right\}$

the cotangent function $= \left\{(\theta, \cot\theta):\ \cot\theta = \dfrac{\cos\theta}{\sin\theta},\ \text{provided } \sin\theta \neq 0\right\}$

the secant function $= \left\{(\theta, \sec\theta):\ \sec\theta = \dfrac{1}{\cos\theta},\ \text{provided } \cos\theta \neq 0\right\}$

the cosecant function $= \left\{(\theta, \csc\theta):\ \csc\theta = \dfrac{1}{\sin\theta},\ \text{provided } \sin\theta \neq 0\right\}$

The sine, cosine, tangent, cotangent, secant, and cosecant functions are called the **trigonometric functions**. Using their definitions and the theorem stated on page 376, you can compute their values in terms of the coordinates (a, b) of any point P, other than the origin, on the terminal side of the angle (Figure 10–8). For example, if $\cos\theta \neq 0$:

$$\tan\theta = \frac{\sin\theta}{\cos\theta} = \frac{\dfrac{b}{\sqrt{a^2 + b^2}}}{\dfrac{a}{\sqrt{a^2 + b^2}}}. \qquad \therefore\ \tan\theta = \frac{b}{a},\ \text{provided } a \neq 0.$$

Similar reasoning leads to the expressions for cot θ, sec θ, and csc θ listed in the following theorem.

THEOREM. If θ is a position angle of a point $P(a, b)$ other than the origin, then

$$\sin\theta = \frac{b}{\sqrt{a^2 + b^2}} \qquad \csc\theta = \frac{\sqrt{a^2 + b^2}}{b}, \ (b \neq 0)$$

$$\cos\theta = \frac{a}{\sqrt{a^2 + b^2}} \qquad \sec\theta = \frac{\sqrt{a^2 + b^2}}{a}, \ (a \neq 0)$$

$$\tan\theta = \frac{b}{a}, \ (a \neq 0) \qquad \cot\theta = \frac{a}{b}, \ (b \neq 0)$$

EXAMPLE 1. Find the values of the trigonometric functions of a position angle of $P(-5, -12)$. Sketch the smallest positive angle of this set.

Solution: $a = -5$, $b = -12$

$$\therefore \sqrt{a^2 + b^2} = \sqrt{(-5)^2 + (-12)^2} = \sqrt{169} = 13$$

$\sin\theta = -\frac{12}{13}$ $\quad \csc\theta = -\frac{13}{12}$

$\cos\theta = -\frac{5}{13}$ $\quad \sec\theta = -\frac{13}{5}$

$\tan\theta = \frac{12}{5}$ $\quad \cot\theta = \frac{5}{12}$

Notice that the values of the trigonometric functions depend only on the position of the terminal side of the angle. Because the measure of an angle in standard position determines the position of its terminal side, you can refer to such an angle simply by giving its measure. For example, you can write "sin 30°" in place of "sine of the angle in standard position whose measure is 30°."

An angle in standard position is frequently classified according to the quadrant in which its terminal side lies. Thus, the angle shown in Figure 10–7 is called a *fourth quadrant angle*, while Figure 10–8 shows θ as a *second quadrant angle*. When the terminal side of the angle lies on a coordinate axis, as in the case of α (alpha) in Figure 10–9, we call the angle a **quadrantal angle**.

· *Figure 10–9* ·

The following table classifies the values of the trigonometric functions of a nonquadrantal angle in standard position as positive or negative numbers according to the quadrant of the angle.

Value	Quadrant			
	I	II	III	IV
$\sin\theta$ and $\csc\theta$	positive	positive	negative	negative
$\cos\theta$ and $\sec\theta$	positive	negative	negative	positive
$\tan\theta$ and $\cot\theta$	positive	negative	positive	negative

Knowing the quadrant in which θ terminates and the value of a trigonometric function of θ, you can determine its other trigonometric function values.

EXAMPLE 2. If θ is the second-quadrant angle of least positive measure for which $\cos\theta = -\frac{2}{3}$, draw θ and find the values of its trigonometric functions.

Solution: Let $P(a, b)$ be a point other than O on the terminal side of θ.

1. Since $\cos\theta = \frac{a}{r} = \frac{-2}{3}$, you can choose $a = -2$ and $r = 3$. Then P is the point in the second quadrant in which the vertical line 2 units to the left of the y-axis intersects the circle with center at the origin and radius 3.

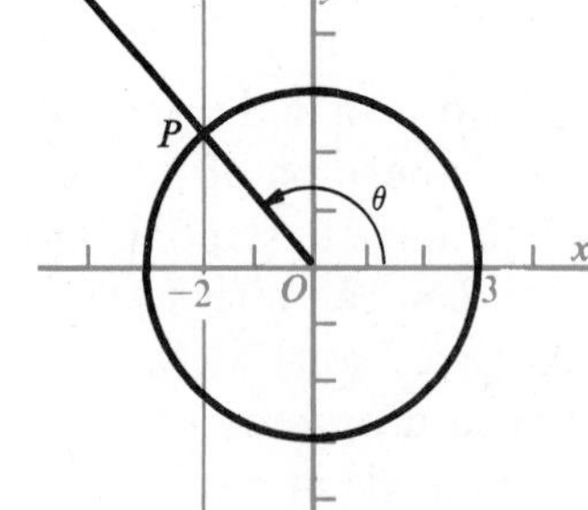

2. Show θ with terminal ray OP.
3. To determine b:

$$a^2 + b^2 = r^2$$
$$(-2)^2 + b^2 = 3^2$$
$$4 + b^2 = 9$$
$$b^2 = 5;\text{ but } b > 0 \text{ (why?)}$$
$$\therefore b = \sqrt{5}$$

4. Use the theorem on page 379 to obtain

$$\sin\theta = \frac{\sqrt{5}}{3} \qquad \csc\theta = \frac{3}{\sqrt{5}} = \frac{3\sqrt{5}}{5}$$

$$\cos\theta = -\frac{2}{3} \qquad \sec\theta = -\frac{3}{2}$$

$$\tan\theta = -\frac{\sqrt{5}}{2} \qquad \cot\theta = -\frac{2}{\sqrt{5}} = -\frac{2\sqrt{5}}{5}$$

Oral Exercises

State the value of the indicated trigonometric function of the angle θ.

SAMPLE. $\cos\theta = -\frac{8}{17}$, $\sin\theta = \frac{15}{17}$; $\cot\theta = ?$ *What you say:* $\cot\theta = -\frac{8}{15}$

1. $\sin\theta = \frac{3}{8}$; $\csc\theta =$ _?_
2. $\cos\theta = -\frac{1}{5}$; $\sec\theta =$ _?_
3. $\sec\theta = -\frac{3}{2}$; $\cos\theta =$ _?_
4. $\csc\theta = \frac{5}{4}$; $\sin\theta =$ _?_
5. $\sin\theta = -\frac{2}{3}$; $\cos\theta = \dfrac{-\sqrt{5}}{3}$; $\tan\theta =$ _?_
6. $\sin\theta = \dfrac{\sqrt{3}}{2}$, $\cos\theta = \frac{1}{2}$; $\cot\theta =$ _?_
7. $\tan\theta = 4$, $\cot\theta =$ _?_
8. $\cot\theta = -5$, $\tan\theta =$ _?_

Name the quadrants in which the terminal side of θ may lie.

9. $\sin\theta > 0$
10. $\cos\theta > 0$
11. $\tan\theta > 0$
12. $\csc\theta < 0$
13. $\sec\theta < 0$
14. $\cot\theta < 0$

Name the quadrant in which the terminal side of θ must lie.

15. $\sin\theta > 0, \cos\theta < 0$
16. $\sin\theta < 0, \cos\theta < 0$
17. $\cos\theta > 0, \tan\theta < 0$
18. $\sin\theta < 0, \tan\theta > 0$
19. $\csc\theta > 0, \cos\theta > 0$
20. $\sec\theta < 0, \sin\theta > 0$
21. $\cot\theta < 0, \sec\theta > 0$
22. $\csc\theta < 0, \tan\theta < 0$

Written Exercises

Draw the smallest positive angle θ in standard position having the point with given coordinates on its terminal side; evaluate the trigonometric functions of θ.

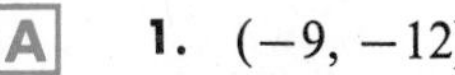

A

1. $(-9, -12)$
2. $(8, 6)$
3. $(\sqrt{3}, 1)$
4. $(-1, -\sqrt{3})$
5. $(2, -2)$
6. $(-3, -3)$
7. $(0, 4)$
8. $(-3, 0)$
9. $(-1, 7)$
10. $(-5, 3)$
11. $(-\sqrt{2}, \sqrt{6})$
12. $(\sqrt{3}, -\sqrt{15})$

In standard position draw the negative angle θ of least numerical measure and terminating in the given quadrant; state the values of the trigonometric functions of θ.

13. $\sin\theta = -\frac{2}{5}$; III
14. $\cos\theta = \frac{3}{7}$; IV
15. $\tan\theta = \frac{5}{4}$; I
16. $\cot\theta = \frac{1}{2}$; III
17. $\cot\theta = -2$; IV
18. $\tan\theta = 3$; I
19. $\sec\theta = 1.5$; IV
20. $\csc\theta = -1.25$; III

Evaluate the trigonometric functions of θ.

21. $\sin \theta = \frac{3}{8}$ and θ is not a first-quadrant angle

22. $\cos \theta = -\frac{1}{2}$ and θ is not a second-quadrant angle

23. $\tan \theta = \sqrt{7}$ and $\sec \theta > 0$

24. $\cot \theta = -1$ and $\csc \theta < 0$

Determine the rectangular coordinates of the point at the given distance from the origin in the stated quadrant, if θ is its position angle.

25. 10; II; $\sin \theta = \frac{4}{5}$

26. $\sqrt{2}$; III; $\cos \theta = -\dfrac{\sqrt{2}}{2}$

27. 4; IV; $\tan \theta = -1$

28. 5; I; $\cot \theta = 1$

Determine all numerical replacements for the question mark for which the given statement is true.

C **29.** $\sin \theta = \cos \theta =$ __?__

30. $\cos \theta \sec \theta = 1$, $\cos \theta =$ __?__

31. $1 + \cos \theta = 3 \cos \theta$, $\tan \theta < 0$, and $\sin \theta =$ __?__

10-4 Special Angles

Referring to Figure 10–6 and the definitions of the trigonometric functions, you can verify the values given in the following table for quadrantal angles. A dash (—) means that no value exists. (Recall that division by 0 is undefined.)

θ	$\sin \theta$	$\cos \theta$	$\tan \theta$	$\csc \theta$	$\sec \theta$	$\cot \theta$
0°	0	1	0	—	1	—
90°	1	0	—	1	—	0
180°	0	−1	0	—	−1	—
270°	−1	0	—	−1	—	0

An angle whose measure is between 0° and 90° is called a **positive acute angle**. Using the origin and any other point P on the terminal side of a positive acute angle θ in standard position, you can form a right triangle whose third vertex is the point of intersection M of the x-axis and the vertical line through P (Figure 10–10). The values of the trigonometric functions of θ can then be expressed in terms of the lengths of the sides of the right triangle OMP:

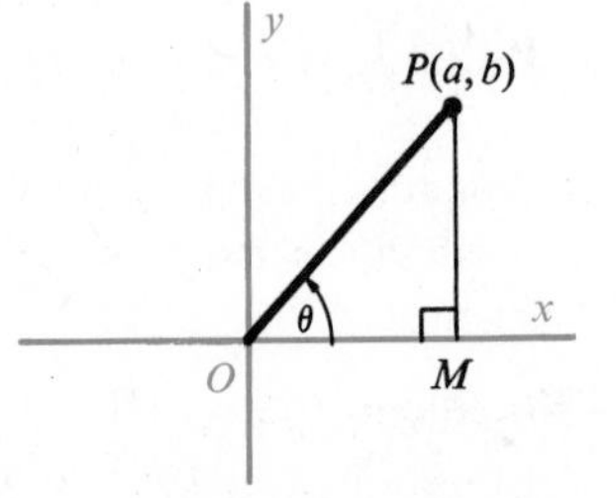

· *Figure 10–10* ·

$$\sin\theta = \frac{b}{\sqrt{a^2+b^2}} = \frac{\textbf{length of side opposite } \theta}{\textbf{length of hypotenuse}}$$

$$\cos\theta = \frac{a}{\sqrt{a^2+b^2}} = \frac{\textbf{length of side adjacent to } \theta}{\textbf{length of hypotenuse}}$$

Similarly, in terms of the sides located relative to the angle θ, you have:

$$\tan\theta = \frac{\textbf{length of opposite side}}{\textbf{length of adjacent side}} \qquad \csc\theta = \frac{\textbf{length of hypotenuse}}{\textbf{length of opposite side}}$$

$$\cot\theta = \frac{\textbf{length of adjacent side}}{\textbf{length of opposite side}} \qquad \sec\theta = \frac{\textbf{length of hypotenuse}}{\textbf{length of adjacent side}}$$

Because these statements do not involve a coordinate system, you can use them to define values for trigonometric functions of any acute angle of a right triangle.

EXAMPLE. In triangle ABC, let a, b, c denote the lengths of the sides opposite angles A, B, C respectively. Find the trigonometric function values for $\angle A$ (read "angle A") and $\angle B$, if $a = 5$, $c = 13$, and C is a right angle.

Solution:

1. Use the Pythagorean Theorem to determine b.

$$b = \sqrt{c^2 - a^2}$$

$$b = \sqrt{13^2 - 5^2} = \sqrt{144} = 12$$

angle	length of opposite side	length of adjacent side	length of hypotenuse
A	5	12	13
B	12	5	13

2. Using the data in the chart, you find the following values.

$\sin A = \frac{5}{13}$, $\cos A = \frac{12}{13}$, $\tan A = \frac{5}{12}$, $\cot A = \frac{12}{5}$, $\csc A = \frac{13}{5}$, $\sec A = \frac{13}{12}$

$\sin B = \frac{12}{13}$, $\cos B = \frac{5}{13}$, $\tan B = \frac{12}{5}$, $\cot B = \frac{5}{12}$, $\csc B = \frac{13}{12}$, $\sec B = \frac{13}{5}$

In right triangle ABC, angles A and B are complementary angles because the sum of their measures is 90°. Notice that

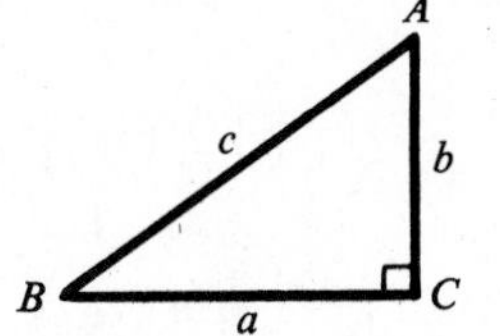

$$\sin B = \frac{b}{c} = \cos A, \qquad \cos B = \frac{a}{c} = \sin A, \qquad \tan B = \frac{b}{a} = \cot A.$$

Also, $\csc B = \sec A$, $\sec B = \csc A$, and $\cot B = \tan A$.

Therefore, if we couple the trigonometric functions into the following pairs of **cofunctions**: the *sine and cosine* functions, the *tangent and cotangent* functions, the *secant and cosecant* functions, we can state the preceding facts as a theorem.

THEOREM. Any trigonometric function of a positive acute angle is equal to the cofunction of the complementary angle.

For example,
$$\sin 60° = \cos 30°$$
$$\tan 20° = \cot 70°$$
$$\csc 45° = \sec 45°$$

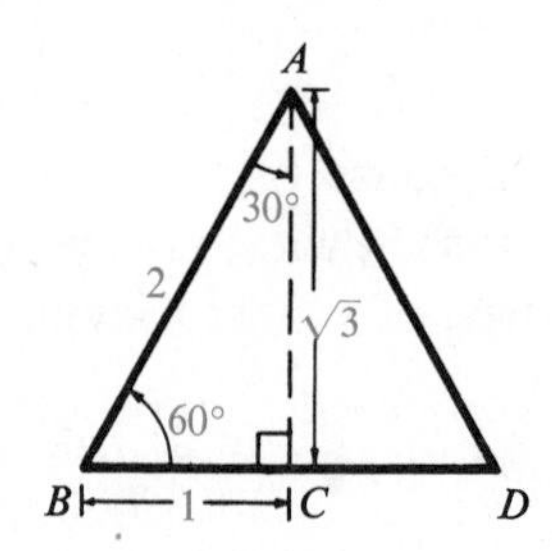

· *Figure 10–11* ·

Figure 10–11 shows an equilateral triangle ABD, each side having length 2 and each angle having measure 60°. Because AC, the perpendicular bisector of side BD, bisects angle A, triangle ABC is a right triangle whose acute angles and sides have the measures indicated in the figure. Correlating each acute angle of this triangle with the lengths of the sides opposite and adjacent to the angle, you can verify the following statements.

$$\sin 60° = \frac{\sqrt{3}}{2} = \cos 30° \qquad \csc 60° = \frac{2}{\sqrt{3}} = \frac{2\sqrt{3}}{3} = \sec 30°$$

$$\cos 60° = \tfrac{1}{2} = \sin 30° \qquad \sec 60° = 2 = \csc 30°$$

$$\tan 60° = \sqrt{3} = \cot 30° \qquad \cot 60° = \frac{1}{\sqrt{3}} = \frac{\sqrt{3}}{3} = \tan 30°$$

To determine the values of the trigonometric functions of an angle of 45°, consider right triangle BCD formed by drawing the diagonal BD of the unit square in Figure 10–12. Since the hypotenuse BD has length $\sqrt{2}$, you find

$$\sin 45° = \frac{1}{\sqrt{2}} = \frac{\sqrt{2}}{2} = \cos 45°$$

$$\tan 45° = \frac{1}{1} = 1 = \cot 45°$$

$$\sec 45° = \sqrt{2} = \csc 45°$$

· *Figure 10–12* ·

The following table summarizes the values of the trigonometric functions of angles of 30°, 60°, and 45°. Picturing Figures 10–11, 10–12, and 10–6 in your mind will enable you to recall the entries in this table as well as in the table for quadrantal angles.

θ	$\sin\theta$	$\cos\theta$	$\tan\theta$	$\csc\theta$	$\sec\theta$	$\cot\theta$
30°	$\frac{1}{2}$	$\frac{\sqrt{3}}{2}$	$\frac{\sqrt{3}}{3}$	2	$\frac{2\sqrt{3}}{3}$	$\sqrt{3}$
45°	$\frac{\sqrt{2}}{2}$	$\frac{\sqrt{2}}{2}$	1	$\sqrt{2}$	$\sqrt{2}$	1
60°	$\frac{\sqrt{3}}{2}$	$\frac{1}{2}$	$\sqrt{3}$	$\frac{2\sqrt{3}}{3}$	2	$\frac{\sqrt{3}}{3}$

It is not necessary to remember all six of the function values for these angles, since the last three are, in order, the reciprocals of the first three.

Written Exercises

Evaluate.

A

1. $\sin 30° + \cos 45° - \sin 45°$

2. $\tan 60° - \cot 30° + \tan 45°$

3. $\tan 180° + \cot 90° - \cot 45°$

4. $\sin 0° + \cos 180° - \sin 270°$

5. $\sin 30° \cos 60° + \cos 30° \sin 60°$

6. $\cos 0° \cos 180° - \sin 0° \sin 180°$

Verify that each of the following statements is true.

7. $\sin^2 30° + \cos^2 30° = \sin^2 45° + \cos^2 45°$ [*Note.* $\sin^2 30° = (\sin 30°)^2$]

8. $1 - 2\sin^2 30° = \cos 60°$

9. $1 + \tan^2 60° = \sec^2 60°$

10. $1 + \cot^2 45° = \csc^2 45°$

11. $2\cos^2 30° - 1 = \cos 60°$

12. $\dfrac{\tan 60° - \tan 30°}{1 + \tan 60° \tan 30°} = \tan 30°$

13. $\dfrac{1 + \cot 30° \cot 60°}{\cot 30° - \cot 60°} - \cot 30° = 0$

14. $\sin 45° = \sqrt{\dfrac{1 - \cos 90°}{2}}$

15. $\cos 90° = \sqrt{\dfrac{1 + \cos 180°}{2}}$

16. $\sec 60° = \tan 60° \tan 30° + 1$

Exercises 17–20 refer to right triangle ABC in the figure.

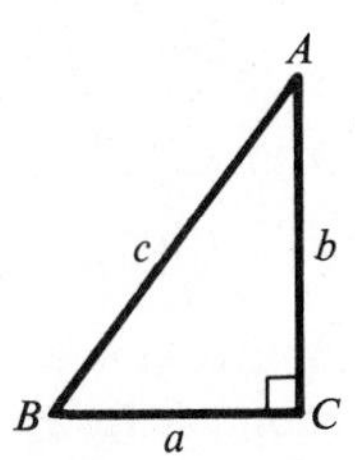

17. Find a, if $b = 4$ and A is 30°.

18. Find c, if $a = 9$ and B is 45°.

19. Find $\sin A$ if $a = 5$ and $b = 9$.

20. Find $\tan B$ if $a = 3$ and $c = 7$.

EVALUATING AND APPLYING TRIGONOMETRIC FUNCTIONS

10–5 Using Tables

Approximations of the values of the trigonometric functions of positive acute angles have been calculated and are available in tables. In Table 6 at the end of the book the measures of angles from $0°00'$ to $45°00'$ at intervals of ten minutes are listed in the first column; angle measures from $45°00'$ to $90°00'$ are listed in the last column, reading *from bottom to top*.

To find a *four-significant figure* approximation of the value of any trigonometric function of an angle with measure between $0°$ and $90°$:

1. Reading in the first or last column, locate the row in which the measure of the angle is listed;
2. In this row find the entry in the column (**a**) at the *top* of which the function is named, if the angle is read at the *left*; (**b**) at the *bottom* of which the function is named, if the angle is read at the *right*.

For example: **a.** $\sin 25°00' \doteq 0.4226$; $\tan 40°50' \doteq 0.8642$

b. $\cos 65°00' \doteq 0.4226$; $\cot 49°10' \doteq 0.8642$

Notice that angles whose measures are given in any one row are complementary angles, while the functions named at the top and bottom of a column are cofunctions.

Notice also that as θ varies in measure from $0°$ to $90°$ the values $\sin \theta$, $\tan \theta$, and $\sec \theta$ increase, but $\cos \theta$, $\cot \theta$, and $\csc \theta$ decrease. This fact is important in using linear interpolation (Section 9–5) to approximate the values of the trigonometric functions of an angle whose measure is between consecutive entries in the table.

EXAMPLE 1. Find $\sin 27°14'$ and $\cos 27°14'$.

Solution:

$$10'\left[\begin{array}{l} \\ 4'\left[\begin{array}{c} \\ \\ \end{array}\right. \end{array}\right.\begin{array}{c|c} \theta & \sin\theta \\ \hline 27°20' & 0.4592 \\ 27°14' & ? \\ 27°10' & 0.4566 \end{array}\left.\begin{array}{r} \\ \left.\begin{array}{c} \\ \\ \end{array}\right]e \end{array}\right]0.0026$$

(a positive number because $\sin 27°20' > \sin 27°10'$)

$$\frac{4}{10} = \frac{e}{0.0026}; \quad e = \frac{4}{10}(0.0026) = 0.0010$$

$\sin 27°14' = 0.4566 + 0.0010$; $\therefore \sin 27°14' = 0.4576$, **Answer.**

Note. In working with approximations of values of trigonometric functions, it is customary to write $=$ instead of $\doteq$.

		θ	$\cos \theta$		
10′		27°20′	0.8884		−0.0013 (a negative number because $\cos 27°20' < \cos 27°10'$)
	4′	27°14′	?	e	
		27°10′	0.8897		

$$\frac{4}{10} = \frac{e}{-0.0013}; \quad e = \frac{4}{10}(-0.0013) = -0.0005$$

$$\cos 27°14' = 0.8897 + (-0.0005); \quad \therefore \cos 27°14' = 0.8892, \textbf{ Answer.}$$

The table also enables you to approximate to the nearest minute the measure of a positive acute angle, if you know a four-significant figure approximation of the value of one of its trigonometric functions.

EXAMPLE 2. Find the measures of the positive acute angles α and β (beta), if $\tan \alpha = 1.025$ and $\cot \beta = 0.0782$.

Solution: In the column labeled **Tan** locate the two consecutive entries between which 1.025 lies:

		α	$\tan \alpha$		
10′		45°50′	1.030		0.006
	n'	?	1.025	0.001	
		45°40′	1.024		

$$\frac{n}{10} = \frac{0.001}{0.006}; \quad n = \frac{1}{6}(10) = 1.7 \doteq 2$$

$\therefore$ the measure of α is approximately $45°40' + 2'$, or $45°42'$, **Answer.**

To determine β, work in the column **Cot**:

		β	$\cot \beta$		
10′		85°40′	0.0758		−0.0029
	n'	?	0.0782	−0.0005	
		85°30′	0.0787		

$$\frac{n}{10} = \frac{-0.0005}{-0.0029}; \quad n = \frac{5}{29}(10) \doteq 2$$

$\therefore \beta = 85°30' + 2'$, or $85°32'$, **Answer.**

Following common usage, we write $=$ in place of $\doteq$ even though β is given only to the nearest minute.

In many practical problems applying trigonometric function values, an angle is described as an *angle of elevation*, or an *angle of depression* (see Figure 10–13). Since the point B is elevated with respect to the observer at A, $\angle CAB$, the angle between the line of sight and the horizontal ray AC through A, is an **angle of elevation**. The point Q is depressed with respect to the observer at R; therefore, $\angle SRQ$, the angle between the line of sight and the horizontal ray RS, is an **angle of depression**.

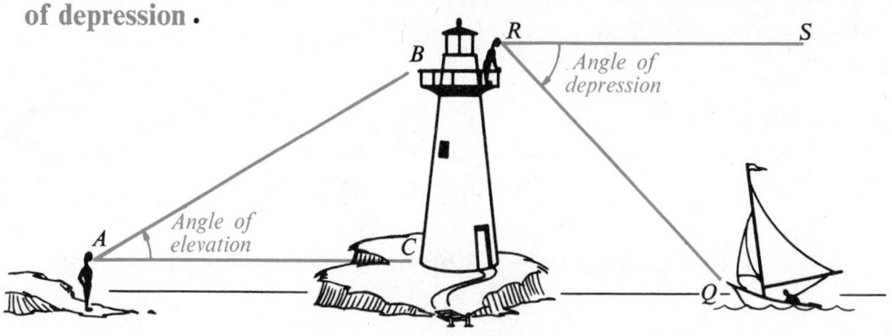

· *Figure 10–13* ·

EXAMPLE 3. The measure of the angle of depression of a buoy from the platform of a radar tower 75 feet above the ocean is 14°. Find the distance of the buoy from the base of the tower if the data given are **(a)** exact; **(b)** approximate.

Solution:

In right triangle BCP:

$\angle CPB$ is

$90° - 14° = 76°;$

$CP = 75$

$\tan \angle CPB = \dfrac{CB}{CP};$

$\tan 76° = \dfrac{CB}{75}$

$CB = 75 \tan 76°$

$CB = 75(4.011)$

(a) 300.8 ft.; **(b)** 300 ft., **Answer.**

Written Exercises

Find the value of each trigonometric function to four significant figures.

1. sin 15°12′	**4.** cos 43°45′	**7.** cot 59°2′	**10.** sec 22°13′
2. tan 32°53′	**5.** tan 71°38′	**8.** csc 48°55′	**11.** csc 80°16′
3. cos 19°27′	**6.** sin 67°9′	**9.** sec 8°6′	**12.** cot 81°1′

Find the measure of each positive acute angle to the nearest minute.

13. $\cos\theta = 0.9219$ **16.** $\cos\alpha = 0.5230$ **19.** $\cot\gamma = 4.480$

14. $\sin\theta = 0.6620$ **17.** $\sin\beta = 0.9608$ **20.** $\csc\beta = 4.292$

15. $\tan\alpha = 1.088$ **18.** $\tan\beta = 1.224$

With the data given for right triangle ABC (in each case C = 90°), find to the nearest unit the measures of its other sides and angles.

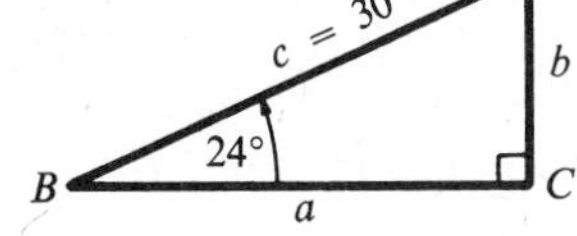

SAMPLE. $B = 24°$; $c = 30$

Solution: 1. To find A: $90° - 24° = 66°$

2. To find a: $\cos B = \frac{a}{c}$ $\cos 24° = \frac{a}{30}$

$a = 30 \cos 24°$

$a = 30(0.9135)$, or $27.41 = 27$

3. To find b: $\sin B = \frac{b}{c}$ $\sin 24° = \frac{b}{30}$

$b = 30 \sin 24°$

$b = 30(0.4067)$, or $12.20 = 12$

B **21.** $A = 27°, c = 6$ **23.** $B = 34°, b = 25$ **25.** $a = 18, c = 40$

22. $B = 42°, b = 20$ **24.** $a = 14, c = 32$ **26.** $a = 3, b = 12$

Since most of the entries in Table 6 are approximations, lengths (not angle measures) computed using them should generally not be given to more than four significant figures, even though the data involved are exact. The following rule comparing the accuracy of angle measure and length is used with the rules on page 354 to decide the accuracy of a computation involving approximations.

Angles measured to the nearest	*correspond to*	*Lengths to*
1°		2 significant figures
10′		3 significant figures
1′		4 significant figures

Problems

Find the results if the data given are (a) exact; (b) approximate.

A **1.** The angle of elevation of the Rock Mountain fire-control tower from the top of Blue Mountain 3 miles away (horizontal distance) is 18°. How much higher than Blue Mountain is the fire-control tower?

2. The angle of elevation of the summit from the bottom of the second lift at Snow Bowl is 33°. If a skier rides 1000 feet on this lift to the summit, what is the vertical distance between the bottom of the lift and the summit?
3. A vein of ore makes an angle of 30° with the horizontal ground. If the width of the vein exposed at the surface is 15 feet, what is the actual width w of the vein?
4. How far from the vertical wall of a building is the base of a thirty-foot ladder which makes a 75° angle with the ground?
5. The angle of depression of an aircraft carrier from an approaching airplane is 52°20′. If the plane is 700 feet above level of the deck of the carrier, how far away is the carrier?
6. The navigator on a bomber finds that the angle of depression of a target 4.00 miles away is 11°40′. At what altitude is the plane flying?
7. Billy's kite has a string 40 feet long and is flying 27 feet above his eye level. Find the angle of elevation of the kite.
8. At an airport, cars drive down a ramp 96 feet long to reach the lower level baggage-claim area 13 feet below the main level. What angle does the ramp make with the ground at the lower level?
9. A surveyor standing in a ravine finds that the angle of elevation of the top of one side is 15°13′. If she is standing 14.00 feet from the base of this side, how deep is the ravine?
10. As an airplane flying north passes directly over a civil defense airwatch unit, another unit 4.30 miles due north finds the angle of elevation of the plane to be 19°17′. Find the altitude of the plane.
11. Find the length of the altitude of an isosceles triangle whose base has length 20 inches and whose base angles each has measure 45°.
12. A chord 16 inches long subtends an angle of 120° at the center of a circle. Find the distance of the chord from the center.

B 13. A pendulum 40 inches long is moved 30° from the vertical. How much is the lower end of the pendulum lifted?

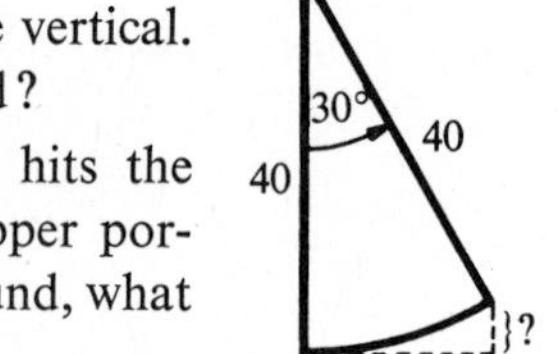

14. The top of a vertical tree broken by the wind hits the ground 25 feet from the foot of the tree. If the upper portion makes an angle of 30° with the horizontal ground, what was the original height of the tree?
15. The angle of depression of the top of the Billings Building from the roof of the Wolcott Building (in the same vertical plane) is 33°10′, and from the 15th floor it is 21°50′. If the distance between the roof and the 15th floor is 101 feet, how far apart are the buildings?

16. From a point on the ground 75.0′ from the base of a building, the angle of elevation of the top of a flagpole on the edge of the roof of the building is 45°20′ and the angle of elevation of the bottom of the flagpole is 38°40′. Find the height of the pole.

10–6 Logarithms of the Values of Trigonometric Functions

Since each value of a trigonometric function of a positive acute angle is a positive number, it has a logarithm. For example:

$$\sin 31° \doteq 0.5150 \quad \text{(Table 6)}$$
$$\log 0.5150 \doteq 9.7118\text{–}10 \quad \text{(Table 5)}$$

$\therefore$ **log sin 31°** $\doteq$ **9.7118–10**, which is read **"logarithm of the sine of an angle of 31°"**

In Table 7 the characteristics and four-significant figure approximations of the mantissas of these logarithms can be read directly for angles measured to the nearest ten minutes, and by interpolation for angles measured to the nearest minute. Note that to conserve space Table 7 gives the logarithms increased by 10. Thus, log sin 31° is listed as 9.7118; you must add -10 to complete this and every other logarithm in the table.

To facilitate interpolation in Table 7, the difference between successive entries is given in the columns headed "*d*" or "*cd*." The numbers in the "*cd*" column are differences common to "L Tan" and "L Cot" and are used with either one. Notice that a difference listed as "43" stands for "0.0043" or for "-0.0043" according as values to which the difference refers increase (L Sin θ, L Tan θ) or decrease (L Cos θ, L Cot θ) with increasing measure of θ.

EXAMPLE 1. Use Table 7 to find log cos 32°26′ and log sec 32°26′.

Solution:

$$10'\left[\begin{array}{c} \\ 6'\left[\begin{array}{c} \\ \\ \end{array}\right.\end{array}\right. \begin{array}{c|c} \theta & \text{L}\cos\theta \\ \hline 32°30' & 9.9260 - 10 \\ 32°26' & ? \\ 32°20' & 9.9268 - 10 \end{array} \left.\begin{array}{c} \\ \\ \end{array}\right]e \left.\begin{array}{c} \\ \\ \\ \end{array}\right] -0.0008$$

$$e = \tfrac{6}{10}(-0.0008) = -0.00048 \doteq -0.0005$$

$\therefore \log\cos 32°26' = 9.9268 - 10 + (-0.0005) = 9.9263 - 10$, **Answer.**

$\log\sec 32°26' = \log 1 - \log\cos 32°26'$ (why?)
$= 10.0000 - 10 - (9.9263 - 10) = 0.0737$, **Answer.**

EXAMPLE 2. What is the angle of ascent of an airplane whose flight path to an altitude of 6750 feet is 38,550 feet long?

Solution: $\sin B = \dfrac{6750}{38550}$

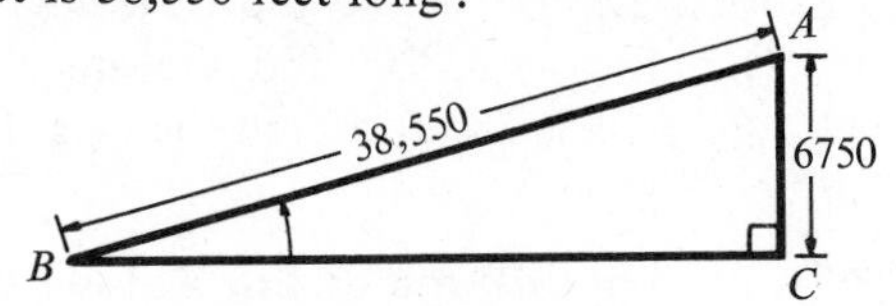

$$\log \sin B = \log 6750 - \log 38550$$

From Table 5: $\log 6750 = 13.8293 - 10$

$\log 38550 = 4.5861 \quad (-)$

$\log \sin B = 9.2432 - 10$

To approximate the measure of angle B, locate consecutive entries between which $9.2431 - 10$ lies in the "L Sin" column of Table 7:

		B	L Sin B		
$10'$		$10°10'$	$9.2468 - 10$		0.0071
	n'	?	$9.2432 - 10$	0.0035	
		$10°00'$	$9.2397 - 10$		

$$\frac{n}{10} = \frac{0.0035}{0.0071}; \quad n = \frac{35}{71}(10) = 5$$

$\therefore$ B is approximately $10°00' + 5'$, or $10°5'$;
the angle of ascent is $10°5'$, **Answer.**

Written Exercises

Using logarithms, find the value of each expression to four significant figures.

A

1. $124 \tan 51°00'$
2. $0.821 \sin 18°10'$
3. $\sin 37°20' \cos 37°20'$
4. $\sin 87°40' \cos 87°40'$
5. $\dfrac{\sin 59°10'}{\sin 24°30'}$
6. $\dfrac{\cot 35°00'}{\tan 25°00'}$
7. $62 \dfrac{\sin 42° \sin 37°}{\sin 79°}$
8. $7.8 \dfrac{\sin 24° \sin 70°}{\sin 46°}$

9. $\dfrac{(\tan 15°)^3}{15 \cos 27°}$

10. $\dfrac{240 \cos 47°}{\sin^2 47°}$

11. $\sqrt{\dfrac{32 \sec 70°}{12 \sin 70°}}$

12. $\sqrt[3]{8 \csc 15° \cos 15°}$

Use logarithms to find the measure of the positive acute angle to the nearest minute.

13. $\cos \theta = \dfrac{4.930}{8.750}$

14. $\tan \theta = \dfrac{7.540}{3.290}$

15. $\sin \alpha = \dfrac{24.30 \sin 32°}{28.9}$

16. $\sin \beta = \dfrac{17.31 \sin 54°}{52.00}$

17. $\cos \alpha = \dfrac{\cos 15° \sin 40°}{\cos 20°}$

18. $\sin \beta = \sqrt{\dfrac{13 \times 34}{52 \times 35}}$

19. $\tan \theta = \dfrac{14.32 \tan 16°24'}{76.9}$

20. $\cot \theta = \dfrac{15.21 \cot 39°14'}{7.30}$

Problems

Use logarithms in solving these problems. Assume linear measures are correct to four significant figures and angle measures to the nearest minute.

1. The Grossmans bought a tent with a center pole 5.250′ high for their camping trip. If the sides of the tent are supposed to make an angle of 55°00′ with the ground, how wide is the tent?
2. From the periscope of a submarine the bridge of a ship is sighted at 0°40′ above the horizon. If the bridge is 25.35 feet above the horizon line, how far is the ship from the submarine?
3. A beam of light traveling 39.50 inches from a source to a horizontal surface hits the surface at an angle of 37°25′. How far above the surface is the light source?
4. A conveyor belt carries bales of hay from the ground to the loft of a barn. If the belt makes an angle of 52°15′ with the vertical wall of the barn, and the loft door is 27.50 feet above the ground, how far does the belt travel from the ground to the loft?
5. The State Highway Commission plans to take a triangular corner plot from the square lot at the intersection of Routes 3 and 102 for the new expressway. If the plot to be taken runs 521.5 feet along Route 3 and 636.4 feet along Route 102, what angles does the third side of this plot make with Routes 3 and 102?

6. An ore boat headed due east on Lake Superior. After it had traveled 17.25 miles, it had been blown 0.8375 miles north of this course by a southwest wind. By what angle did the boat's actual course differ from its intended course?

7. Two surveyors stand 11.38 yards apart on the east bank of the Wachaw River. One stands directly opposite a large rock on the west bank, and the other finds the angle between the perpendicular from the rock to the first surveyor and the line of sight between the rock and himself to be 22°17′. How wide is the riyer?

8. The slant height of the Bowers' roof is 14.36 feet. The eaves extend one foot beyond the house on either side. If the roof makes an angle of 33°19′ with the attic floor, how high above the floor does the roof rise?

B 9. The lens of a camera forms on the film an inverted image of the object being photographed, as indicated in the sketch. The object is 10.3 feet away from the lens, the lens is 4.9 inches from the film, and angle A is 27°31′. How high is the image on the film?

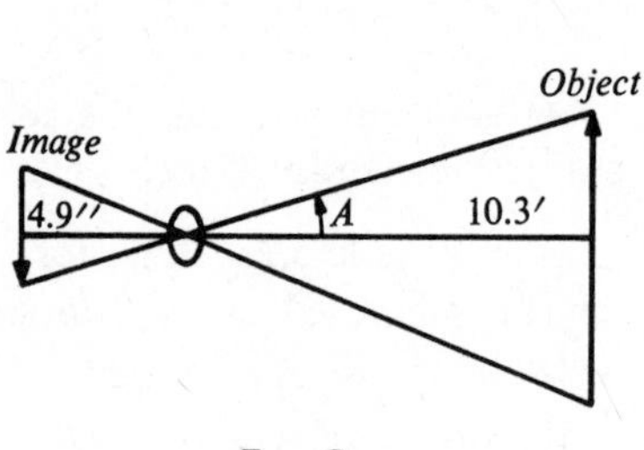

Ex. 9

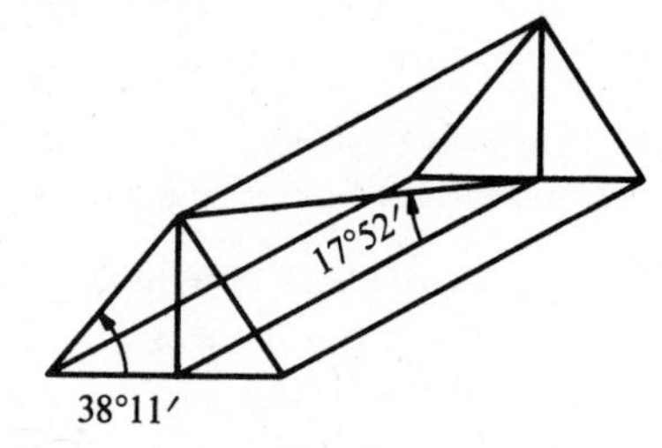

Ex. 10

10. Ingots of an alloy are cast in the shape of a prism with isosceles triangles as ends. The base of a triangular end is 8″ long, and the sides form a 38°11′ angle with the base. The line connecting the apex of a triangular end with the midpoint of the base of the opposite end forms an angle of 17°52′ with the line joining the midpoints of the bases of either end. Find the volume of the ingot. (Volume = area of cross section × depth.)

11. From the top of a mountain 12,350 feet high, the angles of depression of two ships lying in a vertical plane with the mountain top measure 18°24′ and 13°39′. Find the distance between the ships.

12. A right triangle whose legs are 36.25 and 84.30 cm. long is inscribed in a circle. What is the length of the diameter of the circle and the measures of the acute angles of the triangle?

10–7 Reference Angles

To see how to use Tables 6 and 7 for angles of any measure, we associate with each angle θ in standard position a first-quadrant angle called the *reference angle* of θ. Let $P(a, b)$ be any point, other than the origin, on the terminal side of θ, and let T be the point in the first quadrant whose coordinates are $(|a|, |b|)$. The acute (or right) angle in standard position with ray OT as terminal side is the **reference angle** of θ and is labeled ρ (rho) in Figure 10–14.

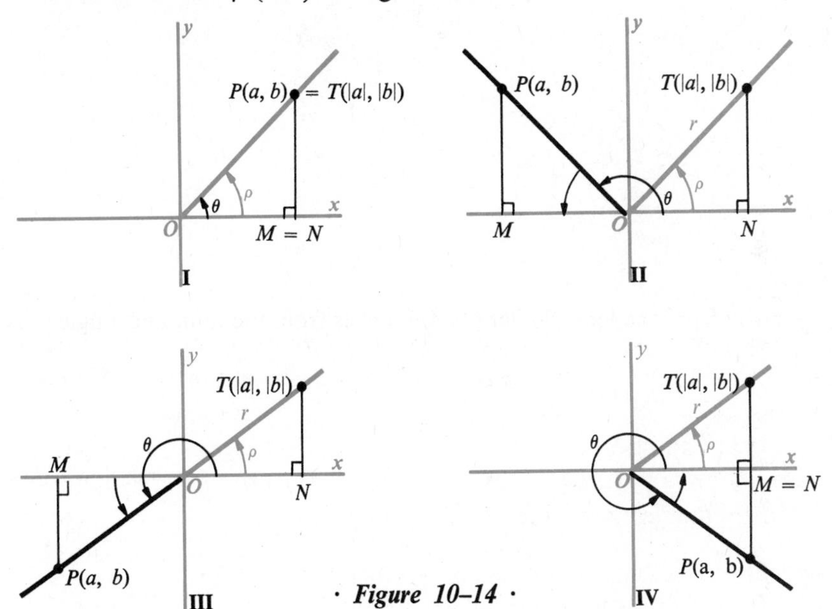

· *Figure 10–14* ·

To determine the relationship between the values of the trigonometric functions of θ and ρ, you must analyze the relationship between a and $|a|$, b and $|b|$ for each quadrant. Notice that in all quadrants $r = \sqrt{a^2 + b^2} = \sqrt{|a|^2 + |b|^2}$.

θ in Quadrant I. $a = |a|$ and $b = |b|$

This means $\sin\theta = \sin\rho$, $\cos\theta = \cos\rho$, and so on.

θ in Quadrant II. $a = -|a|$ and $b = |b|$

$$\sin\theta = \frac{b}{r} = \frac{|b|}{r} = \sin\rho$$

$$\cos\theta = \frac{a}{r} = \frac{-|a|}{r} = -\cos\rho \qquad \tan\theta = \frac{b}{a} = \frac{|b|}{-|a|} = -\tan\rho$$

Similarly, $\csc\theta = \csc\rho$, $\sec\theta = -\sec\rho$, $\cot\theta = -\cot\rho$.

By considering θ in the other quadrants, you can verify the other entries in the table. Notice that you can obtain the value of any function of θ by multiplying the value of the corresponding function of ρ by 1 or -1 according as the value of the function of θ is positive or negative. (See the chart on page 380.)

Value	Quadrant in which θ Terminates			
	I	II	III	IV
$\sin \theta$	$\sin \rho$	$\sin \rho$	$-\sin \rho$	$-\sin \rho$
$\cos \theta$	$\cos \rho$	$-\cos \rho$	$-\cos \rho$	$\cos \rho$
$\tan \theta$	$\tan \rho$	$-\tan \rho$	$\tan \rho$	$-\tan \rho$
$\csc \theta$	$\csc \rho$	$\csc \rho$	$-\csc \rho$	$-\csc \rho$
$\sec \theta$	$\sec \rho$	$-\sec \rho$	$-\sec \rho$	$\sec \rho$
$\cot \theta$	$\cot \rho$	$-\cot \rho$	$\cot \rho$	$-\cot \rho$

In Figure 10–14, you can see that $\angle POM$ has the same measure as ρ. This assertion is true because the lengths of the corresponding sides of right triangles POM and TON are equal since $MP = NT = |b|$, $OM = ON = |a|$, $OT = OP = \sqrt{a^2 + b^2}$. Hence, the measures of the corresponding angles must be equal. This means that you can determine the measure of ρ by finding the measure of the acute angle formed by the terminal side of θ and the x-axis.

EXAMPLE 1. Find $\sin 210°$ and $\tan 210°$.

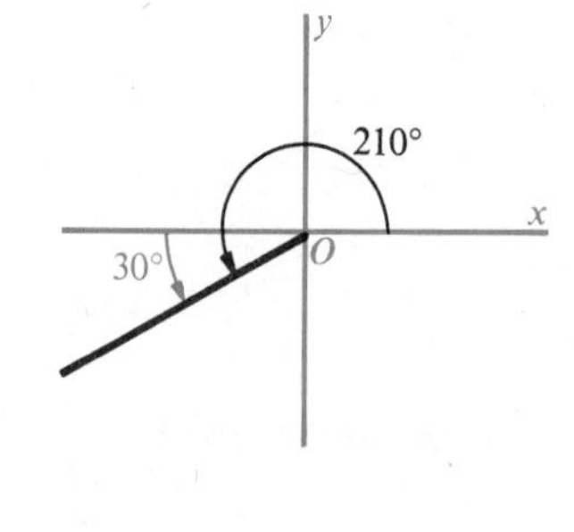

Solution:

1. Sketch the angle in standard position.
2. ρ measures: $210° - 180° = 30°$.
3. Since the angle terminates in Quadrant III,

$$\sin 210° = -\sin 30° = -\tfrac{1}{2} = -0.5000$$

$$\tan 210° = \tan 30° = \frac{\sqrt{3}}{3} \doteq 0.5774$$

To determine the measure of the reference angle when the measure of θ is greater than 360° or less than 0°, you use the fact that *angles in standard position whose measures differ by an integral multiple of* 360° *are coterminal.*

EXAMPLE 2. Find four significant figure approximations of $\cos 708°20'$ and $\sin 708°20'$.

Solution:

1. $708°20' - 1 \cdot 360° = 348°20'$.
2. $360° - 348°20' = 359°60' - 348°20' = 11°40'$

$$\left.\begin{aligned} \cos 708°20' &= \cos 11°40' = 0.9793 \\ \sin 708°20' &= -\sin 11°40' = -0.2022 \end{aligned}\right\} \text{Table 6}$$

Written Exercises

In standard position, draw the angle with given measure. Label and give the measure of its reference angle.

1. $120°$ **4.** $-60°$ **7.** $760°$ **10.** $-315°$
2. $225°$ **5.** $-150°$ **8.** $1040°$ **11.** $-240°$
3. $330°$ **6.** $-94°$ **9.** $-20°$ **12.** $540°$

Copy each table and fill in the blanks with exact values.

13.

	θ	30°	150°	210°	330°
a.	$\sin\theta$	?	?	?	?
b.	$\cos\theta$	?	?	?	?
c.	$\tan\theta$	?	?	?	?

14.

	θ	−45°	−135°	−225°	−315°
a.	$\sin\theta$	?	?	?	?
b.	$\cos\theta$	?	?	?	?
c.	$\tan\theta$	?	?	?	?

15.

	θ	45°	135°	225°	315°
a.	$\sin\theta$	?	?	?	?
b.	$\cos\theta$	?	?	?	?
c.	$\tan\theta$	?	?	?	?

16.

	θ	60°	120°	240°	300°
a.	$\sin\theta$	?	?	?	?
b.	$\cos\theta$	?	?	?	?
c.	$\tan\theta$	?	?	?	?

Express as a function of a positive acute angle.

17. $\cos 160°$
18. $\sin 130°$
19. $\tan 200°$
20. $\cos 310°$
21. $\cot 440°$
22. $\sec 195°$
23. $\sin(-355°)$
24. $\cos(-1045°)$
25. $\csc(-39°20')$
26. $\cot(-54°40')$

Find each value to four significant figures.

27. $\sin 310°$
28. $\cos 165°$
29. $\tan(-59°)$
30. $\cot(-140°)$
31. $\log|\cos(114°30')|$
32. $\log|\sin(225°50')|$

If θ is a positive angle terminating in the given quadrant and measuring less than one rotation, determine its measure to the nearest ten minutes.

33. $\cot\theta = 0.1853$; III
34. $\tan\theta = -0.5658$; II
35. $\cos\theta = 0.8601$; IV
36. $\sin\theta = -0.6734$; III
37. $\log|\sin\theta| = 9.9584 - 10$; IV
38. $\log|\cos\theta| = 9.8699 - 10$; II

Determine, correct to tenths, the rectangular coordinates of the point *P* for which *OP* has the given length and whose position angle has the given measure.

B

39. 5; 125°
40. 12; $-40°$
41. 8.3; 267°
42. 12.5; 140°
43. 10; $-15°$
44. 52; 224°

Determine the distance *OP* to tenths, and the measure of the smallest positive position angle of *P*, to the nearest degree.

45. $P(4, 3)$
46. $P(5, 12)$
47. $P(-7, -2)$
48. $P(-3.4, -8.2)$
49. $P(7.1, -0.5)$
50. $P(-0.8, 4.2)$

VECTORS

10–8 Adding Vectors

To specify the velocity of an airplane you must give both the direction and magnitude of the velocity. Quantities whose designation requires both magnitude and direction are called **vector quantities** and are represented by directed line segments or arrows called **vectors**. Units of length on the arrow indicate the units of magnitude of the vector quantity, and the direction of the arrow indicates the direction of the vector quantity.

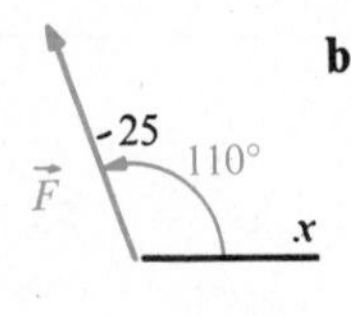

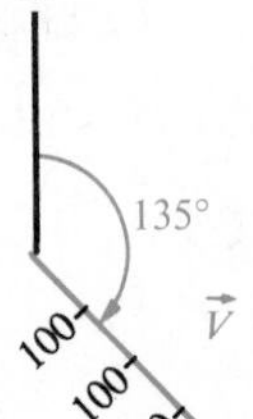

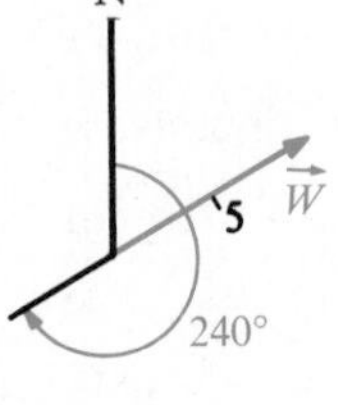

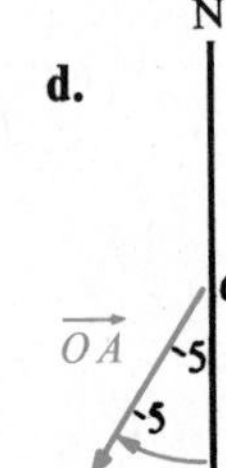

· *Figure 10–15* ·

In Figure 10–15, vectors represent:

a. A force $\overrightarrow{F}$ of 50 pounds at 110° (the angle is measured counterclockwise from the positive *x*-axis to the vector).

b. A velocity $\overrightarrow{V}$ of 400 m.p.h. at 135° (the angle, called the *heading*, *bearing*, or *course*, is measured clockwise from north to the vector).

c. Wind velocity $\overrightarrow{W}$ of 10 knots from 240° (the angle is measured clockwise from north to the direction *from* which the wind blows).

d. A displacement $\overrightarrow{OA}$ from *O* to *A* of 15 miles S35°W (the angle is described by a ray turned from south 35° west to the vector).

The last three illustrations show the use of the north-south line as reference in specifying direction angles in navigation and surveying. In Figure 10–16 are other examples of this technique.

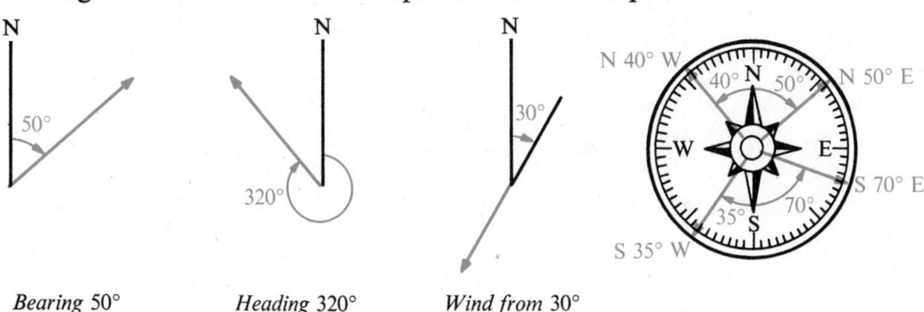

· *Figure 10–16* ·

Vectors such as $\overrightarrow{BR}$ and $\overrightarrow{CD}$ in Figure 10–17 are equivalent vectors; that is, they have the same magnitude and direction. We may think of a point as representing a vector of length 0, a *zero vector*. All zero vectors are considered equivalent.

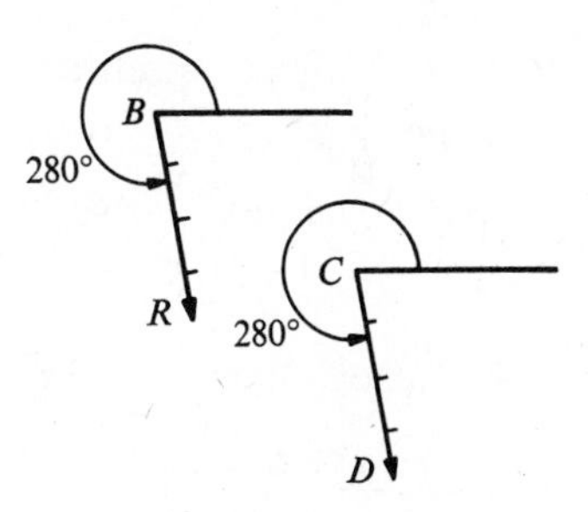

· *Figure 10–17* ·

The scale drawing in Figure 10–18 pictures the motion of a ship which sailed 30 miles due east ($\overrightarrow{ST}$), turned, and then sailed 40 miles N30°E ($\overrightarrow{TP}$). Because the vector $\overrightarrow{SP}$ represents the single motion that would bring the ship to the same final position as the combination of given displacements, we call $\overrightarrow{SP}$ the *sum* or *resultant* of $\overrightarrow{ST}$ and $\overrightarrow{TP}$ and write: $\overrightarrow{SP} = \overrightarrow{ST} + \overrightarrow{TP}$. Measuring $\overrightarrow{SP}$ and $\angle TSP$ on the scale drawing, you can estimate that this resultant displacement is 60 miles, N55°E.

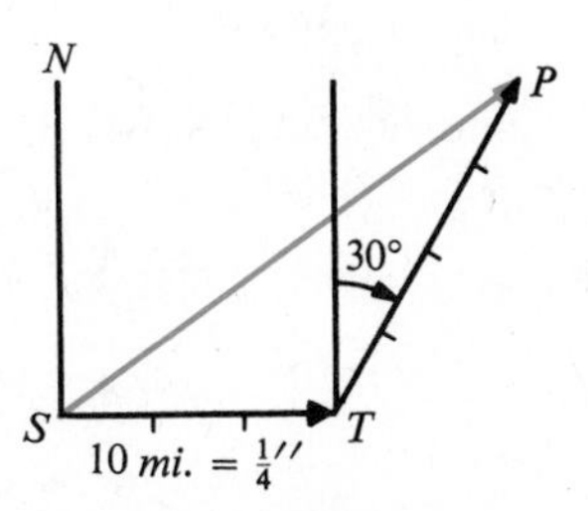

· *Figure 10–18* ·

To define the resultant of any two vectors, we use the fact that given a vector $\overrightarrow{CD}$ and a point B, then there is a unique vector $\overrightarrow{BR}$ at B equivalent to $\overrightarrow{CD}$ (Figure 10–19).

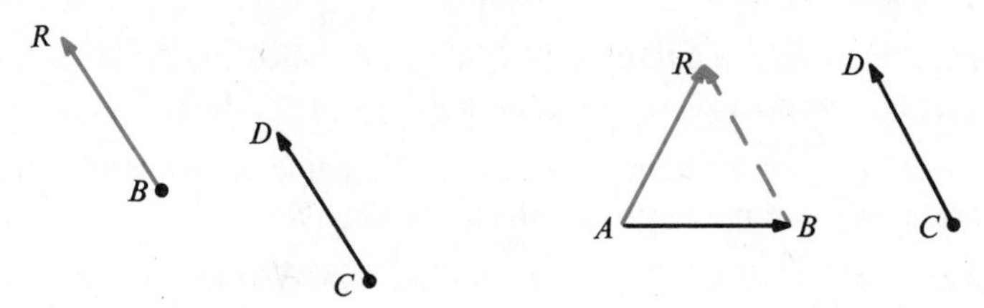

· *Figure 10–19* · · *Figure 10–20* ·

If $\overrightarrow{AB}$ and $\overrightarrow{CD}$ are any two vectors and if $\overrightarrow{BR}$ is the vector at B equivalent to $\overrightarrow{CD}$, then the **sum** or **resultant** of $\overrightarrow{AB}$ and $\overrightarrow{CD}$ is $\overrightarrow{AR}$; that is, $\overrightarrow{AB} + \overrightarrow{CD} = \overrightarrow{AR}$ (Figure 10–20).

EXAMPLE. An airplane whose air speed is 400 miles per hour flies in easterly winds blowing at 100 miles per hour. Determine the resultant velocity of the plane if its heading is **(a)** 90°; **(b)** 270°; **(c)** 0°. Give results to the nearest m.p.h. and nearest degree.

Solution:

a. **(1)** At A draw $\overrightarrow{AB}$ to represent wind velocity.

(2) At B draw $\overrightarrow{BR}$ to represent the plane's airspeed and heading.

(3) The resultant is $\overrightarrow{AR}$.

∴ The resultant velocity is 300 m.p.h. due east, **Answer.**

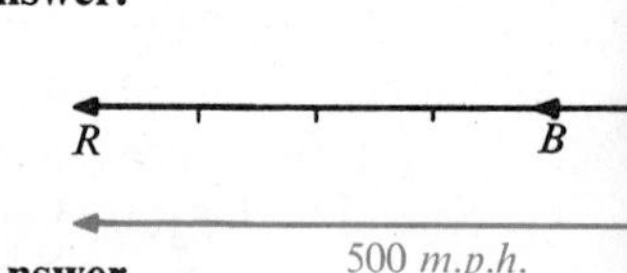

b. Repeat Steps 1–3 of **a.**

The resultant velocity is 500 m.p.h. due west, **Answer.**

c. Use trigonometry in right triangle ABR.

The heading is $270° + A$, where $\angle A = \angle RAB$.

$$\tan A = \frac{BR}{AB} = \frac{400}{100} = 4$$

$$A = 76°$$

$$270° + 76° = 346°$$

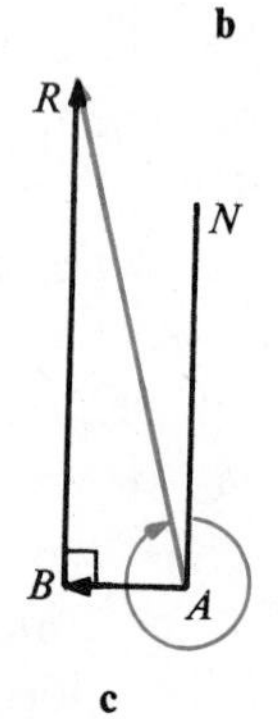

Magnitude of $\overrightarrow{AR}$ is AR.

$$\begin{aligned}(AR)^2 &= (AB)^2 + (BR)^2 = (100)^2 + (400)^2\\ &= (100)^2(4^2 + 1^2) = (100)^2(17)\\ AR &= 100\sqrt{17} = 100(4.123). \quad AR = 412\end{aligned}$$

$\therefore$ The resultant velocity is approximately 412 m.p.h. on course 346°, **Answer.**

Written Exercises

Find the resultant of the vectors by using **(a)** a scale drawing; **(b)** trigonometry. Express angle measures to the nearest degree; magnitudes to the nearest unit.

A

1. Forces of 120 lb. to the left and 50 lb. up.
2. Forces of 40 lb. to the right and 70 lb. down.
3. Velocities of 25 m.p.h. south and 30 m.p.h. east.
4. Velocities of 15 m.p.h. north and 10 m.p.h. west.
5. Displacements of 12 km. north and 8 km. east.
6. Displacements of 50 ft. west and 20 ft. south.

B

7. Forces of 6 kg. at 50° and 10 kg. at 140°.
8. Forces of 16 gm. at 240° and 28 gm. at 150°.
9. Displacements of 7 mi. N20°E and 14 mi. S70°E.
10. Displacements of 18 ft. S50°W and 9 ft. N40°W.
11. Airspeed of 600 m.p.h. at a heading of 225° and wind velocity of 18 m.p.h. from 135°.
12. Airspeed of 350 m.p.h. at a heading of 70° and wind velocity of 50 m.p.h. from 340°.

Problems

Assume data given is exact.

1. Jenny walks 1 block east along a vacant lot and then 2 blocks north to a friend's house. Phil starts at the same point and walks diagonally through the vacant lot coming out at the same point as Jenny. If Jenny walked 217 feet east and 400 feet north, how far did Phil walk?
2. A Major League baseball diamond is a square having 90 foot sides. If the pitcher stands 60 feet 6 inches from home plate, how far is he from 2nd base?

3. In a naval maneuver two ships rendezvous at Point A. One then proceeds east 10 miles and north 14 miles to Point B. At what bearing should the second ship head to meet the first ship at Point B?
4. A jet heads due west at 627 m.p.h. If a 25 m.p.h. north wind is blowing, what is the plane's ground speed and course?

B

5. At what bearing and speed would a pilot head if she wants to fly due north at 345 m.p.h. when a 40 m.p.h. west wind is blowing?
6. At what bearing and speed should the navigator direct the captain of a ship to head, if the captain wants to steam straight ahead at 18.2 knots when seas of 7.4 knots are hitting the ship broadside?
7. Jim can swim at a rate of 3 m.p.h. If he heads for a point directly across a river in which the current is 10 m.p.h., by how many degrees does the direction in which he actually swims differ from his intended direction? If the river is 32 yards wide, will he make it across before reaching the falls 112 yards downstream?
8. In a military test, a ballistic missile has a target 250 miles east and 280 miles south of its launching site. How far must it travel to the target? If a second missile is sent from the target site to intercept the first missile, at what heading should it be sent?

10–9 Resolving Vectors

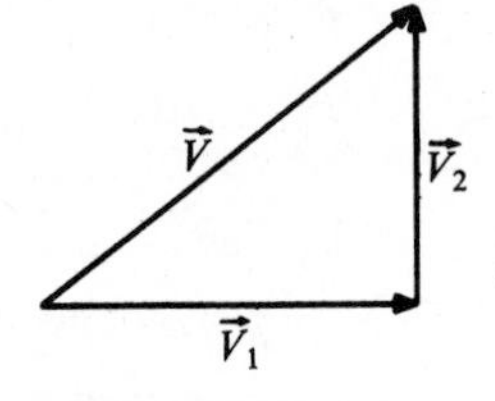

· *Figure 10–21* ·

Two vectors such as $\vec{V_1}$ and $\vec{V_2}$ in Figure 10–21 whose sum is $\vec{V}$ are called **components** of $\vec{V}$. Expressing a vector in a plane as a sum of two components in definite directions (usually at right angles to each other) is called **resolving the vector.** Of particular interest are the horizontal and vertical components of a vector.

EXAMPLE 1. In opening a vertical window from the top by means of a window pole, a man pulls with a force of 50 pounds. To the nearest pound, what part of the man's force lowers the window if the pole makes an angle of 25° with the window?

Solution:

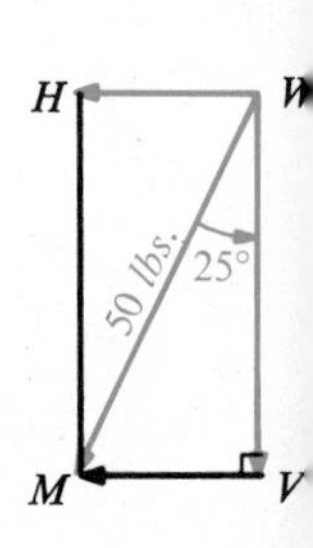

1. Draw a right triangle; label it to represent the given force and angle.

2. $\cos 25° = \frac{WV}{50} = 0.9063$ $\quad$ $WV = 50(0.9063)$, or 45.3

$\therefore$ The force lowering the window is about 45 pounds, **Answer.**

By solving the equation $\sin 25° = \frac{VM}{50}$, you can show the horizontal force pulling on the window to be about 21 pounds.

Figure 10–22 diagrams the forces acting on an object at A on a plane inclined at an angle θ with the horizontal. $\overrightarrow{AW}$ represents the force of gravity pulling the object towards the center of the earth with a pull equal to the weight of the object. Its components are $\overrightarrow{AB}$ parallel to the plane, and $\overrightarrow{BW}$ perpendicular to the plane. Because $\overrightarrow{AB}$ denotes the force tending to pull the object down the plane, the length of $\overrightarrow{AB}$ tells the magnitude of the smallest braking force that will keep the object from moving. If θ measures 10° and $\overrightarrow{AW}$ represents the weight of a 2700-pound automobile, you find the magnitude of this minimum brake force, to the nearest pound, as follows:

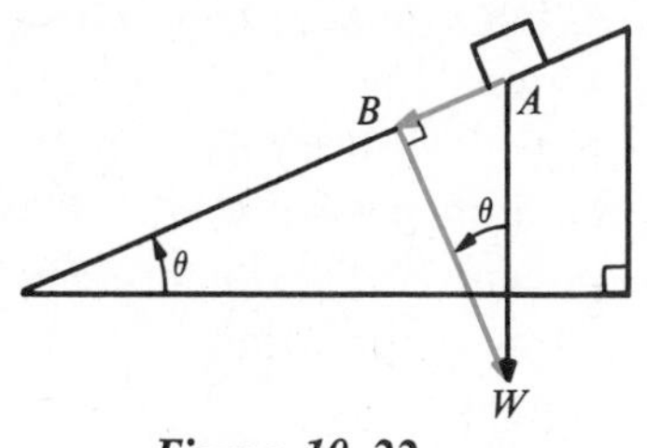

· *Figure 10–22* ·

$$\mathbf{\sin 10^\circ = \frac{AB}{AW} = \frac{AB}{2700}. \quad AB = 2700 \sin 10^\circ \doteq 2700\,(0.1736)}$$

$AB \doteq 468.7.$ $\quad\therefore$ **The minimum brake force required is 469 lb.**

Can you find the resultant of two vectors whose horizontal and vertical components are known? You can if you assume that *the component of the resultant in each direction is the sum of the components of the vectors in that direction.*

EXAMPLE 2. In one hour how far *north* will an airplane fly if its airspeed and heading are 600 m.p.h. at 40°00′ and if winds of 120 m.p.h. are blowing *in* the direction (not *from*) N30°00′W.

Solution:

Let $\overrightarrow{DE}$ = the north component of wind velocity
$\overrightarrow{CB}$ = the north component of airspeed
$\overrightarrow{AN}$ = the total velocity *due north*

Then: $\overrightarrow{AN} = \overrightarrow{DE} + \overrightarrow{CB}$

(*not to scale*)

In $\triangle ADE$: $\sin 60^\circ = \dfrac{DE}{120}$

$$DE = 120 \sin 60^\circ$$
$$\doteq 120(0.8660)$$
$$DE \doteq 103.9$$

In $\triangle ABC$: $\sin 50^\circ = \dfrac{CB}{600}$

$$CB = 600 \sin 50^\circ$$
$$= 600(0.7660)$$
$$CB = 459.6$$

$\therefore AN \doteq 103.9 + 459.6 \doteq 563.5$ $\qquad$ 564 miles north, **Answer.**

Explain why the plane will fly about 326 miles east during that hour.

Do you see that you can specify a vector at a point by giving an ordered pair of numbers indicating its horizontal and vertical components? For example, at T, $[2, -3]$ denotes a vector whose horizontal component is a vector of *length 2 to the right* and whose vertical component *is a vector of length 3 down* (Figure 10–23). When the initial point is the origin in a coordinate plane, the numbers indicating the components of the vector are also the coordinates of the terminal point (Figure 10–24).

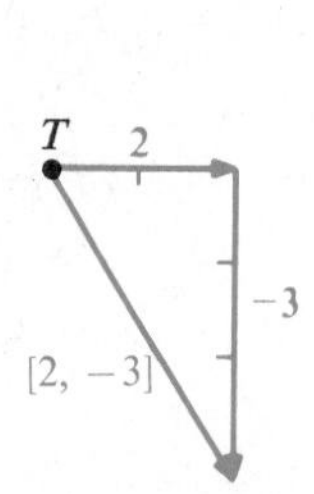

· *Figure 10–23* ·

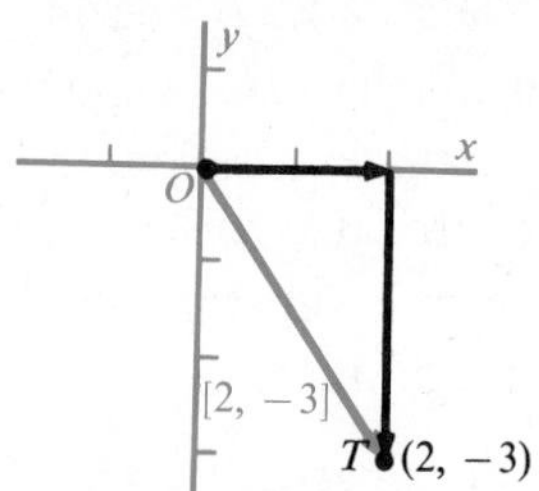

· *Figure 10–24* ·

Written Exercises

Determine the horizontal and vertical components of the vector having the given length and direction.

A

1. 12, N45°W
2. 100, S15°E
3. 24, bearing 110°
4. 36, bearing 220°
5. 15, course 90°
6. 160, heading 180°

If P is a point at the given distance from the origin and having a position angle of given measure, approximate to tenths the horizontal and vertical components of $\overrightarrow{OP}$.

7. 12; 42°
8. 16; 81°
9. 52; 134°
10. 40; 234°
11. 700; −290°
12. 64; −100°

Each ordered pair specifies a vector at the origin of a coordinate system. Draw the vectors, determine the components of their resultant, and draw the resultant.

SAMPLE. $[3, -1]; [5, 1]$

Solution:

$$[3, -1] + [5, 1] = [3 + 5, -1 + 1]$$
$$= [8, 0], \textbf{ Answer.}$$

B

13. $[-4, 2]; [0, 6]$
14. $[-1, -1]; [3, 4]$
15. $[0, 0]; [7, -2]$

16. $[0, -2]; [-5, -1]$
17. $[6, -6]; [-6, 6]$
18. $[-7, -7]; [7, 7]$
19. $[4, 8]; [-8, -16]$
20. $[-3, 2]; [0, 0]$

Let $[a, b]$, $[c, d]$, and $[e, f]$ denote vectors at the origin of a coordinate system. **(a)** Verify each statement if $a = -5$, $b = 3$, $c = 7$, $d = -2$, $e = 4$, $f = 1$; **(b)** prove that each statement is true for every replacement of a, b, c, d, e, and f by real numbers.

C **21.** $[a, b] + [c, d] = [c, d] + [a, b]$

22. $([a, b] + [c, d]) + [e, f] = [a, b] + ([c, d] + [e, f])$

23. $[a, b] + [0, 0] = [a, b]$

24. There is a vector $[x, y]$ such that $[a, b] + [x, y] = [0, 0]$.

Problems

Assume data given is exact.

A **1.** A boy is pulling his brother on a sled. The rope makes an angle of 38° with the sled. If the boy is exerting a pull of 30 lb. on the rope, what force is being exerted on the sled to pull it forward?

2. A force of 240 lb. is to be resolved into two component forces which are at right angles to each other. If one force is $33\frac{1}{3}\%$ greater than the other, what is the larger force?

3. A plane flies on course N25°E at 540 m.p.h. How many miles north of its starting point will it be at the end of an hour and a half?

4. How much force is wasted when a girl pushes with a force of 90 lb. on the handle of a lawn mower while holding it at **(a)** an angle of 30° above the ground, and **(b)** an angle of 45° above the ground?

B **5.** The string to a box kite makes a 60° angle with the ground. If the string will break when subjected to a 30 lb. force and if the kite requires a minimum horizontal force of 5 lb. to fly, what is the possible range of the horizontal force of the wind in which the kite could be flown?

6. A wire cable on a crane can withstand a 20-ton tension. If the crane is extended at an angle of 50° from the vertical, what is the greatest weight it can lift to leave a safety margin of two tons in the wire?

7. A river flows from north to south. To cross from the east bank directly to the west bank a boat captain finds that she must keep on a course of 284°. If the trip takes fifteen minutes when the boat travels 12.4 m.p.h., **(a)** how wide is the river, and **(b)** how swift is the current?

8. A theater marquee is supported by two equal steel cables which make angles of 40° with the building. If the marquee weighs 600 lb., what is the tension in each cable?

9. A mirror weighing 20 lb. is supported at the top corners by a taut wire which passes around a nail embedded in the wall. If the corners and the nail form an angle of 130°, what is the total pull on the wire?

WORKING WITH COMPLEX NUMBERS

10–10 Complex Numbers

In a plane a point like $P(2, 1)$ determines a vector $[2, 1]$ ($\overrightarrow{OP}$ in Figure 10–25) from the origin to the point. Since every point of the x-axis determines one and only one horizontal vector at O, the familiar pairing of the points of a number line with the real numbers suggests a one-to-one correspondence between the set of horizontal vectors and the set of real numbers (Figure 10–26).

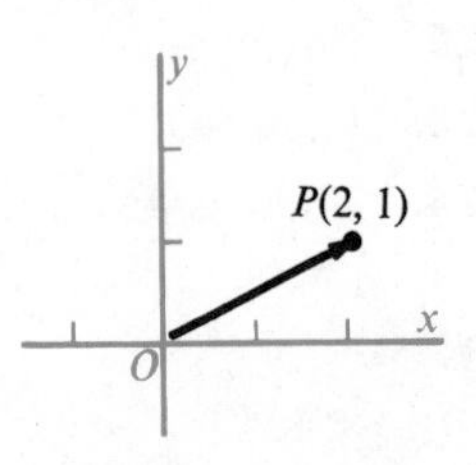

· *Figure 10–25* ·

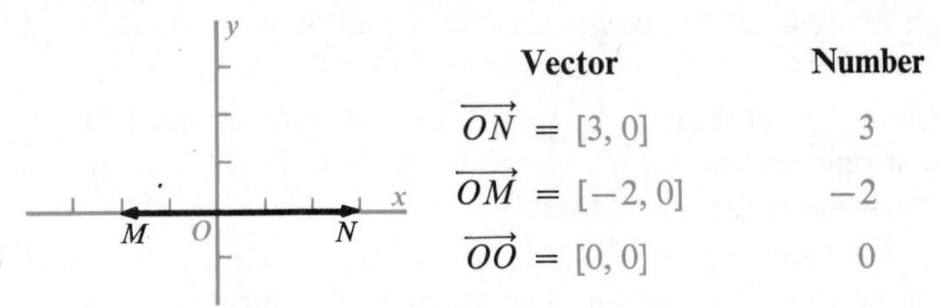

Vector	Number
$\overrightarrow{ON} = [3, 0]$	3
$\overrightarrow{OM} = [-2, 0]$	-2
$\overrightarrow{OO} = [0, 0]$	0

· *Figure 10–26* ·

Can you find numbers to pair with the vertical vectors from O? To maintain a 1-1 correspondence between numbers and vectors, we need *new* numbers as partners of the vertical vectors. We use the letter i, the symbol $1i$, or the expression $0 + 1i$ to designate the partner of $[0, 1]$, and in general ai (also written ia) or $0 + ai$ to name the number corresponding to $[0, a]$ (Figure 10–27). By agreement, $0i = 0 + 0i = 0$, and $i0 = 0 + i0 = 0$.

Vector	Number
$\overrightarrow{OR} = [0, 1]$	i or $0 + 1i$
$\overrightarrow{OS} = [0, 2]$	$2i$ or $0 + 2i$
$\overrightarrow{OT} = [0, -1]$	$-i$ or $0 + (-i)$
$\overrightarrow{OV} = [0, -3]$	$-3i$ or $0 + (-3i)$

· *Figure 10–27* ·

The vector $\overrightarrow{OP}$ in Figure 10–28 has $\overrightarrow{ON}$ as its horizontal component and $\overrightarrow{OS}$ as its vertical component. Since $\overrightarrow{OP} = \overrightarrow{ON} + \overrightarrow{OS}$, you pair $\overrightarrow{OP}$ with the "sum" of the partners of $\overrightarrow{ON}$ and $\overrightarrow{OS}$: $3 + 2i$. In general, you pair the vector $[a, b]$ with $a + bi$ (also written $a + ib$).

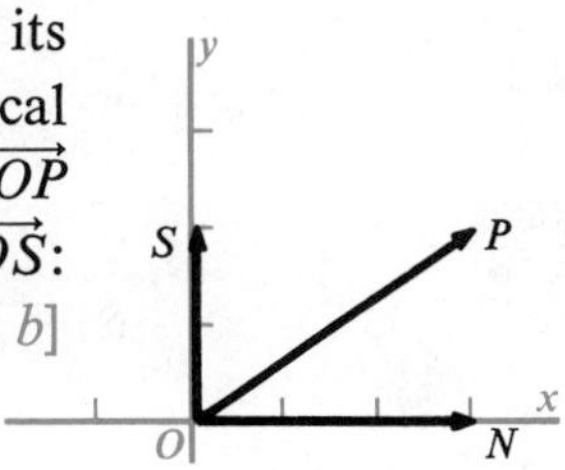

· *Figure 10–28* ·

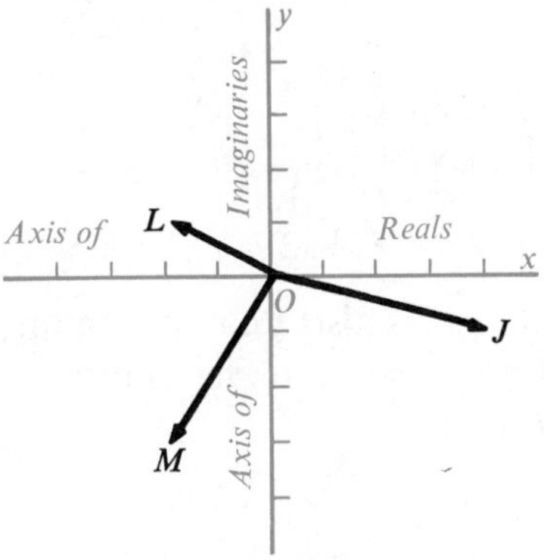

· *Figure 10–29* ·

Vector	Number
$\overrightarrow{OL} = [-2, 1]$	$-2 + 1i$
$\overrightarrow{OM} = [-2, -3]$	$-2 + (-3i)$
$\overrightarrow{OJ} = [4, -1]$	$4 + (-1i)$

Expressions in the *standard form* $a + bi$ where a and b denote real numbers represent elements of the **set of complex numbers**. A complex number is

1. a *real number* if, like 3 or 0, it is denoted by $a + 0i$ or a;

2. an *imaginary number* if, like $-2 + 3i$, it is denoted by $a + bi$, $b \neq 0$.

Imaginary numbers such as $2i$ and $-3i$, which have the form $0 + bi$ or bi, are called *pure imaginary numbers.*

To *plot a complex number in a complex plane* means to draw the associated vector or to mark its terminal point in the plane (Figures 10–26, 10–27, 10–29). Can you suggest why, as shown in Figure 10–29, the x-axis is called the *axis of reals* (or the *real axis*), and the y-axis, the *axis of imaginaries* (or the *imaginary axis*)?

The fact that vectors at the origin are equal if and only if their corresponding components are equal suggests the following **definition of equality** in the set of complex numbers.

If a, b, c, and d denote real numbers, then $a + bi = c + di$ if and only if $a = c$ and $b = d$.

For example, $7 + 2i = (4 + 3) + (8 - 6)i$ because $7 = 4 + 3$ and $2 = 8 - 6$; but $7 + 2i \neq 2 + 7i$, because $7 \neq 2$.

Adding vectors by finding sums of corresponding components leads to the following **definition of addition** in the set of complex numbers.

> If a, b, c, and d denote real numbers, then
> $(a + bi) + (c + di) = (a + c) + (b + d)i.$

For example:
$(5 + 3i) + (-7 + 6i) = (5 - 7) + (3 + 6)i = -2 + 9i.$

To simplify notation, the symbol $\boldsymbol{a + (-bi)}$ is often written $\boldsymbol{a - bi}$.

Thus, $(3 - 5i) + (-2 + 2i) = (3 - 2) + (-5 + 2)i = 1 - 3i.$

Do you see that the sum of complex numbers is also a complex number, so that the system of complex numbers is closed under addition? The following example indicates other properties.

EXAMPLE 1. Verify:

a. $(3 + 2i) + (-7 + 3i) = (-7 + 3i) + (3 + 2i)$

b. $[(3 + 2i) + (-7 + 3i)] + (4 - 2i) = (3 + 2i) + [(-7 + 3i) + (4 - 2i)]$

c. $(3 + 2i) + (0 + 0i) = 3 + 2i$

d. $(3 + 2i) + (-3 - 2i) = 0 + 0i$

Solution:

a. $(3 + 2i) + (-7 + 3i) = (3 + (-7)) + (2 + 3)i = -4 + 5i$
$(-7 + 3i) + (3 + 2i) = (-7 + 3) + (3 + 2)i = -4 + 5i$

b. $[(3 + 2i) + (-7 + 3i)] + (4 - 2i) = (-4 + 5i) + (4 - 2i) = 0 + 3i$
$(3 + 2i) + [(-7 + 3i) + (4 - 2i)] = (3 + 2i) + (-3 + 1i) = 0 + 3i$

c. $(3 + 2i) + (0 + 0i) = (3 + 0) + (2 + 0)i = 3 + 2i$

d. $(3 + 2i) + (-3 - 2i) = (3 - 3) + (2 - 2)i = 0 + 0i$

The commutative and associative properties suggested by **(a)** and **(b)** of this example hold for all sums of complex numbers. Also, as **(c)** suggests, the **identity element** for **addition** is $\mathbf{0 + 0}i$ or 0. Moreover, every complex number $a + bi$ has a unique **additive inverse**: $\boldsymbol{-(a + bi) = (-a) + (-bi)}$.

As in the system of real numbers, you subtract a complex number by adding its additive inverse.

EXAMPLE 2. $(5 + 7i) - (-3 + 4i) = (5 + 7i) + [3 + (-4i)] = 8 + 3i$

Oral Exercises

Give the number associated with the vector in the diagram.

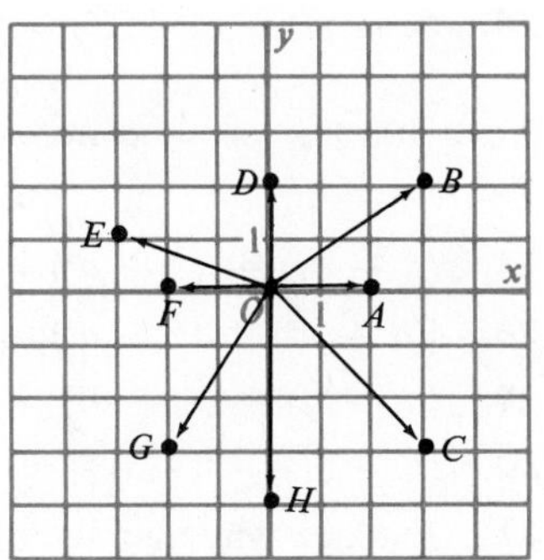

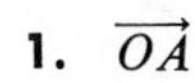

1. $\overrightarrow{OA}$
2. $\overrightarrow{OB}$
3. $\overrightarrow{OC}$
4. $\overrightarrow{OD}$
5. $\overrightarrow{OE}$
6. $\overrightarrow{OF}$
7. $\overrightarrow{OG}$
8. $\overrightarrow{OH}$

Give the additive inverse of each number and state whether the given number and its additive inverse are real numbers, pure imaginary numbers, or imaginary (but not pure imaginary) numbers.

9. $4 + 3i$
10. $-7i$
11. 2
12. $-5 + 0i$
13. $0 + 0i$
14. $-6 + 2i$
15. $0 + 8i$
16. $\sqrt{2} + i$

Written Exercises

In a complex plane plot each number and its additive inverse.

A

1. $-3 + 5i$
2. $-7 + 2i$
3. $8 - 3i$
4. $1 - 6i$
5. $4i$
6. $-3i$
7. 0
8. 6
9. $-1 + i$
10. $-3 - 3i$
11. $-2 - 5i$
12. -3

Let r be the first complex number and s the second. Compute **(a)** $r + s$; **(b)** $r - s$; **(c)** $s - r$.

13. $3 + 7i, i$
14. $16 + 3i, 1 - i$
15. $-i, 1 + 3i$
16. $-4i, (3 + 1i)$
17. $7, 2 - 3i$
18. $-6, -5 + 8i$

Simplify:

B

19. $(5 + 3i) + (2 - 4i) - (3 - 8i)$
20. $(-4 + 2i) - (6 + 8i) + (13 - 2i)$
21. $-(7 - 3i) + (4 + i) - (-1)$
22. $-(8 + 2i) - (1 - 6i) - 3i$

Determine real numbers x and y for which the equation is true.

23. $(x + yi) + (7 - 3i) = 5 + 2i$

24. $(x + yi) - (4 + 2i) = 6 - 8i$

25. $2x + yi = 1 + (3 + 5i)$

26. $x + 2yi = i + (-2 + 7i)$

Prove that the following statements are true for all real values of a, b, c, d, e, and f.

C **27.** $(a + bi) + (c + di) = (c + di) + (a + bi)$

28. $[(a + bi) + (c + di)] + (e + fi) = (a + bi) + [(c + di) + (e + fi)]$

29. $(a + bi) + (0 + 0i) = a + bi$

30. $(a + bi) + [(-a) + (-bi)] = 0 + 0i$

31. Explain why the set of pure imaginary numbers together with 0 is closed under addition.

32. Show by an example that the set of imaginary numbers is not closed under addition.

10–11 Multiplying Pure Imaginary Numbers

Can you describe the multiplication of real numbers in terms of the vectors representing them in the complex plane? Figure 10–30 shows that multiplying a real number such as 3 or -2 by 1 leaves the vector representing the real number unchanged; but multiplication by -1 rotates that vector counterclockwise through 180°, the angle of the vector of -1.

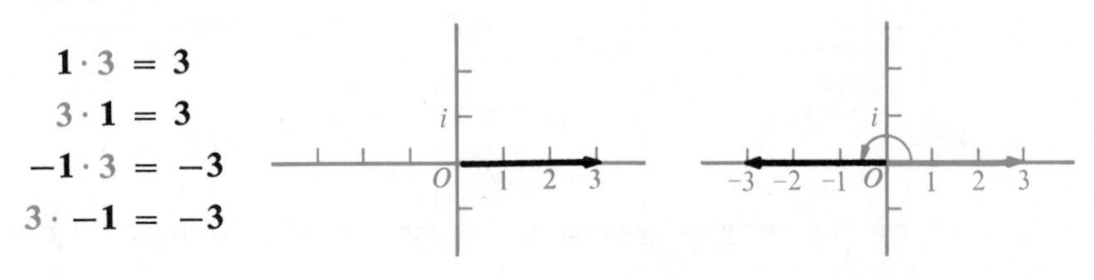

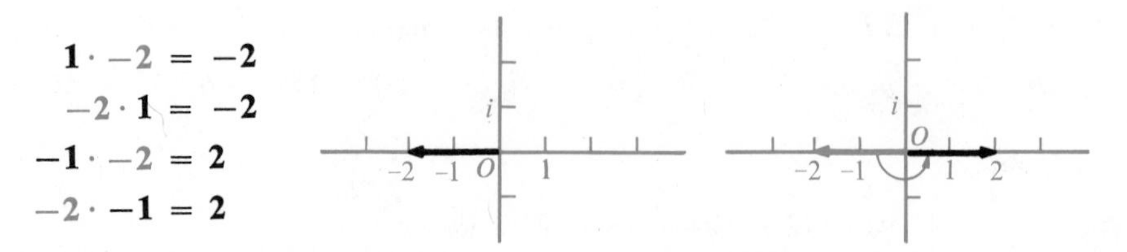

· *Figure 10–30* ·

To maintain this pattern, multiplication of a number by i should rotate the vector of the number through 90°, the angle of the vector of i.

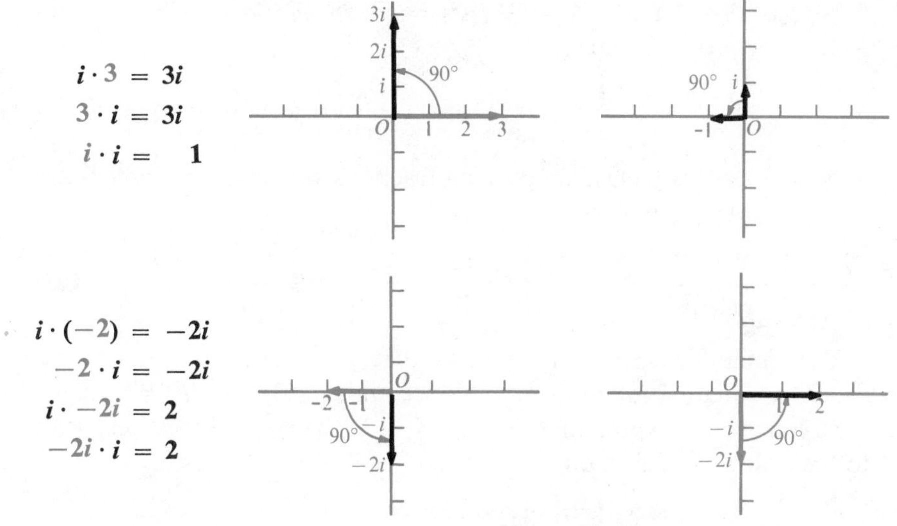

· *Figure 10–31* ·

The examples in Figure 10–31 suggest these definitions:

1. $i \cdot i = -1$; that is, $i^2 = -1$.
2. $a \cdot i = ai$ for every real number a.

By requiring that multiplication continue to have the commutative and associative properties, you can discover how to express in standard form any product of real or pure imaginary numbers. Study the following examples. Do you see that the product of a nonzero real and a pure imaginary number is a pure imaginary number, but the product of two pure imaginary numbers is a real number?

$$2(5i) = (2 \cdot 5)i = 10i;\ 4i(-3) = (4 \cdot -3)i = -12i$$

$$7i(6i) = (7 \cdot 6)(i \cdot i) = 42i^2 = 42(-1) = -42$$

$$-15i(\tfrac{1}{3}i) = (-15 \cdot \tfrac{1}{3})i^2 = -5(-1) = 5$$

When you simplify successive powers of i, you find the values repeating in cycles of four, according to the pattern i, -1, $-i$, 1.

$i^1 = i$

$i^2 = -1$

$i^3 = i^2 \cdot i = -1 \cdot i = -i$

$i^4 = i^2 \cdot i^2 = (-1)(-1) = 1$

$i^5 = i^4 \cdot i = 1 \cdot i = i$

$i^6 = i^4 \cdot i^2 = 1(-1) = -1$

$i^7 = i^4 \cdot i^3 = 1(-i) = -i$

$i^8 = i^4 \cdot i^4 = 1 \cdot 1 = 1$

Notice also that $i(-i) = -1(i^2) = (-1)(-1) = 1$. Thus, i and $-i$ are reciprocals; that is,

$$\frac{1}{i} = -i \quad \text{and} \quad \frac{1}{-i} = i.$$

You can use this fact in simplifying fractions whose denominators are pure imaginary numbers.

$$\frac{9}{6i} = \frac{9}{6} \cdot \frac{1}{i} = \frac{3}{2} \cdot -i = -\frac{3}{2}i; \quad \frac{12}{i^3} = \frac{12}{-i} = 12 \cdot \frac{1}{-i} = 12 \cdot i = 12i$$

The definition $i^2 = -1$ suggests that you write $i = \sqrt{-1}$, and call i "a square root of -1." Notice that $(i\sqrt{3})^2 = 3i^2 = -3$, so that you would expect that $i\sqrt{3} = \sqrt{-3}$. These observations lead to the following definition:

For every positive real number r, $i\sqrt{r} = \sqrt{-r}$.

Thus, in the set of complex numbers you have the square roots of *all* real numbers.

To simplify a square-root radical whose radicand is a negative number, *first* express the radical as the product of a real number and i. *Then*, use the properties of the real roots of real numbers (Chapter 7) to simplify this product.

EXAMPLE 1. $\sqrt{-16} + \sqrt{-49} = i\sqrt{16} + i\sqrt{49} = 4i + 7i = 11i$

EXAMPLE 2.
$$\begin{aligned} 5\sqrt{-48} - \tfrac{1}{3}\sqrt{-27} &= 5i\sqrt{48} - \tfrac{1}{3}i\sqrt{27} \\ &= 5i \cdot 4\sqrt{3} - \tfrac{1}{3}i \cdot 3\sqrt{3} \\ &= 20i\sqrt{3} - i\sqrt{3} = 19i\sqrt{3} \end{aligned}$$

EXAMPLE 3.
$$\begin{aligned} \sqrt{-8} \cdot \sqrt{-2} &= i\sqrt{8} \cdot i\sqrt{2} \\ &= \sqrt{8 \cdot 2} \cdot i^2 = \sqrt{16}(-1) = -4 \end{aligned}$$

Note that if you wrote $\sqrt{-8} \cdot \sqrt{-2} = \sqrt{-8 \cdot -2} = \sqrt{16} = 4$, you would obtain an incorrect result because you would have applied properties proved only for radicals denoting *real numbers.* This is why it is important to follow the order of operations indicated above.

EXAMPLE 4.
$$\begin{aligned} \frac{14}{\sqrt{-7}} &= \frac{14}{i\sqrt{7}} = -\frac{14i}{\sqrt{7}} \\ &= -\frac{14i \cdot \sqrt{7}}{\sqrt{7} \cdot \sqrt{7}} = -\frac{14\sqrt{7}\,i}{7} = -2\sqrt{7}\,i \end{aligned}$$

Oral Exercises

Express in standard form.

1. $2i \cdot 4$
2. $5 \cdot 6i$
3. $3i(-8)$
4. $-2i(-2)$
5. $i(-i)$
6. $-i(-i)$
7. $5i(4i)$
8. $-3i(-7i)$
9. $-4i(11i)$
10. $12i(-3i)$
11. $\frac{18i}{3}$
12. $\frac{-36i}{12}$
13. $\frac{9i}{3i}$
14. $\frac{16i}{2i}$
15. $\frac{-21i}{-7i}$
16. $\frac{-32i}{-8i}$
17. $\sqrt{-6}$
18. $\sqrt{-11}$
19. $\sqrt{-4}$
20. $\sqrt{-9}$
21. $\frac{5}{i}$
22. $\frac{7}{-i}$
23. $\frac{a}{-i}$
24. $\frac{a}{i}$

Written Exercises

Simplify. Assume that *x* and *y* denote positive real numbers.

A

1. i^9
2. i^{24}
3. i^{14}
4. i^{17}
5. $(i\sqrt{5})^2$
6. $(i\sqrt{7})^2$
7. $\sqrt{-\frac{1}{2}}$
8. $\sqrt{-\frac{5}{8}}$
9. $5\sqrt{-48}$
10. $7\sqrt{-128}$
11. $2\sqrt{-7} \cdot 3\sqrt{-5}$
12. $4\sqrt{-11} \cdot \sqrt{-1}$
13. $\sqrt{-16} \cdot \sqrt{-10}$
14. $\sqrt{-9} \cdot \sqrt{-3}$
15. $\sqrt{125} \cdot \sqrt{-5}$
16. $\sqrt{-2}\,\sqrt{98}$
17. $\sqrt{-\frac{1}{4}}\,\sqrt{-16}$
18. $\sqrt{-\frac{1}{3}}\,\sqrt{-27}$
19. $6\sqrt{-\frac{4}{3}}\,\sqrt{3}$
20. $12\sqrt{6}\,\sqrt{-\frac{25}{6}}$
21. $\frac{i\sqrt{8}}{i\sqrt{2}}$
22. $\frac{i\sqrt{216}}{i\sqrt{6}}$
23. $\frac{12\sqrt{-10}}{4\sqrt{-5}}$
24. $\frac{5\sqrt{-14}}{20\sqrt{-7}}$
25. $\frac{8\sqrt{-24}}{2\sqrt{-3}}$
26. $\frac{2\sqrt{-2}}{\sqrt{-8}}$
27. $\frac{5}{20\sqrt{-1}}$
28. $\frac{8}{4\sqrt{-1}}$
29. $\frac{6}{\sqrt{-3}}$

30. $\dfrac{2}{\sqrt{-2}}$

31. $\dfrac{70}{5\sqrt{-7}}$

32. $\dfrac{20}{2\sqrt{-5}}$

33. $5\sqrt{-2} + \sqrt{-8}$

34. $-7\sqrt{-3} + \sqrt{-27}$

35. $\sqrt{-9} + \sqrt{-25} - \sqrt{-5}$

36. $\sqrt{-64} + \sqrt{-7} - \sqrt{-49}$

37. $\frac{1}{3}\sqrt{63} - \sqrt{-28}$

38. $\frac{1}{4}\sqrt{80} + \sqrt{-125}$

B 39. $-\sqrt{-\frac{5}{4}} - \sqrt{-\frac{1}{5}}$

40. $2\sqrt{-\frac{1}{3}} - \sqrt{-\frac{4}{75}}$

41. $\frac{1}{2}\sqrt{-128} - \frac{1}{5}\sqrt{-200} + 7\sqrt{-8}$

42. $\frac{1}{7}\sqrt{-245} - 3\sqrt{-28} - \frac{1}{3}\sqrt{-63}$

43. $\dfrac{1}{i} - \dfrac{1}{i^2} + \dfrac{1}{i^3} - \dfrac{1}{i^4}$

44. $4i + 6i^2 - i^3 + 2i^4$

45. $i + 2i^2 + 3i^3 + i^4$

46. $\dfrac{1}{i} + \dfrac{1}{i^2} + \dfrac{1}{i^3} + \dfrac{1}{i^4}$

C 47. $\sqrt{-4x^4} - \sqrt{-25x^4} + \sqrt{-100x^4}$

48. $\sqrt{-\dfrac{x}{4}} + \sqrt{-\dfrac{x}{16}} - \sqrt{-\dfrac{x}{64}}$

49. $-\sqrt{-18y^2} + \sqrt{-2y^2} - \sqrt{-8y^2}$

50. $\sqrt{-3y^6} - \sqrt{-27y^6} + \sqrt{-12y^6}$

10–12 Complex Numbers and Quadratic Equations

If the complex numbers are to satisfy the distributive, as well as the commutative and associative laws, then you should be able to multiply a pair of complex numbers such as $2 + 3i$ and $5 + 7i$ just as you multiply binomials:

$$\begin{aligned}(2 + 3i)(5 + 7i) &= 2(5 + 7i) + 3i(5 + 7i)\\ &= 2 \cdot 5 + 2 \cdot 7i + 3i \cdot 5 + 3i \cdot 7i\\ &= 10 + 14i + 15i + 21i^2\\ \therefore (2 + 3i)(5 + 7i) &= 10 - 21 + (14 + 15)i = -11 + 29i\end{aligned}$$

This example suggests the following **definition of multiplication** in the set of complex numbers.

> If a, b, c, and d denote real numbers, then
> $(a + bi)(c + di) = (ac - bd) + (ad + bc)i.$

Because equality, addition, and multiplication of complex numbers have been defined so that the properties of equality, addition, and multiplication stated on page 32 for the set of real numbers are also valid when restated for the set of complex numbers, concepts and methods based on these properties apply in working with complex numbers, just as with real numbers.

EXAMPLE 1. Use the quadratic formula to solve $x^2 + 2x + 7 = 0$ over the set of complex numbers.

Solution:

$$x = \frac{-b \pm \sqrt{b^2 - 4ac}}{2a}; a = 1, b = 2, c = 7$$

$$x = \frac{-2 \pm \sqrt{2^2 - 4(1)(7)}}{2(1)}$$

$$x = \frac{-2 \pm \sqrt{4 - 28}}{2} = \frac{-2 \pm \sqrt{-24}}{2}$$

$$x = \frac{-2 \pm 2i\sqrt{6}}{2} = -1 \pm i\sqrt{6}$$

Check: $(-1 + i\sqrt{6}) + (-1 - i\sqrt{6}) \stackrel{?}{=} -2; -2 = -2$ ✓

$$(-1 + i\sqrt{6})(-1 - i\sqrt{6}) \stackrel{?}{=} 7$$

$$(-1)^2 - (i\sqrt{6})^2 \stackrel{?}{=} 7$$

$$1 + 6 = 7 \checkmark$$

$\{-1 + i\sqrt{6}, -1 - i\sqrt{6}\}$, **Answer.**

Numbers such as $-1 + i\sqrt{6}$ and $-1 - i\sqrt{6}$ which have the form $a + bi$ **and** $a - bi$ (a and b, real) are called **conjugates** of each other. As in Example 1, the quadratic formula indicates that when the discriminant $b^2 - 4ac$ of a quadratic equation with real coefficients is a negative number, the equation has two imaginary roots which are conjugates of each other. Thus:

A quadratic equation with *real* coefficients has two equal real roots if $b^2 - 4ac = 0$; two unequal real roots if $b^2 - 4ac > 0$; and two unequal imaginary roots if $b^2 - 4ac < 0$.

Do you see that $(a + bi)(a - bi) = a^2 + b^2$? This means that the product of nonzero conjugate complex numbers is a positive real number. You can use this fact to express the quotient of complex numbers in standard form.

EXAMPLE 2. Express $\frac{2 + 5i}{3 - i}$ in standard form.

Solution: *Plan:* Use the Property of Fractions (page 165) to multiply the numerator and denominator by the conjugate of the denominator.

$$\frac{2 + 5i}{3 - i} = \frac{(2 + 5i)(3 + i)}{(3 - i)(3 + i)}$$

$$= \frac{(6 - 5) + (2 + 15)i}{9 + 1} = \frac{1 + 17i}{10}$$

$$= \frac{1}{10} + \frac{17}{10}i, \textbf{ Answer.}$$

Oral Exercises

Express in standard form.

1. $7(-3 + 4i)$
2. $3(2 + 5i)$
3. $-5(3 - 2i)$
4. $-8(4 - i)$
5. $\frac{9 + 6i}{3}$
6. $\frac{12 - 4i}{2}$
7. $\frac{4 - 2i\sqrt{2}}{2}$
8. $\frac{18 - 6i\sqrt{7}}{6}$
9. $2i(7 + 4i)$
10. $5i(1 - 3i)$

If a, b, and c are real numbers ($a \neq 0$) for which $b^2 - 4ac$ has the given value, state the nature of the roots of the equation $ax^2 + bx + c = 0$.

SAMPLE. -7 *What you say:* Since -7 is negative, the roots are unequal imaginary numbers.

11. 27
12. 16
13. -6
14. 0
15. -4
16. -5
17. 3
18. -1

Written Exercises

Solve each equation over the set of complex numbers.

A

1. $x^2 - 9x + 18 = 0$
2. $x^2 - x + 1 = 0$
3. $y^2 - y + 3 = 0$
4. $y^2 - 5y - 3 = 0$
5. $3n^2 = 5n - 7$
6. $2n^2 = 3n - 1$
7. $\frac{v^2}{2} + \frac{3v}{5} = \frac{3}{10}$
8. $\frac{v}{2} + \frac{2}{3} = \frac{v^2}{6}$

Express in standard form.

9. $(5 + 6i)(6i - 5)$

10. $(7i - 1)(1 + 7i)$

11. $(3 + i)^2$

12. $(2 - 5i)^2$

13. $(7 - \sqrt{-2})^2$

14. $(1 + \sqrt{-6})^2$

15. $(-2 + 6i)(3 + 4i)$

16. $(3 + i)(3 + 7i)$

17. $(1 + \sqrt{-25})(\sqrt{-36} - 2)$

18. $(\sqrt{-49} - 3)(2 - \sqrt{-1})$

B **19.** $\dfrac{5 + i}{-i}$

20. $\dfrac{1 - 3i}{i}$

21. $\dfrac{20i}{i - 3}$

22. $\dfrac{15i}{i + 2}$

23. $\dfrac{2 + i}{7 - 5i}$

24. $\dfrac{-2 + 3i}{1 - i}$

25. The conjugate of $\dfrac{i}{1 - i}$

26. The reciprocal of $1 + \dfrac{1}{i^3}$

Solve if x denotes **(a)** a real number, **(b)** a complex number.

C **27.** $x^2 - 2ix - 3 = 0$

28. $ix^2 + 3x - 2i = 0$

29. Prove: The sum of a complex number and its conjugate is a real number.

30. Prove: The difference between an imaginary number and its conjugate is a pure imaginary number.

Determine real values of x and y for which each statement is true.

31. $\dfrac{x + y}{i} + x - y + 4 = 0$

32. $-i(x + 3y) + (2x - y + 1) = \dfrac{8}{i}$

Chapter Summary

Inventory of Structure and Method

1. If (a, b) are the coordinates of a point, not the origin, on the terminal side of a position angle θ, then $\cos\theta = \dfrac{a}{\sqrt{a^2 + b^2}}$ and $\sin\theta = \dfrac{b}{\sqrt{a^2 + b^2}}$. Certain combinations of sine and cosine of an angle θ produce values of other trigonometric functions: $\tan\theta = \dfrac{\sin\theta}{\cos\theta}$, and $\cot\theta$, $\sec\theta$, $\csc\theta$ are the reciprocals of tan θ, cos θ, sin θ, respectively. The exact values of certain **special angles** may be found.

2. From the table you can find a value for a function of any angle θ in terms of the value of a function of the **reference angle** of θ.
3. You can solve many practical problems by applying trigonometric function values or by using their logarithms. The **resultant** of vectors, parallel or perpendicular to each other, and the horizontal and vertical **components** of a given vector can be found similarly.
4. A **complex number,** $a + bi$, where a and b are real numbers, is a real number if $b = 0$, is an **imaginary** number if $b \neq 0$, and is a pure imaginary number if $a = 0$, $b \neq 0$. Each complex number is paired with a vector at the origin or with a point in the **complex plane.** If a, b, c, and d are real numbers, then $a + bi = c + di$ if, and only if, $a = c$ and $b = d$.
5. Complex numbers may be added and multiplied: For real numbers a, b, c, and d, $a + bi + c + di = (a + c) + (b + d)i$; and $(a + bi)(c + di) = (ac - bd) + (ad + bc)i$. The closure, associative, commutative, and distributive properties hold for the set of complex numbers.
6. You use the fact that the product of nonzero **conjugate** complex numbers is a positive real number to express the quotient of complex numbers in standard form.

Vocabulary and Spelling

ray (*p. 371*)
vertex (of a ray) (*p. 371*)
(directed) angle (*p. 371*)
positive angle (*p. 371*)
negative angle (*p. 371*)
initial side (*p. 372*)
terminal side (*p. 372*)
degree (*p. 372*)
coterminal angles (*p. 372*)
standard position (*p. 373*)
position angle (*p. 373*)
unit circle (*p. 374*)
sine (sin θ) (*p. 375*)
cosine (cos θ) (*p. 375*)
tangent (tan θ) (*p. 378*)
cotangent (cot θ) (*p. 378*)
secant (sec θ) (*p. 378*)
cosecant (csc θ) (*p. 378*)
trigonometric functions (*p. 378*)
first (second, third, fourth) quadrant angle (*p. 379*)
quadrantal angle (*p. 379*)
special angles (*p. 382*)
cofunction (*p. 384*)
angle of elevation (*p. 388*)
angle of depression (*p. 388*)
reference angle (*p. 395*)
vector quantity (*p. 398*)
vector (*p. 398*)
heading (bearing, course) (*p. 399*)
equivalent vectors (*p. 399*)
zero vector (*p. 399*)
resultant (*p. 399*)
component vectors (*p. 402*)
resolving a vector (*p. 402*)
i (*p. 406*)
complex number (*p. 407*)
standard form (*p. 407*)

imaginary number (*p. 407*)
pure imaginary number (*p. 407*)
complex plane (*p. 407*)
axis of reals (*p. 407*)
axis of imaginaries (*p. 407*)
conjugate numbers (*p. 415*)

Chapter Test and Review

10–1 **1.** For $P(\sqrt{5}, -2)$, draw a positive and a negative angle in standard position with ray OP as terminal side.

10–2 **2.** Find $\sin \theta$ and $\cos \theta$, if θ is a position angle of $T(2, -\sqrt{5})$.

3. If $\cos \theta = -\frac{5}{7}$, and θ terminates in Quadrant II, find $\sin \theta$.

10–3 **4.** Draw the smallest positive angle having point $(-3, \sqrt{7})$ on its terminal side and find the trigonometric functions of the angle.

10–4 **5.** Evaluate $2(\cos 60° \tan 45° + \sin 60° \tan 30°)$.

6. Solve for x: $\tan x = \cot 32°$, $0° < x < 90°$.

10–5 **7.** Find $\cos 56°13'$.

8. From the lookout post on a ship, the angle of depression of a raft is $11°20'$. If the post is $94'$ above sea level, how far, to the nearest foot is the raft from the ship?

10–6 **9.** Using logarithms, find the positive acute angle B to the nearest minute: $\sin B = \dfrac{48.1 \cos 42°50'}{61.7}$.

10. Find to the nearest tenth of a centimeter the longer side of a rectangle if the shorter side makes an angle of 66° with the diagonal which measures 56.4 centimeters. Use logarithms.

10–7 **Express as a function of a positive acute angle.**

11. $\cos 112°$ **12.** $\sin(-200°)$ **13.** $\tan 575°$

10–8 **14.** Give **(a)** the magnitude, and **(b)** the direction, of the resultant of displacements of 9 m. west and 40 m. north.

10–9 **15.** Find to the nearest tenth the horizontal and vertical components of a vector of length 13 and bearing 130°.

10–10 **16.** If $m = 3 - 2i$ and $n = 5 - 5i$, find $m - n$.

10–11 **17.** Simplify: $2\sqrt{-32} - \sqrt{\frac{9}{2}}$

10–12 **18.** Express in standard form: $\dfrac{5 - \sqrt{-3}}{5 + \sqrt{-3}}$.

19. Solve $2x^2 = 4x - 3$ over the set of complex numbers.

Review the sections listed at the left-hand margin if your test results show this to be advisable.

CHAPTER 11

. . . a convex mirror distorting a pattern of parallel lines

Trigonometric Identities and Formulas

The trigonometric functions with which you are now acquainted are interrelated in a number of interesting and very useful ways. In this chapter you will become familiar with many of these relationships that are powerful tools in attacking more advanced mathematical problems and that also serve to clarify basic concepts in the fields of classical and modern physics.

IDENTITIES INVOLVING ONE ANGLE

11–1 The Fundamental Identities

Since the statement $(2x + 1)(2x - 1) = 4x^2 - 1$ is true for every replacement of x by a number, it is true in particular when x is replaced by the real number, $\sin 7°$; that is,

$$(2 \sin 7° + 1)(2 \sin 7° - 1) = 4(\sin 7°)^2 - 1.$$

Indeed, for *every* angle θ in standard position you may write the true statement:

$$\mathbf{(2 \sin \theta + 1)(2 \sin \theta - 1) = 4 \sin^2 \theta - 1}$$

where "$\sin^2 \theta$" means "$(\sin \theta)^2$" and is read, "the square of $\sin \theta$."

An equation which involves at least one variable whose domain is the set of angles in standard position is called a **trigonometric equation.** A trigonometric equation, such as $(2 \sin \theta + 1)(2 \sin \theta - 1) = 4 \sin^2 \theta - 1$, that is true for all values of the variables for which both of its members are defined is called a **trigonometric identity.**

Trigonometric identities depend on the definitions of the trigonometric functions, as well as on the algebra of real numbers. Can you explain why each of the following statements is true for every angle θ for which the functions involved are defined?

1. $\tan \theta = \dfrac{\sin \theta}{\cos \theta}$
2. $\cot \theta = \dfrac{\cos \theta}{\sin \theta}$
3. $\sec \theta = \dfrac{1}{\cos \theta}$
4. $\csc \theta = \dfrac{1}{\sin \theta}$
5. $\cot \theta = \dfrac{1}{\tan \theta}$

Identities **1–4** follow directly from the definitions of the trigonometric functions (page 378). To see that identity **5** is a by-product of identities **1** and **2**, notice that if $\sin \theta \neq 0$ and $\cos \theta \neq 0$, you have:

$$\frac{1}{\tan \theta} = \frac{1}{\frac{\sin \theta}{\cos \theta}} \quad \text{(using identity 1)}$$

$$= \frac{\cos \theta}{\sin \theta} \quad \text{(using the properties of real numbers)}$$

$$= \cot \theta \quad \text{(using identity 2)}$$

$$\therefore \cot \theta = \frac{1}{\tan \theta}$$

By recalling that, for every angle θ in standard position, $(\cos \theta, \sin \theta)$ are the coordinates of a point of the unit circle whose equation is $x^2 + y^2 = 1$ (Section 10–2), you can discover the identity:

$$(\cos \theta)^2 + (\sin \theta)^2 = 1, \text{ or}$$

6. $\sin^2 \theta + \cos^2 \theta = 1.$

If you divide each member of **6** by $\cos^2 \theta$, you can derive another identity,

$$\frac{\sin^2 \theta}{\cos^2 \theta} + 1 = \frac{1}{\cos^2 \theta}, \text{ or } 1 + \left(\frac{\sin \theta}{\cos \theta}\right)^2 = \left(\frac{1}{\cos \theta}\right)^2, \qquad \cos \theta \neq 0$$

Using identities **1** and **3**, you find

7. $1 + \tan^2 \theta = \sec^2 \theta.$

Can you suggest how to derive the following identity?

8. $1 + \cot^2 \theta = \csc^2 \theta.$

Identities **1–8** are called the **fundamental trigonometric identities.** Using them and the properties of real numbers, you can write any expression involving values of the trigonometric functions of an angle θ in terms of the value of $\sin \theta$ or any other trigonometric function of θ.

EXAMPLE 1. Express $\cos\theta$ in terms of $\sin\theta$.

Solution:

$$\sin^2\theta + \cos^2\theta = 1$$
$$\cos^2\theta = 1 - \sin^2\theta$$
$$\therefore \cos\theta = \sqrt{1 - \sin^2\theta}, \quad \theta \text{ in Quadrant I or IV}$$
$$\text{or } \cos\theta = -\sqrt{1 - \sin^2\theta}, \quad \theta \text{ in Quadrant II or III}$$

The result of Example 1 suggests the following method of finding $\cos\theta$, given that θ is a second-quadrant angle with $\sin\theta = \frac{3}{5}$.

$$\cos\theta = -\sqrt{1 - \sin^2\theta} = -\sqrt{1 - (\tfrac{3}{5})^2} = -\sqrt{\tfrac{16}{25}} = -\tfrac{4}{5}$$

EXAMPLE 2. In terms of $\cos\alpha$ find an expression equivalent to $(1 + \sin\alpha)(\sec\alpha - \tan\alpha)$.

Solution: The given expression denotes a real number provided $\cos\alpha \neq 0$. Since identities **1** and **3** introduce no additional restrictions, you may use them to write:

$$(1 + \sin\alpha)(\sec\alpha - \tan\alpha) = (1 + \sin\alpha)\left(\frac{1}{\cos\alpha} - \frac{\sin\alpha}{\cos\alpha}\right)$$

$$= (1 + \sin\alpha)\left(\frac{1 - \sin\alpha}{\cos\alpha}\right) = \frac{1 - \sin^2\alpha}{\cos\alpha} = \frac{\cos^2\alpha}{\cos\alpha} \quad \text{(using } \mathbf{6}\text{)}$$

$\therefore (1 + \sin\alpha)(\sec\alpha - \tan\alpha) = \cos\alpha$, provided $\cos\alpha \neq 0$, **Answer.**

Oral Exercises

Express the following in terms of a single trigonometric function.

1. $\dfrac{\sin\theta}{\cos\theta}$

2. $1 + \tan^2\beta$

3. $\dfrac{\cos^2 u}{\sin^2 u}$

4. $1 - \cos^2\phi$

5. $\tan\theta\sec\theta\cos\theta$

6. $\csc\theta\sin\theta\cot\theta$

7. $\sin^2 q + \cos^2 q + \tan^2 q$

8. $\cos^2\rho + \sin^2\rho + \cot^2\rho$

9. $\csc^2\phi - \cot^2\phi + \tan^2\phi$

10. $\tan\gamma\cot\gamma - \cos^2\gamma \quad (\gamma = \text{gamma})$

11. $\dfrac{(\sin^2\alpha + \cos^2\alpha)(\sec^2\alpha - \tan^2\alpha)}{\tan\alpha}$

12. $\dfrac{\sin\alpha(\csc^2\alpha - \cot^2\alpha)}{\cos\alpha\sec\alpha}$

13. $\dfrac{\sqrt{\sec^2\theta - 1}}{\sqrt{\csc^2\theta - 1}}$

14. $\dfrac{\sqrt{1 - \sin^2\theta}}{\sqrt{1 + \tan^2\theta}}$

Written Exercises

A

1. Express in terms of $\cos\theta$: **(a)** $\sin\theta$; **(b)** $\tan\theta$; **(c)** $\csc\theta$.

2. Express in terms of $\tan\theta$: **(a)** $\cos\theta$; **(b)** $\csc\theta$; **(c)** $\sec\theta$.

3. Express in terms of $\csc\alpha$: **(a)** $\cos^2\alpha$ **(b)** $\tan^2\alpha$; **(c)** $\sec^2\alpha$.

4. Express in terms of $\sin\beta$: **(a)** $\cot^2\beta$; **(b)** $\sec^2\beta$; **(c)** $\cos^2\beta$.

θ terminates in the given quadrant; find the values of its trigonometric functions.

5. IV; $\cos\theta = \frac{4}{5}$

6. III; $\tan\theta = \frac{8}{15}$

7. II; $\csc\theta = \frac{13}{12}$

8. III; $\sin\theta = -\frac{7}{25}$

9. Express in terms of $\sin A$: $\tan^2 A(\csc^2 A - 1) + \tan A\cos A$.

10. Express in terms of $\sec\theta$: $\sin\theta\csc\theta + \dfrac{\sin\theta}{\cos\theta\cot\theta}$.

B

11. Express in terms of $\tan\theta$: $\csc^2\theta(\sec^2\theta - 1)(\sin\theta\cos\theta)$.

12. Express in terms of $\cos\theta$: $1 + \tan^2\theta - \dfrac{\sin^2\theta}{\csc^2\theta - 1}$.

Express in terms of sine and cosine functions only, and simplify.

13. $\left(\dfrac{\cos\gamma - \sec\gamma}{\sec\gamma} + \cos^2\gamma\tan^2\gamma\right)\left(\dfrac{\tan\gamma - \sin\gamma}{\tan\gamma}\right)$

14. $(\tan u + \sin u)(1 - \cos u) + \dfrac{\cos u}{\csc u}$

15. $\dfrac{\sqrt{\cot^2\beta + 1}}{\csc\beta}\left(\dfrac{\cot^2\beta\sec^2\beta - 1}{\csc\beta\cot^2\beta\sin\beta}\right)$

16. $\sin\alpha\sec\alpha\left(\cos\alpha + \dfrac{\csc\alpha}{\sec^2\alpha}\right) + (\csc\alpha + \sec\alpha)$

Find the value of the following expressions if $\sin\theta = \frac{13}{85}$ and $\cos\theta = \frac{84}{85}$.

17. $\cos\theta\left(\dfrac{\sin\theta\sec\theta + \tan\theta}{\sec\theta\tan\theta}\right)$

18. $\dfrac{\cot\theta + \cos\theta}{\sec\theta + \tan\theta}$

19. $\sin\theta + \dfrac{\sqrt{1 + \cos\theta}}{\sqrt{\sec\theta - 1}} \cdot \dfrac{\sqrt{1 - \cos\theta}}{\sqrt{\sec\theta + 1}}$

20. $(\cos\theta - \sin\theta)\left(\dfrac{\sqrt{\csc\theta + 1}}{\sqrt{1 - \sin\theta}} \cdot \dfrac{\sqrt{\csc\theta - 1}}{\sqrt{\sin\theta + 1}}\right)$

11–2 Proving Identities

You can sometimes verify that an equation is a trigonometric identity by using the properties of numbers, and substitution from the fundamental identities, to transform the more complicated member of the equation to the form of the simpler member.

EXAMPLE 1. Prove the identity:

$$2 \csc^2 \theta = \frac{1}{1 + \cos \theta} + \frac{1}{1 - \cos \theta}.$$

Proof:

Notice that the given equation is meaningful if and only if $1 \pm \cos \theta \neq 0$ and $\sin \theta \neq 0$. (Why?)

1. Choose the right member (R.M.) to be transformed. $\quad \dfrac{1}{1 + \cos \theta} + \dfrac{1}{1 - \cos \theta}$
2. Add the fractions in this member. (Equality holds provided $1 \pm \cos \theta \neq 0$.) $\quad = \dfrac{(1 - \cos \theta) + (1 + \cos \theta)}{(1 + \cos \theta)(1 - \cos \theta)}$

   $= \dfrac{2}{1 - \cos^2 \theta}$
3. Substitute: $1 - \cos^2 \theta = \sin^2 \theta$. $\quad = \dfrac{2}{\sin^2 \theta}$
4. Substitute: $\sin \theta = \dfrac{1}{\csc \theta}$. (Valid provided $\sin \theta \neq 0$.) $\quad = \dfrac{2}{\dfrac{1}{\csc^2 \theta}}$
5. Multiply numerator and denominator by $\csc^2 \theta$. (Valid because $\csc \theta \neq 0$.) $\quad = \dfrac{2 \csc^2 \theta}{1}$

Since the steps transforming the right-hand member introduced no new restrictions, the identity has been proved valid.

$$\therefore\ 2 \csc^2 \theta = \frac{1}{1 + \cos \theta} + \frac{1}{1 - \cos \theta}.$$

EXAMPLE 2. Verify: $\dfrac{\sin \theta}{1 - \cos \theta} = \dfrac{1 + \cos \theta}{\sin \theta}$.

Proof:

1. Choose either member, say the left, to be transformed. $\quad \dfrac{\sin \theta}{1 - \cos \theta}$
2. Multiply the numerator and denominator by $1 + \cos \theta$, which is the numerator of the right member. (Valid if $\cos \theta \neq -1$.) $\quad = \dfrac{\sin \theta\,(1 + \cos \theta)}{(1 - \cos \theta)(1 + \cos \theta)}$
3. Simplify. $\quad = \dfrac{\sin \theta\,(1 + \cos \theta)}{1 - \cos^2 \theta}$
4. Substitute: $1 - \cos^2 \theta = \sin^2 \theta$. $\quad = \dfrac{\sin \theta\,(1 + \cos \theta)}{\sin^2 \theta}$
5. Divide numerator and denominator by $\sin \theta$. (Valid if $\sin \theta \neq 0$.) $\quad = \dfrac{1 + \cos \theta}{\sin \theta}$

Are the steps in Example 2 (p. 425) consistent with the restrictions implied by the given equation? The members of that equation are *both* defined if and only if $\cos\theta \neq 1$ and $\sin\theta \neq 0$. But $\sin\theta \neq 0$ means that θ is coterminal with neither 0° nor 180° and therefore that $\cos\theta \neq 1$ or -1. Thus, the transformations introduced no additional restrictions.

$$\therefore \frac{\sin\theta}{1 - \cos\theta} = \frac{1 + \cos\theta}{\sin\theta}$$

Often it is convenient to transform each member of a proposed identity to the same expression in terms of sine and cosine or other functions. Checking to see that the steps in the following example are consistent with the restrictions in the equation is left to you.

EXAMPLE 3. Verify: $\tan\beta + \cot\beta = \sec\beta\csc\beta$.

Proof:

$\text{L.M.} = \dfrac{\sin\beta}{\cos\beta} + \dfrac{\cos\beta}{\sin\beta}$	$\text{R.M.} = \dfrac{1}{\cos\beta}\cdot\dfrac{1}{\sin\beta}$
$= \dfrac{\sin^2\beta + \cos^2\beta}{\cos\beta\sin\beta}$	$= \dfrac{1}{\cos\beta\sin\beta}$
$= \dfrac{1}{\cos\beta\sin\beta}$	

$$\therefore \tan\beta + \cot\beta = \sec\beta\csc\beta.$$

Written Exercises

Prove the following identities.

A

1. $\sin\theta\cot\theta = \cos\theta$

2. $\cos A\tan A = \sin A$

3. $\dfrac{\sin^2\theta + \cos^2\theta}{\cos\theta} = \sec\theta$

4. $\dfrac{1 + \sin\alpha}{\sin\alpha} = 1 + \csc\alpha$

5. $\dfrac{\sin\alpha - 1}{\cos\alpha} = \tan\alpha - \sec\alpha$

6. $1 - \sin B\cos B\tan B = \cos^2 B$

7. $\sin\alpha + \cos\alpha\cot\alpha = \csc\alpha$

8. $1 - 2\sin^2 x = 2\cos^2 x - 1$

9. $\cos\alpha(\csc\alpha - \sec\alpha) = \cot\alpha - 1$

10. $\csc\beta(\csc\beta + \cot\beta) = \dfrac{1}{1 - \cos\beta}$

11. $\sin^4\alpha - \cos^4\alpha = 2\sin^2\alpha - 1$

12. $\tan^4\rho - \sec^4\rho = 1 - 2\sec^2\rho$

13. $\dfrac{\sin\beta + \tan\beta}{1 + \cos\beta} = \tan\beta$

14. $\sec\delta + \tan\delta = \dfrac{\cos\delta}{1 - \sin\delta}$

15. $(1 + \csc \alpha)(1 - \sin \alpha) = \cot \alpha \cos \alpha$

16. $(1 + \tan \theta + \sec \theta)^2 = 2(1 + \sec \theta)(\tan \theta + \sec \theta)$

17. $(1 + \sec \beta)(\sec \beta - 1) = \dfrac{\sin \beta \sec \beta}{\cos \beta \csc \beta}$

18. $(\csc \beta - 1)(1 + \csc \beta) = \dfrac{\csc \beta \cos \beta}{\sec \beta \sin \beta}$

19. $\dfrac{\sin \delta \cos \delta}{1 + \cos \delta} - \dfrac{\sin \delta}{1 - \cos \delta} = -(\cot \delta \cos \delta + \csc \delta)$

20. $\dfrac{\sin \delta + \cos \delta}{\sec \delta + \tan \delta} + \dfrac{\cos \delta - \sin \delta}{\sec \delta - \tan \delta} = 2 - 2 \sin^2 \delta \sec \delta$

21. $\dfrac{\sec n}{1 - \cos n} = \dfrac{\sec n + 1}{\sin^2 n}$

22. $\dfrac{\tan n}{\tan n + \sin n} = \dfrac{1 - \cos n}{\sin^2 n}$

23. $\dfrac{1 + \sec \gamma}{\sec \gamma - 1} + \dfrac{1 + \cos \gamma}{\cos \gamma - 1} = 0$

24. $\dfrac{\sec^2 \gamma(1 + \csc \gamma) - \tan \gamma(\sec \gamma + \tan \gamma)}{\csc \gamma(1 + \sin \gamma)} - 1 = 0$

B **25.** $\dfrac{\tan A - \sin A}{\tan A \sin A} = \dfrac{\tan A \sin A}{\tan A + \sin A}$

26. $\dfrac{\csc A}{1 + \sec A} = \dfrac{\cot A}{1 + \cos A}$

27. $\dfrac{\csc C + \cot C}{\csc C - \cot C} = \csc^2 C(1 + 2 \cos C + \cos^2 C)$

28. $\dfrac{\sin C + \cos C - 1}{\sin C - \cos C + 1} = \dfrac{\cos C}{\sin C + 1}$

29. $\dfrac{\sin^3 B + \cos^3 B}{\sin^2 B + 2 \sin B \cos B + \cos^2 B} = \dfrac{1}{\sin B + \cos B} - \dfrac{\cos B}{1 + \cot B}$

30. $\dfrac{\cos B - \sin B}{\cos^3 B - \sin^3 B} = \dfrac{1}{\tan B \cos^2 B + 1}$

C **31.** $\dfrac{1 - \cos x}{\sin x} = \sqrt{\dfrac{\csc x - \cot x}{\csc x + \cot x}}$ or $\dfrac{1 - \cos x}{\sin x} = -\sqrt{\dfrac{\csc x - \cot x}{\csc x + \cot x}}$

32. $\tan x(\csc x + 1) = \sqrt{\dfrac{\sin x + 1}{1 - \sin x}}$ or $\tan x(\csc x + 1) = -\sqrt{\dfrac{\sin x + 1}{1 - \sin x}}$

33. $\dfrac{\sin^2 \theta + 2 \cos \theta - 1}{2 + \cos \theta - \cos^2 \theta} = \dfrac{1}{1 + \sec \theta}$

34. $\dfrac{2 \tan \alpha \sec \alpha + \sec \alpha}{3 + \tan \alpha - 2 \sec^2 \alpha} = \dfrac{1}{\cos \alpha - \sin \alpha}$

IDENTITIES INVOLVING TWO ANGLES

11–3 The Distance Formula

Suppose P and Q are the points shown in Figure 11–1. To find the distance PQ, you take the steps described below:

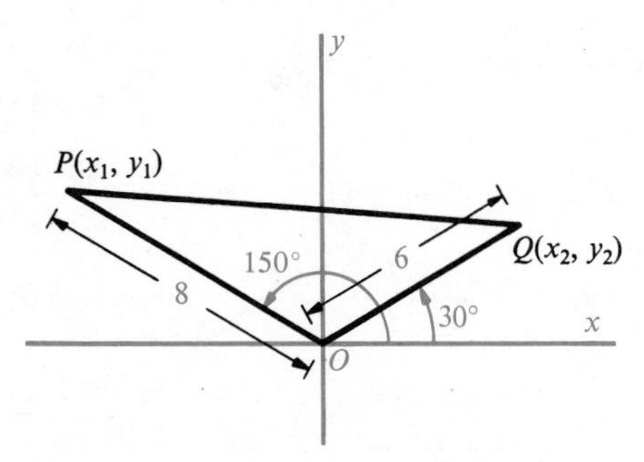

· *Figure 11-1* ·

1. Use the theorem on page 376 to determine the rectangular coordinates (x_1, y_1) of P and (x_2, y_2) of Q.

P: $x_1 = 8 \cos 150° = 8(-\frac{1}{2}\sqrt{3}) = -4\sqrt{3}$;

$y_1 = 8 \sin 150° = 8(\frac{1}{2}) = 4.$

Q: $x_2 = 6 \cos 30° = 6(\frac{1}{2}\sqrt{3}) = 3\sqrt{3}$; $y_2 = 6 \sin 30° = 6(\frac{1}{2}) = 3$

2. Use the distance formula: $(PQ)^2 = (x_1 - x_2)^2 + (y_1 - y_2)^2$

$(PQ)^2 = (-4\sqrt{3} - 3\sqrt{3})^2 + (4 - 3)^2 = 49(3) + 1 = 148$

$\therefore PQ = 2\sqrt{37}$

By following the steps above, you can derive a formula for the square of the distance between any points P and Q in terms of their respective position angles, α and β, and distances from the origin, p and q (Figure 11–2).

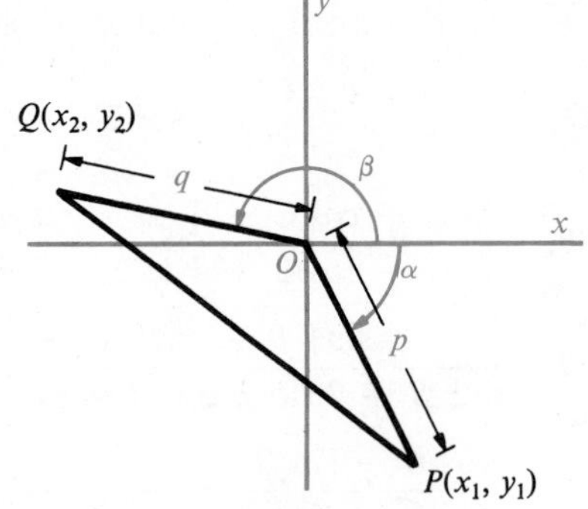

· *Figure 11–2* ·

1. P: $x_1 = p \cos \alpha$; $y_1 = p \sin \alpha$

Q: $x_2 = q \cos \beta$; $y_2 = q \sin \beta$

2. $(PQ)^2 = (x_1 - x_2)^2 + (y_1 - y_2)^2$

$= (p \cos \alpha - q \cos \beta)^2 + (p \sin \alpha - q \sin \beta)^2$

$= p^2 \cos^2 \alpha - 2pq \cos \alpha \cos \beta + q^2 \cos^2 \beta$
$\quad + p^2 \sin^2 \alpha - 2pq \sin \alpha \sin \beta + q^2 \sin^2 \beta$

$= p^2(\cos^2 \alpha + \sin^2 \alpha) + q^2(\cos^2 \beta + \sin^2 \beta)$
$\quad - 2pq(\cos \alpha \cos \beta + \sin \alpha \sin \beta)$

$= p^2 \cdot 1 + q^2 \cdot 1 - 2pq(\cos \alpha \cos \beta + \sin \alpha \sin \beta)$

$$\therefore \mathbf{(PQ)^2 = p^2 + q^2 - 2pq(\cos \alpha \cos \beta + \sin \alpha \sin \beta)}$$

EXAMPLE. Approximate $(PQ)^2$, correct to tenths, if P is 10 units from the origin and has a position angle of 590°, and if Q has coordinates (15, 0).

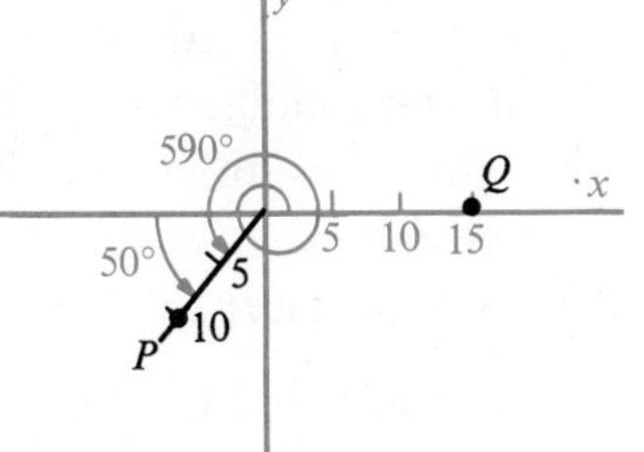

Solution: $p = 10$; measure of α is 590°; therefore, its reference angle measures 50°; $q = 15$; measure of β is 0°.

$$(PQ)^2 = 10^2 + 15^2 - 2(10)(15)(\cos 590° \cos 0° + \sin 590° \sin 0°)$$
$$= 100 + 225 - 300[(-\cos 50°) \cdot 1 + (-\sin 50°) \cdot 0]$$
$$\doteq 325 - 300(-0.6428 + 0)$$
$$\therefore (PQ)^2 \doteq 517.8, \textbf{ Answer.}$$

Written Exercises

Find to the nearest tenth the square of the distance between the points.

1. P, 5 units from the origin, with position angle 17° and Q, 3 units from the origin, with position angle 107°.
2. P, 5 units from the origin with position angle 732° and Q, 9 units from the origin, with position angle 642°.
3. M (−6, 0) and N, $4\frac{1}{2}$ units from the origin, with position angle 25°.
4. M (0, 3) and N, 7 units from the origin, with position angle 72°.
5. X, 4 units from the origin, with position angle 195° and Y, 6 units from the origin, with position angle −12°.
6. X, 3.2 units from the origin, with position angle 165° and Y, 2.1 units from the origin, with position angle −108°.
7. S, with x-coordinate 3 and position angle 435° and T, 15 units from the origin, with position angle −265°.
8. S, $\frac{9}{2}$ units from the origin, with position angle 9° and T, with y-coordinate $-\frac{15}{2}$ and position angle −23°.
9. C (5, 7) and D, 2 units from the origin, with position angle 261°.
10. C, 21 units from the origin, with position angle 912° and D (10, −1).
11. G, with x-coordinate −5 and position angle 141° and H, with y-coordinate −12 and position angle −112°.
12. G, with y-coordinate $-\frac{5}{2}$ and position angle 680° and H, with x-coordinate $-\frac{1}{2}$ and position angle 100°.

11–4 The Cosine of the Difference of Two Angles

In Figure 11–3, the angle $\alpha - \beta$ has the terminal side of β as its initial side, the terminal side of α as its terminal side, and the difference between 30°, the measure of α, and 90°, the measure of β, as its measure: $30° - 90° = -60°$.

Does $\cos(\alpha - \beta)$ equal $\cos \alpha - \cos \beta$?

$$\cos(\alpha - \beta) = \cos(-60°) = \tfrac{1}{2}$$
$$\cos \alpha = \cos 30° = \tfrac{1}{2}\sqrt{3}$$
$$\cos \beta = \cos 90° = 0$$
$$\cos \alpha - \cos \beta = \tfrac{1}{2}\sqrt{3} - 0 = \tfrac{1}{2}\sqrt{3}$$

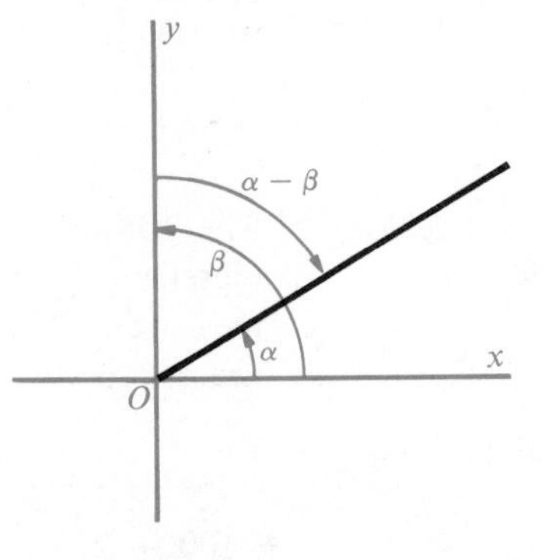

· *Figure 11–3* ·

You see, in this case, $\cos(\alpha - \beta)$ is *not* equal to $\cos \alpha - \cos \beta$.

To discover the relationships among the trigonometric functions of α, β, and $\alpha - \beta$, let α and β be any angles in standard position, and let point P (on the terminal side of α) and Q (on the terminal side of β) be 1 unit from the origin (Figure 11–4).

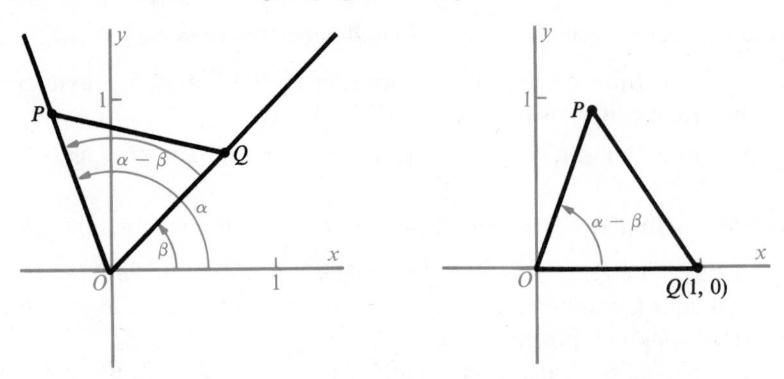

· *Figure 11–4* · · *Figure 11–5* ·

Using the distance formula of Section 11–3 with 1 in place of p and q,

$$(PQ)^2 = 1^2 + 1^2 - 2(1)(1)(\cos \alpha \cos \beta + \sin \alpha \sin \beta)$$
$$\therefore\ (PQ)^2 = 2 - 2(\cos \alpha \cos \beta + \sin \alpha \sin \beta) \quad *$$

Now choose a new coordinate system in which Q is the point $(1, 0)$; ray OQ, the terminal side of β, is the positive x-axis; and the angle $\alpha - \beta$ is in standard position (Figure 11–5, drawn to show the new x-axis as a horizontal line). To compute $(PQ)^2$ in this coordinate system, notice the following:

Q is 1 unit from the origin with a position angle of $0°$;
P is 1 unit from the origin with $\alpha - \beta$ as its position angle.

Therefore,

$$(PQ)^2 = 1^2 + 1^2 - 2(1)(1)[\cos \underset{P}{(\alpha - \beta)} \cos \underset{Q}{0°} + \sin \underset{P}{(\alpha - \beta)} \sin \underset{Q}{0°}]$$
$$= 1 + 1 - 2[1 \cdot \cos(\alpha - \beta) + 0 \cdot \sin(\alpha - \beta)]$$
$$\therefore (PQ)^2 = 2 - 2\cos(\alpha - \beta) \quad *$$

Equate the expressions for $(PQ)^2$ in the starred (*) equations:

$$2 - 2\cos(\alpha - \beta) = 2 - 2(\cos\alpha\cos\beta + \sin\alpha\sin\beta).$$

This leads to the *formula for the cosine of the difference of two angles:*

$$\cos(\alpha - \beta) = \cos\alpha\cos\beta + \sin\alpha\sin\beta.$$

This result now enables you to write the formula in the last line of page 428 in the simpler form $(PQ)^2 = p^2 + q^2 - 2pq\cos(\alpha - \beta)$ for the distance between any points P and Q.

Since α and β are any angles in standard position, the formula for $\cos(\alpha - \beta)$ is an identity in which you can substitute for α and β any angles whatever.

EXAMPLE 1. Determine the exact value of $\cos 15°$.

Solution:

$$15° = 45° - 30°$$
$$\therefore \cos 15° = \cos(45° - 30°)$$
$$= \cos 45° \cos 30° + \sin 45° \sin 30°$$
$$= \frac{\sqrt{2}}{2} \cdot \frac{\sqrt{3}}{2} + \frac{\sqrt{2}}{2} \cdot \frac{1}{2}$$
$$\therefore \cos 15° = \frac{\sqrt{6} + \sqrt{2}}{4}, \textbf{ Answer.}$$

Could you have used $60° - 45°$ for $15°$? Try it.

Since the formula for $\cos(\alpha - \beta)$ is valid for any angle α, it is true in particular when the measure of α is $90°$. Thus,

$$\cos(90° - \beta) = \cos 90° \cos\beta + \sin 90° \sin\beta$$
$$= 0 \cdot \cos\beta + 1 \cdot \sin\beta = 0 + \sin\beta$$
$$\therefore \cos(90° - \beta) = \sin\beta$$

Because the last equation is an identity in β, it remains valid when you replace β by $90° - \beta$. In this way you obtain

$$\cos[90° - (90° - \beta)] = \sin(90° - \beta)$$
$$\cos\beta = \sin(90° - \beta),$$

or

$$\mathbf{\sin(90° - \beta) = \cos\beta}$$

Furthermore, since $\tan(90° - \beta) = \dfrac{\sin(90° - \beta)}{\cos(90° - \beta)} = \dfrac{\cos\beta}{\sin\beta} = \cot\beta$,

$$\mathbf{\tan(90° - \beta) = \cot\beta,}$$

provided the function values are defined. The proofs of the following identities are left as Exercises 11, 12, 13 below:

$$\mathbf{\cot(90° - \beta) = \tan\beta, \quad \sec(90° - \beta) = \csc\beta, \quad \csc(90° - \beta) = \sec\beta}$$

Compare these results, showing that *cofunctions of complementary angles are equal*, with the theorem stated on page 384.

Written Exercises

Express each of the following in the form cos θ for suitable θ and then evaluate cos θ to four decimal places.

A

1. $\cos 260° \cos 190° + \sin 260° \sin 190°$

2. $\cos 310° \cos 80° + \sin 310° \sin 80°$

3. $\frac{1}{2}\cos 40° - \frac{\sqrt{3}}{2}\sin 40°$

4. $\frac{\sqrt{2}}{2}(\cos 25° + \sin 25°)$

Express as the cosine of the difference of two angles, and evaluate.

5. $\cos 75°$ **6.** $\cos 195°$ **7.** $\cos 255°$ **8.** $\cos 105°$

Verify as identities.

9. $\cos(45° - \beta) = \frac{\sqrt{2}}{2}(\cos\beta + \sin\beta)$

10. $\cos(150° - \beta) = -\frac{1}{2}(\sqrt{3}\cos\beta - \sin\beta)$

Prove that the following are identities.

11. $\cot(90° - \beta) = \tan\beta$

12. $\csc\beta = \sec(90° - \beta)$

13. $\csc(90° - \beta) = \sec\beta$

14. $\cos(180° - \beta) = -\cos\beta$

Simplify:

B

15. $\cos(90° - \alpha)\sin(180° - \beta) + \cos(360° - \alpha)\sin(90° - \beta)$

16. $\cos(\alpha - 90°)\sin(90° - \beta) + \sin(\beta - 270°)\cos(90° - \alpha)$

17. $\tan(90° - \beta)\tan(180° - \beta)\sec\beta + \csc\alpha\sin(90° - \alpha)\csc(90° - \alpha)$

18. $\csc(90° - \theta)\sec(360° - \theta) - \tan(720° + \theta)\cot(450° - \theta)$

11–5 Functions of Sums and Differences of Angles

Several important identities are consequences of the formula: $\cos(\alpha - \beta) = \cos\alpha\cos\beta + \sin\alpha\sin\beta$. For example, if α has measure 0°, you find that

$$\cos(0° - \beta) = \cos 0°\cos\beta + \sin 0°\sin\beta$$
$$\cos(-\beta) = 1\cdot\cos\beta + 0\cdot\sin\beta$$
$$\therefore\ \mathbf{\cos(-\beta) = \cos\beta}$$

To find an expression for $\sin(-\beta)$ in terms of $\sin\beta$, replace β by $-\beta$ in the identity $\sin\beta = \cos(90° - \beta)$ derived in Section 11–4.

$$\begin{aligned}
\sin(-\beta) &= \cos[90° - (-\beta)]\\
\therefore\ \sin(-\beta) &= \cos(90° + \beta)\\
&= \cos[\beta - (-90°)]\\
&= \cos\beta\cos(-90°) + \sin\beta\sin(-90°)\\
&= \cos\beta\cdot 0 + \sin\beta\cdot(-1)\\
\therefore\ \mathbf{\sin(-\beta)} &= \mathbf{-\sin\beta}
\end{aligned}$$

It is left as an exercise for you to prove the following identities.

$$\mathbf{\tan(-\beta) = -\tan\beta} \qquad \mathbf{\cot(-\beta) = -\cot\beta}$$
$$\mathbf{\sec(-\beta) = \sec\beta} \qquad \mathbf{\csc(-\beta) = -\csc\beta}$$

Using the fact that $\alpha + \beta = \alpha - (-\beta)$, you can now derive a *formula for the cosine of the sum of two angles:*

$$\begin{aligned}
\cos(\alpha + \beta) &= \cos[\alpha - (-\beta)]\\
&= \cos\alpha\cos(-\beta) + \sin\alpha\sin(-\beta)\\
&= \cos\alpha\cos\beta + \sin\alpha(-\sin\beta)
\end{aligned}$$

$$\mathbf{\cos(\alpha + \beta) = \cos\alpha\cos\beta - \sin\alpha\sin\beta}$$

Because the sine of an angle equals the cosine of its complement, you can also obtain a formula for $\sin(\alpha + \beta)$:

$$\begin{aligned}\sin(\alpha + \beta) &= \cos[90^\circ - (\alpha + \beta)] \\ &= \cos[(90^\circ - \alpha) - \beta] \\ &= \cos(90^\circ - \alpha)\cos\beta + \sin(90^\circ - \alpha)\sin\beta\end{aligned}$$

$$\therefore\ \sin(\alpha + \beta) = \sin\alpha\cos\beta + \cos\alpha\sin\beta$$

Replace β by $-\beta$ in the formula just derived and you obtain:

$$\begin{aligned}\sin[\alpha + (-\beta)] &= \sin\alpha\cos(-\beta) + \cos\alpha\sin(-\beta) \\ \sin(\alpha - \beta) &= \sin\alpha\cos\beta + \cos\alpha\,(-\sin\beta)\end{aligned}$$

$$\therefore\ \sin(\alpha - \beta) = \sin\alpha\cos\beta - \cos\alpha\sin\beta$$

EXAMPLE 1. Simplify: $\sin 160^\circ \cos 20^\circ + \cos 160^\circ \sin 20^\circ$.

Solution:

$$\begin{aligned}\sin 160^\circ \cos 20^\circ + \cos 160^\circ \sin 20^\circ &= \sin(160^\circ + 20^\circ) \\ &= \sin 180^\circ = 0\end{aligned}$$

$\therefore\ \sin 160^\circ \cos 20^\circ + \cos 160^\circ \sin 20^\circ = 0$, **Answer.**

EXAMPLE 2. Determine $\sin(\alpha - \beta)$, if α is a third-quadrant angle for which $\cos\alpha = -\frac{3}{5}$ and β is a second-quadrant angle with $\sin\beta = \frac{8}{17}$.

Solution:

$\cos\alpha = -\frac{3}{5}$; $\sin\beta = \frac{8}{17}$ Given

$\therefore\ \sin\alpha = -\frac{4}{5}$; $\cos\beta = -\frac{15}{17}$ Using method of Sec. 10–3 or 11–1.

$$\begin{aligned}\sin(\alpha - \beta) &= \sin\alpha\cos\beta - \cos\alpha\sin\beta \\ &= -\tfrac{4}{5}(-\tfrac{15}{17}) - (-\tfrac{3}{5})(\tfrac{8}{17}) \\ &= \tfrac{60}{85} + \tfrac{24}{85}\end{aligned}$$

$\therefore\ \sin(\alpha - \beta) = \frac{84}{85}$, **Answer.**

Can you derive a formula for $\tan(\alpha + \beta)$? If $\cos(\alpha + \beta) \neq 0$,

$$\tan(\alpha + \beta) = \frac{\sin(\alpha + \beta)}{\cos(\alpha + \beta)}$$

$$\tan(\alpha + \beta) = \frac{\sin\alpha\cos\beta + \cos\alpha\sin\beta}{\cos\alpha\cos\beta - \sin\alpha\sin\beta}$$

Assuming $\cos\alpha \neq 0$ and $\cos\beta \neq 0$, you can transform the fraction in the right-hand member of this identity into an equivalent fraction. By dividing numerator and denominator by $\cos\alpha\cos\beta$,

$$\tan(\alpha+\beta) = \frac{\dfrac{\sin\alpha\cos\beta}{\cos\alpha\cos\beta} + \dfrac{\cos\alpha\sin\beta}{\cos\alpha\cos\beta}}{\dfrac{\cos\alpha\cos\beta}{\cos\alpha\cos\beta} - \dfrac{\sin\alpha\sin\beta}{\cos\alpha\cos\beta}}$$

$$\tan(\alpha+\beta) = \frac{\tan\alpha + \tan\beta}{1 - \tan\alpha\tan\beta}$$

Rewriting this identity with $-\beta$ in place of β and simplifying the result, you will obtain

$$\tan(\alpha-\beta) = \frac{\tan\alpha - \tan\beta}{1 + \tan\alpha\tan\beta}$$

for all angles α and β for which the functions involved are defined.

Written Exercises

Simplify.

A

1. $\cos(-\beta)\sec(-\beta) - \csc\beta\sin(-\beta)$
2. $\tan\beta\cos\beta - \cot(-\beta)\sec(-\beta) - \csc\beta - \sin(-\beta)$
3. $\cos 137^\circ \cos 47^\circ + \sin 137^\circ \sin 47^\circ$
4. $\sin 26^\circ \cos 94^\circ + \cos 26^\circ \sin 94^\circ$
5. $\cos 708^\circ \sin 753^\circ - \sin 708^\circ \cos 753^\circ$
6. $\cos 157^\circ \cos 173^\circ - \sin 157^\circ \sin 173^\circ$

Apply the formulas involving sums and differences of angles to find the exact value of each of the following.

7. $\tan 75^\circ$ **9.** $\sin 15^\circ$ **11.** $\cos 285^\circ$ **13.** $\tan 255^\circ$ **15.** $\sin 195^\circ$

8. $\sin 75^\circ$ **10.** $\tan 15^\circ$ **12.** $\sin 285^\circ$ **14.** $\cos 165^\circ$ **16.** $\cot 165^\circ$

17. If α is a first-quadrant angle with $\sin\alpha = \frac{4}{5}$ and β is a second-quadrant angle with $\cos\beta = -\frac{51}{149}$, find **(a)** $\sin(\alpha+\beta)$; **(b)** $\cos(\alpha+\beta)$; **(c)** $\sin(\alpha-\beta)$; **(d)** $\cos(\alpha-\beta)$; **(e)** $\tan(\alpha+\beta)$; **(f)** $\tan(\alpha-\beta)$.

18. If α is a third-quadrant angle with $\csc \alpha = -\frac{13}{5}$ and β is a fourth-quadrant angle with $\sec \beta = \frac{25}{7}$, find **(a)** $\sin(\alpha + \beta)$; **(b)** $\cos(\alpha + \beta)$; **(c)** $\sin(\alpha - \beta)$; **(d)** $\cos(\alpha - \beta)$; **(e)** $\tan(\alpha + \beta)$; **(f)** $\tan(\alpha - \beta)$.

If θ is a third-quadrant angle with $\sin \theta = -\frac{8}{17}$ and ρ a first-quadrant angle with $\sec \rho = \frac{5}{3}$, find each of the following.

19. **(a)** $\tan(\theta + \rho)$; **(b)** $\cot(\theta + \rho)$; **(c)** $\cos(\rho + \theta)$; **(d)** $\sin(\rho - \theta)$

20. **(a)** $\tan(\theta - \rho)$; **(b)** $\cot(\theta - \rho)$; **(c)** $\cos(\rho - \theta)$; **(d)** $\sin(\rho + \theta)$

Evaluate ($n \in \{\text{integers}\}$).

21. $\csc 60^\circ \left(\dfrac{\tan 47^\circ + \tan 13^\circ}{1 - \tan 13^\circ \tan 47^\circ}\right)$

22. $\dfrac{\tan 279^\circ - \tan 144^\circ}{\tan 144^\circ \tan 279^\circ + 1} + \sec 139^\circ \cos 139^\circ$

23. $\cos(n \cdot 180^\circ + 45^\circ)$

24. $\sin(n \cdot 90^\circ + 30^\circ)$

Prove.

B **25.** $\tan(135^\circ - x) = \dfrac{\sin x + \cos x}{\sin x - \cos x}$

26. $\tan(x + 60^\circ) = \dfrac{4 \tan x + \sqrt{3} \sec^2 x}{\sec^2 x - 4 \tan^2 x}$

27. $\dfrac{\cos(A + B)}{\cos(A - B)} = \dfrac{1 - \tan A \tan B}{1 + \tan A \tan B}$

28. $\dfrac{\sin(A + B)}{\cos(A - B)} = \dfrac{\sin A + \cos A \tan B}{\cos A + \sin A \tan B}$

11-6 Double- and Half-Angle Identities

When you replace α by β in the formulas for $\sin(\alpha + \beta)$, $\cos(\alpha + \beta)$, and $\tan(\alpha + \beta)$, you obtain identities known as the *double-angle* formulas.

$$\sin(\beta + \beta) = \sin \beta \cos \beta + \cos \beta \sin \beta$$

$$\therefore \ \sin 2\beta = 2 \sin \beta \cos \beta$$

$$\cos(\beta + \beta) = \cos \beta \cos \beta - \sin \beta \sin \beta$$

$$\cos 2\beta = \cos^2 \beta - \sin^2 \beta$$

$$\tan(\beta + \beta) = \frac{\tan \beta + \tan \beta}{1 - \tan \beta \tan \beta}$$

$$\tan 2\beta = \frac{2 \tan \beta}{1 - \tan^2 \beta}$$

Alternative forms of the formula for $\cos 2\beta$ result when you use the identity $\sin^2 \beta + \cos^2 \beta = 1$ to transform the right-hand member of $\cos 2\beta = \cos^2 \beta - \sin^2 \beta$.

$\cos 2\beta = \cos^2 \beta - \sin^2 \beta$	$\cos 2\beta = \cos^2 \beta - \sin^2 \beta$
$= \cos^2 \beta - (1 - \cos^2 \beta)$	$= (1 - \sin^2 \beta) - \sin^2 \beta$
$\cos 2\beta = 2\cos^2 \beta - 1$	$\cos 2\beta = 1 - 2\sin^2 \beta$

EXAMPLE 1. Evaluate: $\sin 22.5° \cos 22.5°$.

Solution: Because $\sin \beta \cos \beta = \frac{1}{2} \sin 2\beta$, you have:

$$\sin 22.5° \cos 22.5° = \tfrac{1}{2} \sin 2(22.5°)$$

$$= \tfrac{1}{2} \sin 45° = \frac{1}{2} \cdot \frac{\sqrt{2}}{2}$$

$$\therefore \sin 22.5° \cos 22.5° = \frac{\sqrt{2}}{4}, \textbf{ Answer.}$$

From the formulas for $\cos 2\beta$, you can derive the *half-angle formulas:*

$$\sin^2 \frac{\theta}{2} = \frac{1 - \cos \theta}{2} \qquad \cos^2 \frac{\theta}{2} = \frac{1 + \cos \theta}{2}$$

$$\tan^2 \frac{\theta}{2} = \frac{1 - \cos \theta}{1 + \cos \theta}$$

To obtain the first formula, transform $\cos 2\beta = 1 - 2\sin^2 \beta$ into the equivalent identity: $\sin^2 \beta = \dfrac{1 - \cos 2\beta}{2}$. Then, replace 2β by θ and β by $\dfrac{\theta}{2}$, and you obtain $\sin^2 \dfrac{\theta}{2} = \dfrac{1 - \cos \theta}{2}$. You can derive the second half-angle formula similarly from the identity $\cos 2\beta = 2\cos^2 \beta - 1$.

Then, $\tan^2 \dfrac{\theta}{2} = \dfrac{\sin^2 \frac{\theta}{2}}{\cos^2 \frac{\theta}{2}} = \dfrac{\frac{1 - \cos \theta}{2}}{\frac{1 + \cos \theta}{2}}$. $\quad \therefore \tan^2 \dfrac{\theta}{2} = \dfrac{1 - \cos \theta}{1 + \cos \theta}$.

Notice that the half-angle formulas give expressions for the squares: $\sin^2 \dfrac{\theta}{2}$, $\cos^2 \dfrac{\theta}{2}$, $\tan^2 \dfrac{\theta}{2}$. Of course, knowing the value of $\cos \theta$, you can use these formulas to determine $\sin \dfrac{\theta}{2}$, $\cos \dfrac{\theta}{2}$, or $\tan \dfrac{\theta}{2}$, *provided that you also know the quadrant in which* $\dfrac{\theta}{2}$ *terminates.*

Depending on the quadrant of θ, we have

$$\sin\frac{\theta}{2} = \sqrt{\frac{1-\cos\theta}{2}} \quad \text{or} \quad -\sqrt{\frac{1-\cos\theta}{2}}$$

$$\cos\frac{\theta}{2} = \sqrt{\frac{1+\cos\theta}{2}} \quad \text{or} \quad -\sqrt{\frac{1+\cos\theta}{2}}$$

$$\tan\frac{\theta}{2} = \sqrt{\frac{1-\cos\theta}{1+\cos\theta}} \quad \text{or} \quad -\sqrt{\frac{1-\cos\theta}{1+\cos\theta}}$$

EXAMPLE 2. Determine the exact values of $\sin 112\frac{1}{2}°$ and $\cos 112\frac{1}{2}°$.

Solution: $112\frac{1}{2} = \frac{1}{2}(225)$. Therefore,

$$\sin^2 112\tfrac{1}{2}° = \sin^2 \tfrac{1}{2}(225°) = \frac{1-\cos 225°}{2} = \frac{1-\left(-\frac{\sqrt{2}}{2}\right)}{2}$$

$$\sin^2 112\tfrac{1}{2}° = \frac{2+\sqrt{2}}{4}$$

$$\cos^2 112\tfrac{1}{2}° = \cos^2 \tfrac{1}{2}(225°) = \frac{1+\cos 225°}{2} = \frac{1+\left(-\frac{\sqrt{2}}{2}\right)}{2}$$

$$\cos^2 112\tfrac{1}{2}° = \frac{2-\sqrt{2}}{4}$$

Since an angle of $112\frac{1}{2}°$ terminates in the second quadrant, $\sin 112\frac{1}{2}° > 0$ and $\cos 112\frac{1}{2}° < 0$. Therefore,

$$\sin 112\tfrac{1}{2}° = \frac{\sqrt{2+\sqrt{2}}}{2}; \ \cos 112\tfrac{1}{2}° = -\frac{\sqrt{2-\sqrt{2}}}{2}, \ \textbf{Answer.}$$

Written Exercises

Find the exact value of the following.

A

1. $\cos^2 75° - \sin^2 75°$

2. $\sin 67.5° \cos 67.5°$

3. $\dfrac{2\tan 105°}{1-\tan^2 105°}$

4. $2\cos^2 165° + 1$

5. $2\sin^2 157.5° - 1$

6. $\dfrac{-2\tan 22.5°}{2-\sec^2 22.5°}$

Using the half-angle formulas, find the exact value of the following.

7. $\sin 15°$ **8.** $\cos 135°$ **9.** $\tan(-195°)$ **10.** $\cot(-292.5°)$

Prove.

B

11. $\cos 2t = \dfrac{\csc^2 t - 2}{\csc^2 t}$

12. $\dfrac{\sin 2\beta}{2 \sin^2 \beta} = \cot \beta$

13. $\tan 2\theta = \dfrac{\sin 4\theta}{1 + \cos 4\theta}$

14. $\tan \dfrac{x}{2} = \dfrac{1 - \cos x}{\sin x}$

15. $\dfrac{1 - \sin 2\theta}{\cos 2\theta} = \dfrac{1 - \tan \theta}{1 + \tan \theta}$

16. $\tan 3\beta = \csc 6\beta - \cot 6\beta$

17. $\sin 3\theta = 3 \sin \theta - 4 \sin^3 \theta$

18. $\cos 3\theta = 4 \cos^3 \theta - 3 \cos \theta$

11-7 Sum and Product Identities

By adding corresponding members of the identities

$$\sin \alpha \cos \beta + \cos \alpha \sin \beta = \sin (\alpha + \beta)$$
$$\sin \alpha \cos \beta - \cos \alpha \sin \beta = \sin (\alpha - \beta),$$

you obtain

$$\mathbf{2 \sin \alpha \cos \beta = \sin(\alpha + \beta) + \sin(\alpha - \beta).^*}$$

The starred (*) identity enables you to convert any product of the sine of an angle and the cosine of another angle into the sum or difference of the sines of two positive angles.

EXAMPLE 1. Express as a sum **(a)** $\sin 17° \cos 13°$; **(b)** $\sin 70° \cos 100°$.

Solution:

a. $2 \sin 17° \cos 13° = \sin(17° + 13°) + \sin(17° - 13°)$
$= \sin 30° + \sin 4°$
$\therefore \sin 17° \cos 13° = \frac{1}{2}(\sin 30° + \sin 4°)$, **Answer.**

b. $2 \sin 70° \cos 100° = \sin(70° + 100°) + \sin(70° - 100°)$
$= \sin 170° + \sin(-30°)$
$\therefore \sin 70° \cos 100° = \frac{1}{2}[\sin 170° + \sin(-30°)]$
But, $\sin(-30°) = -\sin 30°$.

Therefore, $\sin 70° \cos 100° = \frac{1}{2}(\sin 170° - \sin 30°)$, **Answer.**

The use of the starred identity to express a sum or difference of the sines of two angles as a product is facilitated by the change in notation shown on the next page.

Let

$$\alpha + \beta = A$$
$$\alpha - \beta = B$$

Transforming this system to express α and β in terms of A and B,

$$2\alpha = A + B \qquad 2\beta = A - B$$
$$\alpha = \frac{A + B}{2} \qquad \beta = \frac{A - B}{2}$$

Under these substitutions, the starred identity can be written:

$$\sin A + \sin B = 2 \sin \tfrac{1}{2}(A + B) \cos \tfrac{1}{2}(A - B).$$

You are to derive

$$\sin A - \sin B = 2 \cos \tfrac{1}{2}(A + B) \sin \tfrac{1}{2}(A - B).$$

EXAMPLE 2. Express as a product: **(a)** $\sin 60° + \sin 30°$;
(b) $\sin 60° - \sin 30°$.

Solution:

a. $\sin 60° + \sin 30° = 2 \sin \dfrac{60° + 30°}{2} \cos \dfrac{60° - 30°}{2}$

$\sin 60° + \sin 30° = 2 \sin 45° \cos 15°$, **Answer.**

b. $\sin 60° - \sin 30° = 2 \cos \dfrac{60° + 30°}{2} \sin \dfrac{60° - 30°}{2}$

$\sin 60° - \sin 30° = 2 \sin 15° \cos 45°$, **Answer.**

The addition and subtraction of corresponding members of the identities

$$\cos \alpha \cos \beta - \sin \alpha \sin \beta = \cos(\alpha + \beta)$$
$$\cos \alpha \cos \beta + \sin \alpha \sin \beta = \cos(\alpha - \beta)$$

produce the identities

$$2 \cos \alpha \cos \beta = \cos(\alpha + \beta) + \cos(\alpha - \beta)$$
$$-2 \sin \alpha \sin \beta = \cos(\alpha + \beta) - \cos(\alpha - \beta)$$

The substitution $\alpha + \beta = A$ and $\alpha - \beta = B$, as before, leads to:

$$\cos A + \cos B = 2 \cos \frac{A + B}{2} \cos \frac{A - B}{2}$$

$$\cos A - \cos B = -2 \sin \frac{A + B}{2} \sin \frac{A - B}{2}$$

EXAMPLE 3. Verify the identity: $\dfrac{\sin 3\theta + \sin\theta}{\cos 3\theta + \cos\theta} = \tan 2\theta$.

Proof:

$$\text{L.M.} = \frac{\sin 3\theta + \sin\theta}{\cos 3\theta + \cos\theta} = \frac{2\sin\dfrac{3\theta+\theta}{2}\cos\dfrac{3\theta-\theta}{2}}{2\cos\dfrac{3\theta+\theta}{2}\cos\dfrac{3\theta-\theta}{2}}$$

$$= \frac{\sin 2\theta\,(2\cos\theta)}{\cos 2\theta\,(2\cos\theta)} = \frac{\sin 2\theta}{\cos 2\theta} = \tan 2\theta$$

$$\therefore \frac{\sin 3\theta + \sin\theta}{\cos 3\theta + \cos\theta} = \tan 2\theta$$

Written Exercises

Write as a sum or difference.

A

1. $2\cos 19^\circ \sin 117^\circ$
2. $\sin(-190^\circ)\cos 105^\circ$
3. $-2\cos 205^\circ \cos(-10^\circ)$
4. $\sin 72^\circ \sin 403^\circ$

Write as a product.

5. $\sin 11^\circ - \sin(-29^\circ)$
6. $4\cos 37^\circ + 4\cos 272^\circ$
7. $2\cos 301^\circ - \frac{1}{2}(4\cos 8^\circ)$
8. $\sin 25^\circ \sin 9^\circ + \sin 111^\circ \sin 25^\circ$

Find the exact value of **(a)** $\sin A + \sin B$, **(b)** $\sin A - \sin B$, **(c)** $\cos A + \cos B$, **(d)** $\cos A - \cos B$, if

9. $A = 75^\circ, B = 15^\circ$
10. $A = 165^\circ, B = 75^\circ$

Verify the following identities.

11. $\dfrac{\sin 4\beta - \sin 2\beta}{\cos 2\beta + \cos 4\beta} = \tan\beta$
12. $\dfrac{\cos 2\beta - \cos 4\beta}{\sin 2\beta - \sin 4\beta} = -\tan 3\beta$
13. $\dfrac{\cos 3\beta + \cos\beta}{\cos\beta - 2\sin^2\beta\cos\beta} = 2$

B

14. $\dfrac{\cos\beta + \cos 2\beta + \cos 3\beta}{\sin 3\beta + \sin 2\beta + \sin\beta} = \cot 2\beta$
15. $\dfrac{\sin(\alpha+\beta+\gamma) + \sin(\alpha-\beta-\gamma)}{\cos(\alpha+\beta+\gamma) - \cos(\alpha-\beta-\gamma)} = \dfrac{\tan\beta\tan\gamma - 1}{\tan\beta + \tan\gamma}$
16. $\dfrac{\cos 10\beta + \cos 2\beta}{-\cos 10\beta + \cos 2\beta} = \dfrac{(1-\tan^2 3\beta)(1-\tan^2 2\beta)}{4\tan 2\beta\tan 3\beta}$

SUMMARY OF BASIC IDENTITIES

Reciprocal Identities

$$\cos\theta \sec\theta = 1 \qquad \sin\theta \csc\theta = 1 \qquad \tan\theta \cot\theta = 1$$

Quotient Identities

$$\tan\theta = \frac{\sin\theta}{\cos\theta} \qquad \cot\theta = \frac{\cos\theta}{\sin\theta}$$

Pythagorean Identities

$$\sin^2\theta + \cos^2\theta = 1 \qquad 1 + \tan^2\theta = \sec^2\theta \qquad 1 + \cot^2\theta = \csc^2\theta$$

Addition Identities

$$\cos(\alpha + \beta) = \cos\alpha\cos\beta - \sin\alpha\sin\beta$$
$$\cos(\alpha - \beta) = \cos\alpha\cos\beta + \sin\alpha\sin\beta$$
$$\sin(\alpha + \beta) = \sin\alpha\cos\beta + \cos\alpha\sin\beta$$
$$\sin(\alpha - \beta) = \sin\alpha\cos\beta - \cos\alpha\sin\beta$$
$$\tan(\alpha + \beta) = \frac{\tan\alpha + \tan\beta}{1 - \tan\alpha\tan\beta} \qquad \tan(\alpha - \beta) = \frac{\tan\alpha - \tan\beta}{1 + \tan\alpha\tan\beta}$$

Double Angle Identities

$$\cos 2\theta = \cos^2\theta - \sin^2\theta \qquad \sin 2\theta = 2\sin\theta\cos\theta$$
$$= 2\cos^2\theta - 1 \qquad \tan 2\theta = \frac{2\tan\theta}{1 - \tan^2\theta}$$
$$= 1 - 2\sin^2\theta$$

Half Angle Identities

$$\left|\cos\frac{\theta}{2}\right| = \sqrt{\frac{1 + \cos\theta}{2}}; \quad \left|\sin\frac{\theta}{2}\right| = \sqrt{\frac{1 - \cos\theta}{2}}; \quad \left|\tan\frac{\theta}{2}\right| = \sqrt{\frac{1 - \cos\theta}{1 + \cos\theta}}$$

Sum and Product Identities

$$2\sin\alpha\cos\beta = \sin(\alpha + \beta) + \sin(\alpha - \beta)$$
$$2\cos\alpha\cos\beta = \cos(\alpha + \beta) + \cos(\alpha - \beta)$$
$$-2\sin\alpha\sin\beta = \cos(\alpha + \beta) - \cos(\alpha - \beta)$$
$$\sin A + \sin B = 2\sin\frac{A + B}{2}\cos\frac{A - B}{2}$$
$$\sin A - \sin B = 2\cos\frac{A + B}{2}\sin\frac{A - B}{2}$$

$$\cos A + \cos B = 2\cos\frac{A+B}{2}\cos\frac{A-B}{2}$$

$$\cos A - \cos B = -2\sin\frac{A+B}{2}\sin\frac{A-B}{2}$$

MISCELLANEOUS IDENTITIES

Prove.

A

1. $\cos\theta\csc\theta\tan\theta = 1$
2. $\csc^2\rho(1 - \sin^2\rho) = \cot^2\rho$
3. $\dfrac{\csc\alpha\sin\beta}{\sec\alpha\cos\beta} = \dfrac{\tan\beta}{\tan\alpha}$
4. $\dfrac{\sin M}{\cot M + \csc M} - \dfrac{\sin M}{\cot M - \csc M} = 2$
5. $\dfrac{\cos^2\beta}{(1 - \sin\beta)^2} = (\sec\beta + \tan\beta)^2$
6. $2\cos^2(45° - \frac{1}{2}\theta) - 1 = \sin\theta$
7. $\tan\gamma + \cot\gamma = 2\csc 2\gamma$
8. $\dfrac{2\tan\rho}{1 + \tan^2\rho} = \sin 2\rho$
9. $\dfrac{2\tan(45° - 0.5x)}{1 - \tan^2(0.5x - 45°)} = \cot x$
10. $\dfrac{\cos 5t\cos 3t + \sin 5t\sin 3t}{\sin 3t - \sin t} = \dfrac{\csc t}{2}$

B

11. $\sin y\cos^3 y - \cos y\sin^3 y = \frac{1}{4}\sin 4y$
12. $\csc^2\dfrac{R}{2} = \dfrac{2\sec R}{\sec R - 1}$
13. $\dfrac{\sin(-\alpha)}{[1 + \cos(180° - \alpha)][\cos(360° - \alpha) + 1]} = -\sec(90° - \alpha)$
14. $\dfrac{\cos(-\alpha)\tan(180° + \alpha) + \sin(180° - \alpha)}{\cot(90° - \alpha)}$
$= \sin(90° + \alpha) + \cos(360° - \alpha)$
15. $\dfrac{1 - (\sin 2\beta + \cos 2\beta)^2}{2\sin 2\beta\cos 2\beta} = -1$
16. $\dfrac{\sin 4\theta\cos 2\theta - \cos 4\theta\sin 2\theta}{\cos^2\theta - \sin^2\theta} = \tan 2\theta$

C

17. $\dfrac{1 - \sin 2\beta}{1 - 4\sin^2\beta + 4\sin^4\beta} = \dfrac{1}{1 + 2\sin\beta\cos\beta}$
18. $\sec^6 p - \tan^6 p = 1 + 3\tan^2 p\sec^2 p$
19. $\cos 20° + \cos 100° + \cos 140° = 0$
20. $1 + \tan C\tan\dfrac{C}{2} = \sec C$

TRIANGLE APPLICATIONS

11–8 The Law of Cosines

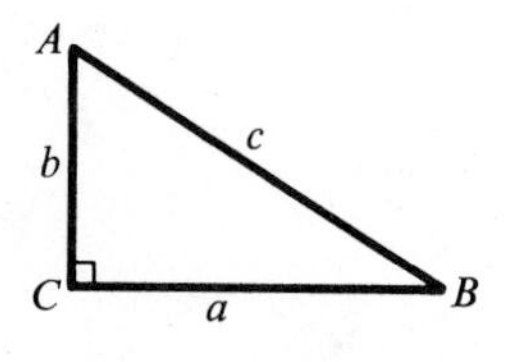

· *Figure 11–6* ·

The formula $c^2 = a^2 + b^2$ is true for every *right* triangle (Figure 11–6). The distance formula (page 431) enables you to derive a similar formula true for *every* triangle.

Given any triangle ABC, choose a coordinate system with origin at C and angle C in standard position (Figure 11–7). Then, vertex B is a units from the origin and has a position angle of 0°; vertex A is b units from the origin and has angle C as position angle; while the distance between A and B is c.

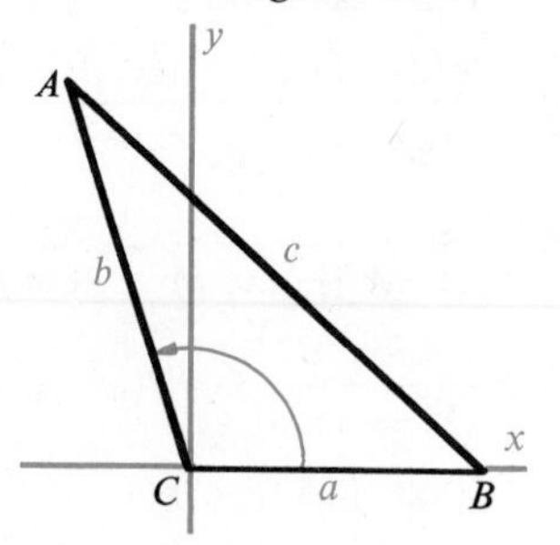

· *Figure 11–7* ·

Applying the distance formula (page 431), you find

$$c^2 = (AB)^2 = a^2 + b^2 - 2ab\cos(C - 0°)$$
$$c^2 = a^2 + b^2 - 2ab\cos C.$$

If C is a right angle, $\cos C = 0$, so that you have the special case of the Pythagorean theorem: $c^2 = a^2 + b^2$. Can you explain why $c^2 < a^2 + b^2$ if the measure of C is between 0° and 90°, but that $c^2 > a^2 + b^2$ if the measure of C is between 90° and 180°?

By chȯosing coordinate systems first with angle A and then with angle B in standard position, you can show similarly that

$$a^2 = b^2 + c^2 - 2bc\cos A; \qquad b^2 = a^2 + c^2 - 2ac\cos B.$$

These results are summarized in the following theorem called the **Law of Cosines**.

THEOREM. In a triangle the square of the length of any side equals the sum of the squares of the lengths of the other two sides decreased by twice the product of the lengths of these two sides and the cosine of their included angle.

EXAMPLE 1. On take-off a rocket exerts on its launch pad a force of 9 tons in the direction shown, while the weight of the pad exerts a 5-ton force vertically downward. Find the magnitude of the resultant of these forces to the nearest ton.

Solution:

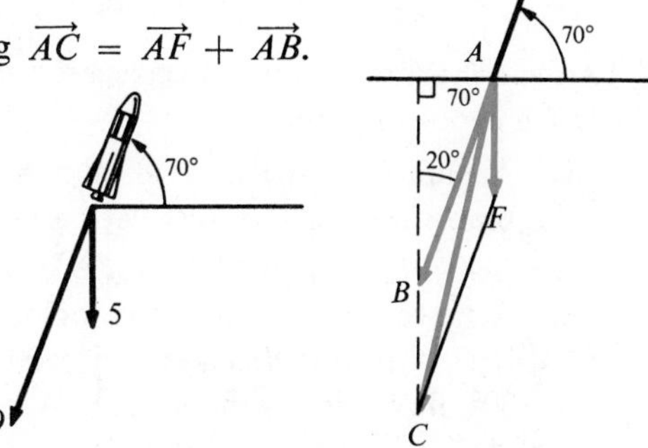

1. Draw the force diagram showing $\overrightarrow{AC} = \overrightarrow{AF} + \overrightarrow{AB}$. Then in triangle ABC, $AB = c = 9$, $BC = a = 5$, and angle ABC has measure $(180 - 20)° = 160°$.

2. To determine AC (b):

$$\begin{aligned} b^2 &= a^2 + c^2 - 2ac \cos B \\ &= 5^2 + 9^2 - 2 \cdot 5 \cdot 9 \cos 160° \\ &= 25 + 81 - 90(-0.9397) \end{aligned}$$

$b^2 = 190.6$; $b = \sqrt{190.6}$, or 14

$\therefore$ the magnitude of the resultant is approximately 14 tons, **Answer.**

EXAMPLE 2. In triangle ABC, $a:b:c = 2:4:5$. To the nearest degree determine the measure of the largest angle of the triangle.

Solution: There exists a positive real number r such that $a = 2r$, $b = 4r$, and $c = 5r$. Since $c > b > a$, $\angle C$ is the largest angle.

From the law of cosines:

$$\begin{aligned} \cos C &= \frac{a^2 + b^2 - c^2}{2ab} \\ &= \frac{(2r)^2 + (4r)^2 - (5r)^2}{2(2r)(4r)} \\ &= \frac{4r^2 + 16r^2 - 25r^2}{16r^2} = -\frac{5}{16} \end{aligned}$$

$\cos C = -0.3125$. $C = 180° - 72° = 108°$, **Answer.**

Written Exercises

Find the required part of $\triangle ABC$ either to the nearest tenth or to the nearest 10 minutes.

1. $a = 7, b = 9, C = 60°; c = ?$
2. $c = 8, a = 5, B = 60°; b = ?$
3. $c = 1.2, b = 1.7, A = 120°; a = ?$
4. $b = 2.3, a = 1.8, C = 120°; c = ?$
5. $c = 82, b = 57, a = 61; B = ?$
6. $a = 29, b = 47, c = 32; B = ?$
7. $a = 71, b = 45, c = 51; A = ?$
8. $a = 35, b = 39, c = 44; A = ?$
9. $c = 2.1, a = 1.8, B = 52° 10'; b = ?$
10. $b = 1.6, c = 2.3, A = 138°40'; a = ?$

Problems

Assume linear measures are correct to two significant figures and angle measures to the nearest degree.

1. A plane's airspeed is 400 m.p.h. on a heading of 135°. If a wind is blowing from the west with a speed of 50 m.p.h., what is the ground speed of the plane?

2. A surveyor at C sights two points A and B on opposite sides of a lake. If C is 5000 ft. from A and 7500 ft. from B, and angle ACB measures 30°, how wide is the lake?

3. Two forces, one of 90 lb. magnitude and the other 180 lb. in magnitude, are applied to the same point. If the angle between their directions measures 52°, what is the magnitude of their resultant?

4. Two forces of 120 lb. and 80 lb. act on a body at an angle of 60°. What is the magnitude of the resultant of the two forces?

5. A ship sails 20 miles on course 35° and then sails 30 miles on course 100°. How far is it from its starting point?

6. From a radar station the bearing of a plane 150 miles away is N50°E. Another plane has bearing S70°E and is 220 miles away. How far apart are the planes?

7. Two cars start from the same point at 9 A.M. and drive along roads which come together in a dead end at an angle of 50°. If one car is traveling 35 m.p.h. in an easterly direction while the other is going at the rate of 45 m.p.h. in a westerly direction, how far apart are they at noon?

8. Two planes, one flying at 300 m.p.h. and the other at 450 m.p.h. left an airport at the same time. Three hours later they were 1200 miles apart. What was the measure of the angle between their flight paths?

9. Find the measure of the angle between two forces of 20 lb. and 15 lb., if the magnitude of their resultant is 26 lb.

10. The measures of two sides of a parallelogram are 50 and 80 inches, while one diagonal is 90 inches long. How long is the other diagonal?

Prove that each formula holds in triangle ABC.

C

11. $1 + \cos A = \dfrac{(b + c + a)(b + c - a)}{2bc}$

12. $1 - \cos A = \dfrac{(a - b + c)(a + b - c)}{2bc}$

13. $\tan \dfrac{A}{2} = \sqrt{\dfrac{(a - b + c)(a + b - c)}{(b + c + a)(b + c - a)}}$ **(Half-angle Law)**

(*Hint:* Use the *half-angle formula* on page 438 and the results of Exercises 11 and 12.)

14. $\tan \frac{A}{2} = \sqrt{\frac{(s-c)(s-b)}{s(s-a)}} = \frac{r}{s-a}$ where $s = \frac{a+b+c}{2}$ and

$r = \sqrt{\frac{(s-a)(s-b)(s-c)}{s}}$. (*Hint*: Use the result of Exercise 13.)

Using logarithms, apply the result of Exercise 14 to determine to the nearest minute the measure of each angle of the triangles with sides as follows.

15. 15.3, 19.2, 13.9

16. 8.16, 9.44, 11.0

17. 17.30, 25.40, 35.52

18. 39.01, 14.00, 43.40

11–9 The Law of Sines

Noting that the coordinates of point A in Figure 11–7 (page 444) are $(b \cos C, b \sin C)$, you can deduce a useful formula for the area K of triangle ABC. Because the y-coordinate of A is the length of the *altitude* AD drawn from A perpendicular to the line containing *base* BC whose length is a (Figure 11–8), you have:

$$K = \tfrac{1}{2}(BC)(AD) = \tfrac{1}{2}a(b \sin C)$$

(base ↓ BC, altitude ↓ AD)

$$K = \tfrac{1}{2}ab \sin C .$$

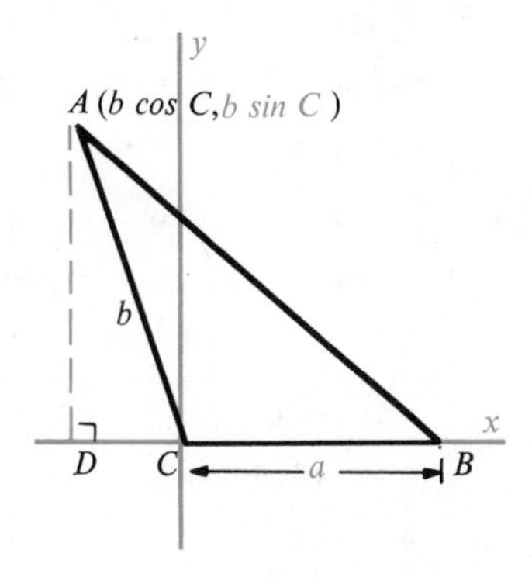

· *Figure 11–8* ·

By choosing the coordinate system appropriately, you can obtain

$$K = \tfrac{1}{2}ac \sin B \quad \textbf{and} \quad K = \tfrac{1}{2}bc \sin A ,$$

to complete the proof of the following theorem.

THEOREM. The area of a triangle equals one-half the product of the lengths of two sides and the sine of their included angle.

This theorem implies that the following compound sentence is true: $\frac{1}{2}bc \sin A = \frac{1}{2}ac \sin B = \frac{1}{2}ab \sin C$. Division of each member by $\frac{1}{2}abc$, yields

$$\frac{\sin A}{a} = \frac{\sin B}{b} = \frac{\sin C}{c} .$$

This relationship, called the **Law of Sines**, is stated in the following theorem.

THEOREM. The sines of the angles of a triangle are proportional to the lengths of the opposite sides.

Notice that if C is a right angle, $\sin C = 1$ and the law of sines yields the familiar right triangle relationships $\sin A = \frac{a}{c}$ and $\sin B = \frac{b}{c}$.

EXAMPLE. A ship is being tracked from two stations A and B 6500 feet apart on a north-south line. At A the ship is observed in the direction N34°E, while at B it is observed in the direction N48°E. How far is the ship from B?

Solution:

1. Draw a diagram picturing the data, with the ship at C.
2. In triangle ABC, denote $\angle CBA$ by B.

$A = 34°$; $c = 6500$

$B = 180° - 48° = 132°$

$C = 180° - [A + B] = 180° - 166° = 14°$

C, a, 48°, B, b, 6500, 34°, A (not to scale)

3. To find CB (a):

$$\frac{a}{\sin A} = \frac{c}{\sin C}, \quad \text{or} \quad a = \frac{c \sin A}{\sin C}. \qquad a = \frac{6500 \sin 34°}{\sin 14°}$$

$$\begin{aligned}
\log a &= \log 6500 + \log \sin 34° - \log \sin 14° \\
\log 6500 &= 3.8129 \\
\log \sin 34° &= \underline{9.7476 - 10} \quad (+) \\
& 13.5605 - 10 \\
\log \sin 14° &= \underline{9.3837 - 10} \quad (-) \\
\log a &= 4.1768 \\
a &= 15{,}020
\end{aligned}$$

To the nearest hundred feet, the ship is 15,000 feet from B, **Answer.**

Written Exercises

Find the required values for $\triangle ABC$ to the nearest tenth.

A

1. $A = 30°, B = 60°; a:b = ?$
2. $C = 120°, A = 45°; c:a = ?$
3. $a = 16, b = 13, \sin A = \frac{2}{3}; B = ?$
4. $b = 34, c = 27, \sin B = 0.9; C = ?$
5. $b = 1.5, \sin A = \frac{2}{5}, \sin B = \frac{4}{7}; a = ?$
6. $c = 7.5, \sin C = 0.7, \sin B = 0.4; b = ?$

Problems

Assume that angle measures are correct to the nearest degree and linear measures to two significant figures.

A

1. A triangle contains angles measuring 35° and 50°. If the side opposite the 35° angle is 12 inches long, find the length of the longest side.

2. Two of the angles of a triangle measure 70° and 67°. If the side opposite the 70° angle is 30 cm. in length, how long is the shortest side?

3. While on opposite ends of a 7.4-mile beach, two men noticed a ship on fire. If lines of sight from the ship to the men made a greater angle with each other than either of the angles of 59° and 40° which they made with the beach, how far was the ship from the nearer man?

4. A parcel of land is in the shape of an isosceles triangle. The base fronts on a road and has a length of 562 ft. If the legs meet at an angle of 22°, how long are they?

5. From an observation post P the distance to a gun position G was 2000 yards. Find the distance between the gun and a target T if angle PGT measures 65° and angle GPT measures 84°.

6. A vertical tree stands on a slope that is inclined at an angle of 10° with the horizontal. When the angle of elevation of the sun measures 25°, the shadow of the tree down the slope is 40 ft. long. How tall is the tree?

B

7. Radio station A is 120 miles due north of station B. Station A receives a distress message from a ship at a bearing of 130°, while station B receives the same message at a bearing of 47°. How long would a helicopter flying at 110 m.p.h. take to reach the ship from station A?

8. A surveyor laying a road due west from A encounters a swamp at B. He changes his direction to N28°W for 2500 yards to C and then turns S37°W. How far must he continue in this direction to reach point D on the east-west line through A?

9. ABC is an equilateral triangle whose side is 18″ long. Lines AD and AE are drawn trisecting angle A and intersecting side BC in points D and E. Find the lengths of segments BD, DE, and EC.

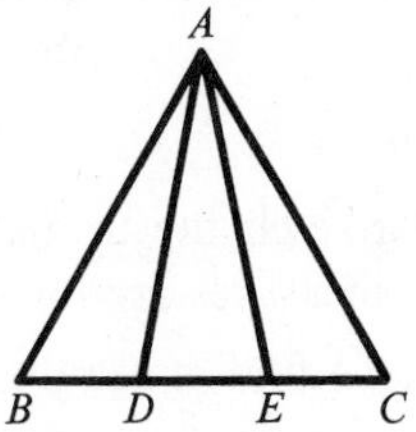

A
B D E C

10. In triangle ABC, prove that if $\frac{\cos A}{b} = \frac{\cos B}{a}$, then the triangle is either an isosceles or a right triangle.

Prove that each formula holds in triangle ABC.

11. $\dfrac{a-b}{b} = \dfrac{\sin A - \sin B}{\sin B}$

12. $\dfrac{a+b}{b} = \dfrac{\sin A + \sin B}{\sin B}$

C **13.** $\dfrac{a-b}{a+b} = \dfrac{\sin A - \sin B}{\sin A + \sin B}$ (*Hint:* Use the results of Exercises 11 and 12.)

14. $\dfrac{a-b}{a+b} = \dfrac{\cos \frac{1}{2}(A+B)\sin \frac{1}{2}(A-B)}{\sin \frac{1}{2}(A+B)\cos \frac{1}{2}(A-B)} = \dfrac{\tan \frac{1}{2}(A-B)}{\tan \frac{1}{2}(A+B)}$

(*Hint:* Use the result of Exercise 13 and the formulas of Section 11–7, page 439.) This is called the **Law of Tangents.**

Using logarithms, apply the result of Exercise 14 to determine to the nearest minute the measures of the other angles of the triangle in which the two sides whose lengths are given form an angle of the indicated measure.

15. 71.30; 36.50; 47°15′

16. 1240; 2413; 24°10′

11–10 Solving Triangles

In Sections 11–8 and 11–9, you have used one relationship, either the law of cosines or the law of sines, to solve problems involving triangles in which you were given the measures of

1. Two sides and the angle included between them, or
2. Three sides, or
3. Two angles and one side.

The process of determining the measures of the remaining sides and angles is called **solving the triangle**. By using both laws, you can sometimes shorten the solution.

EXAMPLE 1. Solve triangle ABC if $a = 7.000$, $b = 6.000$, and the measure of C is 24°20′.

Solution:

1. Sketch the triangle and label the parts whose measures are known.

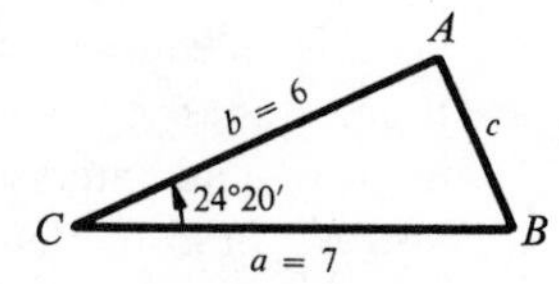

2. To find c, use the law of cosines:

$$\begin{aligned} c^2 &= a^2 + b^2 - 2ab\cos C \\ &= 7^2 + 6^2 - 2(7)(6)\cos 24°20' \\ &\doteq 49 + 36 - 84(0.9112) \\ c^2 &\doteq 85 - 76.5408 \doteq 8.459 \end{aligned}$$

$$\begin{aligned} 2\log c &= \log 8.459 \\ \log c &= \tfrac{1}{2}(0.9274) \\ \log c &= 0.4637 \\ c &= 2.909 \end{aligned}$$

3. Use the law of sines to find the measure of the *smaller* of the remaining angles, namely B.

$$\frac{\sin B}{b} = \frac{\sin C}{c}, \text{ or } \sin B = \frac{b \sin C}{c}$$

$$\log \sin B = \log b + \log \sin C - \log c$$

$b = 6$ $\qquad \log b = 0.7782$

$C = 24°20'$ $\qquad \log \sin C = 9.6149 - 10 \quad (+)$

$$10.3931 - 10$$

$$\log c = 0.4637 \quad (-) \quad \text{[from Step 2]}$$

$$\log \sin B = 9.9294 - 10$$

$$B = 58°13', \text{ or } 180° - 58°13' = 121°47'$$

Since B is the smaller of the angles A and B, it must be an acute angle. (Why?) Therefore, $B = 58°13'$.

4. To find A: $\quad A + B + C = 180°$

$$A + 58°13' + 24°20' = 180° \qquad A = 97°27'$$

5. Check by comparing your results with the sketch, and by substituting the results in a relationship not employed in the solution. For example,

$$\frac{\sin A}{a} = \frac{\sin B}{b}, \text{ or } \log \sin A - \log a = \log \sin B - \log b:$$

$\log \sin 97°27' = \log \sin 82°33' = 9.9963 - 10$
$\log 7 = 0.8451$
$9.1512 - 10$

$\log \sin 58°13' = 9.9294 - 10$
$\log 6 = 0.7782$
$9.1512 - 10$

$c = 2.909$, $A = 97°27'$, $B = 58°13'$, **Answer.**

EXAMPLE 2. Solve triangle ABC if $a = 10.00$, $b = 15.00$, and $c = 20.00$.

Solution: (*Plan*)

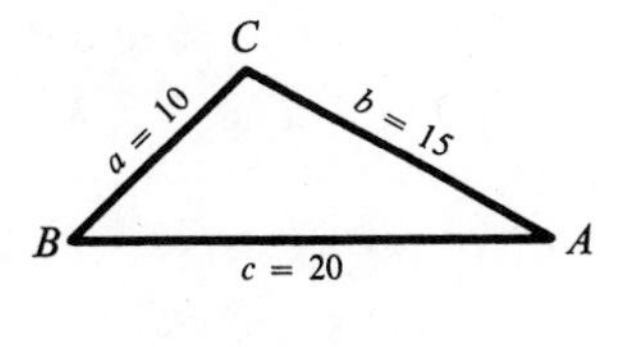

1. Sketch and label the triangle.
2. Use the law of cosines to determine the measure of the *largest* angle, namely C:

$$\cos C = \frac{a^2 + b^2 - c^2}{2ab}.$$

3. The remaining angles must be acute. (Why?) Use the law of sines to find the measure of one of them, say A: $\sin A = \dfrac{a \sin C}{c}$.
4. Use $A + B + C = 180°$ to find B.
5. Check by using $\dfrac{\sin A}{a} = \dfrac{\sin B}{b}$.

Carrying through the steps of the calculation is left to you.

When the measures of two angles and one side of a triangle are known, you use the fact that the sum of the measures of the angles is 180° to find the measure of the other angle, and the law of sines to find the lengths of the other sides. You also use the law of sines in solving a triangle when you know the *lengths of two of its sides and the measure of an angle opposite one of them.* This information is called *ambiguous,* however, because fitting the data there may be no, one, or two triangles.

Suppose, for example, that A, a, and b are known. By sketching $\angle A$ and measuring the distance b on one of its sides, you have the possibilities suggested in Figure 11–9 [$A < 90°$] and Figure 11–10 [$A \geq 90°$].

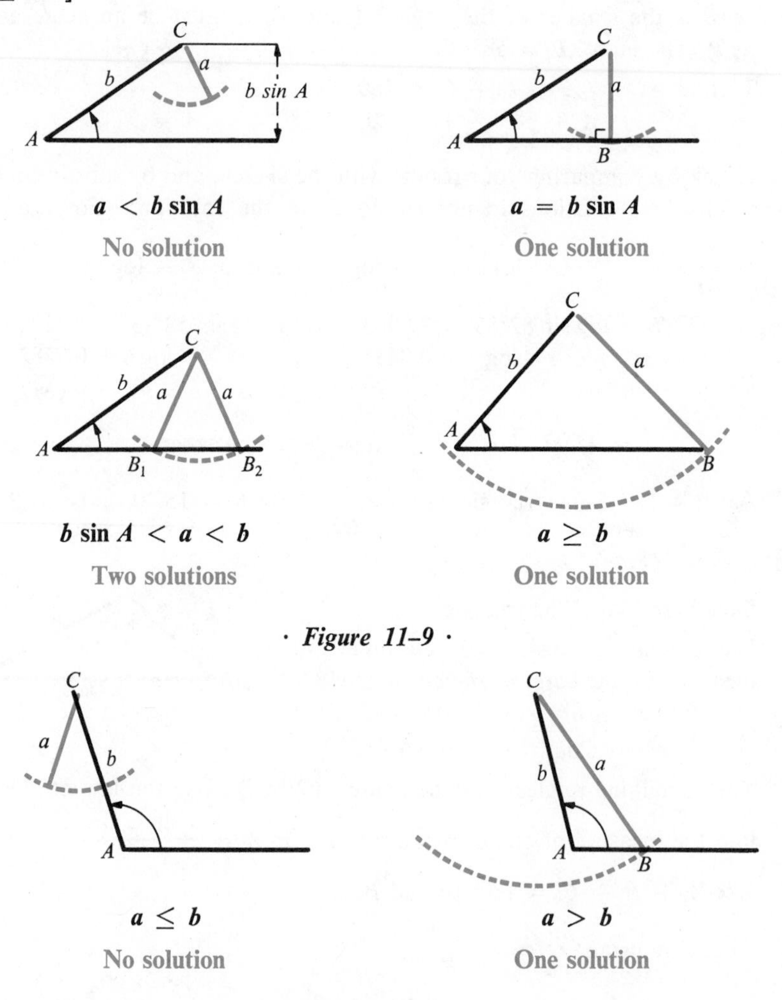

· *Figure 11–9* ·

· *Figure 11–10* ·

EXAMPLE 3. Solve triangle ABC, if $a = 14.00$, $b = 18.00$, $A = 35°00'$.

Solution:

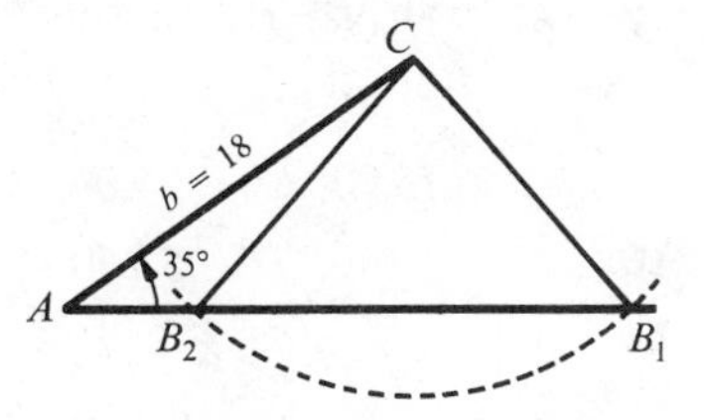

1. Sketching the triangle suggests that there are two solutions.

2. To determine B, use $\sin B = \dfrac{b \sin A}{a}$.

$$\log \sin B = \log b + \log \sin A - \log a$$

$$\begin{array}{lrl}
b = 18 & \log b = & 1.2553 \\
A = 35° & \log \sin A = & 9.7586 - 10 \quad (+) \\
 & & \overline{11.0139 - 10} \\
a = 14 & \log a = & 1.1461 \qquad (-) \\
 & \log \sin B = & \overline{9.8678 - 10}
\end{array}$$

$$B = 47°32', \text{ or } B = 180° - 45°32' = 132°28'$$

3. To determine C, use $C = 180° - A - B$.

$$C = 180° - 35° - 47°32' \quad \Big| \quad C = 180° - 35° - 132°28'$$
$$\therefore\ C = 97°28' \qquad\qquad \text{or } C = 12°32'$$

4. To determine c, use $c = \dfrac{a \sin C}{\sin A}$.

Completing Step 4 to find $c = 24.20$ or $c = 5.295$, and checking, are left to you.

$B = 47°32'$, $C = 97°28'$, $c = 24.20$; or
$B = 132°28'$, $C = 12°32'$, $c = 5.295$, **Answer.**

Among the exercises are examples of the other cases pictured in Figures 11–9 and 11–10.

Written Exercises

Find the measures of the other parts of each triangle ABC fitting the following data. Assume that angles have been measured to the nearest minute and sides to four significant figures.

A

1. $a = 5.000$, $b = 9.000$, $c = 12.00$
2. $a = 25.00$, $c = 4.000$, $B = 37°40'$
3. $b = 20.00$, $c = 60.00$, $A = 40°00'$
4. $c = 0.8000$, $A = 25°30'$, $B = 70°50'$
5. $b = 130.0$, $c = 150.0$, $B = 110°00'$

6. $a = 0.700$, $b = 0.800$, $c = 1.000$
7. $b = 15.00$, $A = 45°00'$, $C = 36°10'$
8. $a = 4130$, $c = 5560$, $C = 64°40'$
9. $c = 75.00$, $a = 54.00$, $A = 29°20'$
10. $a = 2.140$, $b = 5.260$, $C = 40°10'$
11. $a = \sqrt{2}$, $b = \sqrt{8}$, $c = 5$
12. $a = 17.40$, $b = 10.30$, $B = 100°30'$
13. $a = 1.250$, $B = 60°35'$, $C = 15°20'$
14. $c = 152.0$, $b = 135.0$, $B = 50°25'$
15. $a = 4900$, $c = 2200$, $C = 30°19'$
16. $a = 7.200$, $b = 5.400$, $c = 13.90$

If *b*, *B*, and *A* are to be parts of triangle *ABC*, determine the values of *b* for which *A* has **(a)** no value; **(b)** one value; **(c)** two values.

B 17. $a = 70$, $B = 120°$ 18. $a = 20$, $B = 45°$

Problems

A 1. A draftsman drew to scale (25 yd. = 1 in.) a map of a development that includes a triangular playground with sides of lengths 75 yd., 85 yd., and 100 yd. On the map what are the measures of the angles of the triangle representing the playground?

2. If a baseball diamond is a square 90.0 feet on a side, and if the pitcher's mound is 60.5 ft. from home plate on the diagonal from home to second base, how far is the pitcher from the three bases?

3. If the approximate distances from the Sun (S) to Earth (E) and Venus (V) were 9.3×10^7 mi. and 6.7×10^7 mi., respectively, when $\angle VES$ measured 28°, find the possible distances from earth to Venus.

4. One minute after passing over checkpoint A, a plane flying due east at 600 miles per hour passes over checkpoint B. As it passes B, what is its bearing from checkpoint C, which is 20 miles from A, 12 miles from B, and north of the line AB?

5. A vertical television mast is mounted on the roof of a building. From a point 750 feet from and on a level with the base of the building, the angles of elevation of the base and top of the mast measure 34° and 50° respectively. How tall is the mast?

6. Find the perimeter of a regular pentagon inscribed in a circle of radius 12 inches.

7. Front Street and Fairview Parkway intersect at an angle of $37°40'$. A car 500 ft. from the intersection is traveling away from it at 60 m.p.h. on Fairview Parkway. Another car 175 ft. from the intersection (on the same side as the first car) is traveling away from it at 40 m.p.h. on Front Street. How far apart are the cars after 15 minutes?

8. A force F of 700 lb. and G of 900 lb. act at a point. Their resultant R makes an angle of $48°$ with F. Find the magnitude of R and the measure of the angle between F and G.

9. The lengths of the diagonals of a parallelogram are 84 cm. and 52 cm. If the diagonals intersect at an angle of $40°$, how long are the sides of the parallelogram?

10. One angle of a rhombus measures $100°$, while the longer diagonal is 3.50 meters in length. How long is the side of the rhombus?

B

11. A ship sailed 2.5×10 miles on course $32°$ and then 1.2×10 miles on course $150°$. What course should the ship set, and what distance must it travel to return to its starting point by the shortest route?

12. Find the measures of the largest and smallest angles in the triangle whose vertices have coordinates $(0, -7)$, $(15, 13)$, and $(-15, 29)$.

13. A plane heading due north with an airspeed of 392 m.p.h. is subject to a 29 m.p.h. wind from $159°20'$. What are the plane's ground speed and course?

14. A pilot wants to maintain a course of $31°$ and ground speed of 400 m.p.h. against a 41 m.p.h. headwind from $343°$. What should her heading and airspeed be?

15. From the top of a lighthouse 150 ft. above the ocean, the angle of depression of a buoy due west of the lighthouse measures $36°$. The angle of depression of another buoy S65°W of the lighthouse measures $24°$. How far apart are the buoys?

16. From two points 6000 feet apart in the plane of the base of a hill, the angles of elevation of the summit measure $19°10'$ and $20°30'$. If the points are on opposite sides of the mountain but in the same vertical plane with the summit, what is the height of the mountain?

C

17. A light ray travels 14″ from a source A to a glass plate and makes an angle having sine 0.8167 and cosine 0.5772 with the top edge of the plate. The ray is refracted at the surface of the plate so that its path makes an angle having sine 0.3827 and cosine 0.9239 with the normal through the point of incidence. If $\angle OBA = 5°30'$, find AB.

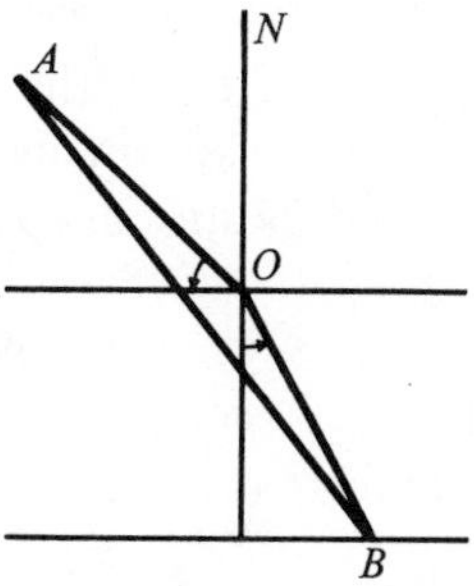

18. A pilot leaves an aircraft carrier and flies south at 360 m.p.h., while the carrier proceeds N30°W at 30 m.p.h. If the pilot has enough fuel to fly 4 hours, how far south can he fly before returning to his ship?

19. A fighter plane has a cruising speed of 600 m.p.h. In what direction should the plane head, and how long will it take to intercept in the shortest time a bomber that is 400 miles due north and flying on course 60° at 350 m.p.h.?

20. A freighter, steaming on course 140° at 20 knots, is 40 nautical miles N20°E of a submarine with a cruising speed of 25 knots. Find the course to be set by the sub to overtake the freighter in the least amount of time, and find this minimum time. (1 knot = 1 nautical mile per hour.)

11–11 Areas of Triangles

Knowing the lengths of two sides, say a and b, of triangle ABC and the measure of their included angle C, you can find the area of the triangle by using the formula (see page 447)

$$K = \tfrac{1}{2}ab \sin C.$$

From the law of sines you have $b = \dfrac{a \sin B}{\sin A}$.
Substituting for b in the area formula, you discover that

$$K = \tfrac{1}{2}a^2 \frac{\sin B \sin C}{\sin A}.$$

You can similarly derive the formulas

$$K = \tfrac{1}{2}b^2 \frac{\sin A \sin C}{\sin B} \text{ and } K = \tfrac{1}{2}c^2 \frac{\sin A \sin B}{\sin C}.$$

With the formulas just derived you can find the area of a triangle if you know the measures of one of its sides and two of its angles.

Given the lengths of three sides of a triangle, you find the area by using the following formula, whose proof is indicated in Exercises 23 and 24 on page 457.

$$K = \sqrt{s(s-a)(s-b)(s-c)},$$

where s is $\dfrac{a+b+c}{2}$, the *semiperimeter* of the triangle.

EXAMPLES. Find the area of triangle ABC, if

1. $b = 16, c = 5, A = 30°$
2. $b = 2, A = 30°, C = 45°$ 3. $a = 5, b = 4, c = 7$

Solutions: 1. $K = \frac{1}{2}bc \sin A = \frac{1}{2} \cdot 16 \cdot 5 \cdot \sin 30° = 8 \cdot 5 \cdot \frac{1}{2} = 20$

2. $B = 180° - A - C = 180° - 75° = 105°$

$$K = \frac{b^2}{2} \frac{\sin A \sin C}{\sin B} = \frac{4 \sin 30° \sin 45°}{2 \sin 105°} \doteq \frac{2(0.50)(0.707)}{(0.966)} \doteq 0.73$$

3. $$s = \frac{a + b + c}{2} = \frac{5 + 4 + 7}{2} = 8$$

$$K = \sqrt{s(s - a)(s - b)(s - c)} = \sqrt{8(3)(4)(1)} = 4\sqrt{6}$$

Written Exercises

A **1–16.** Find the area of the triangle or triangles (if any) fitting the data in Exercises 1–16, pages 453–454.

B **Find the measure of the indicated part of the triangle ABC determined by the given data.**

17. $K = 1340; A = 39°, B = 58°; c = ?$

18. $K = 15.90, c = 5.670; a = 41.00; A > 90°; B = ?$

Find the area of each parallelogram.

19. The adjacent sides are 22 in. and 15 in. long, and one angle measures 80°.

20. The diagonals are 100 and 120 cm. long and intersect at an angle of 42°.

21. The diagonals of the quadrilateral have lengths m and n and meet at angle θ. Prove the area of the figure to be $\frac{1}{2}mn \sin \theta$.

Prove that each formula holds in triangle ABC.

C **22.** $K = \frac{1}{2}c^2 \frac{\sin A \sin B}{\sin (A + B)}$ **23.** $K = bc \sin \frac{1}{2}A \cos \frac{1}{2}A$

24. $K = \sqrt{s(s - a)(s - b)(s - c)}$ where $s = \frac{a + b + c}{2}$. (*Hint:* Use the half-angle formulas, page 438, and the results of Exs. 11 and 12, page 446.)

Extra for Experts

Trigonometric Form of Complex Numbers

Let the point $P(a, b)$ represent the complex number $a + bi$ in the complex plane. Then a position angle θ of P is called an **amplitude** of the complex number, while the distance OP or r is called the **absolute value**, or **modulus**, of the number. Since $r = \sqrt{a^2 + b^2}$, $a = r \cos \theta$ and $b = r \sin \theta$, you can express the complex number in the **trigonometric form** $a + bi = r(\cos \theta + i \sin \theta)$. For example, if $a + bi = 1 - i$, then $a = 1, b = -1, r = \sqrt{2}$.

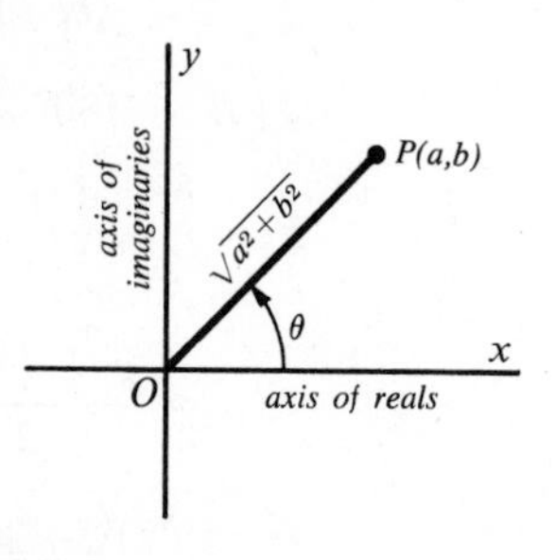

Therefore, $\cos \theta = \frac{1}{\sqrt{2}}$, $\sin \theta = -\frac{1}{\sqrt{2}}$, and θ is 315°; thus $1 - i = \sqrt{2}\,(\cos 315° + i \sin 315°)$.

If $z_1 = r_1(\cos \theta_1 + i \sin \theta_1)$, and $z_2 = r_2(\cos \theta_2 + i \sin \theta_2)$ are complex numbers in trigonometric form, you can verify that

$$z_1z_2 = r_1r_2[(\cos \theta_1 \cos \theta_2 - \sin \theta_1 \sin \theta_2) + i(\sin \theta_1 \cos \theta_2 + \cos \theta_1 \sin \theta_2)]$$

$$\therefore\ z_1z_2 = r_1r_2\,[\cos(\theta_1 + \theta_2) + i \sin(\theta_1 + \theta_2)]$$

Similarly, if $z_2 \neq 0$, you have

$$\frac{z_1}{z_2} = \frac{r_1}{r_2}\,[\cos(\theta_1 - \theta_2) + i \sin(\theta_1 - \theta_2)]$$

These results mean that to multiply complex numbers, you multiply their absolute values and add their amplitudes; to divide complex numbers, you divide the absolute values and find the difference of their amplitudes. Thus, if $z_1 = 6(\cos 150° + i \sin 150°)$, and $z_2 = 2(\cos 30° + i \sin 30°)$, you have

$$\begin{aligned} z_1z_2 &= 6 \cdot 2[\cos(150° + 30°) + i \sin(150° + 30°)] \\ &= 12(\cos 180° + i \sin 180°) = -12 \end{aligned}$$

$$\begin{aligned} z_1 \div z_2 &= (6 \div 2)[\cos(150° - 30°) + i \sin(150° - 30°)] \\ &= 3(\cos 120° + i \sin 120°) = -\frac{3}{2} + \frac{i3\sqrt{3}}{2} \end{aligned}$$

Squaring the complex number $r(\cos \theta + i \sin \theta)$, you obtain

$$[r(\cos \theta + i \sin \theta)]^2 = r^2(\cos 2\theta + i \sin 2\theta).$$

(Why?) In general, for any integer n, it is true that

$$[r(\cos \theta + i \sin \theta)]^n = r^n(\cos n\theta + i \sin n\theta)$$

Exercises

Write the numbers in the following pairs in trigonometric form. Using that form, find the product and the quotients of the numbers and then write the results in standard form.

1. $-10 + 10i;\ 5 + 5i$
2. $2 - 2i;\ 1 + i$
3. $-1 - i\sqrt{3};\ -\sqrt{3} - i$
4. $-i;\ \ 3 - 3\sqrt{3}\,i$

Use trigonometric form in computing the indicated powers. Write the result in standard form.

5. $(-1 - i)^4$
6. $(-1 + \sqrt{3}\,i)^6$
7. $(\sqrt{2} + i\sqrt{2})^{-8}$
8. Prove: Two complex numbers are equal if and only if their absolute values are equal and their amplitudes are coterminal angles.
9. Find the three roots of $z^3 = 27$. *Hint:* If $z = r(\cos\theta + i\sin\theta)$, $r^3(\cos 3\theta + i\sin 3\theta) = 27(\cos 0° + i\sin 0°)$. Use Exercise 8.

Chapter Summary

Inventory of Structure and Method

1. The **fundamental trigonometric identities,** together with other derived identities, allow you to transform trigonometric expressions into simpler ones and also to prove that certain equations are identities.
2. The **distance** between P and Q can be expressed also in terms of position angles of the points and their distances from the origin.

$$(PQ)^2 = p^2 + q^2 - 2pq(\cos\alpha\cos\beta + \sin\alpha\sin\beta)$$

From this formula you can derive formulas for values of functions of the *difference* and the **sum of two angles,** and then for functions of **double** and of **half a given angle.**
The **sum** or the **difference** of the **sines** or the **cosines of two angles** can be transformed into a **product.**
3. When the measures of three parts, including one side, of a triangle are known, the remaining parts can be found by the **Law of Cosines:** $a^2 = b^2 + c^2 - 2bc\cos A$, or by the **Law of Sines:**

$$\frac{a}{\sin A} = \frac{b}{\sin B} = \frac{c}{\sin C}$$

When the known parts of the triangle are the lengths of **two sides** and the measure of an **angle opposite** one of them, there may be no, one, or two solutions.

4. The area of a triangle is given by $K = \frac{1}{2}ab \sin C$; by $K = \frac{1}{2}a^2 \dfrac{\sin B \sin C}{\sin A}$; by $K = \sqrt{s(s - a)(s - b)(s - c)}$ where s denotes the semiperimeter.

Vocabulary and Spelling

trigonometric equation (*p. 421*)
trigonometric identity (*p. 421*)
fundamental identities (*p. 422*)
Law of Cosines (*p. 444*)
Law of Sines (*p. 447*)
solving a triangle (*p. 450*)

Chapter Test and Review

11-1 **1.** Express $\tan^2 \theta$ in terms of $\sin \theta$.

11-2 **2.** *Prove:* $(\tan A + \cot A)^2 = \sec^2 A + \csc^2 A$.

11-3 **3.** Find $(MN)^2$ for $M(4, 120°)$ and $N(6, 30°)$.

11-4 **4.** Express $\cos(x - 90°)$ as a function of x.

11-5 **5.** $\sin A = \frac{5}{13}$, A in Q. II; $\sec B = \frac{4}{3}$, B in Q. IV.
Find **(a)** $\sin(A + B)$; **(b)** $\tan(A - B)$.

11-6 **6.** If $\tan \theta = 3\sqrt{7}$, θ in Q. III, find $\cos \dfrac{\theta}{2}$.

7. *Prove:* $\dfrac{1 + \sin 2\alpha}{\cos \alpha + \sin \alpha} = \dfrac{\cos 2\alpha}{\cos \alpha - \sin \alpha}$.

11-7 **8.** Express as a function of an acute angle: $\cos 310° + \cos 190°$

11-8 **9.** In triangle ABC, $a = 6$, $b = 9$, $C = 120°$. Find c to the nearest unit.

11-9 **10.** Port A bears 295°50′ from ship C; port B bears 258°50′ from C. If B is 84 miles due south of A, how far, to the nearest mile, is C from the nearer port?

11-10 **11.** In triangle ABC, $c = 20$ and $B = 40°$. How many different triangles are possible if **(a)** $b = 10$; **(b)** $b = 18$, **(c)** $b = 20$; **(d)** $b = 25$; **(e)** $b = 20 \sin 40°$.

11-11 **12.** Find the area of triangle RST if $r = 12.0$, $t = 15.0$, and $S = 114°30'$.

A Duel with Life

One of the most powerful ideas in modern mathematics is that of group theory. The study of abstract groups has clarified the structure of the number system, uncovered surprising similarities between the underlying structures of algebra and geometry, and helped to explain physical phenomena such as the behavior of electrons in an atom. A "group" in the mathematical sense is simply a set of elements, together with an operation defined for them, which has the properties of closure, associativity, existence of an identity element, and existence of an inverse or reciprocal for every element. You are familiar with this concept as it applies to the number system in your study of algebra; for example, the set of integers under the operation of addition is a group. The term "group" was first used in its mathematical sense by a 21-year old French mathematician, Évariste Galois (Gal wah), in his feverishly scribbled will, written the night before his death.

The brief life of Galois, who was born near Paris in 1811, was one of continual frustration. Twice he tried to enter the École Polytechnique, then the leading school for training mathematicians, but failed the entrance examination. By the age of seventeen he had made a number of noteworthy mathematical discoveries which he submitted to the Academy of Sciences, but through carelessness his paper was never presented and was later lost. Two years later he again submitted some significant work which was lost before being read.

Discouraged with scholarly pursuits, Galois became a radical in politics and supported a party opposed to the king, Louis Philippe. He was imprisoned on trumped-up charges as a dangerous revolutionist and was later released only to be maneuvered by his political enemies into the senseless duel of honor in which he was killed. Before his death Galois wrote to a friend, "Preserve my memory, since fate has not given me life enough for my country to know my name." Today, mathematicians throughout the world know his name for his work with groups and with the conditions for solution of algebraic equations.

CHAPTER 12

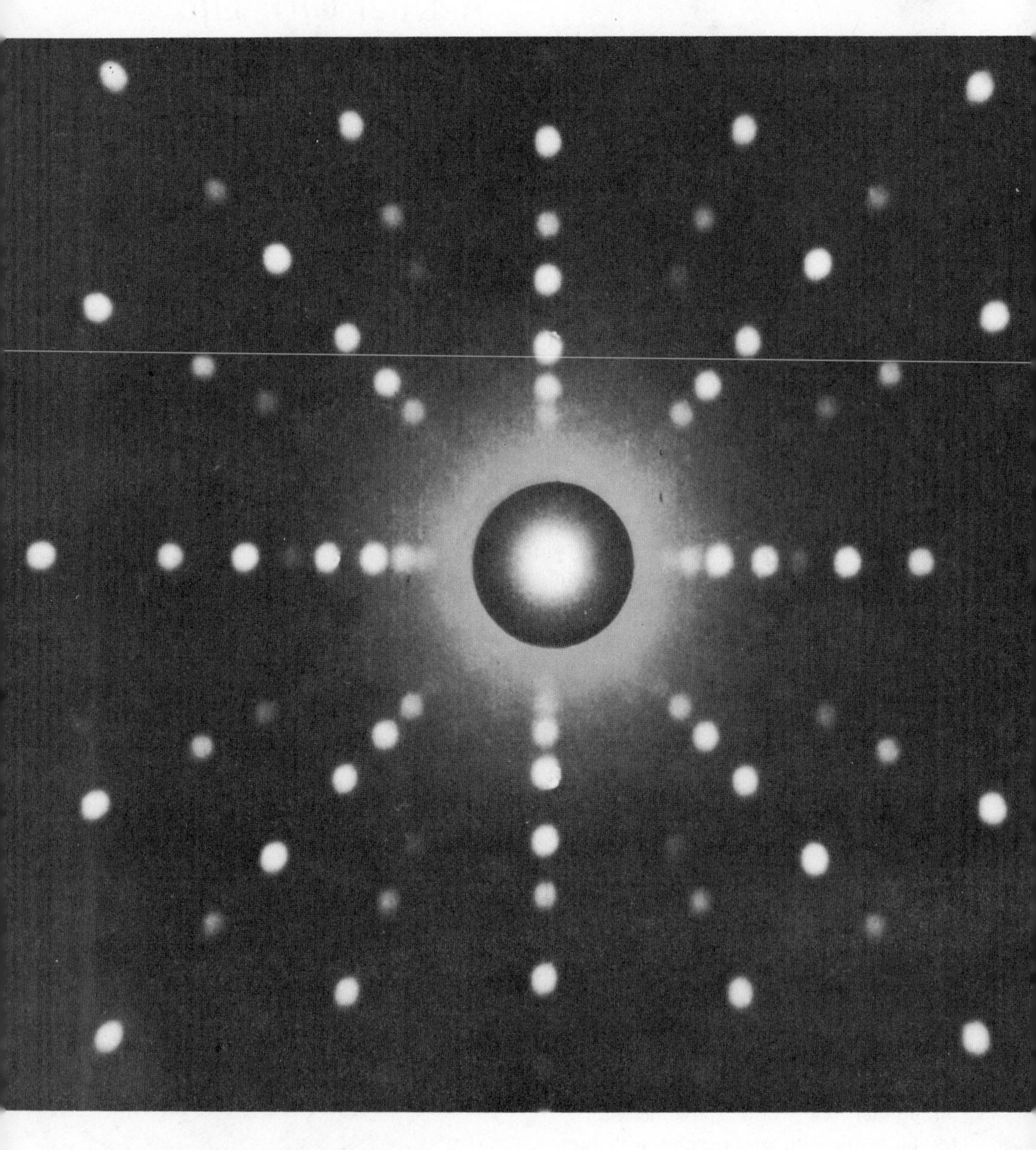

. . . a two-fold symmetry appearing as x-rays diffracted by a synthetic ceramic

The Circular Functions and Their Inverses

In many applications, functions such as $\{(x, \sin x)\}$ describe situations in which x may not denote an angle. The rhythmic motion of the heart, the periodic fluctuation of prices and of employment levels, the oscillation of a vibrating spring, earthquake tremors recorded on a seismograph, microwave communications, all involve the trigonometric functions of numbers, which you study in this chapter.

VARIATION AND GRAPHS

12–1 Measuring Arcs and Angles

Figure 12–1 shows the point $T(1, 0)$ on the unit circle $\{(x, y): x^2 + y^2 = 1\}$, whose circumference is 2π. A point starting at T and moving around the circle to a point P travels along a circular arc, $\widehat{TP}$. If you know the length of the arc $[m(\widehat{TP})]$, and the direction of motion, then you can locate P.

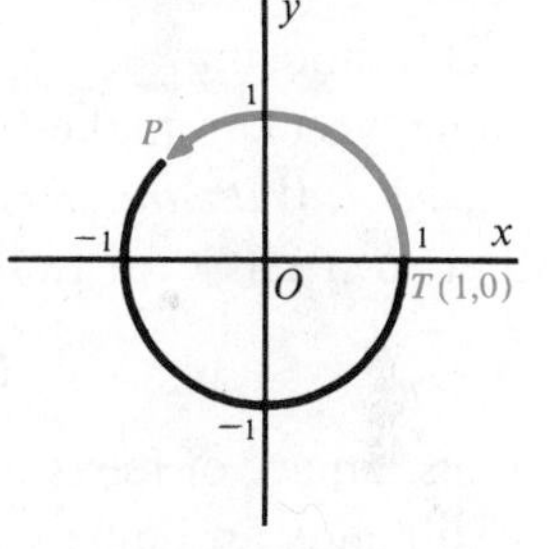

Figure 12–1

Figure 12–2 shows various positions of P corresponding to different arc lengths. Notice that positive measures have been assigned to arcs generated by counterclockwise motion and negative measures to arcs generated by clockwise motion. The terminal point of an arc with measure 0 is the initial point T itself.

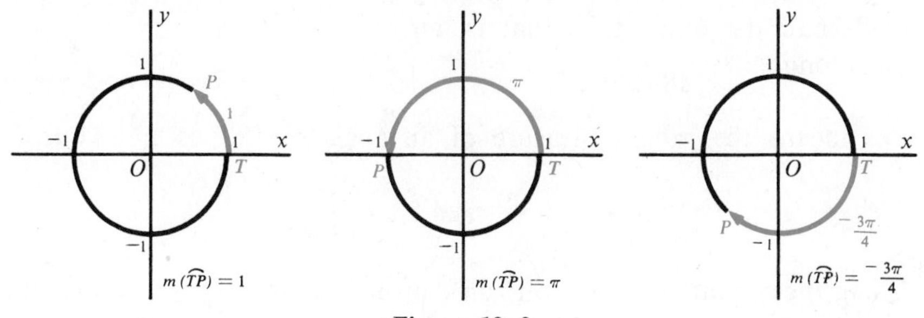

Figure 12–2

Can you explain why arcs whose measures differ by integral multiples of 2π will have the same terminal point? Figure 12–3 shows three coterminal arcs; note that arcs of more than one revolution are indicated by multiple curves.

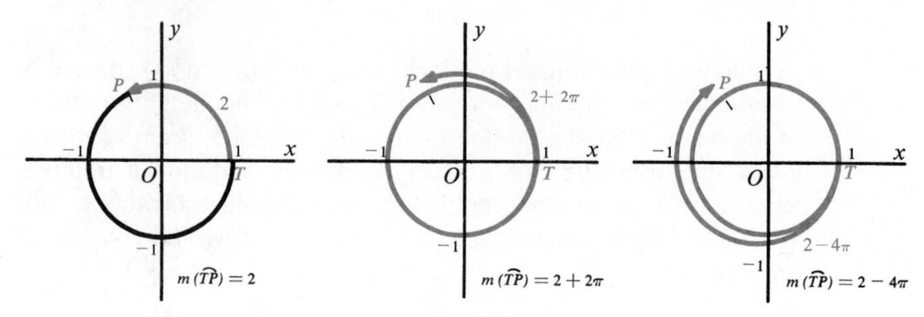

· *Figure 12–3* ·

In geometry you learn that the length s of a circular arc is proportional to the radius r *and* the measure of the central angle θ subtended by the arc (Figure 12–4); that is,

$$s = kr\theta.$$

By choosing an appropriate unit to measure the angle, you can make the constant of proportionality k be 1. *With this measurement system*, $s = r\theta$; so that in a circle of radius 1, you have $s = 1 \cdot \theta$, or

· *Figure 12–4* ·

$$s = \theta \text{ and } \theta = s.$$

Thus, an arc of measure 1 on a circle of radius 1 subtends an angle whose measure is 1. We call this unit of angular measure, **1 radian**, written 1^R.

Can you find the radian measure of an angle of 180°? Because such an angle subtends half the unit circle, that is, an arc π units long,

$$180° = \pi^R;$$

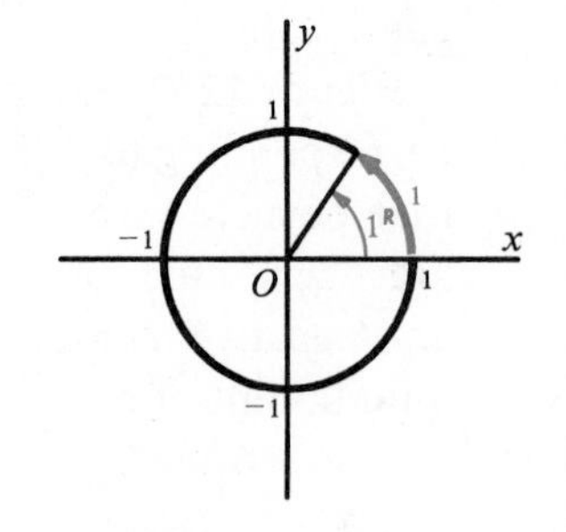

· *Figure 12–5* ·

this means the radian measure of an angle of 180° is π^R. Thus,

$$1^R = \frac{180°}{\pi} \text{ and } 1° = \frac{\pi^R}{180}$$

Using these relationships, you can convert radian measure to degrees and degrees to radians. Because $\pi \doteq 3.14159$, you find $1^R \doteq 57°18'$ and $1° \doteq 0.01745^R$.

EXAMPLE 1. Convert $\frac{1}{2}^{R}$ to degree measure.

Solution: $$\frac{1^{R}}{2} = \left(\frac{1}{2}\cdot\frac{180}{\pi}\right)^{\circ} = \frac{90^{\circ}}{\pi} \doteq \frac{90^{\circ}}{3.1416} \doteq 28.65^{\circ}, \text{ or } \doteq 28^{\circ}39',$$ **Answer.**

EXAMPLE 2. Convert 30° to radian measure.

Solution: $$30^{\circ} = \left(30\cdot\frac{\pi}{180}\right)^{R} = \frac{\pi^{R}}{6} \doteq \frac{3.1416^{R}}{6}, \text{ or } \doteq 0.5236^{R},$$ **Answer.**

EXAMPLE 3. The angular speed of a point on a wheel is 120 RPM (revolutions per minute). Express this speed in radians per second and find the distance to the nearest inch that the point travels in 10 seconds if it is 6 inches from the center of the wheel.

Solution: 120 RPM $= 120(2\pi)$, or 240π radians per minute.

$\therefore$ the angular speed is $\frac{240\pi}{60}$, or 4π radians per second. In 10 seconds, the point travels an arc with central angle $10 \cdot 4\pi$, or 40π radians. Therefore, the distance traveled is the length of this arc:

$$s = r\theta$$
$$= 6 \cdot 40\pi = 240\pi \doteq 754$$ 754 inches, **Answer.**

Written Exercises

Give the exact radian measure of each of the following.

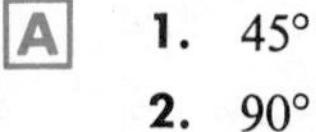

1. 45°
2. 90°
3. 300°
4. -180°
5. -330°
6. 450°
7. 720°
8. -15°
9. -75°
10. -360°
11. 270°
12. 210°

Using $\pi \doteq 3.1416$, convert each measure to the nearest hundredth of a radian.

13. $11\frac{1}{2}^{\circ}$
14. 90°
15. -160°
16. 430°

Convert each measure to the nearest degree.

17. $-\frac{3\pi^{R}}{4}$
18. $-\pi^{R}$
19. $\frac{11\pi^{R}}{6}$
20. $\frac{7\pi^{R}}{12}$
21. $-\frac{9\pi^{R}}{4}$
22. 0^{R}
23. 2^{R}
24. 3^{R}
25. $\frac{1}{4}^{R}$
26. -1.5^{R}
27. -0.8^{R}
28. 0.03^{R}

Give the exact value of each of the following.

29. $\sin \frac{\pi^R}{3}$ **32.** $\sin\left(-\frac{\pi^R}{2}\right)$ **35.** $\cos n\pi^R$, n an integer

30. $\cos \frac{\pi^R}{4}$ **33.** $\cos\left(-\frac{\pi^R}{6}\right)$ **36.** $\sin(2n + 1)\pi^R$, n an integer

31. $\tan \pi^R$ **34.** $\cot \frac{5\pi^R}{6}$

On a circle of radius 24 cm., what is the length of the arc intercepted by a central angle of given measure?

37. 3^R **38.** $\frac{\pi^R}{6}$ **39.** $60°$ **40.** $150°$

What is the radius of a circle on which an arc 18 ft. long subtends a central angle of given measure?

41. $\frac{3}{4}^R$ **42.** π^R **43.** $120°$ **44.** $360°$

45. What is the speed in feet per minute of a point on the rim of a wheel of diameter 6 feet, turning at the rate of 5 RPM?

46. An automobile is traveling at the rate of 60 mph (88 ft. per sec.). If a tire is 15 in. in radius, find the measure of the angle through which the wheel turns in 3 sec.

47. To the nearest hundred miles per minute, what is the speed of an earth satellite traveling in a circular orbit 600 miles high if it completes 1 orbit every 80 minutes? (Use 4000 mi. for earth's radius.)

48. If the eye can detect a movement of 0.1 in. per sec., how long must the minute hand of a clock be for the movement of its tip to be detected?

49. Show that the length of an arc subtended by a central angle of $d°$ in a circle of radius r is given by $s = \frac{\pi r d}{180}$.

50. Show that the velocity v of a point on the edge of a circular disk of radius r ft. turning at p RPM is $2\pi pr$ ft. per min.

12-2 The Circular Functions

Every real number t is the measure of one and only one arc with initial point T on the circle $\{(x, y)\colon x^2 + y^2 = 1\}$. Hence each real number determines a unique ordered pair of numbers (a, b) which are the coordinates of the terminal point P of the arc (Figure 12-6, next page). The set of all ordered pairs (t, a) is called the **cosine** function over the real numbers; the set of all pairs (t, b) is the sine function over the real numbers. We write: $\cos t = a$ and $\sin t = b$.

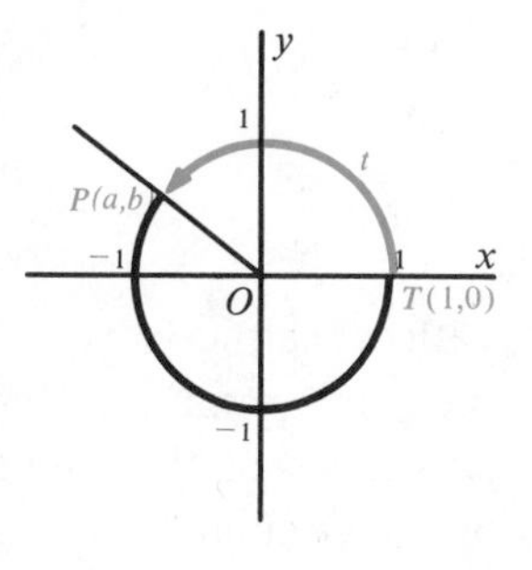

· *Figure 12–6* ·

What is the relationship between these new functions and the cosine and sine functions whose domain is the set of angles in standard position (Chapter 10)? Notice that an arc of measure t subtends at O an angle in standard position with measure t^{R}. Since $P(a, b)$ is a point one unit from the origin on the terminal side of this angle, you have

$$\cos t^{\mathrm{R}} = a \text{ and } \sin t^{\mathrm{R}} = b.$$

Thus:

$$\cos t^{\mathrm{R}} = \cos t, \text{ and } \sin t^{\mathrm{R}} = \sin t.$$

Because of these relationships, you need not distinguish between $\cos t^{\mathrm{R}}$ and $\cos t$, or between $\sin t^{\mathrm{R}}$ and $\sin t$. For example, you can write cos 2 to mean either "cosine of the number 2" or "cosine of the angle whose measure is 2^{R}." On the other hand, in referring to an angle whose measure is given in degrees, you *always use the degree symbol.* Notice that $\cos 2° \neq \cos 2$; in fact, $\cos 2° \doteq 0.9994$; but $\cos 2$ or $\cos 2^{\mathrm{R}} \doteq \cos 114°35' \doteq -0.4160$.

In terms of the cosine and sine functions, you can define the *tangent, cotangent, secant, and cosecant functions over the real numbers*, just as we did in Section 10–3 for angles. For example, the tangent function is the following set of ordered pairs of *real numbers:*

$$\left\{(t, \tan t)\text{: } \tan t = \frac{\sin t}{\cos t},\ \cos t \neq 0\right\}.$$

The six "trigonometric" functions over the real numbers are sometimes called the circular functions, to distinguish them from the trigonometric functions for angles. However, to find the value of a circular function for any given real number, you can consider the real number as the radian measure of an angle and then evaluate the corresponding trigonometric function for that angle.

EXAMPLE 1. Find the value of **(a)** $\sin(-\frac{1}{2})$; **(b)** $\cos \frac{2\pi}{3}$; **(c)** $\tan \frac{9\pi}{4}$.

Solution:

a. $-\frac{1}{2}^{\mathrm{R}} \doteq -28°39'$; $\therefore \sin(-\frac{1}{2}) \doteq \sin(-28°39') \doteq -0.4795$

b. $\frac{2\pi^{\mathrm{R}}}{3} = 120°$; $\therefore \cos \frac{2\pi}{3} = \cos 120° = -\frac{1}{2}$

(*continued on page* 468)

c. $\frac{9\pi}{4} = 2\pi + \frac{\pi}{4}$; $\therefore$ an angle of $\frac{9\pi^R}{4}$ is coterminal with an angle of $\frac{\pi^R}{4}$.

Since $\frac{\pi^R}{4} = 45°$, $\tan\frac{9\pi}{4} = \tan 45° = 1$.

Because the values of the trigonometric functions of t radians equal the corresponding values of the circular functions of the real number t, properties of the trigonometric functions can be interpreted in terms of the circular functions. For example, identities such as those in the first column below, which were proved for the set of angles, can be restated as valid identities over the real numbers (column 2).

$\sin^2\theta + \cos^2\theta = 1$	$\sin^2 t + \cos^2 t = 1$
$\cos(90° - \beta) = \sin\beta$	$\cos\left(\frac{\pi}{2} - x\right) = \sin x$
$\sin(-\alpha) = -\sin\alpha$	$\sin(-u) = -\sin u$

EXAMPLE 2. Evaluate $\sin\left(\pi + \frac{\pi}{6}\right)$.

Solution:

$$\sin\left(\pi + \frac{\pi}{6}\right) = \sin\pi\cos\frac{\pi}{6} + \cos\pi\sin\frac{\pi}{6}$$
$$= 0\cdot\frac{\sqrt{3}}{2} + (-1)\frac{1}{2} = -\frac{1}{2}, \textbf{ Answer.}$$

Written Exercises

Find the exact value of the circular functions of each of the following numbers.

A

1. 0 **4.** $-\pi$ **7.** $-\frac{2}{3}\pi$ **10.** 9π

2. $\frac{\pi}{2}$ **5.** $\frac{5\pi}{6}$ **8.** $-\frac{11\pi}{6}$ **11.** $\frac{\pi}{12}$

3. $\frac{\pi}{4}$ **6.** $\frac{4\pi}{3}$ **9.** $-\frac{7\pi}{2}$ **12.** $\frac{\pi}{8}$

Find each value to the nearest hundredth. Use $1^R \doteq 57°18'$; $0.1^R \doteq 5°44'$.

13. $\sin 1.6$ **14.** $\tan 0.4$ **15.** $\tan(-2.1)$ **16.** $\cos(-3)$

At time t (in sec.) the displacement d (in ft.), velocity v (in ft. per. sec.), and acceleration a (in ft. per sec.^{2}) of a weight hanging on a certain vibrating spring are given by $d = \frac{1}{3}\cos 3t$, $v = -\sin 3t$, and $a = -3\cos 3t$. Find d, v, and a for the following values of t.

17. 0 **18.** $\frac{1}{12}\pi$ **19.** $\frac{1}{2}\pi$ **20.** $\frac{1}{3}\pi$

At time t (in sec.) the voltage V and the current I (in amperes) in a circuit are given by $V = 100 \sin 260t$ and $I = 25 \sin 260(t - 0.001)$. Find V and I at the following times.

21. 0 sec. **22.** 0.001 sec. **23.** 0.005 sec. **24.** 0.01 sec.

Evaluate each of the following if n denotes an integer.

B **25.** $\cos\left(n\pi + \frac{\pi}{4}\right)$

26. $\tan\left[(2n + 1)\frac{\pi}{2} - \frac{\pi}{3}\right]$

27. $\cot\left(n \cdot \frac{\pi}{4}\right)$

28. $\sin\left(\frac{n\pi}{2} + \frac{\pi}{6}\right)$

Prove each identity over the set of real numbers.

29. $\dfrac{\cos^2 x - \sin(\pi + x)\sin(\pi - x)}{\csc(\pi - x)} = \sin x$

30. $\dfrac{\sin(\pi - y)}{1 + \cos y} - \cot(\pi - y) = \csc y$

31. $\tan^2 x - \sin^2 x = \tan^2 x \sin^2 x$

32. $\sin^6 v + \cos^6 v = 1 - 3 \sin^2 v \cos^2 v$

33. $\dfrac{2 \cos^2 4t}{\sin 8t} = \dfrac{\sin 8t}{1 - \cos 8t}$

34. $2 \cos 3d(\cos 3d - 1) = \cos 6d - 2 \cos 3d + 1$

35. $\cos\left(\frac{\pi}{3} + y\right) + \cos\left(\frac{\pi}{3} - y\right) = \cos y$

36. $\dfrac{\tan(r + s) - \tan s}{1 + \tan(r + s)\tan s} = \tan r$

C **37.** $\dfrac{\cos 12y - \sin 6y + \cos 6y - \sin 12y}{\cos 12y + \cos 6y} = 1 - \tan 9y$

38. $\dfrac{2 \cos k}{\cos k \sin 2k + \sin k \cos 2k - \sin k} = \cot k + \tan 2k$

39. If $\sin u = \sin v$, prove that there is an integer n for which $u = v + 2n\pi$ or $u = (\pi - v) + 2n\pi$.

40. If $\cos u = \cos v$, prove that there is an integer n for which $u = v + 2n\pi$, or $u = (2\pi - v) + 2n\pi$.

Graphs of Cosine and Sine Functions

In Figure 12–7, the terminal points of arcs of length t for various convenient values of t between 0 and 2π have been indicated on the unit circle. Recall that for each value of t the abscissa of the terminal point is $\cos t$, while the ordinate is $\sin t$. Therefore, by noting the pattern of change in the coordinates of the terminal point, you can see the variation in the values of these functions as t varies from 0 to 2π.

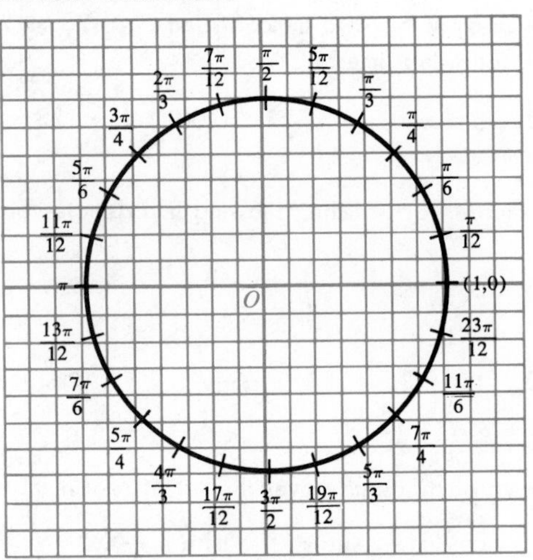

· *Figure 12–7* ·

When t increases from	$\cos t$	$\sin t$
0 to $\frac{\pi}{2}$	decreases from 1 to 0	increases from 0 to 1
$\frac{\pi}{2}$ to π	decreases from 0 to -1	decreases from 1 to 0
π to $\frac{3\pi}{2}$	increases from -1 to 0	decreases from 0 to -1
$\frac{3\pi}{2}$ to 2π	increases from 0 to 1	increases from -1 to 0

For t greater than 2π or less than 0, the values of $\cos t$ and $\sin t$ repeat the patterns of the interval from 0 to 2π, because for every integer n, $\cos(t + n \cdot 2\pi) = \cos t$ and $\sin(t + n \cdot 2\pi) = \sin t$. Whenever f is a function such that for a nonzero constant p, $f(x + p) = f(x)$ for each x in the domain of f, then f is called a **periodic function**. The smallest such *positive* constant p is called the **period** of f. Thus, the cosine and sine functions are periodic with period 2π.

You can picture the variation and periodicity of these functions by drawing their graphs. The graph of $\{(x, y): y = \sin x\}$ is shown in Figure 12–8. It is a smooth curve obtained by joining the points whose coordinates are given in the table and then repeating the pattern in both directions along the x-axis. Note that the scales on the axes are equal. However, for convenience, 3.14 units have been marked off on the x-axis to denote π, and the numbers $\frac{\pi}{2}, \frac{\pi}{3}, \frac{\pi}{6}$, etc., have been shown. Note that $\frac{\sqrt{2}}{2} \doteq 0.71$ and $\frac{\sqrt{3}}{2} \doteq 0.87$.

x	0	$\frac{\pi}{6}$	$\frac{\pi}{3}$	$\frac{\pi}{2}$	$\frac{2\pi}{3}$	$\frac{5\pi}{6}$	π	$\frac{7\pi}{6}$	$\frac{4\pi}{3}$	$\frac{3\pi}{2}$	$\frac{5\pi}{3}$	$\frac{11\pi}{6}$	2π
y = sin x	0	$\frac{1}{2}$	$\frac{\sqrt{3}}{2}$	1	$\frac{\sqrt{3}}{2}$	$\frac{1}{2}$	0	$-\frac{1}{2}$	$-\frac{\sqrt{3}}{2}$	-1	$-\frac{\sqrt{3}}{2}$	$-\frac{1}{2}$	0

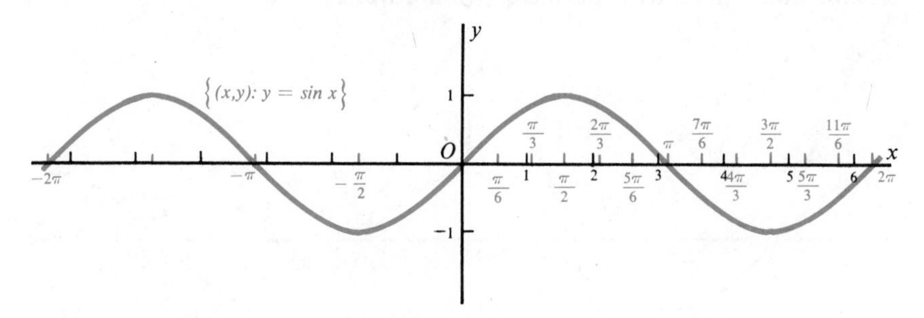

· *Figure 12–8* ·

Figure 12–9 shows the graph of $\{(x, y): y = \cos x\}$.

x	0	$\frac{\pi}{6}$	$\frac{\pi}{3}$	$\frac{\pi}{2}$	$\frac{2\pi}{3}$	$\frac{5\pi}{6}$	π	$\frac{7\pi}{6}$	$\frac{4\pi}{3}$	$\frac{3\pi}{2}$	$\frac{5\pi}{3}$	$\frac{11\pi}{6}$	2π
y = cos x	1	$\frac{\sqrt{3}}{2}$	$\frac{1}{2}$	0	$-\frac{1}{2}$	$-\frac{\sqrt{3}}{2}$	-1	$-\frac{\sqrt{3}}{2}$	$-\frac{1}{2}$	0	$\frac{1}{2}$	$\frac{\sqrt{3}}{2}$	1

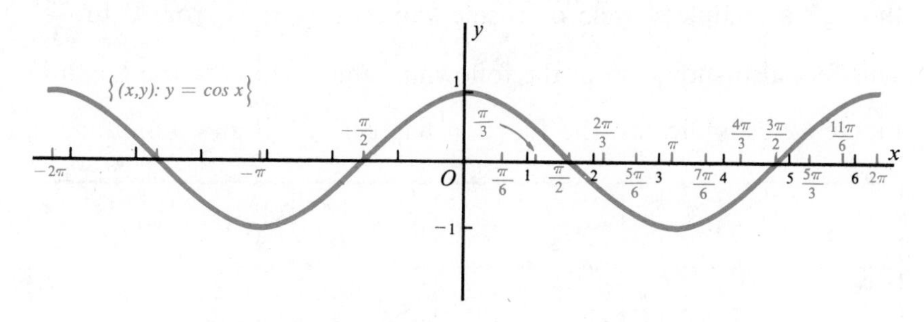

· *Figure 12–9* ·

The curves in Figures 12–8 and 12–9 are called *sinusoidal waves.*

Both curves have 1 as maximum ordinate and -1 as minimum ordinate. When a periodic function has a maximum value M and a minimum value m, the **amplitude** of the function is $\frac{M - m}{2}\cdot$ Thus, the amplitude of the sine and cosine functions is $\frac{1 - (-1)}{2} = 1$.

To draw the graph of $\{(x, y)\colon y = 3 \cos x\}$, notice that each ordinate of this graph is 3 times the corresponding ordinate of the curve in Figure 12–9. Therefore, as shown in Figure 12–10, this function has period 2π and amplitude 3. In general, the graph of any function of the form $\{(x, y)\colon y = a \cos x\}$, or $\{(x, y)\colon y = a \sin x\}$, $a \neq 0$, is a sinusoidal curve with period 2π and amplitude $|a|$.

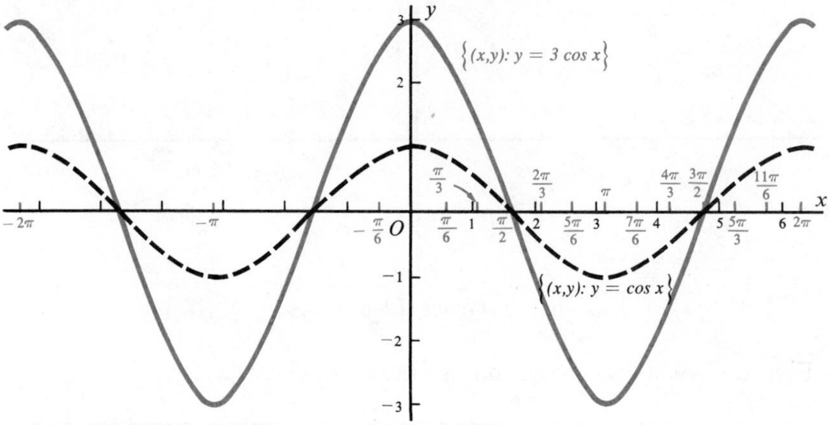

· *Figure 12–10* ·

To draw the graph of $\{(x, y)\colon y = \cos 3x\}$, notice that as x varies from 0 to $\frac{2\pi}{3}$, $3x$ varies from 0 to 2π. Therefore, $\cos 3x$ will run through a complete cycle of cosine values as x runs from 0 to $\frac{2\pi}{3}\cdot$ This fact also shows up in the following table. Thus, as the graph in Figure 12–11 indicates, the function has period $\frac{2\pi}{3}$ and amplitude 1.

x	0	$\frac{\pi}{18}$	$\frac{\pi}{9}$	$\frac{\pi}{6}$	$\frac{2\pi}{9}$	$\frac{5\pi}{18}$	$\frac{\pi}{3}$	$\frac{7\pi}{18}$	$\frac{4\pi}{9}$	$\frac{\pi}{2}$	$\frac{5\pi}{9}$	$\frac{11\pi}{18}$	$\frac{2\pi}{3}$
3x	0	$\frac{\pi}{6}$	$\frac{\pi}{3}$	$\frac{\pi}{2}$	$\frac{2\pi}{3}$	$\frac{5\pi}{6}$	π	$\frac{7\pi}{6}$	$\frac{4\pi}{3}$	$\frac{3\pi}{2}$	$\frac{5\pi}{3}$	$\frac{11\pi}{6}$	2π
y = cos 3x	1	$\frac{\sqrt{3}}{2}$	$\frac{1}{2}$	0	$-\frac{1}{2}$	$-\frac{\sqrt{3}}{2}$	-1	$-\frac{\sqrt{3}}{2}$	$-\frac{1}{2}$	0	$\frac{1}{2}$	$\frac{\sqrt{3}}{2}$	1

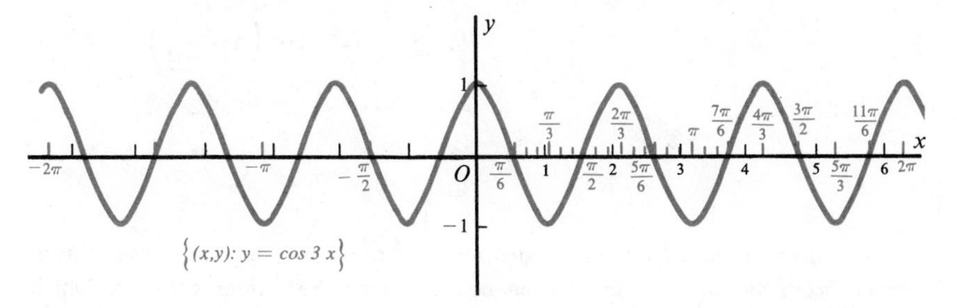

· *Figure 12–11* ·

In general, the graph of a function of the form $\{(x, y): y = a \cos bx\}$, or $\{(x, y): y = a \sin bx\}$, $a \neq 0$, $b \neq 0$, is a sinusoidal curve with amplitude $|a|$ and period $\frac{2\pi}{|b|}$. By using this fact, you can quickly sketch the curve by locating its maximum and minimum points and the points where it crosses the x-axis.

EXAMPLE. Sketch the graph of $\{(x, y): y = 2 \cos \frac{1}{3}x\}$ over 1 period.

Solution: Amplitude $= 2$; period $= \frac{2\pi}{\frac{1}{3}} = 6\pi$.

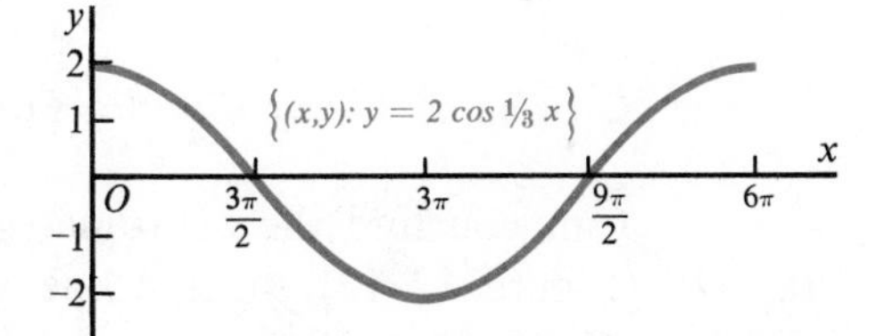

Over the interval $0 \leq x \leq 6\pi$:

1. the maximum points occur at the ends of the interval: $(0, 2)$, $(6\pi, 2)$
2. the minimum occurs at the middle of the interval: $(3\pi, -2)$
3. the curve crosses the x-axis at the quarter and three-quarter points: $\left(\frac{3\pi}{2}, 0\right)$ and $\left(\frac{9\pi}{2}, 0\right)$

With this information, the curve is sketched as shown.

Written Exercises

Determine the amplitude and period p of each function f whose values are indicated, and then sketch the graph over the following interval of two periods $-p \leq x \leq p$.

1. $f(x) = 2 \cos x$
2. $f(x) = \frac{1}{2} \cos x$
3. $f(x) = \frac{1}{3} \sin x$
4. $f(x) = 4 \sin x$
5. $f(x) = \sin 3x$
6. $f(x) = \cos 2x$
7. $f(x) = \cos \frac{1}{2}x$
8. $f(x) = \sin \frac{1}{3}x$
9. $f(x) = 2 \sin 4x$
10. $f(x) = -2 \cos 4x$
11. $f(x) = -4 \cos \frac{1}{2}x$
12. $f(x) = 6 \sin \frac{1}{2}x$

B

13. $f(x) = \cos \pi x$

14. $f(x) = \sin \dfrac{\pi x}{2}$

15. $f(x) = 2 \sin\left(x - \dfrac{\pi}{3}\right)$

16. $f(x) = 2 \cos\left(x + \dfrac{\pi}{3}\right)$

17. $f(x) = 1 + \sin x$

18. $f(x) = 2 + \cos x$

Over the given interval draw the graphs of f and g in the same coordinate system. From the graphs find to the nearest tenth the values of x for which f(x) = g(x).

19. $f(x) = \sin x$
$g(x) = 2 \cos x,\ 0 \le x < 2\pi$

20. $f(x) = \sin 2x$
$g(x) = 3 \cos x,\ 0 \le x < 2\pi$

21. $f(x) = \cos \pi x$
$g(x) = x,\ 0 \le x < 2$

22. $f(x) = \sin \pi x$
$g(x) = x - 1,\ 0 \le x < 2$

23. $f(x) = \sin\left(\dfrac{\pi}{2} - x\right)$
$g(x) = x,\ 0 \le x \le 2\pi$

24. $f(x) = \cos\left(x + \dfrac{\pi}{4}\right)$
$g(x) = \sin\left(x + \dfrac{3\pi}{4}\right),$
$-\pi \le x \le \pi$

12–4 Graphs of Other Circular Functions

Can you find the coordinates of the point of intersection of ray OP (Figure 12–12) and the line $x = 1$ which is tangent to the unit circle? Since ray OP has slope $\dfrac{\sin t}{\cos t}$, or $\tan t$, it is contained in the line $y = (\tan t)x$. Therefore, for P in the first or fourth quadrant, the ray intersects the line $x = 1$ at the point $G(1, \tan t)$.

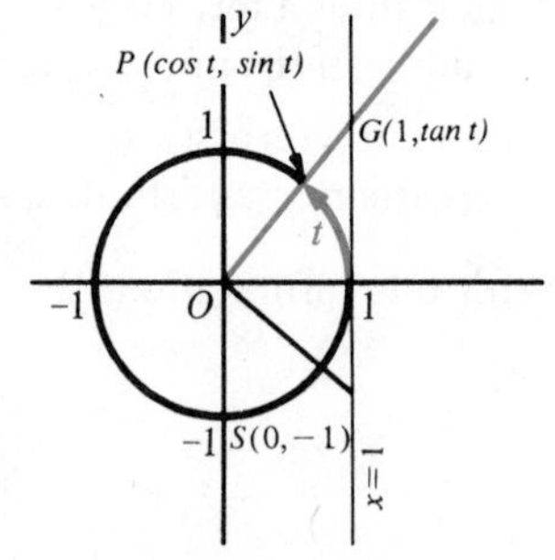

· Figure 12–12 ·

This means that you can visualize the variation in the value of $\tan t$ as t varies from $-\dfrac{\pi}{2}$ to $\dfrac{\pi}{2}$ by noting the change in the ordinate of G as P moves counterclockwise on the circle from $S(0, -1)$. For P at S, that is, $t = -\dfrac{\pi}{2}$, there is no value of $\tan t$. (Where is G?) As t varies from $-\dfrac{\pi}{2}$ to 0, $\tan t$ increases through all negative numbers to zero.

As t goes from 0 to $\frac{\pi}{2}$, $\tan t$ increases from zero through all positive numbers.

To see the variation in $\tan t$ for $\frac{\pi}{2} < t < \frac{3\pi}{2}$, consider Figure 12–13, which shows that for P in the second or third quadrant, ray OP intersects the line $x = -1$ in the point $(-1, -\tan t)$. Can you explain why $\tan t$ runs through all negative numbers, 0, and then all positive numbers as t varies from $\frac{\pi}{2}$ to $\frac{3\pi}{2}$? This suggests that the tangent function has period π, a fact confirmed by the following identity:

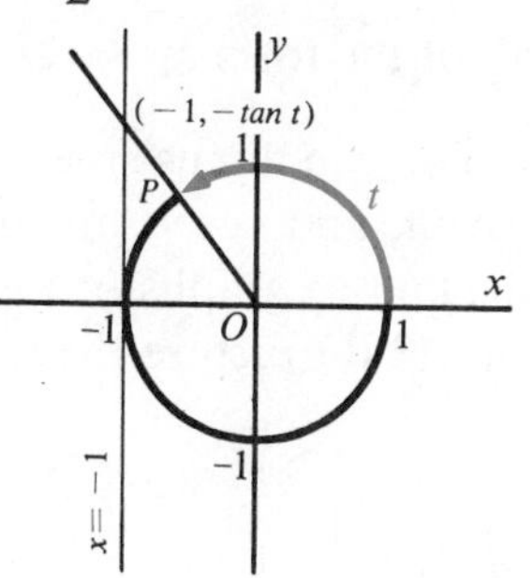

· *Figure 12–13* ·

For every integer n:

$$\tan(t + n\pi) = \frac{\tan t + \tan n\pi}{1 - \tan n\pi \tan t} = \frac{\tan t + 0}{1 - 0 \cdot \tan t} = \tan t$$

The graph of $\{(x, y): y = \tan x\}$ pictures the variation described above and is obtained by repeating the pattern shown by plotting points over one period (Figure 12–14).

x	$-\frac{\pi}{2}$	$-\frac{\pi}{3}$	$-\frac{\pi}{4}$	$-\frac{\pi}{6}$	0	$\frac{\pi}{6}$	$\frac{\pi}{4}$	$\frac{\pi}{3}$	$\frac{\pi}{2}$
y = tan x	—	$-\sqrt{3}$	-1	$-\frac{\sqrt{3}}{3}$	0	$\frac{\sqrt{3}}{3}$	1	$\sqrt{3}$	—

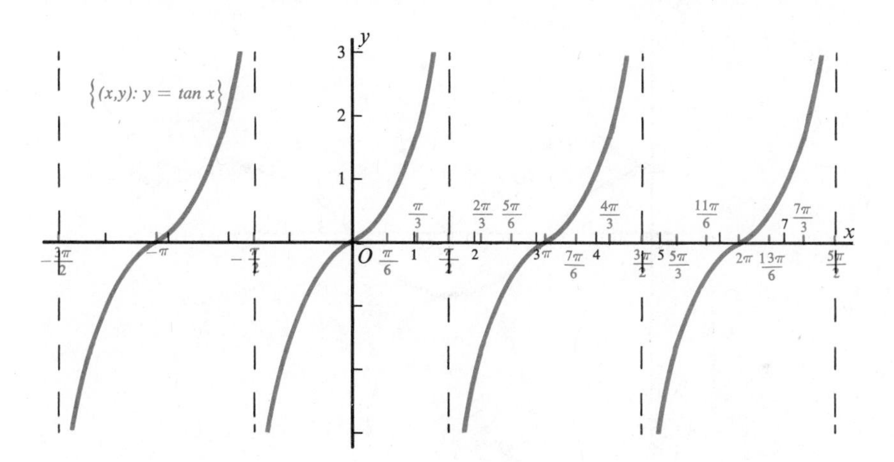

· *Figure 12–14* ·

Because $\tan x$ does not exist when x is replaced by any odd multiple of $\frac{\pi}{2}$, the equations of the dash lines (the asymptotes) in the figure are all of the form $x = (2n + 1)\frac{\pi}{2}$, where n is any integer.

You can discuss the variations and draw the graphs of the cotangent, secant, and cosecant functions by referring to a table of values or to the known graphs of their reciprocal functions. Figures 12–15, 12–16, and 12–17 picture the graphs of each pair of reciprocal functions.

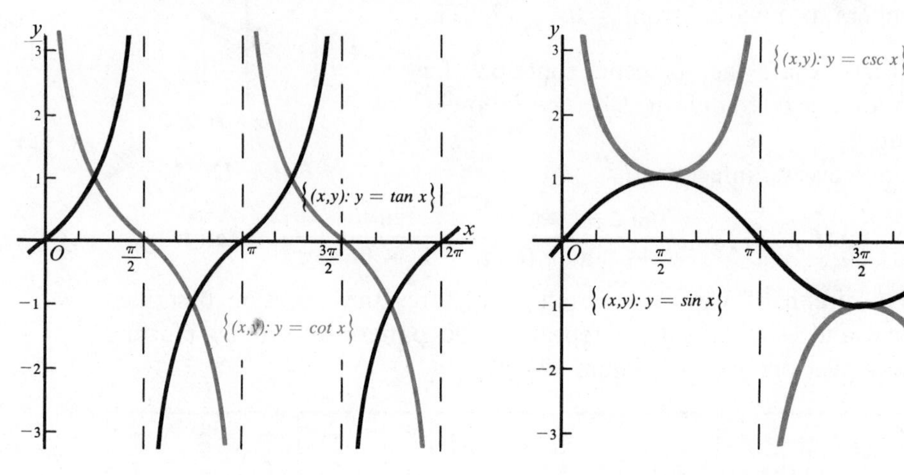

· *Figure 12–15* ·

· *Figure 12–16* ·

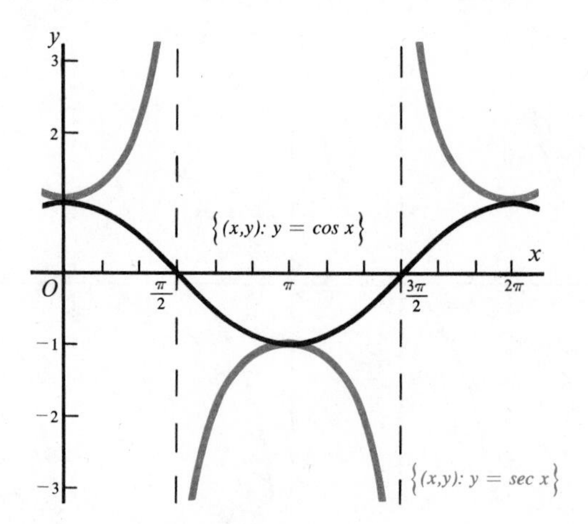

· *Figure 12–17* ·

Written Exercises

Determine the period of each function f and sketch the graph over an interval two periods in length.

A

1. $f(x) = \tan x$
2. $f(x) = \cot x$
3. $f(x) = 2 \cot x$
4. $f(x) = \frac{1}{2} \tan x$
5. $f(x) = \sec x$
6. $f(x) = \csc x$
7. $f(x) = \frac{1}{2} \csc x$
8. $f(x) = 2 \sec x$
9. $f(x) = \tan 2x$
10. $f(x) = \tan \frac{1}{2}x$
11. $f(x) = -\cot \frac{1}{2}x$
12. $f(x) = \cot 2x$
13. Does the tangent function have an amplitude? Justify your answer.
14. Does the secant function have an amplitude? Justify your answer.

Describe the variation of each value as t varies from

(a) 0 to π **(b)** π to 2π **(c)** 0 to $-\pi$ **(d)** $-\pi$ to $-\dfrac{3\pi}{2}$

15. $\tan t$ and $\cot t$
16. $\sin t$ and $\csc t$
17. $\cos t$ and $\sec t$
18. $\sin^2 t$ and $\cos^2 t$

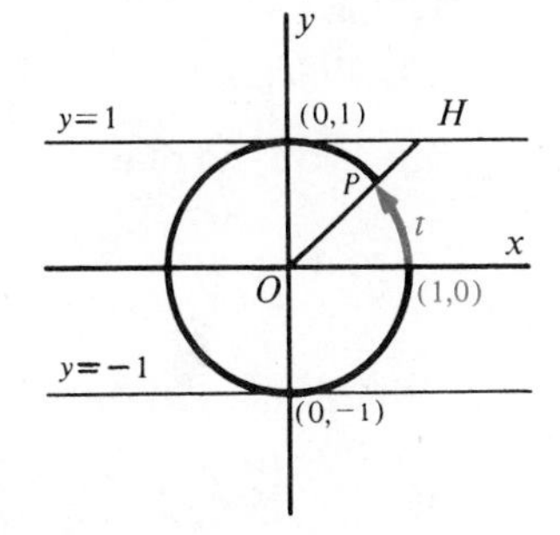

Refer to the figure to discuss the variation of each function in terms of the x-coordinate of H (Ex. 19) and the distance OH (Ex. 20).

C

19. cotangent function
20. cosecant function

From the graphs of f and g, find to the nearest tenth the values of x for which $f(x) = g(x)$.

21. $f(x) = x$
$g(x) = \tan x, \; -\pi \leq x < \pi$

22. $f(x) = \tan\left(x + \dfrac{\pi}{4}\right)$
$g(x) = \frac{1}{2}$

INVERSE FUNCTIONS AND GRAPHS

12-5 Inverse Values

Over the real numbers the solution set of the equation $\cos x = \frac{1}{2}$ consists of $\dfrac{\pi}{3}$, $-\dfrac{\pi}{3}$, and all the numbers which differ from either of these by an integral multiple of 2π. Thus, the solution set is $\{x\colon x = 2n\pi \pm \dfrac{\pi}{3};\ n, \text{any integer}\}$. We give this *infinite* set of numbers a special name: *arccos* $\frac{1}{2}$, or $\cos^{-1} \frac{1}{2}$, each of which can be read "arc cosine $\frac{1}{2}$," "*inverse cosine* $\frac{1}{2}$," or "the set of numbers whose cosine is $\frac{1}{2}$." (If you use the symbol $\cos^{-1} \frac{1}{2}$, be careful not to confuse it with $(\cos \frac{1}{2})^{-1}$, or $\frac{1}{\cos \frac{1}{2}}$.)

In general, **arccos *a*** is the set of numbers for which the value of the cosine is a; that is, it is the solution set of the equation $\cos x = a$. For example:

$$\arccos 0 = \left\{\frac{\pi}{2}, -\frac{\pi}{2}, \frac{3\pi}{2}, -\frac{3\pi}{2}, \ldots\right\}$$

$$= \left\{t: t = \frac{(2n+1)\pi}{2}; n, \text{ any integer}\right\}.$$

Since it is convenient to omit the words "n, any integer," throughout this chapter n will be understood to have the set of integers as replacement set.

Similarly, we define the sets *arcsin a*, *arctan a*, *arccot a*, and so on. Can you explain why, provided $a \neq 0$, $\text{arccot } a = \arctan \frac{1}{a}$, $\text{arcsec } a = \arccos \frac{1}{a}$ and $\text{arccsc } a = \arcsin \frac{1}{a}$?

EXAMPLE 1. Specify by roster $\arcsin\left(-\frac{\sqrt{2}}{2}\right)$.

Solution:

$$\arcsin\left(-\frac{\sqrt{2}}{2}\right) = \left\{x: \sin x = -\frac{\sqrt{2}}{2}\right\}$$

$$= \left\{\frac{5\pi}{4}, \frac{7\pi}{4}, -\frac{3\pi}{4}, -\frac{\pi}{4}, \ldots\right\}$$

$$= \left\{x: x = \frac{5\pi}{4} + 2n\pi, \text{ or } \frac{7\pi}{4} + 2n\pi\right\},$$

Answer.

***EXAMPLE 2.** If $t \in \arctan \frac{1}{3}$, find $\sin t$.

Solution 1: Since $t \in \arctan \frac{1}{3}$:

$\tan t = \frac{1}{3}$; and $\cot t = 3$

$\csc^2 t = 1 + \cot^2 t = 1 + 3^2 = 10$

$\therefore \csc t = \sqrt{10}$ or $-\sqrt{10}$

$\sin t = \frac{\sqrt{10}}{10}$ or $-\frac{\sqrt{10}}{10}$

**Note.* You will sometimes see exercises of this kind stated more briefly, as "Find $\sin(\arctan \frac{1}{3})$."

Solution 2. The terminal side of an angle of t radians is the ray from O through the point $(3, 1)$ or $(-3, -1)$. Referring to the diagram, you have

$$\sin t = \frac{1}{\sqrt{10}} = \frac{\sqrt{10}}{10}, \text{ or}$$

$$\sin t = -\frac{\sqrt{10}}{10}.$$

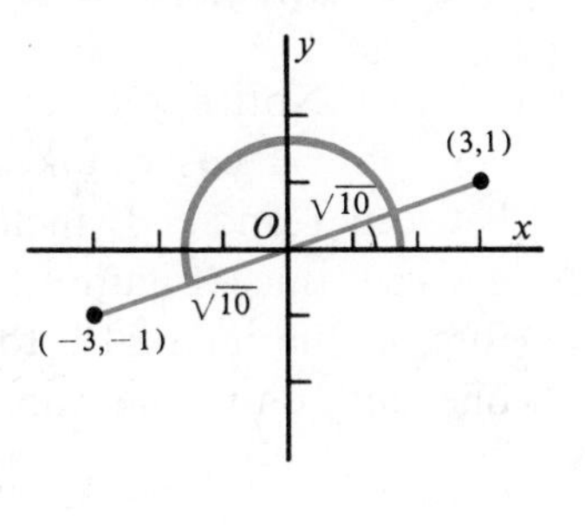

Written Exercises

Specify each set by roster.

1. $\arccos 1$
2. $\arcsin 0$
3. $\arctan 0$
4. $\arcsin \frac{1}{2}$
5. $\arccos\left(-\frac{\sqrt{2}}{2}\right)$
6. $\arctan 1$
7. $\arctan (-1)$
8. $\operatorname{arcsec} (-2)$
9. $\operatorname{arccsc}\left(-\frac{2\sqrt{3}}{3}\right)$
10. $\arcsin 3$
11. $\arccos (-2)$
12. $\operatorname{arccot} \sqrt{3}$

Find the intersection of the set $\{t\colon 0 \leq t < 2\pi\}$ and the given set.

13. $\operatorname{arcsec} \sqrt{2}$
14. $\arctan (-\sqrt{3})$
15. $\arcsin (-1)$
16. $\arccos \frac{\sqrt{3}}{2}$
17. $\operatorname{arccot} 0$
18. $\operatorname{arccsc} 0$

If t belongs to the given set, find the values of the indicated numbers.

19. $\arccos \frac{1}{3}$; $\sin t$
20. $\arctan 2$; $\cos t$
21. $\arcsin (-\frac{1}{5})$; $\tan t$
22. $\operatorname{arccsc} \frac{5}{4}$; $\tan t$
23. $\operatorname{arccot} (-0.1)$; $\sec t$
24. $\operatorname{arcsec} (-2)$; $\csc t$

Name the least nonnegative member of each set.

SAMPLE. $\arctan\left(\cot \frac{\pi}{5}\right)$

Solution:

$$\cot \frac{\pi}{5} = \tan\left(\frac{\pi}{2} - \frac{\pi}{5}\right) = \tan \frac{3\pi}{10}; \therefore \arctan\left(\cot \frac{\pi}{5}\right) = \arctan\left(\tan \frac{3\pi}{10}\right)$$

The least nonnegative member of this set is $\frac{3\pi}{10}$, **Answer.**

B

25. $\arccos\left(\cos \frac{\pi}{6}\right)$
26. $\arcsin\left(\sin \frac{2\pi}{3}\right)$
27. $\arctan\left[\tan\left(-\frac{\pi}{4}\right)\right]$
28. $\arcsin\left(\csc \frac{\pi}{8}\right)$
29. $\arccos[\cos(-1)]$
30. $\arcsin[\sin(-1)]$

12–6 The Inverse Circular Functions

Notice that as x varies from 0 to π, the cosine function $\{(x, y): y = \cos x\}$ takes on each value in its range, {the real numbers between 1 and -1, inclusive}, once and only once (Figure 12–18). Therefore, in the interval 0 to π, there is one and only one solution of the equation $\cos x = \frac{1}{2}$, namely, $\frac{\pi}{3}$. We call this unique solution the *principal value of the set arccos* $\frac{1}{2}$ and denote it by *Arccos* $\frac{1}{2}$ (or $Cos^{-1}\,\frac{1}{2}$).

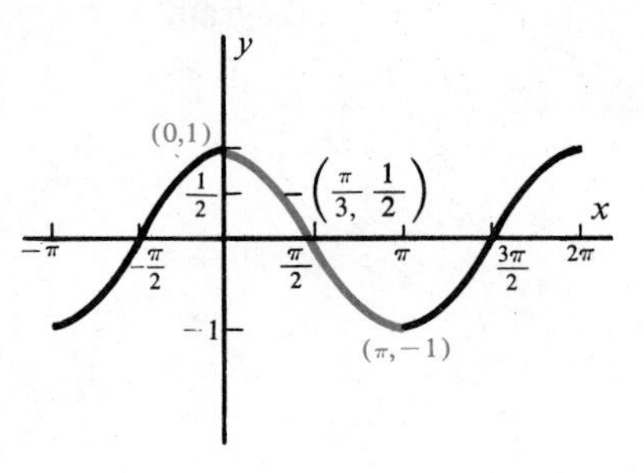

· *Figure 12–18* ·

In general, if a is any real number such that $-1 \leq a \leq 1$, **Arccos *a*** is the unique member of the set arccos a which is between 0 and π, inclusive. Thus, *y = Arccos a if and only if $\cos y = a$ and $0 \leq y \leq \pi$.* For example, Arccos 1 = 0, and $\text{Arccos}\left(-\frac{\sqrt{2}}{2}\right) = \frac{3\pi}{4}$.

The set of all ordered pairs (x, Arccos x) where $-1 \leq x \leq 1$ is called the **Arc cosine function.** Its range is the set of numbers from 0 to π, inclusive. To obtain the graph of this function, you interchange the coordinates of the ordered pairs of the cosine function. Therefore, the resulting graph, shown in red in Figure 12–19, is part of the reflection of the cosine curve in the line $y = x$. (See page 345.)

· *Figure 12–19* ·

By continuing the curve in both directions along the y-axis, you produce the graph of the *relation* $\{(x, y): y = \text{arccos}\, x\}$.

Looking at the graph of $\{(x, y): y = \sin x\}$ (Figure 12–20), you see that for any number b such that $-1 \leq b \leq 1$, there is one and only one value of x such that $\sin x = b$ and $-\frac{\pi}{2} \leq x \leq \frac{\pi}{2}$. We call this value of x the *principal value of the set arcsin b* and denote it by **Arcsin *b*.**

Thus, $\text{Arcsin}\,\frac{1}{2} = \frac{\pi}{6}$ and $\text{Arcsin}\left(-\frac{\sqrt{2}}{2}\right) = -\frac{\pi}{4}$.

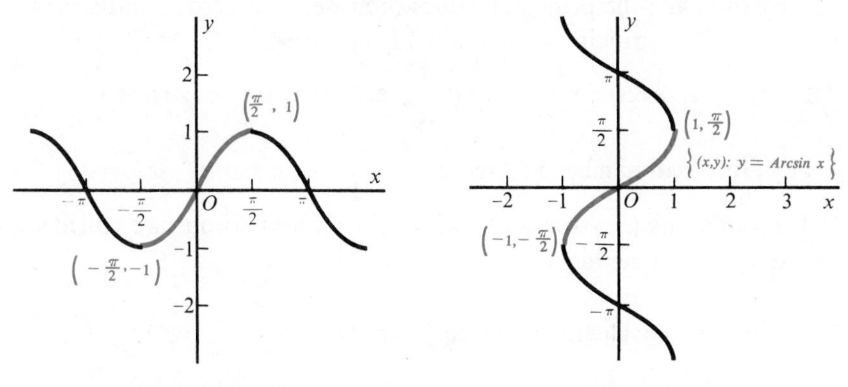

· *Figure 12–20* ·

· *Figure 12–21* ·

Figure 12–21 shows in red the graph of the **Arc sine function,** $\{(x, y): y = \text{Arcsin } x\}$. Continuing this curve produces the graph of the *relation* $\{(x, y): y = \arcsin x\}$.

The graph of the tangent function in Figure 12–22 indicates that for any real number c there is a unique solution of the equation $\tan x = c$ with $-\frac{\pi}{2} < x < \frac{\pi}{2}$. We call this number the *principal value of the set arctan c* and designate it by **Arctan *c*.** For example, $\text{Arctan } 1 = \frac{\pi}{4}$ and $\text{Arctan } (-\sqrt{3}) = -\frac{\pi}{3}$.

Figure 12–23 shows in red the graph of the **Arc tangent function,** $\{(x, y): y = \text{Arctan } x\}$. Repeating the pattern produces the graph of the *relation* $\{(x, y): y = \arctan x\}$.

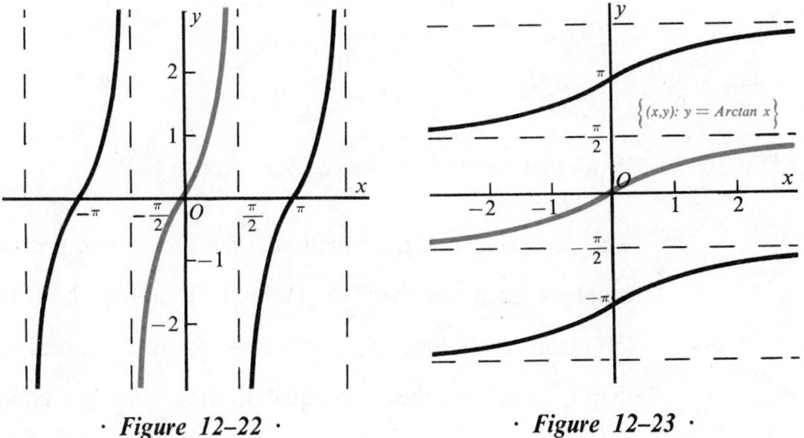

· *Figure 12–22* ·

· *Figure 12–23* ·

We can define the principal values of arcsec x, arccsc x, and arccot x in terms of the principal values already specified.

If $|x| \geq 1$, Arcsec x = Arccos $\frac{1}{x}$, and Arccsc x = Arcsin $\frac{1}{x}$.

For every real number x, Arccot $x = \frac{\pi}{2} -$ Arctan x.

The functions (x, Arccos x), (x, Arcsin x), and so on, are called the **inverse circular functions.**

EXAMPLE 1. Evaluate $\cos[\text{Arcsin}\,(-\frac{5}{13})]$.

Solution:

Let $t = \text{Arcsin}(-\frac{5}{13})$. Then $\sin t = -\frac{5}{13}$ *and* $-\frac{\pi}{2} < t < 0$.

$\therefore \cos t = \sqrt{1 - \sin^2 t} = \sqrt{1 - (-\frac{5}{13})^2} = \frac{12}{13}$, **Answer.**

EXAMPLE 2. Evaluate $\tan[\text{Arctan}\,\frac{3}{4} + \text{Arccos}(-\frac{3}{5})]$.

Solution: Let $u = \text{Arctan}\,\frac{3}{4}$ and $v = \text{Arccos}(-\frac{3}{5})$.

Then $\tan u = \frac{3}{4}$ and

$\cos v = -\frac{3}{5}$ and $\frac{\pi}{2} < v < \pi$.

y
5
4
x
−3

From the sketch:

$\tan v = -\frac{4}{3}$

Since
$$\tan(u + v) = \frac{\tan u + \tan v}{1 - \tan u \tan v},$$

$$\tan[\text{Arctan}\,\tfrac{3}{4} + \text{Arccos}(-\tfrac{3}{5})] = \frac{\frac{3}{4} + (-\frac{4}{3})}{1 - \frac{3}{4}(-\frac{4}{3})} = -\frac{7}{24}, \textbf{ Answer.}$$

EXAMPLE 3. Prove that $\text{Arcsin}\,\frac{1}{4} + \text{Arccos}\,\frac{7}{8} = \text{Arcsin}\,\frac{11}{16}$.

Proof: The left member of the equation is the sum of two positive numbers, each less than $\frac{\pi}{4}\cdot$ (Why?) Therefore, both the left member and the right member are positive numbers less than $\frac{\pi}{2}\cdot$ Hence, they are equal if their sines are equal, or if their values for any other circular function are equal. (Why?)

$$\sin(\text{Arcsin } \tfrac{1}{4} + \text{Arccos } \tfrac{7}{8}) \stackrel{?}{=} \sin(\text{Arcsin } \tfrac{11}{16})$$

Let $u = \text{Arcsin } \frac{1}{4}$ and $v = \text{Arccos } \frac{7}{8}$ | $\frac{11}{16}$

$\sin u = \frac{1}{4}$ $\qquad \cos v = \frac{7}{8}$

$\cos u = \dfrac{\sqrt{15}}{4}$ $\qquad \sin v = \dfrac{\sqrt{15}}{8}$

$$\sin(u + v) = \sin u \cos v + \cos u \sin v$$

$$= \frac{1}{4} \cdot \frac{7}{8} + \frac{\sqrt{15}}{4} \cdot \frac{\sqrt{15}}{8}$$

$$= \tfrac{7}{32} + \tfrac{15}{32} = \tfrac{11}{16}$$

$$\therefore \text{Arcsin } \tfrac{1}{4} + \text{Arccos } \tfrac{7}{8} = \text{Arcsin } \tfrac{11}{16}.$$

By restating this section and the preceding one in terms of the trigonometric functions over the set of angles, you can also discuss trigonometric inverses. For example, $\arcsin \frac{1}{2}$ can be interpreted as the set of angles θ whose sine is $\frac{1}{2}$; that is,

$$\arcsin \tfrac{1}{2} = \{\theta : \theta = 30° + n(360°), \text{ or } 150° + n(360°)\}.$$

EXAMPLE 4. Prove: $\text{Arcsin } b = \text{Arctan } \dfrac{b}{\sqrt{1 - b^2}}$.

Proof: Let $t = \text{Arcsin } b$ and $u = \text{Arctan } \dfrac{b}{\sqrt{1 - b^2}}$.

Then, $-\dfrac{\pi}{2} \leq t \leq \dfrac{\pi}{2}$, and $-\dfrac{\pi}{2} < u < \dfrac{\pi}{2}$.

Therefore, $t = u$ if and only if $\sin t = \sin u$. (Why?)

But $\sin t = \sin(\text{Arcsin } b) = b$.

$$\sin u = \sin\left(\text{Arctan } \frac{b}{\sqrt{1 - b^2}}\right) = b \text{ (from each figure below)}$$

$\therefore \sin t = \sin u$, and $t = u$. That is, $\text{Arcsin } b = \text{Arctan } \dfrac{b}{\sqrt{1 - b^2}}$.

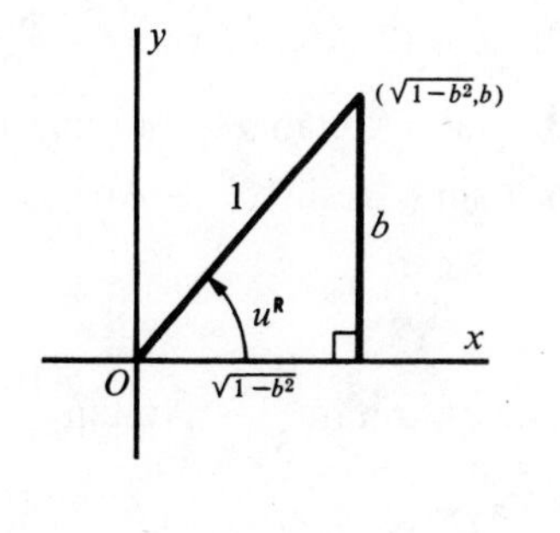

$b \geq 0$

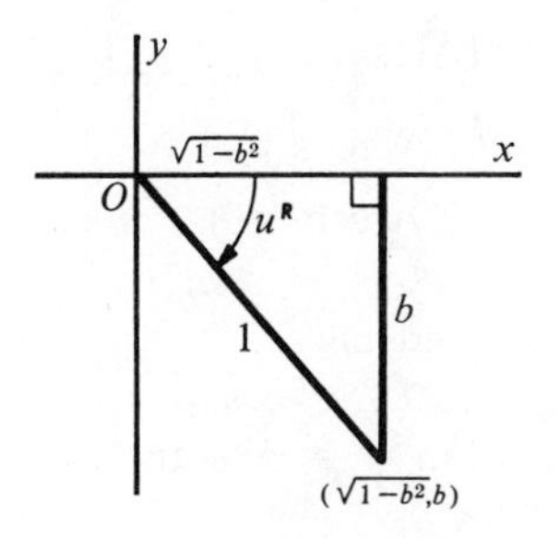

$b < 0$

Oral Exercises

State the domain and range of each function **(a)** as an inverse circular function; **(b)** as an inverse trigonometric function.

1. Arc cosine
2. Arc sine
3. Arc tangent
4. Arc secant
5. Arc cosecant
6. Arc cotangent

Identify each of the following in the set of **(a)** real numbers; **(b)** angles.

7. $\text{Arctan } 1$
8. $\text{Arcsin } \frac{\sqrt{3}}{2}$
9. $\text{Arccos}(-\frac{1}{2})$
10. $\text{Arctan}(-\sqrt{3})$
11. $\text{Arcsin}\left(-\frac{\sqrt{2}}{2}\right)$
12. $\text{Arcsin } 0$
13. $\text{Arccos}\left(\sin \frac{3\pi}{2}\right)$
14. $\text{Arcsin}\left(\tan \frac{3\pi}{4}\right)$
15. $\text{Arctan}(\cos \pi)$

Written Exercises

Evaluate each of the following.

A

1. $\cos(\text{Arctan } \frac{5}{12})$
2. $\sin(\text{Arccot } \frac{4}{3})$
3. $\tan(\text{Arcsin } \frac{8}{17})$
4. $\cot(\text{Arccos } \frac{12}{13})$
5. $\sin[\text{Arccos}(-\frac{2}{5})]$
6. $\cos[\text{Arcsin}(-\frac{3}{4})]$
7. $2 \sec(\text{Arctan } 2)$
8. $2 \csc[\text{Arctan}(-3)]$
9. $\cot[\text{Arctan}(-\frac{1}{3})]$
10. $\tan(\text{Arcsec } 4)$
11. $\tan 2(\text{Arccos } \frac{3}{5})$
12. $\sin \frac{1}{2}[\text{Arctan}(-\frac{7}{24})]$
13. $\sec 2[\text{Arctan}(-\frac{12}{5})]$
14. $\cos(\frac{1}{2} \text{Arcsin } \frac{8}{17})$
15. $\sin(\text{Arctan } \frac{1}{2} + \text{Arctan } \frac{1}{3})$
16. $\cos[\text{Arcsin } \frac{4}{5} + \text{Arctan}(-\frac{8}{15})]$
17. $\tan[\text{Arcsin}(-\frac{12}{13}) - \text{Arccot } \frac{24}{7}]$
18. $\sin[\text{Arcsin}(-\frac{15}{17}) - \text{Arccos } \frac{7}{25}]$

Express in terms of *x* and *y*.

B

19. $\cos(\text{Arcsin } 2x),\ x \le 0$
20. $\sin(\frac{1}{2} \text{Arccos } y),\ y \le 0$
21. $\tan(2 \text{Arccos } y^2)$
22. $\cos(2 \text{Arccos } x),\ x > \frac{\sqrt{2}}{2}$
23. $\tan(\text{Arctan } x - \text{Arctan } y)$
24. $\sin(\text{Arcsin } x^2 + \text{Arccos } x^2)$

Prove each identity.

25. $\text{Arctan } \frac{2}{3} + \text{Arctan } \frac{1}{5} = \frac{\pi}{4}$
26. $\text{Arctan } \frac{4}{3} - \text{Arctan } \frac{1}{7} = \frac{\pi}{4}$
27. $\text{Arcsin } \frac{12}{13} + \text{Arccos } \frac{3}{5} = \text{Arccos}(-\frac{33}{65})$

28. $\text{Arcsin } \frac{1}{3} - \text{Arccos } \frac{7}{11} = \text{Arcsin } (-\frac{17}{33})$

29. $2 \text{ Arcsin } \frac{3}{5} + \text{Arccos } \frac{3}{5} = \pi - \text{Arcsin } \frac{4}{5}$

30. $2 \text{ Arctan } 2 - \text{Arctan}\left(-\frac{1}{7}\right) = \frac{3\pi}{4}$

31. $\text{Arcsin } a = \frac{\pi}{2} - \text{Arccos } a$

32. $\text{Arctan } c^2 + \text{Arctan } \frac{1}{c^2} = \frac{\pi}{2}$

33. $\text{Arcsin } \frac{2b}{1 + b^2} = 2 \text{ Arctan } b$

34. $2 \text{ Arccos } x^2 = \text{Arccos } (2x^4 - 1)$

Solve each equation.

C **35.** $\text{Arccos}(2x^2 - 1) = \text{Arccos } 1$

36. $\text{Arctan}(y^2 - 1) = \text{Arctan}(y + 1)$

37. $\text{Arctan } x + \text{Arctan } 3x = \text{Arctan } 2$

38. $\text{Arccos } x + 2 \text{ Arcsin } x = \text{Arccos}(-\frac{1}{2}),\ x > 0.$

Sketch the graph of each function.

39. $\{(x, y): y = 2 \text{ Arcsin } x\}$

40. $\{(x, y): y = 2 \text{ Arccos } x\}$

41. $\{(x, y): y = \text{Arccot } x\}$

42. $\{(x, y): y = \text{Arcsec } x\}$

OPEN SENTENCES

12–7 General and Particular Solutions

You can employ algebraic transformations (Chapters 2–7), trigonometric identities, and properties of the inverse functions to solve open sentences involving trigonometric and circular functions.

EXAMPLE 1. Solve $(2 \cos x + 1)(\tan x - 1) = 0.$

Solution: The equation is equivalent (see page 57) to the compound sentence

either $2 \cos x + 1 = 0$ or $\tan x - 1 = 0$

$2 \cos x = -1$

$\cos x = -\frac{1}{2}$

The solution set is $\arccos(-\frac{1}{2})$, or

$$\left\{x\colon x = \frac{2\pi}{3} + 2n\pi, \text{ or } \frac{4\pi}{3} + 2n\pi\right\}$$

$\tan x = 1$

The solution set is arctan 1, or

$$\left\{x\colon x = \frac{\pi}{4} + 2n\pi \text{ or } \frac{5\pi}{4} + 2n\pi\right\}$$

Checking these values in the original equation is left to you.

$$\left\{x : x = \frac{2\pi}{3} + 2n\pi, \frac{4\pi}{3} + 2n\pi, \frac{\pi}{4} + 2n\pi, \frac{5\pi}{4} + 2n\pi\right\}$$ **Answer.**

The answer given in Example 1 is called the **general solution** of the open sentence because it indicates all the members in the solution set. The subset consisting of the solutions in a particular interval, usually taken to be $0 \leq x < 2\pi$, is called the **particular solution**. The particular solution in Example 1 is $\left\{\frac{2\pi}{3}, \frac{4\pi}{3}, \frac{\pi}{4}, \frac{5\pi}{4}\right\}$.

EXAMPLE 2. Find the particular solution of $\cos 2y + 2 = \sin y$ for $0 \leq y < 2\pi$.

Solution:

Plan: To obtain an equation involving only $\sin y$, replace $\cos 2y$ by $1 - 2\sin^2 y$; simplify. Then solve the resulting equation by factoring.

$$\cos 2y + 2 = \sin y$$
$$1 - 2\sin^2 y + 2 = \sin y$$
$$2\sin^2 y + \sin y - 3 = 0$$
$$(2\sin y + 3)(\sin y - 1) = 0$$

$2\sin y + 3 = 0$	$\sin y - 1 = 0$
$\sin y = -\frac{3}{2}$	$\sin y = 1$
There is no number whose sine is less than -1.	$\left\{\frac{\pi}{2}\right\}$, **Answer.**

EXAMPLE 3. To the nearest degree, determine the angles between 0° and 360° satisfying $\sec^2\theta - 2\tan\theta - 3 = 0$.

Solution:

Plan: Replace $\sec^2\theta$ by $1 + \tan^2\theta$. Then use the quadratic formula to solve the resulting equation.

$$\sec^2\theta - 2\tan\theta - 3 = 0$$
$$1 + \tan^2\theta - 2\tan\theta - 3 = 0$$
$$\tan^2\theta - 2\tan\theta - 2 = 0$$
$$\tan\theta = \frac{-(-2) \pm \sqrt{(-2)^2 - 4(1)(-2)}}{2(1)}$$
$$\tan\theta = \frac{2 \pm \sqrt{12}}{2} = 1 \pm \sqrt{3}$$

$\tan\theta = 2.732$	$\tan\theta = -0.7321$
From Table 6: $\theta = 70°$, or $180° + 70°$	$\theta = 180° - 36°$, or $360° - 36°$

70°, 250°, 144°, 324°, **Answer.**

You can state the general solution of Example 3 as follows:
$\{\theta\colon \theta = n \cdot 180° + \text{Arctan}(1 + \sqrt{3})\} \cup \{\theta\colon \theta = n \cdot 180° + \text{Arctan}(1 - \sqrt{3})\}$.

Written Exercises

Solve the following open sentences for $0 \le x < 2\pi$, or for $0° \le \theta < 360°$. Give approximations of values of x to the nearest tenth and of θ to the nearest degree.

A

1. $\cos x + 1 = 0$

2. $\sin^2 x = 0$

3. $2 \cos x - \sqrt{3} = 0$

4. $2 \sin x + \sqrt{3} = 0$

5. $2 \sec \theta - 2\sqrt{3} \ge 0$

6. $2 + \sec \theta \le 0$

7. $\tan \theta(\csc \theta + 2) = 0$

8. $\cos \theta(\tan \theta - \sqrt{3}) = 0$

9. $\cot^2 \theta + \cot \theta = 0$

10. $\csc^2 x + 2 \csc x = 0$

11. $\tan^2 x - 3 \le 0$

12. $1 - \cot^2 \theta \ge 0$

13. $2 \cos \theta \csc \theta = \sqrt{3} \csc \theta$

14. $2 \sin \theta \sec \theta = \sec \theta$

15. $2 \cos^2 x - \cos x = 1$

16. $1 + \cos \theta - 2 \sin^2 \theta = 0$

17. $\tan^2 \theta - 5 \tan \theta + 1 = 0$

18. $\csc^2 x + 11 \csc x - 12 = 0$

19. $\cot^2 x - \csc x = 1$

20. $\tan^2 \theta + 3 \sec \theta + 3 = 0$

21. $\sin \theta + 4 \csc \theta + 5 = 0$

22. $3 \sec \theta - \cos \theta - 2 = 0$

23. $\sin 2x + 2 \cos x = 0$

24. $\cos 2x - 2 \cos x = 0$

25. $\sin^2 \theta - 2 \sin \theta - 1 = 0$

26. $\sec^2 \theta + 4 \sec \theta + 1 = 0$

27. $2 \cos^4 x - 3 \cos^2 x + 1 = 0$

28. $4 \sin^4 x + 3 \sin^2 x - 1 = 0$

State the general solution of each of the following equations over the set of (a) real numbers; (b) angles.

B

29. $\sin x = \cos x$

30. $\tan x = \cot x$

31. $4 \sin^2 x = 3 \tan^2 x - 1$

32. $\tan^2 x = 9 \cos^2 x + \sin^2 x$

Solve each open sentence over the real numbers for which $-\pi < x \le \pi$.

33. $0 \le \sin x \le 1$

34. $\cot x \ge 1$

35. $\tan x \le \sin x$

36. $\sin x \le \cos x$

37. $\tan^2 x - 1 \le 0$

38. $2 \sin^2 x - 1 \le 0$

12–8 Additional Sentences

Open sentences involving values of circular functions of an algebraic expression such as $\frac{1}{2}x$, $3x$, or $2x - \frac{\pi}{3}$, can often be solved by *first* determining suitable replacements for the given expression and then finding the corresponding replacements for x.

EXAMPLE 1. Solve $\sin 3x + \sin x = \cos x$ for $0 \leq x < 2\pi$.

Solution: *Plan:* Transform the left member by using the identity $\sin A + \sin B = 2 \sin \frac{A+B}{2} \cos \frac{A-B}{2}$.

$$\sin 3x + \sin x = \cos x$$

$$2 \sin \frac{3x + x}{2} \cos \frac{3x - x}{2} = \cos x$$

$$2 \sin 2x \cos x = \cos x$$

$$(2 \sin 2x - 1)\cos x = 0$$

$$2 \sin 2x - 1 = 0 \quad\Big|\quad \cos x = 0$$

$$\sin 2x = \frac{1}{2} \quad\Big|\quad x = \frac{\pi}{2}, \frac{3\pi}{2}$$

Since $0 \leq x < 2\pi$, $0 \leq 2x < 4\pi$,

$$\therefore\ 2x = \frac{\pi}{6}, \frac{5\pi}{6}, \frac{13\pi}{6}, \frac{17\pi}{6}$$

$$x = \frac{\pi}{12}, \frac{5\pi}{12}, \frac{13\pi}{12}, \frac{17\pi}{12}. \qquad \left\{\frac{\pi}{12}, \frac{5\pi}{12}, \frac{13\pi}{12}, \frac{17\pi}{12}, \frac{\pi}{2}, \frac{3\pi}{2}\right\}, \textbf{ Answer.}$$

EXAMPLE 2. Solve $\cos \frac{1}{2}y + \sin \frac{1}{2}y = 1$.

Solution:

1. Transform the equation to one having $\cos \frac{1}{2}y$ as its left member.

$$\cos \tfrac{1}{2}y + \sin \tfrac{1}{2}y = 1$$
$$\cos \tfrac{1}{2}y = 1 - \sin \tfrac{1}{2}y$$

2. Square each member of the equation obtained in Step 1 and then substitute $1 - \sin^2 \frac{1}{2}y$ for $\cos^2 \frac{1}{2}y$.

$$\cos^2 \tfrac{1}{2}y = 1 - 2 \sin \tfrac{1}{2}y + \sin^2 \tfrac{1}{2}y$$
$$1 - \sin^2 \tfrac{1}{2}y = 1 - 2 \sin \tfrac{1}{2}y + \sin^2 \tfrac{1}{2}y$$
$$2 \sin^2 \tfrac{1}{2}y - 2 \sin \tfrac{1}{2}y = 0$$

3. Solve the resulting equation by factoring.

$$\sin \tfrac{1}{2}y(\sin \tfrac{1}{2}y - 1) = 0$$

$$\sin \tfrac{1}{2}y = 0 \quad\Big|\quad \sin \tfrac{1}{2}y - 1 = 0$$

$$\tfrac{1}{2}y = 0 + 2n\pi \text{ or } \pi + 2n\pi \quad\Big|\quad \sin \tfrac{1}{2}y = 1$$

$$\quad\Big|\quad \tfrac{1}{2}y = \frac{\pi}{2} + 2n\pi$$

$$\therefore\ y = 4n\pi \text{ or } 2\pi + 4n\pi \quad\Big|\quad y = \pi + 4n\pi$$

4. Because the squaring transformation in Step 2 may not produce an equivalent equation, it is essential to check in the original equation.

$$\cos \tfrac{1}{2}(4n\pi) + \sin \tfrac{1}{2}(4n\pi) \stackrel{?}{=} 1$$
$$1 + 0 = 1 \checkmark$$
$$\cos \tfrac{1}{2}(2\pi + 4n\pi) + \sin \tfrac{1}{2}(2\pi + 4n\pi) \stackrel{?}{=} 1$$
$$-1 + 0 \stackrel{?}{=} 1, \text{ No}$$
$$\cos \tfrac{1}{2}(\pi + 4n\pi) + \sin \tfrac{1}{2}(\pi + 4n\pi) \stackrel{?}{=} 1$$
$$0 + 1 = 1 \checkmark$$

$\{y: y = 4n\pi \text{ or } (4n + 1)\pi\}$, **Answer.**

Written Exercises

Solve the following equations for $0 \le x < 2\pi$, or for $0° \le \theta < 360°$. Give approximations of values of x to the nearest tenth and of θ to the nearest degree

A

1. $\tan^2 2x = 3$
2. $2 \sin^2 \frac{1}{2}x = 1$
3. $2 \cos \pi x + 1 = 0$
4. $\tan \pi x - 1 = 0$
5. $\cos 2\theta(3 - 4 \sin^2 \theta) = 0$
6. $\cot 2\theta(1 - \sec^2 \theta) = 0$
7. $(4 \cos^2 2\theta + 1) \sin \frac{1}{3}\theta = 0$
8. $\tan \frac{1}{3}\theta(4 \csc^2 2\theta - 1) = 0$
9. $\tan 3x + \cot 6x = \dfrac{2}{\sqrt{3}}$
10. $3 \sec^2 2x - 2\sqrt{3} \tan 2x = 6$
11. $\tan \theta = 3 \tan \dfrac{\theta}{2}$
12. $\tan\left(\dfrac{\pi}{4} + 3\theta\right) = 2 \tan 6\theta$
13. $\sin 3x \cos x + \cos 3x \sin x = 1$
14. $2 \cos x \cos 2x - 2 \sin x \sin 2x = 1$

B

15. $\sin \dfrac{x}{2} - \cos \dfrac{x}{2} = \sqrt{2}$
16. $\sqrt{3} \cos(\theta - 10°) + \sin(\theta - 10°) = -1$
17. $3 \sin 3\theta + 4 \cos 3\theta = 5$
18. $12 \sin \frac{1}{2}\theta + 5 \cos \frac{1}{2}\theta = 13$

Give the general solution of each equation. If the equation is an identity, state this fact and prove it.

19. $\sin\left(2x + \dfrac{2\pi}{3}\right) + \sin\left(2x - \dfrac{2\pi}{3}\right) = \sin \dfrac{\pi}{4}$
20. $\sin\left(\dfrac{\pi}{3} - \dfrac{1}{2}x\right) + \sin\left(\dfrac{\pi}{3} + \dfrac{1}{2}x\right) = \sin \dfrac{\pi}{3}$
21. $\cos^4 3\theta - \sin^4 3\theta = \cos 6\theta$

22. $1 - \cos^6 5x = \sin^2 5x(1 + \cos^2 5x + \cos^4 5x)$

23. $\sin 2\theta \tan^2 2\theta - \tan 2\theta = \sin 2\theta$

24. $\sqrt{\frac{1}{2}(2 - \sin 2x)} = \cos x$

25. $\sin \frac{x}{2} \tan \frac{x}{4} = 1 - \cos \frac{x}{2}$

26. $\dfrac{\cos(2x + 1) - \cos 2x}{\cos(x + \frac{1}{2}) - \cos x} = 2[\cos(x + \frac{1}{2}) + \cos x]$

Solve each system for $0° \leq \theta < 360°$.

27. $r = 3$
$r^2 = 18 \cos 2\theta$

28. $r = \sin 2\theta$
$r = \cos 4\theta$

29. $r = \cos 3\theta$
$r = 1 - \cos 3\theta$

30. $r = \sin \theta - 1$
$r^2 = \frac{1}{2} \sin \theta$

Chapter Summary

Inventory of Structure and Method

1. A **radian** is the central angle subtended in a circle of radius 1 by an arc of length 1. Therefore $180° = \pi^R$. In a circle of radius r, a central angle θ *measured in radians* intercepts an arc of length $r\theta$.
2. For a real number t the value of a **circular function** equals the value of the corresponding trigonometric function for an angle of t radians.
3. Because the circular functions are periodic functions, their graphs consist of basic patterns repeated over each interval of length one **period.** Therefore, there is an infinite set of numbers for which a given circular function has any one of its values. For example, arcsin $\frac{1}{3}$ is the infinite set of numbers whose sine is $\frac{1}{3}$. The principal value in one of these sets is obtained by specifying the interval to which the value must belong.
4. Using trigonometric identities and the usual algebraic transformations, you solve equations involving the circular or trigonometric functions.

Vocabulary and Spelling

radian (*p. 464*)
circular functions (*p. 466*)
periodic functions (*p. 470*)
period (*p. 470*)
sinusoidal wave (*p. 471*)
amplitude (*p. 472*)
inverse cosine (sine, etc.) (*p. 478*)
arccos a, etc. (*p. 478*)
principal value (*p. 480*)
inverse circular functions (*p. 480*)
general solution (*p. 486*)
particular solution (*p. 486*)

Chapter Test

12–1 **1.** Convert the angle measure from degrees to radians or from radians to degrees. Give results to the nearest tenth of a radian, or to the nearest degree.

(a) $-120°$ (b) $\frac{13}{4}\pi^R$ (c) $\frac{1}{3}^R$

2. Two points on the equator differ by 10° in longitude. Find the distance between them if earth's radius is taken to be 4000 mi.

12–2 **3.** Give the exact value: (a) $\cos\left(-\dfrac{8\pi}{3}\right)$ (b) $\tan\left(\dfrac{5\pi}{6}\right)$

12–3 **4.** Draw the graph of $\{(x, y): y = 3 \sin 2x\}$, for $-\pi \leq x \leq \pi$.

12–4 **5.** Draw the graph of $\{(x, y): y = \tan \frac{1}{2}x\}$, over one period.

12–5 **6.** Give a roster of the set $\arcsin(-\frac{1}{2})$.

7. If $t \in \arctan \frac{5}{12}$, find $\sin t$ and $\cos t$.

12–6 **8.** Find $\cos\left[\text{Arccos}\dfrac{\sqrt{2}}{2} - \text{Arcsin}\,(-\frac{3}{5})\right]$.

9. Prove: $\text{Arctan } 2 + \text{Arctan } 3 = \pi - \text{Arctan } 1$.

12–7 **10.** Solve for $0 \leq x < 2\pi$, or $0° \leq \theta < 360°$.

(a) $\cos 2\theta = 4 \cos \theta$ (b) $1 + \cos^2 x = 2 \sin^2 x - \frac{5}{2} \sin x$

12–8 **11.** Find the general solution and the particular solution for $0 \leq x < 2\pi$ of $\sin 2x - \sin 4x = 2 \sin x$

Extra for Experts

Irrational Trigonometric Values and Logarithms

Using the method of Section 7–2, you can prove that certain values of trigonometric functions are irrational.

EXAMPLE 1. Prove that sin 10° is irrational.

Solution:

Writing the identity (Exercise 17, page 439) $\sin 3\theta = 3 \sin \theta - 4 \sin^3 \theta$, with 10° in place of θ, you have $\sin 30° = 3 \sin 10° - 4 \sin^3 10°$. Then, replacing sin 30° by $\frac{1}{2}$ and sin 10° by x, you obtain: $\frac{1}{2} = 3x - 4x^3$, or $8x^3 - 6x + 1 = 0$. By the theorem on page 256, the only possible rational roots of this equation are the numbers 1, $\frac{1}{2}$, $\frac{1}{4}$, $\frac{1}{8}$, and their negatives. By substituting each of these values in turn in the equation, you can verify that none is a root. Therefore, x, or sin 10°, denotes an irrational number.

You can also use the identity $\cos 3\theta = 4\cos^3\theta - 3\cos\theta$ (Exercise 18, page 439) to show that certain values of $\cos\theta$ are irrational, and by using some of your other identities, you can extend these proofs of irrationality to include many additional values of the trigonometric functions.

Another kind of argument can be used to show that $\log n$ is irrational for certain values of n.

EXAMPLE 2. Prove that log 3 is irrational.

Proof: Could $\log 3 = \frac{a}{b}$ where a and b are positive integers? If there are such integers, then $10^{\frac{a}{b}} = 3$. Raising each member to the bth power gives $10^a = 3^b$. But for any positive integer a, 10^a has a numeral ending in 0, while for any positive integer b, 3^b ends in 1, 3, 7, or 9. Hence, there are no positive integers a and b for which $10^a = 3^b$. It follows that log 3 is irrational.

This method can be employed to prove that $\log n$, where n is any positive rational number except an integral power of 10, is irrational.

Exercises

1. Use the identity for $\cos 3\theta$ to prove that $\cos 20°$ is irrational.
2. Use the identity $\cos 2\theta = 1 - 2\sin^2\theta$ and the fact that $\cos 20°$ is irrational to prove that $\sin 10°$ is irrational. (*Hint:* Show that assuming $\sin 10° = \frac{a}{b}$ leads to a contradiction.)
3. Use the identity $\cos 4\theta = 8\cos^4\theta - 8\cos^2\theta + 1$ to prove that $\cos 15°$ is irrational.

Use the method of Example 2 to prove that the following are irrational numbers.

4. log 5 **5.** log 3 + log 5. (*Hint:* log 3 + log 5 = log 15.)

Cumulative Review: Chapters 10-12

1. Find the trigonometric function values of a position angle of $P(1, -2\sqrt{2})$.
2. If $\sin\alpha = \frac{2\sqrt{10}}{7}$, α in Q.II, find $\tan\alpha$.
3. Evaluate **(a)** $\sin\frac{\pi}{4}\cos\frac{\pi}{6}\tan\frac{\pi}{3}$; **(b)** $\cos 0°(\tan 45° - \sin 90°)$.
4. Express as a function of a positive acute angle.

   a. $\cos 328°$ **b.** $\cos -515°$ **c.** $\tan 257°$ **d.** $\tan \frac{13}{15}\pi$

5. Simplify: **(a)** $2\sqrt{-6} \cdot \sqrt{-3}$; **(b)** i^{58}; **(c)** $10\,(2 - i)^{-1}$
6. Solve for x and y: $(3 + 4i)x + (i - 2)y = 7 + 2i$.
7. Solve $\cos(2n + 30°) = \sin 50°$ for $0° < n < 90°$.

Express as a function of a single acute angle.

8. $\sin 280° - \sin 100°$
9. $\cos 335° + \cos 95°$

Using logarithms, find x to the nearest minute, a to the nearest unit.

10. $\sin x = \dfrac{.6726 \cos 38°23'}{\sin 132°30'}$
11. $a = \dfrac{3270 \sin 23°48' \sin 41°52'}{\sin 65°40'}$
12. How many radians are there in the angle subtended at the center of a circle, radius 12″, by an 18″ arc?
13. **a.** State the period and the amplitude of $f(x) = 3 \cos \frac{3}{2}x$.

    b. Sketch the graph of $f(x)$ for $-\dfrac{\pi}{3} \leq x \leq 2\pi$.

    c. In the interval in **(b)**, how many values are there for which $\cos \frac{3}{2}x = -1$?
14. Change to radian measure: **(a)** 162°; **(b)** 795°.
15. Find the intersection of $\{p\colon -\pi \leq p \leq 3\pi\}$ and the set **(a)** $\arccos(-\frac{1}{2})$; **(b)** $\arcsin \dfrac{\sqrt{3}}{2}$.
16. Find **(a)** $\cos \text{Arcsin}\,\frac{1}{5}$; **(b)** $\sin \text{Arccos}(-\frac{7}{9})$; **(c)** $\cos \text{Arctan}(-2\sqrt{2})$
17. *Prove:* $\text{Arccos}\,\frac{1}{3} + \text{Arcsin}\,\frac{4}{9}\sqrt{2} = \text{Arccos}\,(-\frac{1}{3})$
18. $4x^2 + 2x + 1 = 0$. **(a)** State the nature of the roots, and **(b)** solve over the set of complex numbers.

Prove as identities.

19. $\dfrac{2 + 2 \cos 2A}{\sin^2 2A} = \csc^2 A$
20. $\dfrac{\tan \theta \tan 2\theta}{\sec 2\theta} = 1 - \cos 2\theta$

Solve for $0° \leq x < 360°$.

21. $5 \sin x = 2 + \cos 2x$
22. $\sec^2 x + \tan x = 3$

Solve $\triangle ABC$ given that

23. $B = 59°$, $C = 64°10'$, $b = 23.0$
24. $b = 37.5$, $c = 43.0$, $A = 54°40'$
25. Find the number of possible triangles having

    a. $b = 52$, $c = 61$, $B = 50°$ **b.** $a = 61$, $b = 52$, $B = 70°$

CHAPTER 13

. . . the sounding board of a grand piano, revealing the long, heavy strings which produce the lowest notes

Progressions and Binomial Expansions

Arranging a set of five elements in a definite order produces an "ordered set." The set of natural numbers is an ordered set which has a first element and in which each member has an immediate successor. In this chapter you will study sequences, which are ordered sets having these two properties. Sequences are important in such areas of mathematics as calculus and topology, and in applications such as actuarial work and queuing theory.

ARITHMETIC PROGRESSIONS

13–1 Arithmetic Progressions

A certain computer can be built with one or more memory units. The first unit provides 8000 words of storage, and each additional unit provides another 4000 words. The following table shows values of $w(n)$, the number of words of storage in a computer with n memory units.

n	1	2	3	4	...
$w(n)$	8000	12,000	16,000	20,000	...

4000 4000 4000

The values of any function whose domain is a set of consecutive natural numbers are said to form a **sequence**, and each value is called a **term** of the sequence. Noting that the function $\{n, w(n)\}$ specified in the table defines a sequence, 8,000, 12,000, 16,000, . . . , in which consecutive terms differ by 4000, you can write the table as follows:

n	1	2	3	4	...	n
$w(n)$	$8000 + 0 \cdot (4000)$	$8000 + 1 \cdot (4000)$	$8000 + 2 \cdot (4000)$	$8000 + 3 \cdot (4000)$	...	$8000 + (n - 1)(4000)$

4000 4000 4000

Do you see that the **general**, or **nth**, **term** of the sequence is given by

$$\mathbf{w(n) = 8000 + (n - 1)(4000)?}$$

This sequence is an example of an *arithmetic progression* (A.P.).

If the difference between any two successive terms in a sequence is a constant, *d*, then the sequence is called an arithmetic progression.

If a is the first term in an arithmetic progression and d is the common difference of successive terms, then the following table gives an expression for each term $t(n)$, also denoted by t_n.

n	1	2	3	⋯	n
t_n	$a + 0 \cdot d$	$a + 1 \cdot d$	$a + 2 \cdot d$	⋯	$a + (n - 1)d$

$d \quad d \quad d \cdots d$

Therefore, the **nth term** in the sequence is given by

$$\mathbf{t_n = a + (n - 1)d.}$$

EXAMPLE. Find the seventeenth term in the arithmetic progression 2, 6, 10, ...

Solution: Find the common difference (any term minus the preceding term).

$$d = 6 - 2 = 4$$

Substitute 2 for a, 4 for d, and 17 for n in the formula $t_n = a + (n - 1)d$.

$$t_{17} = 2 + (17 - 1)4$$
$$t_{17} = 2 + 16(4) = 66, \textbf{ Answer.}$$

A sequence is **finite** if it has a last term, and **infinite** if it does not. Be careful not to draw conclusions from just a few terms in a sequence. For example, the sequence beginning 3, 5, 7, will have 9 as its next term if the sequence is an arithmetic progression, but if it is the sequence of prime numbers, the next term is 11. The nth term of the sequence beginning 5, 7, 9 can be $2n + 3$; but it can also be $n^3 - 6n^2 + 13n - 3$, as you can verify by replacing n with 1, 2, and 3 successively. There are infinitely many general terms for any sequence that is identified by only a few terms.

Written Exercises

Write the first four terms in an A.P. using the given values for a and d..

A

1. $a = 1, d = 2$

2. $a = -3, d = 3.5$

3. $a = 2, d = -1.3$

4. $a = -3, d = -3$

5. $a = 1, d = 2k$

6. $a = \sin 90°, d = \sin 30°$

Find the nth term of the A.P. having the given values for a, d, and n.

7. $a = 1, d = 3, n = 10$

8. $a = 2, d = 2, n = 16$

9. $a = -2, d = 4, n = 21$

10. $a = -2, d = 3, n = 5$

11. $a = 3i, d = -2i, n = 8$

12. $a = 3, d = -1, n = 25$

13. $a = \cos 45°, d = \cos 135°$
$n = 20$

14. $a = -2, d = -3, n = 12$

Find the term asked for in each of the following arithmetic progressions.

15. The thirtieth term of $\frac{1}{3}, 1, 1\frac{2}{3}, \cdots$.

16. The eighth term of $i, 0.8i, 0.6i, \cdots$.

17. The eleventh term of $3\sqrt{3}, 6\sqrt{3}, 9\sqrt{3}, \cdots$.

18. The thirty-fifth term of $(\sqrt{2} + 1), \sqrt{2}, (\sqrt{2} - 1), \cdots$.

19. The fortieth term of $(x - y), x, (x + y), \cdots$.

20. The eighteenth term of $-3x^2, -x^2, x^2, \cdots$.

21. Which term of 2, 9, 16, . . . is 142?

22. Which term of 4, -1, -6, . . . is -141?

Draw the graph of the function f whose domain is $\{1, 2, 3, 4, 5\}$ and whose values are given by the indicated formula.

23. $f(n) = 1 + 3n$

24. $f(n) = 2n + 5$

25. $f(n) = 1 - \frac{1}{3}n$

26. $f(n) = -0.75n + 0.5$

27. $f(n) = 4 + n(\sin 30°)$

28. $f(n) = 4 - n(\cos 60°)$

Problems

A

1. A man takes a job at $6000 a year. He receives annual increases in pay of $500. What is his salary during his seventh year in the job?

2. Diana's beginning salary is $5400. With yearly increases of $300, when will she reach $9000?

3. A Christmas Savings Club, which helps members to save money for Christmas shopping, requires each member to deposit $5 the first week and to increase his deposit by $1 weekly for nine weeks. How much is the final deposit?

4. Mr. Pickering opens a savings account when his son is in the sixth grade to provide for his son's college education. If he deposits $1000 the first year and increases his deposits by $125 each year after that, how much will he deposit when his son is a senior in high school?
5. A college student typing a research paper finds that she can type 5 words per minute faster each $\frac{1}{2}$ hour she types. If she starts at 37 words per minute at 7:30 P.M., how fast is she typing at 9:00 P.M.?
6. A ball which rolls off a penthouse terrace falls 16 feet the first second, 48 feet the next second, and 80 the third second. If it continues to fall in this manner, how far does it fall the seventh second?

B

7. A missile fired vertically upward rises 15,840 feet the first second, 15,808 feet the following second, and 15,776 feet the third second.
   a. How many feet does it rise the 45th second? **b.** How many feet and in what direction does it move the ninth minute after it is fired?
8. At the end of one year, the trade-in value of a certain automobile is $500 less than the original cost. Each year thereafter the trade-in value decreases by $200. If the original cost of the automobile is $4000, what is the trade-in value at the end of n years? When is the trade-in value 0?
9. The third term of an A.P. is 14; the ninth term is -1. Find the first three terms. (*Hint:* $a + 2d = 14$, etc.)
10. The fifth term of an A.P. is 9; the fourteenth term is 45. Write the first three terms.

13–2 Arithmetic Means

What is the first term of an arithmetic progression whose third term is 3 and whose seventh term is 9? One way to answer this question is to represent the progression schematically, _ _ 3 _ _ _ 9, and then find the common difference by considering the progression whose first term is 3 and whose fifth term is 9.

Using $t_n = a + (n - 1)d$,

$$9 = 3 + (5 - 1)d,$$

and you find that $d = \frac{3}{2}$. You can then find the first term in the progression whose third (last) term is 3 and whose common difference is $\frac{3}{2}$. Again, you use $t_n = a + (n - 1)d$.

$$3 = a + (3 - 1)\tfrac{3}{2}$$
$$3 = a + 3$$
$$a = 0$$

and the required first term is 0.

Knowing the common difference, you can also insert the remaining terms in the sequence. Since the common difference is $\frac{3}{2}$, the progression

$$\underline{0}\ \_\ \underline{3}\ \_\ \_\ \_\ \underline{9} \quad \text{becomes} \quad \underline{0}\ \underline{\tfrac{3}{2}}\ \underline{3}\ \underline{\tfrac{9}{2}}\ \underline{6}\ \underline{\tfrac{15}{2}}\ \underline{9}.$$

The terms between two given terms in an arithmetic progression are called **arithmetic means** between the given terms. Thus $\frac{9}{2}$, 6, and $\frac{15}{2}$ are the three arithmetic means between 3 and 9.

EXAMPLE. Insert the four arithmetic means between 1 and 11.

Solution: Substitute 11 for t_n, 1 for a, and 6 for n in

$t_n = a + (n - 1)d$, and solve for d.

$$11 = 1 + (6 - 1)d$$
$$11 = 1 + 5d$$
$$d = 2$$

The required means are obtained by adding 2.

1, 3, 5, 7, 9, 11, **Answer.**

A single arithmetic mean inserted between two numbers is the **average** or **arithmetic mean** of the two numbers. For example, the arithmetic mean of 0 and 3 is half their sum, or $\frac{3}{2}$.

Written Exercises

Insert the given number of arithmetic means in each case.

A

1. Five, between 4 and 22
2. Three, between 18 and -10
3. Six, between -2 and 12
4. Seven, between 11 and 13
5. Five, between 1 and -1
6. Nine, between -10 and 0
7. Five, between 8 and 80
8. Three, between tan 45° and tan 135°

Find the arithmetic mean of the given terms.

9. 5 and 73
10. 7 and 15
11. -28 and 2
12. -9 and -7

B

13. $3a$ and $3b$
14. $a + bi$ and $a - bi$
15. $(1 + \sqrt{5})$ and $(\sqrt{5} - 1)$
16. sin 75° and sin 15°

C

17. Show that if a and b are both even integers, or both odd integers, then their arithmetic mean is an integer.

18. Show that if a and b are integers, and one is even and one is odd, then their arithmetic mean is not an integer.

19. Show that if $a < b$, and if the arithmetic mean of a and b is c, then $a < c < b$.

20. Show that if b^2 is the arithmetic mean of a^2 and c^2, then $\frac{1}{c+a}$ is the arithmetic mean of $\frac{1}{b+c}$ and $\frac{1}{a+b}$. (Assume $a^2 \neq c^2$.)

Problems

A

1. The seven weights in a set for an analytic balance are in arithmetic progression. If the largest is 25 grams and the smallest 1 gram, what are the other weights?

2. If an income tax is 1% on the first thousand dollars of net income, 2% on the second thousand, and so on, what is the tax rate on the last thousand dollars of a net income of $7400?

3. A young man's annual salary increased for five years in A.P. If his salary the first year was $4,400 and his salary the fifth year was $6,000, what was his salary during each of the other years?

4. A man driving along an interstate toll road at 60 m.p.h. (88 ft./sec.) applies the brake as he approaches a tollbooth and comes to a complete stop in 22 sec. If the speeds at which he travels in successive seconds are in A.P., how fast did he travel the seventh second after braking?

B

5. The arithmetic mean of two numbers is 9. If the sum of the squares of the numbers is 50 more than the square of 20, find the numbers.

6. The arithmetic mean of two numbers is $\frac{1}{3}$ the larger number and $\frac{1}{2}$ the square of the smaller number. Find the numbers.

7. The product of two nonzero numbers is $\frac{2}{5}$ the larger number and $\frac{4}{9}$ their arithmetic mean. Find the smaller number.

8. The reciprocal of one number is 5 times the reciprocal of another. Seven times their arithmetic mean is 4 greater than their product. Find all such pairs of numbers.

9. In the equation $ax^2 + bx + c = 0$, the product of the roots is -7, $a = 1$, and the sum of the roots is the arithmetic mean of a and c. Find b and c.

10. A circle whose radius is 10 has its center at the origin. The arithmetic mean of the coordinates of a point on the circle is 7. Find the coordinates of all such points.

13–3 Sum of an Arithmetic Progression

A **series** is the indicated sum of the terms in a sequence. Thus, associated with the sequence 3, 6, 9, 12 is the series $3 + 6 + 9 + 12$. You can find a simple expression for the sum S_n of the first n terms of an arithmetic progression. First, consider the terms of any arithmetic series in the usual order, and then in reversed order. Use the letter l to denote the nth or last term.

$$S_n = a + (a + d) + (a + 2d) + \ldots + [a + (n - 1)d]$$
$$S_n = l + (l - d) + (l - 2d) + \ldots + [l - (n - 1)d]$$

If you add the corresponding members of these two equations, you find that the sum of the terms involving d is 0, and you have

$$2S_n = (a + l) + (a + l) + \ldots + (a + l)$$

where $(a + l)$ occurs n times. Therefore, $2S_n = n(a + l)$, or

$$S_n = \frac{n}{2}(a + l).$$

If you write this as $S_n = n\left(\frac{a + l}{2}\right)$, you can see that the sum is just n times the arithmetic mean of the first and last terms. Since l is the nth term, $l = a + (n - 1)d$. Therefore you can replace l in the formula for the sum with $a + (n - 1)d$ to obtain

$$S_n = \frac{n}{2}[a + a + (n - 1)d]$$

or

$$S_n = \frac{n}{2}[2a + (n - 1)d]$$

EXAMPLE 1. Find the sum of eighteen terms of the arithmetic progression beginning 4, 7, 10, ...

Solution: The common difference is 3. Using $S_n = \frac{n}{2}[2a + (n - 1)d]$, replace n with 18, a with 4, and d with 3.

$$S_{18} = \tfrac{18}{2}[2(4) + (18 - 1)3]$$

$$S_{18} = 9[8 + 17(3)] = 9[59] = 531, \textbf{ Answer.}$$

You can use the Greek letter Σ (sigma) to abbreviate the writing of a series. For instance, to abbreviate the writing of the series

$$3 + 6 + 9 + 12 + 15 + 18 + 21 + 24, \text{ or}$$
$$3(1) + 3(2) + 3(3) + 3(4) + \cdots + 3(8)$$

first observe that the general term is $3n$; then write $\sum_{n=1}^{8} 3n$ (read "the summation from 1 to 8 of $3n$"), where it is understood that you are to add all terms obtained from $3n$ by replacing n with the consecutive integers from 1 to 8 inclusive. The symbol $\sum$ is called the **summation sign**, the expression $3n$ is called the summand, and the letter n the index. The replacement set of n is the range of summation.

EXAMPLE 2. Write $\sum_{k=1}^{5} 4k$ in expanded form.

Solution: Replace k with the integers 1 to 5 in turn.

$$\sum_{k=1}^{5} 4k = 4(1) + 4(2) + 4(3) + 4(4) + 4(5)$$
$$= 4 + 8 + 12 + 16 + 20, \textbf{ Answer.}$$

EXAMPLE 3. Write $1 + 3 + 5 + 7 + 9$, using summation notation.

Solution:

1	2	3	4	5
1	3	5	7	9
↓	↓	↓	↓	↓
$2\cdot1 - 1$	$2\cdot2 - 1$	$2\cdot3 - 1$	$2\cdot4 - 1$	$2\cdot5 - 1$

(differences between successive terms: 2, 2, 2, 2)

A general term for the series is $2n - 1$. Since there are five terms,

$$\therefore \sum_{n=1}^{5} (2n - 1), \textbf{ Answer.}$$

Oral Exercises

State each series in expanded form.

1. $\sum_{i=2}^{4} i$ **2.** $\sum_{i=3}^{7} i$ **3.** $\sum_{j=1}^{3} 2j$ **4.** $\sum_{j=2}^{4} 2j$

5. $\sum_{i=1}^{3} (i + 1)$

6. $\sum_{i=1}^{3} (i - 1)$

7. $\sum_{k=2}^{4} (2k + 1)$

8. $\sum_{k=3}^{5} (2k - 1)$

9. $\sum_{j=3}^{5} -j$

10. $\sum_{j=2}^{4} -2j$

11. $\sum_{i=1}^{3} (4 - i)$

12. $\sum_{p=2}^{4} (10 - p)$

13. $\sum_{k=2}^{4} (10 - 2k)$

14. $\sum_{k=3}^{5} (2 - 2k)$

15. $\sum_{i=10}^{12} (i + 2)$

16. $\sum_{i=50}^{52} (i + 2)$

Written Exercises

Find the sum of the arithmetic series.

1. $\sum_{j=1}^{5} 3j$

2. $\sum_{j=1}^{10} 4j$

3. $\sum_{k=1}^{10} (4k - 2)$

4. $\sum_{k=1}^{20} (3k - 1)$

5. $\sum_{n=1}^{15} \frac{1}{2}(n + 1)$

6. $\sum_{n=1}^{50} \frac{1}{4}(n + 2)$

7. $\sum_{q=1}^{10} (2 - q)$

8. $\sum_{q=1}^{8} (4 - 2q)$

Find the sum of the arithmetic progression having the given data.

9. $a = 6, d = 4, n = 17$

10. $a = \frac{1}{5}, d = \frac{2}{5}, n = 16$

11. $d = -4, l = -32, n = 12$

12. $d = 1, l = 7, n = 10$

13. $a = 0, d = -\frac{1}{2}, l = -50$

14. $a = 13, d = 4, l = 89$

Write the first three terms of each arithmetic progression.

15. $a = 3, l = 17, S_n = 100$

16. $a = \frac{2}{3}, l = 7\frac{1}{3}, S_n = 48$

17. $n = 12, l = 1, S_n = -24$

18. $n = 7, l = 7, S_n = 25\frac{1}{2}$

19. $a = \frac{3}{4}, l = \frac{3}{32}, S_n = 6\frac{3}{4}$

20. $a = 0.85, n = 7, S_n = 15.05$

21. $d = 0.7, n = 5, S_n = -47.44$

22. $d = 5, n = 11, S_n = 275$

23. $a = 8, n = 17, S_n = 183.6$

24. $l = -41, d = -2, S_n = -441$

Use summation notation to write each sum.

25. $2 + 5 + 8 + 11$

26. $1 - 1 - 3 - 5$

27. $2 + \frac{3}{2} + 1 + \frac{1}{2} + 0$

28. $12 + 9 + 6 + 3$

Solve for the variable in red.

SAMPLE. $\sum_{i=1}^{3} (ai - 2) = 9.$

Solution: Expand $\sum_{i=1}^{3} (ai - 2) = 9$, and solve for a.

$$a(1) - 2 + a(2) - 2 + a(3) - 2 = 9$$
$$6a - 6 = 9$$
$$6a = 15$$
$$a = \tfrac{5}{2}, \textbf{ Answer.}$$

B

29. $\sum_{i=4}^{6} ai = 30$

30. $\sum_{i=3}^{5} bi = 48$

31. $\sum_{i=3}^{5} (xi + 3) = 45$

32. $\sum_{i=10}^{13} (yi - 5) = 210$

33. $\sum_{k=1}^{6} (k \csc x - 7) = 0;\ 0 \leq x \leq 2\pi$

34. $\sum_{t=4}^{7} (t \cos y + 3) = 23;\ 0 \leq y \leq 2\pi$

C

35. If $\sum_{i=1}^{3} (ai + b) = 15$, and $\sum_{i=2}^{4} (ai + b) = 21$, find a and b.

36. If $\sum_{i=3}^{6} (ai + b) = -46$, and $\sum_{i=1}^{3} (ai + b) = -2$, find a and b.

37. Find: $\sum_{k=1}^{99} \log 2^k$.

38. Find: $\sum_{n=1}^{100} \log \tan^n \frac{\pi}{4}$

Problems

A

1. How much did an aeronautical engineer with Fairfield Aircraft earn in ten years if her starting salary was $6000 and she received annual increases of $350?
2. The carillon in a campus bell tower chimes as many times as the hour. How many times does it chime between 8:00 A.M. and 5 P.M.?
3. In the front section of the physics lecture hall, there are 25 seats in the first row and 2 seats more in each following row. How many seats are there in the front 10 rows?

4. Some boys on the beach decided to form a human pyramid having one person fewer in each successive layer. If there are six boys in the bottom layer, how many are there in the pyramid?

5. If the taxi rate is 70¢ for the first mile and 40¢ for each additional mile, what is the fare from a suburb to the airport, 12 miles away?

6. The annual cost of repairs for a certain automobile increases $50 each year. If the cost of repairs at the end of the first year is $25, what is the total amount spent on repairs for an automobile kept 7 years?

7. In a match game in which the object is to avoid picking up the last match, four rows of matches are placed on the table. If the numbers of matches in each row are consecutive integers and the second largest row has six matches, how many matches are used in the game?

8. A student taking a test consisting of ten questions is told that each question after the first is worth two credits more than the preceding question. If the third question on the test is worth five credits, what is the maximum score that the student can obtain?

9. John repays the $675 he owes his brother by making monthly payments. If the first payment is $10 and every other payment is $5 more than that of the preceding month, how long does it take him to pay off his debt?

10. Over a number of weeks Arnold Renault saved $12.15 from his weekly allowance. If he saved 25¢ the first week, and every week following this he saved 5¢ more than the preceding week, for how many weeks did he save?

B 11. Find the sum of the first 25 odd positive integers.

12. Find the sum of the positive integers less than 100 and divisible by 6.

13. Anne and Hester are both reading an 1100-page historical novel. Anne reads 50 pages a day and Hester reads 10 pages the first day, 20 the second, 30 the third, and so on. After how many days will they be on the same page?

14. The largest integer in an arithmetic progression of consecutive even integers is nine times the smallest integer. The sum of the arithmetic progression is 90. Find the numbers.

15. At the end of each month a credit union charges interest equal to one per cent of the unpaid balance of a loan. A man borrows $100 from the credit union and pays back $10 at the end of each month for ten months. If his first payment is made one month after the date of the loan, what is the total amount of interest charged?

16. From two towns 363 miles apart, Jack and Jill set out to meet each other. If Jill travels 1 mile the first day, 3 the second, 5 the third, and so on (in A.P.), and Jack travels 2 miles the first day, 6 the second, 10 the third, and so on (in A.P.), when will they meet?

GEOMETRIC PROGRESSIONS AND SERIES

13–4 Geometric Progression

Under conditions favorable to the growth of certain bacteria, one organism can divide into two every half-hour. The number of bacteria thus produced in successive half-hours, starting with a single organism, may be presented in a chart.

Number of half-hours	1	2	3	4	5	...
Number of bacteria	2	4	8	16	32	...

The number of bacteria at each half-hour is a term in the sequence 2, 4, 8, 16, 32, ... You can find an expression for the general term, t_n, of this sequence by noting that each term is twice the preceding term in the sequence. Thus, the table can be written as follows:

Number of half-hours	1	2	3	4	...	n
Number of bacteria	$2 \cdot 2^0$	$2 \cdot 2^1$	$2 \cdot 2^2$	$2 \cdot 2^3$	...	$2 \cdot 2^{n-1}$

Do you see that the general or nth term of the sequence is given by

$$t_n = 2 \cdot 2^{n-1}?$$

This sequence is an example of a *geometric progression* (G.P.).

If the ratio r of every pair of two successive terms in a sequence is a constant, then the sequence is called a geometric progression.

If a is the first term of a geometric progression, and r is the common ratio, then the following table shows an expression for each term, t_n.

n	1	2	3	...	n
t_n	$a \cdot r^0$	$a \cdot r^1$	$a \cdot r^2$	...	$a \cdot r^{n-1}$

Therefore, the nth term in the sequence is given by

$$\boldsymbol{t_n = ar^{n-1}}.$$

EXAMPLE. What is the sixth term in the geometric progression 3, 12, 48, . . .?

Solution: Find the ratio r by dividing any term by the preceding term, $r = \frac{48}{12} = 4$. Use $t_n = ar^{n-1}$, replacing a by 3, r by 4, and n by 6.

$t_6 = 3 \cdot 4^{6-1}$

$t_6 = 3 \cdot 4^5 = 3(1024) = 3072$, **Answer.**

Oral Exercises

State whether each of the given four-term sequences forms a geometric progression, an arithmetic progression, or neither. If the sequence is an arithmetic progression, give the common difference; if it is a geometric progression, give the common ratio.

1. $2, 10, 50, 250$
2. $5, 15, 45, 135$
3. $24, 8, 2\frac{2}{3}, \frac{8}{9}$
4. $2, 3, 4\frac{1}{2}, 6\frac{3}{4}$
5. $-3, 6, -12, 24$
6. $\frac{1}{32}, -\frac{1}{16}, \frac{1}{8}, -\frac{1}{4}$
7. $2, -2, 2, -2$
8. $\cos 180°, -2\cos 0°, 4\cos 180°, -8\cos 0°$
9. $48, 36, 24, 12$
10. $-\sqrt{5}, -\sqrt{15}, -3\sqrt{5}, -3\sqrt{15}$
11. $\sqrt{3}, 2\sqrt{3} + 2, 3\sqrt{3} + 4, 4\sqrt{3} + 6$
12. p, prq, pr^2q^2, pr^3q^3
13. $2, 3, 5, 8$
14. $\sin 30°, \sin^2 210°, \sin^3 30°, \sin^4 210°$

Written Exercises

Write the first four terms of each geometric progression.

A

1. $a = 1, r = 3$
2. $a = -9, r = 2$
3. $a = \frac{3}{4}, r = \frac{1}{2}$
4. $a = -3, r = -\frac{1}{3}$
5. $a = 12, r = \sin \frac{3\pi}{2}$
6. $a = 7.7, r = \sec 60°$

Find t_n in each of the following geometric progressions.

7. $a = 4, n = 4, r = 4$
8. $a = 12, n = 5, r = \frac{1}{3}$
9. $5, 10, 20, \ldots; n = 7$
10. $39, 13, 4\frac{1}{3}, \ldots; n = 9$
11. $2\sqrt{7}, 6\sqrt{7}, 18\sqrt{7}, \ldots; n = 6$
12. $-\sqrt{3}, \sqrt{6}, -2\sqrt{3}, \ldots; n = 10$

Draw the graph of the function f whose domain is $\{1, 2, 3, 4, 5\}$ and whose values are given by the indicated formula.

13. $f(n) = 5 \cdot 2^{n-1}$
14. $f(n) = -3 \cdot 2^{n-1}$
15. $f(n) = (-3)^{n-1}$
16. $f(n) = (-1)^{n-1}$
17. $f(n) = (\sin 210°)^{n-1}$
18. $f(n) = -9 \cot^{2n-2} 30°$

B

19. There are two geometric progressions of real numbers with a first term of 7 and a fifth term of 112. Find the two values for r.

20. There are two geometric progressions of real numbers having -1 as the first term and -625 as the fifth term. Find the two values for r.

21. In a geometric progression whose first term is 5 and whose common ratio is -5, there is a term $t_n = 3125$. What is the value of n?

22. The first term of a geometric progression is 27 and the common ratio is $\frac{1}{3}$. For what value of n is $t_n = \frac{1}{3}$?

23. Which term of the geometric progression 2, -6, 18, . . . is 162?

24. Which term of the geometric progression 243, -81, 27, . . . is $-\frac{1}{9}$?

25. The seventh term of a geometric progression is 256 and the first term is 4. What is the fifth term?

26. Find the eighth term of a geometric progression whose first term is 2 and whose sixth term is $\frac{1}{16}$.

C

27. Prove that the logarithms of n positive numbers in geometric progression are in arithmetic progression.

28. In a geometric progression of positive numbers, each term after the second is the sum of the two preceding terms. Find the common ratio.

Problems

A

1. A man who invested in stock found that in one year through dividends his income increased by 5%. If his income were to continue to increase at this rate for five more years and his original income was $2000, what would his income be at the end of this time?

2. A father gives his son $1 on his 12th birthday and decides to double his gift each following year. How much did the boy receive on his 21st birthday?

3. A boy states that one of his ancestors in the tenth generation before him was on the *Mayflower*. How many ancestors of that generation does he have, assuming that there is no duplication?

4. There are seven houses; in each are seven cats. Each cat kills seven mice. Each mouse would have eaten seven ears of wheat. Each ear of wheat will produce seven measures of grain. How much grain is saved?

5. A Town Planning Commission finds that because of the new missile plant the population has been increasing by 10% annually. If the population is now 15,000, what population may be expected at the end of four years? (Answer to the nearest hundred.)

6. If the value of a car depreciates 20% the first year and 5% each year after that, what is the value of a 4-year old car which originally sold for $3000?

B

7. A side of an equilateral triangle is 20 inches long. A second equilateral triangle is inscribed in it by joining the midpoints of the sides of the first triangle. The process is continued, as shown in the accompanying diagram. Find the perimeter of the fifth inscribed equilateral triangle.

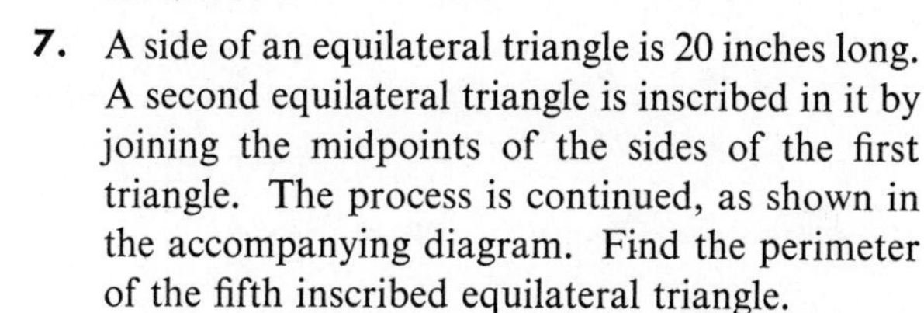

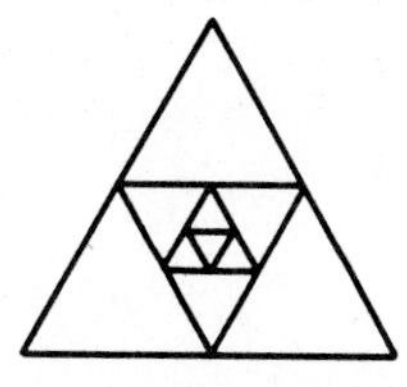

8. A jar contains 500 cubic inches of air. On its first stroke, an air pump removes 20% of the air, leaving 80% of 500 cubic inches of air in the jar. On the second stroke, the pump removes 20% of the remaining air, and so on. How much air is left in the jar after the fifth stroke of the piston?

C

9. The length of each oscillation of a pendulum is 90% of the length of the preceding oscillation. How many oscillations are required for the pendulum to damp down to one which has less than half the length of the initial oscillation?

10. Filled to capacity, a tank contains 10 gallons of pure antifreeze. One gallon of liquid is drawn out and the tank is filled with water. If this operation is repeated several times, after how many operations will there be less than 1 gallon of pure antifreeze left in the tank?

13–5 Geometric Means

The terms between two given terms in a geometric progression are called the **geometric means** between the given terms. To insert geometric means between numbers in a G.P., you must find the common ratio by using the formula $t_n = ar^{n-1}$.

EXAMPLE 1. Insert the three real geometric means between 1 and 81.

Solution: Since $a = 1$ and $t_n = 81$, substitute 1 for a, 81 for t_n, and 5 for n in $t_n = ar^{n-1}$.

$81 = 1\,r^{5-1}$

$81 = r^4$

$r = \sqrt[4]{81}$ or $-\sqrt[4]{81}$; $r = 3$ or -3

Multiply 1 successively by 3 or -3 to generate the required geometric means.

1, 3, 9, 27, 81 or 1, -3, 9, -27, 81, **Answer.**

A single geometric mean inserted between two numbers is called the **geometric mean (mean proportional)** of the numbers. If m is the geometric mean of a and b, a, m, b form a geometric progression and:

$$\frac{m}{a} = \frac{b}{m}$$

$$\therefore m^2 = ab; \quad m = \sqrt{ab}, \quad \text{or} \quad m = -\sqrt{ab}.$$

EXAMPLE 2. Find the geometric mean of 5 and 10.

Solution: Set $a = 5$, $b = 10$ and substitute in $m = \sqrt{ab}$, $m = -\sqrt{ab}$.

$$m = \sqrt{(5)(10)} = \sqrt{50}, \text{ or } m = -\sqrt{50}$$

$5\sqrt{2}$ or $-5\sqrt{2}$, **Answer.**

Oral Exercises

State the positive geometric mean of the two given numbers.

1. 2 and 8
2. 12 and 3
3. 1 and 4
4. 1 and 9
5. 2 and 32
6. 2 and 50
7. $\frac{1}{2}$ and 8
8. $\frac{1}{2}$ and 18
9. $\frac{1}{8}$ and 32
10. $\frac{1}{3}$ and 27
11. 3 and 5
12. 1 and 7
13. 1 and 16
14. 4 and 9
15. 2 and 7
16. 3 and 10
17. 5 and 7
18. 5 and 6

Written Exercises

Insert the given number of real geometric means and write the resulting finite geometric progression.

1. Two, between 1 and 27.
2. Three, between 1 and 256.
3. Four, between -7 and -224.
4. Three, between $\frac{1}{525}$ and $\frac{25}{21}$.
5. Five, between m^2 and m^{14}.
6. Two, between m^2 and m^{14}.
7. One positive, between 5 and 45.
8. One positive, between $\frac{1}{9}$ and $\frac{1}{441}$.
9. One negative, between 3 and 48.
10. One negative, between 2.5 and 10.

11. One negative, between $\sin z$ and $\csc z$.

12. One negative, between $\tan \theta$ and $\cot \theta$.

13. Two, between $\frac{a^3}{b}$ and $\frac{b^3}{a}$.

14. One, between $|x|$ and $4|x|$.

15. Show that if b is the geometric mean of a and c, then b^2 is the geometric mean of a^2 and c^2.

16. From the result of Exercise 15 deduce that the squares of the terms of a geometric progression also form a geometric progression.

17. The third term of a G.P. is 5 and the sixth term is $\frac{8}{\sqrt{5}}$. Find the intervening terms.

18. The fourth term of a G.P. is 2 and the seventh term is -2. Find the intervening terms.

B **19.** The product of three real numbers in G.P. is -64. The first is 4 times the third. Find the numbers.

20. Three numbers are in the ratio 2:5:6. If the first number is left unchanged, the second increased by 8, and the third increased by 6, the results will be in geometric progression. Find the original numbers.

21. Find the first term in a geometric progression whose common ratio is 2 and whose sixth term is 96.

22. Find the first term in a geometric progression whose common ratio is 3 and whose fifth term is 324.

23. If $-\frac{64}{9}$ is the sixth term of a geometric progression whose common ratio is $-\frac{2}{3}$, what is the first term of the progression?

24. If $\frac{81}{16}$ is the fifth term of a geometric progression whose common ratio is $-\frac{3}{4}$, what is the first term?

C **25.** Prove that the arithmetic mean of two different positive numbers a and b is greater than their positive geometric mean. [*Hint:* $(a - b)^2 > 0$.]

26. Use the result of Exercise 25 to prove that for any three different positive numbers a, b, and c, $(a + b)(b + c)(c + a) > 8abc$.

13–6 Geometric Series

The sum of the terms in a geometric progression is a **geometric series**. You can find an expression for such a sum by writing the general geometric series in expanded form, and directly beneath this writing the results of multiplying each term in the series by $-r$.

$$S_n = a + ar + ar^2 + \dots + ar^{n-2} + ar^{n-1}$$

$$-rS_n = -ar - ar^2 - ar^3 - \dots - ar^{n-1} - ar^n.$$

Adding the corresponding members of each equation, you have

$$S_n - rS_n = a - ar^n,$$

since the sum of the terms in the right member between a and $-ar^n$ is 0. Factoring the left member, you have

$$(1 - r)S_n = a - ar^n$$

$$\mathbf{S_n = \frac{a - ar^n}{1 - r} \text{ (provided } r \neq 1)}$$

EXAMPLE 1. Find the sum of eight terms in the geometric series whose first term is 1 and whose common ratio is 2.

Solution: Substitute 1 for a, 2 for r, and 8 for n in

$$S_n = \frac{a - ar^n}{1 - r}.$$

$$S_8 = \frac{1 - 1(2)^8}{1 - 2}$$

$$S_8 = \frac{1 - 256}{-1} = 255, \textbf{ Answer.}$$

Because $S_n = \dfrac{a - ar^n}{1 - r}$ we can write $S_n = \dfrac{a - r(ar^{n-1})}{1 - r}$. If l denotes the last term of the sequence, $l = ar^{n-1}$. Substituting l for ar^{n-1}, we obtain

$$\mathbf{S_n = \frac{a - rl}{1 - r} \quad (r \neq 1).}$$

EXAMPLE 2. Find the sum of a geometric series whose first term is 4, whose last term is 324, and whose common ratio is 3.

Solution: Substitute 4 for a, 3 for r, and 324 for l in

$$S_n = \frac{a - rl}{1 - r}.$$

$$S_n = \frac{4 - 3(324)}{1 - 3}$$

$$S_n = \frac{4 - 972}{-2} = \frac{-968}{-2} = 484, \textbf{ Answer.}$$

Written Exercises

Find the sum of the geometric series.

SAMPLE. $\sum_{j=1}^{4} 4(3)^{j-1}$

Solution: By inspection, $a = 4$, $r = 3$, and $n = 4$.

Substitute in $S_n = \dfrac{a - ar^n}{1 - r}$.

$$S_4 = \frac{4 - 4(3)^4}{1 - 3}$$

$$S_4 = \frac{4 - 4(81)}{-2} = \frac{4 - 324}{-2} = \frac{-320}{-2} = 160, \textbf{ Answer.}$$

A

1. $\sum_{j=1}^{7} 5(2)^{j-1}$

2. $\sum_{j=1}^{3} 5(4)^{j-1}$

3. $\sum_{k=1}^{6} 12(\frac{1}{2})^{k-1}$

4. $\sum_{r=1}^{5} 9(\frac{1}{3})^{r-1}$

5. $\sum_{k=1}^{6} 3(-\frac{1}{3})^{k-1}$

6. $\sum_{j=1}^{7} 2(-\frac{1}{2})^{j-1}$

7. $\sum_{k=1}^{6} -\frac{2}{5}(\frac{1}{2})^{k-1}$

8. $\sum_{j=1}^{7} -\frac{1}{2}(-\frac{1}{3})^{j-1}$

Find the sum of the indicated geometric progression.

9. $a = 4, l = 324, r = 3$

10. $a = 4, l = 324, r = -3$

11. $a = 27, r = \tan^2 30°, n = 6$

12. $a = 1, r = \csc 30°, n = 7$

13. $a = 64, r = -\frac{1}{4}, l = \frac{1}{4}$

14. $a = 64, r = \frac{1}{4}, l = \frac{1}{4}$

15. $1000, 100, 10, \ldots; n = 7$

16. $1200, 12, 0.12, \ldots; n = 5$

Of the values *a*, *l*, *n*, *r*, and S_n, three are given. Find the other two.

B

17. $n = 9, r = 2, S_n = 1022$

18. $n = 5, r = \frac{1}{3}, S_n = \frac{121}{81}$

19. $a = -2, n = 3, S_n = -1302$

20. $a = -2, n = 3, S_n = -14$

21. $a = 5, r = -2, S_n = -25$

22. $a = 17, r = -\frac{1}{2}, S_n = \frac{187}{16}$

23. $a = 30, l = 0.003, S_n = 33.333$

24. $a = 200, l = 0.02, S_n = 202.02$

Problems

A

1. The diameter of each successive layer of a wedding cake is $\frac{2}{3}$ the previous layer. If the diameter of the first layer of a 5-layer cake is 15 inches, find the sum of the circumferences of all the layers.

2. If there have been no intermarriages, how many ancestors have you had in the ten generations preceding you?

3. A man sends out two letters on Saturday, with instructions to the recipients to write letters to two friends by the following Saturday, asking them to do likewise. If there are no duplications and no one breaks the chain, how many letters are sent in the first eight Saturdays?

4. A large fraternal organization has a telephone communication system in which the secretary calls three men of Group A, who each call three men of Group B. Each of the nine men in Group B then calls three men of Group C, and so on. The groups are lettered through the alphabet to Group G. How many men are in the organization?

5. A side of a square is 10 inches. The midpoints of its sides are joined to form an inscribed square, and the process is continued as shown in the diagram. Find the sum of the perimeters of the first five squares formed in this way.

6. A side of an equilateral triangle is 12 inches. The midpoints of its sides are joined to form an inscribed equilateral triangle, and the process is continued. Find the sum of the perimeters of the first five equilateral triangles in the resulting figure.

7. If the half-life of the Uranium 230 isotope is 20.8 days, how much of a given amount of the isotope will be left after 104 days?

8. A certain lathe makes a total of 211 revolutions in the first five seconds after the motor is turned off. In any one second, its speed is two-thirds of its speed during the preceding second. What was its speed in revolutions per second at the time the motor was turned off?

B

9. The sum of the first and second terms of a geometric progression is -3, and the sum of the fifth and sixth terms is $-\frac{3}{16}$. Find the sum of the first 8 terms.

10. The sum of the first two terms of a geometric progression is 36, and the product of the first and third terms is nine times the second term. Find the sum of the first seven terms.

11. In a certain credit union, money left on deposit for one year earns 4% interest at the end of the year. If you invested $100 at the beginning

of each year in this credit union and did not withdraw the interest due at the end of the year, how much would you have on deposit at the end of the 10th year?

12. At the end of each quarter a bank pays 1% interest on money left on deposit from the beginning of the quarter. If you wished to save $1000 over a two-year period, how much would you have to deposit in this bank at the beginning of each quarter? Assume that you do not withdraw the interest due at the end of each quarter.

13–7 Infinite Geometric Series

The repeating decimal (see page 190) 0.454545 . . . can be written $\frac{45}{100} + \frac{45}{10000} + \frac{45}{1000000} + \ldots$. Do you see that this is a geometric series whose first term is $\frac{45}{100}$, whose ratio is $\frac{1}{100}$, and which has infinitely many terms? To see whether this series corresponds to a rational number, consider the formula for the sum of a geometric progression,

$$S_n = \frac{a - ar^n}{1 - r},$$

which can be written in the form

$$S_n = \frac{a(1 - r^n)}{1 - r} = \frac{a}{1 - r}(1 - r^n).$$

If you replace a by $\frac{45}{100}$ and r by $\frac{1}{100}$, you have

$$S_n = \frac{\frac{45}{100}}{1 - \frac{1}{100}}\left[1 - \left(\frac{1}{100}\right)^n\right] = \frac{5}{11}\left[1 - \left(\frac{1}{100}\right)^n\right].$$

Since $\left|\frac{1}{100}\right| < 1$, $\left(\frac{1}{100}\right)^n$ grows smaller and smaller as n grows larger and larger; in fact, $\left(\frac{1}{100}\right)^n$ can be made to differ from 0 by as little as desired by simply taking n large enough. That is, by letting n increase indefinitely, the sum

$$S_n = \frac{5}{11}\left[1 - \left(\frac{1}{100}\right)^n\right]$$

can be made to approach S where

$$S = \frac{5}{11}[1 - 0].$$

We say that the *limit* of S_n, as n increases without bound, is $\frac{5}{11}$.

In general, if $|r| < 1$, it can be shown that r^n grows closer and closer to 0 as n grows larger and larger, so that the factor $1 - r^n$ approaches $1 - 0$ or 1. From this fact it will follow that the sum $S_n = \frac{a}{1 - r}(1 - r^n)$ approaches $\frac{a}{1 - r}$. Therefore, we define the sum S of an infinite geometric progression whose ratio r satisfies $|r| < 1$ by

$$\mathbf{S = \frac{a}{1 - r}}.$$

EXAMPLE. Find the sum of an infinite geometric series whose first term is 6 and whose ratio is $\frac{1}{3}$.

Solution: Replace a with 6 and r with $\frac{1}{3}$ in $S = \frac{a}{1 - r}$

$$S = \frac{6}{1 - \frac{1}{3}}$$

$$S = \frac{6}{\frac{2}{3}} = 9, \textbf{ Answer.}$$

Written Exercises

Find the sum of the infinite geometric series indicated below.

A

1. $a = 4, r = \frac{1}{2}$

2. $a = 6, r = -\frac{1}{3}$

3. $a = 0.6, r = 0.1$

4. $a = 0.23, r = 0.01$

5. $2, 1, \frac{1}{2}, \ldots$

6. $9, 3, 1, \ldots$

7. $9, -6, 4, \ldots$

8. $50, -30, 18, \ldots$

9. $0.1, 0.01, 0.001, \ldots$

10. $0.9, 0.09, 0.009, \ldots$

11. $18, 12, 8, \ldots$

12. $\sqrt{6}, \sqrt{2}, \sqrt{\frac{2}{3}}, \ldots$

Write the first three terms of the infinite geometric progression.

13. $a = 3, S = 3\frac{1}{3}$

14. $a = 3, S = 2\frac{1}{4}$

15. $r = \frac{2}{3}, S = 18$

16. $r = 0.01, S = \frac{3}{11}$

Change each of the following repeating decimals to an equivalent common fraction.

17. $0.5555\ldots$

18. $0.8888\ldots$

19. $0.\overline{12}$

20. $0.\overline{72}$

21. $0.1\overline{2}$

22. $0.2\overline{5}$

23. $0.\overline{675}$

24. $0.\overline{297}$

Problems

A

1. A rubber ball dropped 40 feet rebounds on each bounce $\frac{2}{5}$ of the distance from which it fell. How far will it travel before coming to rest?

2. A rubber ball dropped 30 feet rebounds on each bounce $\frac{3}{8}$ of the distance from which it fell. How far will it travel before coming to rest?

3. A side of a square is 12 inches. The midpoints of its sides are joined to form an inscribed square, and this process is continued as shown in the diagram. Find the sum of the perimeters of the squares if this process is continued without end.

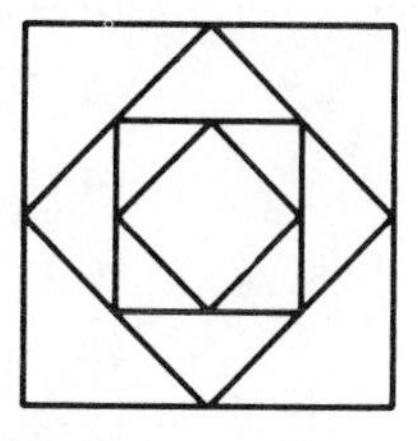

4. A side of an equilateral triangle is 10 inches. The midpoints of its sides are joined to form an inscribed equilateral triangle and the process is continued. Find the sum of the perimeters of the triangles if the process is continued without end.

5. Find the sum of the areas of the squares in Problem 3.

6. Find the sum of the areas of the triangles in Problem 4.

B

7. A "snowflake" curve is constructed as follows: The sides of an equilateral triangle are trisected, and the middle third of the trisection serves as a base for a new equilateral triangle, following which this segment is deleted from the figure. The process is continued. If the side of the initial equilateral triangle is of length 1, what is the area enclosed by the snowflake curve if the process is continued without end?

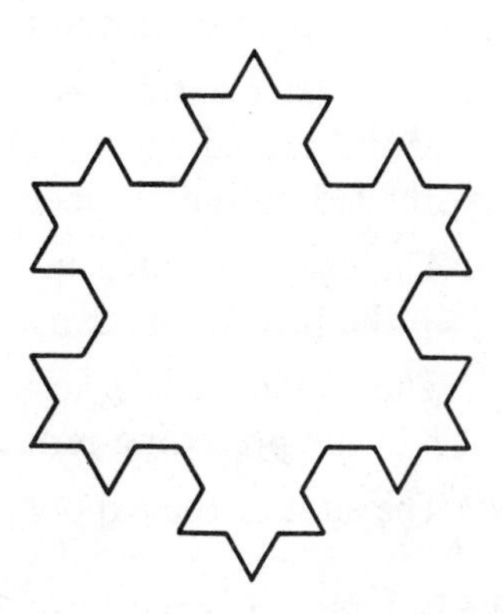

8. Show that the figure described in Problem 7 has no perimeter, that is, that the perimeter is of unbounded length.

C

9. If $|x| < 1$, find the sum S of the series $1 + 3x + 5x^2 + 7x^3 + \cdots$. (*Hint:* Consider $S - xS$.)

10. Find the fallacy in the following argument.

$$\text{Let } S = 1 + 2 + 2^2 + 2^3 + \cdots$$

$$= 1 + 2(1 + 2 + 2^2 + \cdots) = 1 + 2 \cdot \frac{1}{1 - 2} = 1 - 2$$

$$\therefore S = -1$$

BINOMIAL EXPANSIONS

13–8 Powers of Binomials

When you expand natural number powers of binomials you discover an interesting pattern.

$$
\begin{aligned}
(a+b)^2 &= a^2 + 2ab + b^2\\
(a+b)^3 &= a^3 + 3a^2b + 3ab^2 + b^3\\
(a+b)^4 &= a^4 + 4a^3b + 6a^2b^2 + 4ab^3 + b^4\\
(a-b)^2 &= a^2 - 2ab + b^2\\
(a-b)^3 &= a^3 - 3a^2b + 3ab^2 - b^3\\
(a-b)^4 &= a^4 - 4a^3b + 6a^2b^2 - 4ab^3 + b^4
\end{aligned}
$$

These examples suggest:

1. The number of terms in the expansion of $(a \pm b)^n$ is $n + 1$.
2. If the binomial is a sum, all terms in the expansion are added; if the binomial is a difference, the terms are alternately added and subtracted, the even-numbered terms being subtracted.
3. The coefficient of the first term is 1.
4. The coefficient of any other term is the product of the coefficient of the preceding term and the exponent of a in the preceding term divided by the number of the preceding term.
5. The exponent of a in any term is one less than the exponent of a in the preceding term.
6. The exponent of b in any term is one greater than the exponent of b in the preceding term.
7. The sum of the exponents of a and b in each term is n.

EXAMPLE. Expand $(x - 2y)^5$.

Solution:

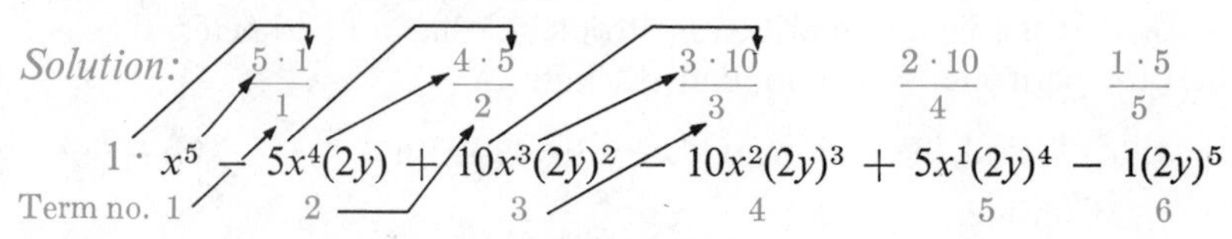

The arrows show how the numerical coefficients of the first four terms are computed. Explain the last two terms.

Simplifying,

$$x^5 - 10x^4y + 40x^3y^2 - 80x^2y^3 + 80xy^4 - 32y^5, \textbf{ Answer.}$$

Written Exercises

Expand each binomial, expressing the result in its simplest form.

A

1. $(c + d)^6$ **7.** $(1 - y^2)^5$ **13.** $\left(a + \frac{x}{2}\right)^6$

2. $(x + y)^5$ **8.** $(x^2 - 1)^8$ **14.** $\left(\frac{a}{2} - y\right)^4$

3. $(m - t)^7$ **9.** $(x + 2)^4$ **15.** $(x^2 - 2)^7$

4. $(r - s)^6$ **10.** $(y - 2)^5$ **16.** $(3 + y^2)^5$

5. $(x + 1)^4$ **11.** $(3x - 1)^3$ **17.** $(r^2 + s^2)^8$

6. $(1 + r)^9$ **12.** $(2k + 3)^3$ **18.** $(r^2 - s^2)^6$

Find the first three terms of each expansion.

19. $(m + t)^8$ **22.** $(a + \frac{1}{3})^7$ **25.** $(\sin x - 3)^6$

20. $(x - y)^{11}$ **23.** $(n^2 + 2)^{12}$ **26.** $(\cos x + 2)^{10}$

21. $(d - \frac{1}{2})^{10}$ **24.** $(n^2 - 3)^9$

Find the value of each expression to the nearest thousandth.

B

27. $(1 + 0.03)^5$ **28.** $(1 + 0.02)^6$ **29.** $(1.04)^8$ **30.** $(1.05)^4$

Given that the binomial expansion $(a + b)^r$ holds for all rational numbers r, find the first three terms in each of the following.

31. $(a + b)^{1/2}$ **32.** $(a - b)^{1/3}$ **33.** $(x + y)^{2/3}$

Find an approximation to the nearest hundredth for each of the following.

34. $\sqrt{1.04}$ *Hint:* $\sqrt{1.04} = (1 + 0.04)^{1/2}$ **35.** $\sqrt[3]{1.08}$

13–9 The General Binomial Expansion

The pattern displayed by the expansion of binomials in the preceding section suggests the *Binomial Theorem*, which states that for any positive integer n the expansion of $(a + b)^n$ is:

$$a^n + \frac{n}{1}a^{n-1}b^1 + \frac{n}{1}\cdot\frac{n-1}{2}a^{n-2}b^2$$

$$+ \frac{n}{1}\cdot\frac{n-1}{2}\cdot\frac{n-2}{3}a^{n-3}b^3 + \dots$$

$$+ \frac{n}{1}\cdot\frac{n-1}{2}\cdot\frac{n-2}{3}\cdots\frac{n-(r-2)}{r-1}a^{n-(r-1)}b^{r-1} + \dots + b^n.$$

The ***r*th** term is

$$\frac{n(n-1)(n-2)\ldots[n-(r-2)]}{1\cdot 2\cdot 3\cdot\ldots\cdot(r-1)}a^{n-(r-1)}b^{r-1}.$$

The product in the denominator, $1 \cdot 2 \cdot 3 \cdot \ldots \cdot (r-1)$, can be written in **factorial notation.** Thus, $(r-1)!$ (read "r minus one, factorial" or "factorial, r minus one") means to form the product of the successive natural numbers $1 \cdot 2 \cdot 3 \cdot \ldots \cdot (r-1)$. For example,

$$5! = 1 \cdot 2 \cdot 3 \cdot 4 \cdot 5 = 120,\ 3! = 1 \cdot 2 \cdot 3 = 6,$$

and

$$7! = 1 \cdot 2 \cdot 3 \cdot 4 \cdot 5 \cdot 6 \cdot 7 = 5040.$$

Therefore, the ***r*th term** in the binomial expansion can be written

$$\frac{n(n-1)(n-2)\ldots[n-(r-2)]}{(r-1)!}a^{n-(r-1)}b^{r-1}.$$

Observe that in the rth term, the exponent of b is $r-1$, the exponent of a is $n-(r-1)$, the denominator of the coefficient is $(r-1)!$, and the numerator of the coefficient is $n(n-1)\ldots[n-(r-2)]$, which consists of $r-1$ consecutive integers decreasing from n.

EXAMPLE. Find the sixth term in the expansion of $(x+2y)^{12}$.

Solution: Here $n = 12$ and $r = 6$.

First find the value of the exponent of b or $2y$; it is $r-1$, or 5.

$$(2y)^5$$

The denominator of the coefficient is $(r-1)!$, or $5!$. $5!$ has five factors.

$$\frac{\quad}{1 \cdot 2 \cdot 3 \cdot 4 \cdot 5}(\ )(2y)^5$$

The numerator is the product of 5 consecutive integers descending from 12.

$$\frac{12(11)(10)(9)(8)}{1 \cdot 2 \cdot 3 \cdot 4 \cdot 5}(\ )(2y)^5$$

The exponent of a, or x, must add to the exponent of $2y$ to give 12.

$$\frac{12(11)(10)(9)(8)}{1 \cdot 2 \cdot 3 \cdot 4 \cdot 5}(x)^7(2y)^5$$

$\therefore$ the exponent of x is 7.

$25344x^7y^5$, **Answer.**

Written Exercises

Find and simplify the specified term in each expansion.

A

1. Third, $(x + m)^4$
2. Fourth, $(y - 1)^8$
3. Fifth, $(2 - x)^6$
4. Third, $(s - 3)^7$
5. Sixth, $(x + y)^{10}$
6. Seventh, $(t - 1)^{12}$
7. Fourth, $(x^2 + 3)^6$
8. Third, $(m^3 - 2)^5$
9. Fifth, $(3d^2 - 2)^5$
10. Sixth, $(2m^3 - x^2)^8$
11. Tenth, $(\tan^2 \theta - 1)^{15}$
12. Twelfth, $(1 + \sec^2 \theta)^{20}$
13. Seventh, $\left(m^2 - \frac{r}{2}\right)^9$
14. Sixth, $\left(\frac{2}{m^2} - \frac{m^2}{x}\right)^7$
15. Middle, $\left(x^2 + \frac{1}{2x}\right)^8$
16. Middle, $\left(2 - \frac{x^2}{y^2}\right)^{10}$

Chapter Summary

Inventory of Structure and Method

1. The **general term** of an **A.P.** is given by the formula $t_n = a + (n - 1)d$. The **sum** of an A.P., $\sum_{i=1}^{n} [a + (i - 1)d]$, can be found from the formula $S_n = \frac{n}{2}(a + l)$, or $S_n = \frac{n}{2}[2a + (n - 1)d.]$

2. The general term of a **G.P.** can be found from the formula $t_n = ar^{n-1}$. The **sum,** $\sum_{i=1}^{n} ar^{i-1}$, is found from $S_n = \frac{a - ar^n}{1 - r}$, or $S_n = \frac{a - rl}{1 - r}$.

3. You can determine any number of arithmetic or of geometric **means** by using the formulas for t_n.

4. When $|r| < 1$, the sum of an **infinite G.P.** having r as common ratio and a as first term is $\frac{a}{1 - r}$. Using this formula, you can express a repeating decimal as an equivalent common fraction.

5. To find any positive integral power of a binomial, use the **Binomial Theorem:**

$$(a + b)^n = a^n + na^{n-1}b + \frac{n(n-1)}{2!}a^{n-2}b^2 + \frac{n(n-1)(n-2)}{3!}a^{n-3}b^3 + \cdots + b^n$$

where the rth term of the expansion is given by

$$\frac{n(n-1)(n-2)\cdots(n-r+2)}{(r-1)!}a^{n-r+1}b^{r-1}$$

Vocabulary and Spelling

sequence (*p. 495*)
term (of a sequence) (*p. 495*)
arithmetic progression (A.P.) (*p. 496*)
finite sequence (*p. 496*)
infinite sequence (*p. 496*)
arithmetic means (*p. 499*)
series (*p. 501*)
summation $\sum_{i=1}^{n} f(i)$ (*p. 502*)
geometric progression (G.P.) (*p. 506*)
Binomial Theorem (expansion) (*p. 519*)
factorial notation ($n!$) (*p. 520*)

Chapter Test and Review

13–1 **1.** Find the 50th term of the A.P.: 38, 35, 32, ...

13–2 **2.** Find the indicated number of arithmetic means between -9 and 11: **(a)** 1, **(b)** 3.

13–3 **3.** Find the sum of 31 terms of the A.P.: 126, 117, 108, ...

4. A man borrows \$500 and repays it by paying \$100 plus 6% interest on the unpaid balance at the end of each year. Find the total interest paid.

13–4 **5.** Find the 10th term of the G.P.: $\sqrt{2}, 1, \frac{\sqrt{2}}{2}, \cdots$.

13–5 **6.** Find the indicated number of geometric means between 256 and 4: **(a)** 1, **(b)** 5.

13–6 **7.** Evaluate $\sum_{n=1}^{6} 18(-\frac{2}{3})^{n-1}$.

13–7 **8.** Find the sum of the infinite G.P.: $5\frac{1}{3}, 2\frac{2}{3}, 1\frac{1}{3}, \ldots$.

13–8 **9.** Expand $(r^2 - 2t)^6$.

13–9 **10.** Express the 5th term of $\left(x - \frac{y}{2}\right)^{10}$ in simple form.

Review the sections listed at the left-hand margin if your test results show this to be advisable.

A Dream Realized

Known as one of the greatest thinkers, perhaps *the* greatest, of the seventeenth century, Gottfried Wilhelm Leibniz (*Libe nitz*) showed genius in many fields: law, religion, diplomacy, literature, philosophy, mathematics. His brilliant mind could not resist venturing into all these areas. Would he have done better to concentrate in one field? Or was it better that he left a legacy of ideas in many areas? These are questions we cannot answer, but we do know that Leibniz's name is high on the honor roll of mathematicians.

He was born in Leipzig (Germany) in 1646, the son of a philosophy professor. His early studies in the classics and philosophy led to a study of logic. He attempted to reform classical logic, and his work foreshadowed that of George Boole, who invented symbolic logic (Boolean algebra) about 1850. Had he pursued his idea of reducing logic to symbols, the history of modern mathematics might have been greatly altered. However, his dream of a universal symbolic language and system of reasoning, which was considered absurd in his time, has been largely realized in modern abstract algebra and symbolic logic.

Leibniz expressed his faith in the power of reason in these words:

> "*Although the whole of this life were said to be nothing but a dream and the physical world nothing but a phantasm, I should call this dream or phantasm real enough, if, using reason well, we were never deceived by it.*"

It was not until the age of twenty-six that Leibniz became interested in mathematics and physics. He is credited with discovering, independently of Newton, the fundamental theorem uniting differential and integral calculus. He also did significant work in combinatorial analysis, devised a computer which performed all arithmetic operations, and stressed the importance of the binary system of numeration which is used extensively in modern electronic computers.

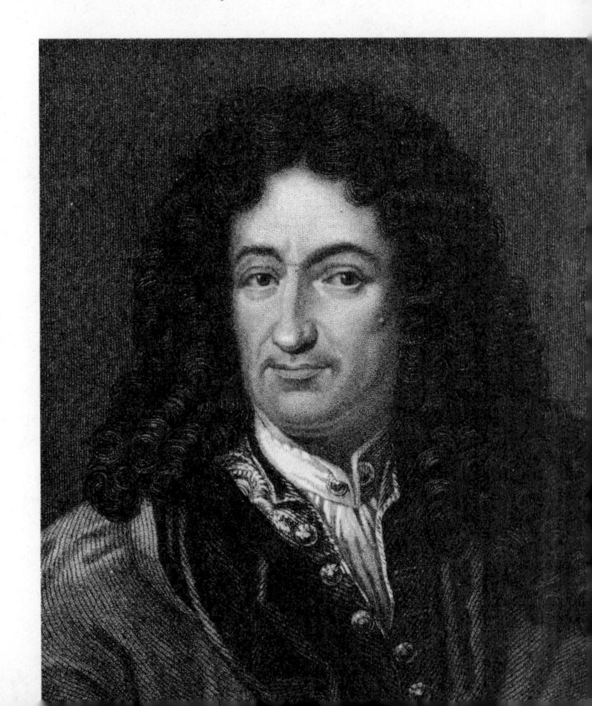

Extra for Experts

Mathematical Induction

Let N denote the set of natural numbers: $N = \{1, 2, 3, 4, \ldots\}$. N has two characteristic properties:

1. N contains the number 1.

2. N is closed with respect to the addition of 1 to each of its members.

Thus, $1 \in N$; $1 + 1$, or $2, \in N$; $2 + 1$, or $3, \in N$; and, in general, if $a \in N$, then $(a + 1) \in N$.

To determine whether a set S *consisting of natural numbers* is actually the set of *all* natural numbers, you subject S to two tests based on the above:

1. Does 1 belong to S?

2. For *each* natural number a in S, is it true that $a + 1$ belongs to S?

When the answer to *both* of these questions is "Yes," then S is N.

EXAMPLE 1. Let S be the solution set of the open sentence $2^x \geq 1 + x$ over the set of natural numbers, N. Prove that $S = N$.

Proof:

1. Is $\in S$? That is, does $2^x \geq 1 + x$ become a true statement when x is replaced by 1?

$$2^x \geq 1 + x$$
$$2^1 \stackrel{?}{\geq} 1 + 1$$
$$2 \geq 2 \checkmark$$

$$\therefore 1 \in S$$

2. If $a \in S$, is $(a + 1) \in S$? That is, if, on replacing x by some natural number a, you obtain a true statement $[2^a \geq 1 + a]$, will you also obtain a true statement when you replace x by $a + 1$?

$$[2^{a+1} \stackrel{?}{\geq} 1 + (a + 1)].$$

Suppose $2^a \geq 1 + a$.

Now $2^{a+1} = 2 \cdot 2^a$

$\therefore 2^{a+1} \geq 2(1 + a)$

But $2(1 + a) = (1 + a) + (1 + a)$

Also, $1 + a \geq 1$

$\therefore 2(1 + a) \geq 1 + (1 + a)$

$\therefore 2^{a+1} \geq 1 + (1 + a) \checkmark$

$$\therefore \text{ if } a \in S, \text{ then } (a + 1) \in S.$$

Because the answers to **1** and **2** are each "Yes," we conclude that $S = N$.

EXAMPLE 2. Prove that the sum of the first n consecutive odd integers is the square of n: $1 + 3 + 5 + \cdots + (2n - 1) = n^2$.

Proof: Let S be the set of natural numbers n for which $1 + 3 + 5 + \cdots + (2n - 1) = n^2$ is a true statement.

1. Is $1 \in S$? For $n = 1$, the equation becomes $1 \stackrel{?}{=} 1^2$; $1 = 1$. ✓
$\therefore 1 \in S$.

2. If $a \in S$, is $(a + 1) \in S$? Suppose that the statement is true for the sum of a odd integers:

$$1 + 3 + 5 + \cdots + (2a - 1) = a^2.$$

To obtain the sum of $(a + 1)$ odd integers, add the next odd integer, namely $2(a + 1) - 1$, or $2a + 1$, to each member of this equation:

$$1 + 3 + 5 + \cdots + (2a - 1) + (2a + 1) = a^2 + 2a + 1$$
$$= (a + 1)^2$$
$$1 + 3 + 5 + \cdots + (2a - 1) + [2(a + 1) - 1] = (a + 1)^2,$$

which says that the sum of the first $(a + 1)$ odd integers is $(a + 1)^2$.

$\therefore$ if the given statement is true when n is replaced by a, it is also true with $a + 1$ in place of n.

Since S passed both tests, $S = N$. This means that we have proved that for every natural number n, $1 + 3 + 5 + \cdots + (2n - 1) = n^2$.

The argument used in Examples 1 and 2 is called *proof by mathematical induction.* You use it to prove theorems which involve special cases corresponding to the successive natural numbers.

Exercises

Prove that each statement is true for all natural numbers n.

1. $1 + 2 + 3 + \cdots + n = \dfrac{n(n + 1)}{2}$

2. $\dfrac{1}{1 \cdot 2} + \dfrac{1}{2 \cdot 3} + \dfrac{1}{3 \cdot 4} + \cdots + \dfrac{1}{n(n + 1)} = \dfrac{n}{n + 1}$

3. If $\sin(\theta + 2\pi) = \sin \theta$, then $\sin(\theta + 2\pi n) = \sin \theta$.

Hint: $\sin(\theta + 2\pi \cdot 1) = \sin \theta$ is given true.

$\therefore \sin[\theta + 2\pi(a + 1)] = \sin[(\theta + 2\pi a) + 2\pi] = \sin(\theta + 2\pi a).$

4. If $\tan(\theta + \pi) = \tan \theta$, then $\tan(\theta + n\pi) = \tan \theta$.

5. Prove that if $1 + 2 + 3 + \cdots + n = \frac{1}{8}(2n + 1)^2$ is true for some positive integer k, then it is true for $k + 1$. Have you proved the relationship for all positive integers by mathematical induction?

6. Prove by mathematical induction that

$1 + 2 + 3 + \cdots + n < \frac{1}{8}(2n + 1)^2$ for every positive integer n.

CHAPTER 14

. . . a photomicrograph of graphite, or the common "lead" in pencils, revealing a flat, circular structure

Polynomial Functions

Often in experimental work, scientists and engineers must find the values of some function to a specified accuracy. Polynomial functions, which you will study in this chapter, are of basic importance in such cases since the values of any function whose graph is a smooth, unbroken curve can be approximated as closely as desired by the values of a polynomial function of sufficiently high degree.

POLYNOMIAL FUNCTIONS OVER THE COMPLEX NUMBERS

14–1 Synthetic Substitution

Functions whose values are given by equations such as $f(x) = \sqrt{2}x + 1$, $g(x) = 2x^2 + ix - 3$, and $h(x) = x^3 - 8$, are called *polynomial functions*. If the set of complex numbers is the domain of these functions, they are **functions over the complex numbers.**

You know how to evaluate a function by direct substitution. For example, if a_0, a_1, a_2, a_3 denote complex numbers and P is the function $\{[x, P(x)]\colon P(x) = a_0x^3 + a_1x^2 + a_2x + a_3\}$, then to evaluate P at 8, you write $P(8) = a_0 8^3 + a_1 8^2 + a_2 8 + a_3$. To discover an easier way to find $P(8)$, study the following sequence of operations.

Step	Result
1. **Multiply a_0 by 8**	$a_0 \cdot 8$
2. **Add a_1**	$a_0 \cdot 8 + a_1$
3. **Multiply the result of Step 2 by 8**	$(a_0 \cdot 8 + a_1) \cdot 8$
4. **Add a_2**	$(a_0 \cdot 8 + a_1) \cdot 8 + a_2$
5. **Multiply the result of Step 4 by 8**	$[(a_0 \cdot 8 + a_1) \cdot 8 + a_2] \cdot 8$
6. **Add a_3**	$[(a_0 \cdot 8 + a_1) \cdot 8 + a_2] \cdot 8 + a_3$

By simplifying the expression in Step 6, you find

$$[(a_0 \cdot 8 + a_1) \cdot 8 + a_2] \cdot 8 + a_3 = a_0 \cdot 8^3 + a_1 \cdot 8^2 + a_2 \cdot 8 + a_3 = P(8)$$

Steps 1–6 are arranged below in three rows. The circled numerals designate each of the steps.

8	a_0	a_1	a_2	a_3
		① $a_0 \cdot 8$	③ $(a_0 \cdot 8 + a_1) \cdot 8$	⑤ $[(a_0 \cdot 8 + a_1) \cdot 8 + a_2] \cdot 8$
	a_0	② $a_0 \cdot 8 + a_1$	④ $(a_0 \cdot 8 + a_1) \cdot 8 + a_2$	⑥ $[(a_0 \cdot 8 + a_1) \cdot 8 + a_2] \cdot 8 + a_3$

If $P(x) = 7x^3 + 3x^2 + 2x - 1$, you can find $P(8)$ by following Steps 1–6, using 7, 3, 2, and -1 in place of a_0, a_1, a_2, and a_3 respectively.

$$\begin{array}{r|rrrr} 8 & 7 & 3 & 2 & -1 \\ & & 56 & 472 & 3792 \\ \hline & 7 & 59 & 474 & \underbrace{3791}_{P(8)} \end{array}$$

Thus $P(8) = 3791$. This process, called **synthetic substitution**, applies to polynomials of any degree over the complex numbers. Notice that $P(x)$ must be written in descending powers of x. Also, if a power is missing, 0 must be written in the corresponding place.

EXAMPLE. If $Q(x) = 2x^4 - 3x^3 + 2x - 1$, find $Q(2)$ and $Q(2i)$.

Solution: Write the coefficients of $Q(x)$ in order, writing 0 where necessary. Then, use synthetic substitution.

$$\begin{array}{r|rrrrr} 2 & 2 & -3 & 0 & 2 & -1 \\ & & 4 & 2 & 4 & 12 \\ \hline & 2 & 1 & 2 & 6 & 11 \end{array}$$

$$\begin{array}{r|rrrrr} 2i & 2 & -3 & 0 & 2 & -1 \\ & & 4i & -8-6i & 12-16i & 32+28i \\ \hline & 2 & -3+4i & -8-6i & 14-16i & 31+28i \end{array}$$

$Q(2) = 11$; $Q(2i) = 31 + 28i$, **Answer.**

Written Exercises

Use synthetic substitution to find the indicated values of the given polynomial over the complex numbers.

$P(x) = 3x^3 - 2x^2 - x - 4$

A

1. $P(2)$ **2.** $P(-1)$ **3.** $P(-3)$ **4.** $P(4)$

$Q(x) = 2x^4 - 3x^3 + x^2 + 1$

5. $Q(3)$ **6.** $Q(-2)$ **7.** $Q(i)$ **8.** $Q(-i)$

$f(y) = 2y^4 - 5y^3 + 5y^2 - 20y - 12$

9. $f(3)$ **10.** $f(2i)$ **11.** $f(-2i)$ **12.** $f(-\frac{1}{2})$

$P(x) = x^3 + 2ix^2 + x + 2i$

13. $P(i)$ **14.** $P(-i)$ **15.** $P(1 - i)$ **16.** $P(2 + i)$

$P(x) = x^3 - (a + b + c)x^2 + (ab + ac + bc)x - abc$

17. $P(a)$ **18.** $P(b)$ **19.** $P(c)$ **20.** $P(0)$

B **21.** If $P(x) = 2x^3 - 3x^2 + 3x - m$, find m so that $P(2) = 6$.

22. If $Q(x) = x^3 - 2x + 5m$, find m so that $Q(-1) = 3$.

23. If $R(x) = 3x^3 + 2x^2 - mx + 2$, find m so that $R(3) = 5$.

24. If $P(x) = x^4 - 2x^3 + x^2 - mx + 2$, find m so that $P(2) = 0$.

25. If $Q(x) = 3x^3 - mx^2 + 3x + 1$, find m so that $Q(-2) = 0$.

26. If $R(x) = 2x^3 + mx^2 - 2x + 3$, find m so that $R(-1) = 4$.

27. If $P(x) = 3x^3 - 2x^2 + ax + b$, find values for a and b so that $P(-2) = -37$ and $P(1) = 2$.

28. If $P(x) = 2x^4 - 3x^2 + ax + b$, find values for a and b so that $P(-2) = 24$ and $P(2) = 20$.

14–2 Remainder and Factor Theorems

By dividing $x^2 - x - 6$, $x^2 - 5x + 6$, $x^3 - 4x^2 + 6x - 4$, and $x^3 + 2x^2 - 7x + 4$ respectively by $x - 2$, you obtain the quotients (Q) and remainders (R) shown in the following chart.

P	Q	R	P(2)
$x^2 - x - 6$	$x + 1$	-4	-4
$x^2 - 5x + 6$	$x - 3$	0	0
$x^3 - 4x^2 + 6x - 4$	$x^2 - 2x + 2$	0	0
$x^3 + 2x^2 - 7x + 4$	$x^2 + 4x + 1$	6	6

Notice that in every case the remainder R equals $P(2)$. This fact illustrates the **Remainder Theorem.**

THEOREM. For every polynomial $P(x)$ of nonzero degree n over the set of complex numbers, and for every complex number r, there exists a polynomial $Q(x)$ of degree $n - 1$, such that

$$P(x) = (x - r)Q(x) + P(r).$$

We shall show how the Remainder Theorem is proved by examining a particular case, the polynomial $P(x) = a_0x^3 + a_1x^2 + a_2x + a_3$, with 8 in place of r.

Now, $P(8) = a_08^3 + a_18^2 + a_28 + a_3$, and

$$\begin{aligned} P(x) - P(8) &= a_0(x^3 - 8^3) + a_1(x^2 - 8^2) + a_2(x - 8) + (a_3 - a_3) \\ &= a_0(x - 8)(x^2 + 8x + 64) + a_1(x - 8)(x + 8) + a_2(x - 8) \\ &= (x - 8)[a_0(x^2 + 8x + 64) + a_1(x + 8) + a_2] \\ &= (x - 8)[a_0x^2 + (a_08 + a_1)x + (a_08^2 + a_18 + a_2)]. \end{aligned}$$

Therefore, if you let $Q(x) = a_0x^2 + (a_08 + a_1)x + (a_08^2 + a_18 + a_2)$,

you have $$P(x) = (x - 8)Q(x) + P(8).$$

You can use this argument to prove the Remainder Theorem for any polynomial of any nonzero degree in x and any divisor $x - r$.

Do you recognize the coefficients of $Q(x)$ in the preceding proof? They are the first three expressions in the last line of the substitution process shown on page 527. Because for any polynomial $P(x)$ you can use the synthetic substitution process to find the quotient $Q(x)$ and the "remainder" $P(r)$ obtained on dividing $P(x)$ by $(x - r)$, synthetic substitution is often called **synthetic division.**

EXAMPLE 1. Use synthetic division to divide $6x^3 - 19x^2 + x + 6$ by $x - 3$.

Solution:

$$\begin{array}{r|rrrr} 3 & 6 & -19 & 1 & 6 \\ & & 18 & -3 & -6 \\ \hline & 6 & -1 & -2 & \mid\ 0 \end{array} \qquad Q(x) = 6x^2 - x - 2; \quad R = 0$$

Check: $6x^3 - 19x^2 + x + 6 = (x - 3)(6x^2 - x - 2) + 0$ ✓

$$\therefore \frac{6x^3 - 19x^2 + x + 6}{x - 3} = 6x^2 - x - 2 + \frac{0}{x - 3} = 6x^2 - x - 2, \textbf{ Answer.}$$

The Remainder Theorem leads to the **Factor Theorem**, which was discussed briefly in Section 4–10:

THEOREM. Over the set of complex numbers, $(x - r)$ is a factor of a polynomial $P(x)$ if and only if r is a root of $P(x) = 0$.

Proof: If r is a root of $P(x) = 0$, then by the definition of root, $P(r) = 0$. Therefore $P(x) = (x - r)Q(x) + 0 = (x - r)Q(x)$, and $(x - r)$ is a factor of $P(x)$. Conversely, if $(x - r)$ is a factor of $P(x)$, then $P(x) = (x - r)Q(x)$, so that $P(r) = (r - r)Q(r) = 0 \cdot Q(r) = 0$.

This theorem can help you identify factors of polynomials.

EXAMPLE 2. Is $(x - 4)$ a factor of $P(x) = x^4 - 3x^3 - x^2 - 11x - 4$?

Solution: If $P(4) = 0$, then $x - 4$ is a factor. Use synthetic substitution to substitute 4 for x.

$$\begin{array}{r|rrrr|r} 4 & 1 & -3 & -1 & -11 & -4 \\ & & 4 & 4 & 12 & 4 \\ \hline & 1 & 1 & 3 & 1 & 0 \end{array}$$

$(x - 4)$ is a factor, **Answer.**

Written Exercises

Use synthetic division to write each of the given polynomials in the form $P(x) = (x - r)Q(x) + P(r)$ when r is as given.

SAMPLE. $P(x) = x^3 + 2x^2 - 2x + 3$; $r = 2$

Solution:

$$\begin{array}{r|rrr|r} 2 & 1 & 2 & -2 & 3 \\ & & 2 & 8 & 12 \\ \hline & 1 & 4 & 6 & 15 \end{array}$$

The first three terms in the bottom row are the coefficients of $Q(x)$ and $P(r) = 15$. $P(x) = (x - 2)(x^2 + 4x + 6) + 15$, **Answer.**

A

1. $P(x) = 3x^3 - 2x^2 + 2x + 1$; $r = 2$
2. $P(x) = 2x^3 + 3x^2 - 2x + 3$; $r = 1$
3. $P(x) = x^3 + 4x^2 + 3x + 2$; $r = -3$
4. $P(x) = 2x^3 + 3x^2 - 2x - 3$; $r = -1$
5. $P(x) = x^4 - 3x^3 - x^2 - 11x - 4$; $r = 3$
6. $P(x) = 2x^4 + x^3 - 2x^2 - 12x - 45$; $r = -2$

Find the quotient and the remainder using synthetic division.

7. $(3x^3 + 11x^2 + 11x + 15) \div (x + 3)$
8. $(2x^3 - 7x^2 - 17x + 10) \div (x - 5)$
9. $(3x^4 - 6x^3 + 3x + 4) \div (x - 2i)$
10. $(2x^4 - 3x^2 + 7x + 3) \div (x + i)$

Use the Factor Theorem to show that the given polynomial has the given factor.

11. $2x^3 - 11x^2 + 12x + 9; (x - 3)$

12. $x^3 + 2x^2 - 5x - 6; (x - 2)$

13. $6x^3 - 7x^2 - 7x + 6: (x + 1)$

14. $x^4 + 3x^3 - 9x - 27; (x + 3)$

Use the Factor Theorem to show that the equation has the given root.

15. $x^4 - 16x^3 + 86x^2 - 176x + 105 = 0; 5$

16. $x^4 - 5x^3 - 13x^2 + 53x + 60 = 0; -1$

17. $x^3 - 3x^2 + x - 3 = 0; i$

18. $x^3 - x^2 + 4x - 4 = 0; -2i$

Find Q(x) in each exercise.

19. $2x^3 - 7x^2 - 21x + 54 = (x - 2)Q(x)$

20. $2x^3 - 7x^2 - 21x + 54 = (x + 3)Q(x)$

21. $2x^3 - 3x^2 - 4x + 1 = (x + 1)Q(x)$

22. $2x^3 - 3x^2 - 4x + 4 = (x - 2)Q(x)$

B **23.** Show that a is a root of $x^3 + (a + 1)x^2 + (a - 2a^2)x = 2a^2$.

24. Show that $2b$ is a root of $x^3 + (4 - b)x^2 - 2(2b + b^2)x = 8b^2$.

25. Show that $1 - 3i$ is a root of $x^4 - 3x^3 + 6x^2 + 2x - 60 = 0$.

26. Show that $2 + 4i$ is a root of $x^4 - 4x^3 + 18x^2 + 8x - 40 = 0$.

Determine m so that the first polynomial is a factor of the second.

27. $x - 3; x^3 - 2x^2 + 3x + m$

28. $x + 1; 2x^4 - 3x^2 + 2x + m$

29. $x - 1; x^3 - 3x^2 + mx - 4$

30. $x - 2; 2x^3 + 3x^2 - mx + 10$

14–3 Depressed Equations

Knowing one root of a polynomial equation, you can sometimes determine the other roots.

EXAMPLE. Find the zeros of the function P where
$P(x) = 2x^3 + x^2 - 4x - 2$.

Solution: (*Plan:* Solve the equation $P(x) = 0$.)

1. Because the coefficients are integers, use the theorem on page 256 to identify possible rational roots, $\frac{p}{q}$.

$$2x^3 + x^2 - 4x - 2 = 0$$

$$\frac{p}{q} \in \left\{\frac{1}{2}, -\frac{1}{2}, 1, -1, 2, -2\right\}$$

2. Use the Factor Theorem and synthetic substitution to test each possibility. By mentally doing the addition steps in the process, you can arrange the work conveniently, as shown.

x				P(x)
	2	1	−4	−2
$\frac{1}{2}$	2	2	−3	$-\frac{7}{2}$
$-\frac{1}{2}$	2	0	−4	0

$\therefore P(x) = (x + \frac{1}{2})(2x^2 - 4) = 0$

3. Solve the *depressed* equation, $2x^2 - 4 = 0$

$2x^2 - 4 = 0$

$x^2 = 2$

$x = \sqrt{2}$ or $-\sqrt{2}$

$\therefore$ the set of zeros of P is $\{-\frac{1}{2}, -\sqrt{2}, \sqrt{2}\}$, **Answer.**

Whenever r is a root of the polynomial equation $P(x) = 0$, you find the remaining roots by solving the **depressed equation** $P(x) \div (x - r) = 0$.

Written Exercises

Find the solution set of each of the following equations.

A

1. $x^3 + 4x^2 + 8x + 5 = 0$
2. $x^3 - 6x^2 + 11x - 6 = 0$
3. $3x^3 - 2x^2 - 8x - 3 = 0$
4. $2x^3 - 13x^2 - 13x - 15 = 0$

Find the zeros of the function.

5. $f = \{[x, P(x)]: P(x) = x^3 - x^2 - 14x + 24\}$
6. $f = \{[x, P(x)]: P(x) = x^3 - 3x^2 - 10x + 24\}$
7. $f = \{[x, P(x)]: P(x) = 2x^4 + 7x^3 + 4x^2 - 7x - 6\}$
8. $f = \{[x, P(x)]: P(x) = 6x^4 - 29x^3 + 40x^2 - 7x - 12\}$

Given the indicated root(s), find the other roots of the equation.

B

9. $ix^3 + 2x^2 + 1 = 0; i$
10. $x^3 - 2ix^2 + x = 2i; -i$
11. $x^4 - 2x^2 - 3 = 0; \sqrt{3}$ and $-\sqrt{3}$
12. $x^4 - 2x^3 - 2x - 1 = 0; i$ and $-i$

14–4 The Fundamental Theorem of Algebra

Over the set of real numbers a polynomial equation may have no solution. For example, $x^2 + 1 = 0$ has no *real* root. But over the set of complex numbers it has two roots, namely i and $-i$. The German mathematician K. F. Gauss in 1799 first proved that every polynomial equation with complex coefficients has at least one root. This result, called the **Fundamental Theorem of Algebra,** leads to the following assertion which we will accept without proof.

THEOREM. Every polynomial equation with complex coefficients and nonzero degree n has exactly n complex roots.

In applying this theorem, you may have to count the same number as a root more than once. For example, 2 is a *double* root of the equation $x^2 - 4x + 4 = 0$.

You recall (page 415) that the imaginary roots of a quadratic equation with *real* coefficients occur in conjugate pairs. Thus, the fact that $1 - 3i$ is a root of $x^2 - 2x + 10 = 0$ implies that $1 + 3i$ is also a root. This property is typical of all polynomial equations with *real* coefficients.

THEOREM. If a polynomial equation with real coefficients has $a + bi$ as a root (a and b real, $b \neq 0$), then $a - bi$ is also a root.

The proof of this theorem is indicated in Exercises 19–24, page 535.

If you know that $P(x) = x^4 - 4x^3 + 8x^2 - 12x + 15 = 0$ has a root $2 + i$, this theorem with the Factor Theorem enables you to solve the equation. Since the equation has real coefficients, *both* $2 + i$ *and* $2 - i$ are roots. Therefore, both $x - (2 + i)$ and $x - (2 - i)$ are factors of the left member. Since neither of these polynomials is a factor of the other, their product $[(x - 2) - i][(x - 2) + i]$, or $x^2 - 4x + 5$, must be a factor of $P(x) = 0$. But $P(x) \div (x^2 - 4x + 5) = x^2 + 3$. The roots of the depressed equation are $i\sqrt{3}$ and $-i\sqrt{3}$; hence, the solution set of $P(x) = 0$ is

$$\{2 \pm i,\ i\sqrt{3},\ -i\sqrt{3}\}.$$

Written Exercises

A

1. If two roots of $x^3 - x^2 + 2x - 2 = 0$ are 1 and $\sqrt{2}i$, what must be the other root? Verify your answer by synthetic substitution.
2. If two roots of $x^3 - 8x^2 + 22x - 20 = 0$ are 2 and $3 + i$, what must be the other root? Verify your answer by synthetic substitution.
3. A cubic equation with real coefficients has roots 3 and $1 - 2i$. What must be the third root? Find the equation.
4. A cubic equation with real coefficients has roots -1 and $3i$. What must be the third root? Find the equation.
5. Given that one root of $2x^3 - 11x^2 + 28x - 24 = 0$ is $2 - 2i$, find the remaining roots.
6. Given that one root of $x^3 - 3x^2 + 4x - 2 = 0$ is $1 + i$, find the remaining roots.

7. Given that one root of $x^4 - 3x^3 + 6x^2 + 2x - 60 = 0$ is $1 - 3i$, find the remaining roots.
8. Given that one root of $x^4 - 10x^3 + 35x^2 - 50x + 34 = 0$ is $4 - i$, find the remaining roots.

Factor each polynomial completely over (a) the real numbers, (b) the complex numbers.

9. $x^3 + x^2 + x + 1$
10. $y^3 + 2y^2 + 2y + 4$
11. $x^3 - 8x + 3$
12. $x^3 - 3x^2 + x + 1$
13. $x^4 + 3x^3 - 8x - 24$
14. $x^4 + 4x^3 - 16x - 16$

State whether each assertion is true. Justify your answer.

15. If $1 + i$ is a root of a polynomial equation, then so is $1 - i$.
16. Every polynomial with real coefficients and odd degree has at least one real root.
17. Every polynomial of positive degree over the set of complex numbers can be written as a product of linear factors.
18. There exists a polynomial equation of degree 2 having $\{3 + i, 4, 3 - i\}$ as solution set.

19. Explain why the conjugate of a real number is the number itself.

Let a, b, c, d, and e denote real numbers. Prove that each statement is true.

20. The conjugate of the sum of $a + bi$ and $c + di$ is the sum of the conjugates of the numbers.
21. The conjugate of the product of $a + bi$ and $c + di$ is the product of the conjugates of the numbers.
22. For each positive integer k, the conjugate of $e \cdot (a + bi)^k$ is $e \cdot (a - bi)^k$. (*Hint:* Use Exercises 21 and 19.)
23. If $P(x) = a_0x^n + a_1x^{n-1} + \cdots + a_0$ is a polynomial with *real* coefficients, then the conjugate of $P(a + bi)$ is $P(a - bi)$. (*Hint:* Use Exercises 20 and 22.)
24. If $P(x)$ is the polynomial described in Exercise 23, and if $P(a + bi) = 0$, then $P(a - bi) = 0$.

POLYNOMIALS WITH REAL COEFFICIENTS

14–5 Descartes' Rule

If, as you view a polynomial in simple form with real coefficients from left to right, the signs associated with the coefficients of two successive terms are opposite, a **variation in sign** is said to occur.

Thus,

$$2x^4 - 3x^3 + 2x^2 + 3x - 1$$

(variations marked 1, 2, 3)

contains three variations in sign. The following fact is known as **Descartes' Rule of Signs.**

> The number of positive real roots of $P(x) = 0$ where $P(x)$ is a polynomial with real coefficients is equal to the number of variations in sign occurring in $P(x)$, or else is fewer than this number by a positive even integer. The number of negative real roots of $P(x) = 0$ is equal to the number of variations in sign occurring in $P(-x)$, or else is fewer than this number by a positive even integer.

EXAMPLE. Determine the possible number of **(a)** positive real roots, and **(b)** negative real roots of $x^4 + 2x^3 - 7x^2 + 3x - 2 = 0$.

Solution:

1. By inspection, in $x^4 + 2x^3 - 7x^2 + 3x - 2$ there are either 3 positive real roots or just one positive real root.

2. Replacing x with $-x$, you have

$$(-x)^4 + 2(-x)^3 - 7(-x)^2 + 3(-x) - 2$$
$$= x^4 - 2x^3 - 7x^2 - 3x - 2$$

By inspection there is one variation in sign, and the equation can have only one negative real root.

There are possibly 3 positive real roots or 1 positive real root, and 1 negative real root, **Answer.**

Do you see that the equation in the example must have at least one positive real root and one negative real root? Since the Fundamental Theorem of Algebra assures you that the equation has *exactly* 4 complex roots, you can state the possibilities for the nature of the roots of $x^4 + 2x^3 - 7x^2 + 3x - 2 = 0$ as follows:

Number of Positive Real Roots	Number of Negative Real Roots	Number of Imaginary Roots
3	1	0
1	1	2

Oral Exercises

In each of the following, apply Descartes' Rule and state the possibilities for the nature of the roots of each polynomial equation.

1. $x^3 - 3x^2 + 2x + 1 = 0$
2. $2x^3 + 3x^2 - 4x + 1 = 0$
3. $x^4 + 1 = 0$
4. $x^5 + 2 = 0$
5. $x^4 + 2x^3 - 3x^2 + x - 3 = 0$
6. $3x^5 - x^3 + x^2 + 2x - 1 = 0$
7. $4x^3 + 3x^2 + 1 = 0$
8. $2x^3 + x^2 - 1 = 0$
9. $x^5 - x^3 - x + 1 = 0$
10. $2x^7 - x^5 - x^3 + 3 = 0$

Written Exercises

A

1. What is the greatest number of real roots that the equation $x^5 + x^3 + x^2 + x + 1 = 0$ may have? The least?
2. What is the greatest number of real roots that $x^5 - x^2 + 1 = 0$ may have? The least?
3. What is the greatest number of real zeros the function $\{(x, y): y = x^4 + x^2 - 1\}$ may have? The least?
4. What is the greatest number of real zeros the function $\{(x, y): y = x^4 + x^3 + x^2 + x + 1\}$ may have? The least?
5. Explain why $2x^6 + x^4 + x^2 + 1 = 0$ can have no real roots.

B

6. Explain why $3x^3 + x^2 + 1 = 0$ must have two imaginary roots.
7. Explain why $4x^5 - x^4 - x^2 - 1 = 0$ must have four imaginary roots.
8. Explain why $2x^5 + x^4 + x^2 + 1 = 0$ must have four imaginary roots.

C

9. Find one real root of $x^5 - x^4 + 3x^3 - 3x^2 + 2x - 2 = 0$ and then apply Descartes' Rule to the depressed equation to show that there are no other real roots.
10. Find one real root of $x^5 + x^4 + 5x^3 + 3x^2 + 4x + 6 = 0$ and show that there are no other real roots.

14–6 Graphing

You have had much practice in graphing first- and second-degree polynomial functions with domain the set of real numbers. You will find synthetic substitution a convenient means of computing $P(x)$ for chosen x when graphing polynomial functions of higher degree over the real numbers.

EXAMPLE. Graph P, if $P(x) = x^3 - 4x^2 + 4$.

Solution: Use synthetic substitution to find values for $P(x)$.

x				P(x)
0	1	−4	0	4
1	1	−3	−3	1
2	1	−2	−4	−4
3	1	−1	−3	−5
4	1	0	0	4
−1	1	−5	5	−1

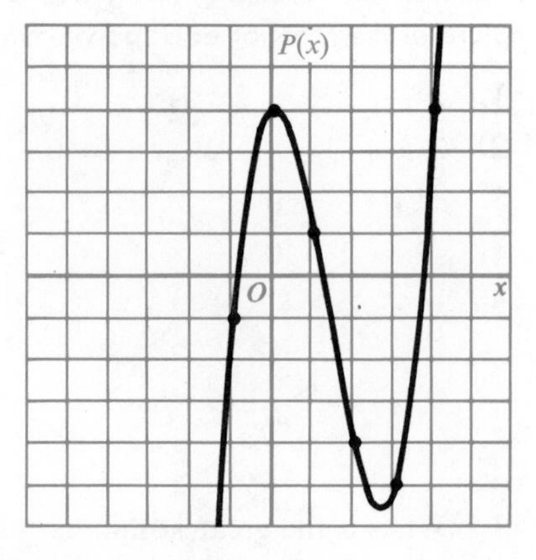

In drawing the graphs of polynomial functions as smooth unbroken curves, you assume the important **Property of Continuity**:

> If P is a polynomial function, and if m is any number between $P(a)$ and $P(b)$, then there is a number c between a and b for which $P(c) = m$.

In other words, P takes on every value between any two of its values. Therefore, you can find approximations for the real zeros of a polynomial function by estimating the x-intercepts of its graph. For instance, in the example above, the function has real zeros of approximately -0.9, 1.2, and 3.7.

Written Exercises

Graph the given polynomial function, and estimate any real zeros.

1. $\{(x, y): y = x^3\}$
2. $\{(x, y): y = 2x^3\}$
3. $\{(x, y): y = x^3 + 1\}$
4. $\{(x, y): y = x^3 - 3\}$
5. $\{(x, y): y = x^3 - 4x\}$
6. $\{(x, y): y = x^3 + 4x\}$
7. $\{(x, y): y = x^3 - 2x^2\}$
8. $\{(x, y): y = x^3 + 2x^2\}$
9. $\{(x, y): y = x^3 + 2x^2 - 5x - 6\}$
10. $\{(x, y): y = 3x^3 - 16x^2 + 12x + 16\}$
11. $\{(x, y): y = x^4 - 4x^3 - 4x^2 + 16x\}$
12. $\{(x, y): y = x^5 - 2x^4 + x^3 - 1\}$

B

13. Observe that if $P(x) = x^2 - 3x + 2$, then $P(0) = 2$ and $P(5) = 12$. The principle of continuity assures you that there must be a number c between 0 and 5 such that $P(c) = 6$. Find c.

14. In Exercise 13, $P(-5) = 42$ and $P(-1) = 6$. Find a number c, $-5 < c < -1$, such that $P(c) = 12$.

15. If $P(x) = x^2 - 4x - 8$, then $P(0) = -8$ and $P(6) = 4$. Find a number c, $0 < c < 6$, such that $P(c) = 0$.

16. In Exercise 15, $P(-4) = 24$. Find a number c, $-4 < c < 0$, such that $P(c) = 0$.

14–7 Location Principle

Consider the three facts:

1. A polynomial function f contains $(3, -4)$ and $(5, 6)$.
2. The property of continuity guarantees that the graph of a polynomial function is a smooth, unbroken curve.
3. Any line parallel to the y-axis can cut the graph of a function in at most one point.

Do you see why these facts imply that f must have a zero between 3 and 5? Fact 1 above means that the graph of f must contain the points $(3, -4)$ and $(5, 6)$ which are shown in Figure 14–1a. Fact 2 assures you that the graph cannot be broken like the one shown in Figure 14–1b. Fact 3 assures you that the graph cannot pass outside the red lines as does the graph in Figure 14–1c. Therefore, the graph must intersect the x-axis in at least one point between 3 and 5. Figure 14–2 shows several possibilities.

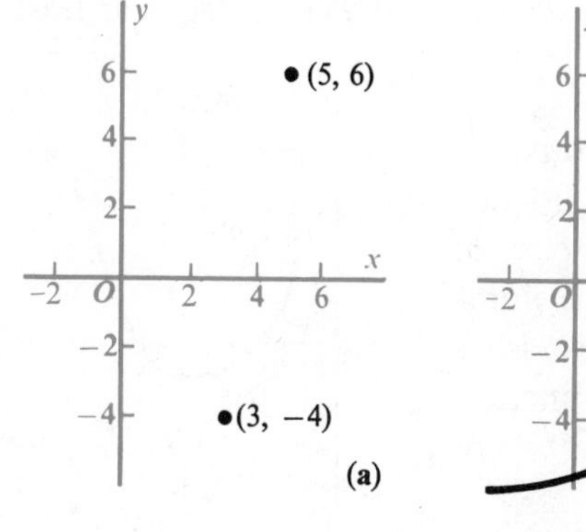

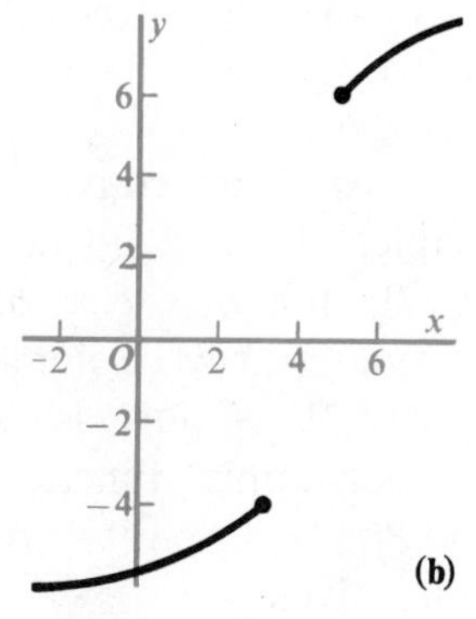

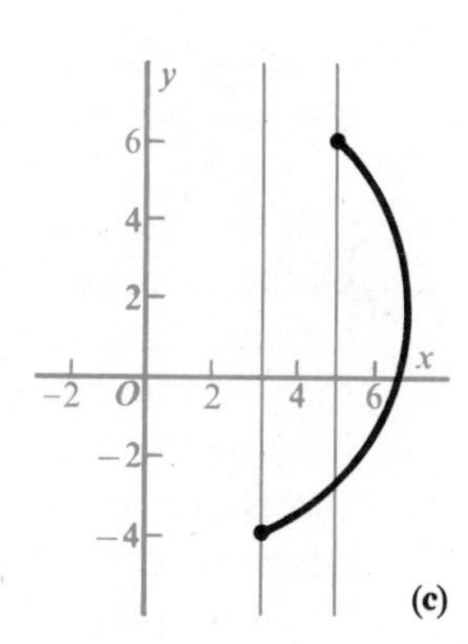

Figure 14–1

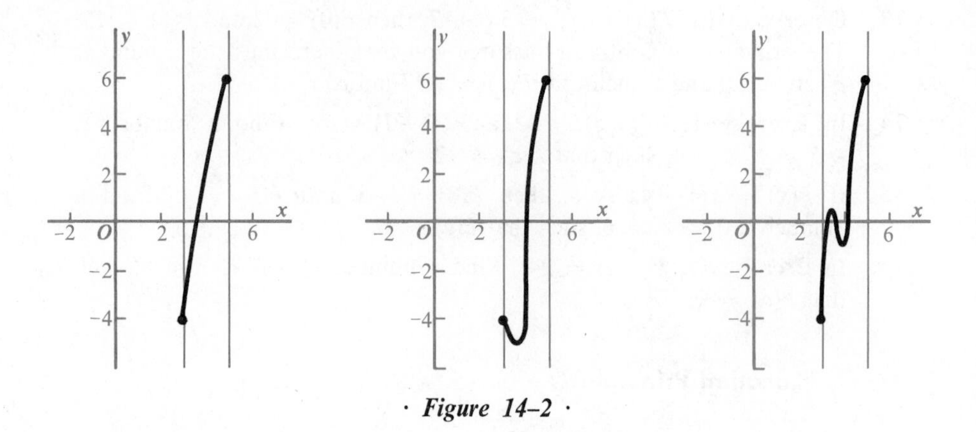

· *Figure 14–2* ·

Facts 2 and 3 above imply the **Location Principle.**

If P is a function whose values are given by a polynomial with real coefficients and if a and b are real numbers such that one of the values $P(a)$ and $P(b)$ is positive and the other is negative, then P has an odd number of zeros between a and b.

EXAMPLE. Show that P, where $P(x) = 10x^3 - 17x^2 + x + 6$, has at least one zero between 0 and -1.

Solution: By inspection, $P(0) = 6$. Using synthetic substitution,

$$\begin{array}{r|rrrr} -1 & 10 & -17 & 1 & 6 \\ & & -10 & 27 & -28 \\ \hline & 10 & -27 & 28 & -22 \end{array}$$

$\therefore P(-1) = -22$. Since $P(0) > 0$ and $P(-1) < 0$, $P(x) = 0$ has at least one root between 0 and -1, **Answer.**

It is important not to assume the converse of the Location Principle. That is, do not assume that if $P(c) = 0$, and $a < c < b$, then $P(a)$ and $P(b)$ must necessarily be numbers on opposite sides of 0. Figure 14–3 shows the graph of a polynomial function where $a < c < b$, and $P(c) = 0$, but where $P(a)$ and $P(b)$ are both positive.

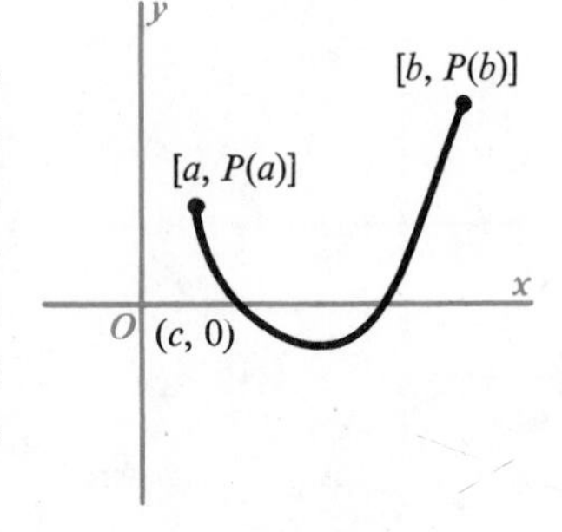

· *Figure 14–3* ·

Written Exercises

In the interval $-4 < x < 4$, locate consecutive integers between which are found zeros of each of the following functions:

SAMPLE. $\{(x, y): y = 12x^3 - 8x^2 - 23x + 12\}$

Solution: Use synthetic substitution to find values for y when $x = -3, -2, -1, 0, 1, 2, 3$, and construct a table of values.

x	−3	−2	−1	0	1	2	3
y	−315	−70	15	12	−7	30	195

By examining the values of y, you will find that there are zeros between -2 and -1, 0 and 1, and 1 and 2, **Answer.**

A

1. $\{(x, y): y = 12x^3 + 16x^2 - 95x - 50\}$
2. $\{(x, y): y = 8x^3 - 12x^2 - 66x + 35\}$
3. $\{(x, y): y = 2x^3 + x^2 + x - 1\}$
4. $\{(x, y): y = 2x^3 - x^2 + x + 1\}$
5. $\{(x, y): y = 6x^4 - x^3 - 6x^2 - 12x - 5\}$
6. $\{(x, y): y = 4x^4 + 8x^3 - x^2 + 8x - 5\}$

Each of the following functions has one real zero between -4 and 4. Locate it between consecutive integers.

7. $\{(x, y): y = 2x^3 - x^2 + 5x - 3\}$
8. $\{(x, y): y = 2x^3 + 7x^2 + 7x + 5\}$
9. $\{(x, y): y = 2x^5 + 5x^4 + 4x + 10\}$
10. $\{(x, y): y = 2x^5 - 3x^4 + 8x^3 - 12x^2 + 8x - 3\}$

14-8 Upper and Lower Bounds for Roots

To identify an interval that contains all the real roots of a polynomial equation, you must find a real number M that equals or is greater than all the real roots of the equation and a real number L that equals or is less than all the real roots. M and L are called **upper** and **lower bounds** for the roots. The following theorem tells how to find bounds for the roots.

THEOREM. Let $P(x)$ be a polynomial with real coefficients, M a nonnegative real number, and L a nonpositive real number. If the coefficients of the quotient and remainder obtained on dividing $P(x)$ by $x - M$ are all denoted by numerals of the same sign (zero may be denoted by 0 or -0), then $P(x) = 0$ has no root greater than M. If the coefficients obtained on dividing $P(x)$ by $x - L$ are denoted by numerals that alternate in sign, then $P(x) = 0$ has no root less than L.

The proof of this theorem is considered in Exercises 9 and 10 at the end of this section. To apply the theorem, you inspect the numbers in the last line of the synthetic substitution of M or L for x in $P(x)$.

EXAMPLE. Find the least nonnegative integer that the theorem above shows to be an upper bound and the greatest nonpositive integer that the theorem above shows to be a lower bound for the roots of $x^3 - 2x^2 + 3x + 5 = 0$.

Solution: Use synthetic substitution with $x = 1, 2, 3, \ldots,$ until an upper bound is reached, and with $x = -1, -2, -3, \ldots$ until a lower bound is reached

	1	−2	3	5	
1	1	−1	2	7	
2	1	0	3	11	→ numerals of the same sign
−1	1	−3	6	−1	→ numerals alternating in sign

∴ the required upper and lower bounds are 2, −1, **Answer.**

Written Exercises

Find the smallest nonnegative integral upper bound and the greatest nonpositive integral lower bound for the real roots of each equation.

A

1. $2x^3 - 3x^2 - 3x + 3 = 0$

2. $z^3 - 6z^2 + 12z - 8 = 0$

3. $y^3 + 3y^2 - 2y - 5 = 0$

4. $2x^3 - 7x^2 - 4 = 0$

5. $x^4 + 3x^3 + 4x^2 - 36 = 0$

6. $x^4 - x^3 - 10x^2 - 2x + 12 = 0$

7. $x^5 + x^4 - 2x - 4 = 0$

8. $x^5 - x^4 + 2x^3 - 3 = 0$

C

9. Let $P(x) = (x - M)Q(x) + P(M)$. Prove that if the terms of $Q(x)$ all have positive or 0 coefficients, and if M is 0 or a positive real number such that $P(M) \geq 0$, $P(x) = 0$ can have no roots greater than M. *Hint:* For all $x > M$, $(x - M) > 0$ and $Q(x) > 0$.

10. Let $P(x) = (x - L)Q(x) + P(L)$. Prove that if L is 0 or a negative real number, and if the coefficients of $Q(x)$ and $P(L)$ are alternately positive and negative numbers, then $P(x) = 0$ can have no roots less than L. *Hint:* Examine the value of $Q(x)$ under the circumstances described and observe that for all $x < L$, $(x - L) < 0$.

14–9 Polynomials and Linear Interpolation

If $P(x) = x^3 - x - 7$, the Location Principle tells you that P has at least one zero between 2 and 3 because $P(2) = -1$ while $P(3) = 17$. However, Descartes' Rule shows that $x^3 - x - 7 = 0$ has exactly one positive root. (Why?) Therefore P has just one zero (call it r) between 2 and 3. To obtain a better approximation of r, we use the method of linear interpolation which you have applied in approximating values of logarithms and trigonometric functions.

Figure 14–4 shows the part of the graph of P over the interval $2 \le x \le 3$. Notice that the line segment joining the points $A(2, -1)$ and $B(3, 17)$ of the graph crosses the x-axis at C, which is near the point where the graph itself crosses. This suggests that the x-coordinate of C is a fairly good approximation of r. Denoting the coordinates of C by $(2 + h_1, 0)$, you have:

$$\textbf{slope of } AC = \textbf{slope of } AB$$

$$\frac{1}{h_1} = \frac{18}{1}$$

$$h_1 = \tfrac{1}{18} \doteq 0.06$$

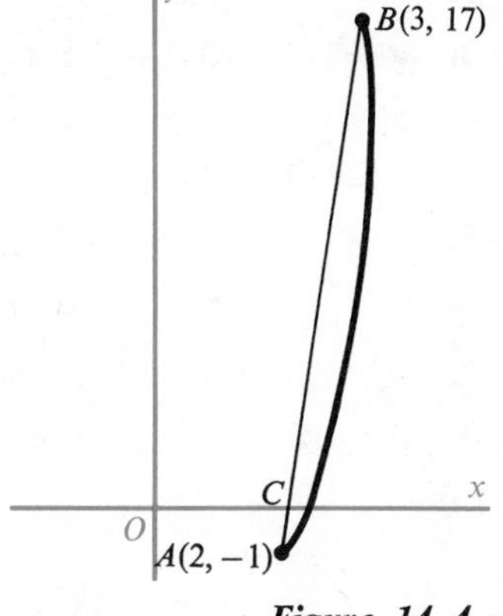

· *Figure 14–4* ·

Therefore, an approximation of the zero of P is $2 + 0.06$, or 2.06. As a check, let us substitute 2.06 synthetically for x in $P(x)$.

$$\begin{array}{l|llll} 2.06 & 1 & 0 & -1 & -7 \\ & & 2.06 & 4.2436 & 6.681816 \\ \hline & 1 & 2.06 & 3.2436 & -0.318184 \doteq -0.3182 \end{array}$$

Thus, $P(2.06)$, or -0.3182, is fairly close to 0.

To obtain an even better approximation of r, we repeat the interpolation over a shorter interval. It is easy to verify by synthetic substitution that $P(2.1) = 0.161$, so that $2.06 < r < 2.1$. Applying interpolation with A replaced by $(2.06, -0.3182)$, B by $(2.1, 0.161)$, and C by $(2.06 + h_2, 0)$ (see fig. below), you find that $\frac{0.3182}{h_2} = \frac{0.4792}{0.04}$, or $h_2 \doteq 0.0266$. Now you have a second approximation for the root, $2.06 + 0.0266 = 2.0866$. This process can be repeated as many times as desired, until you have an approximation of the root to any precision you wish. To three decimal places, the root sought in this example is 2.087.

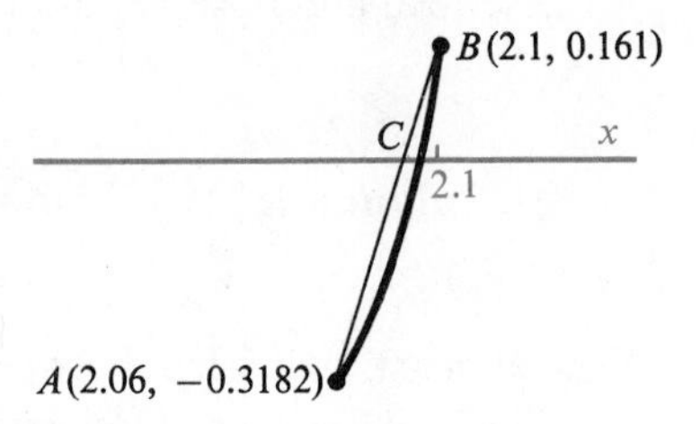

· *Figure 14–5* ·

Written Exercises

Find the indicated zero to the nearest hundredth.

A
1. $y = x^3 + 3x^2 - 9x + 4$ between 0 and 1
2. $y = x^3 - 3x + 1$ between 1 and 2
3. $y = x^3 - 3x^2 - 2x + 5$ between 1 and 2
4. $y = x^3 - 4x^2 - 6x + 8$ between 0 and 1
5. $y = -x^3 - 2x - 20$ between -2 and -3
6. $y = 2x^3 - x^2 + 3x + 1$ between -1 and 0

B
7. All real zeros of the function $\{(x, y) : y = x^3 + x - 1\}$
8. All real zeros of the function $\{(x, y) : y = x^3 + 7x + 7\}$

Chapter Summary

Inventory of Structure and Method

1. **Synthetic Substitution or Division** may be used in finding $P(r)$ for given values for r.
2. The **Remainder Theorem** states that for every polynomial $P(x)$, of degree n $(n \geq 1)$, and every complex number r, there is a polynomial $Q(x)$, of degree $n - 1$, such that $P(x) = (x - r) \cdot Q(x) + P(r)$. This leads to the *Factor Theorem:* $x - r$ is a factor of $P(x)$ if and only if r is a root of $P(x) = 0$.
3. The **Property of Continuity:** For $P(x)$ a polynomial and m a number be-

tween $P(a)$ and $P(b)$, there is a number c between a and b for which $P(c) = m$.

4. Knowing a root of a polynomial equation, apply the Factor Theorem to obtain the **depressed equation** and solve the latter.
5. The **Fundamental Theorem of Algebra** implies that every polynomial equation of degree n with complex coefficients has exactly n complex roots.

   Conjugate Complex Roots: If $P(x)$ is a polynomial with real coefficients and $a + bi$ (a and b real numbers, $b \neq 0$) is a root of $P(x) = 0$, then $a - bi$ is also a root.
6. To help you locate real roots of $P(x) = 0$, a polynomial equation with real coefficients, note:

   Rational Roots: Use the theorem stated on page 256.

   Descartes' Rule of Signs: The number of positive real roots of $P(x) = 0$ is equal to $n - 2k$ where n is the number of variations in sign of $P(x)$ and $k \in \{0, 1, 2, 3 \ldots\}$. For negative roots, apply the rule to $P(-x)$.

   Location Principle: If a and b are real numbers and $P(a)$ and $P(b)$ are represented by numerals of opposite sign for real numbers a and b, then there is an odd number of roots between a and b.

   Bounds: For a nonnegative number M, if the last line of the synthetic substitution of M in $P(x)$ contains only numerals of the same sign, then M is an upper bound for the roots of $P(x) = 0$. For a nonpositive number L, if these numerals alternate in sign, then L is a lower bound for the roots of $P(x) = 0$.
7. To approximate **irrational roots** of $P(x) = 0$, use linear interpolation.

Vocabulary and Spelling

polynomial function (*p. 527*)
synthetic substitution (*p. 528*)
Remainder Theorem (*p. 529*)
Factor Theorem (*p. 530*)
synthetic division (*p. 530*)
depressed equation (*p. 533*)
Fundamental Theorem of Algebra (*p. 533*)
variation in sign (*p. 535*)
Descartes' Rule (of Signs)(*p. 536*)
Property of Continuity (*p. 538*)
Location Principle (*p. 540*)
upper bound (*p. 541*)
lower bound (*p. 541*)
linear interpolation (*p. 543*)

Chapter Test and Review

14–1 1. If $P(x) = 2x^3 - 5x - 3$, find **(a)** $P(-1)$, **(b)** $P(3)$, by synthetic substitution.

14–2 2. In each case, use synthetic division to find the quotient and

the remainder and state whether the divisor is a factor of the dividend. **a.** $(4x^3 - 12x^2 + 3x + 10) \div (x - 2)$
b. $(3x^3 + 12x^2 - 5x - 13) \div (x + 4)$

14–3 **3.** Find the solution set of $2n^3 + 3n^2 - 11n - 6 = 0$.

14–4 **4.** A cubic equation with real coefficients has 2 and $-2 + i$ as two of its roots. Find the third root and write the equation.

14–5 **5.** Give the possibilities for the number of roots of each kind for the equation $y^5 + 3y^4 + 2y^2 - y + 1 = 0$.

14–6 **6.** Graph the function $\{(x, y): y = x^3 + x^2 - 7x - 3\}$, estimating any real zeros to the nearest tenth.

14–7 **7.** Given $\{(x, y): y = 4x^3 - 3x^2 - 5x + 1 = 0\}$, locate the real zeros between consecutive integers.

14–8 **8.** Find upper and lower bounds for the real roots of $x^3 - x^2 - 10x + 6 = 0$.

14–9 **9.** Approximate the root between 2 and 3 to the nearest hundredth: $x^3 - 2x - 5 = 0$.

Extra for Experts

Analytic Proofs

Many of the theorems of Euclidean geometry can be proved by using algebraic methods. This is especially true of theorems about polygons. Such proofs are called *analytic.* The properties of polygons with which you must work are those involving the notions of length, bisection, and the parallelism or perpendicularity of line segments.

EXAMPLE 1. Prove that the diagonals of a rectangle are equal.

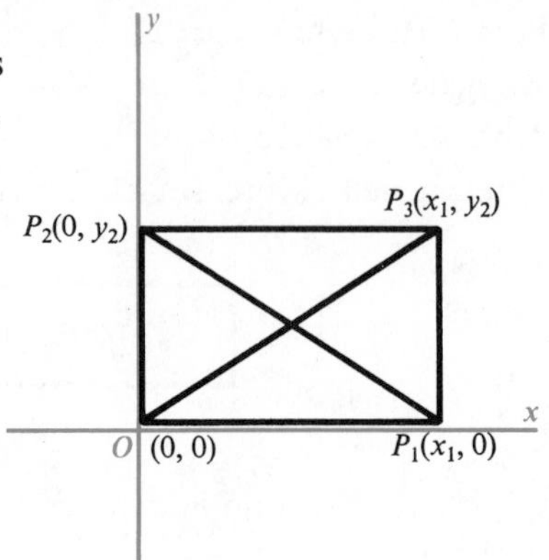

Solution: You can establish a Cartesian coordinate system as shown in the figure. If the coordinates of P_1 are $(x_1, 0)$ and those of P_2 are $(0, y_2)$, then, because $P_1P_3 \parallel OP_2$ and $P_2P_3 \parallel OP_1$, the coordinates of P_3 must be (x_1, y_2). From the distance formula,

$$OP_3 = \sqrt{(x_1 - 0)^2 + (y_2 - 0)^2} = \sqrt{x_1^2 + y_2^2},$$
$$P_1P_2 = \sqrt{(0 - x_1)^2 + (y_2 - 0)^2} = \sqrt{x_1^2 + y_2^2}$$

and the theorem is proved.

There are several features of this proof worthy of comment. Do you see that you can locate the origin of your coordinate system and direct the axes in any way you please? Since the location of the origin and the direction of the axes of a coordinate system have nothing to do with the size or shape of any figure in the plane, it is therefore to your advantage to place the axes in such a way as to minimize the algebraic difficulties in each proof. On the other hand, you must be careful not to restrict the generality of your argument in any way. Thus, you cannot assign numerical coordinates to vertices or use figures with special characteristics such as isosceles triangles for triangles, parallelograms for quadrilaterals, or squares for rectangles.

In theorems involving the concept of bisection, you may need to recall that if $P_1(x_1, y_1)$ and $P_2(x_2, y_2)$ are any two points in the plane, then the midpoint of the line segment joining P_1 and P_2 has coordinates

$$\left(\frac{x_1 + x_2}{2}, \frac{y_1 + y_2}{2}\right).$$

If the theorem you are trying to prove is concerned with parallel or perpendicular lines, you will probably wish to use the slope concept in its proof.

EXAMPLE 2. Prove that the diagonals of a rhombus are perpendicular.

Solution: By definition, a rhombus is a parallelogram with two adjacent sides of equal measure. We can let one vertex of the rhombus determine the origin of a Cartesian coordinate system and let the x-axis be drawn along one side of the rhombus, as shown.

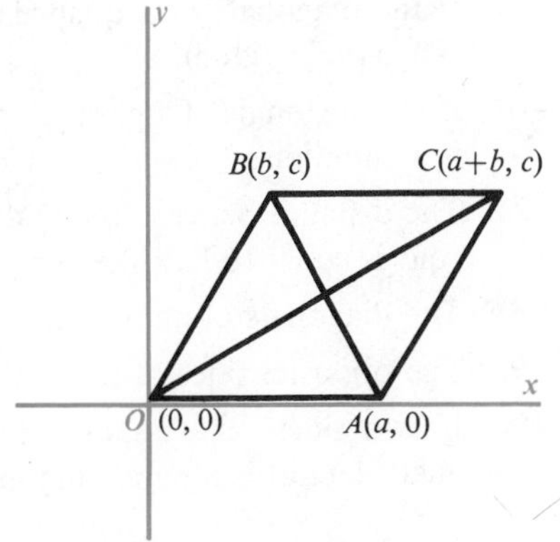

Let the x-coordinate of B be b. Then, to find c (the y-coordinate of B), use the fact that $OB = OA$:

$$\sqrt{b^2 + c^2} = a;$$

$\therefore c = \sqrt{a^2 - b^2}$. Since lines BC and OA are parallel, B and C have the same y-coordinate, namely, c or $\sqrt{a^2 - b^2}$. To find d (the x-coordinate of C), use the fact that lines AC and OB are parallel and have equal slopes:

$$\frac{\sqrt{a^2 - b^2}}{d - a} = \frac{\sqrt{a^2 - b^2}}{b};$$

$\therefore d - a = b$ (why?), and $d = a + b$.

Now, to prove that diagonals OC and BA are perpendicular, you must show that the product of their slopes is -1 (see page 304).

$$m_{OC} \cdot m_{BA} \stackrel{?}{=} -1$$

$$\left(\frac{\sqrt{a^2 - b^2}}{a + b}\right)\left(\frac{\sqrt{a^2 - b^2}}{b - a}\right) \stackrel{?}{=} -1$$

$$\frac{a^2 - b^2}{b^2 - a^2} = -1$$

Therefore, the diagonals are perpendicular.

Exercises

Give an analytic proof of each of the following theorems.

1. The medians to the equal sides in an isosceles triangle are equal.
2. If the diagonals of a rectangle are perpendicular, the rectangle is a square.
3. If a line bisects one side of a triangle and its parallel to a second side, then it bisects the third side.
4. The line joining the midpoints of two sides of a triangle is parallel to the third side and is equal in length to one half of it.
5. If the diagonals of a quadrilateral bisect each other, the quadrilateral is a parallelogram.
6. If the diagonals of a parallelogram are perpendicular, the parallelogram is a rhombus.
7. The distance between the midpoints of the nonparallel sides of a trapezoid is equal to half the sum of the lengths of the parallel sides.
8. The diagonals of an isosceles trapezoid are equal.
9. The opposite sides of a parallelogram are equal in length.
10. If two sides of a quadrilateral are parallel and equal in length, the quadrilateral is a parallelogram.

Statistics

One of the most rapidly growing fields attracting mathematicians today is that of statistics. The statistician works in a variety of areas including market research, psychological tests and measurements, industrial quality control, management science, opinion analysis, medical studies, and investigations in all the biological and physical sciences.

The statistician uses high-speed data-processing systems to help him summarize and interpret data. The data may represent information about a sample from a large population, for example, all the cars produced by a factory each month, or all the cases of cancer detected each year. On the basis of the data for the sample, the skilled statistician is able to deduce within certain limits of reliability properties of the population or of other samples. The statistician may also design experiments in advance so that the data to be collected can be validly interpreted to reveal the information sought.

The statistician needs an excellent general background in mathematics. In particular, he must know algebra, calculus, set theory, and modern probability theory. In the final chapter of this book, you will find a brief introduction to the study of probability. In addition to knowing mathematics, the statistician should have training in the special area in which he works. It is not hard to see that a statistician in the field of biology needs to understand both biology and statistics.

Do you like to analyze the past and guess at the future? If so, you may enjoy a career in statistics, where scientific methods are employed to make intelligent guesses and rational decisions.

This mathematician is constructing a statistical model for analyzing production data.

CHAPTER 15

. . . the delicate structure of a spider web maintained by the equilibrium of forces on each strand

Matrices and Determinants

Introduced in 1858, matrix theory today has applications in such diverse fields as inventory control in factories, quantum theory in physics, cost analysis in transportation and other industries, deployment problems in military operations, and data analysis in sociology and psychology. In this chapter you will learn some basic concepts of matrix theory and their use in solving systems of linear equations.

MATRICES

15–1 Terminology

A **matrix** is a rectangular array of numbers, exhibited between brackets or double lines. Examples of matrices are:

$$\begin{bmatrix} 0 & 1 & 2 \\ 3 & -1 & 4 \end{bmatrix}, \quad \begin{bmatrix} 1 & 0 \\ 3 & 0 \end{bmatrix}, \quad \begin{Vmatrix} 4 \\ 3 \end{Vmatrix}, \quad [1 \;\; 2]$$

The individual numbers that make up a matrix are called the **entries** or **elements** of the matrix and, in this book, will always be understood to be real numbers. The number of rows (horizontal) and columns (vertical) determine the **dimensions** of the matrix. The sample matrices above are 2×3 (read "two by three"), 2×2, 2×1, and 1×2 matrices, respectively, the number of rows always preceding the number of columns. A matrix that contains only one row or one column is called a **row matrix** or **column matrix**.

Capital letters are used to denote matrices, as, for example, $A_{3\times2}$, $B_{2\times3}$, $C_{3\times1}$, and so on, where the subscript gives the dimensions of the matrix. When the dimensions are clear from the context, the subscript is omitted. If all the entries in a matrix are zeros, the matrix is called a **zero matrix**. Thus,

$$\begin{bmatrix} 0 & 0 \\ 0 & 0 \\ 0 & 0 \end{bmatrix}$$

is a 3×2 zero matrix, symbolized by $O_{3\times2}$.

Two matrices are equal if and only if they have the same dimensions and the same *corresponding* (occupying the same relative position) entries. Thus,

$$\begin{bmatrix} 1 & 0 \\ 2 & 1 \end{bmatrix} = \begin{bmatrix} \frac{2}{2} & 0 \\ \frac{4}{2} & \frac{2}{2} \end{bmatrix}, \begin{bmatrix} 0 & 1 & 3 \\ 2 & -1 & 0 \end{bmatrix} = \begin{bmatrix} 0 & \frac{2}{2} & \frac{6}{2} \\ \frac{4}{2} & -\frac{2}{2} & 0 \end{bmatrix}$$

but

$$\begin{bmatrix} 1 & 0 \\ 2 & 1 \end{bmatrix} \neq \begin{bmatrix} 1 & 2 \\ 0 & 1 \end{bmatrix}, \begin{bmatrix} 0 & 0 \\ 0 & 0 \end{bmatrix} \neq \begin{bmatrix} 0 & 0 & 0 \\ 0 & 0 & 0 \end{bmatrix}.$$

Associated with every matrix A, is a matrix A^{T} (read "A transpose") which is the matrix formed by interchanging the rows and columns of A. Thus,

$$\text{if } A = \begin{bmatrix} 1 & 2 \\ 3 & 4 \end{bmatrix}, \text{ then } A^{\mathsf{T}} = \begin{bmatrix} 1 & 3 \\ 2 & 4 \end{bmatrix}.$$

Oral Exercises

State the dimensions of each of the given matrices.

1. $\begin{bmatrix} 1 & 2 \\ 3 & 1 \end{bmatrix}$

2. $\begin{bmatrix} 2 & 1 & 3 \\ 0 & 1 & 2 \end{bmatrix}$

3. $[2 \;\; 1 \;\; 3]$

4. $\begin{bmatrix} 2 & 0 \\ 1 & 1 \\ 3 & 2 \end{bmatrix}$

5. $[2]$

6. $[0]$

7. $\begin{bmatrix} 2 \\ 1 \\ 3 \end{bmatrix}$

8–14. State the dimensions of the transpose of each of the matrices 1–7.

Let $A = \begin{bmatrix} 3 & 1 & 2 \\ 4 & 5 & 6 \\ 9 & 7 & 8 \end{bmatrix}$. State each of the following.

15. The entries in the second row.

16. The entries in the third column.

17. The entry in the first row and third column.

18. The entry in the second row and first column.

19. The entry in the first row and second column.

20. The entry in the third row and third column.

21. The transpose of A.

22. The zero matrix of the same dimensions.

Written Exercises

Find each x, y, and z.

A

1. $\begin{bmatrix} x & 0 \\ 2 & 1 \end{bmatrix} = \begin{bmatrix} 3 & 0 \\ 2 & 1 \end{bmatrix}$

2. $\begin{bmatrix} 0 & y \\ 1 & 5 \end{bmatrix} = \begin{bmatrix} 0 & 2 \\ 1 & 5 \end{bmatrix}$

3. $\begin{bmatrix} x & 3 \\ 1 & y \end{bmatrix} = \begin{bmatrix} 2 & 3 \\ 1 & 4 \end{bmatrix}$

4. $\begin{bmatrix} x & 3 & 0 \\ 0 & 1 & y \end{bmatrix} = \begin{bmatrix} 2 & z & 0 \\ 0 & 1 & 3 \end{bmatrix}$

5. $\begin{bmatrix} x & 2 & 1 \\ 0 & 3 & 2 \end{bmatrix} = \begin{bmatrix} 1 & y & z \\ 0 & 3 & 2 \end{bmatrix}$

6. $\begin{bmatrix} x & 0 \\ y & 2 \end{bmatrix} = \begin{bmatrix} 3 & 0 \\ 4 & 2 \end{bmatrix}$

7. $\begin{bmatrix} 0 & x \\ 2 & 1 \end{bmatrix}^T = \begin{bmatrix} 0 & 2 \\ 3 & 1 \end{bmatrix}$

8. $\begin{bmatrix} 0 & 2 \\ x & 1 \end{bmatrix}^T = \begin{bmatrix} 0 & 3 \\ 2 & 1 \end{bmatrix}$

15–2 Addition and Scalar Multiplication

Just as the sum of two real numbers is a unique real number, the sum of two matrices is a unique matrix.

The sum of two matrices of the same dimensions is the matrix whose entries are the sums of the corresponding entries of the matrices being added.

For example,

$$\begin{bmatrix} 2 & 1 & 3 \\ 1 & -1 & 0 \end{bmatrix} + \begin{bmatrix} 0 & 1 & 2 \\ -1 & 1 & 2 \end{bmatrix} = \begin{bmatrix} (2+0) & (1+1) & (3+2) \\ (1-1) & (-1+1) & (0+2) \end{bmatrix}$$

$$= \begin{bmatrix} 2 & 2 & 5 \\ 0 & 0 & 2 \end{bmatrix}.$$

Only matrices of the same dimensions can be added. The sum of two matrices not of the same dimensions is not defined. You can show that matrix addition is commutative and associative.

Because the sum of the zero matrix $O_{m \times n}$ and any other matrix $A_{m \times n}$ is $A_{m \times n}$, the zero matrix is the identity element for addition in the set of $m \times n$ matrices. For example,

$$\begin{bmatrix} a & b \\ c & d \end{bmatrix} + \begin{bmatrix} 0 & 0 \\ 0 & 0 \end{bmatrix} = \begin{bmatrix} a & b \\ c & d \end{bmatrix}.$$

Also, the additive inverse (or negative) of the matrix $A_{m\times n}$ is the matrix $-A_{m\times n}$, each of whose entries is the negative of the corresponding entry in A. For example,

$$\text{if } A = \begin{bmatrix} a & b \\ c & d \end{bmatrix}, \text{ then } -A = \begin{bmatrix} -a & -b \\ -c & -d \end{bmatrix},$$

$$\text{because } \begin{bmatrix} a & b \\ c & d \end{bmatrix} + \begin{bmatrix} -a & -b \\ -c & -d \end{bmatrix} = \begin{bmatrix} 0 & 0 \\ 0 & 0 \end{bmatrix}.$$

As with real numbers, to subtract a matrix $B_{m\times n}$ from another, $A_{m\times n}$, will mean to add $-B_{m\times n}$ to $A_{m\times n}$. Thus

$$A_{m\times n} - B_{m\times n} = A_{m\times n} + (-B_{m\times n}).$$

In working with matrices, we call any real number a **scalar**. The product of a scalar r and a matrix $A_{m\times n}$ is the matrix $rA_{m\times n}$, each of whose entries is r times the corresponding entry of A. For example,

$$r\begin{bmatrix} 1 & 3 \\ -1 & 2 \end{bmatrix} = \begin{bmatrix} r & 3r \\ -r & 2r \end{bmatrix} \text{ and } 3\begin{bmatrix} 1 & 0 \\ 2 & 3 \\ -1 & 1 \end{bmatrix} = \begin{bmatrix} 3 & 0 \\ 6 & 9 \\ -3 & 3 \end{bmatrix}.$$

Scalar multiplication, that is, the product of a scalar and a matrix, can be shown to be commutative and associative.

Written Exercises

Find the sum.

A

1. $\begin{bmatrix} 3 & 1 \\ 2 & 0 \end{bmatrix} + \begin{bmatrix} 1 & -3 \\ 1 & 2 \end{bmatrix}$

2. $\begin{bmatrix} 3 & 1 \\ -1 & 0 \end{bmatrix} + \begin{bmatrix} -3 & 2 \\ 1 & 0 \end{bmatrix}$

3. $\begin{bmatrix} 1 & 3 & -1 \\ 2 & 1 & 3 \end{bmatrix} + \begin{bmatrix} 0 & -3 & 1 \\ -2 & -1 & -3 \end{bmatrix}$

4. $\begin{bmatrix} 2 & 1 & 1 \\ 1 & 2 & 1 \end{bmatrix} + \begin{bmatrix} 0 & 1 & 2 \\ 3 & 4 & 5 \end{bmatrix}$

5. $\begin{bmatrix} 1 & 0 & 1 \\ 2 & 1 & 0 \\ 0 & -1 & 1 \end{bmatrix} + \begin{bmatrix} 2 & 1 & 0 \\ 0 & 1 & 1 \\ 1 & 0 & 2 \end{bmatrix}$

6. $\begin{bmatrix} 3 & -1 & 0 \\ 2 & 1 & 4 \\ 1 & 1 & 1 \end{bmatrix} + \begin{bmatrix} 0 & 0 & 1 \\ 0 & 1 & 0 \\ 0 & 0 & 1 \end{bmatrix}$

Find the product.

7. $3\begin{bmatrix} 1 & 3 \\ -1 & 0 \end{bmatrix}$

8. $-1\begin{bmatrix} 2 & 7 \\ 3 & -5 \end{bmatrix}$

9. $-2\begin{bmatrix} 1 & 0 \\ 2 & 1 \\ 0 & 3 \end{bmatrix}$

10. $4\begin{bmatrix} 1 & 1 \\ 2 & 1 \\ 0 & 2 \end{bmatrix}$

11. $-3\begin{bmatrix} 1 & 2 & 2 \\ 0 & 1 & 1 \\ 3 & 1 & 2 \end{bmatrix}$

12. $-5\begin{bmatrix} 1 & 0 & 0 \\ 0 & 1 & 0 \\ 0 & 0 & 1 \end{bmatrix}$

Find a single matrix equal to each of the following.

13. $2\begin{bmatrix} 1 & 3 \\ -1 & 2 \end{bmatrix} - 1\begin{bmatrix} 0 & 2 \\ 1 & 3 \end{bmatrix}$

14. $3\begin{bmatrix} 2 & 1 \\ 0 & 2 \end{bmatrix} + \begin{bmatrix} -2 & 1 \\ 3 & 4 \end{bmatrix}$

15. $3\begin{bmatrix} 2 & 1 & 2 \\ -1 & 3 & 4 \\ 0 & 1 & 1 \end{bmatrix} - 2\begin{bmatrix} 1 & 0 & 2 \\ 3 & -1 & 4 \\ 0 & 2 & 1 \end{bmatrix}$

16. $4\begin{bmatrix} 1 & 0 & 0 \\ 0 & 1 & 0 \\ 0 & 0 & 1 \end{bmatrix} - 3\begin{bmatrix} 1 & 0 & 0 \\ 0 & 1 & 0 \\ 0 & 0 & 1 \end{bmatrix}$

Solve for the variable matrix in each equation.

SAMPLE. $3\begin{bmatrix} a & b \\ c & d \end{bmatrix} - 2\begin{bmatrix} 1 & 3 \\ 5 & 0 \end{bmatrix} = 4\begin{bmatrix} -1 & 2 \\ 3 & 2 \end{bmatrix}$

Solution:

1. Do all indicated multiplications. $\begin{bmatrix} 3a & 3b \\ 3c & 3d \end{bmatrix} + \begin{bmatrix} -2 & -6 \\ -10 & 0 \end{bmatrix} = \begin{bmatrix} -4 & 8 \\ 12 & 8 \end{bmatrix}$

2. To each member add $\begin{bmatrix} 2 & 6 \\ 10 & 0 \end{bmatrix}$, the additive inverse of $\begin{bmatrix} -2 & -6 \\ -10 & 0 \end{bmatrix}$.

$$\begin{bmatrix} 3a & 3b \\ 3c & 3d \end{bmatrix} + \begin{bmatrix} -2 & -6 \\ -10 & 0 \end{bmatrix} + \begin{bmatrix} 2 & 6 \\ 10 & 0 \end{bmatrix} = \begin{bmatrix} -4 & 8 \\ 12 & 8 \end{bmatrix} + \begin{bmatrix} 2 & 6 \\ 10 & 0 \end{bmatrix}$$

$$\begin{bmatrix} 3a & 3b \\ 3c & 3d \end{bmatrix} + \begin{bmatrix} 0 & 0 \\ 0 & 0 \end{bmatrix} = \begin{bmatrix} -2 & 14 \\ 22 & 8 \end{bmatrix}$$

$$\begin{bmatrix} 3a & 3b \\ 3c & 3d \end{bmatrix} = \begin{bmatrix} -2 & 14 \\ 22 & 8 \end{bmatrix}$$

3. Solve for a, b, c, and d.

$3a = -2$ $\quad 3b = 14$ $\quad 3c = 22$ $\quad 3d = 8$

$a = -\frac{2}{3}$ $\quad b = \frac{14}{3}$ $\quad c = \frac{22}{3}$ $\quad d = \frac{8}{3}$

$\begin{bmatrix} -\frac{2}{3} & \frac{14}{3} \\ \frac{22}{3} & \frac{8}{3} \end{bmatrix}$, **Answer.**

B **17.** $\begin{bmatrix} u & v \\ w & x \end{bmatrix} + 2\begin{bmatrix} -2 & 1 \\ 3 & 0 \end{bmatrix} = 3\begin{bmatrix} 1 & -2 \\ 3 & 1 \end{bmatrix}$

18. $\begin{bmatrix} u & v \\ w & x \end{bmatrix} - 3\begin{bmatrix} 1 & 4 \\ 0 & 1 \end{bmatrix} = -1\begin{bmatrix} 3 & 2 \\ 1 & 5 \end{bmatrix}$

19. $4\begin{bmatrix} a & b & c \\ d & e & f \\ g & h & i \end{bmatrix} - 3\begin{bmatrix} 2 & 1 & 0 \\ 0 & 1 & 1 \\ 0 & 1 & 2 \end{bmatrix} = \begin{bmatrix} 1 & 0 & 2 \\ 0 & 1 & -1 \\ 1 & 1 & 3 \end{bmatrix}$

20. $2\begin{bmatrix} a & b & c \\ d & e & f \\ g & h & i \end{bmatrix} + 3\begin{bmatrix} -1 & 0 & 2 \\ 0 & 1 & 3 \\ 0 & 0 & 2 \end{bmatrix} = -2\begin{bmatrix} 1 & 0 & 2 \\ -1 & 3 & 1 \\ 1 & 0 & 0 \end{bmatrix}$

Let r and s be any real numbers, and let $A = \begin{bmatrix} a_1 & b_1 \\ c_1 & d_1 \end{bmatrix}$, $B = \begin{bmatrix} a_2 & b_2 \\ c_2 & d_2 \end{bmatrix}$, $C = \begin{bmatrix} a_3 & b_3 \\ c_3 & d_3 \end{bmatrix}$. Prove that each of the following assertions is true.

C **21.** $A + B = B + A$

22. $rB = Br$

23. $r(A + B) = rA + rB$

24. $(A^T)^T = A$

25. $(A + B) + C = A + (B + C)$

26. $(A + B)^T = A^T + B^T$

27. $-1 \cdot A = -A$

28. $(rs)A = r(sA)$

29. Explain why the set of 2×2 matrices is closed with respect to **(a)** addition; **(b)** scalar multiplication.

30. What is the identity element with respect to scalar multiplication?

15–3 Matrix Multiplication

Consider $\boldsymbol{A} = [\boldsymbol{a} \quad \boldsymbol{b} \quad \boldsymbol{c}]$ and $\boldsymbol{B} = \begin{bmatrix} x_1 & x_2 \\ y_1 & y_2 \\ z_1 & z_2 \end{bmatrix}$, where A has 3 columns and B has 3 rows.

Suppose the numbers a, b, and c represent the number of cases of corn, spinach, and peas purchased each week by a supermarket, while x_1, y_1, and z_1 represent the cost per case of each, respectively, the first week, and x_2, y_2, z_2 the costs the second week. How much would the supermarket have to pay for these items? For the first week, the cost of the corn is $a \cdot x_1$, of the spinach $b \cdot y_1$, and of the peas $c \cdot z_1$; by adding these products, you obtain the total cost, $ax_1 + by_1 + cz_1$. Similarly, for the second week, you have a total cost of $ax_2 + by_2 + cz_2$.

The process of adding the products obtained by multiplying the elements of a row in one matrix by the corresponding elements of a column in another matrix offers a useful meaning to attach to the product of two matrices, illustrated on the following page.

$$[1 \quad 3 \quad -1]\cdot\begin{bmatrix}2\\1\\3\end{bmatrix} = [(1\times 2)+(3\times 1)+(-1\times 3)] = [2]$$

$$\begin{bmatrix}a & b\\c & d\end{bmatrix}\cdot\begin{bmatrix}u & v\\w & x\end{bmatrix} = \begin{bmatrix}au+bw & av+bx\\cu+dw & cv+dx\end{bmatrix}$$

The element in the *first row and first column* of the product is found by multiplying each element in the *first row* of the *first* matrix by the corresponding element in the *first column* of the *second* matrix, and adding them.

The element in the *first row and second column* of the product is found by multiplying each element in the *first row* of the *first* matrix by the corresponding element in the *second column* of the *second* matrix and adding them.

Can you state how to get the element in the *second row and first column* of the product and also the element in the *second row and second column*?

EXAMPLE. Multiply $\begin{bmatrix}1 & 0 & -1\\2 & 1 & 3\\3 & -1 & 2\end{bmatrix}\begin{bmatrix}-1 & 0 & 2\\3 & 1 & -4\\1 & 0 & 0\end{bmatrix}$

Solution:

$$\begin{bmatrix}1 & 0 & -1\\2 & 1 & 3\\3 & -1 & 2\end{bmatrix}\begin{bmatrix}-1 & 0 & 2\\3 & 1 & -4\\1 & 0 & 0\end{bmatrix} = \begin{bmatrix}-2 & & \\ & & \\ & & \end{bmatrix}$$

$$\begin{bmatrix}1 & 0 & -1\\2 & 1 & 3\\3 & -1 & 2\end{bmatrix}\begin{bmatrix}-1 & 0 & 2\\3 & 1 & -4\\1 & 0 & 0\end{bmatrix} = \begin{bmatrix}-2 & 0 & \\ & & \\ & & \end{bmatrix}$$

$$\begin{bmatrix}1 & 0 & -1\\2 & 1 & 3\\3 & -1 & 2\end{bmatrix}\begin{bmatrix}-1 & 0 & 2\\3 & 1 & -4\\1 & 0 & 0\end{bmatrix} = \begin{bmatrix}-2 & 0 & 2\\ & & \\ & & \end{bmatrix}$$

$$\begin{bmatrix}1 & 0 & -1\\2 & 1 & 3\\3 & -1 & 2\end{bmatrix}\begin{bmatrix}-1 & 0 & 2\\3 & 1 & -4\\1 & 0 & 0\end{bmatrix} = \begin{bmatrix}-2 & 0 & 2\\4 & & \\ & & \end{bmatrix}$$

$$\begin{bmatrix}1 & 0 & -1\\2 & 1 & 3\\3 & -1 & 2\end{bmatrix}\begin{bmatrix}-1 & 0 & 2\\3 & 1 & -4\\1 & 0 & 0\end{bmatrix} = \begin{bmatrix}-2 & 0 & 2\\4 & 1 & 0\\-4 & -1 & 10\end{bmatrix}$$

We are now ready to state the definition of matrix multiplication:

The product of an $m \times n$ matrix ($A_{m \times n}$) and an $n \times p$ matrix ($B_{n \times p}$) is the $m \times p$ matrix ($C_{m \times p}$) whose entry in the ath row and bth column is the sum of the products of the corresponding entries in the ath row of A and the bth column of B.

Notice that the two matrices to be multiplied must be such that each row in the first matrix has the same number of entries as each column of the second matrix. Thus, if the left matrix is an $m \times n$ matrix, the right matrix must be an $n \times p$ matrix. The product will then be an $m \times p$ matrix.

Matrix multiplication differs from that of real numbers in that it is not, in general, commutative. For example,

$$\begin{bmatrix} 1 & 0 \\ 2 & -1 \end{bmatrix} \begin{bmatrix} 1 & 2 \\ -1 & 3 \end{bmatrix} = \begin{bmatrix} 1 & 2 \\ 3 & 1 \end{bmatrix},$$

while

$$\begin{bmatrix} 1 & 2 \\ -1 & 3 \end{bmatrix} \begin{bmatrix} 1 & 0 \\ 2 & -1 \end{bmatrix} = \begin{bmatrix} 5 & -2 \\ 5 & -3 \end{bmatrix}.$$

It is therefore necessary to find a product in the order in which it is written. AB means the *left-multiplication* of B by A, and BA means the *right-multiplication* of B by A. Thus, in the multiplication above,

if $A = \begin{bmatrix} 1 & 0 \\ 2 & -1 \end{bmatrix}$ and $B = \begin{bmatrix} 1 & 2 \\ -1 & 3 \end{bmatrix}$, $AB = \begin{bmatrix} 1 & 2 \\ 3 & 1 \end{bmatrix}$ and $BA = \begin{bmatrix} 5 & -2 \\ 5 & -3 \end{bmatrix}$

A *square* matrix whose main diagonal from upper left to lower right consists of entries of 1, while all other entries are 0, is called an **identity matrix** and denoted by I. You can show that the identity matrices

$$\begin{bmatrix} 1 & 0 \\ 0 & 1 \end{bmatrix} \text{ and } \begin{bmatrix} 1 & 0 & 0 \\ 0 & 1 & 0 \\ 0 & 0 & 1 \end{bmatrix}$$

are the identity elements for multiplication in the set of 2×2 and 3×3 matrices respectively. For example,

$$\begin{bmatrix} 1 & 0 \\ 0 & 1 \end{bmatrix} \begin{bmatrix} a & b \\ c & d \end{bmatrix} = \begin{bmatrix} a & b \\ c & d \end{bmatrix} = \begin{bmatrix} a & b \\ c & d \end{bmatrix} \begin{bmatrix} 1 & 0 \\ 0 & 1 \end{bmatrix}$$

Now consider the product

$$\begin{bmatrix} -2 & 1 \\ -4 & 2 \end{bmatrix}\begin{bmatrix} 2 & 3 \\ 4 & 6 \end{bmatrix} = \begin{bmatrix} 0 & 0 \\ 0 & 0 \end{bmatrix}.$$

Do you see that in matrix multiplication, the fact that $AB = O$ does not imply that either $A = O$ or $B = O$?

The associative law $(AB)C = A(BC)$ is valid for matrix multiplication, as are the two distributive laws:

$$\boldsymbol{AB + AC = A(B + C)} \text{ and}$$
$$\boldsymbol{BA + CA = (B + C)A}.$$

Written Exercises

Multiply.

A

1. $[3 \quad 2 \quad 1]\begin{bmatrix} 1 \\ -1 \\ 2 \end{bmatrix}$

2. $[-1 \quad 3 \quad 2]\begin{bmatrix} 0 \\ 1 \\ 2 \end{bmatrix}$

3. $\begin{bmatrix} 3 & 0 \\ 1 & 2 \end{bmatrix}\begin{bmatrix} -1 & 2 \\ 0 & 1 \end{bmatrix}$

4. $\begin{bmatrix} 1 & -3 \\ -1 & 2 \end{bmatrix}\begin{bmatrix} 1 & -1 \\ 0 & 2 \end{bmatrix}$

5. $\begin{bmatrix} 1 & 0 & -1 \\ 2 & 0 & 1 \\ 1 & 1 & 3 \end{bmatrix}\begin{bmatrix} -1 & 1 & 2 \\ 2 & 1 & 1 \\ 1 & 1 & 2 \end{bmatrix}$

6. $\begin{bmatrix} -2 & 1 & 0 \\ 0 & 1 & 1 \\ -1 & 2 & 1 \end{bmatrix}\begin{bmatrix} -3 & 0 & 1 \\ 1 & 2 & -1 \\ -1 & 1 & 3 \end{bmatrix}$

7. $\begin{bmatrix} 1 & 0 & 0 \\ 0 & 0 & 1 \\ 0 & 1 & 0 \end{bmatrix}\begin{bmatrix} a & b & c \\ d & e & f \\ g & h & i \end{bmatrix}$

8. $\begin{bmatrix} 1 & 0 & 0 \\ 0 & 2 & 0 \\ 0 & 0 & 1 \end{bmatrix}\begin{bmatrix} a & b & c \\ d & e & f \\ g & h & i \end{bmatrix}$

B

9. If $A = \begin{bmatrix} 0 & 1 \\ 1 & 0 \end{bmatrix}$, find A^2; A^3; $(-A)^2$.

10. If $B = \begin{bmatrix} 1 & 0 & -1 \\ 2 & 1 & 3 \\ 0 & 1 & 1 \end{bmatrix}$, find B^2; B^3; $(-B)^2$.

11. If $A = \begin{bmatrix} 1 & -1 \\ 0 & 2 \end{bmatrix}$, $B = \begin{bmatrix} -1 & -1 \\ 0 & -1 \end{bmatrix}$, and $C = \begin{bmatrix} 2 & 1 \\ 1 & 3 \end{bmatrix}$, show that $AB + AC = A(B + C)$. Also, show that $A(B + C) \neq (B + C)A$.

12. If $A = \begin{bmatrix} 2 & 5 \\ 1 & 3 \end{bmatrix}$ and $B = \begin{bmatrix} 3 & -5 \\ -1 & 2 \end{bmatrix}$, show that $AB = BA = I$.

13. If $A = \begin{bmatrix} 0 & 1 \\ 3 & 2 \end{bmatrix}$ and $B = \begin{bmatrix} 1 & 0 \\ 2 & 1 \end{bmatrix}$, show that $(A - B)^2 \neq A^2 - 2AB + B^2$.

14. Let A and B be 2×2 matrices. Show that $(AB)^{\mathsf{T}} = B^{\mathsf{T}}A^{\mathsf{T}}$.

15–4 The Determinant Function δ.

You can associate with each 2×2 matrix $A = \begin{bmatrix} a & b \\ c & d \end{bmatrix}$ a real number, $ad - bc$, called the **determinant** of the matrix. You form the determinant by adding the product ad of the entries on one diagonal of the matrix to the negative of the product bc of the entries on the other diagonal. Thus,

$$\begin{bmatrix} a & b \\ c & d \end{bmatrix}.$$

The association of the number $ad - bc$ with the 2×2 matrix A constitutes a function since each 2×2 matrix is paired with one and only one real number. This function, denoted by δ (delta), is composed of the ordered pairs $(A, \delta(A))$. The domain of the function is the set of 2×2 matrices, and the range is the set of real numbers.

EXAMPLE 1. If $A = \begin{bmatrix} 3 & 1 \\ 2 & -5 \end{bmatrix}$ find $\delta(A)$.

Solution: $\delta(A) = [3 \times (-5)] - [1 \times 2] = -15 - 2 = -17$, **Answer.**

Determinants can be defined for *square matrices* of any dimension (*order*). For example, if A is the matrix of order 3

$$\begin{bmatrix} a_1 & b_1 & c_1 \\ a_2 & b_2 & c_2 \\ a_3 & b_3 & c_3 \end{bmatrix}$$

we define $\delta(A) = a_1b_2c_3 + a_2b_3c_1 + a_3b_1c_2 - a_2b_1c_3 - a_1b_3c_2 - a_3b_2c_1$.

Notice that this sum of products displays all the possible arrangements of the subscripts of the letters a, b, and c. A convenient scheme for finding the terms in this sum is as follows:

1. Copy the first two columns of the matrix in order to the right of the third column.

$$\begin{matrix} a_1 & b_1 & c_1 & a_1 & b_1 \\ a_2 & b_2 & c_2 & a_2 & b_2 \\ a_3 & b_3 & c_3 & a_3 & b_3 \end{matrix}$$

2. In turn, multiply each entry in the first row by the other two entries on the diagonal going from left to right. The products are the first three terms in the determinant.

$$\begin{matrix} a_1 & b_1 & c_1 & a_1 & b_1 \\ a_2 & b_2 & c_2 & a_2 & b_2 \\ a_3 & b_3 & c_3 & a_3 & b_3 \\ & & + & + & + \end{matrix}$$

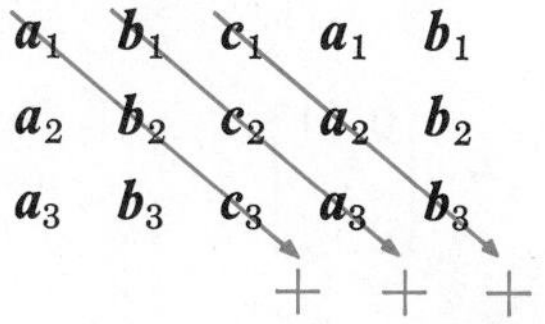

3. Similarly, multiply each entry in the first row, starting from the right, by the other two entries on the diagonal going from right to left. The negatives of these products are the last three terms in the determinant.

$$\begin{matrix} a_1 & b_1 & c_1 & a_1 & b_1 \\ a_2 & b_2 & c_2 & a_2 & b_2 \\ a_3 & b_3 & c_3 & a_3 & b_3 \\ - & - & - & & \end{matrix}$$

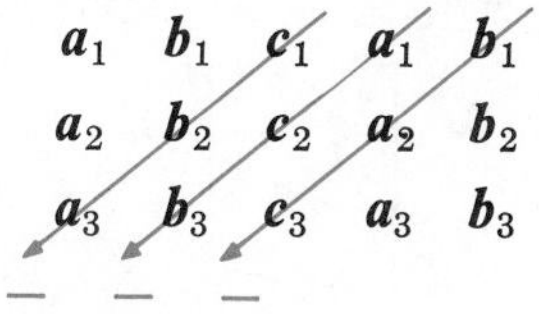

EXAMPLE 2. If $A = \begin{bmatrix} 1 & 3 & 4 \\ 2 & -1 & 3 \\ 0 & 1 & 1 \end{bmatrix}$, find $\delta(A)$.

Solution:

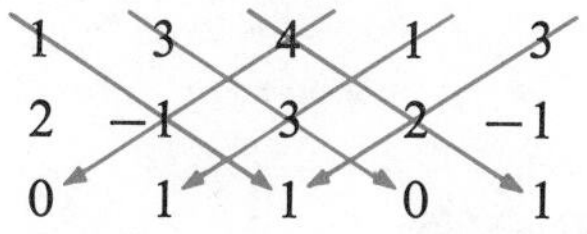

$$\begin{matrix} 1 & 3 & 4 & 1 & 3 \\ 2 & -1 & 3 & 2 & -1 \\ 0 & 1 & 1 & 0 & 1 \end{matrix}$$

$$\delta(A) = (-1) + (0) + (8) - (6) - (3) - (0)$$

$$\delta(A) = -2, \textbf{ Answer.}$$

Sometimes the determinant of a matrix is displayed in the same form as the matrix, but with vertical bars enclosing the entries rather than brackets. Thus,

$$\textbf{if } A = \begin{bmatrix} a_1 & b_1 & c_1 \\ a_2 & b_2 & c_2 \\ a_3 & b_3 & c_3 \end{bmatrix}, \ \delta(A) = \begin{vmatrix} a_1 & b_1 & c_1 \\ a_2 & b_2 & c_2 \\ a_3 & b_3 & c_3 \end{vmatrix}.$$

The entries are then called the **elements** of the determinant and the number of entries in any row (or column) is called the **order** of the determinant.

Written Exercises

Find $\delta(A)$ if A is the matrix in each exercise.

A

1. $\begin{bmatrix} 1 & 2 \\ -1 & 3 \end{bmatrix}$

2. $\begin{bmatrix} 0 & 1 \\ 2 & 1 \end{bmatrix}$

3. $\begin{bmatrix} 3 & 1 \\ 2 & -5 \end{bmatrix}$

4. $\begin{bmatrix} 3 & 2 \\ -1 & 5 \end{bmatrix}$

5. $\begin{bmatrix} 2 & 3 \\ 4 & 6 \end{bmatrix}$

6. $\begin{bmatrix} 1 & 2 \\ 4 & 8 \end{bmatrix}$

7. $\begin{bmatrix} 1 & 0 & 2 \\ 1 & 1 & 0 \\ 1 & -1 & 2 \end{bmatrix}$

8. $\begin{bmatrix} 2 & 1 & 0 \\ 1 & -1 & 3 \\ 0 & 1 & 2 \end{bmatrix}$

9. $\begin{bmatrix} 3 & 1 & 4 \\ 1 & 2 & -1 \\ 0 & 0 & 2 \end{bmatrix}$

10. $\begin{bmatrix} 8 & 1 & 3 \\ 2 & -1 & 4 \\ 1 & -1 & 2 \end{bmatrix}$

11. $\begin{bmatrix} 3 & 2 & -1 \\ 0 & 1 & 3 \\ 3 & 3 & 2 \end{bmatrix}$

12. $\begin{bmatrix} 1 & 2 & 3 \\ 2 & 1 & 1 \\ 3 & 3 & 4 \end{bmatrix}$

If A and B are 2×2 matrices and a is a scalar:

B

13. Show that $\delta(aA) = a^2\,\delta(A)$.

14. Show that $\delta(A^{\mathsf{T}}) = \delta(A)$.

15. Show that $\delta(AB) = \delta(A) \cdot \delta(B)$.

16. Show that $\delta(A - A^{\mathsf{T}}) = \delta(A^{\mathsf{T}} - A)$.

2 × 2 MATRICES

15–5 The Inverse of a Matrix

The product

$$\begin{bmatrix} \mathbf{2} & \mathbf{3} \\ \mathbf{1} & \mathbf{2} \end{bmatrix}\begin{bmatrix} \mathbf{2} & \mathbf{-3} \\ \mathbf{-1} & \mathbf{2} \end{bmatrix} = \begin{bmatrix} \mathbf{4-3} & \mathbf{-6+6} \\ \mathbf{2-2} & \mathbf{-3+4} \end{bmatrix} = \begin{bmatrix} \mathbf{1} & \mathbf{0} \\ \mathbf{0} & \mathbf{1} \end{bmatrix}$$

is the identity matrix I. When the product of two real numbers is the multiplicative identity 1, the numbers are called multiplicative inverses. Similarly, any two matrices A and B such that $AB = BA = I$, are called **inverses**. Customarily, B is denoted by A^{-1} which is always understood to be the inverse of the matrix A.

You know that every real number a, except 0, has a multiplicative inverse $1/a$. Does every 2×2 matrix A have an inverse A^{-1}? To answer this question, let

$A = \begin{bmatrix} a & b \\ c & d \end{bmatrix}$ and then see whether you can find a matrix

$A^{-1} = \begin{bmatrix} u & v \\ x & y \end{bmatrix}$ such that $AA^{-1} = I$. You have

$$\begin{bmatrix} a & b \\ c & d \end{bmatrix} \begin{bmatrix} u & v \\ x & y \end{bmatrix} = \begin{bmatrix} 1 & 0 \\ 0 & 1 \end{bmatrix}$$

$$\begin{bmatrix} au + bx & av + by \\ cu + dx & cv + dy \end{bmatrix} = \begin{bmatrix} 1 & 0 \\ 0 & 1 \end{bmatrix}$$

This last equation is true *if and only if*

$$au + bx = 1 \qquad av + by = 0$$

$$cu + dx = 0 \qquad cv + dy = 1$$

Provided $ad - bc \neq 0$, you can solve these pairs of equations for u and x, and for v and y, respectively, and find

$$u = \frac{d}{ad - bc} \qquad v = \frac{-b}{ad - bc}$$

$$x = \frac{-c}{ad - bc} \qquad y = \frac{a}{ad - bc}$$

Since each denominator is $\delta(A)$, you have if $\delta(A) \neq 0$,

$$A^{-1} = \frac{1}{\delta(A)} \begin{bmatrix} d & -b \\ -c & a \end{bmatrix}$$

Thus, you can find the inverse of any 2×2 matrix *provided its determinant is not 0.* If $\delta(A) = 0$, A has no inverse. Notice what the equation says to do to find A^{-1}: interchange a and d, replace b and c with their respective negatives, and multiply the resulting matrix by $\frac{1}{\delta(A)}$.

EXAMPLE. If $A = \begin{bmatrix} 2 & -1 \\ 1 & 3 \end{bmatrix}$, find A^{-1}.

Solution: $\delta(A) = 6 - (-1) = 7$, so A^{-1} exists. Now interchange 2 and 3, replace -1 and 1 with 1 and -1 respectively, and multiply the resulting matrix by $\frac{1}{7}$.

$$A^{-1} = \frac{1}{7}\begin{bmatrix} 3 & 1 \\ -1 & 2 \end{bmatrix},$$ **Answer.**

Check: $$\frac{1}{7}\begin{bmatrix} 3 & 1 \\ -1 & 2 \end{bmatrix}\begin{bmatrix} 2 & -1 \\ 1 & 3 \end{bmatrix} = \frac{1}{7}\begin{bmatrix} 7 & 0 \\ 0 & 7 \end{bmatrix} = \begin{bmatrix} 1 & 0 \\ 0 & 1 \end{bmatrix}$$

You should always check by actual multiplication to see that you have found the inverse correctly.

The inverse of a square matrix A of order $n > 2$ is more difficult to find than the inverse of a 2×2 matrix, but it always exists if $\delta(A) \neq 0$. A matrix that has an inverse is said to be **invertible**. If A and B are invertible matrices, you can show that

$$(AB)^{-1} = B^{-1}A^{-1}$$

Let $X = B^{-1}A^{-1}$. Then, multiplying on the left by B,

$$BX = B(B^{-1}A^{-1}) = (BB^{-1})A^{-1}$$
$$BX = IA^{-1}$$
$$BX = A^{-1}$$ Now, multiplying on the left by A,
$$A(BX) = AA^{-1}$$
$$(AB)X = I.$$

But this says that X is the inverse of AB, which you wished to show.

Written Exercises

Find the inverse of each matrix. If the matrix is not invertible, so state.

A

1. $\begin{bmatrix} 1 & 3 \\ 2 & 1 \end{bmatrix}$

2. $\begin{bmatrix} 3 & -1 \\ 4 & 2 \end{bmatrix}$

3. $\begin{bmatrix} 1 & 2 \\ -1 & 3 \end{bmatrix}$

4. $\begin{bmatrix} 0 & 1 \\ 1 & 0 \end{bmatrix}$

5. $\begin{bmatrix} 1 & 2 \\ 2 & 4 \end{bmatrix}$

6. $\begin{bmatrix} 3 & -1 \\ 6 & -2 \end{bmatrix}$

7. $\begin{bmatrix} 4 & 5 \\ 0 & 1 \end{bmatrix}$

8. $\begin{bmatrix} 1 & 0 \\ 0 & 1 \end{bmatrix}$

9. $\begin{bmatrix} -1 & 3 \\ -2 & 4 \end{bmatrix}$ **10.** $\begin{bmatrix} 1 & -3 \\ 2 & 2 \end{bmatrix}$ **11.** $\begin{bmatrix} -1 & 3 \\ 1 & -2 \end{bmatrix}$ **12.** $\begin{bmatrix} 2 & 2 \\ 3 & 5 \end{bmatrix}$

Solve each of the given equations for A.

SAMPLE. $\begin{bmatrix} 1 & 3 \\ 2 & 7 \end{bmatrix} A = \begin{bmatrix} 4 & 1 \\ -2 & 3 \end{bmatrix}$

Solution:

1. Find the inverse of $\begin{bmatrix} 1 & 3 \\ 2 & 7 \end{bmatrix}$. Its determinant is 1.

$$\begin{bmatrix} 1 & 3 \\ 2 & 7 \end{bmatrix}^{-1} = \frac{1}{1}\begin{bmatrix} 7 & -3 \\ -2 & 1 \end{bmatrix}$$

2. Left-multiply each member of the equation by the inverse.

$$\begin{bmatrix} 7 & -3 \\ -2 & 1 \end{bmatrix}\begin{bmatrix} 1 & 3 \\ 2 & 7 \end{bmatrix} A = \begin{bmatrix} 7 & -3 \\ -2 & 1 \end{bmatrix}\begin{bmatrix} 4 & 1 \\ -2 & 3 \end{bmatrix}$$

$$\begin{bmatrix} 1 & 0 \\ 0 & 1 \end{bmatrix} A = \begin{bmatrix} 34 & -2 \\ -10 & 1 \end{bmatrix}$$

$$A = \begin{bmatrix} 34 & -2 \\ -10 & 1 \end{bmatrix}, \textbf{ Answer.}$$

B

13. $\begin{bmatrix} 1 & 2 \\ 1 & 3 \end{bmatrix} A = \begin{bmatrix} 0 & 1 \\ -1 & 2 \end{bmatrix}$

14. $\begin{bmatrix} 2 & 1 \\ 1 & 1 \end{bmatrix} A = \begin{bmatrix} 3 & -1 \\ 2 & 2 \end{bmatrix}$

15. $\begin{bmatrix} 3 & 2 \\ 2 & 2 \end{bmatrix} A = \begin{bmatrix} 5 & 0 \\ -1 & -1 \end{bmatrix}$

16. $\begin{bmatrix} 4 & 2 \\ 1 & 1 \end{bmatrix} A = \begin{bmatrix} 2 & 3 \\ 0 & 1 \end{bmatrix}$

17. $\begin{bmatrix} 5 & 3 \\ 3 & 2 \end{bmatrix} A - \begin{bmatrix} 1 & 3 \\ 2 & 1 \end{bmatrix} = \begin{bmatrix} 1 & 2 \\ -1 & 3 \end{bmatrix}$ (*Hint*: Transform by addition first.)

18. $\begin{bmatrix} 3 & 4 \\ 2 & 3 \end{bmatrix} A + \begin{bmatrix} 3 & -1 \\ 1 & 2 \end{bmatrix} = \begin{bmatrix} 0 & 2 \\ -1 & 1 \end{bmatrix}$

C

19. Show that $[A^{\mathsf{T}}]^{-1} = [A^{-1}]^{\mathsf{T}}$, if A is any 2×2 invertible matrix.

20. Show that $\delta(A^{-1}) = \dfrac{1}{\delta(A)}$, if A is any 2×2 invertible matrix.

21. Restate the sentence $AX + B = C$ to express X in terms of the matrices A, B, and C.

15–6 Solution of Systems of Linear Equations

Systems of linear equations in two variables can be represented in the form of matrix equations. First observe that

$$\begin{bmatrix} a_1 & b_1 \\ a_2 & b_2 \end{bmatrix} \begin{bmatrix} x \\ y \end{bmatrix} = \begin{bmatrix} a_1x + b_1y \\ a_2x + b_2y \end{bmatrix}.$$

Now if

$$\begin{aligned} a_1x + b_1y &= c_1 \\ a_2x + b_2y &= c_2, \end{aligned}$$

you can write the equivalent matrix equation

$$\begin{bmatrix} a_1 & b_1 \\ a_2 & b_2 \end{bmatrix} \begin{bmatrix} x \\ y \end{bmatrix} = \begin{bmatrix} c_1 \\ c_2 \end{bmatrix},$$

which is in the form $AX = B$, where A is a 2×2 matrix called the **coefficient matrix** of the system, and X and B are 2×1 matrices. If A is invertible, you can solve $AX = B$ for X as follows:

$$\begin{aligned} AX &= B \\ A^{-1}AX &= A^{-1}B \\ IX &= A^{-1}B \\ X &= A^{-1}B. \end{aligned}$$

Thus, if

$$\begin{bmatrix} a_1 & b_1 \\ a_2 & b_2 \end{bmatrix} \begin{bmatrix} x \\ y \end{bmatrix} = \begin{bmatrix} c_1 \\ c_2 \end{bmatrix},$$

then

$$\begin{bmatrix} x \\ y \end{bmatrix} = \begin{bmatrix} a_1 & b_1 \\ a_2 & b_2 \end{bmatrix}^{-1} \begin{bmatrix} c_1 \\ c_2 \end{bmatrix}$$

$$\begin{bmatrix} x \\ y \end{bmatrix} = \frac{1}{\delta(A)} \begin{bmatrix} b_2 & -b_1 \\ -a_2 & a_1 \end{bmatrix} \begin{bmatrix} c_1 \\ c_2 \end{bmatrix}.$$

EXAMPLE. Find the solution set of the system

$$\begin{aligned} 2x - 3y &= 1 \\ x + 4y &= 6 \end{aligned}$$

Solution:

1. Write the matrix equation

$$\begin{bmatrix} 2 & -3 \\ 1 & 4 \end{bmatrix} \begin{bmatrix} x \\ y \end{bmatrix} = \begin{bmatrix} 1 \\ 6 \end{bmatrix}$$

2. Find the inverse of the coefficient matrix.

$$\begin{bmatrix} 2 & -3 \\ 1 & 4 \end{bmatrix}^{-1} = \frac{1}{11}\begin{bmatrix} 4 & 3 \\ -1 & 2 \end{bmatrix}$$

3. Left-multiply each member of the matrix equation by this inverse.

$$\begin{bmatrix} x \\ y \end{bmatrix} = \frac{1}{11}\begin{bmatrix} 4 & 3 \\ -1 & 2 \end{bmatrix}\begin{bmatrix} 1 \\ 6 \end{bmatrix} = \frac{1}{11}\begin{bmatrix} 22 \\ 11 \end{bmatrix} = \begin{bmatrix} 2 \\ 1 \end{bmatrix}$$

Hence,

$$\begin{bmatrix} x \\ y \end{bmatrix} = \begin{bmatrix} 2 \\ 1 \end{bmatrix}. \quad \{(2, 1)\}, \textbf{ Answer.}$$

If the coefficient matrix is not invertible, the equations are either dependent or inconsistent.

Written Exercises

Find the solution set for the given system by means of matrices. If the system is dependent or inconsistent, so state.

1. $x + 2y = 5$
$x + 3y = 7$

2. $2x + 5y = 9$
$x + 2y = 4$

3. $3x - 4y = -6$
$2x - 3y = -5$

4. $5x - 2y = 1$
$2x - y = 0$

5. $3x + y = 1$
$x - 2y = -2$

6. $2x - 3y = -7$
$3x + 2y = -4$

7. $x + 2y = 3$
$2x + 4y = 6$

8. $2x - 3y = 7$
$4x - 6y = 9$

9. $3x + 5y = 35$
$2x - 3y = -2$

10. $2x - 3y = -20$
$2x + 3y = 40$

DETERMINANTS

15–7 Expansion by Minors

Because determinants resemble matrices, you must be careful to ascertain which of the two you are working with before performing any mathematical operations with them. A matrix is an array of numbers; a determinant is a particular real number defined by an array and computed from it by a definite rule, called "expanding the determinant."

There is another way to expand a determinant called **expansion by minors.** The **minor** of an element in a determinant is the determinant resulting from the deletion of the row and column containing the element. For example, in the determinant

$$\begin{vmatrix} 1 & 2 & 3 \\ -1 & 0 & -2 \\ 4 & -4 & 6 \end{vmatrix},$$

the minor of the element 2 is $\begin{vmatrix} \not{1} & \not{2} & \not{3} \\ -1 & \not{0} & -2 \\ 4 & \not{-4} & 6 \end{vmatrix}$ or $\begin{vmatrix} -1 & -2 \\ 4 & 6 \end{vmatrix}$;

the minor of -2 is $\begin{vmatrix} 1 & 2 & \not{3} \\ -1 & \not{0} & \not{-2} \\ 4 & -4 & \not{6} \end{vmatrix}$ or $\begin{vmatrix} 1 & 2 \\ 4 & -4 \end{vmatrix}$; and so on.

The value of a third-order determinant as defined in Section 15–4 can be rewritten

$$\begin{vmatrix} a_1 & b_1 & c_1 \\ a_2 & b_2 & c_2 \\ a_3 & b_3 & c_3 \end{vmatrix} = a_1b_2c_3 - a_1b_3c_2 + b_1c_2a_3 - b_1c_3a_2 + c_1a_2b_3 - c_1a_3b_2.$$

Factoring, you obtain

$$a_1(b_2c_3 - b_3c_2) - b_1(c_3a_2 - c_2a_3) + c_1(a_2b_3 - a_3b_2).$$

The terms in the parentheses are the minors of a_1, b_1, and c_1, respectively, and if these minors are denoted by A_1, B_1, and C_1,

$$\begin{vmatrix} a_1 & b_1 & c_1 \\ a_2 & b_2 & c_2 \\ a_3 & b_3 & c_3 \end{vmatrix} = a_1A_1 - b_1B_1 + c_1C_1.$$

The expression on the right is the expansion of the determinant by minors about the first row. It can be shown that you can expand a determinant by minors about any row or any column as follows:

1. Multiply each element in the chosen row or column by its minor.
2. Multiply the product obtained by 1 or -1 according as the sum of the number of the row and the number of the column containing the element is an even integer or an odd integer.
3. Add the resulting products.

EXAMPLE. Expand $\begin{vmatrix} 2 & 1 & 3 \\ 5 & -1 & 4 \\ 1 & -2 & 3 \end{vmatrix}$ by the minors of the first column.

Solution: Write the products of each element in the first column and its minor. Use the negative of the product in the second row, since $2 + 1 = 3$, which is an odd integer.

$$2\begin{vmatrix} -1 & 4 \\ -2 & 3 \end{vmatrix} - 5\begin{vmatrix} 1 & 3 \\ -2 & 3 \end{vmatrix} + 1\begin{vmatrix} 1 & 3 \\ -1 & 4 \end{vmatrix}$$

$$= 2(5) - 5(9) + 1(7) = 10 - 45 + 7 = -28, \textbf{ Answer.}$$

This method of expanding determinants is general. Do you see that it gives us a means of defining a fourth-order determinant?

$$\text{Consider the matrix } A = \begin{bmatrix} a_1 & b_1 & c_1 & d_1 \\ a_2 & b_2 & c_2 & d_2 \\ a_3 & b_3 & c_3 & d_3 \\ a_4 & b_4 & c_4 & d_4 \end{bmatrix}.$$

$$\text{Let } A_1 = \begin{vmatrix} b_2 & c_2 & d_2 \\ b_3 & c_3 & d_3 \\ b_4 & c_4 & d_4 \end{vmatrix} \qquad B_1 = \begin{vmatrix} a_2 & c_2 & d_2 \\ a_3 & c_3 & d_3 \\ a_4 & c_4 & d_4 \end{vmatrix}$$

$$C_1 = \begin{vmatrix} a_2 & b_2 & d_2 \\ a_3 & b_3 & d_3 \\ a_4 & b_4 & d_4 \end{vmatrix} \qquad D_1 = \begin{vmatrix} a_2 & b_2 & c_2 \\ a_3 & b_3 & c_3 \\ a_4 & b_4 & c_4 \end{vmatrix}$$

We then define $\delta(A)$ as follows:

$$\boldsymbol{\delta(A) = a_1A_1 - b_1B_1 + c_1C_1 - d_1D_1}$$

Notice that A_1, B_1, C_1, and D_1 are analogous to what are defined as minors in the case of a third-order determinant. We therefore call them minors of the fourth-order determinant $\begin{vmatrix} a_1 & b_1 & c_1 & d_1 \\ a_2 & b_2 & c_2 & d_2 \\ a_3 & b_3 & c_3 & d_3 \\ a_4 & b_4 & c_4 & d_4 \end{vmatrix}$ with respect to the first row.

It can be shown that if the determinant is expanded according to the minors of any other row or column the same value $\delta(A)$ will be obtained.

Each of the minors, being third-order determinants, can themselves be developed by minors. Thus the development of a fourth-order determinant can be made to depend on the development of second-order determinants.

Clearly a fifth-order determinant can be defined in terms of fourth-order determinants, a sixth-order determinant in terms of fifth-order determinants, and so on, each of these eventually depending on second-order determinants.

Written Exercises

Expand the given determinant about the given row or column.

A

1. $\begin{vmatrix} 1 & 2 & 1 \\ 3 & 4 & 2 \\ 5 & 6 & 3 \end{vmatrix}$; row 1

2. $\begin{vmatrix} 3 & 1 & -2 \\ 2 & -1 & 2 \\ 1 & 1 & 0 \end{vmatrix}$; row 3

3. $\begin{vmatrix} 0 & -1 & -2 \\ 1 & 3 & 0 \\ 2 & 4 & 1 \end{vmatrix}$; row 2

4. $\begin{vmatrix} 1 & -1 & 2 \\ 4 & 0 & 1 \\ 2 & 1 & 3 \end{vmatrix}$; column 2

5. $\begin{vmatrix} 1 & -1 & 4 \\ 1 & -2 & 5 \\ 1 & -3 & 6 \end{vmatrix}$; column 1

6. $\begin{vmatrix} 1 & 2 & 0 \\ 3 & 1 & 1 \\ -1 & 4 & 1 \end{vmatrix}$; column 3

Expand the given determinant about any row or any column.

7. $\begin{vmatrix} 2 & 1 & 3 \\ -5 & 0 & 2 \\ 6 & 1 & 4 \end{vmatrix}$

8. $\begin{vmatrix} 3 & 2 & 4 \\ -2 & 1 & 6 \\ 0 & 2 & 1 \end{vmatrix}$

9. $\begin{vmatrix} 0 & 2 & 4 \\ 2 & 6 & 3 \\ 0 & 7 & 4 \end{vmatrix}$

10. $\begin{vmatrix} 3 & 2 & 3 \\ 1 & -4 & 2 \\ 0 & 0 & 1 \end{vmatrix}$

Solve each of the given equations for x.

11. $\begin{vmatrix} 3 & 1 & -2 \\ 0 & x & 1 \\ 4 & -2 & -1 \end{vmatrix} = 0$

12. $\begin{vmatrix} x & 2 & 3 \\ 1 & x & 3 \\ 1 & -1 & 1 \end{vmatrix} = 5$

Evaluate.

B **13.** $\begin{vmatrix} 1 & 0 & 1 & 0 \\ 3 & -1 & 0 & 2 \\ 1 & 4 & 1 & 1 \\ 3 & 1 & -1 & 2 \end{vmatrix}$

14. $\begin{vmatrix} 1 & -3 & 2 & 1 \\ 2 & -1 & 3 & 0 \\ 3 & 2 & 1 & 0 \\ -1 & 1 & 3 & 1 \end{vmatrix}$

15-8 Properties of Determinants

Determinants have properties that may help you simplify their expansion. While these properties will be illustrated with third-order determinants and presented without proof, they are general, and apply to determinants of any order.

Property 1. If any two rows or any two columns of a determinant are interchanged, the resulting determinant is the negative of the original determinant.

$$\begin{vmatrix} 1 & 0 & 2 \\ -1 & 1 & 0 \\ 2 & -1 & 3 \end{vmatrix} = 3 + 0 + 2 - 0 - 0 - 4 = 1$$

$$\begin{vmatrix} -1 & 1 & 0 \\ 1 & 0 & 2 \\ 2 & -1 & 3 \end{vmatrix} = 0 + 4 + 0 - 3 - 2 - 0 = -1$$

Property 2. If two rows or two columns of a determinant are identical, the determinant is 0.

$$\begin{vmatrix} 1 & 1 & 2 \\ -1 & -1 & 0 \\ 2 & 2 & 3 \end{vmatrix} = -3 + 0 - 4 + 3 - 0 + 4 = 0$$

Property 3. If all the rows and columns of a determinant are interchanged in order, the resulting determinant equals the original one.

$$\begin{vmatrix} 1 & 0 & 2 \\ -1 & 1 & 0 \\ 2 & -1 & 3 \end{vmatrix} = 3 + 0 + 2 - 0 - 0 - 4 = 1$$

$$\begin{vmatrix} 1 & -1 & 2 \\ 0 & 1 & -1 \\ 2 & 0 & 3 \end{vmatrix} = 3 + 2 + 0 - 0 - 0 - 4 = 1$$

Property 4. If the elements of one row or one column are multiplied by the real number k, the resulting determinant is k times the original one.

$$\begin{vmatrix} 1 & 0 & 2 \\ -1 & 1 & 0 \\ 2 & -1 & 3 \end{vmatrix} = 3 + 0 + 2 - 0 - 0 - 4 = 1$$

$$\begin{vmatrix} 3 & 0 & 2 \\ -3 & 1 & 0 \\ 6 & -1 & 3 \end{vmatrix} = 9 + 0 + 6 - 0 - 0 - 12 = 3$$

(Note: This property of a determinant differs from and should not be confused with the scalar multiplication of a matrix.)

Property 5. If one row or one column has 0 for every element, the determinant is 0.

$$\begin{vmatrix} 1 & 0 & 2 \\ -1 & 0 & 0 \\ 2 & 0 & 3 \end{vmatrix} = 0 + 0 + 0 - 0 - 0 - 0 = 0$$

Property 6. If each element of one row or one column is multiplied by a real number k and if the resulting products are then added to the corresponding elements of another row or another column, respectively, the resulting determinant equals the original one.

$$\begin{vmatrix} 1 & 0 & 2 \\ -1 & 1 & 0 \\ 2 & -1 & 3 \end{vmatrix} = 3 + 0 + 2 - 0 - 0 - 4 = 1$$

$$\begin{vmatrix} 1+3(2) & 0 & 2 \\ -1+3(0) & 1 & 0 \\ 2+3(3) & -1 & 3 \end{vmatrix} = \begin{vmatrix} 7 & 0 & 2 \\ -1 & 1 & 0 \\ 11 & -1 & 3 \end{vmatrix} = 21+0+2-0-0-22 = 1$$

EXAMPLE 1. Evaluate $\begin{vmatrix} 1 & 3 & 7 \\ 2 & 5 & 16 \\ -3 & 9 & 15 \end{vmatrix}$

Solution: **1.** Multiply the first row by -2 and add to the second row.

$$\begin{vmatrix} 1 & 3 & 7 \\ 2+(-2)1 & 5+(-2)3 & 16+(-2)7 \\ -3 & 9 & 15 \end{vmatrix} = \begin{vmatrix} 1 & 3 & 7 \\ 0 & -1 & 2 \\ -3 & 9 & 15 \end{vmatrix}$$

2. Multiply the first row by 3 and add to the third row.

$$\begin{vmatrix} 1 & 3 & 7 \\ 0 & -1 & 2 \\ -3+3\cdot 1 & 9+3\cdot 3 & 15+3\cdot 7 \end{vmatrix} = \begin{vmatrix} 1 & 3 & 7 \\ 0 & -1 & 2 \\ 0 & 18 & 36 \end{vmatrix}$$

3. Expand by minors about column 1.

$$1\begin{vmatrix} -1 & 2 \\ 18 & 36 \end{vmatrix} - 0\begin{vmatrix} 3 & 7 \\ 18 & 36 \end{vmatrix} + 0\begin{vmatrix} 3 & 7 \\ -1 & 2 \end{vmatrix} = -72, \textbf{ Answer.}$$

EXAMPLE 2. Evaluate $\begin{vmatrix} 1 & 3 & -4 \\ 3 & 2 & 6 \\ 1 & 3 & -4 \end{vmatrix}$

Solution: The first and third rows are identical. 0, **Answer.**

Written Exercises

Evaluate each of the given determinants. Use any of the properties 1–6 to simplify the work.

1. $\begin{vmatrix} 3 & 9 & 6 \\ 4 & -4 & 4 \\ 10 & 5 & 20 \end{vmatrix}$ **2.** $\begin{vmatrix} 25 & 40 & 15 \\ -3 & 6 & 21 \\ 8 & 12 & 20 \end{vmatrix}$ **3.** $\begin{vmatrix} 29 & 26 & 22 \\ 25 & 31 & 27 \\ 63 & 54 & 46 \end{vmatrix}$

4. $\begin{vmatrix} 28 & 27 & 25 \\ 31 & 30 & 26 \\ 36 & 35 & 30 \end{vmatrix}$ **5.** $\begin{vmatrix} 26 & 29 & 29 \\ 25 & 30 & 27 \\ 25 & 28 & 26 \end{vmatrix}$ **6.** $\begin{vmatrix} 35 & 73 & 16 \\ 38 & 80 & 23 \\ 32 & 67 & 16 \end{vmatrix}$

7. $\begin{vmatrix} 29 & 30 & 33 \\ 35 & 38 & 42 \\ 28 & 29 & 32 \end{vmatrix}$ **8.** $\begin{vmatrix} 13 & 16 & 19 \\ 27 & 33 & 39 \\ 28 & 34 & 40 \end{vmatrix}$ **9.** $\begin{vmatrix} 22 & 32 & 27 \\ 27 & 41 & 34 \\ 20 & 30 & 25 \end{vmatrix}$

B **10.** $\begin{vmatrix} 1 & 1 & 1 & 1 \\ 2 & 3 & 4 & 5 \\ 1 & 3 & 6 & 10 \\ 1 & 4 & 10 & 20 \end{vmatrix}$ **11.** $\begin{vmatrix} 30 & 11 & 20 & 38 \\ 12 & 6 & 0 & 18 \\ 11 & -2 & 36 & 3 \\ 19 & 6 & 17 & 22 \end{vmatrix}$ **12.** $\begin{vmatrix} 2 & 1 & 1 & 1 \\ 1 & 2 & 1 & 1 \\ 1 & 1 & 2 & 1 \\ 1 & 1 & 1 & 2 \end{vmatrix}$

15-9 Cramer's Rule

You can use determinants to solve a system of three linear equations in three variables. Consider the system

$$\begin{aligned} a_1x + b_1y + c_1z &= d_1 \\ a_2x + b_2y + c_2z &= d_2 \\ a_3x + b_3y + c_3z &= d_3. \end{aligned}$$

If D denotes the determinant of the coefficient matrix,

$$D = \begin{vmatrix} a_1 & b_1 & c_1 \\ a_2 & b_2 & c_2 \\ a_3 & b_3 & c_3 \end{vmatrix}.$$

Suppose (x, y, z) denotes a solution of the system. Then

$$xD = x\begin{vmatrix} a_1 & b_1 & c_1 \\ a_2 & b_2 & c_2 \\ a_3 & b_3 & c_3 \end{vmatrix} = \begin{vmatrix} a_1x & b_1 & c_1 \\ a_2x & b_2 & c_2 \\ a_3x & b_3 & c_3 \end{vmatrix}.$$

Applying Property 6 from the preceding section, you can write

$$xD = \begin{vmatrix} a_1x + b_1y + c_1z & b_1 & c_1 \\ a_2x + b_2y + c_2z & b_2 & c_2 \\ a_3x + b_3y + c_3z & b_3 & c_3 \end{vmatrix} = \begin{vmatrix} d_1 & b_1 & c_1 \\ d_2 & b_2 & c_2 \\ d_3 & b_3 & c_3 \end{vmatrix}$$

from which, if $D \neq 0$,

$$x = \frac{\begin{vmatrix} d_1 & b_1 & c_1 \\ d_2 & b_2 & c_2 \\ d_3 & b_3 & c_3 \end{vmatrix}}{D} = \frac{\begin{vmatrix} d_1 & b_1 & c_1 \\ d_2 & b_2 & c_2 \\ d_3 & b_3 & c_3 \end{vmatrix}}{\begin{vmatrix} a_1 & b_1 & c_1 \\ a_2 & b_2 & c_2 \\ a_3 & b_3 & c_3 \end{vmatrix}}.$$

If you designate the determinant in the numerator by D_x, you may write $x = \dfrac{D_x}{D}$.

Similarly, it can be shown that

$$y = \frac{\begin{vmatrix} a_1 & d_1 & c_1 \\ a_2 & d_2 & c_2 \\ a_3 & d_3 & c_3 \end{vmatrix}}{\begin{vmatrix} a_1 & b_1 & c_1 \\ a_2 & b_2 & c_2 \\ a_3 & b_3 & c_3 \end{vmatrix}} = \frac{D_y}{D}; \quad z = \frac{\begin{vmatrix} a_1 & b_1 & d_1 \\ a_2 & b_2 & d_2 \\ a_3 & b_3 & d_3 \end{vmatrix}}{\begin{vmatrix} a_1 & b_1 & c_1 \\ a_2 & b_2 & c_2 \\ a_3 & b_3 & c_3 \end{vmatrix}} = \frac{D_z}{D}.$$

Thus, if $D \neq 0$, we have found expressions for x, y, z. You can verify by substitution that these values actually do satisfy the three given equations.

Notice that the determinants in the numerators are the same as D except that the coefficients of the variable for which you are solving have been replaced by the constant terms d_1, d_2, and d_3. This rule for the solution of linear systems of equations is known as **Cramer's Rule.**

If the denominator determinant has a value of zero, then the system contains either dependent or inconsistent equations.

EXAMPLE. Find the solution set of the system

$$\begin{aligned} 2x - y - z &= 1 \\ 2x - 3y - 4z &= 0 \\ x + y - z &= 4 \end{aligned}$$

Solution: Set $x = \dfrac{D_x}{D}$, $y = \dfrac{D_y}{D}$, and $z = \dfrac{D_z}{D}$.

$$D = \begin{vmatrix} 2 & -1 & -1 \\ 2 & -3 & -4 \\ 1 & 1 & -1 \end{vmatrix} = 6 + 4 - 2 - 2 + 8 - 3 = 11$$

$$D_x = \begin{vmatrix} 1 & -1 & -1 \\ 0 & -3 & -4 \\ 4 & 1 & -1 \end{vmatrix} = 3 + 16 + 0 - 0 + 4 - 12 = 11$$

$$D_y = \begin{vmatrix} 2 & 1 & -1 \\ 2 & 0 & -4 \\ 1 & 4 & -1 \end{vmatrix} = 0 - 4 - 8 + 2 + 32 - 0 = 22$$

$$D_z = \begin{vmatrix} 2 & -1 & 1 \\ 2 & -3 & 0 \\ 1 & 1 & 4 \end{vmatrix} = -24 + 0 + 2 + 8 - 0 + 3 = -11$$

$$x = \frac{D_x}{D} = \frac{11}{11} = 1, \quad y = \frac{D_y}{D} = \frac{22}{11} = 2, \quad z = \frac{D_z}{D} = \frac{-11}{11} = -1$$

$\{(1, 2, -1)\}$, **Answer.**

Written Exercises

Find the solution set of the given system by means of Cramer's rule.

A

1. $x + y + z = 6$
$2x - y - z = -3$
$x - 3y + 2z = 1$

2. $x - y + z = 3$
$3x + 2y - z = 1$
$4x - 2y - 3z = -2$

3. $x - 2y - 3z = 3$
$y + x - z = 2$
$2x - 3y = 5z + 5$

4. $x + 4y - 3z = 0$
$x - z = y + 7$
$z = 2x + 3y + 5$

5. $2x + 3y + 4z = 3$
$x - 2z = 0$
$3y - 8z = -1$

6. $3x - 4z = 0$
$6x + 4y = -1$
$8y + 2z = 5$

7. $x + y - z = 2$
$2x - 3y + z = 4$
$4x - y + 3z = 1$

8. $2x + 3y - z = 20$
$4x - 5y + 2z = 11$
$7x - 4y + 3z = 33$

9. $x - 2y + 3z = 6$
$2x + y - z = 4$
$3x - y + 2z = -1$

10. $3x + 2y - 5z = 4$
$-x + y + 3z = 1$
$2x + 3y - 2z = 6$

Cayley, Invariants, and Matrices

Many of us are familiar with the words "relativity," "space-time," and "Lorentz transformation" although we probably are not aware of their meaning or implication. They are part of the vocabulary of the "special theory of relativity" developed by Einstein and other modern physicists in their attempt to find expressions for the laws of nature that do not depend upon the frame of reference of the observer. Thus, a natural phenomenon as seen by an astronaut traveling through space could be transformed into an equation describing the same phenomenon as viewed by a man on the earth. Much of the mathematical theory which laid the foundation for this work was formulated by Arthur Cayley, an Englishman who lived during the reign of Queen Victoria. His work is an excellent example of research done in abstract mathematics which later proved to be of great practical significance to the development of physics.

Even as a boy, Cayley made his mathematical genius apparent, and his teachers urged him to devote himself to mathematics. He studied at Cambridge, where he took top honors and was employed as a tutor for three years following his graduation. During this time he produced the outline for much of his later work.

The theory of algebraic invariants, developed by Cayley and his friend and coworker James Joseph Sylvester, was among his greatest works. By an invariant is meant a property that is unaltered by a particular transformation. For example, the nature of the roots (whether real or complex) of a quadratic equation in x is unaltered by replacing x by a real linear expression $gx + r$. The concept of invariance which grew from Cayley's observations has been important in physics, as noted above, and in projective geometry and topology, where certain properties of figures remain the same although the figures are distorted or deformed. Another field which Cayley developed, one with which you are now familiar, is the algebra of matrices. He devised the laws of matrix addition and multiplication which you have just studied. His work in matrices has been invaluable to physicists, particularly in the field of quantum mechanics.

Chapter Summary

Inventory of Structure and Method

1. The rational operations may be performed in the system of matrices with some restrictions. The **sum of two matrices** of the *same dimensions* is the matrix whose entries are the sums of the corresponding entries of the matrices to be added.
   In the set of $m \times n$ matrices, the **additive identity** element is the zero matrix, $O_{m\times n}$; the **additive inverse** of $A_{m\times n}$ is $-A_{m\times n}$. The **product** of a **scalar** r and a matrix A is the matrix each of whose entries is r times the corresponding entry of A.
   Matrix addition and scalar multiplication are both **associative** and **commutative.**
2. The **product of matrices** $A_{m\times n}$ and $B_{n\times p}$ is a matrix $C_{m\times p}$ whose entry in row i and column j is the sum of the products of the corresponding entries in row i of A and column j of B. Matrix multiplication is **associative** but not **commutative**; a product is found in the order in which it is written. Multiplication is **distributive with respect to addition.**
   In the set of square matrices, the **multiplicative identity** is I, such that $AI = IA = A$. Provided $\delta(A) \neq 0$, A has a **multiplicative inverse** A^{-1}, such that $AA^{-1} = A^{-1}A = I$.
3. You may find the **determinant** of a matrix directly from the definition or by expansion by minors. Often, you can simplify the expansion of determinants by applying their properties.
4. You use determinants in solving linear systems in two and in three variables by **Cramer's Rule.**

Vocabulary and Spelling

matrix (*p. 551*)
entry (of a matrix) (*p. 551*)
dimensions (of a matrix) (*p. 551*)
row matrix (*p. 551*)
column matrix (*p. 551*)
zero matrix (*p. 551*)
corresponding entries (*p. 552*)
transpose (A^{T}) of A (*p. 552*)
scalar multiplication (*p. 554*)
matrix multiplication (*p. 556*)
left-multiplication (*p. 558*)
right-multiplication (*p. 558*)
square matrix (*p. 558*)
identity matrix (I) (*p. 558*)
determinant (δ) (*p. 560*)
order of a square matrix (*p. 560*)
elements of a determinant (*p. 561*)
order of a determinant (*p. 561*)
inverse matrix (A^{-1}) (*p. 563*)
invertible matrix (*p. 564*)
coefficient matrix (*p. 566*)
expansion by minors (*p. 567*)
minor of an element (*p. 568*)

Chapter Test and Review

15-1 **1.** Solve for x: $\begin{bmatrix} 3 & 2 \\ -1 & 5 \end{bmatrix} = \begin{bmatrix} 3 & -1 \\ x & 5 \end{bmatrix}^T$

15-2 **2.** Find the sum: $\begin{bmatrix} 8 & -3 & 1 \\ -7 & 5 & -6 \end{bmatrix} + \begin{bmatrix} -3 & -5 & -4 \\ 2 & 5 & -1 \end{bmatrix}$

15-3 **3.** Multiply: $\begin{bmatrix} -5 & 2 & 6 \\ 0 & -3 & 1 \end{bmatrix} \times \begin{bmatrix} -2 \\ 3 \\ 1 \end{bmatrix}$

15-4 **4.** Evaluate $\delta(A)$ if $A = \begin{bmatrix} 7 & -1 & 2 \\ -3 & 0 & -3 \\ 0 & 4 & 1 \end{bmatrix}$

15-5 **5.** Solve for A: $\begin{bmatrix} 3 & 6 \\ 2 & 5 \end{bmatrix} A = \begin{bmatrix} -1 & 5 \\ -3 & 3 \end{bmatrix}$

15-6 **6.** Use matrices to solve the system: $8x - y = 7$
$2x + 3y = -8$

15-7 **7.** Solve for x: $\begin{vmatrix} 4 & 1 & -3 \\ -2 & 5 & -1 \\ 0 & x & 4 \end{vmatrix} = 18$

15-8 **8.** Evaluate: $\begin{vmatrix} 17 & 27 & 32 & -14 \\ 6 & 9 & 10 & -5 \\ -4 & -6 & 14 & -7 \\ 8 & 12 & -5 & 3 \end{vmatrix}$

15-9 **9.** Use Cramer's Rule to find the solution set:

$$\begin{aligned} 3x + 3y + 4z &= -1 \\ x + y + 10z &= 4 \\ 3x + 5y - 2z &= 0 \end{aligned}$$

CHAPTER 16

. . . probability theory in action

Permutations, Combinations, and Probability

Today many problems which formerly could not be analyzed in mathematical terms because they involved uncertainty or chance are being discussed in terms of probability theory. Economists, psychologists, and sociologists are finding an increasing use for the methods of probability in the study and analysis of human situations. Some weather forecasters even give their predictions in terms of the odds for or against rain!

PERMUTATIONS

16–1 Fundamental Counting Principles

Let A be the set of *three* integers $\{0, 1, 2\}$ and B the set of *two* integers $\{7, 8\}$. Can you find the number of different ordered pairs (a, b) in which the first entry is an element of A and the second is an element of B? For each of the *three* ways that you can choose the first entry in such an ordered pair, there are *two* ways in which to choose the second entry. Thus the set of all these ordered pairs is

$$\{(0, 7), (0, 8), (1, 7), (1, 8), (2, 7), (2, 8)\},$$

which contains $3 \cdot 2 = 6$ elements. The set of ordered pairs is called the **Cartesian product** of A and B and is denoted by $\boldsymbol{A \times B}$. This example illustrates a fundamental principle of counting:

> If a finite set A contains r elements and a finite set B contains s elements, then there are rs different ordered pairs (a, b) where $a \in A$ and $b \in B$ (that is, $A \times B$ contains rs elements).

This principle can be extended to any number of sets and applied in many counting situations.

EXAMPLE 1. How many even natural numbers are there having a three-digit numeral?

Solution: To help you think through such problems, you can make a diagram such as this: [| |] or: — — —. The hundreds digit is any one of the nine elements of {1, 2, 3, 4, 5, 6, 7, 8, 9}; therefore, you write 9 in the first space: [9 | |]. Tens digit is any element of {0, 1, 2, 3, 4, 5, 6, 7, 8, 9}, so write 10 in the second space: [9 | 10 |]. Units digit is any one of the five elements of {0, 2, 4, 6, 8}, so write 5 in the third space: [9 | 10 | 5]. The fundamental principle tells you that there are 9×10 ways of choosing both hundreds and tens digits and, therefore, $(9 \times 10) \times 5$, or 450, different even natural numbers having a three-digit numeral. 450, **Answer.**

Since the union of {0, 1, 2} and {7, 8} is the set {0, 1, 2, 7, 8}, you can see that the number of elements in the union is the sum of the numbers of elements in the given sets: $5 = 3 + 2$. On the other hand, the union of {0, 1, 2} and {2, 7} has only *four* elements {0, 1, 2, 7}, because the number 2 is a member of both of the given sets, that is, $\{2\} = \{0, 1, 2\} \cap \{2, 7\}$. These examples illustrate a second fundamental counting principle:

If a finite set A contains r elements, a finite set B contains s elements, and their intersection $(A \cap B)$ contains t elements, then the union of A and B $(A \cup B)$ contains $r + s - t$ elements.

When the sets A and B have no element in common, that is, $A \cap B = \emptyset$, we say that A and B are **disjoint.** Thus, the number of elements in the union of disjoint sets is the sum of the numbers of elements in the sets.

EXAMPLE 2. How many positive odd integers less than 10,000 can be represented, using the digits 0, 3, 6, 9?

Solution: Since you can have numerals with 1, 2, 3, or 4 digits, you consider these cases separately. In each case, you first fill units place with an odd digit (either 3 or 9) and then fill the remaining places. The table shows the number of odd integers representable in each case. Note that 0 cannot be the initial digit in any of the numerals.

Digits in Numeral	1	2	3	4
Number of Odd Integers	2	2×3	$2 \times 4 \times 3$	$2 \times 4 \times 4 \times 3$

Total Number
of These Odd Integers $= 2 + 6 + 24 + 96 = 128$, **Answer.**

Written Exercises

Find the number of elements in $A \times B$, $A \cap B$, and $A \cup B$.

1. $A = \{1, 2, 3\}$; $B = \{3, 4\}$
2. $A = \{7, 8\}$; $B = \{5, 7, 9\}$
3. $A = \{J, Q, K\}$; $B = \{J, Q\}$
4. $A = \{H, T\}$; $B = \{1, 2, 3\}$
5. $A = B = \{a, b, c\}$
6. $A = B = \{1, 2, 3, 4, 5, 6\}$
7. How many sequences of two letters each can be formed?
8. How many three-digit numerals can be written using the symbols 6, 7, and 8?
9. How many different ways can ten questions on a true-false test be answered?
10. An automobile manufacturer produces 7 models, each available in 6 different colors. In addition, the buyer can choose one of 4 different upholstery fabrics and one of 5 different colors for the interior. How many varieties of cars can be ordered from the manufacturer?
11. How many different telephone numbers can be formed from **(a)** two different letters and five digits if the first digit cannot be 0; **(b)** seven digits if the third cannot be 0?
12. In long-distance direct dialing, the area code consists of three digits and the local number of seven digits. Taking the area code into consideration, how many telephone numbers can be formed if the sixth digit cannot be 0?
13. Each row of a four-rowed signal device contains a red and a green light. If at most one light can be lit in any one row, how many different signals can be sent by this device?
14. A witness to a holdup reports that the license of the getaway car consisted of 6 different digits. He remembers the first three but has forgotten the remainder. How many licenses do the police have to check?
15. In how many ways can you write four-digit numerals, using the digits 3, 4, 5, 6, and 7, if you may use a digit as many times as desired in any one numeral?
16. How many three-letter arrangements can be made of the letters P, R, I, M, and E, if any letter may be repeated?

B

17. How many positive odd integers whose numerals contain three digits can be formed, using the digits 1, 2, 3, 4, and 5? (*Hint:* Fill the units place with an odd digit; then fill the remaining places.)

18. How many positive even integers of three digits can be formed from the digits 1, 2, 3, 4, 5, and 6? (*Hint:* Fill the units place with an even digit; then fill the remaining places.)

19. How many positive odd integers less than 70,000 can be represented, using the digits 2, 3, 4, 5, and 6?

20. How many positive integers <8000 can be represented, using 3, 5, 6, 7?

21. How many auto license plates of four symbols can be made in which at least two of the symbols are letters and the rest are digits?

22. How many three-letter code words can be made if at least one of the letters must be one of the vowels: A, E, I, O, or U?

16–2 Linear and Circular Permutations

You can list the members of the set $\{a, b, c\}$ in six different orders:

$$\begin{array}{ccc} a\,b\,c & b\,a\,c & c\,a\,b \\ a\,c\,b & b\,c\,a & c\,b\,a \end{array}$$

Each ordering, or arrangement, of the letters is called a *permutation* of the set $\{a, b, c\}$. A **permutation** is any arrangement of the elements of a set in a definite order.

Studying the preceding example suggests a pattern for the number of permutations of a set. Notice that the first letter listed can be any member of $\{a, b, c\}$. This means there are 3 choices for first place, so we write 3 in the first space of the diagram: $\boxed{3 \mid \mid }$. *After a letter has been selected for first place*, the choice for second place is made from the set of 2 letters remaining. Therefore, write 2 in the second space: $\boxed{3 \mid 2 \mid }$. *After letters have been assigned to both the first and the second places*, there is only 1 choice for third place; so write 1 in the third space: $\boxed{3 \mid 2 \mid 1}$. Thus, the number of permutations of $\{a, b, c\}$ is

$$3 \times 2 \times 1 = 3! = 6$$

This example illustrates the following fact:

The number of permutations of a set containing *n* different elements is *n*!.

EXAMPLE 1. In how many ways can you arrange five different books on a shelf?

Solution: The problem asks for the number of permutations of five things taken five at a time. Thus, $5! = 5 \cdot 4 \cdot 3 \cdot 2 \cdot 1$ or 120 ways, **Answer.**

Now suppose you are asked to find the number of permutations of five books taken only three at a time. In the diagram | | | |, the first space could be filled in five ways, the second in four ways, and the last in three. Thus | 5 | 4 | 3 | would represent the situation. From the fundamental principle there are $5 \cdot 4 \cdot 3 = 60$ ways in which the books could be arranged.

In a set the number of permutations of n different elements taken r at a time is denoted by ${}_nP_r$. Other representations are $P(n, r)$ and P^n_r. To obtain a formula for ${}_nP_r$, notice that the diagram representing the situation contains r spaces to be filled as shown:

n	$n - 1$	$n - 2$	...	$n - (r - 1)$

Thus,

$${}_nP_r = n(n - 1)(n - 2) \ldots [n - (r - 1)].$$

Notice also that if $r = n$, ${}_nP_n = n!$.

EXAMPLE 2. In how many ways can you appoint a president, a secretary, and a treasurer in a club containing twelve members?

Solution: The number of permutations of twelve things taken three at a time is ${}_{12}P_3 = 12 \cdot 11 \cdot 10 = 1320$, **Answer.**

There is a special type of permutation, called a **circular permutation**, which is an arrangement of objects about a circular framework. A common example is the seating of people around a circular table. In such an arrangement there is no first place, so that if each person shifts his position one place counterclockwise (or clockwise) the relative positions are not changed. In fact, each person can shift position n times and return to his original position without disturbing the arrangement. Therefore, if you use the formula for a linear permutation to find the number of possible arrangements, you will have counted each different arrangement n times. Thus, there are $n! \div n = (n - 1)!$ distinguishable permutations.

EXAMPLE 3. In how many ways can five persons be seated around a circular table?

Solution: Since this is a circular permutation of 5 things, there are $(5 - 1)! = 4! = 24$ possible different seating arrangements. You may think of this in a slightly different manner: Since a rotation of any permutation does not produce a new permutation, one of the positions can be considered fixed, and | 1 | 4 | 3 | 2 | 1 | describes the situation. We see again that there are 24 different arrangements. 24, **Answer.**

In problems involving people seated around a table, we consider an arrangement as seen by a person walking around the table in a clockwise direction to be different from the same arrangement as seen by a person walking in a counterclockwise direction. In problems involving arrangements about objects which do not have a definite top or bottom, however, such as key rings and bracelets, we may flip over any arrangement read in clockwise order to get an arrangement identical to the original arrangement read in counterclockwise order. Since the clockwise and counterclockwise readings of such a circular arrangement in the plane represent the same arrangement, there are only half as many different arrangements as in the case in which the circular framework could not be flipped. There are, then, $\frac{(n-1)!}{2}$ different permutations.

Written Exercises

A

1. In how many ways can the letters of the word PHOENIX be arranged if each letter is used only once in each arrangement?
2. Seven salesmen are to be assigned to seven different counters in a department store. How many ways can the assignment be made?
3. A school has six sections of first-year algebra. In how many ways can a pair of twins be assigned to algebra classes if their parents have requested that they be placed in different classes?
4. A symphony concert is to consist of five works: 2 modern, 2 of the classical period, and a piano concerto for soloist and orchestra. If the concerto is the last work on the program, how many ways can the program be arranged?
5. How many 4-letter radio station call letters can be made if the first letter must be W or K and no letter may be repeated?

6. A beauty salon has 4 assistants who wash hair, 2 stylists who cut hair, and a manicurist. By how many different arrangements of the personnel in the salon may a woman have her hair washed, cut, and then her nails manicured?

7. A business school gives courses in typing, shorthand, transcription, business English, technical writing, and accounting. In how many ways may a student arrange his program if he has three courses a day?

8. A sandlot baseball team has 13 players. If there are three pitchers, two catchers, two center-fielders, and one of each other position, how many 9-player starting teams can be fielded?

9. How many permutations of the letters A N S W E R end in a vowel?

10. How many permutations of the letters E Q U I N O X end in a consonant?

11. How many permutations of the letters M O D E R N have consonants in the second and third positions?

12. How many even integers whose numerals contain three digits can be formed using the digits 1, 2, 3, 4, 5 if no digit is repeated in a numeral?

13. How many odd natural numbers are there having a 4-digit numeral in which no digit is repeated?

14. How many numbers divisible by 5 can be formed from the digits 1, 2, 3, 4, 5, 6, using each digit exactly once in each numeral?

15. To lead a certain cheer, the seven cheerleaders form a circle, each facing the center. In how many orders can they arrange themselves?

16. A milliner wants to arrange six different flowers around the brim of a hat. In how many orders can she place them?

17. In how many ways can five keys be arranged on a key ring?

18. In how many ways can a girl arrange nine charms on a bracelet?

19. In how many ways can five men and five girls be seated at a round table so that each girl is between two men?

20. In how many ways can four young couples be seated at a round table so that girls and boys are seated alternately?

B

21. Show that ${}_6P_4 = 6({}_5P_3)$.

22. Show that ${}_nP_4 = n({}_{n-1}P_3)$.

23. Show that ${}_5P_r = 5({}_4P_{r-1})$.

24. Show that ${}_5P_3 - {}_5P_2 = 2({}_5P_2)$.

25. Show that ${}_nP_4 - {}_nP_3 = (n - 4)({}_nP_3)$.

26. Show that ${}_nP_r - {}_nP_{r-1} = (n - r){}_nP_{r-1}$.

C

27. Solve for n: ${}_nP_3 = 3({}_{n-1}P_2)$.

28. Solve for n: ${}_nP_4 = 8({}_{n-1}P_3)$.

29. Solve for n: ${}_nP_4 = 4({}_nP_3)$.

30. Solve for n: ${}_nP_r = k({}_{n-1}P_{r-1})$.

16–3 Permutations of Elements Not All Different

In the name *Bob* you can distinguish between the two *b*'s because one is a capital letter. Since $\{B, o, b\}$ is a set of three different elements, the number of permutations of the set is ${}_3P_3 = 3!$, or 6. They are:

B o b	*o B b*	*b B o*
b o B	*o b B*	*B b o*

In the verb *bob* the two *b*'s are alike. Therefore, permutations which differ only in rearrangement of these two letters are indistinguishable. Since there are two permutations of the *b*'s among themselves (${}_2P_2 = 2!$), there are only three distinguishable permutations of the letters *b o b* taken three at a time:

b o b *o b b* *b b o*

Thus, the number of permutations of three elements taken three at a time when two of the elements are alike is given by

$$\frac{{}_3P_3}{{}_2P_2} = \frac{3!}{2!}.$$

In general, if n elements are taken n at a time. and n_1 of the elements are alike, then the number P of distinguishable permutations is $\boldsymbol{P = n! \div n_1!}$. Thus when the letters C R O S S E S are taken seven at a time, $P = 7! \div 3!$.

The formula can be extended to cases in which n_1 elements are alike, n_2 others are alike, and so on. For example, among the eight letters I N F I N I T E, two *n*'s are alike and three *i*'s are alike, so that the number of permutations of the eight letters taken eight at a time is $8! \div (2!)(3!)$. Likewise, the number of permutations of the ten letters A P P E A R A N C E, taken ten at a time, is $10! \div (3!)(2!)(2!)$.

Formally,

The number of distinguishable permutations of n elements taken n at a time, with n_1 elements alike, n_2 of another kind alike, and so on, is

$$\frac{n!}{n_1!\,n_2!\ldots}$$

Written Exercises

Find the number of permutations of all the letters of each word.

A

1. sequence
2. maximum
3. minimum
4. abscissa
5. difference
6. discriminant
7. progression
8. mathematics
9. characteristic
10. dependent
11. mantissa
12. trigonometry

13. How many signals can be made by displaying six flags all at one time on a vertical flagpole if the flags differ only in color, three of them being red, two white, and one green?

14. In how many ways can five pennies, two nickels, and a dime be distributed among eight boys seated in a row if each receives a coin?

How many different five-digit numerals can be made in each case?

15. 3, 4, and 7 may each be used once; 5 may be used twice.

16. 6, 7, and 8 may each be used once; 9 may be used twice.

17. 3 may be used three times; 5 may be used twice.

18. 2 and 3 may each be used twice; 4 may be used once.

COMBINATIONS

16–4 Counting Subsets

Can you list the three-element subsets of the set T where $T = \{a, b, c, d\}$? To obtain any of these subsets, all you have to do is remove one of the members of the original set. Thus, T has four subsets with three elements:

$$\{a, b, c\} \qquad \{a, b, d\} \qquad \{a, c, d\} \qquad \{b, c, d\}$$

You can classify the *permutations* of T's elements taken three at a time according to the three-element subset involved in each permutation. For example, the 3!, or 6, arrangements

$$\begin{matrix} a\,b\,c & b\,a\,c & c\,a\,b \\ a\,c\,b & b\,c\,a & c\,b\,a \end{matrix}$$

are the permutations of the subset $\{a, b, c\}$. Similarly, each of the other three-element subsets yield 3! other permutations of the letters

a, b, c, and d taken three at a time. In fact, if you let ${}_4C_3$ denote the number of three-element subsets of the four-element set s, you have

$$ {}_4C_3 \times 3! = {}_4P_3 \quad \text{or} \quad {}_4C_3 = \frac{{}_4P_3}{3!}. $$

This formula is consistent with our observation that ${}_4C_3 = 4$, since

$$ \frac{{}_4P_3}{3!} = \frac{4 \cdot 3 \cdot 2}{1 \cdot 3 \cdot 2} = 4. $$

Moreover, the formula suggests the general relationship between ${}_nC_r$, the number of r-element subsets of a set with n elements and ${}_nP_r$, the number of permutations of the n elements taken r at a time for $0 < r < n$:

$$ {}_n\boldsymbol{C}_r = \frac{{}_n\boldsymbol{P}_r}{\boldsymbol{r!}}. $$

Since ${}_nP_r = n(n-1)(n-2) \cdots [n-(r-1)]$, this means

$$ {}_nC_r = \frac{n(n-1)(n-2) \cdots [n-(r-1)]}{r!}. $$

Note that the numerator and the denominator on the right are both products of r elements.

An r-element subset of a set with n elements is often called a **combination** of n elements taken r at a time. Thus, ${}_nC_r$, also denoted by $\binom{n}{r}$, $C(n, r)$, or C_r^n, is the number of combinations of n elements taken r at a time.

EXAMPLE. How many different committees of four persons can be formed from a club with 10 members?

Solution: The problem asks for the number of combinations of ten things taken four at a time. Substitute 10 for n and 4 for r in

$$ {}_nC_r = \frac{n(n-1)(n-2) \cdots (n-r+1)}{r!} $$

$$ {}_{10}C_4 = \frac{10 \cdot 9 \cdot 8 \cdot 7}{1 \cdot 2 \cdot 3 \cdot 4} = 210, \textbf{ Answer.} $$

If you multiply the numerator and denominator of the expression for ${}_nC_r$ by $(n - r)!$, you obtain:

$${}_nC_r = \frac{n(n-1)(n-2)\ldots(n-r+1)(n-r)(n-r-1)\ldots 3\cdot 2\cdot 1}{r!(n-r)!}$$

$${}_nC_r = \frac{n!}{r!(n-r)!}$$

Does the symbol ${}_nC_0$ have meaning? It is the number of subsets with no elements in a set having n elements. Since there is just one such subset, namely $\emptyset$, the empty set, ${}_nC_0 = 1$. If you use the formula for ${}_nC_r$ in this case, you have

$${}_nC_0 = \frac{n!}{0!n!} = \frac{1}{0!}, \quad \text{or}$$

$$1 = \frac{1}{0!}$$

Therefore, for the formula to hold, we must *define* **0!** to be **1**. Now, you should verify that this definition makes the formula for ${}_nC_r$ valid also in the case $r = n$.

You can discover a useful fact about ${}_nC_r$ by noticing that whenever r elements are selected from a set of n elements, $n - r$ elements are left behind. Therefore, the combinations of r elements selected and the combinations of $n - r$ elements left are paired, one-to-one, and are consequently the same in number; that is,

$${}_nC_r = {}_nC_{n-r}.$$

You can use this fact to simplify computations; for example;

$${}_{50}C_{48} = {}_{50}C_2 = \frac{50\cdot 49}{1\cdot 2} = 1225.$$

Written Exercises

A

1. How many combinations can be formed from the letters D R E A M, taking two at a time? Show the combinations.
2. How many combinations can be formed from the letters N I L E, taking two at a time? Write the combinations.
3. How many straight lines can be formed by joining any two of five points, no three of which are in a straight line?

4. Seven points lie on the circumference of a circle. How many chords can be drawn joining them?

5. In how many ways can a student choose to answer five questions out of eight on an examination, if the order of his answers is of no importance?

6. Eva's Hamburger Haven sells hamburgers with cheese, lettuce, tomato, relish, ketchup, or mustard. How many different hamburgers can be made, choosing any three of the "extras"?

7. Julie owes letters to her grandmother, her uncle, her cousin, and two school friends. Tuesday night she decides to write to two of them. From how many combinations can she choose?

8. Local 352 is holding an election of four officers. In how many ways can they be chosen from a membership of 75? (Disregard order.)

9. A quality control engineer has to inspect a sample of 5 fuses from a box of 100. How many different samples can he choose?

10. The twelve engineers in the instrumentation department of Ajax Missile Corp. are to divide into project groups of four persons each. How many possible groups are there?

B **11.** Six points lie on the circumference of a circle. How many inscribed triangles can be drawn having these points as vertices?

12. Eleven points lie on the circumference of a circle. How many inscribed hexagons can be drawn having these points as vertices?

13. If 6 students are to be chosen from 12 to participate in an honors section of a course, in how many ways can this group be selected? In how many ways can the group not chosen to participate be selected?

14. How many ways can a chemistry student choose 5 experiments to perform out of 10? In how many ways can 10 things be divided into 2 equal groups?

15. How many different five-card hands can be drawn from a pack of 52 cards? (Set up solution and estimate answer.)

16. How many different thirteen-card hands can be dealt from the 52 cards in a pack? (Set up solution and estimate answer.)

17. Find n, given ${}_nC_2 = {}_{100}C_{98}$.

18. Find n if ${}_nC_5 = {}_nC_3$.

C **19.** Prove ${}_nC_r = {}_nC_{n-r}$ by using the formula ${}_nC_r = \dfrac{n!}{(n-r)!r!}$.

20. Show that the total number of subsets of a set with n elements is 2^n. *Hint.* Each member of the set either is or is not selected in forming a subset.

16–5 Combinations Formed from Several Sets

Bayville High School sends a committee of three boys and two girls from its Driver Education Class to represent the school at the city's Junior Driving Safety Council meetings. If there are nine boys and five girls in the Driver Education Class, in how many ways may the committee be selected? To solve this problem, you ask yourself how many subsets containing three boys are possible in a set containing nine boys. You have ${}_9C_3 = \frac{9 \cdot 8 \cdot 7}{1 \cdot 2 \cdot 3} = 84$. How many subsets of two girls can be formed from a set containing five girls? ${}_5C_2 = \frac{5 \cdot 4}{1 \cdot 2} = 10$. Then there are ${}_9C_3 \cdot {}_5C_2 = 84 \cdot 10 = 840$ different committees possible.

In general, in working with combinations formed from several groups, you find the possible combinations for each group and then apply the fundamental principle. Sometimes you have to permute the elements of the groups after selecting them.

EXAMPLE. Suppose you have eight historical novels and five biographies. In how many orders can you arrange four historical novels and two biographies on a bookshelf which holds six books?

Solution: Possible combinations of historical novels:

$$ {}_8C_4 = \frac{8 \cdot 7 \cdot 6 \cdot 5}{1 \cdot 2 \cdot 3 \cdot 4} = 70 $$

Possible combinations of biographies:

$$ {}_5C_2 = \frac{5 \cdot 4}{1 \cdot 2} = 10 $$

Possible ways of selecting the six books:

$$ {}_8C_4 \cdot {}_5C_2 = 70 \cdot 10 = 700. $$

Each of the 700 possible combinations consists of six different books. Since ${}_6P_6 = 6!$, each combination can be arranged in 6! different orders. Thus there are 720 permutations for each combination. The total number of permutations, then, is $700 \cdot 720$, or 504,000. 504,000, **Answer.**

Written Exercises

A

1. Mrs. Henry McGrath has five hats, nine winter dresses, three handbags, and six pairs of shoes. How many different winter outfits does she have?
2. On a geometry test, each student may select one theorem to prove from three which are given and two constructions to perform from three which are given. In how many ways can a student make his selection?
3. Students in an English class are to write a report on two books read outside of class. For the first, they may choose from four different books, and for the second, from three different books. How many different choices of reports are there? (Disregard order.)
4. There are ten men and six women in a repertory theatre group. Four of the men can play male leads, and the others play supporting roles. Three of the women play female leads, and the others play supporting roles. In how many ways can a play with male and female leads and two male and three female supporting roles be cast?
5. A chef interested in using up some leftover meats and vegetables decides to make a stew consisting of three kinds of meat and four vegetables. If there are five different meats and seven different vegetables available, how many different kinds of stew can the chef make?

B

6. Seven boys and seven girls were nominated for homecoming king and queen. How many ways can a king, a queen, and her court of two girls be chosen?
7. A bridge deck has thirteen cards of each suit. How many 13-card hands having seven spades are there? How many hands having exactly seven spades, three hearts, two diamonds, and one club are there?
8. A deck of cards has thirteen cards of each suit. How many 10-card hands having three cards of one kind and two of another are there? How many hands having three 10's and two queens are there?
9. A department-store window designer has eight spring dresses, four shorts-and-shirt outfits, and seven bathing suits from which to choose three dresses, two shorts-and-shirt outfits, and two bathing suits. How many ways can she arrange these on seven manikins?
10. The executive division of a business organization proposed three speakers for the annual banquet, the sales department proposed two, the production department proposed two, and the accounting department proposed one. If there is to be one speaker from each department, how many ways can they be arranged on one side of the head table?
11. How many five-letter arrangements of the letters REGIONAL consisting of three consonants and two vowels can be formed if no letter is repeated?

12. How many four-letter arrangements of the letters C A P S U L E having three consonants and one vowel can be formed if no letter is repeated?

C

13. Using three of the letters of S Q U A R E and two of the letters of F O O T, how many arrangements of five different letters are possible?

14. Using three letters of A R T I C L E and three of S H O W, how many arrangements of six different letters are possible?

15. How many numerals having five different digits can be formed from the digits 1, 2, 3, 4, 5, 6, 7, 8, 9, if each numeral is to be written with three odd digits and two even digits?

16. If there are twelve desks in the front row of a classroom, in how many ways can three students be seated? In how many ways can they be seated next to each other?

16–6 The Binomial Theorem and Pascal's Triangle

You can look at the expansion of a positive integral power of a binomial (Section 13–8) from the point of view of combinations of terms selected from each of the binomial factors. Consider the following expansion:

$$\begin{aligned}(a + b)^3 &= (a + b)(a + b)(a + b)\\ &= aaa + baa + aab + aba + bba + bab + abb + bbb.\end{aligned}$$

You obtain each product shown in the expansion by multiplying three variables, one from each of the binomial factors of $(a + b)^3$. The term baa, for example, is the result of choosing b from the first binomial factor, a from the second, and a from the third. Do you see that the products baa, aab, and aba are the ones occurring when you select b from one factor and a from both of the other factors? Thus, if you combine similar terms in the expansion to obtain

$$(a + b)^3 = a^3 + 3a^2b + 3ab^2 + b^3,$$

then 3, the coefficient of a^2b, is the number of ways of selecting one b from the three factors; that is, ${}_3C_1$. Similarly, because you obtain a^3 by choosing no b from the three factors, the coefficient of a^3 is 1, or ${}_3C_0$. In fact, you can rewrite the expansion as follows:

$$(a + b)^3 = {}_3C_0a^3 + {}_3C_1a^2b + {}_3C_2ab^2 + {}_3C_3b^3$$

The reasoning used in determining the coefficients in the expansion of $(a + b)^3$ can be extended to determining the coefficients in the expansion of $(a+b)^n$. Thus,

$$(a+b)^n = {}_nC_0\, a^n + {}_nC_1\, a^{n-1}\, b + {}_nC_2\, a^{n-2}\, b^2 + \ldots + {}_nC_n\, b^n,$$

where the **rth** term is ${}_nC_{r-1}a^{n-(r-1)}b^{r-1}$.

If you write the expansions of $(a+b)^n$ for successive values of n in the form of a triangle, you have

$$\begin{aligned}
(a+b)^0 &= 1\\
(a+b)^1 &= a+b\\
(a+b)^2 &= a^2+2ab+b^2\\
(a+b)^3 &= a^3+3a^2b+3ab^2+b^3\\
(a+b)^4 &= a^4+4a^3b+6a^2b^2+4ab^3+b^4
\end{aligned}$$

Now, looking only at the coefficients, you see the triangle:

$$\begin{array}{ccccccccc}
 & & & & 1 & & & & \\
 & & & 1 & & 1 & & & \\
 & & 1 & & 2 & & 1 & & \\
 & 1 & & 3 & & 3 & & 1 & \\
1 & & 4 & & 6 & & 4 & & 1
\end{array}$$

Do you see that you can write the next row in this triangle by inspection? Notice that each term is the sum of the two terms to the right and to the left of it in the row directly above. Thus, the next row is:

$$\begin{array}{ccccccccccc}
 & 1 & & 4 & & 6 & & 4 & & 1 & \\
 & & + & & + & & + & & + & & \\
1 & & 5 & & 10 & & 10 & & 5 & & 1
\end{array}$$

This array is known as **Pascal's Triangle**, named after the French mathematician and philosopher Blaise Pascal. You can generate the rth term in the nth row of the triangle by the relationship

$$ {}_nC_r = {}_{n-1}C_{r-1} + {}_{n-1}C_r. \qquad (n \geq r+1)$$

EXAMPLE 1. Expand: $(x+2y)^4$.

Solution:

$$\begin{aligned}
(x+2y)^4 &= {}_4C_0x^4 + {}_4C_1x^3(2y) + {}_4C_2x^2(2y)^2 + {}_4C_3x(2y)^3 + {}_4C_4(2y)^4\\
&= 1x^4 + 4x^3(2y) + 6x^2(4y^2) + 4x(8y^3) + 1(16y^4)\\
&= x^4 + 8x^3y + 24x^2y^2 + 32xy^3 + 16y^4,
\end{aligned}$$

Answer.

EXAMPLE 2. Find the sixth term in the expansion of $(a + 3b)^9$.

Solution: The rth term is given by ${}_nC_{r-1}a^{n-(r-1)}(3b)^{r-1}$.
Hence, the 6th term $= {}_9C_{6-1}a^{9-(6-1)}(3b)^{6-1}$.

$$\text{Since } {}_9C_5 = {}_9C_4 = \frac{9 \cdot 8 \cdot 7 \cdot 6}{1 \cdot 2 \cdot 3 \cdot 4} = 126,$$

6th term $= 126a^4(3b)^5 = 126a^4(243b^5) = 30{,}618a^4b^5$, **Answer.**

Written Exercises

Expand the given binomial.

A

1. $(1 + 3y)^4$
2. $(2x + 1)^5$
3. $\left(2 + \frac{y}{2}\right)^6$
4. $\left(\frac{x}{3} + 3\right)^6$
5. $\left(2 - \frac{y}{3}\right)^6$
6. $\left(\frac{x}{3} - 1\right)^7$

Find the given term in the given expansion.

B

7. The fifth term in $(x + y)^{10}$
8. The sixth term in $(a + b)^{11}$
9. The fourth term in $\left(2 - \frac{b}{2}\right)^{10}$
10. The eighth term in $\left(2 - \frac{b}{2}\right)^{10}$
11. The fourteenth term in $(5 + a)^{15}$
12. The fifteenth term in $(2x - 1)^{17}$

C

13. Prove: ${}_nC_2 = {}_{n-1}C_1 + {}_{n-1}C_2$, if $n \geq 3$.
14. Prove: ${}_nC_r = {}_{n-1}C_{r-1} + {}_{n-1}C_r$, if $n \geq r + 1$.

PROBABILITY

16–7 Sample Spaces and Events

Suppose you conduct an experiment by tossing three coins — a dime, a nickel, and a quarter. If h represents heads and t tails, any possible outcome of the experiment is an element of:

$$\{(h, h, h), (h, h, t), (h, t, h), (h, t, t), (t, h, h), (t, h, t), (t, t, h), (t, t, t)\},$$

where the components of the ordered triples represent in order the result on the dime, the nickel, and the quarter. This set is called a *sample space* or *universe* of the experiment. A **sample space** is a set S

of elements that correspond one-to-one with the outcomes of an experiment. Each of the elements corresponding to an outcome is called a **sample point**

EXAMPLE 1. Each letter of the word *logarithm* is written on a card and the cards are shuffled. List a sample space for the outcome of drawing one card.

Solution: {l, o, g, a, r, i, t, h, m}, **Answer.**

Now suppose you were interested in whether the letter drawn in Example 1 was a vowel. You can call the drawing of a vowel an *event*, and in this case, the event is the occurrence of any of the outcomes o, a, or i. The set {o, a, i} can be seen to be a subset of the sample space. An **event** is any subset of a sample space.

EXAMPLE 2. Two marbles are to be drawn from a bag known to contain only red marbles and blue marbles. List a sample space for the experiment, and then list the event that both marbles are the same color.

Solution: Since the marbles must be either red or blue, a sample space is $\{(r, r), (r, b), (b, r), (b, b)\}$. The event that both are the same color is $\{(r, r), (b, b)\}$, **Answer.**

It is convenient to discuss the sample space for an experiment involving two distinct occurrences, such as two marbles, as the Cartesian product of the sample spaces of each of the occurrences. In the preceding example, the sample space for the drawing of the first marble is $A = \{r, b\}$ and for the drawing of the second is $B = \{r, b\}$ The sample space for the experiment, listed in the Solution, is simply $A \times B$ (Figure 16–1).

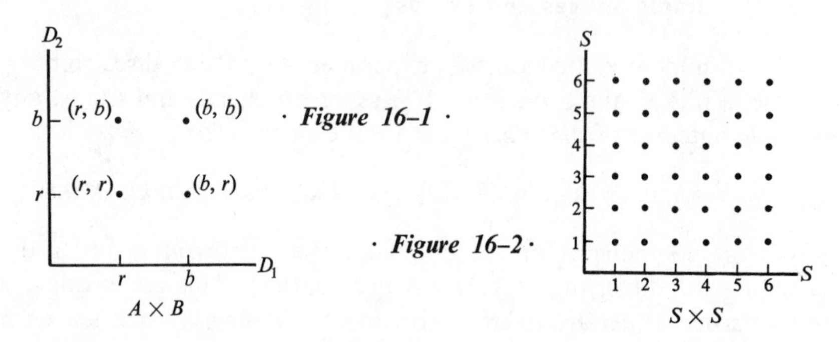

· *Figure 16–1* ·

· *Figure 16–2* ·

As another example, consider the experiment involving the throwing of two dice. Each die has as sample space $S = \{1, 2, 3, 4, 5, 6\}$, and the experiment has as a sample space $S \times S$ (Figure 16–2).

EXAMPLE 3. From five cards numbered 0, 1, 2, 3, 4, two cards are drawn in succession. Specify by roster **(a)** a sample space; **(b)** the event that the sum of the numbers on the cards is greater than 6.

Solution: **a.** $\{(0, 1), (1, 0), (0, 2), (2, 0), (0, 3), (3, 0), (0, 4), (4, 0), (1, 2), (2, 1), (1, 3), (3, 1), (1, 4), (4, 1), (2, 3), (3, 2), (2, 4), (4, 2), (3, 4), (4, 3)\}$

b. The event described is $\{(3, 4), (4, 3)\}$, **Answer.**

Written Exercises

A

1. A number is chosen at random from the digits 1 to 9, inclusive. List a sample space. List the event that the number is even.

2. A number is chosen at random from the integers -4 to 4, inclusive. List a sample space. List the event that the number is positive.

3. A letter is chosen at random from the word PURCHASE. List a sample space. List the event that the letter is a vowel.

4. A letter is chosen at random from the word NUMBER. List a sample space. List the event that the letter is not a vowel.

5. Two numbers are chosen at random from the integers 1, 2, 3, and 4. List a sample space. List the event that the sum of the numbers is an even integer.

6. Two numbers are chosen at random from among the integers from -2 to 2, inclusive. List a sample space. List the event that the sum of the numbers is 0.

7. Two letters are chosen at random from the word LETTER. List a sample space. List the event that both letters are the same.

8. Two letters are chosen at random from the word SEASON. List a sample space. List the event that both letters are vowels.

B

9. A die is thrown and a coin is tossed. List a sample space. List the event the number on the die is odd.

10. Two bags contain marbles, the first bag containing white and red marbles, and the second containing white, red, and green marbles. A marble is drawn from each bag. List a sample space. List the event that neither marble is red.

16–8 Meaning of Mathematical Probability

Consider the following experiment: From a bag containing 5 blue and 12 white marbles, draw one marble, record its color, then replace it.

If the experiment is designed so that each marble is just as likely to be drawn as any other, we say that the experiment has 17 *equally likely* outcomes. The event that a white marble is drawn consists of 12 outcomes. Therefore, if you repeat the experiment many times, it seems reasonable to expect that about $\frac{12}{17}$ of the time you will find that you have drawn a white marble. This ratio, $\frac{12}{17}$, is called the *probability* that the outcome of any single trial of the experiment will be the drawing of a white marble. This example suggests the following definition:

Let S be a sample space of an experiment in which there are n possible outcomes, each equally likely. If an event A is a subset of S such that A contains h elements, then the probability of the event A, denoted by $P(A)$, is given by $P(A) = \frac{h}{n}$.

EXAMPLE 1. If two cards are drawn at random from a standard bridge deck containing 52 cards, what is the probability that both cards drawn are face cards (Jack, Queen, King)?

Solution: Since there are 52 cards in the deck, there are ${}_{52}C_2$ ways in which two cards can be drawn at random. There are 12 face cards in the deck, 4 Jacks, 4 Queens, and 4 Kings, so that there are ${}_{12}C_2$ ways in which the two cards drawn can be face cards. If A represents the drawing of two face cards, then

$$P(A) = \frac{{}_{12}C_2}{{}_{52}C_2} = \frac{132}{2652} = \frac{11}{221}, \text{ **Answer.**}$$

In the previous example the answer $\frac{1}{22}$ does not tell you anything that you can accept as a certainty. It does not, for example, tell you that if you perform the experiment 22 times you will get one and only one draw of 2 white marbles. You might get one such draw, or you might get none, or you might get 22. What $\frac{1}{22}$ does tell you is that if you perform the experiment a very great number of times, the ratio of the number of times you draw 2 white marbles to the total number of draws will come close to $\frac{1}{22}$.

An event A in the sample space S is called *certain* if $A = S$; it is called *impossible* if $A = \emptyset$. Since $P(S) = \frac{n}{n} = 1$, while $P(\emptyset) = \frac{0}{n} = 0$, the probability is 1 for a certain event and 0 for an impossible one. Do you see that the probability of an event which is neither certain nor impossible is a number between 0 and 1?

By the symbol $\overline{A}$ (read "the **complement** of A"), we mean the set of the elements of S that are *not* members of A. If A has h members, then $\overline{A}$ contains $n - h$ elements. Therefore, $P(\overline{A})$ is the probability that A does *not* occur, and:

$$\mathbf{P(\overline{A}) = \frac{n - h}{n} = 1 - \frac{h}{n} = 1 - P(A).}$$

The **odds** that the event A will occur are given by

$$\mathbf{\frac{P(A)}{P(\overline{A})}, \text{ or } \frac{h}{n - h}.}$$

Thus, in the original experiment the odds are *12 to 5 in favor of* drawing a white marble, or *5 to 12 against* drawing a white marble.

EXAMPLE 2. What are the odds that a marble drawn at random from a bag containing 40 marbles will be white, if there are 24 white marbles in the bag?

Solution:

The probability that the marble is white: $P(A) = \frac{24}{40} = \frac{3}{5}$;

the probability that the marble is *not* white: $P(\overline{A}) = 1 - \frac{3}{5} = \frac{2}{5}$;

$\therefore$ the odds that the marble drawn is white: $\frac{P(A)}{P(\overline{A})} = \frac{\frac{3}{5}}{\frac{2}{5}} = \frac{3}{2}$.

3 to 2, **Answer.**

Written Exercises

A

1. Mrs. Glenhaven invites 10 relatives to a family party: her mother, 2 uncles, 3 brothers, and 4 cousins. Suppose that the chances of any one of the guests arriving first are equally likely. What is the probability that the first guest is an uncle? a brother? an uncle or a brother? a brother or a cousin?

2. One card is drawn from a pack consisting of 13 different cards each of clubs and spades (black cards) and hearts and diamonds (red cards). Express each of the following probabilities:

a. The card is the king of diamonds.

b. The card is a 7.

c. The card is a spade.

d. The card is red.

e. The card is a 9 or a 10.

3. Out of 24 people who placed ads to sell household belongings in a neighborhood paper one week, 18 made a sale within a week. If Mrs. Rumford places an ad to sell a table in the paper the following week, what are the odds that she will sell it within a week? (Assume that the probability of sale is the same each week.)

4. If the probability that it will rain on a given day is $\frac{1}{3}$,

a. What is the probability that it will not rain?

b. What are the odds that it will rain?

c. What are the odds that it will not rain?

5. You are the first person to draw one of 24 slips of paper, numbered consecutively from 1 to 24.

a. What is the probability of drawing a number exactly divisible by 3?

b. What are the odds in favor of drawing an odd number?

c. What are the odds against drawing a number exactly divisible by 4?

6. At a fashion show a door prize of a fur coat is given to the person whose ticket stub is drawn from a bowl. If 35 tickets (numbered 1–35) were sold,

a. What is the probability that the winning ticket bears a number > 20? < 30?

b. What is the probability that the number on the winning ticket is divisible by 2? by 3?

7. A Chinese fortune cookie producer has four different fortunes: A, B, C, and D, one of which is placed in each cookie. He has three times as many *A* fortunes as *B*, and twice as many *B* as *C* and *D*. If you take a cookie at random from a bag of thirty cookies,

a. What is the probability that it contains fortune *A*?

b. What is the probability that it contains fortune *B*?

c. What is the probability that it contains fortune *C* or *D*?

d. What is the sum of these probabilities?

8. Of the 500,000 income tax returns that come into a branch of a state tax bureau, 500,000 returns are checked for arithmetic and 50,000 returns are analyzed thoroughly. If Mrs. Willoughby's return is at this branch,

a. What is the probability that it will be inspected for arithmetic?

b. What is the probability that it will both be inspected for arithmetic and be thoroughly analyzed?

c. What is the probability that it will not be analyzed thoroughly?

9. A bag contains 2 white marbles, 4 blue marbles, and 6 red marbles. A marble is drawn at random from the bag. What is the probability that

a. it is white?
b. it is blue?
c. it is red?
d. it is not white?
e. it is not blue?
f. it is black?

10. In Exercise 9, three marbles are drawn from the bag. What is the probability that

a. they are all blue?
b. they are all red?
c. they are all white?
d. none of them is red?
e. not all of them are red?
f. none is black?

11. Three cards are drawn from a deck of 52 cards. What is the probability that:

a. they are all spades?
b. they are all red cards?
c. none of them is a club?
d. all of them are aces?

12. In Exercise 11 what are the odds that:

a. all three cards are spades?
b. they are all red cards?
c. none is a club?
d. all of them are aces?

B

13. Ten cards, the 2 through the 6 of spades and the 2 through the 6 of diamonds, are shuffled thoroughly and then taken one by one from the top of the deck and placed on the table. How many arrangements are possible? What is the probability that each card is next to a card bearing the same numeral?

14. In an extra-sensory-perception experiment, a blindfolded subject has two rows of blocks before him. Each row has blocks numbered 1 to 10 arranged in random order. The subject is to place one hand on a block in the first row and then try to place his other hand on the block having the same numeral in the second row. If the subject has no ESP, what is the probability of his making a match on the first try?

15. If the letters of the word *algebra* are placed at random in a row, what is the probability that two successive letters will be *a*?

16. If the letters of the word *about* are placed at random in a row, what is the probability that three successive letters will be vowels?

16–9 Mutually Exclusive Events

Venn diagrams offer a convenient means of visualizing events in sample spaces. Figure 16–3 shows the sample space S for the experiment of drawing a number from $\{1, 2, 3, 4, 5, 6, 7, 8\}$. The figure also shows two events A and B in S. A is the drawing of a number less than 4, so that $A = \{1, 2, 3\}$. B is the drawing of an even number; that is, $B = \{2, 4, 6, 8\}$. Therefore, $P(A) = \frac{3}{8}$ and $P(B) = \frac{4}{8} = \frac{1}{2}$.

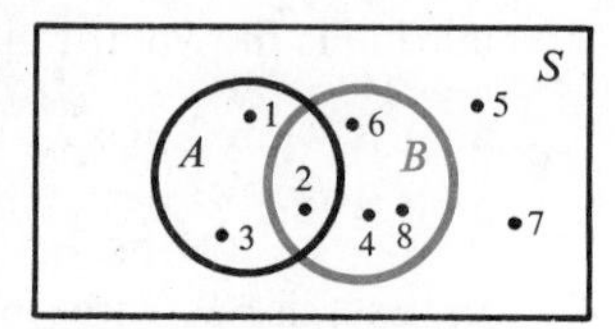

· *Figure 16–3* ·

What is the probability that either A or B (or both) will occur? This amounts to asking for $P(A \cup B)$. Since $A \cup B = \{1, 2, 3, 4, 6, 8\}$, $P(A \cup B) = \frac{6}{8} = \frac{3}{4}$. To see the relationship between $P(A \cup B)$, $P(A)$, and $P(B)$ notice that the intersection of A and B $(A \cap B)$, is $\{2\}$. Also, $P(\{2\}) = \frac{1}{8}$ and

$$P(A \cup B) = \frac{6}{8} = \frac{3 + 4 - 1}{8} = \frac{3}{8} + \frac{4}{8} - \frac{1}{8}.$$

$$\downarrow \qquad \downarrow \qquad \downarrow$$

$$\mathbf{P(A \cup B) = P(A) + P(B) - P(A \cap B).}$$

You can prove that this relationship holds for any two events A and B in a sample space. If the events have no outcome in common, that is, $A \cap B = \emptyset$, we say that the events are **mutually exclusive**.

In this case, $P(A \cap B) = P(\emptyset) = 0$. Thus:

If A and B are mutually exclusive events,

$$P(A \cup B) = P(A) + P(B).$$

EXAMPLE. From 8 girls and 6 boys, a group of 4 students is to be chosen at random to participate in an opinion poll. What is the probability that more than 2 girls will be chosen?

Solution: The group of 4 will contain *more than* 2 girls providing it contains exactly 3 girls and 1 boy (event A) *or else* it contains *exactly* 4 girls and no boys (event B).

Since $A \cap B = \emptyset$, $P(A \cup B) = P(A) + P(B)$.

$$P(A) = \frac{{}_8C_3 \times {}_6C_1}{{}_{14}C_4} = \frac{56 \times 6}{1001} = \frac{48}{143}$$

$$P(B) = \frac{{}_8C_4 \times {}_6C_0}{{}_{14}C_4} = \frac{70 \times 1}{1001} = \frac{10}{143}$$

$\therefore P(A \cup B) = \frac{48}{143} + \frac{10}{143} = \frac{58}{143}$, **Answer.**

Written Exercises

A

1. Two dice are rolled. What is the probability that: **(a)** The sum of the numbers is 4? **(b)** One or both of the numbers are 5? **(c)** Either the sum of the numbers is 4 or one or both of the numbers are 5?
2. Two dice are rolled. What is the probability that: **(a)** The sum of the numbers is 5? **(b)** Just one of the numbers is 6? **(c)** Either the sum of the numbers is 5, or just one of the numbers is 6?
3. If two cards are drawn from a standard deck of 52 cards, what is the probability that: **(a)** Both are spades? **(b)** Both are kings? **(c)** Either both are spades or both are kings?
4. If two cards are drawn from a standard deck of 52 cards, what is the probability that: **(a)** Both are aces? **(b)** Both are queens? **(c)** Either both are aces or both are queens?
5. If two cards are drawn from a standard deck of 52 cards, what is the probability that: **(a)** Both are red? **(b)** Both are queens? **(c)** Either both are red or both are queens?
6. If two cards are drawn from a standard deck of 52 cards, what is the probability that: **(a)** Both are black? **(b)** One is the ace of spades? **(c)** Either both are black or one is the ace of spades?

B

7. One bag contains 3 red, 2 black, and 2 white balls. Another bag contains 1 red, 1 black, and 3 white balls. If a ball is drawn at random from each bag, find the probability that either both or none is black.
8. If a 5-volume set of books is randomly placed on a shelf, what is the probability that they will be arranged in either proper or reverse order?

16–10 Independent and Dependent Events

Suppose two balls are drawn at random from a bag containing 4 red and 3 black balls. What is the probability that both balls selected are red?

Let A be the event of drawing a red ball the first time, and B, the event of drawing a red ball the second time. The sample space S of the experiment depends on whether or not the first ball drawn is returned to the bag before the second ball is chosen. The question amounts to asking for $P(A \cap B)$.

Case I. The first ball is replaced before the second is drawn.

The sample space S consists of all ordered pairs (x, y) where both x and y denote elements of a set of 7 outcomes (4 red, 3 black). The first fundamental counting principle (page 581) implies that S contains $7 \times 7 = 49$ elements. Since $A \cap B$ consists of the ordered pairs of the form (red, red), there are $4 \times 4 = 16$ elements in $A \cap B$. Therefore,

$$P(A \cap B) = \frac{16}{49} = \frac{4}{7} \cdot \frac{4}{7}.$$

Note:

$$P(A \cap B) = P(A) \cdot P(B).$$

Case II. The first ball is not replaced before the second is drawn.

Any one of 7 balls may be selected on the first draw. But since the experiment is performed *without replacement*, one of only 6 balls may be chosen on the second draw. Therefore, there are 7×6, or 42, ordered pairs possible. The number of these that are of the form (red, red) is 4×3, or 12, because any of the 4 red balls can be the first, but there are only 3 choices for the second red ball. Thus,

$$P(A \cap B) = \frac{12}{42} = \frac{2}{7}$$

Analyzing this result as follows, $P(A \cap B) = \frac{12}{42} = \frac{4}{7} \cdot \frac{3}{6}$, you can see that $\frac{4}{7} = P(A)$. We can interpret the second factor, $\frac{3}{6}$, as the *probability that the second ball drawn is red under the condition that the first ball drawn was red*, and denote it by $P(B|A)$.

This example suggests a general law:

Let $P(A)$ denote the probability of an event A, and $P(B|A)$ denote the probability of an event B after event A has occurred. If $P(A \cap B)$ is the probability that A and B occur, then:

$$P(A \cap B) = P(A) \cdot P(B|A).$$

If $P(B|A) = P(B)$, we say that events A and B are *independent*. This means that the probability of one does not depend on the occurrence of the other. For example, in Case I, where the balls are drawn *with replacement*, the events A and B are independent because the outcome on the first draw does not affect the outcome on the second draw. Thus, two events A and B are **independent** if and only if

$$\mathbf{P(A \cap B) = P(A) \cdot P(B).}$$

Two events that are not independent are said to be **dependent**.

EXAMPLE 1. Throw two dice. Event A is the throwing of two numbers whose difference is 2. Event B is the throwing of at least one 3. Graph the sample space and indicate each event on the graph. Are the events dependent or independent?

Solution: From the graph at right, you can easily find $P(A)$, $P(B)$ and $P(A \cap B)$.

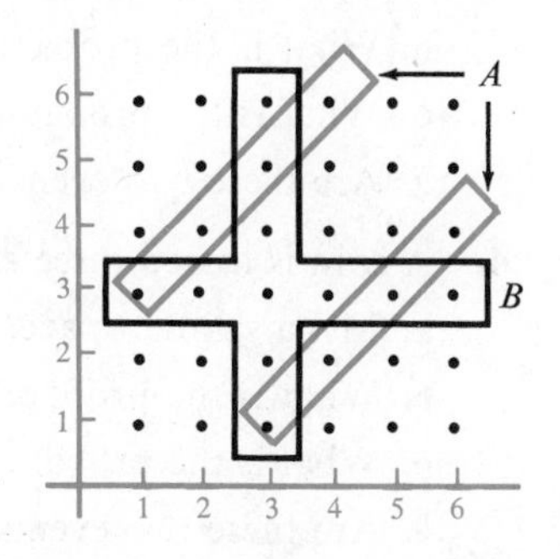

$P(A) = \frac{8}{36} = \frac{2}{9}$ $\quad P(B) = \frac{11}{36}$

$P(A \cap B) = \frac{4}{36} = \frac{1}{9}$

Does $\frac{2}{9} \times \frac{11}{36} = \frac{1}{9}$? No.

$\therefore$ A and B are dependent, **Answer.**

EXAMPLE 2. Throw a die and toss a coin. What is the probability that both a number less than 4 and a tail result?

Solution: The probability that a number is less than 4 is $P(A) = \frac{3}{6} = \frac{1}{2}$. The probability of a tail is $P(B) = \frac{1}{2}$. The probability of both is therefore $P(A \cap B) = P(A) \times P(B) = \frac{1}{2} \times \frac{1}{2} = \frac{1}{4}$, **Answer.**

EXAMPLE 3. Three cards labeled d, g, o respectively are laid in a row, face up. What is the probability that they spell *dog*?

Solution 1: There are $3! = 6$ possible arrangements. One of these spells *dog*. Therefore, the desired probability is $\frac{1}{6}$, **Answer.**

Solution 2: Let the events be X: *first card is labeled d;* Y: *second card is o;* and Z: *third card is g.* Then

$$P[(X \cap Y) \cap Z] = [P(X) \cdot P(Y|X)] \cdot P(Z|X \cap Y)$$
$$= [\tfrac{1}{3} \quad \cdot \quad \tfrac{1}{2}] \cdot 1 = \tfrac{1}{6}, \textbf{ Answer.}$$

Written Exercises

A

1. A red and a green die are thrown. Let A be the event that the sum of the resulting numbers is 7, and B be the event that the red die shows a 6.
   a. Graph a sample space. **b.** Graph events A and B.
   c. Show that A and B are independent.

2. Two red dice are thrown. Let A be the event that the sum of the resulting numbers is 7, and B be the event that at least one of the dice shows a 6.
   a. Graph a sample space. **b.** Graph events A and B.
   c. Show that A and B are dependent.

3. A coin is tossed three successive times.
   a. List a sample space.
   b. What is the probability that at least two tosses produce heads?
   c. What is the probability that at least one toss produces a tail?
   d. Are these two events independent?

4. A coin is tossed three successive times.
   a. List a sample space.
   b. What is the probability that the first two tosses produce heads?
   c. What is the probability that the last toss produces a tail?
   d. Are these two events independent?

5. A die is rolled and a coin is tossed.
   a. Graph a sample space.
   b. What is the probability that a number less than 4 is thrown?
   c. What is the probability that a head is tossed?
   d. Are these events independent?

6. A die is thrown and a coin is tossed.
   a. Graph a sample space.
   b. What is the probability that the die shows an even number?
   c. What is the probability that a tail is tossed?
   d. Are these events independent?

7. A card is drawn from a standard deck of 52 cards, replaced, the deck is shuffled, and a second card is drawn. What is the probability that both cards are kings? That both cards are hearts?

8. A pair of dice is thrown twice. What is the probability that both throws are 7's? That both throws are 3's?

9. An urn contains 8 white marbles and 5 black marbles. Two marbles are drawn successively from the urn, the first being returned before the drawing of the second. What is the probability that both marbles are black? That both marbles are the same color?

10. A die is rolled and a card is drawn from a standard deck of 52 cards. What is the probability that the die will show an even number and that the card will be a heart? That the die will show a 3 and the card will be a 3?

11. There are twelve people present at a business conference of a company. Seven of them are executives, three are salesmen, and two are secretaries. Three of the executives and one salesman are stockholders in the company. A fly in the room lands at random on the hand of one of the persons present.

a. What is the probability that the fly lands on an executive?

b. What is the probability that the fly lands on a stockholder?

c. Are these events independent?

12. In Exercise 11, nine of the members of the meeting are men and three are women.

a. What is the probability that the fly lands on a man?

b. What is the probability that the fly lands on a secretary?

c. Are these events independent?

B

13. If the probability that John will solve a certain problem is $\frac{2}{3}$, that Mary will solve it is $\frac{3}{4}$, and that Bill will solve it is $\frac{1}{2}$, what is the probability that: **(a)** At least one person will solve it? **(b)** Mary and Bill will solve it but John will not? **(c)** John and Mary will solve it but Bill will not? **(d)** At least two people will solve it?

14. The probability that Bob will ask Julie to the Senior Prom is $\frac{1}{4}$, that Jack will ask her is $\frac{1}{2}$, and that Tom will ask her is $\frac{7}{8}$. What is the probability that: **(a)** At least one of the three asks her? **(b)** That Bob and Jack ask her? **(c)** That Jack and Tom ask her but Bob does not? **(d)** That at least two of them ask her?

15. A pair of dice is thrown twice. What is the probability that: **(a)** The sum of the numbers on the first throw is 7 and the sum on the second throw is also 7? **(b)** The sum of the numbers on the first throw is 3 and the sum on the second throw is also 3? **(c)** The sum of the numbers on the first throw is the same as the sum on the second throw?

16. A single die is thrown three times. What is the probability that: **(a)** All three numbers thrown were 3's? **(b)** Exactly two of the numbers thrown were the same? **(c)** That one of the numbers thrown was a 3? **(d)** That exactly two of the numbers thrown were the same, and just one number was 3?

Chapter Summary

Inventory of Structure and Method

1. If finite sets A, B, and $A \cap B$ contain r, s, and t elements, respectively, then $A \times B$ contains rs elements and $A \cup B$ contains $r + s - t$ elements.

   From the **Fundamental Principles** you can derive a formula for the number of **permutations** of n elements, r at a time:

$$_nP_r = n(n - 1)(n - 2) \ldots (n - (r - 1)).$$

   There are also formulas in the cases where some of the elements are the same and where there is a circular arrangement.

2. The number of **combinations** of n things, r at a time, is given by $_nC_r = \frac{_nP_r}{r!}$. Also, $_nC_r = {}_nC_{n-r}$.

   The **coefficients of the expansion** $(a + b)^n$ can be expressed as combinations.

3. If there are h ways in which an event A can occur, in n possible outcomes, then the **probability** of A is $P(A) = \frac{h}{n}$, and the *odds* in favor of A are $\frac{h}{n - h}$.

   Probabilities may be discussed in terms of **sample spaces** and **events**, and their graphs.

4. The probability that at least *one* of the events A and B will occur is given by $P(A \cup B) = P(A) + P(B) - P(A \cap B)$. When A and B are **mutually exclusive**, $P(A \cap B) = 0$.

5. The probability that *two* events A and B will occur is given by $P(A \cap B)$ where $P(A \cap B) = P(A) \cdot P(B|A)$.

Vocabulary and Spelling

Chapter Test and Review

16–1 **1.** There are 2 major routes from Colorado Springs to Denver and 3 from Denver to Cheyenne. From how many different routes may a tourist choose when traveling between Colorado Springs and Cheyenne?

16–2 **2.** From a homeroom of 25, in how many ways can you choose a president, a student council representative and an intramural captain if no student may hold two offices?

16–3 **3.** From the letters of *rootstock* how many distinguishable permutations may be formed?

16–4 **4.** In order to have a game of touch football 12 boys must choose 2 teams of 6. How many different pairs of teams are possible?

16–5 **5.** In how many ways can you select a committee of 4 boys and 3 girls from a club with a membership of 9 boys and 7 girls?

16–6 **6.** Find and simplify the seventh term of $\left(\frac{r^3}{2} - 1\right)^{10}$.

16–7 **7.** Two letters are randomly selected from $\{a, b, c, d, e\}$. **(a)** Specify the sample space by roster. **(b)** Specify by roster the event that both of the selected letters are consonants.

16–8 **8.** A blindfolded person draws a marble from a bowl in which there are 3 red, 5 black and 4 white marbles. What are the odds that the drawn marble is *not* black?

16–9 **9.** A team of 3 is chosen from a group of 5 men and 4 women astronauts. What is the probability that the team contains at least 2 women?

16–10 **10.** From a standard deck of 52 cards, a card is drawn at random; a second card is drawn without replacement. Find the probability that either both are aces or else both are deuces.

11. Two cards are dealt from a well-shuffled bridge deck. What is the probability that **(a)** both are red, **(b)** both are aces, **(c)** both are aces and at least one is red, **(d)** both are aces or at least one is red?

Cumulative Review: Chapters 13-16

1. Insert 4 arithmetic means between 60 and 25.
2. The second and third terms of a G.P. are 5 and $\frac{25}{3}$. Find the first and fourth terms of this G.P.
3. A clock strikes the hour and once each half-hour. How many times will the clock strike from 2:59 P.M. through 9:31 P.M.?
4. Find the sum of the first five terms of the G.P. $6, 8, \frac{32}{3}, \cdots$.
5. Evaluate: (a) $\sum_{j=1}^{18} \frac{3}{4}(48 - 2j)$ (b) $\sum_{i=2}^{8} 64(\frac{1}{2})^{i-1}$
6. Show that $\tan \alpha$ is the geometric mean of $\sec \alpha + 1$ and $\sec \alpha - 1$ if α is in the first or third quadrants.
7. Expand: (a) $\left(4 + \frac{x}{2}\right)^5$ (b) $\left(\frac{x}{4} - 2\right)^6$
8. Find the seventh term of $\left(\frac{n}{2} - 2\right)^{15}$
9. Convert $0.0\overline{46}$ to a common fraction.
10. Give the solution set over the set of complex numbers.
    (a) $2x^3 + 12x + 90 = 0$ (b) $a^4 + 8a - 3a^3 = 24$
11. Given that 3 is a root of $x^4 - 7x^3 + kx^2 = 18$, find k.
12. If $P(x) = 3\cos^3 x - 2\cos x - 1$, find $P\left(\frac{5\pi}{6}\right)$.
13. Show that matrix multiplication is not commutative using
    $A = \begin{bmatrix} 2 & 3 \\ -1 & 1 \end{bmatrix}$ and $B = \begin{bmatrix} 7 & 4 \\ 5 & 8 \end{bmatrix}$.
14. Solve for X: $X\begin{bmatrix} 17 & 33 \\ 10 & 19 \end{bmatrix} = \begin{bmatrix} 4 & 9 \\ 3 & 5 \end{bmatrix}$
15. Solve using matrices: $3x + 5y = 1$
    $2x - 7y = 11$
16. Simplify:
    (a) $3\begin{bmatrix} 2 & -1 \\ 6 & 3 \end{bmatrix} - \frac{1}{4}\begin{bmatrix} 8 & 4 \\ -12 & 16 \end{bmatrix}$ (b) $\begin{bmatrix} -3 & 0 \\ 1 & 5 \\ 2 & 6 \end{bmatrix} \times \begin{bmatrix} -1 & 3 \\ 0 & 2 \end{bmatrix}$
17. A nursery operator places tulip bulbs in lots of 16. He plants 4 and sells the remaining 12 only if all 4 grow.
    (a) In how many ways can he choose 4 bulbs from a lot for testing?
    (b) If a lot contains 3 defective bulbs, what is the probability that he will fail to sell the remaining 12 when, in fact, all are good?

APPENDIX

TABLE 1

FORMULAS

Circle	$A = \pi r^2$, $C = 2\pi r$	Cube	$V = s^3$
Parallelogram	$A = bh$	Rectangular Box	$V = lwh$
Right Triangle	$A = \frac{1}{2}bh$, $c^2 = a^2 + b^2$	Right Circular Cylinder	$V = \pi r^2 h$
Square	$A = s^2$	Pyramid	$V = \frac{1}{3}Bh$
Trapezoid	$A = \frac{1}{2}h(b + b')$	Right Circular Cone	$V = \frac{1}{3}\pi r^2 h$
Triangle	$A = \frac{1}{2}bh$	Sphere	$V = \frac{4}{3}\pi r^3$
Sphere	$A = 4\pi r^2$		

TABLE 2

AMERICAN SYSTEM OF WEIGHTS AND MEASURES

LENGTH

12 inches	=	1 foot
3 feet	=	1 yard
$5\frac{1}{2}$ yards	=	1 rod
5280 feet	=	1 land mile
6076 feet	=	1 nautical mile

AREA

144 square inches	=	1 square foot
9 square feet	=	1 square yard
160 square rods	=	1 acre
640 acres	=	1 square mile

VOLUME

1728 cubic inches	=	1 cubic foot
27 cubic feet	=	1 cubic yard

WEIGHT

16 ounces	=	1 pound
2000 pounds	=	1 ton
2240 pounds	=	1 long ton

CAPACITY

Dry Measure

2 pints	=	1 quart
8 quarts	=	1 peck
4 pecks	=	1 bushel

Liquid Measure

16 fluid ounces	=	1 pint
2 pints	=	1 quart
4 quarts	=	1 gallon
231 cubic inches	=	1 gallon

METRIC SYSTEM OF WEIGHTS AND MEASURES

LENGTH	10 millimeters (mm)	= 1 centimeter (cm)	=	0.3937 inch
	100 centimeters	= 1 meter (m)	=	39.37 inches
	1000 meters	= 1 kilometer (km)	=	0.6214 mile
CAPACITY	1000 milliliters (ml)	= 1 liter (l)	=	1.057 quart
	1000 liters (l)	= 1 kiloliter (kl)	=	264.2 gallons
WEIGHT	1000 milligrams (mg)	= 1 gram (g)	=	0.0353 ounce
	1000 grams	= 1 kilogram (kg)	=	2.205 pounds

TABLE 3 SQUARES AND SQUARE ROOTS

N	N^2	$\sqrt{N}$	$\sqrt{10N}$	N	N^2	$\sqrt{N}$	$\sqrt{10N}$
1.0	1.00	1.000	3.162	**5.5**	30.25	2.345	7.416
1.1	1.21	1.049	3.317	**5.6**	31.36	2.366	7.483
1.2	1.44	1.095	3.464	**5.7**	32.49	2.387	7.550
1.3	1.69	1.140	3.606	**5.8**	33.64	2.408	7.616
1.4	1.96	1.183	3.742	**5.9**	34.81	2.429	7.681
1.5	2.25	1.225	3.873	**6.0**	36.00	2.449	7.746
1.6	2.56	1.265	4.000	**6.1**	37.21	2.470	7.810
1.7	2.89	1.304	4.123	**6.2**	38.44	2.490	7.874
1.8	3.24	1.342	4.243	**6.3**	39.69	2.510	7.937
1.9	3.61	1.378	4.359	**6.4**	40.96	2.530	8.000
2.0	4.00	1.414	4.472	**6.5**	42.25	2.550	8.062
2.1	4.41	1.449	4.583	**6.6**	43.56	2.569	8.124
2.2	4.84	1.483	4.690	**6.7**	44.89	2.588	8.185
2.3	5.29	1.517	4.796	**6.8**	46.24	2.608	8.246
2.4	5.76	1.549	4.899	**6.9**	47.61	2.627	8.307
2.5	6.25	1.581	5.000	**7.0**	49.00	2.646	8.367
2.6	6.76	1.612	5.099	**7.1**	50.41	2.665	8.426
2.7	7.29	1.643	5.196	**7.2**	51.84	2.683	8.485
2.8	7.84	1.673	5.292	**7.3**	53.29	2.702	8.544
2.9	8.41	1.703	5.385	**7.4**	54.76	2.720	8.602
3.0	9.00	1.732	5.477	**7.5**	56.25	2.739	8.660
3.1	9.61	1.761	5.568	**7.6**	57.76	2.757	8.718
3.2	10.24	1.789	5.657	**7.7**	59.29	2.775	8.775
3.3	10.89	1.817	5.745	**7.8**	60.84	2.793	8.832
3.4	11.56	1.844	5.831	**7.9**	62.41	2.811	8.888
3.5	12.25	1.871	5.916	**8.0**	64.00	2.828	8.944
3.6	12.96	1.897	6.000	**8.1**	65.61	2.846	9.000
3.7	13.69	1.924	6.083	**8.2**	67.24	2.864	9.055
3.8	14.44	1.949	6.164	**8.3**	68.89	2.881	9.110
3.9	15.21	1.975	6.245	**8.4**	70.56	2.898	9.165
4.0	16.00	2.000	6.325	**8.5**	72.25	2.915	9.220
4.1	16.81	2.025	6.403	**8.6**	73.96	2.933	9.274
4.2	17.64	2.049	6.481	**8.7**	75.69	2.950	9.327
4.3	18.49	2.074	6.557	**8.8**	77.44	2.966	9.381
4.4	19.36	2.098	6.633	**8.9**	79.21	2.983	9.434
4.5	20.25	2.121	6.708	**9.0**	81.00	3.000	9.487
4.6	21.16	2.145	6.782	**9.1**	82.81	3.017	9.539
4.7	22.09	2.168	6.856	**9.2**	84.64	3.033	9.592
4.8	23.04	2.191	6.928	**9.3**	86.49	3.050	9.644
4.9	24.01	2.214	7.000	**9.4**	88.36	3.066	9.695
5.0	25.00	2.236	7.071	**9.5**	90.25	3.082	9.747
5.1	26.01	2.258	7.141	**9.6**	92.16	3.098	9.798
5.2	27.04	2.280	7.211	**9.7**	94.09	3.114	9.849
5.3	28.09	2.302	7.280	**9.8**	96.04	3.130	9.899
5.4	29.16	2.324	7.348	**9.9**	98.01	3.146	9.950
5.5	30.25	2.345	7.416	**10**	100.00	3.162	10.000

TABLE 4 CUBES AND CUBE ROOTS

N	N^3	$\sqrt[3]{N}$	$\sqrt[3]{10N}$	$\sqrt[3]{100N}$	N	N^3	$\sqrt[3]{N}$	$\sqrt[3]{10N}$	$\sqrt[3]{100N}$
1.0	1.000	1.000	2.154	4.642	**5.5**	166.375	1.765	3.803	8.193
1.1	1.331	1.032	2.224	4.791	**5.6**	175.616	1.776	3.826	8.243
1.2	1.728	1.063	2.289	4.932	**5.7**	185.193	1.786	3.849	8.291
1.3	2.197	1.091	2.351	5.066	**5.8**	195.112	1.797	3.871	8.340
1.4	2.744	1.119	2.410	5.192	**5.9**	205.379	1.807	3.893	8.387
1.5	3.375	1.145	2.466	5.313	**6.0**	216.000	1.817	3.915	8.434
1.6	4.096	1.170	2.520	5.429	**6.1**	226.981	1.827	3.936	8.481
1.7	4.913	1.193	2.571	5.540	**6.2**	238.328	1.837	3.958	8.527
1.8	5.832	1.216	2.621	5.646	**6.3**	250.047	1.847	3.979	8.573
1.9	6.859	1.239	2.668	5.749	**6.4**	262.144	1.857	4.000	8.618
2.0	8.000	1.260	2.714	5.848	**6.5**	274.625	1.866	4.021	8.662
2.1	9.261	1.281	2.759	5.944	**6.6**	287.496	1.876	4.041	8.707
2.2	10.648	1.301	2.802	6.037	**6.7**	300.763	1.885	4.062	8.750
2.3	12.167	1.320	2.844	6.127	**6.8**	314.432	1.895	4.082	8.794
2.4	13.824	1.339	2.884	6.214	**6.9**	328.509	1.904	4.102	8.837
2.5	15.625	1.357	2.924	6.300	**7.0**	343.000	1.913	4.121	8.879
2.6	17.576	1.375	2.962	6.383	**7.1**	357.911	1.922	4.141	8.921
2.7	19.683	1.392	3.000	6.463	**7.2**	373.248	1.931	4.160	8.963
2.8	21.952	1.409	3.037	6.542	**7.3**	389.017	1.940	4.179	9.004
2.9	24.389	1.426	3.072	6.619	**7.4**	405.224	1.949	4.198	9.045
3.0	27.000	1.442	3.107	6.694	**7.5**	421.875	1.957	4.217	9.086
3.1	29.791	1.458	3.141	6.768	**7.6**	438.976	1.966	4.236	9.126
3.2	32.768	1.474	3.175	6.840	**7.7**	456.533	1.975	4.254	9.166
3.3	35.937	1.489	3.208	6.910	**7.8**	474.552	1.983	4.273	9.205
3.4	39.304	1.504	3.240	6.980	**7.9**	493.039	1.992	4.291	9.244
3.5	42.875	1.518	3.271	7.047	**8.0**	512.000	2.000	4.309	9.283
3.6	46.656	1.533	3.302	7.114	**8.1**	531.441	2.008	4.327	9.322
3.7	50.653	1.547	3.332	7.179	**8.2**	551.368	2.017	4.344	9.360
3.8	54.872	1.560	3.362	7.243	**8.3**	571.787	2.025	4.362	9.398
3.9	59.319	1.574	3.391	7.306	**8.4**	592.704	2.033	4.380	9.435
4.0	64.000	1.587	3.420	7.368	**8.5**	614.125	2.041	4.397	9.473
4.1	68.921	1.601	3.448	7.429	**8.6**	636.056	2.049	4.414	9.510
4.2	74.088	1.613	3.476	7.489	**8.7**	658.503	2.057	4.431	9.546
4.3	79.507	1.626	3.503	7.548	**8.8**	681.472	2.065	4.448	9.583
4.4	85.184	1.639	3.530	7.606	**8.9**	704.969	2.072	4.465	9.619
4.5	91.125	1.651	3.557	7.663	**9.0**	729.000	2.080	4.481	9.655
4.6	97.336	1.663	3.583	7.719	**9.1**	753.571	2.088	4.498	9.691
4.7	103.823	1.675	3.609	7.775	**9.2**	778.688	2.095	4.514	9.726
4.8	110.592	1.687	3.634	7.830	**9.3**	804.357	2.103	4.531	9.761
4.9	117.649	1.698	3.659	7.884	**9.4**	830.584	2.110	4.547	9.796
5.0	125.000	1.710	3.684	7.937	**9.5**	857.375	2.118	4.563	9.830
5.1	132.651	1.721	3.708	7.990	**9.6**	884.736	2.125	4.579	9.865
5.2	140.608	1.732	3.733	8.041	**9.7**	912.673	2.133	4.595	9.899
5.3	148.877	1.744	3.756	8.093	**9.8**	941.192	2.140	4.610	9.933
5.4	157.464	1.754	3.780	8.143	**9.9**	970.299	2.147	4.626	9.967
5.5	166.375	1.765	3.803	8.193	**10**	1000.000	2.154	4.642	10.000

TABLE 5 COMMON LOGARITHMS OF NUMBERS*

N	0	1	2	3	4	5	6	7	8	9
10	0000	0043	0086	0128	0170	0212	0253	0294	0334	0374
11	0414	0453	0492	0531	0569	0607	0645	0682	0719	0755
12	0792	0828	0864	0899	0934	0969	1004	1038	1072	1106
13	1139	1173	1206	1239	1271	1303	1335	1367	1399	1430
14	1461	1492	1523	1553	1584	1614	1644	1673	1703	1732
15	1761	1790	1818	1847	1875	1903	1931	1959	1987	2014
16	2041	2068	2095	2122	2148	2175	2201	2227	2253	2279
17	2304	2330	2355	2380	2405	2430	2455	2480	2504	2529
18	2553	2577	2601	2625	2648	2672	2695	2718	2742	2765
19	2788	2810	2833	2856	2878	2900	2923	2945	2967	2989
20	3010	3032	3054	3075	3096	3118	3139	3160	3181	3201
21	3222	3243	3263	3284	3304	3324	3345	3365	3385	3404
22	3424	3444	3464	3483	3502	3522	3541	3560	3579	3598
23	3617	3636	3655	3674	3692	3711	3729	3747	3766	3784
24	3802	3820	3838	3856	3874	3892	3909	3927	3945	3962
25	3979	3997	4014	4031	4048	4065	4082	4099	4116	4133
26	4150	4166	4183	4200	4216	4232	4249	4265	4281	4298
27	4314	4330	4346	4362	4378	4393	4409	4425	4440	4456
28	4472	4487	4502	4518	4533	4548	4564	4579	4594	4609
29	4624	4639	4654	4669	4683	4698	4713	4728	4742	4757
30	4771	4786	4800	4814	4829	4843	4857	4871	4886	4900
31	4914	4928	4942	4955	4969	4983	4997	5011	5024	5038
32	5051	5065	5079	5092	5105	5119	5132	5145	5159	5172
33	5185	5198	5211	5224	5237	5250	5263	5276	5289	5302
34	5315	5328	5340	5353	5366	5378	5391	5403	5416	5428
35	5441	5453	5465	5478	5490	5502	5514	5527	5539	5551
36	5563	5575	5587	5599	5611	5623	5635	5647	5658	5670
37	5682	5694	5705	5717	5729	5740	5752	5763	5775	5786
38	5798	5809	5821	5832	5843	5855	5866	5877	5888	5899
39	5911	5922	5933	5944	5955	5966	5977	5988	5999	6010
40	6021	6031	6042	6053	6064	6075	6085	6096	6107	6117
41	6128	6138	6149	6160	6170	6180	6191	6201	6212	6222
42	6232	6243	6253	6263	6274	6284	6294	6304	6314	6325
43	6335	6345	6355	6365	6375	6385	6395	6405	6415	6425
44	6435	6444	6454	6464	6474	6484	6493	6503	6513	6522
45	6532	6542	6551	6561	6571	6580	6590	6599	6609	6618
46	6628	6637	6646	6656	6665	6675	6684	6693	6702	6712
47	6721	6730	6739	6749	6758	6767	6776	6785	6794	6803
48	6812	6821	6830	6839	6848	6857	6866	6875	6884	6893
49	6902	6911	6920	6928	6937	6946	6955	6964	6972	6981
50	6990	6998	7007	7016	7024	7033	7042	7050	7059	7067
51	7076	7084	7093	7101	7110	7118	7126	7135	7143	7152
52	7160	7168	7177	7185	7193	7202	7210	7218	7226	7235
53	7243	7251	7259	7267	7275	7284	7292	7300	7308	7316
54	7324	7332	7340	7348	7356	7364	7372	7380	7388	7396

*Mantissas, decimal points omitted. Characteristics are found by inspection.

TABLE 5 COMMON LOGARITHMS OF NUMBERS

N	0	1	2	3	4	5	6	7	8	9
55	7404	7412	7419	7427	7435	7443	7451	7459	7466	7474
56	7482	7490	7497	7505	7513	7520	7528	7536	7543	7551
57	7559	7566	7574	7582	7589	7597	7604	7612	7619	7627
58	7634	7642	7649	7657	7664	7672	7679	7686	7694	7701
59	7709	7716	7723	7731	7738	7745	7752	7760	7767	7774
60	7782	7789	7796	7803	7810	7818	7825	7832	7839	7846
61	7853	7860	7868	7875	7882	7889	7896	7903	7910	7917
62	7924	7931	7938	7945	7952	7959	7966	7973	7980	7987
63	7993	8000	8007	8014	8021	8028	8035	8041	8048	8055
64	8062	8069	8075	8082	8089	8096	8102	8109	8116	8122
65	8129	8136	8142	8149	8156	8162	8169	8176	8182	8189
66	8195	8202	8209	8215	8222	8228	8235	8241	8248	8254
67	8261	8267	8274	8280	8287	8293	8299	8306	8312	8319
68	8325	8331	8338	8344	8351	8357	8363	8370	8376	8382
69	8388	8395	8401	8407	8414	8420	8426	8432	8439	8445
70	8451	8457	8463	8470	8476	8482	8488	8494	8500	8506
71	8513	8519	8525	8531	8537	8543	8549	8555	8561	8567
72	8573	8579	8585	8591	8597	8603	8609	8615	8621	8627
73	8633	8639	8645	8651	8657	8663	8669	8675	8681	8686
74	8692	8698	8704	8710	8716	8722	8727	8733	8739	8745
75	8751	8756	8762	8768	8774	8779	8785	8791	8797	8802
76	8808	8814	8820	8825	8831	8837	8842	8848	8854	8859
77	8865	8871	8876	8882	8887	8893	8899	8904	8910	8915
78	8921	8927	8932	8938	8943	8949	8954	8960	8965	8971
79	8976	8982	8987	8993	8998	9004	9009	9015	9020	9025
80	9031	9036	9042	9047	9053	9058	9063	9069	9074	9079
81	9085	9090	9096	9101	9106	9112	9117	9122	9128	9133
82	9138	9143	9149	9154	9159	9165	9170	9175	9180	9186
83	9191	9196	9201	9206	9212	9217	9222	9227	9232	9238
84	9243	9248	9253	9258	9263	9269	9274	9279	9284	9289
85	9294	9299	9304	9309	9315	9320	9325	9330	9335	9340
86	9345	9350	9355	9360	9365	9370	9375	9380	9385	9390
87	9395	9400	9405	9410	9415	9420	9425	9430	9435	9440
88	9445	9450	9455	9460	9465	9469	9474	9479	9484	9489
89	9494	9499	9504	9509	9513	9518	9523	9528	9533	9538
90	9542	9547	9552	9557	9562	9566	9571	9576	9581	9586
91	9590	9595	9600	9605	9609	9614	9619	9624	9628	9633
92	9638	9643	9647	9652	9657	9661	9666	9671	9675	9680
93	9685	9689	9694	9699	9703	9708	9713	9717	9722	9727
94	9731	9736	9741	9745	9750	9754	9759	9763	9768	9773
95	9777	9782	9786	9791	9795	9800	9805	9809	9814	9818
96	9823	9827	9832	9836	9841	9845	9850	9854	9859	9863
97	9868	9872	9877	9881	9886	9890	9894	9899	9903	9908
98	9912	9917	9921	9926	9930	9934	9939	9943	9948	9952
99	9956	9961	9965	9969	9974	9978	9983	9987	9991	9996

TABLE 6 VALUES OF TRIGONOMETRIC FUNCTIONS

Angle	Sin	Cos	Tan	Cot	Sec	Csc	
0° 00′	.0000	1.0000	.0000	- - - -	1.000	- - - -	**90° 00′**
10′	.0029	1.0000	.0029	343.8	1.000	343.8	**50′**
20′	.0058	1.0000	.0058	171.9	1.000	171.9	**40′**
30′	.0087	1.0000	.0087	114.6	1.000	114.6	**30′**
40′	.0116	.9999	.0116	85.94	1.000	85.95	**20′**
50′	.0145	.9999	.0145	68.75	1.000	68.76	**10′**
1° 00′	.0175	.9998	.0175	57.29	1.000	57.30	**89° 00′**
10′	.0204	.9998	.0204	49.10	1.000	49.11	**50′**
20′	.0233	.9997	.0233	42.96	1.000	42.98	**40′**
30′	.0262	.9997	.0262	38.19	1.000	38.20	**30′**
40′	.0291	.9996	.0291	34.37	1.000	34.38	**20′**
50′	.0320	.9995	.0320	31.24	1.001	31.26	**10′**
2° 00′	.0349	.9994	.0349	28.64	1.001	28.65	**88° 00′**
10′	.0378	.9993	.0378	26.43	1.001	26.45	**50′**
20′	.0407	.9992	.0407	24.54	1.001	24.56	**40′**
30′	.0436	.9990	.0437	22.90	1.001	22.93	**30′**
40′	.0465	.9989	.0466	21.47	1.001	21.49	**20′**
50′	.0494	.9988	.0495	20.21	1.001	20.23	**10′**
3° 00′	.0523	.9986	.0524	19.08	1.001	19.11	**87° 00′**
10′	.0552	.9985	.0553	18.07	1.002	18.10	**50′**
20′	.0581	.9983	.0582	17.17	1.002	17.20	**40′**
30′	.0610	.9981	.0612	16.35	1.002	16.38	**30′**
40′	.0640	.9980	.0641	15.60	1.002	15.64	**20′**
50′	.0669	.9978	.0670	14.92	1.002	14.96	**10′**
4° 00′	.0698	.9976	.0699	14.30	1.002	14.34	**86° 00′**
10′	.0727	.9974	.0729	13.73	1.003	13.76	**50′**
20′	.0756	.9971	.0758	13.20	1.003	13.23	**40′**
30′	.0785	.9969	.0787	12.71	1.003	12.75	**30′**
40′	.0814	.9967	.0816	12.25	1.003	12.29	**20′**
50′	.0843	.9964	.0846	11.83	1.004	11.87	**10′**
5° 00′	.0872	.9962	.0875	11.43	1.004	11.47	**85° 00′**
10′	.0901	.9959	.0904	11.06	1.004	11.10	**50′**
20′	.0929	.9957	.0934	10.71	1.004	10.76	**40′**
30′	.0958	.9954	.0963	10.39	1.005	10.43	**30′**
40′	.0987	.9951	.0992	10.08	1.005	10.13	**20′**
50′	.1016	.9948	.1022	9.788	1.005	9.839	**10′**
6° 00′	.1045	.9945	.1051	9.514	1.006	9.567	**84° 00′**
10′	.1074	.9942	.1080	9.255	1.006	9.309	**50′**
20′	.1103	.9939	.1110	9.010	1.006	9.065	**40′**
30′	.1132	.9936	.1139	8.777	1.006	8.834	**30′**
40′	.1161	.9932	.1169	8.556	1.007	8.614	**20′**
50′	.1190	.9929	.1198	8.345	1.007	8.405	**10′**
7° 00′	.1219	.9925	.1228	8.144	1.008	8.206	**83° 00′**
10′	.1248	.9922	.1257	7.953	1.008	8.016	**50′**
20′	.1276	.9918	.1287	7.770	1.008	7.834	**40′**
30′	.1305	.9914	.1317	7.596	1.009	7.661	**30′**
40′	.1334	.9911	.1346	7.429	1.009	7.496	**20′**
50′	.1363	.9907	.1376	7.269	1.009	7.337	**10′**
8° 00′	.1392	.9903	.1405	7.115	1.010	7.185	**82° 00′**
10′	.1421	.9899	.1435	6.968	1.010	7.040	**50′**
20′	.1449	.9894	.1465	6.827	1.011	6.900	**40′**
30′	.1478	.9890	.1495	6.691	1.011	6.765	**30′**
40′	.1507	.9886	.1524	6.561	1.012	6.636	**20′**
50′	.1536	.9881	.1554	6.435	1.012	6.512	**10′**
9° 00′	.1564	.9877	.1584	6.314	1.012	6.392	**81° 00′**
	Cos	Sin	Cot	Tan	Csc	Sec	Angle

TABLE 6 VALUES OF TRIGONOMETRIC FUNCTIONS

Angle	Sin	Cos	Tan	Cot	Sec	Csc	
9° 00′	.1564	.9877	.1584	6.314	1.012	6.392	81° 00′
10′	.1593	.9872	.1614	6.197	1.013	6.277	50′
20′	.1622	.9868	.1644	6.084	1.013	6.166	40′
30′	.1650	.9863	.1673	5.976	1.014	6.059	30′
40′	.1679	.9858	.1703	5.871	1.014	5.955	20′
50′	.1708	.9853	.1733	5.769	1.015	5.855	10′
10° 00′	.1736	.9848	.1763	5.671	1.015	5.759	80° 00′
10′	.1765	.9843	.1793	5.576	1.016	5.665	50′
20′	.1794	.9838	.1823	5.485	1.016	5.575	40′
30′	.1822	.9833	.1853	5.396	1.017	5.487	30′
40′	.1851	.9827	.1883	5.309	1.018	5.403	20′
50′	.1880	.9822	.1914	5.226	1.018	5.320	10′
11° 00′	.1908	.9816	.1944	5.145	1.019	5.241	79° 00′
10′	.1937	.9811	.1974	5.066	1.019	5.164	50′
20′	.1965	.9805	.2004	4.989	1.020	5.089	40′
30′	.1994	.9799	.2035	4.915	1.020	5.016	30′
40′	.2022	.9793	.2065	4.843	1.021	4.945	20′
50′	.2051	.9787	.2095	4.773	1.022	4.876	10′
12° 00′	.2079	.9781	.2126	4.705	1.022	4.810	78° 00′
10′	.2108	.9775	.2156	4.638	1.023	4.745	50′
20′	.2136	.9769	.2186	4.574	1.024	4.682	40′
30′	.2164	.9763	.2217	4.511	1.024	4.620	30′
40′	.2193	.9757	.2247	4.449	1.025	4.560	20′
50′	.2221	.9750	.2278	4.390	1.026	4.502	10′
13° 00′	.2250	.9744	.2309	4.331	1.026	4.445	77° 00′
10′	.2278	.9737	.2339	4.275	1.027	4.390	50′
20′	.2306	.9730	.2370	4.219	1.028	4.336	40′
30′	.2334	.9724	.2401	4.165	1.028	4.284	30′
40′	.2363	.9717	.2432	4.113	1.029	4.232	20′
50′	.2391	.9710	.2462	4.061	1.030	4.182	10′
14° 00′	.2419	.9703	.2493	4.011	1.031	4.134	76° 00′
10′	.2447	.9696	.2524	3.962	1.031	4.086	50′
20′	.2476	.9689	.2555	3.914	1.032	4.039	40′
30′	.2504	.9681	.2586	3.867	1.033	3.994	30′
40′	.2532	.9674	.2617	3.821	1.034	3.950	20′
50′	.2560	.9667	.2648	3.776	1.034	3.906	10′
15° 00′	.2588	.9659	.2679	3.732	1.035	3.864	75° 00′
10′	.2616	.9652	.2711	3.689	1.036	3.822	50′
20′	.2644	.9644	.2742	3.647	1.037	3.782	40′
30′	.2672	.9636	.2773	3.606	1.038	3.742	30′
40′	.2700	.9628	.2805	3.566	1.039	3.703	20′
50′	.2728	.9621	.2836	3.526	1.039	3.665	10′
16° 00′	.2756	.9613	.2867	3.487	1.040	3.628	74° 00′
10′	.2784	.9605	.2899	3.450	1.041	3.592	50′
20′	.2812	.9596	.2931	3.412	1.042	3.556	40′
30′	.2840	.9588	.2962	3.376	1.043	3.521	30′
40′	.2868	.9580	.2994	3.340	1.044	3.487	20′
50′	.2896	.9572	.3026	3.305	1.045	3.453	10′
17° 00′	.2924	.9563	.3057	3.271	1.046	3.420	73° 00′
10′	.2952	.9555	.3089	3.237	1.047	3.388	50′
20′	.2979	.9546	.3121	3.204	1.048	3.356	40′
30′	.3007	.9537	.3153	3.172	1.049	3.326	30′
40′	.3035	.9528	.3185	3.140	1.049	3.295	20′
50′	.3062	.9520	.3217	3.108	1.050	3.265	10′
18° 00′	.3090	.9511	.3249	3.078	1.051	3.236	72° 00′
	Cos	Sin	Cot	Tan	Csc	Sec	Angle

TABLE 6 VALUES OF TRIGONOMETRIC FUNCTIONS

Angle	Sin	Cos	Tan	Cot	Sec	Csc	
18° 00′	.3090	.9511	.3249	3.078	1.051	3.236	72° 00′
10′	.3118	.9502	.3281	3.047	1.052	3.207	50′
20′	.3145	.9492	.3314	3.018	1.053	3.179	40′
30′	.3173	.9483	.3346	2.989	1.054	3.152	30′
40′	.3201	.9474	.3378	2.960	1.056	3.124	20′
50′	.3228	.9465	.3411	2.932	1.057	3.098	10′
19° 00′	.3256	.9455	.3443	2.904	1.058	3.072	71° 00′
10′	.3283	.9446	.3476	2.877	1.059	3.046	50′
20′	.3311	.9436	.3508	2.850	1.060	3.021	40′
30′	.3338	.9426	.3541	2.824	1.061	2.996	30′
40′	.3365	.9417	.3574	2.798	1.062	2.971	20′
50′	.3393	.9407	.3607	2.773	1.063	2.947	10′
20° 00′	.3420	.9397	.3640	2.747	1.064	2.924	70° 00′
10′	.3448	.9387	.3673	2.723	1.065	2.901	50′
20′	.3475	.9377	.3706	2.699	1.066	2.878	40′
30′	.3502	.9367	.3739	2.675	1.068	2.855	30′
40′	.3529	.9356	.3772	2.651	1.069	2.833	20′
50′	.3557	.9346	.3805	2.628	1.070	2.812	10′
21° 00′	.3584	.9336	.3839	2.605	1.071	2.790	69° 00′
10′	.3611	.9325	.3872	2.583	1.072	2.769	50′
20′	.3638	.9315	.3906	2.560	1.074	2.749	40′
30′	.3665	.9304	.3939	2.539	1.075	2.729	30′
40′	.3692	.9293	.3973	2.517	1.076	2.709	20′
50′	.3719	.9283	.4006	2.496	1.077	2.689	10′
22° 00′	.3746	.9272	.4040	2.475	1.079	2.669	68° 00′
10′	.3773	.9261	.4074	2.455	1.080	2.650	50′
20′	.3800	.9250	.4108	2.434	1.081	2.632	40′
30′	.3827	.9239	.4142	2.414	1.082	2.613	30′
40′	.3854	.9228	.4176	2.394	1.084	2.595	20′
50′	.3881	.9216	.4210	2.375	1.085	2.577	10′
23° 00′	.3907	.9205	.4245	2.356	1.086	2.559	67° 00′
10′	.3934	.9194	.4279	2.337	1.088	2.542	50′
20′	.3961	.9182	.4314	2.318	1.089	2.525	40′
30′	.3987	.9171	.4348	2.300	1.090	2.508	30′
40′	.4014	.9159	.4383	2.282	1.092	2.491	20′
50′	.4041	.9147	.4417	2.264	1.093	2.475	10′
24° 00′	.4067	.9135	.4452	2.246	1.095	2.459	66° 00′
10′	.4094	.9124	.4487	2.229	1.096	2.443	50′
20′	.4120	.9112	.4522	2.211	1.097	2.427	40′
30′	.4147	.9100	.4557	2.194	1.099	2.411	30′
40′	.4173	.9088	.4592	2.177	1.100	2.396	20′
50′	.4200	.9075	.4628	2.161	1.102	2.381	10′
25° 00′	.4226	.9063	.4663	2.145	1.103	2.366	65° 00′
10′	.4253	.9051	.4699	2.128	1.105	2.352	50′
20′	.4279	.9038	.4734	2.112	1.106	2.337	40′
30′	.4305	.9026	.4770	2.097	1.108	2.323	30′
40′	.4331	.9013	.4806	2.081	1.109	2.309	20′
50′	.4358	.9001	.4841	2.066	1.111	2.295	10′
26° 00′	.4384	.8988	.4877	2.050	1.113	2.281	64° 00′
10′	.4410	.8975	.4913	2.035	1.114	2.268	50′
20′	.4436	.8962	.4950	2.020	1.116	2.254	40′
30′	.4462	.8949	.4986	2.006	1.117	2.241	30′
40′	.4488	.8936	.5022	1.991	1.119	2.228	20′
50′	.4514	.8923	.5059	1.977	1.121	2.215	10′
27° 00′	.4540	.8910	.5095	1.963	1.122	2.203	63° 00′
	Cos	Sin	Cot	Tan	Csc	Sec	Angle

TABLE 6 VALUES OF TRIGONOMETRIC FUNCTIONS

Angle	Sin	Cos	Tan	Cot	Sec	Csc	
27° 00′	.4540	.8910	.5095	1.963	1.122	2.203	**63° 00′**
10′	.4566	.8897	.5132	1.949	1.124	2.190	**50′**
20′	.4592	.8884	.5169	1.935	1.126	2.178	**40′**
30′	.4617	.8870	.5206	1.921	1.127	2.166	**30′**
40′	.4643	.8857	.5243	1.907	1.129	2.154	**20′**
50′	.4669	.8843	.5280	1.894	1.131	2.142	**10′**
28° 00′	.4695	.8829	.5317	1.881	1.133	2.130	**62° 00′**
10′	.4720	.8816	.5354	1.868	1.134	2.118	**50′**
20′	.4746	.8802	.5392	1.855	1.136	2.107	**40′**
30′	.4772	.8788	.5430	1.842	1.138	2.096	**30′**
40′	.4797	.8774	.5467	1.829	1.140	2.085	**20′**
50′	.4823	.8760	.5505	1.816	1.142	2.074	**10′**
29° 00′	.4848	.8746	.5543	1.804	1.143	2.063	**61° 00′**
10′	.4874	.8732	.5581	1.792	1.145	2.052	**50′**
20′	.4899	.8718	.5619	1.780	1.147	2.041	**40′**
30′	.4924	.8704	.5658	1.767	1.149	2.031	**30′**
40′	.4950	.8689	.5696	1.756	1.151	2.020	**20′**
50′	.4975	.8675	.5735	1.744	1.153	2.010	**10′**
30° 00′	.5000	.8660	.5774	1.732	1.155	2.000	**60° 00′**
10′	.5025	.8646	.5812	1.720	1.157	1.990	**50′**
20′	.5050	.8631	.5851	1.709	1.159	1.980	**40′**
30′	.5075	.8616	.5890	1.698	1.161	1.970	**30′**
40′	.5100	.8601	.5930	1.686	1.163	1.961	**20′**
50′	.5125	.8587	.5969	1.675	1.165	1.951	**10′**
31° 00′	.5150	.8572	.6009	1.664	1.167	1.942	**59° 00′**
10′	.5175	.8557	.6048	1.653	1.169	1.932	**50′**
20′	.5200	.8542	.6088	1.643	1.171	1.923	**40′**
30′	.5225	.8526	.6128	1.632	1.173	1.914	**30′**
40′	.5250	.8511	.6168	1.621	1.175	1.905	**20′**
50′	.5275	.8496	.6208	1.611	1.177	1.896	**10′**
32° 00′	.5299	.8480	.6249	1.600	1.179	1.887	**58° 00′**
10′	.5324	.8465	.6289	1.590	1.181	1.878	**50′**
20′	.5348	.8450	.6330	1.580	1.184	1.870	**40′**
30′	.5373	.8434	.6371	1.570	1.186	1.861	**30′**
40′	.5398	.8418	.6412	1.560	1.188	1.853	**20′**
50′	.5422	.8403	.6453	1.550	1.190	1.844	**10′**
33° 00′	.5446	.8387	.6494	1.540	1.192	1.836	**57° 00′**
10′	.5471	.8371	.6536	1.530	1.195	1.828	**50′**
20′	.5495	.8355	.6577	1.520	1.197	1.820	**40′**
30′	.5519	.8339	.6619	1.511	1.199	1.812	**30′**
40′	.5544	.8323	.6661	1.501	1.202	1.804	**20′**
50′	.5568	.8307	.6703	1.492	1.204	1.796	**10′**
34° 00′	.5592	.8290	.6745	1.483	1.206	1.788	**56° 00′**
10′	.5616	.8274	.6787	1.473	1.209	1.781	**50′**
20′	.5640	.8258	.6830	1.464	1.211	1.773	**40′**
30′	.5664	.8241	.6873	1.455	1.213	1.766	**30′**
40′	.5688	.8225	.6916	1.446	1.216	1.758	**20′**
50′	.5712	.8208	.6959	1.437	1.218	1.751	**10′**
35° 00′	.5736	.8192	.7002	1.428	1.221	1.743	**55° 00′**
10′	.5760	.8175	.7046	1.419	1.223	1.736	**50′**
20′	.5783	.8158	.7089	1.411	1.226	1.729	**40′**
30′	.5807	.8141	.7133	1.402	1.228	1.722	**30′**
40′	.5831	.8124	.7177	1.393	1.231	1.715	**20′**
50′	.5854	.8107	.7221	1.385	1.233	1.708	**10′**
36° 00′	.5878	.8090	.7265	1.376	1.236	1.701	**54° 00′**
	Cos	Sin	Cot	Tan	Csc	Sec	Angle

TABLE 6 VALUES OF TRIGONOMETRIC FUNCTIONS

Angle	Sin	Cos	Tan	Cot	Sec	Csc	
36° 00′	.5878	.8090	.7265	1.376	1.236	1.701	**54° 00′**
10′	.5901	.8073	.7310	1.368	1.239	1.695	**50′**
20′	.5925	.8056	.7355	1.360	1.241	1.688	**40′**
30′	.5948	.8039	.7400	1.351	1.244	1.681	**30′**
40′	.5972	.8021	.7445	1.343	1.247	1.675	**20′**
50′	.5995	.8004	.7490	1.335	1.249	1.668	**10′**
37° 00′	.6018	.7986	.7536	1.327	1.252	1.662	**53° 00′**
10′	.6041	.7969	.7581	1.319	1.255	1.655	**50′**
20′	.6065	.7951	.7627	1.311	1.258	1.649	**40′**
30′	.6088	.7934	.7673	1.303	1.260	1.643	**30′**
40′	.6111	.7916	.7720	1.295	1.263	1.636	**20′**
50′	.6134	.7898	.7766	1.288	1.266	1.630	**10′**
38° 00′	.6157	.7880	.7813	1.280	1.269	1.624	**52° 00′**
10′	.6180	.7862	.7860	1.272	1.272	1.618	**50′**
20′	.6202	.7844	.7907	1.265	1.275	1.612	**40′**
30′	.6225	.7826	.7954	1.257	1.278	1.606	**30′**
40′	.6248	.7808	.8002	1.250	1.281	1.601	**20′**
50′	.6271	.7790	.8050	1.242	1.284	1.595	**10′**
39° 00′	.6293	.7771	.8098	1.235	1.287	1.589	**51° 00′**
10′	.6316	.7753	.8146	1.228	1.290	1.583	**50′**
20′	.6338	.7735	.8195	1.220	1.293	1.578	**40′**
30′	.6361	.7716	.8243	1.213	1.296	1.572	**30′**
40′	.6383	.7698	.8292	1.206	1.299	1.567	**20′**
50′	.6406	.7679	.8342	1.199	1.302	1.561	**10′**
40° 00′	.6428	.7660	.8391	1.192	1.305	1.556	**50° 00′**
10′	.6450	.7642	.8441	1.185	1.309	1.550	**50′**
20′	.6472	.7623	.8491	1.178	1.312	1.545	**40′**
30′	.6494	.7604	.8541	1.171	1.315	1.540	**30′**
40′	.6517	.7585	.8591	1.164	1.318	1.535	**20′**
50′	.6539	.7566	.8642	1.157	1.322	1.529	**10′**
41° 00′	.6561	.7547	.8693	1.150	1.325	1.524	**49° 00′**
10′	.6583	.7528	.8744	1.144	1.328	1.519	**50′**
20′	.6604	.7509	.8796	1.137	1.332	1.514	**40′**
30′	.6626	.7490	.8847	1.130	1.335	1.509	**30′**
40′	.6648	.7470	.8899	1.124	1.339	1.504	**20′**
50′	.6670	.7451	.8952	1.117	1.342	1.499	**10′**
42° 00′	.6691	.7431	.9004	1.111	1.346	1.494	**48° 00′**
10′	.6713	.7412	.9057	1.104	1.349	1.490	**50′**
20′	.6734	.7392	.9110	1.098	1.353	1.485	**40′**
30′	.6756	.7373	.9163	1.091	1.356	1.480	**30′**
40′	.6777	.7353	.9217	1.085	1.360	1.476	**20′**
50′	.6799	.7333	.9271	1.079	1.364	1.471	**10′**
43° 00′	.6820	.7314	.9325	1.072	1.367	1.466	**47° 00′**
10′	.6841	.7294	.9380	1.066	1.371	1.462	**50′**
20′	.6862	.7274	.9435	1.060	1.375	1.457	**40′**
30′	.6884	.7254	.9490	1.054	1.379	1.453	**30′**
40′	.6905	.7234	.9545	1.048	1.382	1.448	**20′**
50′	.6926	.7214	.9601	1.042	1.386	1.444	**10′**
44° 00′	.6947	.7193	.9657	1.036	1.390	1.440	**46° 00′**
10′	.6967	.7173	.9713	1.030	1.394	1.435	**50′**
20′	.6988	.7153	.9770	1.024	1.398	1.431	**40′**
30′	.7009	.7133	.9827	1.018	1.402	1.427	**30′**
40′	.7030	.7112	.9884	1.012	1.406	1.423	**20′**
50′	.7050	.7092	.9942	1.006	1.410	1.418	**10′**
45° 00′	.7071	.7071	1.000	1.000	1.414	1.414	**45° 00′**
	Cos	Sin	Cot	Tan	Csc	Sec	Angle

TABLE 7

FOUR-PLACE LOGARITHMS OF VALUES OF TRIGONOMETRIC FUNCTIONS*

Angle	L Sin	d	L Tan	cd	L Cot	d	L Cos	
0° 0′	—		—		—		10.0000	90° 0′
						0		
10′	7.4637		7.4637		12.5363		10.0000	50′
		3011		3011		0		
20′	7.7648		7.7648		12.2352		10.0000	40′
		1760		1761		0		
30′	7.9408		7.9409		12.0591		10.0000	30′
		1250		1249		0		
40′	8.0658		8.0658		11.9342		10.0000	20′
		969		969		0		
50′	8.1627		8.1627		11.8373		10.0000	10′
		792		792		1		
1° 0′	8.2419		8.2419		11.7581		9.9999	89° 0′
		669		670		0		
10′	8.3088		8.3089		11.6911		9.9999	50′
		580		580		0		
20′	8.3668		8.3669		11.6331		9.9999	40′
		511		512		0		
30′	8.4179		8.4181		11.5819		9.9999	30′
		458		457		1		
40′	8.4637		8.4638		11.5362		9.9998	20′
		413		415		0		
50′	8.5050		8.5053		11.4947		9.9998	10′
		378		378		1		
2° 0′	8.5428		8.5431		11.4569		9.9997	88° 0′
		348		348		0		
10′	8.5776		8.5779		11.4221		9.9997	50′
		321		322		1		
20′	8.6097		8.6101		11.3899		9.9996	40′
		300		300		0		
30′	8.6397		8.6401		11.3599		9.9996	30′
		280		281		1		
40′	8.6677		8.6682		11.3318		9.9995	20′
		263		263		0		
50′	8.6940		8.6945		11.3055		9.9995	10′
		248		249		1		
3° 0′	8.7188		8.7194		11.2806		9.9994	87° 0′
		235		235		1		
10′	8.7423		8.7429		11.2571		9.9993	50′
		222		223		0		
20′	8.7645		8.7652		11.2348		9.9993	40′
		212		213		1		
30′	8.7857		8.7865		11.2135		9.9992	30′
		202		202		1		
40′	8.8059		8.8067		11.1933		9.9991	20′
		192		194		1		
50′	8.8251		8.8261		11.1739		9.9990	10′
		185		185		1		
4° 0′	8.8436		8.8446		11.1554		9.9989	86° 0′
		177		178		0		
10′	8.8613		8.8624		11.1376		9.9989	50′
		170		171		1		
20′	8.8783		8.8795		11.1205		9.9988	40′
		163		165		1		
30′	8.8946		8.8960		11.1040		9.9987	30′
		158		158		1		
40′	8.9104		8.9118		11.0882		9.9986	20′
		152		154		1		
50′	8.9256		8.9272		11.0728		9.9985	10′
		147		148		2		
5° 0′	8.9403		8.9420		11.0580		9.9983	85° 0′
		142		143		1		
10′	8.9545		8.9563		11.0437		9.9982	50′
		137		138		1		
20′	8.9682		8.9701		11.0299		9.9981	40′
		134		135		1		
30′	8.9816		8.9836		11.0164		9.9980	30′
		129		130		1		
40′	8.9945		8.9966		11.0034		9.9979	20′
		125		127		2		
50′	9.0070		9.0093		10.9907		9.9977	10′
		122		123		1		
6° 0′	9.0192		9.0216		10.9784		9.9976	84° 0′
		119		120		1		
10′	9.0311		9.0336		10.9664		9.9975	50′
		115		117		2		
20′	9.0426		9.0453		10.9547		9.9973	40′
		113		114		1		
30′	9.0539		9.0567		10.9433		9.9972	30′
		109		111		1		
40′	9.0648		9.0678		10.9322		9.9971	20′
		107		108		2		
50′	9.0755		9.0786		10.9214		9.9969	10′
		104		105		1		
7° 0′	9.0859		9.0891		10.9109		9.9968	83° 0′
		102		104		2		
10′	9.0961		9.0995		10.9005		9.9966	50′
		99		101		2		
20′	9.1060		9.1096		10.8904		9.9964	40′
		97		98		1		
30′	9.1157		9.1194		10.8806		9.9963	30′
		95		97		2		
40′	9.1252		9.1291		10.8709		9.9961	20′
		93		94		2		
50′	9.1345		9.1385		10.8615		9.9959	10′
		91		93		1		
8° 0′	9.1436		9.1478		10.8522		9.9958	82° 0′
		89		91		2		
10′	9.1525		9.1569		10.8431		9.9956	50′
		87		89		2		
20′	9.1612		9.1658		10.8342		9.9954	40′
		85		87		2		
30′	9.1697		9.1745		10.8255		9.9952	30′
		84		86		2		
40′	9.1781		9.1831		10.8169		9.9950	20′
		82		84		2		
50′	9.1863		9.1915		10.8085		9.9948	10′
		80		82		2		
9° 0′	9.1943		9.1997		10.8003		9.9946	81° 0′
	L Cos	d	L Cot	cd	L Tan	d	L Sin	Angle

* These tables give the logarithms increased by 10. Hence in each case 10 should be subtracted.

TABLE 7

FOUR-PLACE LOGARITHMS OF VALUES OF TRIGONOMETRIC FUNCTIONS

Angle	L Sin	d	L Tan	cd	L Cot	d	L Cos	
9° 0′	9.1943	79	9.1997	81	10.8003	2	9.9946	**81° 0′**
10′	9.2022	78	9.2078	80	10.7922	2	9.9944	**50′**
20′	9.2100	76	9.2158	78	10.7842	2	9.9942	**40′**
30′	9.2176	75	9.2236	77	10.7764	2	9.9940	**30′**
40′	9.2251	73	9.2313	76	10.7687	2	9.9938	**20′**
50′	9.2324	73	9.2389	74	10.7611	2	9.9936	**10′**
10° 0′	9.2397	71	9.2463	73	10.7537	3	9.9934	**80° 0′**
10′	9.2468	70	9.2536	73	10.7464	2	9.9931	**50′**
20′	9.2538	68	9.2609	71	10.7391	2	9.9929	**40′**
30′	9.2606	68	9.2680	70	10.7320	3	9.9927	**30′**
40′	9.2674	66	9.2750	69	10.7250	2	9.9924	**20′**
50′	9.2740	66	9.2819	68	10.7181	3	9.9922	**10′**
11° 0′	9.2806	64	9.2887	66	10.7113	2	9.9919	**79° 0′**
10′	9.2870	64	9.2953	67	10.7047	3	9.9917	**50′**
20′	9.2934	63	9.3020	65	10.6980	2	9.9914	**40′**
30′	9.2997	61	9.3085	64	10.6915	3	9.9912	**30′**
40′	9.3058	61	9.3149	63	10.6851	2	9.9909	**20′**
50′	9.3119	60	9.3212	63	10.6788	3	9.9907	**10′**
12° 0′	9.3179	59	9.3275	61	10.6725	3	9.9904	**78° 0′**
10′	9.3238	58	9.3336	61	10.6664	2	9.9901	**50′**
20′	9.3296	57	9.3397	61	10.6603	3	9.9899	**40′**
30′	9.3353	57	9.3458	59	10.6542	3	9.9896	**30′**
40′	9.3410	56	9.3517	59	10.6483	3	9.9893	**20′**
50′	9.3466	55	9.3576	58	10.6424	3	9.9890	**10′**
13° 0′	9.3521	54	9.3634	57	10.6366	3	9.9887	**77° 0′**
10′	9.3575	54	9.3691	57	10.6309	3	9.9884	**50′**
20′	9.3629	53	9.3748	56	10.6252	3	9.9881	**40′**
30′	9.3682	52	9.3804	55	10.6196	3	9.9878	**30′**
40′	9.3734	52	9.3859	55	10.6141	3	9.9875	**20′**
50′	9.3786	51	9.3914	54	10.6086	3	9.9872	**10′**
14° 0′	9.3837	50	9.3968	53	10.6032	3	9.9869	**76° 0′**
10′	9.3887	50	9.4021	53	10.5979	3	9.9866	**50′**
20′	9.3937	49	9.4074	53	10.5926	4	9.9863	**40′**
30′	9.3986	49	9.4127	51	10.5873	3	9.9859	**30′**
40′	9.4035	48	9.4178	52	10.5822	3	9.9856	**20′**
50′	9.4083	47	9.4230	51	10.5770	4	9.9853	**10′**
15° 0′	9.4130	47	9.4281	50	10.5719	3	9.9849	**75° 0′**
10′	9.4177	46	9.4331	50	10.5669	3	9.9846	**50′**
20′	9.4223	46	9.4381	49	10.5619	4	9.9843	**40′**
30′	9.4269	45	9.4430	49	10.5570	3	9.9839	**30′**
40′	9.4314	45	9.4479	48	10.5521	4	9.9836	**20′**
50′	9.4359	44	9.4527	48	10.5473	4	9.9832	**10′**
16° 0′	9.4403	44	9.4575	47	10.5425	3	9.9828	**74° 0′**
10′	9.4447	44	9.4622	47	10.5378	4	9.9825	**50′**
20′	9.4491	42	9.4669	47	10.5331	4	9.9821	**40′**
30′	9.4533	43	9.4716	46	10.5284	3	9.9817	**30′**
40′	9.4576	42	9.4762	46	10.5238	4	9.9814	**20′**
50′	9.4618	41	9.4808	45	10.5192	4	9.9810	**10′**
17° 0′	9.4659	41	9.4853	45	10.5147	4	9.9806	**73° 0′**
10′	9.4700	41	9.4898	45	10.5102	4	9.9802	**50′**
20′	9.4741	40	9.4943	44	10.5057	4	9.9798	**40′**
30′	9.4781	40	9.4987	44	10.5013	4	9.9794	**30′**
40′	9.4821	40	9.5031	44	10.4969	4	9.9790	**20′**
50′	9.4861	39	9.5075	43	10.4925	4	9.9786	**10′**
18° 0′	9.4900		9.5118		10.4882		9.9782	**72° 0′**
	L Cos	d	L Cot	cd	L Tan	d	L Sin	Angle

TABLE 7

FOUR-PLACE LOGARITHMS OF VALUES OF TRIGONOMETRIC FUNCTIONS

Angle	L Sin	d	L Tan	cd	L Cot	d	L Cos	
18° 0′	9.4900		9.5118		10.4882		9.9782	**72° 0′**
		39		43		4		
10′	9.4939		9.5161		10.4839		9.9778	**50′**
		38		42		4		
20′	9.4977		9.5203		10.4797		9.9774	**40′**
		38		42		4		
30′	9.5015		9.5245		10.4755		9.9770	**30′**
		37		42		5		
40′	9.5052		9.5287		10.4713		9.9765	**20′**
		38		42		4		
50′	9.5090		9.5329		10.4671		9.9761	**10′**
		36		41		4		
19° 0′	9.5126		9.5370		10.4630		9.9757	**71° 0′**
		37		41		5		
10′	9.5163		9.5411		10.4589		9.9752	**50′**
		36		40		4		
20′	9.5199		9.5451		10.4549		9.9748	**40′**
		36		40		5		
30′	9.5235		9.5491		10.4509		9.9743	**30′**
		35		40		4		
40′	9.5270		9.5531		10.4469		9.9739	**20′**
		36		40		5		
50′	9.5306		9.5571		10.4429		9.9734	**10′**
		35		40		4		
20° 0′	9.5341		9.5611		10.4389		9.9730	**70° 0′**
		34		39		5		
10′	9.5375		9.5650		10.4350		9.9725	**50′**
		34		39		4		
20′	9.5409		9.5689		10.4311		9.9721	**40′**
		34		38		5		
30′	9.5443		9.5727		10.4273		9.9716	**30′**
		34		39		5		
40′	9.5477		9.5766		10.4234		9.9711	**20′**
		33		38		5		
50′	9.5510		9.5804		10.4196		9.9706	**10′**
		33		38		4		
21° 0′	9.5543		9.5842		10.4158		9.9702	**69° 0′**
		33		37		5		
10′	9.5576		9.5879		10.4121		9.9697	**50′**
		33		38		5		
20′	9.5609		9.5917		10.4083		9.9692	**40′**
		32		37		5		
30′	9.5641		9.5954		10.4046		9.9687	**30′**
		32		37		5		
40′	9.5673		9.5991		10.4009		9.9682	**20′**
		31		37		5		
50′	9.5704		9.6028		10.3972		9.9677	**10′**
		32		36		5		
22° 0′	9.5736		9.6064		10.3936		9.9672	**68° 0′**
		31		36		5		
10′	9.5767		9.6100		10.3900		9.9667	**50′**
		31		36		6		
20′	9.5798		9.6136		10.3864		9.9661	**40′**
		30		36		5		
30′	9.5828		9.6172		10.3828		9.9656	**30′**
		31		36		5		
40′	9.5859		9.6208		10.3792		9.9651	**20′**
		30		35		5		
50′	9.5889		9.6243		10.3757		9.9646	**10′**
		30		36		6		
23° 0′	9.5919		9.6279		10.3721		9.9640	**67° 0′**
		29		35		5		
10′	9.5948		9.6314		10.3686		9.9635	**50′**
		30		34		6		
20′	9.5978		9.6348		10.3652		9.9629	**40′**
		29		35		5		
30′	9.6007		9.6383		10.3617		9.9624	**30′**
		29		34		6		
40′	9.6036		9.6417		10.3583		9.9618	**20′**
		29		35		5		
50′	9.6065		9.6452		10.3548		9.9613	**10′**
		28		34		6		
24° 0′	9.6093		9.6486		10.3514		9.9607	**66° 0′**
		28		34		5		
10′	9.6121		9.6520		10.3480		9.9602	**50′**
		28		33		6		
20′	9.6149		9.6553		10.3447		9.9596	**40′**
		28		34		6		
30′	9.6177		9.6587		10.3413		9.9590	**30′**
		28		33		6		
40′	9.6205		9.6620		10.3380		9.9584	**20′**
		27		34		5		
50′	9.6232		9.6654		10.3346		9.9579	**10′**
		27		33		6		
25° 0′	9.6259		9.6687		10.3313		9.9573	**65° 0′**
		27		33		6		
10′	9.6286		9.6720		10.3280		9.9567	**50′**
		27		32		6		
20′	9.6313		9.6752		10.3248		9.9561	**40′**
		27		33		6		
30′	9.6340		9.6785		10.3215		9.9555	**30′**
		26		32		6		
40′	9.6366		9.6817		10.3183		9.9549	**20′**
		26		33		6		
50′	9.6392		9.6850		10.3150		9.9543	**10′**
		26		32		6		
26° 0′	9.6418		9.6882		10.3118		9.9537	**64° 0′**
		26		32		7		
10′	9.6444		9.6914		10.3086		9.9530	**50′**
		26		32		6		
20′	9.6470		9.6946		10.3054		9.9524	**40′**
		25		31		6		
30′	9.6495		9.6977		10.3023		9.9518	**30′**
		26		32		6		
40′	9.6521		9.7009		10.2991		9.9512	**20′**
		25		31		7		
50′	9.6546		9.7040		10.2960		9.9505	**10′**
		24		32		6		
27° 0′	9.6570		9.7072		10.2928		9.9499	**63° 0′**
	L Cos	d	L Cot	cd	L Tan	d	L Sin	Angle

TABLE 7

FOUR-PLACE LOGARITHMS OF VALUES OF TRIGONOMETRIC FUNCTIONS

Angle	L Sin	d	L Tan	cd	L Cot	d	L Cos	
27° 0′	9.6570	25	9.7072	31	10.2928	7	9.9499	63° 0′
10′	9.6595	25	9.7103	31	10.2897	6	9.9492	50′
20′	9.6620	24	9.7134	31	10.2866	7	9.9486	40′
30′	9.6644	24	9.7165	31	10.2835	6	9.9479	30′
40′	9.6668	24	9.7196	30	10.2804	7	9.9473	20′
50′	9.6692	24	9.7226	31	10.2774	7	9.9466	10′
28° 0′	9.6716	24	9.7257	30	10.2743	6	9.9459	62° 0′
10′	9.6740	23	9.7287	30	10.2713	7	9.9453	50′
20′	9.6763	24	9.7317	31	10.2683	7	9.9446	40′
30′	9.6787	23	9.7348	30	10.2652	7	9.9439	30′
40′	9.6810	23	9.7378	30	10.2622	7	9.9432	20′
50′	9.6833	23	9.7408	30	10.2592	7	9.9425	10′
29° 0′	9.6856	22	9.7438	29	10.2562	7	9.9418	61° 0′
10′	9.6878	23	9.7467	30	10.2533	7	9.9411	50′
20′	9.6901	22	9.7497	29	10.2503	7	9.9404	40′
30′	9.6923	23	9.7526	30	10.2474	7	9.9397	30′
40′	9.6946	22	9.7556	29	10.2444	7	9.9390	20′
50′	9.6968	22	9.7585	29	10.2415	8	9.9383	10′
30° 0′	9.6990	22	9.7614	30	10.2386	7	9.9375	60° 0′
10′	9.7012	21	9.7644	29	10.2356	7	9.9368	50′
20′	9.7033	22	9.7673	28	10.2327	8	9.9361	40′
30′	9.7055	21	9.7701	29	10.2299	7	9.9353	30′
40′	9.7076	21	9.7730	29	10.2270	8	9.9346	20′
50′	9.7097	21	9.7759	29	10.2241	7	9.9338	10′
31° 0′	9.7118	21	9.7788	28	10.2212	8	9.9331	59° 0′
10′	9.7139	21	9.7816	29	10.2184	8	9.9323	50′
20′	9.7160	21	9.7845	28	10.2155	7	9.9315	40′
30′	9.7181	20	9.7873	29	10.2127	8	9.9308	30′
40′	9.7201	21	9.7902	28	10.2098	8	9.9300	20′
50′	9.7222	20	9.7930	28	10.2070	8	9.9292	10′
32° 0′	9.7242	20	9.7958	28	10.2042	8	9.9284	58° 0′
10′	9.7262	20	9.7986	28	10.2014	8	9.9276	50′
20′	9.7282	20	9.8014	28	10.1986	8	9.9268	40′
30′	9.7302	20	9.8042	28	10.1958	8	9.9260	30′
40′	9.7322	20	9.8070	27	10.1930	8	9.9252	20′
50′	9.7342	19	9.8097	28	10.1903	8	9.9244	10′
33° 0′	9.7361	19	9.8125	28	10.1875	8	9.9236	57° 0′
10′	9.7380	20	9.8153	27	10.1847	9	9.9228	50′
20′	9.7400	19	9.8180	28	10.1820	8	9.9219	40′
30′	9.7419	19	9.8208	27	10.1792	8	9.9211	30′
40′	9.7438	19	9.8235	28	10.1765	9	9.9203	20′
50′	9.7457	19	9.8263	27	10.1737	8	9.9194	10′
34° 0′	9.7476	18	9.8290	27	10.1710	9	9.9186	56° 0′
10′	9.7494	19	9.8317	27	10.1683	8	9.9177	50′
20′	9.7513	18	9.8344	27	10.1656	9	9.9169	40′
30′	9.7531	19	9.8371	27	10.1629	9	9.9160	30′
40′	9.7550	18	9.8398	27	10.1602	9	9.9151	20′
50′	9.7568	18	9.8425	27	10.1575	8	9.9142	10′
35° 0′	9.7586	18	9.8452	27	10.1548	9	9.9134	55° 0′
10′	9.7604	18	9.8479	27	10.1521	9	9.9125	50′
20′	9.7622	18	9.8506	27	10.1494	9	9.9116	40′
30′	9.7640	17	9.8533	26	10.1467	9	9.9107	30′
40′	9.7657	18	9.8559	27	10.1441	9	9.9098	20′
50′	9.7675	17	9.8586	27	10.1414	9	9.9089	10′
36° 0′	9.7692		9.8613		10.1387		9.9080	54° 0′
	L Cos	d	L Cot	cd	L Tan	d	L Sin	Angle

TABLE 7

FOUR-PLACE LOGARITHMS OF VALUES OF TRIGONOMETRIC FUNCTIONS

Angle	*L Sin*	*d*	*L Tan*	*cd*	*L Cot*	*d*	*L Cos*	
36° 0′	9.7692		9.8613		10.1387		9.9080	**54° 0′**
10′	9.7710	18	9.8639	26	10.1361	10	9.9070	**50′**
20′	9.7727	17	9.8666	27	10.1334	9	9.9061	**40′**
30′	9.7744	17	9.8692	26	10.1308	9	9.9052	**30′**
40′	9.7761	17	9.8718	26	10.1282	10	9.9042	**20′**
50′	9.7778	17	9.8745	27	10.1255	9	9.9033	**10′**
37° 0′	9.7795	17	9.8771	26	10.1229	10	9.9023	**53° 0′**
10′	9.7811	16	9.8797	26	10.1203	9	9.9014	**50′**
20′	9.7828	17	9.8824	27	10.1176	10	9.9004	**40′**
30′	9.7844	16	9.8850	26	10.1150	9	9.8995	**30′**
40′	9.7861	17	9.8876	26	10.1124	10	9.8985	**20′**
50′	9.7877	16	9.8902	26	10.1098	10	9.8975	**10′**
38° 0′	9.7893	16	9.8928	26	10.1072	10	9.8965	**52° 0′**
10′	9.7910	17	9.8954	26	10.1046	10	9.8955	**50′**
20′	9.7926	16	9.8980	26	10.1020	10	9.8945	**40′**
30′	9.7941	15	9.9006	26	10.0994	10	9.8935	**30′**
40′	9.7957	16	9.9032	26	10.0968	10	9.8925	**20′**
50′	9.7973	16	9.9058	26	10.0942	10	9.8915	**10′**
39° 0′	9.7989	16	9.9084	26	10.0916	10	9.8905	**51° 0′**
10′	9.8004	15	9.9110	26	10.0890	10	9.8895	**50′**
20′	9.8020	16	9.9135	25	10.0865	11	9.8884	**40′**
30′	9.8035	15	9.9161	26	10.0839	10	9.8874	**30′**
40′	9.8050	15	9.9187	26	10.0813	10	9.8864	**20′**
50′	9.8066	16	9.9212	25	10.0788	11	9.8853	**10′**
40° 0′	9.8081	15	9.9238	26	10.0762	10	9.8843	**50° 0′**
10′	9.8096	15	9.9264	26	10.0736	11	9.8832	**50′**
20′	9.8111	15	9.9289	25	10.0711	11	9.8821	**40′**
30′	9.8125	14	9.9315	26	10.0685	11	9.8810	**30′**
40′	9.8140	15	9.9341	26	10.0659	10	9.8800	**20′**
50′	9.8155	15	9.9366	25	10.0634	11	9.8789	**10′**
41° 0′	9.8169	14	9.9392	26	10.0608	11	9.8778	**49° 0′**
10′	9.8184	15	9.9417	25	10.0583	11	9.8767	**50′**
20′	9.8198	14	9.9443	26	10.0557	11	9.8756	**40′**
30′	9.8213	15	9.9468	25	10.0532	11	9.8745	**30′**
40′	9.8227	14	9.9494	26	10.0506	12	9.8733	**20′**
50′	9.8241	14	9.9519	25	10.0481	11	9.8722	**10′**
42° 0′	9.8255	14	9.9544	25	10.0456	11	9.8711	**48° 0′**
10′	9.8269	14	9.9570	26	10.0430	12	9.8699	**50′**
20′	9.8283	14	9.9595	25	10.0405	11	9.8688	**40′**
30′	9.8297	14	9.9621	26	10.0379	12	9.8676	**30′**
40′	9.8311	14	9.9646	25	10.0354	11	9.8665	**20′**
50′	9.8324	13	9.9671	25	10.0329	12	9.8653	**10′**
43° 0′	9.8338	14	9.9697	26	10.0303	12	9.8641	**47° 0′**
10′	9.8351	13	9.9722	25	10.0278	12	9.8629	**50′**
20′	9.8365	14	9.9747	25	10.0253	11	9.8618	**40′**
30′	9.8378	13	9.9772	25	10.0228	12	9.8606	**30′**
40′	9.8391	13	9.9798	26	10.0202	12	9.8594	**20′**
50′	9.8405	14	9.9823	25	10.0177	12	9.8582	**10′**
44° 0′	9.8418	13	9.9848	25	10.0152	13	9.8569	**46° 0′**
10′	9.8431	13	9.9874	26	10.0126	12	9.8557	**50′**
20′	9.8444	13	9.9899	25	10.0101	12	9.8545	**40′**
30′	9.8457	13	9.9924	25	10.0076	13	9.8532	**30′**
40′	9.8469	12	9.9949	25	10.0051	12	9.8520	**20′**
50′	9.8482	13	9.9975	26	10.0025	13	9.8507	**10′**
45° 0′	9.8495	13	10.0000	25	10.0000	12	9.8495	**45° 0′**
	L Cos	*d*	*L Cot*	*cd*	*L Tan*	*d*	*L Sin*	*Angle*

GLOSSARY

Abscissa: The first coordinate in an ordered pair of numbers which is associated with a point in the coordinate plane. (p. 81)

Absolute value: For every nonzero real number a, its absolute value is defined to be the greater number of the pair a and $-a$. (p. 15) See also **Modulus of a complex number.**

Acute angle: An angle whose measure is between 0° and 90° (called, in particular, a positive acute angle). (p. 382)

Addition Property of Equality: If a, b, and c denote real numbers and if $a = b$, then $a + c = b + c$. (p. 18)

Addition Property of Order: Let a, b, and c denote real numbers. If $a < b$, then $a + c < b + c$. If $a > b$, then $a + c > b + c$. (p. 49)

Additive inverse: The additive inverse of a real number a is the real number whose sum with a is 0. (p. 14)

Algebraic expressions: Numerical expressions, variables, and indicated sums, products, differences, and quotients containing variables. (p. 39)

Amplitude of a complex number: A position angle θ of a point P which represents a complex number in the complex plane. (p. 458)

Amplitude of a periodic function: When a periodic function has a maximum value M and a minimum value m, its amplitude is $\frac{M - m}{2}$. (p. 472)

Angle: The set of points composing two rays with a common vertex, together with a rotation that sends one ray into the other. (p. 371)

Angle of depression: The angle between the horizontal ray through an observer and the line of sight from the observer through an object below the observer. (p. 388)

Angle of elevation: The angle between the horizontal ray through an observer and the line of sight from the observer through an object above the observer. (p. 388)

Antilogarithm: If $\log x = a$, then x is called the antilogarithm of a. (p. 351)

Arithmetic means: The terms between two given terms in an arithmetic progression. (p. 499). A single arithmetic mean inserted between two numbers is the *average* or *arithmetic mean* of the two numbers. (p. 499)

Arithmetic progression: A sequence in which the difference between any two successive terms is a constant, d. (p. 496)

Associative axioms for addition and multiplication: If a, b, and c denote real numbers, then $(a + b) + c = a + (b + c)$ and $(ab)c = a(bc)$. (p. 11)

Axiom (postulate): A basic statement that is assumed to be true. (p. 8) See p. 32 for a listing of the axioms for the real numbers.

Axiom of Additive Inverses: If a denotes any real number, there is a unique real number denoted by $-a$, such that $a + (-a) = 0$ and $(-a) + a = 0$. (p. 15)

Axiom of Comparison: If a and b denote real numbers, then one and only one of the following statements is true: $a < b$, $a = b$, $a > b$. (p. 9)

Axiom of Multiplicative Inverses: If a represents any nonzero real number, there is a unique real number denoted by $\frac{1}{a}$, such that $a \cdot \frac{1}{a} = 1$ and $\frac{1}{a} \cdot a = 1$. (p. 15)

Axiom of One: The set of real numbers contains a unique element 1 having the property that if a denotes any real number, $1 \cdot a = a$ and $a \cdot 1 = a$. (p. 15)

Axiom of Zero: The set of real numbers contains a unique element 0 having the property that if a denotes any real number, $0 + a = a$ and $a + 0 = a$. (p. 14)

Axis: A reference line, such as the horizontal and vertical axes in a coordinate plane. (p. 81)

Axis of symmetry (of a parabola): The line through the focus perpendicular to the directrix. (p. 310)

Binomial: A polynomial of two terms. (p. 40)

Cartesian product: The set of all ordered pairs (a, b) in which the first entry is an element of one set, A, and the second entry is an element of another set, B. The Cartesian product of sets A and B is denoted by $A \times B$. (p. 581)

Characteristic: The integral, or whole number, part of a logarithm. (p. 350)

Circle: A set of points equidistant from a given point, called the center. (p. 306)

Circular function: A function, such as the *sine function over the set of real numbers*, for which values in the domain are real numbers which are measures of arcs on a unit circle. (p. 467) Compare with the *trigonometric sine function* for which elements in the domain are angles.

Closure axioms for addition and multiplication: If a and b denote real numbers, then $a + b$ represents a unique real number, and ab represents a unique real number. (p. 11)

Cofunctions: The following pairs of trigonometric functions are cofunctions: sine and cosine, tangent and cotangent, secant and cosecant. (p. 384)

Combination: A subset containing r elements of a set with n elements is often called a combination of n elements taken r at a time. (p. 590)

Combined variation: Any combination of direct and inverse variation. (p. 321)

Common logarithms: Logarithms to the base 10. (p. 349)

Commutative axioms for addition and multiplication: If a and b denote real numbers, then $a + b = b + a$ and $ab = ba$. (p. 11)

Completing the square: Transforming a quadratic expression into the square of a binomial. (p. 328)

Complex fraction: A fraction whose numerator or denominator (or both) contains one or more fractions or powers involving negative exponents. (p. 173)

Complex number: A number of the form $a + bi$ where a is a real number and bi is any pure imaginary number. If $b = 0$, $a + bi$ is a real number; if $b \neq 0$, $a + bi$ is an imaginary number. (p. 407)

Components of a vector: Two vectors whose sum is another vector, $\vec{V}$, are called components of $\vec{V}$. (p. 402)

Conjugates: Two complex numbers in the form $a + bi$ and $a - bi$ are called conjugates of each other. (p. 415)

Consistent equations: Equations whose graphs intersect in just one point. (pp. 95, 106)

Constant function: A function which has the same second coordinate in all its ordered pairs. (p. 214)

Constant of proportionality (variation): In an equation of the form $y = mx$, $m \neq 0$, which specifies a direct variation, m is the constant of proportionality. (p. 217) In an equation of the form $xy = k$, $k \neq 0$, which specifies an inverse variation, k is the constant of proportionality. (p. 319)

Constant term: The numerical term, or term of degree zero, in a polynomial in simple form. (p. 136)

Converse statements: Each of two statements is the converse of the other if the hypothesis of each statement is the conclusion of the other. (p. 56)

Coordinate: The number paired with a point on the number line. (p. 8)

Coordinate systems: *A plane rectangular coordinate system* is a one-to-one correspondence (established by means of perpendicular lines) between the set of all points in a plane and the set of all ordered pairs of real numbers. (p. 82) A *coordinate system in space* is a one-to-one correspondence (established by means of perpendicular planes) between the set of all points in space and the set of all ordered triples of real numbers. (p. 104)

Cosecant function: The set of ordered pairs $\{(\theta, \csc \theta): \csc \theta = \frac{1}{\sin \theta}$, provided $\sin \theta \neq 0\}$, whose domain is a subset of the set of angles θ in standard position. (p. 378)

Cosine function: If θ is any angle in standard position, and if (a, b) denotes the coordinates of the point one unit from the origin on the terminal side of θ, then the set of all ordered pairs (θ, a) is called the cosine function. (p. 375)

Cotangent function: The set of ordered pairs $\{(\theta, \cot\theta): \cot\theta = \frac{\cos\theta}{\sin\theta}$, provided $\sin\theta \neq 0\}$, whose domain is a subset of the set of angles θ in standard position. (p. 378)

Coterminal angles: Angles having the same initial and terminal sides. (p. 372)

Degree: A unit of angle measure. One degree is $\frac{1}{360}$ of a complete counterclockwise rotation. (p. 372)

Degree of a monomial: The sum of the exponents of the variables in the monomial. (p. 40)

Degree of a polynomial: The greatest of the degrees of the terms in the polynomial. (p. 40)

Dependent equations: Equations in a system which are equivalent. The graphs of such equations coincide. (pp. 95, 109)

Determinant of a matrix: A particular real number associated with each square matrix.

Direct variation: Any linear function specified by an equation of the form $y = mx$, where m is a nonzero constant. (p. 217)

Discriminant: The expression $b^2 - 4ac$ is called the discriminant of the quadratic equation $ax^2 + bx + c = 0$. (p. 283)

Disjoint sets: Two sets which have no element in common. (p. 582)

Distance formula: For points $P_1(x_1, y_1)$ and $P_2(x_2, y_2)$ in a coordinate plane, $d(P_1, P_2) = \sqrt{(x_2 - x_1)^2 + (y_2 - y_1)^2}$. (p. 300)

Distributive Axiom of Multiplication with Respect to Addition: If a, b, and c denote real numbers, then: (1) $a(b + c) = (ab) + (ac)$; (2) $(b + c)a = (ba) + (ca)$. (p. 27)

Division Property of Order: Let a, b, and c denote real numbers. If $a < b$, then: $\frac{a}{c} < \frac{b}{c}$, provided $c > 0$; and $\frac{a}{c} > \frac{b}{c}$, provided $c < 0$. If $a > b$, then: $\frac{a}{c} > \frac{b}{c}$, provided $c > 0$; and $\frac{a}{c} < \frac{b}{c}$, provided $c < 0$. (p. 50)

Domain (of a relation): The set of all the first coordinates of the ordered pairs in the relation. (p. 209)

Domain (of a variable): The set whose elements may serve as replacements for a variable. Also called the *replacement set* or *universe*. (p. 6)

Ellipse: In a plane, a set of points for each of which the sum of the distances from two given points (the foci) is a given constant. (p. 312)

Empty set: The set which has no members. Also called the *null* set. (p. 2)

Equation: A statement that two numerical expressions designate the same number. (p. 3)

Equivalent equations: Equations which have exactly the same solution set. (p. 44)

Equivalent expressions: Expressions which represent the same number for every value of the variable(s) they contain. (p. 41)

Equivalent inequalities: Inequalities which have the same solution set. (p. 50)

Equivalent systems: Two systems of equations which have the same solution set. (p. 96)

Equivalent vectors: Vectors which have the same magnitude and direction. (p. 399)

Event: See **Sample space.**

Exponent: In a power, the number of times the base occurs as a factor. In the power 2^3, 3 is the exponent. (p. 39)

Exponential form: A form in which radical expressions are written as powers, or as products of powers. For example, the radical expression $\sqrt{a^5bc^{-6}}$ in exponential form is $a^{\frac{5}{2}} b^{\frac{1}{2}} c^{-3}$. (p. 339)

Exponential function with base b: The function of the form $\{(x, y): y = b^x, b > 0, b \neq 1\}$. (p. 346)

Extremes of a proportion: In the proportion $\frac{y_1}{x_1} = \frac{y_2}{x_2}$, y_1 and x_2 are called the extremes. (p. 218)

Factorial notation: A notation for the product of certain successive natural numbers. For example, 5! (five factorial) is the product $5 \cdot 4 \cdot 3 \cdot 2 \cdot 1$. (p. 520)

Factor Theorem: Over the set of complex numbers, $(x - r)$ is a factor of a polynomial $P(x)$ if and only if r is a root of $P(x) = 0$. (p. 530)

Fractional equation: An equation in which a variable appears in the denominator of a fraction. (p. 184)

Function: A relation which assigns to each element in the domain a *single* element in the range. (p. 213)

Fundamental Theorem of Algebra: Every polynomial equation with complex coefficients has at least one root. (p. 533)

Geometric means: The terms between two given terms in a geometric progression are called the geometric means between the given terms. A *single* geometric mean inserted between two numbers is called the *geometric mean*, or the *mean proportional*, of the two numbers. (pp. 509–510)

Geometric progression: A sequence in which the ratio r of every pair of two successive terms is a constant. (p. 506)

Graph: On a number line, the point associated with a number. (p. 8). On a coordinate plane, the point associated with an ordered pair of numbers. (p. 81). On a coordinate system in space, the point associated with an ordered triple of numbers. (p. 104)

Greatest common factor: The greatest integer that is a factor of two or more given integers. (p. 131). The monomial with the greatest constant coefficient and the greatest degree which is a factor of each of several given monomials. (p. 132)

Half-plane: Part of a plane, bounded by a line in the plane. (p. 111)

Hyperbola: A set of points in a plane such that for each point of the set the absolute value of the difference of its distances from two given points (called foci) is a constant. (p. 315)

Hypotenuse: The side opposite the right angle in a right triangle. (p. 299)

Identity: An equation which is true for every numerical replacement of the variable(s) in the equation. (p. 41)

Identity element for addition: Because the sum of 0 and any given number is identical to the given number, we call 0 the identity element for addition. (p. 14)

Identity element for multiplication: Because the product of 1 and any given real number is identical to the given number, we call 1 the identity element for multiplication. (p. 15)

Identity matrix: A square matrix whose main diagonal from upper left to lower right consists of entries of 1, while all other entries are 0. (p. 558)

Inconsistent equations: Equations which have no common solution. (pp. 95, 108)

Independent equations: Equations which are not equivalent. (pp. 95, 106)

Inequality: A statement that two numerical expressions represent different numbers. (p. 3)

Infinite set: A set for which the process of counting elements continues without end. (p. 2)

Integer: A member of the set $\{\ldots, -3, -2, -1, 0, 1, 2, 3, \ldots\}$. (p. 2)

Intersection of sets: The set of all elements belonging to both of two given sets. (p. 54)

Inverse functions: A function is the inverse of a given function if it may be obtained by interchanging the coordinates in each ordered pair of the given function. (p. 344)

Inverse matrices: Any two matrices A and B such that $AB = BA = I$ (the identity matrix) are called inverse matrices. (p. 563)

Inverse of a relation: The relation obtained by interchanging the coordinates in each ordered pair in a given relation. (p. 344)

Inverse variation: Any function $\{(x, y): xy = k\}$ where k is a nonzero constant. (p. 319)

Invertible matrix: A matrix that has an inverse. (p. 564)

Irrational equation: See **Radical equation.**

Irrational number: A real number which is not rational. (p. 257)

Irreducible polynomial: A polynomial which cannot be expressed as a product of polynomials of lower degree belonging to a given set. (p. 137)

Joint variation: A variable varies jointly as two or more other variables if it varies directly as the product of those variables. (p. 321)

Law of Cosines: In a triangle, the square of the length of any side equals the sum of the squares of the lengths of the other two sides decreased by twice the product of the lengths of these two sides and the cosine of their included angle. (p. 444)

Law of Sines: The sines of the angles of a triangle are proportional to the lengths of the opposite sides. (p. 448)

Leading coefficient: The coefficient of the term of highest degree of a polynomial. (p. 256)

Least common multiple: The least positive integer that has two or more given integers as a factor. (p. 131) The monomial with the least constant coefficient and the least degree which has each of several given monomials as a factor. (p. 132)

Linear equation: An equation in which each term is either a constant or a monomial of degree 1. (p. 82)

Linear function: A function F is a linear function provided there exist real numbers b and m ($m \neq 0$) such that for every x in the domain of F, $F(x) = mx + b$. (p. 217)

Linear interpolation: A process in which we assume that a small part of the graph of a function is a straight line in order to approximate the value of the function at a given point. It is used to find approximate values of logarithms. (p. 353)

Linear programming: A branch of mathematics concerned with solving practical problems involving linear inequalities. (p. 114)

Linear term: The term of first degree in a polynomial in simple form. (p. 136)

Logarithm of *a* to the base *b*: If a denotes any positive real number and b any positive real number except 1, there is a unique real number called the logarithm of a to the base b ($\log_b a$) which is the exponent in the power of b that equals a; that is, $\log_b a = n$ if and only if $a = b^n$. (p. 347)

Logarithmic function with base *b*: A function of the form $\{(x, y): y = \log_b x, b > 0, b \neq 1, x > 0\}$. (p. 347)

Mantissa: The decimal, or fractional, part of a logarithm. (p. 350)

Mapping: A concept of a function in which one thinks of the function as a mapping of the elements of its domain onto the elements of its range. (p. 344)

Matrix: A rectangular array of numbers exhibited between brackets or double lines. Individual numbers that make up a matrix are called *entries* or *elements*. (p. 551)

Means of a proportion: In the proportion $\frac{y_1}{x_1} = \frac{y_2}{x_2}$, x_1 and y_2 are called the means. (p. 218)

Modulus of a complex number: In the complex plane, the distance from the origin to a point P, where P represents a complex number, $a + bi$. Also called the *absolute value*. (p. 458)

Monomial: A term which is either a numeral, a variable, or a product of a numeral and one or more variables. (p. 39)

Multiplication Property of Equality: If a, b, and c denote real numbers, and if $a = b$, then $ac = bc$. (p. 19)

Multiplication Property of Order: Let a, b, and c denote real numbers. If $a < b$, then: $ac < bc$, provided $c > 0$; and $ac > bc$, provided $c < 0$. If $a > b$, then: $ac > bc$, provided $c > 0$; and $ac < bc$, provided $c < 0$. (p. 49)

Multiplication Property of Zero: If a denotes any real number, then $0 \cdot a = 0$ and $a \cdot 0 = 0$. (p. 15)

Multiplicative inverse: Two numbers whose product is 1 are called *multiplicative inverses*, or *reciprocals*, of each other. (p. 15)

Natural numbers: Members of the set $\{1, 2, 3, 4, \ldots\}$. (p. 2)

nth root: For every positive integer n, any solution of $x^n = b$ is called an nth root of b. (p. 252)

Numeral (Numerical expression): A symbol used to designate a number. (p. 3)

Numerical coefficient of a monomial: The numerical factor of a monomial. (p. 40)

One-to-one correspondence: A pairing of the elements of two sets such that every member of one set has exactly one partner in the other set and no element in either set is without a partner. (p. 2)

One-to-one function: A function for which distinct elements of its domain are mapped onto distinct elements of its range. (p. 344)

Open sentence: A sentence which contains a variable. (p. 6)

Ordered pair of numbers: A pair of numbers in which the order is important. (p. 78)

Ordinate: The second coordinate in an ordered pair of numbers which is associated with a point in the coordinate plane. (p. 81)

Parabola: Any curve consisting of the set of points equidistant from a fixed line (the directrix) and a fixed point (the focus) not on the line. (p. 309)

Parallel lines: In a plane, lines having the same slope, or no slope. (p. 92)

Per cent: A per cent denotes a fraction whose denominator is 100. (p. 179)

Percentage: The product of a base number multiplied by a per cent. (p. 179)

Periodic function: A function f such that for a nonzero constant p, $f(x + p) = f(x)$ for each x in the domain of f. p is called the *period* of f. (p. 470)

Permutation: Any arrangement of the elements of a set in a definite order. (p. 584) A *circular permutation* is a special type of arrangement about a circular framework. (p. 585)

Point-slope form of an equation: An equation in the form $(y - y_1) = m(x - x_1)$. This is an equation for a line which contains point (x_1, y_1) and has slope m. (p. 91)

Polynomial: A monomial or a sum of monomials. (p. 40)

Polynomial equation in simple form: An equation having 0 as one member and a polynomial in simple form as the other member. (p. 256)

Power: The number named by an expression in the form of a^n, where n denotes the number of times a is used as a factor. (p. 39)

Prime number: An integer greater than 1 that has no positive integral factors other than itself and 1. (p. 130)

Prime polynomial: An irreducible polynomial whose greatest monomial factor is 1. (p. 137)

Proof: A form of logical reasoning leading from an hypothesis to a conclusion. (p. 19)

Property of the Negative of a Sum: If a and b denote real numbers, the negative of their sum is the sum of their negatives: $-(a + b) = (-a) + (-b)$. (p. 16)

Property of the Reciprocal of a Product: If a and b denote nonzero real numbers, the reciprocal of their product is the product of their reciprocals: $\frac{1}{ab} = \frac{1}{a} \cdot \frac{1}{b}$. (p. 16)

Proportion: An equality of ratios. (p. 218)

Quadrant: One of the four regions into which the plane is separated by the coordinate axes. (p. 81)

Quadrantal angle: An angle in standard position whose terminal side lies on a coordinate axis. (p. 379)

Quadratic formula: $x = \frac{-b \pm \sqrt{b^2 - 4ac}}{2a}$; this equation is equivalent to the general quadratic equation, $ax^2 + bx + c = 0$. (p. 275)

Quadratic function: A function whose values are given by a quadratic polynomial, $ax^2 + bx + c$, where a, b, and c are real numbers, $a \neq 0$. (p. 226)

Quadratic term: The term of second degree in a polynomial in simple form. (p. 136)

Radian: An angular measure. The measure of 1 radian is assigned to an angle subtended by an arc of measure 1 on a circle of radius 1. (p. 464)

Radical: The symbol $\sqrt[n]{b}$ is called a radical and is read "the principal nth root of b," or "the nth root of b." (p. 253)

Radical equation (irrational equation): An equation having a variable in a radicand. (p. 287)

Radicand: The expression under a radical sign. (p. 253)

Radius of a circle: The distance between each of its points and the center. (p. 306)

Range (of a relation): The set of all the second coordinates of the ordered pairs in the relation. (p. 209)

Rational algebraic expression: Any expression that is the quotient of two polynomials. (p. 166)

Rational number: Any number which can be represented by a fraction whose numerator is an integer and whose denominator is a nonzero integer. (p. 166)

Rational operation: Addition, multiplication, subtraction, and division (except by 0) are the rational operations. (p. 259)

Rationalizing the denominator: Transforming a term involving radicals and fractions into an equivalent fraction with denominator free of radicals. (p. 266)

Real number: Any positive or negative number or 0. (p. 8)

Reciprocal: See **Multiplicative inverse.**

Reference angle: With each angle θ in standard position a reference angle ρ in the first quadrant is associated such that the absolute values of the trigonometric functions of ρ and θ are equal. (p. 395)

Reflexive Axiom of Equality: For any real number a, $a = a$. (p. 11)

Relation: Any set of ordered pairs. (p. 209)

Remainder Theorem: For every polynomial $P(x)$ of nonzero degree n over the set of complex numbers, and for every complex number r, there exists a polynomial $Q(x)$ of degree $n - 1$, such that $P(x) = (x - r)\,Q(x) + P(r)$. (p. 529)

Resultant: The sum of two vectors. (p. 400)

Root index: In the expression $\sqrt[n]{a}$, n is the root index. (p. 253)

Sample space: In probability, a set S of elements that correspond one-to-one with the outcomes of an experiment. Each of the elements corresponding to an outcome is called a *sample point*. An *event* is any subset of a sample space. (p. 598)

Scalar: In working with matrices, a term used for a real number. (p. 554)

Secant function: The set of ordered pairs $\{(\theta, \sec\theta): \sec\theta = \frac{1}{\cos\theta}$, provided $\cos\theta \neq 0\}$ whose domain is a subset of the set of angles θ in standard position. (p. 378)

Sequence: The values of any function whose domain is a set of consecutive natural numbers is said to form a sequence. Each value is called a *term* of the sequence. (p. 495)

Series: The indicated sum of the terms in a sequence. (p. 501)

Set: A collection of objects. The objects in a set are called the *members* or *elements* of the set. (p. 1)

Simultaneous equations: Two or more equations which represent two or more conditions imposed at the same time on the same variables. (p. 96)

Sine function: If θ is any angle in standard position, and if (a, b) denotes the coordinates of the point one unit from the origin on the terminal side of θ, then the set of all ordered pairs (θ, b) is called the sine function. (p. 375)

Slope: If (x_1, y_1) are the coordinates of a point P in the plane, and (x_2, y_2) are the coordinates of a different point Q, then the slope of line PQ is $\frac{y_2 - y_1}{x_2 - x_1}$. (p. 85)

Slope-intercept form of an equation: An equation of the form $y = mx + b$. This is an equation for the line having slope m and y-intercept b. (p. 91)

Solution set (truth set): For an open sentence in one variable, the subset of the domain for which the open sentence is true. (p. 6) For an open sentence in two variables, the set of ordered pairs of numbers which belong to the replacement sets of the variables for which the sentence is true. (p. 78)

Standard position (of an angle): The placement of an angle on a coordinate plane such that the vertex of the angle is at the origin and the initial side of the angle is on the positive side of the x-axis. (p. 373)

Subset: If each element of set A is also an element of set B, we say that A is a subset of B. (p. 2)

Substitution Axiom of Equality: For all real numbers a, b, c, and d: (1) if $a = b$ and $a + c = d$, then $b + c = d$; (2) if $a = b$ and $ac = d$, then $bc = d$. (p. 11)

Subtraction Property of Order: Let a, b, and c denote real numbers. If a $< b$, then $a - c < b - c$. If $a > b$, then $a - c > b - c$. (p. 50)

Symmetric axiom of equality: For any real numbers a and b, if $a = b$, then $b = a$. (p. 11)

Symmetry with respect to the x-axis: If a curve has the property that whenever the point (r, t) belongs to it, then the point $(r, -t)$ also belongs to it, then the curve is said to be symmetric with respect to the x-axis. (p. 311)

Symmetry with respect to the y-axis: If a curve has the property that whenever the ordered pair (r, t) belongs to it, then $(-r, t)$ also belongs to it, then the curve is said to be symmetric with respect to the y-axis. (p. 227)

Tangent function: The set of ordered pairs $\{(\theta, \tan\theta): \tan\theta = \frac{\sin\theta}{\cos\theta}$, provided $\cos\theta \neq 0\}$ whose domain is a subset of the set of angles θ in standard position. (p. 378)

Theorem: An assertion to be (or that has been) proved. (p. 19)

Trace of a plane: In a three-dimensional coordinate system, a line in which a plane intersects a coordinate plane. (p. 105)

Transitive Axiom of Equality: For all real numbers a, b, and c, if $a = b$, and $b = c$, then $a = c$. (p. 11)

Transitive Property of Order: Let a, b, and c denote real numbers: (1) if $a < b$ and $b < c$, then $a < c$; (2) if $a > b$ and $b > c$, then $a > c$. (p. 9)

Trigonometric functions: See **Sine, Cosine, Tangent, Cotangent, Secant,** and **Cosecant.**

Trinomial: A polynomial of three terms. (p. 40)

Union (of sets): The set consisting of all elements belonging to at least one of two given sets. (p. 54)

Value of f at x: The second coordinate of the ordered pair of f whose first coordinate is x. (p. 213)

Variable: A symbol which may represent any member of a specified set. The members of the set are called the **values** of the variable. A variable with just one value is called a **constant.** (p. 6)

Vector: A directed line segment or arrow. Vectors are used to represent *vector quantities*, whose designation requires both magnitude and direction. (p. 398)

Vertex (of a parabola): The point in which a parabola intersects its axis. (p. 310)

x-intercept: The abscissa of the point in which a line intersects the x-axis. (p. 93)

y-intercept: The ordinate of the point in which a line intercepts the y-axis. (p. 91)

Zero of a function: In the domain of a function f, any value of x which satisfies the equation $f(x) = 0$. (p. 284)

LIST OF SYMBOLS

Symbol	Meaning	PAGE
a^n	the *n*th power of *a*	39
A^{T}	*A* transpose	552
$\aleph_0$	aleph null	248
$\lvert a \rvert$	absolute value	15
$-a$	additive inverse of *a*, or the negative of *a*	15
$\widehat{TP}$	arc *TP*	463
$\cos^{-1}$	arccosine	478
$A \times B$	Cartesian product	581
$_nC_r$	combinations of *n* elements taken *r* at a time	590
$\overline{A}$	complement of *A*	601
$\equiv$	congruence	198
$\ldots$	continue unendingly	2
$^\circ$	degree	372
$'$	minute	372
$''$	second	372
$\in$	is an element of	1
$\notin$	is not an element of	1
$\emptyset$	empty set	3
$=$	equals *or* is equal to	3
$\neq$	does not equal	3
$\doteq$	equals approximately	192
$f(x)$	*f* of *x* *or* the value of *f* at *x*	213
$!$	factorial	520
$\sum$	sigma (summation sign)	502
$>$	is greater than	8
$<$	is less than	9
$\geq$	is greater than or equal to	9
$\leq$	is less than or equal to	9
$\cap$	intersection	54
A^{-1}	inverse matrix	563
1^{R}	1 radian	464
$\{\ \}$	set	1
$\subset$	subset	2
$\therefore$	therefore	13
$\cup$	union	54
$\overrightarrow{AB}$	the vector *AB*	399
x_1	*x* sub one	85
$_nP_r$	permutations of *n* things taken *r* at a time	585

Greek letters

Symbol	Meaning	PAGE
α, β, γ	alpha, beta, gamma	
δ	delta, determinant function	560
θ, π, ρ	theta, pi, rho	

INDEX

Numerals in **boldface** *refer to the pages on which terms are defined or explained.*

Answers for

Odd-Numbered Exercises

Modern Algebra and Trigonometry

STRUCTURE AND METHOD

BOOK TWO

Revised Edition

MARY P. DOLCIANI
SIMON L. BERMAN
WILLIAM WOOTON

HOUGHTON MIFFLIN COMPANY · BOSTON
NEW YORK · ATLANTA · GENEVA, ILL. · DALLAS · PALO ALTO

ANSWERS FOR ODD-NUMBERED EXERCISES

Pages 4–5 Written Exercises **A** **1.** 9 **3.** 0 **5.** 2 **7.** 1 **9.** $\neq$ **11.** 6 **13.** $\neq$ **B** **15.** $=$ **17.** 0 **19.** 3 **21.** $\{-7\}, \{27\}, \{14\}$ **23.** $\{-7, 27, 14\}$ **25.** $\{-7, 14\}, \{-7, 27, 14\}$ **27.** Yes **29.** No **31.** No **33.** Yes **35.** $8 = 2^3$; $16 = 2^4$

Pages 7–8 Written Exercises **A** **1.** {F. D. Roosevelt, Truman, Eisenhower} **3.** {Dolciani, Berman, Wooton} **5.** $\{2, 4, 6, \ldots\}$ **7.** $\{\ldots, -3, -2, -1, 1, 2, 3, \ldots\}$ **B** **9.** $\{\{0, 1\}, \{0\}, \{1\}, \emptyset\}$ **11.** $\{5, 6\}$ **13.** $\{\emptyset\}$

Pages 13–14 Written Exercises **A** **1.** a. Closed; b. Closed **3.** a. Not closed; b. Not closed **5.** a. Closed; b. Closed **7.** a. Not closed; b. Closed **9.** a. Not closed; b. Closed **C** **11.** a. 6; b. Yes; c. Comm. and assoc. **13.** a. 8; b. Yes; c. Not comm., not assoc.

Page 18 Written Exercises **A** **1.** $\{6, -6\}$ **3.** $\{-4\}$ **5.** $\{0\}$ **7.** $\emptyset$ **9.** $\{2\}$ **11.** $\{2, -2\}$ **13.** $\{5\}$ **15.** $\{1, -1\}$ **B** **17.** $\emptyset$ **25.** $\emptyset$

Page 26 Written Exercises **A** **1.** 98.0 **3.** -41 **5.** -36 **7.** 61.2 **9.** 0 **11.** 3 **13.** 0 **15.** -15 **17.** -21 **19.** 0 **21.** -13 **23.** 0 **25.** 10° **27.** 4.4° **33.** Not closed **35.** Closed

Page 30 Written Exercises **A** **1.** 0 **3.** 24 **5.** 290 **7.** -90 **9.** 2 **11.** 0 **13.** 40 **15.** 0 **17.** 3 **19.** -10

Page 33 Chapter Test **1.** Not equal **3.** 10 **7.** a. Not closed; b. Not closed **9.** Axiom of closure for add. **11.** $\{3, -3\}$ **15.** $170\frac{2}{3}$

Pages 34–36 Chapter Review **3.** equal **5.** F **7.** F **9.** T **11.** $\emptyset$ **13.** $\{0\}$ **15.** $\{1, 2, 3, \ldots\}$ **17.** {integers} **19.** $\emptyset$ **21.** number, coordinate **23.** $-3, x, 2$ **29.** a. Not closed; b. Closed **31.** a. Not closed; b. Not closed **33.** Trans. prop. of equality **35.** Add. prop. of equality **37.** Assoc. prop. of mult. **39.** Subst. axiom **41.** additive **43.** $-3 + 2$ **45.** $\{-2\frac{1}{2}\}$ **47.** $\{t: t \geq 0\}$ **49.** $\{-1\}$ **51.** axiom, theorem **55.** subtraction, commutative **57.** Not closed **59.** a. -2; b. 8 **61.** a. -7; b. 5 **63.** -1.9 **65.** 42 **67.** -2

Pages 42–43 Written Exercises **A** **1.** 35 **3.** 6 **5.** -8 **7.** $11x - 6$ **9.** 0 **11.** $-5r - 3$ **13.** $22x + 10xy - 22y$ **B** **15.** $8x^3 + 11x^2 + 2x - 17$ **17.** $5b^3 - 3b^2 + b + 5$ **19.** $2x^3 - 3x^3y + 16x^2y^2 + 10xy^3$ **21.** $25t + 26s$ **23.** $27a + 22$ **25.** $20x^2 - 13x + 12$ **27.** 144 **29.** -20 **31.** -56 **33.** 36 **35.** Yes **37.** No **39.** Yes

Pages 47–48 Written Exercises **A** **1.** $\{3\}$ **3.** $\{-8\}$ **5.** $\{-3\}$ **7.** $\{4\}$ **9.** $\{49\}$ **11.** $\{1.56\}$ **13.** $\{-2\frac{1}{2}\}$ **15.** $\{6\}$ **17.** $\{\frac{3}{5}\}$ **19.** $\{19\}$ **21.** $\{86\frac{1}{2}\}$ **23.** $\{4\}$ **B** **25.** {real nos.} **27.** $\emptyset$ **29.** $\{\frac{2}{9}\}$ **31.** $\{\frac{3}{2}\}$ **33.** $\{-1\}$ **35.** $\{\frac{1}{3}\}$ **37.** $\emptyset$ **C** **39.** 6 **41.** 16 **43.** 81 **45.** 3

Pages 51–52 Written Exercises **A** **1.** $\{x: x \leq -1\}$ **3.** $\{z: z < -10\}$ **5.** $\{a: a \geq 12\}$ **7.** $\{m: m < -4\}$ **9.** $\{c: c < -5\}$ **11.** $\{t: t < 0\}$ **13.** {real nos.} **B** **15.** $\{a: a \geq 1\frac{3}{7}\}$ **17.** $\{d: d < 1\}$ **19.** $\{p: p \leq 0\}$

Pages 55–56 Written Exercises **A** **1.** $\{x: -2 < x < 2\}$ **3.** $\{-2, 12\}$ **5.** $\{5, -4\}$ **7.** $\{y: y > 7$ or $y < 1\}$ **9.** $\{y: -5 \leq y \leq -4\}$ **11.** $\{h: h \leq -\frac{1}{5}$ or $h \geq 1\}$ **B** **13.** $\{-6, -5, -4, -3, -2, -1, 0, 1, 2, 3\}$ **15.** $\{-1, 0, 1, 2\}$ **17.** $\{0, 1, 2, 3, 4\}$ **19.** $\{\ldots, -1, 0, 1, \ldots\}$ **31.** $\{2, 3, 6\}$

Page 59 Written Exercises **A** **1.** $\{2, -6\}$ **3.** $\{0, -30\}$ **5.** $\{-\frac{1}{2}, 0, 8\}$ **7.** $\{1\frac{1}{2}, 3, 4\}$ **B** **9.** $\{\frac{1}{2}, -\frac{1}{3}\}$ **11.** $\{-8\}$ **13.** {real nos.}

Pages 65–67 Problems **A** **1.** 3,100 mi, 31,000 mi **3.** 5 yr, 35 yr **5.** 3 quarters, 12 dimes **7.** 40 **9.** 23 in, 24 in, 25 in **11.** 81 sq in **13.** 82 **15.** 35 mph, 45 mph **17.** 40 mph **19.** 15°, 75° **21.** 38°, 71° **23.** 8 cm, 4 cm **B** **25.** Bill, \$105; Mary, \$65 **27.** 8 tables and 16 chairs **29.** Widow: between \$4000 and \$6000; sons: between \$2000 and \$3000

Pages 72–73 Chapter Test **1.** $m^3r^2 + 3m^2r^3 - 2mr^4 - 3$; 5th degree **3.** $\{3\}$ **5.** $\{n: n \leq -2\}$ **7.** $\{h: 1 \leq h < 3\}$ **9.** $\{-\frac{1}{3}, 2\frac{1}{2}\}$ **11.** 12 lb

Pages 73–75 Chapter Review **1.** denominator **3.** monomial, monomials **5.** $-s^2t + 3st - 14st^2$ **7.** equivalent, solution set **9.** $\{-3\}$ **11.** $\{-9\}$ **13.** 4 **15.** F **17.** F (if $c < 0$) **19.** $\{m: m \neq 2\}$ **21.** $\{2, 4\}$ **23.** $\emptyset$ **25.** $\{s: -\frac{2}{3} \leq s \leq 3\}$ **27.** $\{n: -4 < n < 2\}$ **33.** If P moves a distance of 5 units along the number line, then P moves from -2 to 3. **35.** $\{0, -3\}$ **37.** domain **41.** 23 **43.** 14 ft, 5 ft

Pages 78–79 Written Exercises A In Ex. 1–20 answers vary. **1.** (3, 4), (2, 6), (6, −2) **3.** (3, 2), ($\frac{1}{5}$, 0),(10, 7) **5.** (−3, 2), (1, −1), (5, −4) **7.** (0, −3), (2, 3), (−1, −6) **9.** (5, 0), (1, 2), (3, 1) **11.** (2, 3), (2, 4), (2, −3) **B 13.** (1, −3), (2, −1), (5, 4) **15.** (1, 3), (−1, 1), (2, 4) **17.** (1, −1), (0, 2), (−2, 0) **19.** (−5, −1), (−8, −2), (−13, −3) **21.** (−3, −11) **23.** ($\frac{3}{2}$, 0), ($-\frac{3}{2}$, 0)

Pages 79–80 Problems A 1–6. Answers vary **7.** 94, 85, 76, 67, 58, 49 **B 9.** {(1, 14), (2, 13), (3, 12), (4, 11), (5, 10), (6, 9), (7, 8), (8, 7), (9, 6), (10, 5), (11, 4), (12, 3), (13, 2), (14, 1)} **11–16.** Answers vary

Page 84 Written Exercises B 31. $k = -10$ **33.** $k = 2$ **35.** (6, −1) **37.** (−2, 3)

Pages 89–90 Written Exercises A 19. Yes; 2 **21.** No **23.** Yes; $-\frac{3}{2}$ **25.** Yes; −2 **B 27.** a. $\frac{3}{4}$; b. (0, −2) **29.** a. $-\frac{5}{3}$; b. (0, −2) **31.** $a = 1$ **33.** $a = -\frac{1}{2}$ **C 35.** $a = -\frac{1}{2}$

Pages 94–95 Written Exercises A 1. $x + y = 5$ **3.** $-3x + y = 5$ **5.** $-x + 2y = -4$ **7.** $x - y = 0$ **9.** $y = -2$ **11.** $x = 10$ **13.** $-x + y = 1$ **15.** $x + 4y = 8$ **17.** $x + 2y = 0$ **19.** $-5x + 2y = 9$ **21.** $y = 3$ **23.** $x = 0$ **B 25.** $y = x + 3$ **27.** $2x + 3y = 11$ **29.** $x = -5$ **31.** $y = 3x - 12$ **33.** $x = -5$ **35.** $y = -7x - 13$ **37.** $3x + 2y = 6$ **C 39.** $x - ay = a - 3a^2$

Pages 99–100 Written Exercises A 1. {(4, 1)}; ind. **3.** {(−3, −3)}; ind. **5.** {(9, 1)}; ind. **7.** $\{(r, s): r - 8s = 11\}$; dep. **9.** {($\frac{1}{2}$, −3)}; ind. **11.** {(60, −13)}; ind. **13.** {($-\frac{37}{7}$, $\frac{40}{7}$)}; ind. **15.** {($\frac{1}{3}$, $\frac{1}{4}$)}; ind. **17.** ∅; inc. **19.** $\{(r, s): 3r - 4s = 15\}$; dep. **B 21.** $\{(\frac{5}{2}a, -\frac{1}{2}a)\}$ **23.** $\{(a + b, a - b)\}$ **25.** $\left\{\left(\frac{bd - ac}{b^2 - a^2}, \frac{bc - ad}{b^2 - a^2}\right)\right\}$ **27.** $\left\{\left(\frac{t}{r}, 0\right)\right\}$ **C 29.** $\left\{\left(\frac{b}{a}, \frac{a}{b}\right)\right\}$ **31.** $a = \frac{35}{11}$, $b = \frac{5}{11}$

Pages 101–103 Problems A 1. $\frac{3}{8}$, $\frac{9}{2}$ **3.** 23°, 67° **5.** 900 @ \$4.00, 700 @ \$2.75 **7.** 1008 lb, 792 lb **9.** 150 mph, 30 mph **11.** 14 girls, 23 boys **13.** Mary, 100 lb; Jane, 97 lb **B 15.** $A = \frac{7}{3}$, $B = 1$ **17.** $m = 4$, $b = -3$ **19.** $R = 6S - 15$ **21.** 51 **23.** 36 **25.** 27 **27.** 3 mph **C 29.** 7 mph, 5 mph

Pages 109–110 Written Exercises A 7. $x + 3y = 6$, $x + 2z = 6$, $3y + 2z = 6$ **9.** $x + 5y = 10$, $x = 10$, $y = 2$ **11.** $x + y = 0$, $x = 0$, $y = 0$ **17.** {($-\frac{1}{3}$, $\frac{8}{3}$, $-\frac{5}{3}$)} **19.** {(1, 3, 4)} **21.** {($\frac{1}{2}$, 1, $-\frac{1}{2}$)} **B 23.** {(−122, 137, −53)} **25.** {(1, 2, −1)} **27.** Infinite solution set **29.** No solutions **31.** {(1, 2, −1)} **33.** No solutions **35.** $A = 1$, $B = \frac{1}{2}$, $C = \frac{1}{8}$ **37.** $A = 3$, $B = 2$, $C = -1$

Pages 116–117 Extra for Experts 1. Max. = 9, min. = −15 **3.** Max. = 10, min. = −4 **5.** a. 400 consoles, 200 portables; b. 400 consoles, 200 portables

Page 119 Chapter Test 1. (3, 6, 8), (4, 8, 5) **3.** (4, −1) **5.** $y = \frac{1}{2}x - 3$ **7.** {($-\frac{1}{2}$, 3)}; ind. **9.** {(3, 4, 1)}

Pages 119–121 Chapter Review 1. ordered pairs, numbers **3.** (−1, 2), (3, −1), (7, −4) **5.** 10, 31, 52, 73, 94 **7.** 13 **9.** −1 **11.** (4, 1) **13.** the ordinates, the abscissas **15.** $-\frac{3}{7}$ **17.** $\frac{3}{5}$ **21.** No **23.** coordinates, satisfy **25.** $y = -x + 3$ **27.** $y = x + 4$ **29.** $y = \frac{2}{3}x - 1$ **31.** inconsistent **33.** {($\frac{3}{2}$, −1)}; ind. **35.** $12\frac{1}{2}$ mph, $2\frac{1}{2}$ mph **37.** {(3, 4, −5)} **39.** half-plane

Pages 126–127 Written Exercises 1. $24x^6$ **3.** $15a^3b^3$ **5.** $-36r^3s^3t^3$ **7.** $60x^2y^4$ **9.** $144s^{10}y^4$ **11.** $-108r^8s^{13}t^9$ **13.** $16a^2$ **15.** $-\frac{4p}{m^2}$ **17.** $-\frac{2x^4}{9y}$ **19.** $\frac{27b^3}{125c^6}$ **B 21.** $-172b^5$ **23.** $28x^2y^2$ **25.** $4x^2 - 20x^4$

Pages 129–130 Written Exercises A 1. $x^4 + 4x^2 + 3$ **3.** $\frac{1}{2}n^2 + 2n - 6$ **5.** $.09x^2 - 1$ **7.** $z^6 - 6z^3 + 9$ **9.** $2x^6 - 9x^3 - 5$ **11.** $x^{4a} + 4x^{2a} + 4$ **13.** $8a^3 + 36a^2b + 54ab^2 + 27b^3$ **15.** $8y^3 - 27$ **17.** $343z^3 + 1$ **B 19.** $a^3 - 3a^2 + a + 1$ **21.** $a^3 + a^2b - ab^2 - b^3$ **23.** $m^3 + m^2n - mn^2 - n^3$ **25.** $x^3 - 5x^2 + 6x$ **27.** $-5x^3 - 30x^2y - 45xy^2$ **29.** $x^3 + 2x^2 - 5x - 6$ **31.** $2a^4 - 11a^3 + 18a^2 - 4a - 8$ **33.** $15t^3 + 24t^2 - 6t$ **35.** $-12x^4 + 3x^2 - x + 6$ **C 37.** $k = 3$ **39.** $k = 2$ **41.** $k = -7$ **43.** {−1}

Pages 132–133 Written Exercises A 1. 2^7 **3.** $2 \cdot 3^2 \cdot 5 \cdot 7$ **5.** 53 **7.** $2^3 \cdot 7^2 \cdot 13$ **9.** 25; 375 **11.** 45; 450 **13.** $2xy$; $10x^2y^3$ **15.** $2rs$; $12r^3s^2$ **17.** 1; $4x^2yz^2$ **19.** $17xz$; $102x^2yz^3$ **B 21.** 1, 2, 4, 7, 14 **23.** 1, 2, p, $2p$ **25.** 168

Page 135 Written Exercises A 1. $2(x - 3)(x + 3)$ **3.** $x(x - 2)(x + 2)$ **5.** $(a^2 + 4)(a - 2)(a + 2)$ **7.** $5(a - 3)^2$ **9.** $-1(k - 18)^2$ **11.** $(x + y)(a - b)$ **13.** $5(b + 7)^2$ **15.** $2(x - 16)^2$ **17.** $(m + n)(m^2 - mn + n^2)$ **19.** $(4x - 1)(16x^2 + 4x + 1)$ **21.** $(3y - 1)(9y^2 + 3y + 1)$ **23.** $(a - 1)(3a - 2x)$

25. $(5 - y)(25 + 5y + y^2)$ **27.** $(9 - 2y)(81 + 18y + 4y^2)$ **B 29.** $(x^2 - 3)(x^4 + 3x^2 + 9)$ **31.** $(mn^2 + d)(m^2n^4 - mn^2d + d^2)$ **33.** $(1 - 2n^2)(1 + 2n^2 + 4n^4)$ **35.** $(a - 1)(a + 1)(a - b)$ **37.** $(x - 1 + y)(x - 1 - y)$ **39.** $(6 + a + 5)^2$ or $(11 + a)^2$ **41.** $(y + 1 + 3t)(y + 1 - 3t)$ **43.** $(x - y)(x + y - 4)$ **C 45.** $(x^a + 1)(x^a - 1)$ **47.** $(t^p - 1)^2$ **49.** $(x - 2y)^3(1 + x - 2y)(1 - x + 2y)$ **51.** $(t - 1)^3(t - 2)(t^2 - t + 1)$

Page 138 Written Exercises A 1. $(x + 5)(x + 1)$ **3.** $(n + 2)(n + 3)$ **5.** $(m + 4s)(m - s)$ **7.** $(y + 6)(y - 2)$ **9.** $(t + 10)(t - 8)$ **11.** $(3 + x)(2 - x)$ **13.** $(6s + 1)^2$ **15.** $(n + 2)(2n - 3)$ **17.** $(n - 70)(n + 50)$ **19.** $2(y - 1)(6y + 7)$ **21.** $(m - 15n)(m - 20n)$ **23.** $(n - 24r)(n + 15r)$ **25.** $6(x + 15)(x - 10)$ **B 27.** $2a^2(a + 9)(a - 4)$ **29.** $(x^a - 1)(x^a - 2)$ **31.** $x^2(x^2 + x + 1)$ **33.** $2(2x - 1)(4x^2 + 2x + 1)$ **35.** $z^2(z^2 + 4)$ **C 37.** $(t^{2m} - 3)(3t^{2m} - 1)$ **39.** $3(x - 2)(3x + 1)$ **41.** $4(y + 2)^2(y - 2)$

Pages 139–140 Written Exercises A 1. $t + 3$; $2(t + 3)$ **3.** $s + 5$; $2(s + 5)(s - 5)$ **5.** x; x^3 **7.** $16y^2(y - 3)$; $96y^3(y + 2)(y - 3)^2$ **B 9.** y; $6y^3(1 - y)(1 + y)$ **11.** $2(x - 1)$; $12x(x - 1)(x - 5)$ **13.** $t^3(t + 1)$; $t^5(t + 1)(t - 1)$ **15.** 1; $(z + 6)(z - 6)$ **17.** 1; $(a + 1)(a - 1)^2$ **C 19.** $v(t - 2)$; $tv^2(t + 2)(t - 2)(t^2 + 4)(t^2 + 2t + 4)$ **21.** $2a(a - 3b)$; $4a^2b(a - 2b)(a + 2b)(a - 3b)$

Pages 142–143 Written Exercises A 1. $\{1, 3\}$ **3.** $\{-4, 8\}$ **5.** $\{0, 9\}$ **7.** $\{3\}$ **9.** $\{3, -3\}$ **11.** $\{0, \frac{5}{2}\}$ **13.** $\{2, 6\}$ **15.** $\{2, \frac{1}{2}\}$ **17.** $\{-\frac{1}{2}, -\frac{2}{3}\}$ **19.** $\{1, -1\}$ **21.** $\{-1, \frac{2}{3}\}$ **23.** $\{2, 3\}$ **25.** $\{24, -15\}$ **B 27.** $\{8a, -2a\}$ **29.** $\left\{\frac{5}{n}, -\frac{8}{n}\right\}$ **31.** $\{0, 3, -2\}$ **33.** $\{0, 6, 1\}$ **35.** $\{1, -1, 2, -2\}$ **C 37.** $\{0, 3, -3, 1, -1\}$ **39.** $\left\{\frac{1}{a + b}\right\}$ **41.** $\{1, -1, \frac{9}{2}\}$ **43.** $\{a + b + 2\}$

Pages 143–144 Problems A 1. 3, 4, 5, 6 or −6, −5, −4, −3 **3.** 14 in **5.** 400 sec **7.** Base, 10 ft; altitude, 8 ft **9.** 12 units × 4 units **11.** 8, 10, 12 or −12, −10, −8 **13.** 10 ft **B 15.** $CE = 8, ED = 6$ or $CE = 6, ED = 8$ **17.** 15 in, 20 in **19.** 2 sec, 198 sec

Pages 147–149 Written Exercises A 1. $5x^2 + 3x - 6$ **3.** $-2x^2 + 3xy + 8y^2$ **5.** $-a^2 + a - 1$ **7.** $4a - 3 + \frac{1}{a}$ **9.** $x + 12$ **11.** $2n + 7$ **13.** $3x - 2$ **15.** $3n^2 - 2n + 3$ **17.** $x - 2 - \frac{2}{x + 6}$ **19.** $x - 3 + \frac{3}{x + 3}$ **21.** $2a^2 + 5a + 2$ **B 23.** $y - a + \frac{2a^2}{y + a}$ **25.** $x^2 - ax + a^2$ **27.** $2t^2 + 2t + \frac{3}{1 - t}$ **29.** $-x^2 + 2x - 8 + \frac{20}{x + 2}$ **31.** $b^2 + 2b + 3$ **33.** $-2x^2 + 15x - 35 - \frac{129x - 76}{2 - 3x - x^2}$ **35.** $a^2 + 2a + 2$ **37.** Yes **C 39.** $k = 8$ **41.** $a = -5, b = 15$

Pages 150–151 Written Exercises A 1. No **3.** Yes **5.** No **7.** Yes **9.** $x - 1$; $2x - 3$ **11.** $x + 2$, $2x - 1$ **13.** $(x + 1)(2x - 3)(3x - 2)$ **15.** $(y - 1)(y - 5)(y - 7)(y - 3)$ **17.** $(y - 1)^2(y + 5)$ **19.** $(x - 1)(x^2 + x + 1)$ **21.** $(t - 2)(t + 2)(t + 3)$ **B 25.** $m = -18$ **27.** $k = 19$

Pages 152–153 Chapter Test 1. $\frac{3b^4}{4c^2}$ **3.** $27t^6 + 8$ **5.** $2s^2t^3$; $144rs^4t^6$ **7.** $(3x - 1)^2(3x + 1)^2$ **9.** $2(n - 21)(n + 4)$ **11.** $n - 1$; $4(n - 1)(n + 1)(n - 8)$ **13.** $\{2, -\frac{7}{3}\}$ **15.** $\{x: x \geq 1\} \cup \{x: x \leq -8\}$ **17.** $(d + 1)(d - 3)(d + 2)$

Pages 153–155 Chapter Review 1. bases **3.** $\frac{d^7}{2a^2c^2}$ **5.** $-\frac{1}{3}n^{2-6s}$ **7.** difference, $m^2 - n^2$ **9.** $x^3 - 19x + 30$ **11.** 62; 372 **13.** $2(6s + 1)^2$ **15.** $(1 + 2ab)^2(1 - 2ab)^2$ **17.** $(1 + a)(x - 5)$ **19.** $2(m + 6)(m + 9)$ **21.** $(h + 8)(8h - 3)$ **23.** 1; $3n(n - 3)$ **25.** $\{0, 9a^2\}$ **27.** $\{8, -2\}$ **29.** $\{\frac{4}{3}, -\frac{9}{4}\}$ **31.** 4 in or 6 in **33.** $\{k: k \leq 0\} \cup \{k: k \geq 2\}$ **35.** 11 **37.** degree, less, degree, 0 **39.** $x - 3$ **41.** $(z + 2)(z - 6)(2z + 1)$

Page 156 Extra for Experts 1. 7 **3.** 18 **5.** 17 **9.** $\{(3, -2)\}$

Pages 161–162 Written Exercises **1.** 16 **3.** $\frac{1}{49}$ **5.** $\frac{1}{9}$ **7.** $\frac{27}{8}$ **9.** $-\frac{1}{216}$ **11.** 625 **13.** .245 **15.** 13 **17.** $\frac{y^5}{x^5}$ **19.** $\frac{b}{6a^3}$ **21.** $\frac{q^7}{p^5r^9}$ **23.** $7a^2$ **B 29.** $x^{-3}(2 - x - 16x^2 + 4x^3)$ **31.** $z^{-4}(7z^5 - z^3 + 2z^2 - 1)$ **33.** $t^{-3}(2 - 3t + 5t^2 + 4t^3 + t^4)$ **C 35.** $(x^2 - 1)^{-3}(-1 - 3x^2)$ **37.** $(2v + 1)^{-2}(2v^2 + 2v - 4)$

Page 164 Written Exercises **A 1.** $\frac{3}{x}$; $\{0\}$ **3.** $\frac{7x}{10}$ or $\frac{0.7x}{1}$; $\emptyset$ **5.** $\frac{t-2}{t}$; $\{0\}$ **7.** $\frac{r}{r-1}$; $\{1\}$ **9.** $\frac{5}{7k+14}$; $\{-2\}$ **11.** $\frac{x}{x(x+3)}$; $\{-3, 0\}$ **B 13.** $\frac{5x+15}{(x-3)(x+1)}$; $\{-1, 3\}$ **15.** $\frac{v-4}{v^2-4}$; $\{-2, 2\}$ **17.** $\frac{z-1}{(z+1)(z-1)}$; $\{-1, 1\}$ **19.** $\frac{5u}{u^2+36}$; $\emptyset$ **21.** $\frac{3+k}{k(k-1)(k+3)}$; $\{-3, 0, 1\}$ **23.** $\frac{c-1}{3c(c-5)(c+2)}$; $\{-2, 0, 5\}$ **C 25.** $\frac{1}{5r(r+s)}$; $\{-s, 0\}$ for r, $\{-r\}$ for s **27.** $\frac{ab}{(a-b)(a-b)}$; $\{b\}$ for a, $\{a\}$ for b **29.** $\frac{t-p}{(t+p)(t-p)}$; $\{-p, p\}$ for t, $\{-t, t\}$ for p **31.** $x \notin \{3, 0, -5, 5\}$ **33.** $n \notin \{0\}$

Pages 166–167 Written Exercises **A 1.** $\frac{5}{243}$ **3.** $\frac{-b}{3a}$ **5.** $x + 3$ **7.** $\frac{t}{t-3}$ **9.** -1 **11.** $\frac{1}{(n+3)^2}$ **13.** 2 **15.** $\frac{1}{a-1}$ **17.** $\frac{2}{x+3}$ **19.** $\frac{2c-1}{2c+1}$ **21.** $\frac{1}{x+6}$ **23.** $\frac{t-2}{t-1}$ **25.** $\frac{k^2+k+1}{2(k+2)}$ **B 27.** 1 **29.** $\frac{(x^2+y^2)(x+y)}{4}$ **31.** $\frac{1-2v}{v^2-2}$ **C 33.** $\frac{-2t(t^2+3)(t^2+21)}{(t^2-6)^4}$ **35.** $\frac{2y(y^3+4)(-4y^3+6y^2+3y-16)}{(2y+1)^5}$

Pages 168–170 Written Exercises **A 1.** $-\frac{3}{4}$ **3.** 24 **5.** $\frac{15a}{2}$ **7.** 2 **9.** $\frac{5b^2}{2}$ **11.** $\frac{3c}{5}$ **13.** $\frac{-30x}{y^2}$ **15.** $\frac{x+1}{x-1}$ **17.** $\frac{1}{y-8}$ **19.** $\frac{2(z+4)}{z-2}$ **21.** 1 **B 23.** $\frac{4}{9a^3c^2}$ **25.** $\frac{2a-1}{2a+1}$ **27.** $\frac{2x+1}{2x+3}$

Pages 172–173 Written Exercises **A 1.** $\frac{7}{5}$ **3.** $\frac{49}{12}$ **5.** 1 **7.** $\frac{5}{4a}$ **9.** $\frac{7x-3}{3x^2}$ **11.** $\frac{26m+n}{12n}$ **13.** $\frac{2a^2-4a+3}{4a^2}$ **15.** $\frac{5x-11}{6}$ **17.** $\frac{17n^2-2n+6}{12n^2}$ **19.** $\frac{x+1}{x}$ **21.** $\frac{x+5}{x+2}$ **23.** $\frac{7x-2}{3x(x+1)}$ **25.** $\frac{4x}{x^2-1}$ **27.** $\frac{1}{12}$ **29.** $\frac{9t^2+1}{3t-1}$ **B 31.** $\frac{-2}{t}$ **33.** $\frac{2}{y^2-y}$ **35.** $\frac{x-3}{2x-1}$ **37.** $\frac{-3}{m^2-1}$ **39.** $\frac{x^4+x-12}{x^2+3}$ **41.** $\frac{r-s}{r^2-rs+s^2}$ **C 43.** $\frac{s(4r-s)}{(2s-r)(s-r)}$ **45.** $\frac{3(2y-3)(y+2)}{(2y+3)(y+3)}$

Pages 174–175 Written Exercises **A 1.** $\frac{25}{4}$ **3.** $\frac{a^2}{a+2}$ **5.** x **7.** $\frac{-a}{c}$ **9.** $\frac{n-1}{n+2}$ **11.** $\frac{1+y}{y^2-y}$ **13.** 1 **15.** $\frac{2a(a-2)}{4-a}$ **B 17.** $\frac{ab}{b+a}$ **19.** $\frac{2a}{a+1}$ **21.** $\frac{t+1}{2t+1}$ **23.** $\frac{t-1}{t+1}$ **25.** $\frac{m^2n^2}{m^2-mn+n^2}$ **C 27.** $\frac{d^2-c^2}{c^2d^2}$ **29.** $\frac{a^2+a+1}{a^2+1}$ **31.** $\frac{(s^2+r^2)(s+r)}{r^2s}$ **33.** $\frac{a-1}{a+1}$

Pages 177–178 Written Exercises **A 1.** $\{6\}$ **3.** $\{-6\}$ **5.** $\emptyset$ **7.** $\{7500\}$ **9.** $\{-\frac{4}{3}, \frac{1}{2}\}$ **11.** $\{-1, 4\}$ **13.** $\{0, -\frac{2}{3}, \frac{5}{12}\}$ **15.** $\{-\frac{33}{7}\}$ **17.** $\{-\frac{1}{2}\}$ **B 19.** $\{(2, 3)\}$ **21.** $\{(-4, -6)\}$ **23.** $\{(-1, 6)\}$ **25.** $\left\{\left(\frac{11}{7}, \frac{-52}{21}\right)\right\}$ **35.** $\frac{1}{81}(9x+1)(9x-1)$ **37.** $\frac{1}{125}(1-5y)(1+5y+25y^2)$ **39.** $\frac{1}{9}(3a-2)(3a-2)$ **41.** $\frac{1}{6}(3t+1)(2t-1)$ **43.** $\frac{1}{12}(x)(3x+2)(4x-3)$

Pages 180–183 Problems **A 1.** C–1, 200 ft; C–5, 350 ft **3.** News Report, 248,000; Fashion World, 35,500 **5.** 12, 18 **7.** 18 min **9.** 6 mi **11.** $\frac{42000}{11}$ in/sec **13.** 6 fluid oz **15.** $2\frac{3}{10}$ oz **17.** $22\frac{1}{2}$ lb 20% copper, $37\frac{1}{2}$ lb 12% copper **19.** 6 tons **B 21.** 24 min **23.** \$127.01 **25.** \$23.81 **27.** $\frac{3}{14}$ hr **29.** 100 lb **C 31.** .14 hr **33.** 312 ft

Pages 186–187 Written Exercises **A 1.** $\{9\}$ **3.** $\{5\}$ **5.** $\{-\frac{5}{2}\}$ **7.** $\emptyset$ **9.** $\{2\}$ **11.** $\{2\}$ **13.** $\emptyset$ **15.** $\{-2, 2\}$ **B 17.** $\{2\}$ **19.** $\{-\frac{1}{4}, 5\}$ **21.** $\{(2, -1)\}$ **23.** $\{(1, 5)\}$ **C 25.** $\{(\frac{1}{2}, -1)\}$ **27.** $\{(-3, -\frac{1}{2})\}$ **29.** $\{2\}$ **31.** $\{24\}$

Pages 187–189 Problems A 1. 15 mph **3.** 7 mph **5.** 30 **7.** 36, 66 **9.** $\frac{63}{56}$ **11.** Mechanic, $3\frac{1}{3}$ hr; helper $6\frac{2}{3}$ hr **13.** 12 mph **15.** $1\frac{1}{3}$ hr **B 17.** 91 mi **19.** $\frac{6}{7}$ **21.** 20 pt/min **23.** \$60 **25.** 10 **27.** 9 **C 29.** 36 ft/min **31.** 12.2 < oz copper < 25.8

Pages 191–192 Written Exercises A 1. 0.12 **3.** $-0.\overline{63}$ **5.** 10.125 **7.** $-0.9\overline{3}$ **9.** $\frac{27,777}{10,000}$ **11.** $\frac{-3}{2500}$ **13.** $\frac{2}{9}$ **15.** $\frac{56}{99}$ **17.** $\frac{7133}{222}$ **19.** $-\frac{4}{1125}$ **B 23.** $x = \frac{2}{11}$

Pages 195–196 Written Exercises A 1. 7.35×10^1 **3.** 6.54×10^0 **5.** 1.76×10^{-2} **7.** 7.09×10^{-3} **9.** 1.237×10^5 **11.** 1.2×10^{-5} **13.** 3.8×10^2 **15.** 10,000 **17.** 0.00001 **19.** 1230 **21.** 0.09873 **23.** 200 **25.** 0.0016 **27.** 60,000 **29.** 0.005 **31.** 1 cm; 0.005 M; $12\frac{1}{2}\%$ **33.** 10 M; 5 M; 2% **35.** $\frac{1}{100,000}$ M; 0.000005 M; $1\frac{1}{4}\%$ **37.** 1000 M; 500 M; 0.4%

Page 196 Problems A 1. 2×10^{10}; 5×10^9 **3.** 2.2×10^{-2} **5.** 2.8×10^{-1} **7.** 4.00×10^{-5} cm **B 9.** 12.25 sq ft, 20.25 sq ft

Pages 201–202 Chapter Test 1. $\frac{3}{400}$ **3.** $-\frac{3c^8}{a^2b^2}$ **5.** $\emptyset$ **7.** $\frac{1}{a}$ **9.** 0 **11.** $\{-16\}$ **13.** 30 mph **15.** 4.32×10^4

Pages 202–205 Chapter Review 1. nonzero, zero **3.** $\frac{3}{2}$; $\frac{9}{4}$ **5.** $\frac{8s^9}{t^6}$ **7.** $3^{-1}h^{-2}k^{-2}mt^{-3}$; $\frac{m}{3h^2k^2t^3}$ **9.** $\{0, 4\}$ **11.** $\emptyset$ **13.** $2r^2 + r$ **15.** $\frac{h^2 + 4h + 16}{h + 4}$ **17.** $\frac{2c^{10}}{5d}$ **19.** $\frac{-y^5}{(y^2 + 4)(y + 2)^2}$ **21.** $\frac{9}{2}(2a - 1)$ **23.** $\frac{3m - 5}{10}$ **25.** $\frac{40x - 5}{4x(4x - 1)}$ **27.** $\frac{x(3x - 1)}{3(x + 2)}$ **29.** $\emptyset$ **31.** $\frac{5}{6}$ **33.** $0.14d$ **35.** 2 hr **37.** \$750 *at* 4%, \$450 at 6% **39.** polynomial **41.** $\{-\frac{1}{2}\}$ **43.** $\{-11, 10\}$ **45.** 12 min, 20 min **47.** $0.7\overline{857142}$ **49.** $-\frac{77}{30}$ **51.** thousandth **53.** 0.01 **55.** integer, 1, 10 **57.** 93.0 **59.** 1.8×10^{-5} **51.** 18,000

Pages 206–207 Cum. Review 1. No values **3.** Some values **5.** 28 **7.** $\frac{14}{33}$ **9.** -3 **11.** $\frac{m^2}{4n^4}$ **13.** 1 **15.** $\frac{4x^3 - 6x^2y}{(x + 3)(4x^2 - 6xy + 9y^2)}$ **17.** $\frac{2n(3n - 5)}{3(2n - 3)}$ **21.** $\{-\frac{2}{3}\}$ **23.** $\{-3a\}$, $a \neq 1$ **25.** $\{-1\}$ **27.** {all reals} **29.** $\{(4, -3)\}$ **33.** 47 **35.** $17\frac{1}{7}$ hr **37.** 55 mph **39.** 1 mph **41.** 45 < no of 4¢ stamps < 55

Pages 215–216 Written Exercises A 1. 1 **3.** 1 **5.** $a^2 - 2a + 1$ **7.** $a^2 - 4a + 4$ **9.** -3 **11.** 9 **13.** 6 **15.** 0 **21.** $\{1, 2, 3, 4\}$; $t(x) = 6x + 1$ **23.** $\{-1, 0, 1\}$; $t(x) = |x|$ **B 25.** 0 **27.** 26 **29.** $3a^2 + 6a + 2$ **31.** 5; 5 **33.** c; c **35.** $y = -2$

Pages 221–222 Written Exercises 1. 90 **3.** 3π **5.** 15 **7.** 5 **9.** 3 **C 19.** 3

Pages 222–223 Problems A 1. 2 lb/sec **3.** 161 g **5.** \$270 **7.** 264 ft/sec **9.** 1000 mi **11.** 2.16 **13.** 1680 ft **15.** 72 **B 17.** $a = \frac{3}{2}$, $b = 2$ **19.** 2

Pages 229–230 Written Exercises A 7. (2, 20) **9.** Neither **11.** $\frac{2}{3}$ **13.** -10 **15.** $-\frac{1}{2}$ **17.** 108 **19.** 3 or -3 **B 21.** 96 **23.** Multiplied by 4 **25.** Multiplied by $\frac{1}{8}$ **C 27.** $-\frac{1}{2}$, $\frac{1}{2}$ **29.** $\frac{4k}{9}$

Pages 230–232 Problems A 1. 5000 lb **3.** 55,102 BTU **5.** 7.3 in **7.** $1066\frac{2}{3}$ **9.** $1\frac{1}{3}$ **11.** 27 ft-lb **13.** 250 **15.** $\frac{4}{9}$ **17.** 4500 cu M; $\frac{4}{25}$ **19.** 0.49 to 1

Pages 235–236 Written Exercises A 9. -17 **11.** $\frac{49}{2}$ **13.** 2, -2 **B 15.** 8, -2 **17.** -7, 5 **19.** 5, -1 **21.** -5, -1 **23.** $a = -4$, $k = 16$ **25.** $a = 2$, $k = -3$

Pages 240–242 Problems B 1. 1260 ft **3.** -16 **5.** 80,000; 320,000 **7.** 275 watts **C 9.** 32, -32 **11.** \$15.00 **13.** $6x - x^2$; 9

Page 243 Written Exercises A 1. 1.7 or -1.7; 2.6 or -2.6 **3.** 3.4 or .6; 5 or -1 **5.** -5 or 0; -2 or -3 **7.** 2.2 or $-.2$; 2.4 or $-.4$

Pages 244–245 Chapter Test 1. {real nos. excluding $\frac{1}{2}$}; {real nos. excluding 0} **3.** Yes **5.** 77 g **9.** 90 sq in; 160 sq in **11.** $-\frac{9}{2}$ **13.** $37\frac{1}{2}$¢ **15.** $x \doteq -.4$ or -5.6; $x \doteq -.6$ or -5.4

Pages 245–247 Chapter Review 1. set; ordered **3.** range **5.** {real nos. excluding 0} **7.** function; (3, 0), (3, −3) **9.** -3; $1 + 4a - 12a^2 - 8a^3$ **11.** 0; 0 **13.** False **15.** True **17.** 33 **21.** 3 **23.** vertex **27.** $\frac{2}{3}$ or $-\frac{2}{3}$ **29.** $x = -2$ **31.** $(-2, -4)$; min. **33.** $x = -\frac{1}{4}$ **39.** $x \doteq .6$ or 5.4

Pages 254–255 Written Exercises A 1. 1.7 **3.** 1.2 **5.** −1.9 **7.** −1.5 **9.** 1.4 **11.** −1.1 **13.** 0.9 **15.** −1.8 **17.** $\{-\frac{7}{6}, \frac{7}{6}\}$ **19.** $\{-\frac{5}{4}\}$ **21.** ∅ **23.** $\{-\frac{10}{11}, \frac{10}{11}\}$ **B 25.** {−12} **27.** 4 **29.** $-\frac{5}{6}$

Pages 258–259 Written Exercises B 15. {1} **17.** {−4, 2, 3} **19.** $\{-\frac{1}{3}\}$ **21.** $\{0, \frac{15}{2}\}$

Page 263 Written Exercises A 1. 2.23 **3.** −1.25 **5–14.** Answers vary

Pages 266–268 Written Exercises 1. 33.9 **3.** 13.4 **5.** 0.775 **7.** 4.58 **9.** 255 **11.** −3.78 **13.** 1 **15.** $\frac{2\sqrt[4]{3}}{3}$ **17.** $-8\sqrt[5]{2}$ **19.** $4x^2\sqrt{2x}; x \geq 0$ **21.** $2x\sqrt[3]{4y}$ **23.** $ab\sqrt[5]{a}$ **25.** $\frac{\sqrt[5]{a^3}}{a}; a \neq 0$ **27.** $\frac{\sqrt[5]{k^4}}{k^2}; k \neq 0$ **29.** $\frac{2y^2\sqrt[6]{2x^4}}{x^2}; x \neq 0$ **31.** $30ab\sqrt[3]{4}$ **33.** $3h\sqrt[4]{3g^2h}; g \geq 0$ and $h \geq 0$ **35.** $6x^2\sqrt{2}; x > 0$ **37.** $\frac{\sqrt{3a^2+1}}{3a^2+1}$ **39.** $\frac{k^2\sqrt[6]{8}}{2}; k \neq 0$ **41.** $|a-2|$ **B 43.** $81r^8$ **45.** $\frac{a}{4}\sqrt[4]{4}; a > 0$ **47.** $\frac{\sqrt{x-1}}{x^2(x-1)}; x > 1$ **49.** $\frac{(x+3)^2\sqrt{x}}{x|x-7|}; x > 0, x \neq 7$ **51.** $\frac{3a}{\sqrt{15a}}$ **53.** $\frac{2(x+1)^2}{\sqrt[3]{4(x+1)^2}}$ **55.** $\frac{7(t^2+3)}{\sqrt[4]{343(t^2+3)^3}}$

Pages 268–269 Problems A 1. $\frac{11\sqrt{6}}{7} \doteq 4$ sec **3.** $4\sqrt{2} \doteq 6$ in **5.** $400\sqrt{2} \doteq 566$ ft/sec **B 7.** $\frac{32\sqrt{77}}{7} \doteq 40$ cm **9.** $\frac{\sqrt{6\pi}}{6} \doteq \frac{5}{7}$

Pages 270–271 Written Exercises A 1. irrational; −7.52 **3.** rational **5.** irrational; 5.13 **7.** irrational; −17.1 **9.** rational **11.** irrational; 4.23 **13.** $\frac{11}{2}\sqrt[4]{5}$ **15.** $-114x\sqrt{x}$ **17.** $3\sqrt[4]{4}(y^2+1)$ **19.** $\sqrt[3]{5y^2}(5y-2) + y^2\sqrt[3]{5}$ **B 21.** $\sqrt{3y}(10-2y)$ **23.** $\frac{-13n}{60}$ **25.** $-\frac{\sqrt{x}}{x^2}$ **27.** $\{\sqrt{2}\}$ **29.** {1} **31.** $\{1-2\sqrt{7}, 1+2\sqrt{7}\}$ **33.** $\left\{-5-\frac{\sqrt{2}}{11}, -5+\frac{\sqrt{2}}{11}\right\}$ **35.** $\{-2\sqrt{3}, 2\sqrt{3}\}$

Pages 272–274 Written Exercises A 1. $30\sqrt{5} - 25\sqrt{2}$ **3.** −1 **5.** $5 + 2\sqrt{6}$ **7.** $\frac{2+\sqrt{3}}{2}$ **9.** $57 - 13\sqrt{6}$ **11.** $\sqrt[4]{4} - 1$ **13.** $a\sqrt[3]{a^2} - \sqrt[3]{a}$ **15.** $\frac{\sqrt{7}-1}{2}$ **17.** $-13(\sqrt{3}-\sqrt{2})$ **19.** $-7(2-\sqrt{5})$ **21.** $\frac{5\sqrt{3}+7}{2}$ **B 23.** 4 **25.** $a + b$ **27.** $\frac{2(a+b)}{a-b}$ **29.** 0 **31.** $\frac{\sqrt{x+1}-2}{x-3}$ **33.** $\frac{\sqrt[3]{25}+\sqrt[3]{5}+1}{4}$ **35.** $\frac{4\sqrt{3}+\sqrt{6}}{7}$ **C 37.** $\frac{1}{\sqrt{z-1}}$ **39.** $-\frac{1}{\sqrt[3]{(x^2+1)^2}}$ **41.** $(y-3\sqrt{3})(y+3\sqrt{3})$ **43.** $(t+\sqrt{6})^2$ **45.** $(n-2\sqrt{3})^2$ **47.** $(a+b+\sqrt{2})(a+b-\sqrt{2})$

Pages 276–277 Written Exercises A 1. {7, −1} **3.** $\{4+\sqrt{17}, 4-\sqrt{17}\}$; {8.1, −0.1} **5.** $\left\{\frac{-5+3\sqrt{5}}{2}, \frac{-5-3\sqrt{5}}{2}\right\}$; {0.9, −5.9} **7.** $\{\frac{2}{3}, -\frac{5}{2}\}$ **9.** $\left\{\frac{-1+\sqrt{13}}{6}, \frac{-1-\sqrt{13}}{6}\right\}$; {0.4, −0.8} **11.** $\left\{\frac{4+2\sqrt{29}}{5}, \frac{4-2\sqrt{29}}{5}\right\}$; {3.0, −1.4} **13.** $\{-\frac{4}{3}\}$ **15.** $\left\{\frac{-4+\sqrt{10}}{3}, \frac{-4-\sqrt{10}}{3}\right\}$; {−0.3, −2.4} **17.** $\{\frac{1}{2}, -\frac{1}{4}\}$ **19.** $\left\{\frac{1+\sqrt{97}}{4}, \frac{1-\sqrt{97}}{4}\right\}$; {2.7, −2.2} **B 21.** $\{\frac{3}{7}, -\frac{2}{5}\}$ **23.** $\left\{\frac{3+\sqrt{57}}{6}, \frac{3-\sqrt{57}}{6}\right\}$; {1.8, −0.8} **25.** $\left\{\frac{1+\sqrt{37}}{2}, \frac{1-\sqrt{37}}{2}\right\}$; {3.5, −2.5} **27.** $\{-1+\sqrt{2}, -1-\sqrt{2}\}$; {0.4, −2.4} **29.** $\left\{\frac{-1+3\sqrt{5}}{2}, \frac{-1-3\sqrt{5}}{2}\right\}$; {2.9, −3.9} **31.** ∅ **33.** $\left\{\frac{\sqrt{6}+\sqrt{2}}{2}, \frac{\sqrt{6}-\sqrt{2}}{2}\right\}$; {1.9, 0.5}

35. $\{-1 + \sqrt{\sqrt{5} + 1}, -1 - \sqrt{\sqrt{5} + 1}$; $\{0.8, -2.8\}$ **C 37.** $\left\{\frac{\sqrt{10} + 3\sqrt{2}}{2}, \frac{\sqrt{10} - 3\sqrt{2}}{2}\right\}$; $\{3.7, -0.5\}$
39. $\left\{-\frac{1 + \sqrt{3}}{2}, 1\right\}$; $\{-1.4, 1\}$ **41.** $\{\sqrt{-2 + \sqrt{5}}, -\sqrt{-2 + \sqrt{5}}\}$; $\{0.5, -0.5\}$ **43.** $\{\sqrt[6]{3}, -\sqrt[6]{3}\}$; $\{1.2, -1.2\}$ **45.** $(x - 1 + \sqrt{2})(x - 1 - \sqrt{2})$ **47.** $y(y + 3 + \sqrt{7})(y + 3 - \sqrt{7})$

Pages 277–279 Problems A 1. $12\frac{1}{2}$ cm; $7\frac{1}{2}$ cm **3.** 9.5 in; 15.5 in **5.** $-3 + \sqrt{11}$ M **B 7.** $384 - 256\sqrt{2}$ sq in **9.** $n = 6$ **11.** 3 in by 3 in; 3 in by $2\frac{1}{2}$ in

Pages 280–281 Written Exercises A 1. $x^2 + 5x + 6 = 0$ **3.** $2x^2 - 3x - 2 = 0$ **5.** $3x^2 - x = 0$ **7.** $6x^2 + 5x + 1 = 0$ **9.** $x^2 + 4x + 4 = 0$ **11.** $x^2 - 6x + 7 = 0$ **13.** $16x^2 + 16x + 1 = 0$ **15.** $x^2 - 2\sqrt{2}\,x - 1 = 0$ **17.** $x^2 - (1 + \sqrt[3]{2})x = 0$ **B 19.** $\frac{2}{5}$; $b = 23$ **21.** $2 - \sqrt{3}$; $c = 3$ **23.** $-\frac{3}{2}$; $c = \frac{27}{2}$ **C 25.** $-4 - 2\sqrt{7}, -4 + 2\sqrt{7}$

Pages 284–285 Written Exercises A 1. 2 unequal rational roots **3.** 2 unequal irrational roots **5.** no real roots **7.** 2 unequal irrational roots **9.** no real roots **11.** 2 points; rational **13.** no points **B 15.** 2 points; irrational **17.** $2\sqrt{5}, -2\sqrt{5}$ **19.** $k < -4$

Pages 286–287 Written Exercises A 1. $\{x: -\sqrt{7} < x < \sqrt{7}\}$ **3.** $\{r: r \leq 0 \text{ or } r \geq \sqrt{3}\}$ **5.** $\{t: -2 \leq t \leq \frac{3}{2}\}$ **7.** $\{v: v \neq -3\}$ **9.** $\{x: x \leq -11 \text{ or } x \geq 1\}$ **11.** $\{\sqrt{3}\}$ **B 13.** $\{x: -\sqrt{2} \leq x \leq 0 \text{ or } x \geq \sqrt{2}\}$ **15.** $\{x: x \leq -1 \text{ or } 2 \leq x \leq 3\}$ **C 17.** $k < -\sqrt{2}$ or $k > \sqrt{2}$

Pages 288–290 Written Exercises A 1. $\{64\}$ **3.** $\{62\}$ **5.** $\{3\}$ **7.** $\{32\}$ **9.** $\{-\frac{1}{8}\}$ **11.** $\{4\}$ **13.** $\{-4, 3\}$ **15.** $\{3\}$ **17.** $\emptyset$ **19.** $\{-4\}$ **21.** $\emptyset$ **23.** $\{2, 3\}$ **25.** $\{1, 7\}$ **27.** $\emptyset$ **B 29.** $\{-\frac{34}{5}, 4\}$ **31.** $\{4\}$ **33.** $\{9\}$ **35.** $\emptyset$ **37.** $d = \frac{3w}{4\pi r^3}$ **39.** $a = \pm\sqrt{c^2 - b^2}$ **41.** $l = \frac{T}{4v^2 - 1}$

Pages 291–292 Chapter Test 1. $\{-\frac{1}{3}, \frac{1}{3}\}$ **5.** $\frac{9}{4}\sqrt{6}$ **7.** $12\sqrt{3} - 52\sqrt{2}$ **9.** $-\frac{\sqrt{2} - 3\sqrt{10}}{22}$ **11.** 3.3 cm by 9.2 cm **13.** 2 different irrational roots; 2 different rational roots; 1 double rational root **15.** $\{-1\}$

Pages 292–295 Chapter Review 1. 2; 2 **3.** $\{-\frac{3}{2}, \frac{3}{2}\}$ **7.** rational **11.** finite; infinite; nonperiodic **13.** 1.72; 1.701001000 . . . **15.** $-\frac{\sqrt{6}}{3}$ **17.** -4 **19.** 0.689 **21.** same index; same radicand **23.** $3\sqrt{3} - 8\sqrt{5}$ **25.** $18\sqrt{3} + 15\sqrt{2}$ **27.** $9 + 3\sqrt{7}$ **29.** $\{1 + \sqrt{11}, 1 - \sqrt{11}\}$; $\{4.3, -2.3\}$ **31.** $\left\{\frac{-\sqrt{3} + 3}{3}, \frac{-\sqrt{3} - 3}{3}\right\}$; $\{0.4, -1.6\}$ **33.** 3.2 ft by 7.7 ft **35.** $-\frac{1}{2}$; $\frac{1}{3}$ **37.** $3x^2 - 16x - 12 = 0$ **39.** 12 **41.** 4 **43.** equal, irrational **45.** unequal, irrational **47.** two **49.** $\{x: x < 1 \text{ or } x > 3\}$ **51.** $\{1, 6\}$

Page 296 Extra for Experts 1. (2, 1, 3, 4) **3.** $(2, \overline{2, 4})$ **5.** $\frac{48}{13}$ **7.** $\frac{1 + \sqrt{5}}{2}$

Page 301 Written Exercises A 1. $(-5, \frac{1}{2})$; 5 **3.** $(\frac{15}{2}, \frac{2}{3})$; 9 **5.** $(\frac{7}{2}, -\frac{3}{2})$; $\sqrt{2}$ **7.** $\left(\frac{3\sqrt{2}}{2}, 1\right)$; $3\sqrt{2}$ **9.** $\left(2\sqrt{5}, \frac{7\sqrt{7}}{2}\right)$; $3\sqrt{3}$ **11.** $(2a, 0)$; $2\sqrt{a^2 + b^2}$ **B 13.** $(9, -10)$ **15.** 12; no; yes; 6 sq units **17.** $3\sqrt{26} + \sqrt{130}$; no; yes; 26 sq units **19.** $4 + 4\sqrt{2}$; yes; yes; 4 sq units

Pages 302–303 Problems A 1. $4\sqrt{5}$ **3.** 25 ft **5.** $2 - \sqrt{2}$ in **7.** 25π sq cm **B 9.** Eastbound, 6 mph; southbound, 10 mph **11.** $3x - 2y = 5$

Pages 305–306 A 1. 5 **3.** no slope **5.** $-\frac{1}{3}$ **7.** $2x - y = -10$ **9.** $5x + 7y = 0$ **B 11.** $24x + 10y = -41$

Page 308 Written Exercises A 1. $x^2 + (y - 4)^2 = 9$ **3.** $(x - 2)^2 + (y + 2)^2 = \frac{49}{4}$ **5.** $(x + 20)^2 + (y - 30)^2 = 5$ **7.** $(x - \frac{9}{4})^2 + (y - \frac{2}{5})^2 = \frac{9}{4}$ **9.** $x^2 + y^2 = r^2$ **B 23.** $\sqrt{10}$; $x^2 + y^2 = 10$ **25.** $\sqrt{41}$; $(x + 1)^2 + (y - 1)^2 = 41$

Pages 311–312 **Written Exercises** **B 15.** $x = \frac{1}{16}y^2$ **17.** $y = -\frac{1}{4}(x + 3)^2 + 5$ **C 19.** $y = 4x - 21$
21. $x^2 + y^2 = -39$, which has no real solns.

Pages 314–315 **Written Exercises** **B 15.** $\frac{x^2}{25} + \frac{y^2}{16} = 1$ **17.** $\frac{x^2}{24} + \frac{y^2}{49} = 1$ **C 19.** $\frac{x^2}{a^2 - c^2} + \frac{y^2}{a^2} = 1$

Pages 317–319 **Written Exercises** **C 21.** $\frac{y^2}{9} - \frac{x^2}{16} = 1$ **23.** $\frac{x^2}{a^2} - \frac{y^2}{c^2 - a^2} = 1$

Pages 321–322 **Written Exercises** **A 7.** 125 **9.** 30, -30 **11.** $\frac{4}{45}$ **B 13.** 12 **15.** $\frac{27}{128}$ **17.** 9 **19.** 32
21. y is halved **C 29.** $2xy = 1$

Pages 322–323 **Problems** **1.** 375 M **3.** 906.25 rpm **5.** 1760 lb **7.** 7.07 ft **9.** approx. 82 min
11. 133.3 lb **13.** 20 lb, 30 lb

Page 325 **Written Exercises** **A 1.** 2 **3.** 0 **5.** 2 **7.** 4 **9.** 2 In Ex. 11–28 given values are approximate.
11. $\{(2, -2), (6, 6)\}$ **13.** $\{(2\frac{1}{3}, 3\frac{2}{3}), (-1\frac{3}{4}, -4\frac{3}{4})\}$ **15.** $\{(0, -6), (4\frac{4}{5}, 3\frac{3}{5})\}$ **17.** $\{(3\frac{3}{4}, 1), (1, 3\frac{3}{4}), (-1, -3\frac{3}{4}),$
$(-3\frac{3}{4}, -1)\}$ **19.** $\emptyset$ **B 21.** $\{(5, 4), (-5, 4), (-5, -4), (5, -4)\}$ **23.** $\{(-7\frac{1}{4}, 12\frac{1}{4}), (-4\frac{1}{2}, -7\frac{1}{4})\}$
25. $\emptyset$ **27.** $\{(4, 4)\}$ **C 37.** $\emptyset$

Pages 327–328 **Written Exercises** **A 1.** $\emptyset$ **3.** $\{(3, 4), (-2, -6)\}$ **5.** $\{(4, 3), (-\frac{56}{13}, -\frac{33}{13})\}$ **7.** $\{(6, 0),$
$(0, -3)\}$ **9.** $\{(\frac{7}{3}, \frac{2}{3}), (3, 2)\}$ **11.** $\emptyset$ **13.** $\emptyset$ **15.** $\{(\frac{1}{20}, -\frac{6}{5}), (\frac{3}{4}, \frac{2}{3})\}$ **17.** $\{(-\frac{1}{2}, 5), (2, 0)\}$ **19.** $\{(\frac{20}{2}, \frac{53}{6}),$
$(-3, 4)\}$ **B 21.** $\{(3, 6)\}$ **23.** $\{(\frac{1}{3}, -\frac{1}{3}), (3, 4)\}$ **25.** $\{(-2, -30), (6, 10)\}$ **C 27.** $\left\{\left(d, \frac{c}{d}\right), \left(-d, -\frac{c}{d}\right)\right\}$

Page 328 **Problems** **A 1.** 7 in, 5 in **3.** 45 in, 24 in **5.** -1, -1 **7.** 4, 6 **B 9.** 0

Pages 330–331 **Written Exercises** **A 1.** $\{(2, -3), (-2, -3), (3, 2), (-3, 2)\}$ **3.** $\left\{\left(-\frac{5}{2}, \frac{\sqrt{82}}{2}\right),\right.$
$\left.\left(-\frac{5}{2}, -\frac{\sqrt{82}}{2}\right), (2, 5), (2, -5)\right\}$ **5.** $\{(4, 3), (-4, -3), (3, 4), (-3, -4)\}$ **7.** $\{(1, 2), (-1, -2), (2, 1),$
$(-2, -1)\}$ **9.** $\{(2, 1), (-2, 1)\}$ **11.** $\{(4, 3), (4, -3), (-4, 3), (-4, -3)\}$ **13.** $\{(\sqrt{11}, 2\sqrt{3}), (\sqrt{11}, -2\sqrt{3}),$
$(-\sqrt{11}, 2\sqrt{3}), (-\sqrt{11}, -2\sqrt{3})\}$ **15.** $\emptyset$ **17.** $\{(\sqrt{2}, 1), (\sqrt{2}, -1), (-\sqrt{2}, 1), (-\sqrt{2}, -1)\}$
B 19. $\{(3, 2), (2, 3)\}$ **21.** $\{(-3, -4), (4, 3)\}$ **23.** $\{(2, 4), (-2, -4), (4, 2)\}$

Pages 331–332 **Problems** **A 1.** 11, 7; 11, -7; -11, 7; -11, -7 **3.** 5, 1; -5, -1 **5.** 15 M, 8 M **7.** 8
9. 34 in, 20 in **B 11.** $(x - 3)^2 + y^2 = 25$ **13.** $a^2 = 64, b^2 = 16$

Page 335 **Chapter Test** **1.** a. $2\sqrt{13}$ b. $(-5, 5)$ **3.** $(-3, 4)$; 6 **5.** $(5, 0), (-5, 0), (0, 2), (0, -2)$ **7.** 20 in
9. $\{(\frac{1}{2}, -3), (\frac{3}{2}, -1)\}$

Pages 335–336 **Chapter Review** **1.** 25 **3.** -2 **9.** $\{(3.1, 0.4), (-1.5, 2.8)\}$ **11.** $\{(3.7, -1.1), (-3.7, 1.1)\}$
13. $\{(\frac{5}{3}, -2)\}$ **15.** $\{(2\sqrt{3}, 3\sqrt{2}), (2\sqrt{3}, -3\sqrt{2}), (-2\sqrt{3}, 3\sqrt{2}), (-2\sqrt{3}, -3\sqrt{2})\}$

Page 337 **Extra for Experts** **1.** $y = \frac{1}{8}x^2 - 1$ **3.** $\frac{x^2}{4} - \frac{y^2}{12} = 1$

Page 341 **Written Exercises** **A 1.** $x^{1/4}y^{5/4}$ **3.** $3a^{-1/2}b^4$ **5.** $6x^{-3}z^{-5/3}$ **7.** $2\sqrt[12]{2^{11}}$ **9.** $\sqrt[12]{2^{11}}$ **11.** $\sqrt{2}$
13. $\sqrt[4]{2}$ **15.** $\frac{1}{625}$ **17.** 40 **19.** 0.09 **21.** $\frac{1}{64}$ **B 23.** $10^{6.3}$ **25.** $2^{0.9}$ **27.** $\sqrt{3}$ **29.** $a^{35/18}$ **31.** $a^{1/2} + b^{1/2}$
33. $t - t^5$ **35.** $\{16\}$ **37.** $\{126\}$ **39.** $\{4\}$

Pages 343–344 **Written Exercises** **A 1.** 2 **3.** $5^{-2\sqrt{2}}$ **5.** $10^{1+\sqrt{3}-\sqrt{6}}$ **7.** $36^{(\sqrt{5}-\sqrt{10})}$ **9.** $\{\frac{3}{2}\}$ **11.** $\{1, -\frac{1}{2}\}$.
13. $\{-2\}$ **15.** $\{-2\}$ **C 25.** $\{(0, 1), (1, 2)\}$

Page 346 **Written Exercises** **A 1.** $f^{-1} = \{(x, y): y = 3x - 6\}$; yes **3.** $f^{-1} = \{(x, y): y = \pm\sqrt{x + 1}\}$;
no **5.** $f^{-1} = \{(x, y): x = 2\}$; no **7.** $f^{-1} = \{(x, y): y = x\}$; yes **9.** $f^{-1} = \{(x, y): y = \pm\sqrt{25 - x^2},$
$x \geq 0\}$; no **11.** $f^{-1} = \{(x, y): y = \pm x, x \geq 0\}$; no **13.** $\{(x, y): y = x\}$

Page 348 **Written Exercises** **A 1.** -1 **3.** $\frac{1}{3}$ **5.** $\frac{4}{3}$ **7.** 2 **9.** -2 **11.** 0 **13.** 3 **15.** 4 **17.** $\frac{1}{256}$ **19.** 1
21. 2 **23.** $\frac{3}{4}$ **B 25.** 4 **27.** 3 **29.** 6 **31.** 8, -8

Page 351 **Written Exercises** **A 1.** 1.9661 **3.** 0.8451 **5.** 3.5752 **7.** 8.3201 − 10 **9.** 9.7924 − 10
11. 1.7952 **13.** 0.7076 **15.** 4.7782 **17.** 27.3 **19.** 347 **21.** 2630 **23.** 94.4 **25.** 39,000 **27.** 0.0725
29. 5.48 **31.** 0.059 **C 33.** $\{x: x > 2 \text{ or } 0 < x < 1\}$

Pages 353–354 **Written Exercises** **A 1.** 1.5112 **3.** 9.7273 − 10 **5.** 7.8764 − 10 **7.** 0.4972
9. 9.9383 − 10 **11.** 8.1878 − 10 **13.** 760.5 **15.** 0.01663 **17.** 9.806 **19.** 42,050 **21.** 0.03475 **23.** 66.94

Page 357 Written Exercises A 1. 410 **3.** 242 **5.** 130 **7.** 174 **9.** -0.01883 **11.** 1.94 **13.** 3.959 **15.** 0.265 **17.** 1.337 **19.** 1.808 **21.** $\{2\}$ **23.** $\{5\}$ **25.** $\{\frac{3}{2}\}$ **B 27.** $\{6\}$ **29.** $\{3\}$

Page 359 Written Exercises A 1. 68.4 **3.** 3.84 **5.** 27.0 **7.** 0.744 **9.** $8.438 \cdot 10^{14}$ **11.** 1.561 **13.** $2.593 \cdot 10^{17}$ **15.** 7.988 **17.** 0.8132 **19.** 160 **B 21.** $\{1, 100\}$

Pages 362–363 Written Exercises A 17. 0.67 **19.** 0.185 **21.** 0.814 **23.** 1.52 **25.** 0.0822 **27.** 0.2073 **29.** -0.16 **31.** 263,900 **33.** -3 **35.** 125 **B 37.** $\frac{22}{5}\sqrt[3]{150}$ **39.** $x\sqrt{x^2 - 1}$

Pages 363–364 Problems A 1. \$4,549 **3.** \$2,691 **5.** \$459 **7.** 3.77 **9.** $27.00 \cdot 10^{20}$ ergs **B 11.** 0.0000458 **13.** 1155 **15.** 12.54 hr **17.** 0.106 **19.** 17.5 years

Page 366 Written Exercises A 1. $\{2.953\}$ **3.** $\{0.6501\}$ **5.** $\{2484\}$ **7.** $\{-79.62, 79.62\}$ **9.** $\{10\}$ **11.** $\{0.6311\}$ **13.** $\{0.7567\}$ **15.** $\{1.610\}$ **B 17.** $\{5.050\}$ **19.** $\{2.393\}$ **21.** $\{0.3825\}$

Page 367 Chapter Test and Review 1. $\frac{125}{27}$ **3.** $f^{-1} = \{(x, y): y = \frac{1}{3}x - 2\}$ **5.** a. $9.8597 - 10$ b. 3.75 **7.** 0.741 **9.** 80.8

Pages 368–369 Cum. Review 1. No **3.** $2\frac{3}{4}$ **5.** -8; 12 **9.** $\left\{\frac{b}{2}\right\}$ **11.** $\{x: -3 < x \leq 2\}$ **13.** $\{-0.3, -2.4\}$ **15.** $\{-1, 3, \frac{5}{2}\}$ **17.** $\{(1.7, 2.7), (1.7, -2.7), (-1.7, 2.7), (-1.7, -2.7)\}$ **19.** $\{(\frac{1}{2}, -3), (\frac{3}{2}, -1)\}$ **21.** straight line; neither **23.** hyperbola; neither; x-axis and y-axis **25.** parabola; neither **27.** a. $6\sqrt[3]{4}$ b. $9\sqrt{2} - 12$ **29.** a. 0.8250 b. 2.7623 c. 4.7492 **31.** 1 **33.** \$2050 **35.** Possible integral values: 9 and 12, 12 and 16, 15 and 20, 18 and 24, 21 and 28, 24 and 32, 27 and 36 ft **37.** a. 46 b. 23; 69

Pages 373–374 Written Exercises In Exs. 1–18 answers vary. **A 1.** 540°, $-180°$ **3.** 420°, $-300°$ **5.** 315°, $-405°$ **7.** 360°, $-720°$ **9.** 360°, $-360°$ **11.** 510°, $-210°$ **19.** $\{(x, y): y = \frac{4}{3}x \text{ and } x \geq 0\}$ **21.** $\{(x, y): y = \frac{1}{2}x \text{ and } x \leq 0\}$ **23.** $\{(x, y): y = -2x \text{ and } x \leq 0\}$ **25.** $\{(x, y): y = 0 \text{ and } x \geq 0\}$

Pages 377–378 Written Exercises A 1. -0.3; 1.0 **3.** -0.9; -0.5 **5.** 0.7; -0.7 **7.** 0.5; -0.9 **9.** 0.5; -0.9 **11.** -0.7; 0.7 **13.** 1.0; 0.0 **15.** 0.2; -1.0 **17.** $\cos\theta = -\frac{8}{17}$; $\sin\theta = -\frac{15}{17}$ **19.** $\cos\theta = -1$; $\sin\theta = 0$ **21.** $\cos\theta = -\frac{1}{2}\sqrt{2}$; $\sin\theta = \frac{1}{2}\sqrt{2}$ **23.** $\cos\theta = \frac{2}{5}\sqrt{5}$; $\sin\theta = \frac{1}{5}\sqrt{5}$ **B 25.** $\cos\theta = \frac{5}{29}\sqrt{29}$; $\sin\theta = -\frac{2}{29}\sqrt{29}$ **27.** $\cos\theta = -\frac{1}{2}\sqrt{2}$; $\sin\theta = \frac{1}{2}\sqrt{2}$ **29.** $\cos\theta = -1$; $\sin\theta = 0$ **31.** $\frac{2}{5}\sqrt{6}, -\frac{2}{5}\sqrt{6}$ **33.** $\frac{1}{2}\sqrt{2}, -\frac{1}{2}\sqrt{2}$

Pages 381–382 Written Exercises A 1. $\sin\theta = -\frac{4}{5}$, $\cos\theta = -\frac{3}{5}$, $\tan\theta = \frac{4}{3}$, $\csc\theta = -\frac{5}{4}$, $\sec\theta = -\frac{5}{3}$, $\cot\theta = \frac{3}{4}$ **3.** $\sin\theta = \frac{1}{2}$, $\cos\theta = \frac{\sqrt{3}}{2}$, $\tan\theta = \frac{1}{3}\sqrt{3}$, $\csc\theta = 2$, $\sec\theta = \frac{2}{3}\sqrt{3}$, $\cot\theta = \sqrt{3}$ **5.** $\sin\theta = -\frac{\sqrt{2}}{2}$, $\cos\theta = \frac{\sqrt{2}}{2}$, $\tan\theta = -1$, $\csc\theta = -\sqrt{2}$, $\sec\theta = \sqrt{2}$, $\cot\theta = -1$ **7.** $\sin\theta = 1$, $\cos\theta = 0$, $\tan\theta$ is undefined, $\csc\theta = 1$, $\sec\theta$ is undefined, $\cot\theta = 0$ **9.** $\sin\theta = \frac{7\sqrt{2}}{10}$, $\cos\theta = -\frac{\sqrt{2}}{10}$, $\tan\theta = -7$, $\csc\theta = \frac{5\sqrt{2}}{7}$, $\sec\theta = -5\sqrt{2}$, $\cot\theta = -\frac{1}{7}$ **11.** $\sin\theta = \frac{\sqrt{3}}{2}$, $\cos\theta = -\frac{1}{2}$, $\tan\theta = -\sqrt{3}$, $\csc\theta = \frac{2\sqrt{3}}{3}$, $\sec\theta = -2$, $\cot\theta = -\frac{\sqrt{3}}{3}$ **B 13.** $\sin\theta = -\frac{2}{5}$, $\cos\theta = -\frac{\sqrt{21}}{5}$, $\tan\theta = \frac{2\sqrt{21}}{21}$, $\csc\theta = -\frac{5}{2}$, $\sec\theta = -\frac{5\sqrt{21}}{21}$, $\cot\theta = \frac{\sqrt{21}}{2}$ **15.** $\sin\theta = \frac{5\sqrt{41}}{41}$, $\cos\theta = \frac{4\sqrt{41}}{41}$, $\tan\theta = \frac{5}{4}$, $\csc\theta = \frac{\sqrt{41}}{5}$, $\sec\theta = \frac{\sqrt{41}}{4}$, $\cot\theta = \frac{4}{5}$ **17.** $\sin\theta = -\frac{\sqrt{5}}{5}$, $\cos\theta = \frac{2\sqrt{5}}{5}$, $\tan\theta = -\frac{1}{2}$, $\csc\theta = -\sqrt{5}$, $\sec\theta = \frac{\sqrt{5}}{2}$, $\cot\theta = -2$ **19.** $\sin\theta = -\frac{\sqrt{5}}{3}$, $\cos\theta = \frac{2}{3}$, $\tan\theta = -\frac{\sqrt{5}}{2}$, $\csc\theta = -\frac{3\sqrt{5}}{5}$, $\sec\theta = \frac{3}{2}$, $\cot\theta = -\frac{2\sqrt{5}}{5}$ **21.** $\sin\theta = \frac{3}{8}$, $\cos\theta = -\frac{\sqrt{55}}{8}$, $\tan\theta = -\frac{3\sqrt{55}}{55}$, $\csc\theta = \frac{8}{3}$, $\sec\theta = -\frac{8\sqrt{55}}{55}$, $\cot\theta = -\frac{\sqrt{55}}{3}$ **23.** $\sin\theta = \frac{\sqrt{14}}{4}$, $\cos\theta = \frac{\sqrt{2}}{4}$, $\tan\theta = \sqrt{7}$, $\csc\theta = \frac{2\sqrt{14}}{7}$, $\sec\theta = 2\sqrt{2}$, $\cot\theta = \frac{\sqrt{7}}{7}$ **25.** $(-6, 8)$ **27.** $(2\sqrt{2}, -2\sqrt{2})$ **C 29.** $\frac{\sqrt{2}}{2}, -\frac{\sqrt{2}}{2}$ **31.** $-\frac{\sqrt{3}}{2}$

Page 385 Written Exercises A 1. $\frac{1}{2}$ **3.** -1 **5.** 1 **7.** $1 = 1$ **9.** $4 = 4$ **11.** $\frac{1}{2} = \frac{1}{2}$ **13.** $0 = 0$ **15.** $0 = 0$ **17.** $\frac{4\sqrt{3}}{3}$ **19.** $\frac{5\sqrt{106}}{106}$

Pages 388–389 Written Exercises A 1. 0.2622 **3.** 0.9429 **5.** 3.012 **7.** 0.6001 **9.** 1.010 **11.** 1.014 **13.** 22° 48′ **15.** 47° 25′ **17.** 73° 54′ **19.** 12° 35′ **B 21.** $B = 63°$, $a = 3$, $b = 5$ **23.** $A = 56°$, $a = 37$, $c = 45$ **25.** $B = 63°$, $A = 27°$, $b = 36$

Pages 389–391 Problems A 1. (a) 0.9747 mi; (b) 1 mi **3.** (a) 7.500 ft; (b) 8 ft **5.** (a) 884.1 ft; (b) 900 ft **7.** (a) 42° 27′; (b) 40° **9.** (a) height of transit + 3.808 ft; (b) same as (a). **11.** (a) 10 in; (b) 10 in **B 13.** (a) 5.36 in; (b) 5 in **15.** (a) 399.2 ft; (b) 399 ft

Pages 392–393 Written Exercises A 1. 153.1 **3.** 0.4822 **5.** 2.071 **7.** 25.44 **9.** 0.001440 **11.** 2.880 **13.** 55° 43′ **15.** 26° 28′ **17.** 48° 39′ **19.** 3° 8′

Pages 393–394 Problems A 1. 7.352 ft **3.** 24.00 in **5.** 39° 20′, 50° 40′ **7.** 27.77 yd **B 9.** 5.106 in **11.** 13,720 ft

Pages 397–398 Written Exercises A 1. 60° **3.** 30° **5.** 30° **7.** 40° **9.** 20° **11.** 60° **13.** a. $\frac{1}{2}$, $\frac{1}{2}$, $-\frac{1}{2}$, $-\frac{1}{2}$; b. $\frac{\sqrt{3}}{2}$, $-\frac{\sqrt{3}}{2}$, $-\frac{\sqrt{3}}{2}$, $\frac{\sqrt{3}}{2}$; c. $\frac{\sqrt{3}}{3}$, $-\frac{\sqrt{3}}{3}$, $\frac{\sqrt{3}}{3}$, $-\frac{\sqrt{3}}{3}$ **15.** a. $\frac{\sqrt{2}}{2}$, $\frac{\sqrt{2}}{2}$, $-\frac{\sqrt{2}}{2}$, $-\frac{\sqrt{2}}{2}$; b. $\frac{\sqrt{2}}{2}$, $-\frac{\sqrt{2}}{2}$, $-\frac{\sqrt{2}}{2}$, $\frac{\sqrt{2}}{2}$; c. 1, -1, 1, -1 **17.** $-\cos 20°$ **19.** $\tan 20°$ **21.** $\cot 80°$ **23.** $\sin 5°$ **25.** $-\csc 39° 20′$ **27.** -0.7660 **29.** -1.664 **31.** $9.6177 - 10$ **33.** 259° 30′ **35.** 329° 20′ **37.** 294° 40′ **B 39.** $(-2.9, 4.1)$ **41.** $(-0.4, -8.3)$ **43.** $(9.7, -2.6)$ **45.** 5.0; 37° **47.** 7.3; 196° **49.** 7.1; 356°

Page 401 Written Exercises A 1. 130 lb at 157° **3.** approx. 39 mph at 130° **5.** approx. 14 km N34°E **B 7.** approx. 12 kg at 109° **9.** approx. 16 mi N83°E **11.** approx. 600 mph at 227°

Pages 401–402 Problems A 1. 455 ft **3.** 35° 32′ **B 5.** approx. 347 mph at 353° 23′ **7.** 73° 18′; yes

Pages 404–405 Written Exercises A 1. $[-6\sqrt{2}, 6\sqrt{2}]$ **3.** $[23, -8]$ **5.** $[15, 0]$ **7.** $[8.9, 8.0]$ **9.** $[-36.1, 37.4]$ **11.** $[239.4, 657.8]$ **B 13.** $[-4, 8]$ **15.** $[7, -2]$ **17.** $[0, 0]$ **19.** $[-4, -8]$ **C 21.** (a) $[2, 1] = [2, 1]$ **23.** (a) $[-5, 3] = [-5, 3]$

Pages 405–406 Problems A 1. 23.64 lb **3.** 734.1 mi **B 5.** 5 lb to 15 lb **7.** (a) 3.008 mi; (b) 3.000 mph **9.** 47.32 lb

Pages 409–410 Written Exercises A 1. $3 - 5i$ **3.** $-8 + 3i$ **5.** $-4i$ **7.** 0 **9.** $1 - i$ **11.** $2 + 5i$ **13.** (a) $3 + 8i$; (b) $3 + 6i$; (c) $-3 - 6i$ **15.** (a) $1 + 2i$; (b) $-1 - 4i$; (c) $1 + 4i$ **17.** (a) $9 - 3i$; (b) $5 + 3i$; (c) $-5 - 3i$ **B 19.** $4 + 7i$ **21.** $-2 + 4i$ **23.** $x = -2, y = 5$ **25.** $x = 2, y = 5$

Pages 413–414 Written Exercises A 1. i **3.** -1 **5.** -5 **7.** $\frac{1}{2}i\sqrt{2}$ **9.** $20i\sqrt{3}$ **11.** $-6\sqrt{35}$ **13.** $-4\sqrt{10}$ **15.** $25i$ **17.** -2 **19.** $12i$ **21.** 2 **23.** $3\sqrt{2}$ **25.** $8\sqrt{2}$ **27.** $-\frac{1}{4}i$ **29.** $-2i\sqrt{3}$ **31.** $-2i\sqrt{7}$ **33.** $7i\sqrt{2}$ **35.** $(8 - \sqrt{5})i$ **37.** $\sqrt{7} - 2i\sqrt{7}$ **B 39.** $-\frac{7}{10}i\sqrt{5}$ **41.** $16i\sqrt{2}$ **43.** 0 **45.** $-1 - 2i$ **B 47.** $7x^2i$ **49.** $-4yi\sqrt{2}$

Pages 416–417 Written Exercises A 1. $\{6, 3\}$ **3.** $\left\{\frac{1 + i\sqrt{11}}{2}, \frac{1 - i\sqrt{11}}{2}\right\}$ **5.** $\left\{\frac{5 + i\sqrt{59}}{6}, \frac{5 - i\sqrt{59}}{6}\right\}$ **7.** $\left\{\frac{-3 + 2\sqrt{6}}{5}, \frac{-3 - 2\sqrt{6}}{5}\right\}$ **9.** -61 **11.** $8 + 6i$ **13.** $47 - 14i\sqrt{2}$ **15.** $-30 + 10i$ **17.** $-32 - 4i$ **B 19.** $-1 + 5i$ **21.** $2 - 6i$ **23.** $\frac{9}{74} + \frac{17}{74}i$ **25.** $-\frac{1}{2} - \frac{1}{2}i$ **C 27.** (a) $\emptyset$; (b) $\{\sqrt{2} + i, -\sqrt{2} + i\}$ **29.** $(a + bi) + (a - bi) = 2a$ **31.** $\{(-2, 2)\}$

Page 419 Chapter Test and Review **3.** $\frac{2\sqrt{6}}{7}$ **5.** 2 **7.** 0.5561 **9.** 34° 52′ **11.** −cos 68° **13.** tan 35° **15.** [10.0, −8.4] **17.** $-\frac{3}{2}\sqrt{2} + 8i\sqrt{2}$ **19.** $\left\{\frac{2 + i\sqrt{2}}{2}, \frac{2 - i\sqrt{2}}{2}\right\}$

Page 424 Written Exercises **A 1.** a. $\sqrt{1 - \cos^2 \theta}$, θ in Q I or II or $-\sqrt{1 - \cos^2 \theta}$, θ in Q III or IV; b. $\frac{\sqrt{1 - \cos^2 \theta}}{\cos \theta}$, Q I or II or $-\frac{\sqrt{1 - \cos^2 \theta}}{\cos \theta}$, Q III or IV c. $\frac{\sqrt{1 - \cos^2 \theta}}{1 - \cos^2 \theta}$, Q I or II or $-\frac{\sqrt{1 - \cos^2 \theta}}{1 - \cos^2 \theta}$, Q III or IV **3.** a. $\frac{\csc^2 \alpha - 1}{\csc^2 \alpha}$; b. $\frac{1}{\csc^2 \alpha - 1}$; c. $\frac{\csc^2 \alpha}{\csc^2 \alpha - 1}$ **5.** $\sin \theta = -\frac{3}{5}$; $\cos \theta = \frac{4}{5}$; $\tan \theta = -\frac{3}{4}$; $\cot \theta = -\frac{4}{3}$; $\sec \theta = \frac{5}{4}$; $\csc \theta = -\frac{5}{3}$ **7.** $\sin \theta = \frac{12}{13}$; $\cos \theta = -\frac{5}{13}$; $\tan \theta = -\frac{12}{5}$; $\cot \theta = -\frac{5}{12}$; $\sec \theta = -\frac{13}{5}$; $\csc \theta = \frac{13}{12}$ **9.** $1 + \sin A$ **B 11.** $\tan \theta$ **13.** 0 **15.** 1 **17.** $\frac{14{,}112}{7{,}225}$ **19.** $\frac{97}{85}$

Page 429 Written Exercises **A 1.** 34 **3.** 105.2 **5.** 94.76 **7.** 32.6 **9.** 108.8 **11.** 257.4

Pages 432–433 Written Exercises **A 1.** cos 70°; 0.3420 **3.** cos 20°; 0.9397 **5.** $\frac{-\sqrt{2} + \sqrt{6}}{4}$ or 0.2588 **7.** $\frac{\sqrt{2} - \sqrt{6}}{4}$ or −0.2588 **B 15.** $\cos(\alpha - \beta)$ **17.** $-\sec \beta + \csc \alpha$

Pages 435–436 Written Exercises **A 1.** 2 **3.** 0 **5.** $\frac{\sqrt{2}}{2}$ **7.** $2 + \sqrt{3}$ **9.** $\frac{\sqrt{6} - \sqrt{2}}{4}$ **11.** $\frac{\sqrt{6} - \sqrt{2}}{4}$ **13.** $2 + \sqrt{3}$ **15.** $\frac{\sqrt{2} - \sqrt{6}}{4}$ **17.** a. $\frac{216}{745}$; b. $-\frac{713}{745}$; c. $-\frac{624}{745}$; d. $\frac{407}{745}$; e. $-\frac{216}{713}$; f. $-\frac{624}{407}$ **19.** a. $\frac{84}{13}$; b. $\frac{13}{84}$; c. $-\frac{13}{85}$; d. $-\frac{36}{85}$ **21.** 2 **23.** $-\frac{\sqrt{2}}{2}$ if n odd, $\frac{\sqrt{2}}{2}$ if n even

Pages 438–439 Written Exercises **A 1.** $-\frac{\sqrt{3}}{2}$ **3.** $\frac{\sqrt{3}}{3}$ **5.** $-\frac{\sqrt{2}}{2}$ **7.** $\frac{\sqrt{2 - \sqrt{3}}}{2}$ **9.** $-\sqrt{7 - 4\sqrt{3}}$

Page 441 Written Exercises **A 1.** sin 136° + sin 98° **3.** −[cos 195° + cos 215°] **5.** 2 cos 9° sin 20° **7.** −4 sin 154.5° sin 146.5° **9.** a. $\frac{\sqrt{6}}{2}$; b. $\frac{\sqrt{2}}{2}$; c. $\frac{\sqrt{6}}{2}$; d. $-\frac{\sqrt{2}}{2}$

Page 445 Written Exercises **1.** 8.2 **3.** 2.5 **5.** 44° 00′ **7.** 95° 10′ **9.** 1.7

Pages 446–447 Problems **A 1.** 440 mph **3.** 250 lb **5.** 43 mi **B 7.** 110 mi **9.** 95° **C 15.** 52° 06′, 82° 04′, 45° 48′ **17.** 27° 00′, 41° 50′, 111° 10′

Page 448 Written Exercises **1.** 0.6 **3.** 33° **5.** 1.05

Pages 449–450 Problems **A 1.** 21 in **3.** 4.8 mi **5.** 3900 yd **B 7.** 48 min **9.** $BD = EC = 6.3$ in, $DE = 5.4$ in **C 15.** 102° 49′, 29° 57′

Pages 453–454 Written Exercises **A 1.** A = 22° 12′, B = 42° 50′, C = 114° 58′ **3.** a = 46.50, B = 16° 03′, C = 123° 57′ **5.** no triangle **7.** a = 10.74, c = 8.96, B = 98° 50′ **9.** b = 105.0, B = 107° 47′, C = 42° 53′ or b = 25.83, B = 13° 33′, C = 137° 07′ **11.** no triangle **13.** b = 1.123, c = 0.3407, A = 104° 5′ **15.** no triangle **B 17.** a. $b \leq 70$; b. $b > 70$; c. no values

Pages 454–456 Problems **A 1.** 77° 05′, 55° 57′, 46° 58′ **3.** 1.329×10^8 mi or 3.132×10^7 mi **5.** 388.1 ft **7.** 49,740 ft **9.** 64.13 cm, 27.69 cm **B 11.** 242°; 22.1 mi **13.** 419.3 mph on course of 358° 36′ **15.** 1735 ft **C 17.** 32.23 in **19.** 30° 20′; 1.1 hr

Page 457 Written Exercises **A 1.** 20.40 **3.** 385.7 **5.** no triangle **7.** 47.52 **9.** 1928 or 474.6 **11.** no triangle **13.** 0.1856 **15.** no triangle **17.** 70.60 **19.** 325.0

Page 459 Extra for Experts **1.** $10\sqrt{2}\,(\cos 135° + i \sin 135°)$; $5\sqrt{2}\,(\cos 45° + i \sin 45°)$; $-100 + 0 \cdot i$; $0 + 2i$ **3.** $2(\cos 240° + i \sin 240°)$; $2(\cos 210° + i \sin 210°)$; $0 + 4i$; $\frac{\sqrt{3}}{2} + \frac{1}{2}i$ **5.** $-4 + 0 \cdot i$ **7.** $\frac{1}{256} + 0 \cdot i$ **9.** 3; $-\frac{3}{2} + \frac{3\sqrt{3}}{2}i$; $-\frac{3}{2} - \frac{3\sqrt{3}}{2}i$

Page 460 Chapter Test and Review **1.** $\frac{\sin^2 \theta}{1 - \sin^2 \theta}$ **3.** 52 **5.** a. $\frac{15 + 12\sqrt{7}}{52}$ b. $\frac{-15 + 12\sqrt{7}}{36 + 5\sqrt{7}}$ **9.** 13 **11.** a. 0; b. 2; c. 1; d. 1; e. 1

Pages 465–466 Written Exercises **A 1.** $\frac{\pi^R}{4}$ **3.** $\frac{5\pi^R}{3}$ **5.** $\frac{-11\pi^R}{6}$ **7.** $4\pi^R$ **9.** $\frac{-5\pi^R}{12}$ **11.** $\frac{3\pi^R}{2}$ **13.** 0.20^R **15.** -2.79^R **17.** $-135°$ **19.** $330°$ **21.** $-405°$ **23.** $115°$ **25.** $14°$ **27.** $-46°$ **29.** $\frac{\sqrt{3}}{2}$ **31.** 0 **33.** $\frac{\sqrt{3}}{2}$ **35.** -1 if n odd, 1 if n even **37.** 72 cm **39.** 25.13 cm **41.** 24 ft **43.** 8.6 ft **B 45.** 94.25 ft/min **47.** 400 mi/min

Pages 468–469 Written Exercises In Ex. 1–12 values are given in order: sin, cos, tan, cot, sec, csc. **A 1.** 0, 1, 0, –, 1, – **3.** $\frac{\sqrt{2}}{2}, \frac{\sqrt{2}}{2}, 1, 1, \sqrt{2}, \sqrt{2}$ **5.** $\frac{1}{2}, -\frac{\sqrt{3}}{2}, -\frac{\sqrt{3}}{3}, -\sqrt{3}, -\frac{2\sqrt{3}}{3}, 2$ **7.** $-\frac{\sqrt{3}}{2}, -\frac{1}{2}, \sqrt{3}, \frac{\sqrt{3}}{3}, -2, -\frac{2\sqrt{3}}{3}$ **9.** 1, 0, –, 0, –, 1 **11.** $\frac{\sqrt{6} - \sqrt{2}}{4}, \frac{\sqrt{2} + \sqrt{6}}{4}, 2 - \sqrt{3}, 2 + \sqrt{3}, \sqrt{6} - \sqrt{2}, \sqrt{6} + \sqrt{2}$ **13.** 1.00 **15.** 1.71 **17.** $d = \frac{1}{3}, v = 0, a = -3$ **19.** $d = 0, v = 1, a = 0$ **21.** $V = 0, I = -6.43$ **23.** $V = 96.36, I = 21.56$ **B 25.** $-\frac{\sqrt{2}}{2}$ if n odd, $\frac{\sqrt{2}}{2}$ if n even **27.** 1 if $n = 1, 5, \cdots, 1 + 4c$ (c an integer); 0 if $n = 2, 6, \cdots, 2 + 4c$ (c an integer); -1 if $n = 3, 7, \cdots, 3 + 4c$ (c an integer); no value if $n = 0, 4, \ldots, 4c$ (c an integer)

Pages 473–474 Written Exercises **A 1.** $2, 2\pi$ **3.** $\frac{1}{3}, 2\pi$ **5.** $1, \frac{2\pi}{3}$ **7.** $1, 4\pi$ **9.** $2, \frac{\pi}{2}$ **11.** $4, 4\pi$ **B 13.** 1, 2 **15.** $2, 2\pi$ **17.** $1, 2\pi$ **19.** 1.1, 4.2 **21.** 0.4 **23.** 0.7

Page 477 Written Exercises **A 1.** π **3.** π **5.** 2π **7.** 2π **9.** $\frac{\pi}{2}$ **11.** 2π **13.** No **C 21.** 0, –0.1, 0.1

Page 479 Written Exercises **A 1.** $\{x: x = 2n\pi\}$ **3.** $\{x: x = n\pi\}$ **5.** $\left\{x: x = \frac{3\pi}{4} + 2n\pi \text{ or } x = \frac{5\pi}{4} + 2n\pi\right\}$ **7.** $\left\{x: x = \frac{3\pi}{4} + n\pi\right\}$ **9.** $\left\{x: x = \frac{4\pi}{3} + 2n\pi \text{ or } x = \frac{5\pi}{3} + 2n\pi\right\}$ **11.** $\emptyset$ **13.** $\left\{\frac{\pi}{4}, \frac{7\pi}{4}\right\}$ **15.** $\left\{\frac{3\pi}{2}\right\}$ **17.** $\left\{\frac{\pi}{2}, \frac{3\pi}{2}\right\}$ **19.** $\frac{2\sqrt{2}}{3}, -\frac{2\sqrt{2}}{3}$ **21.** $\frac{\sqrt{6}}{12}, -\frac{\sqrt{6}}{12}$ **23.** $\sqrt{101}, -\sqrt{101}$ **B 25.** $\frac{\pi}{6}$ **27.** $\frac{3\pi}{4}$ **29.** 1

Pages 484–485 Written Exercises **A 1.** $\frac{12}{13}$ **3.** $\frac{8}{15}$ **5.** $\frac{\sqrt{21}}{5}$ **7.** $2\sqrt{5}$ **9.** -3 **11.** $-\frac{24}{7}$ **13.** $-\frac{169}{119}$ **15.** $\frac{\sqrt{2}}{2}$ **17.** $-\frac{323}{36}$ **B 19.** $\sqrt{1 - 4x^2}, -\frac{1}{2} \leq x \leq 0$ **21.** $\frac{2y^2\sqrt{1 - y^4}}{2y^4 - 1}, |y| \leq 1$ **23.** $\frac{x - y}{1 + xy}$, $xy \neq -1, x \neq \frac{n \cdot \pi}{2}, y \neq \frac{n \cdot \pi}{2}$ **35.** $\{-1, 1\}$ **37.** $\{\frac{1}{3}\}$

Page 487 Written Exercises **A 1.** $\{3.1\}$ **3.** $\{0.5, 5.8\}$ **5.** $\{\theta: 55° \leq \theta < 90° \text{ or } 270° < \theta \leq 305°\}$ **7.** $\{0°, 180°, 210°, 330°\}$ **9.** $\{90°, 135°, 270°, 315°\}$ **11.** $\{x: 0 \leq x \leq 1.0 \text{ or } 2.1 \leq x \leq 4.2 \text{ or } 5.2 \leq x < 6.3\}$ **13.** $\{30°, 330°\}$ **15.** $\{0, 2.1, 4.2\}$ **17.** $\{12°, 78°, 192°, 258°\}$ **19.** $\{0.5, 2.6, 4.7\}$ **21.** $\{270°\}$ **23.** $\{1.6, 4.7\}$ **25.** $\{204°, 336°\}$ **27.** $\{0, 0.8, 2.4, 3.1, 3.9, 5.5\}$ **B 29.** *a.* $\left\{x: x = \frac{\pi}{4} + n\pi\right\}$; *b.* $\{\theta: \theta = 45° + n \cdot 180°\}$ **31.** a. $\left\{x: x = \frac{\pi}{4} + \frac{n\pi}{2}\right\}$; b. $\{\theta: \theta = 45° + n \cdot 90°\}$ **C 33.** $\{x: 0 \leq x \leq \pi\}$ **35.** $\left\{x: -\frac{\pi}{2} < x \leq 0 \text{ or } \frac{\pi}{2} < x \leq \pi\right\}$ **37.** $\left\{x: -\pi < x \leq -\frac{3\pi}{4} \text{ or } -\frac{\pi}{4} \leq x \leq \frac{\pi}{4} \text{ or } \frac{3\pi}{4} \leq x \leq \pi\right\}$

Pages 489–490 Written Exercises A 1. {0.5, 1.0, 2.1, 2.6, 3.7, 4.2, 5.2, 5.8} **3.** {0.7, 1.3, 2.7, 3.3, 4.7, 5.3} **5.** {45°, 135°, 225°, 315°, 60°, 120°, 240°, 300°} **7.** {0°} **9.** {0.2, 0.3, 1.2, 1.4, 2.3, 2.4, 3.3, 3.5, 4.4, 4.5, 5.4, 5.6} **11.** {0°, 60°, 300°} **13.** {0.4, 2.0, 3.5, 5.1} **B 15.** {4.7} **17.** {12°, 132°, 252°} **19.** $\left\{x: x = \frac{5\pi}{8} + n\pi \text{ or } x = \frac{7\pi}{8} + n\pi\right\}$ **21.** identity **23.** $\{\theta: \theta = (2n + 1) \cdot 90° \text{ or } \theta = 30° + n \cdot 360°$ or $\theta = 150° + n \cdot 360°\}$ **25.** identity **27.** {30°, 150°, 210°, 330°} **29.** {20°, 100°, 140°, 220°, 260°, 340°}

Page 491 Chapter Test 1. a. −2.1; b. 585°; c. 19° **3.** a. $-\frac{1}{2}$; b. $-\frac{\sqrt{3}}{3}$ **7.** $\sin t = \frac{5}{13}, -\frac{5}{13}$; $\cos t = \frac{12}{13}, -\frac{12}{13}$ **11.** $\left\{x: x = n\pi \text{ or } x = \frac{\pi}{3} + \frac{2n\pi}{3}\right\}$; $\left\{0, \frac{\pi}{3}, \pi, \frac{5\pi}{3}\right\}$

Pages 492–493 Cum. Review 1. $\sin\theta = -\frac{2\sqrt{2}}{3}$; $\cos\theta = \frac{1}{3}$; $\tan\theta = -2\sqrt{2}$; $\csc\theta = -\frac{3\sqrt{2}}{4}$; $\sec\theta = 3$; $\cot\theta = -\frac{\sqrt{2}}{4}$ **3.** a. $\frac{3\sqrt{2}}{4}$; b. 0 **5.** a. $-6\sqrt{2}$; b. −1; c. $4 + 2i$ **7.** 5° **9.** cos 35° or sin 55° **11.** $a = 967$ **13.** a. $p = \frac{4\pi}{3}$, $a = 3$; c. $2{:}\ \frac{2\pi}{3}$, 2π **15.** a. $\left\{-\frac{2\pi}{3}, \frac{2\pi}{3}, \frac{4\pi}{3}, \frac{8\pi}{3}\right\}$; b. $\left\{\frac{\pi}{3}, \frac{2\pi}{3}, \frac{7\pi}{3}, \frac{8\pi}{3}\right\}$ **21.** {30°, 150°} **23.** $A = 56°50'$; $c = 24.2$; $a = 22.5$ **25.** 2; 0

Page 497 Written Exercises A 1. 1, 3, 5, 7 **3.** 2, 0.7, −0.6, −1.9 **5.** 1, $1 + 2k$, $1 + 4k$, $1 + 6k$ **7.** 28 **9.** 78 **11.** $-11i$ **13.** $-9\sqrt{2}$ **15.** $19\frac{2}{3}$ **17.** $33\sqrt{3}$ **19.** $x + 38y$ **21.** 21st

Pages 497–498 Problems A 1. $9000 **3.** $14 **5.** 52 wd/min **B 7.** a. 14,432 ft; b. 1408 ft. down **9.** 19, $16\frac{1}{2}$, 14

Pages 499–500 Written Exercises A 1. 4, 7, 10, 13, 16, 19, 22 **3.** −2, 0, 2, 4, 6, 8, 10, 12 **5.** 1, $\frac{2}{3}$, $\frac{1}{3}$, 0, $-\frac{1}{3}$, $-\frac{2}{3}$, −1 **7.** 8, 20, 32, 44, 56, 68, 80 **9.** 39 **11.** −13 **B 13.** $\frac{3}{2}(a + b)$ **15.** $\sqrt{5}$

Page 500 Problems A 1. 5 g, 9 g, 13 g, 17 g, 21 g **3.** $4800, $5200, $5600 **B 5.** −3, 21 **7.** $\frac{2}{5}$ **9.** $b = 3$, $c = -7$

Pages 503–504 Written Exercises A 1. 45 **3.** 200 **5.** $67\frac{1}{2}$ **7.** −35 **9.** 646 **11.** −120 **13.** −2525 **15.** 3, $4\frac{5}{9}$, $6\frac{1}{9}$ **17.** −5, $-\frac{49}{11}$, $-\frac{43}{11}$ **19.** $\frac{3}{4}$, $\frac{113}{160}$, $\frac{53}{80}$ **21.** −10.888, −10.188, −9.488 **23.** 8, 8.35, 8.70 **25.** $\sum_{n=0}^{3} (2 + 3n)$ **27.** $\sum_{n=0}^{4} \left(2 - \frac{n}{2}\right)$ **B 29.** 2 **31.** 3 **33.** 30°, 150° **C 35.** $a = 2, b = 1$ **37.** 1490.1

Pages 504–505 Problems A 1. $75,750 **3.** 340 **5.** $5.10 **7.** 22 **9.** 15 mo **B 11.** 625 **13.** 9 **15.** $5.50

Pages 507–508 Written Exercises A 1. 1, 3, 9, 27 **3.** $\frac{3}{4}$, $\frac{3}{8}$, $\frac{3}{16}$, $\frac{3}{32}$ **5.** 12, −12, 12, −12 **7.** 256 **9.** 320 **11.** $486\sqrt{7}$ **B 19.** −2, 2 **21.** 5 **23.** 5 **25.** 64

Pages 508–509 Problems A 1. $2682.10 **3.** 1024 **5.** 22,000 **B 7.** 1.875 in **C 9.** 7

Pages 510–511 Written Exercises A 1. 1, 3, 9, 27 **3.** −7, −14, −28, −56, −112, −224 **5.** $m^2, m^4, m^6, m^8, m^{10}, m^{12}, m^{14}$ or $m^2, -m^4, m^6, -m^8, m^{10}, -m^{12}, m^{14}$ **7.** 5, 15, 45 **9.** 3, −12, 48 **11.** sin z, −1, csc z **13.** $\frac{a^3}{b}$, $a\sqrt[3]{ba^2}$, $b\sqrt[3]{b^2a}$, $\frac{b^3}{a}$ **17.** $\frac{10}{\sqrt{5}}$, 4 **B 19.** −8, −4, −2 or 8, −4, 2 **21.** 3 **23.** 54

Page 513 Written Exercises A 1. 635 **3.** $23\frac{5}{8}$ **5.** $2\frac{20}{81}$ **7.** $-\frac{63}{80}$ **9.** 484 **11.** $40\frac{4}{9}$ **13.** $51\frac{1}{4}$ **15.** 1111.111 **B 17.** $a = 2, l = 512$ **19.** $r = 25, l = 1250$ or $r = -26, l = -1352$ **21.** $l = -40, n = 4$ **23.** $r = \frac{1}{10}, n = 5$

Pages 514–515 Problems A 1. 39.1π **3.** 510 **5.** $70 + 30\sqrt{2}$ in **7.** $\frac{1}{32}$ **B 9.** $-3\frac{63}{64}$ **11.** $1250

Page 516 Written Exercises A 1. 8 **3.** $\frac{2}{3}$ **5.** 4 **7.** $\frac{27}{5}$ **9.** $\frac{1}{9}$ **11.** 54 **13.** 3, 0.3, 0.03 **15.** 6, 4, $\frac{8}{3}$ **17.** $\frac{5}{9}$ **19.** $\frac{4}{33}$ **21.** $\frac{11}{90}$ **23.** $\frac{25}{37}$

Page 517 Problems A 1. $93\frac{1}{3}$ ft **3.** $96 + 48\sqrt{2}$ in **5.** 288 sq in **B 7.** $\frac{2\sqrt{3}}{5}$ sq units **C 9.** $\frac{1 + x}{(1 - x)^2}$

Page 519 Written Exercises A 1. $c^6 + 6c^5d + 15c^4d^2 + 20c^3d^3 + 15c^2d^4 + 6cd^5 + d^6$ **3.** $m^7 - 7m^6t + 21m^5t^2 - 35m^4t^3 + 35m^3t^4 - 21m^2t^5 + 7mt^6 - t^7$ **5.** $x^4 + 4x^3 + 6x^2 + 4x + 1$ **7.** $1 - 5y^2 + 10y^4 - 10y^6 + 5y^8 - y^{10}$ **9.** $x^4 + 8x^3 + 24x^2 + 32x + 16$ **11.** $27x^3 - 27x^2 + 9x - 1$ **13.** $a^6 + 3a^5x + \frac{15}{4}a^4x^2 + \frac{5}{2}a^3x^3 + \frac{15}{16}a^2x^4 + \frac{3}{16}ax^5 + \frac{1}{64}x^6$ **15.** $x^{14} - 14x^{12} + 84x^{10} - 280x^8 + 560x^6 - 672x^4 + 448x^2 - 128$ **17.** $r^{16} + 8r^{14}s^2 + 28r^{12}s^4 + 56r^{10}s^6 + 70r^8s^8 + 56r^6s^{10} + 28r^4s^{12} + 8r^2s^{14} + s^{16}$ **19.** $m^8 + 8m^7t + 28m^6t^2$ **21.** $d^{10} - 5d^9 + \frac{45}{4}d^8$ **23.** $n^{24} + 24n^{22} + 264n^{20}$ **25.** $\sin^6 x - 18\sin^5 x + 135\sin^4 x$ **B 27.** 1.159 **29.** 1.369 **31.** $a^{1/2} + \frac{1}{2}a^{-1/2}b - \frac{1}{8}a^{-3/2}b^2$ **33.** $x^{2/3} + \frac{2}{3}x^{-1/3}y - \frac{1}{9}x^{-4/3}y^2$ **35.** 1.03

Page 521 Written Exercises A 1. $6x^2m^2$ **3.** $60x^4$ **5.** $252x^5y^5$ **7.** $540x^6$ **9.** $240d^2$ **11.** $-5005\tan^{12}\theta$ **13.** $\frac{21}{16}m^6r^6$ **15.** $\dfrac{35x^4}{8}$

Page 522 Chapter Test and Review 1. -109 **3.** -279 **5.** $\frac{1}{16}$ **7.** $9\frac{23}{27}$ **9.** $r^{12} - 12r^{10}t + 60r^8t^2 - 160r^6t^3 + 240r^4t^4 - 192r^2t^5 + 64t^6$

Pages 528–529 Written Exercises A 1. 10 **3.** -100 **5.** 91 **7.** $2 + 3i$ **9.** 0 **11.** 0 **13.** 0 **15.** $3 - i$ **17.** 0 **19.** 0 **B 21.** 4 **23.** 32 **25.** $-\frac{29}{4}$ **27.** $a = 2, b = -1$

Pages 531–532 Written Exercises A 1. $(x - 2)(3x^2 + 4x + 10) + 21$ **3.** $(x + 3)(x^2 + x) + 2$ **5.** $(x - 3)(x^3 - x - 14) - 46$ **7.** $3x^2 + 2x + 5; 0$ **9.** $3x^3 + (-6 + 6i)x^2 - (12 + 12i)x + (27 - 24i)$; $52 + 54i$ **19.** $2x^2 - 3x - 27$ **21.** $2x^2 - 5x + 1$ **B 27.** -18 **29.** 6

Page 533 Written Exercises A 1. $\{-1, -\frac{3}{2} + \frac{1}{2}i\sqrt{11}, -\frac{3}{2} - \frac{1}{2}i\sqrt{11}\}$ **3.** $\left\{-1, \dfrac{5}{6} + \dfrac{\sqrt{61}}{6}, \dfrac{5}{6} - \dfrac{\sqrt{61}}{6}\right\}$ **5.** $\{-4, 2, 3\}$ **7.** $\{-2, -\frac{3}{2}, -1, 1\}$ **B 9.** $\frac{1}{2}i(1 - \sqrt{5}), \frac{1}{2}i(1 + \sqrt{5})$ **11.** $i, -i$

Pages 534–535 Written Exercises A 1. $-\sqrt{2}\,i$ **3.** $1 + 2i$; $x^3 - 5x^2 + 11x - 15 = 0$ **5.** $2 + 2i, \frac{3}{2}$ **7.** $-2, 1 + 3i, 3$ **9.** a. $(x^2 + 1)(x + 1)$; b. $(x + i)(x - i)(x + 1)$ **11.** a. $(x + 3)\left(x - \dfrac{3}{2} - \dfrac{\sqrt{5}}{2}\right)\left(x - \dfrac{3}{2} + \dfrac{\sqrt{5}}{2}\right)$; b. same as a. **13.** a. $(x - 2)(x + 3)(x^2 + 2x + 4)$; b. $(x - 2)(x + 3)(x + 1 - i\sqrt{3})(x + 1 + i\sqrt{3})$ **B 15.** F **17.** T

Page 537 Written Exercises A 1. 3; 1 **3.** 2; 2 **C 9.** 1

Pages 538–539 Written Exercises A 1. 0 **3.** -1 **5.** $-2, 0, 2$ **7.** 0, 2 **9.** $-3, -1, 2$ **11.** $-2, 0, 2, 4$ **B 13.** 4 **15.** $2 + 2\sqrt{3}$

Page 541 Written Exercises A 1. $-1, 0; 2, 3$ **3.** 0, 1 **5.** $-1, 0; 1, 2$ **7.** 0, 1 **9.** $-2, -3$

Pages 542–543 Written Exercises A 1. $3; -2$ **3.** $2; -4$ **5.** $2; -4$ **7.** $2; -2$

Page 544 Written Exercises A 1. 0.58 **3.** 1.20 **5.** -2.47 **B 7.** 0.68

Pages 545–546 Chapter Test and Review 1. a. 0; b. 36 **3.** $\{-3, -\frac{1}{2}, 2\}$ **5.** 2 pos. real, 1 neg. real, 2 imag. or 0 pos. real, 1 neg. real, 4 imag. **7.** $-1, 0; 0, 1; 1, 2$ **9.** 2.09

Page 553 Written Exercises A 1. $x = 3$ **3.** $x = 2, y = 4$ **5.** $x = 1, y = 2, z = 1$ **7.** $x = 3$

Pages 554–556 Written Exercises A 1. $\begin{bmatrix} 4 & -2 \\ 3 & 2 \end{bmatrix}$ **3.** $\begin{bmatrix} 1 & 0 & 0 \\ 0 & 0 & 0 \end{bmatrix}$ **5.** $\begin{bmatrix} 3 & 1 & 1 \\ 2 & 2 & 1 \\ 1 & -1 & 3 \end{bmatrix}$ **7.** $\begin{bmatrix} 3 & 9 \\ -3 & 0 \end{bmatrix}$ **9.** $\begin{bmatrix} -2 & 0 \\ -4 & -2 \\ 0 & -6 \end{bmatrix}$ **11.** $\begin{bmatrix} -3 & -6 & -6 \\ 0 & -3 & -3 \\ -9 & -3 & -6 \end{bmatrix}$ **13.** $\begin{bmatrix} 2 & 4 \\ -3 & 1 \end{bmatrix}$ **15.** $\begin{bmatrix} 4 & 3 & 2 \\ -9 & 11 & 4 \\ 0 & -1 & 1 \end{bmatrix}$ **B 17.** $\begin{bmatrix} 7 & -8 \\ 3 & 3 \end{bmatrix}$ **19.** $\begin{bmatrix} \frac{7}{4} & \frac{3}{4} & \frac{1}{2} \\ 0 & 1 & \frac{1}{2} \\ \frac{1}{4} & 1 & \frac{9}{4} \end{bmatrix}$

Pages 559–560 Written Exercises A 1. [3] **3.** $\begin{bmatrix} -3 & 6 \\ -1 & 4 \end{bmatrix}$ **5.** $\begin{bmatrix} -2 & 0 & 0 \\ -1 & 3 & 6 \\ 4 & 5 & 9 \end{bmatrix}$ **7.** $\begin{bmatrix} a & b & c \\ g & h & i \\ d & e & f \end{bmatrix}$ **B 9.** $\begin{bmatrix} 1 & 0 \\ 0 & 1 \end{bmatrix}; \begin{bmatrix} 0 & 1 \\ 1 & 0 \end{bmatrix}; \begin{bmatrix} 1 & 0 \\ 0 & 1 \end{bmatrix}$

Page 562 Written Exercises A 1. 5 **3.** -17 **5.** 0 **7.** -2 **9.** 10 **11.** 0

Pages 564–565 **A 1.** $\begin{bmatrix} -\frac{1}{5} & \frac{3}{5} \\ \frac{2}{5} & -\frac{1}{5} \end{bmatrix}$ **3.** $\begin{bmatrix} \frac{3}{5} & -\frac{2}{5} \\ \frac{1}{5} & \frac{1}{5} \end{bmatrix}$ **5.** No inverse **7.** $\begin{bmatrix} \frac{1}{4} & -\frac{5}{4} \\ 0 & 1 \end{bmatrix}$ **9.** $\begin{bmatrix} 2 & -\frac{3}{2} \\ 1 & -\frac{1}{2} \end{bmatrix}$ **11.** $\begin{bmatrix} 2 & 3 \\ 1 & 1 \end{bmatrix}$
B 13. $\begin{bmatrix} 2 & -1 \\ -1 & 1 \end{bmatrix}$ **15.** $\begin{bmatrix} 6 & 1 \\ -\frac{13}{2} & -\frac{3}{2} \end{bmatrix}$ **17.** $\begin{bmatrix} 1 & -2 \\ -1 & 5 \end{bmatrix}$

Page 567 **A 1.** $\{(1, 2)\}$ **3.** $\{(2, 3)\}$ **5.** $\{(0, 1)\}$ **7.** $\{(x, y)\colon x + 2y = 3\}$, dependent **9.** $\{(5, 4)\}$

Pages 570–571 **A 1.** 0 **3.** 5 **5.** 0 **7.** 13 **9.** 40 **11.** $x = -2$ **B 13.** -15

Pages 573–574 **A 1.** -300 **3.** 132 **5.** -101 **7.** 5 **9.** 0 **11.** 18

Page 576 **1.** $\{(1, 2, 3)\}$ **3.** $\{(-1, 1, -2)\}$ **5.** $\{(\frac{1}{2}, \frac{1}{3}, \frac{1}{4})\}$ **7.** $\{(\frac{13}{10}, -\frac{21}{20}, -\frac{7}{4})\}$ **9.** inconsistent

Page 579 **1.** $x = 2$ **3.** $\begin{bmatrix} 22 \\ -8 \end{bmatrix}$ **5.** $\begin{bmatrix} \frac{13}{3} & \frac{7}{3} \\ -\frac{7}{3} & -\frac{1}{3} \end{bmatrix}$ **7.** $x = -7$ **9.** $\{(-3, 2, \frac{1}{2})\}$

Pages 583–584 **A 1.** 6; 1; 4 **3.** 6; 2; 3 **5.** 9; 3; 3 **7.** 676 **9.** 1024 **11.** a. 585×10^5; b. 9×10^6 **13.** 80
15. 625 **B 17.** 75 **19.** 1562 **21.** 1, 565, 616

Pages 586–587 **A 1.** 5040 **3.** 30 **5.** 27,600 **7.** 120 **9.** 240 **11.** 288 **13.** 2240 **15.** 720 **17.** 12
19. 2880 **C 27.** $n = 3$ **29.** $n = 7$

Page 589 **A 1.** 6720 **3.** 420 **5.** 302,400 **7.** 4,989,600 **9.** 908,107,200 **11.** 10,080 **13.** 60 **15.** 60 **17.** 10

Pages 591–592 **A 1.** 10 **3.** 10 **5.** 56 **7.** 10 **9.** 75,287,520 **B 11.** 20 **13.** 924; 924 **15.** 2.6×10^6 **17.** 100

Pages 594–595 **A 1.** 810 **3.** 12 **5.** 350 **B 7.** approx. 5.6×10^9; approx. 5×10^8 **9.** approx. 3.6×10^7
11. 2880 **C 13.** 7200 **15.** 7200

Page 597 **A 1.** $1 + 12y + 54y^2 + 108y^3 + 81y^4$ **3.** $64 + 96y + 60y^2 + 20y^3 + \frac{15}{4}y^4 + \frac{3}{8}y^5 + \frac{1}{64}y^6$
5. $64 - 64y + \frac{80}{3}y^2 - \frac{160}{27}y^3 + \frac{20}{27}y^4 - \frac{4}{81}y^5 + \frac{1}{729}y^6$ **B 7.** $210x^6y^4$ **9.** $-1920b^3$ **11.** $2625a^{13}$

Pages 599–600 **A 1.** {1, 2, 3, 4, 5, 6, 7, 8, 9}; {2, 4, 6, 8} **3.** {P, U, R, C, H, A, S, E}; {U, A, E}
5. {(1, 2), (1, 3), (1, 4), (2, 3), (2, 4), (3, 4), (2, 1), (3, 1), (4, 1), (3, 2), (4, 2), (4, 3)}; {(1, 3), (2, 4), (3, 1), (4, 2)}
7. {(L, E), (L, T), (L, R), (E, T), (E, E), (E, R), (T, T), (T, R), (E, L), (T, L), (R, L), (T, E), (R, E), (R, T)}; {(E, E), (T, T)}
B 9. {(1, H), (1, T), (2, H), (2, T), (3, H), (3, T), (4, H), (4, T), (5, H), (5, T), (6, H), (6, T)}; {(1, H), (1, T), (3, H), (3, T), (5, H), (5, T)}

Pages 602–604 **A 1.** $\frac{1}{5}$; $\frac{3}{10}$; $\frac{1}{2}$; $\frac{7}{10}$ **3.** 3 to 1 **5.** a. $\frac{1}{3}$; b. 1 to 1; c. 3 to 1 **7.** a. $\frac{3}{5}$; b. $\frac{1}{5}$; c. $\frac{1}{5}$; d. 1
9. a. $\frac{1}{6}$; b. $\frac{1}{3}$; c. $\frac{1}{2}$; d. $\frac{5}{6}$; e. $\frac{2}{3}$; f. 0 **11.** a. $\frac{11}{850}$; b. $\frac{2}{17}$; c. $\frac{703}{1700}$; d. $\frac{1}{5525}$ **B 13.** 3,628,800; $\frac{1}{945}$ **15.** $\frac{2}{7}$

Page 605 **A 1.** a. $\frac{1}{12}$; b. $\frac{11}{36}$; c. $\frac{7}{18}$ **3.** a. $\frac{1}{17}$; b. $\frac{1}{221}$; c. $\frac{14}{221}$ **5.** a. $\frac{25}{102}$; b. $\frac{1}{221}$; c. $\frac{55}{221}$ **B 7.** $\frac{22}{35}$

Pages 608–609 **A 3.** a. {(H, T, T), (H, H, T), (H, H, H), (H, T, H), (T, H, H), (T, T, H), (T, H, T), (T, T, T)};
b. $\frac{1}{2}$; c. $\frac{7}{8}$; d. no **5.** b. $\frac{1}{2}$; c. $\frac{1}{2}$; d. yes **7.** $\frac{1}{169}$, $\frac{1}{16}$ **9.** $\frac{25}{169}$; $\frac{89}{169}$ **11.** a. $\frac{7}{12}$; b. $\frac{1}{3}$; c. no **B 13.** a. $\frac{23}{24}$; b. $\frac{1}{8}$;
c. $\frac{1}{4}$; d. $\frac{17}{24}$ **15.** Assume dice distinguishable. a. $\frac{1}{36}$; b. $\frac{1}{324}$; c. $\frac{73}{648}$

Page 611 **1.** 6 **3.** 30,240 **5.** 4410 **7.** a. {*ab*, *ac*, *ad*, *ae*, *bc*, *bd*, *be*, *cd*, *ce*, *de*, *ba*, *ca*, *da*, *ea*, *cb*, *db*, *eb*, *dc*, *ec*, *ed*}; b. {*bc*, *bd*, *cd*, *cb*, *db*, *de*} **9.** $\frac{17}{42}$ **11.** a. $\frac{25}{102}$; b. $\frac{1}{221}$; c. $\frac{5}{1326}$; d. $\frac{501}{663}$

Page 612 (1970 edition) **1.** 10 **3.** 49 **5.** a. $6415\frac{1}{2}$; b. $\frac{364}{3}$ **7.** a. $\frac{1}{729}r^6 + \frac{2}{81}r^5s + \frac{5}{27}r^4s^2 + \frac{20}{27}r^3s^3 + \frac{5}{3}r^2s^4 + 2rs^5 + s^6$; b. $a^8 - 4a^7b + 7a^6b^2 - 7a^5b^3 + \frac{35}{8}a^4b^4 - \frac{7}{4}a^3b^5 + \frac{7}{16}a^2b^6 - \frac{1}{16}ab^7 + \frac{1}{256}b^8$ **9.** $\frac{23}{990}$
11. 14 **15.** $\{(\frac{54}{19}, \frac{107}{57})\}$ **17.** a. 1820; b. $\frac{17}{28}$

Page 612 (1973 edition) **1.** 32, 39, 46, 53 **3.** 49 **5.** a. $391\frac{1}{2}$; b. $63\frac{1}{2}$ **7.** a. $1024 + 640x + 160x^2 + 20x^3 + \frac{5}{4}x^4 + \frac{1}{32}x^5$; b. $\frac{1}{4096}x^6 - \frac{3}{256}x^5 + \frac{15}{64}x^4 - \frac{5}{2}x^3 + 15x^2 - 48x + 64$ **9.** $\frac{23}{495}$ **11.** 14 **15.** $\{(2, -1)\}$
17. a. 1820; b. $\frac{17}{28}$

2-14329